PEARSON CUSTOM
MATHEMATICS

Calculus III
92.231

PEARSON

Senior Vice President, Editorial: Patrick F. Boles
Senior Acquisitions Editor: Debbie Coniglio
Development Editor: Christina Martin
Editorial Assistant: Jeanne Martin
Operations Manager: Eric M. Kenney
Production Manager: Jennifer Berry
Art Director: Renée Sartell
Cover Designer: Josh Read

This special edition published in cooperation with Pearson Learning Solutions.

Printed in the United States of America.

Please visit our website at *www.pearsonlearningsolutions.com*.

Attention bookstores: For permission to return any unsold stock, contact us at *pe-uscustomreturns@pearson.com*.

Pearson Learning Solutions, 501 Boylston Street, Suite 900, Boston, MA 02116
A Pearson Education Company
www.pearsoned.com

V092

ISBN 10: 1-269-70932-1
ISBN 13: 978-1-269-70932-3

Table of Contents

11

Parametric and Polar Curves

Chapter Preview   Until now, all our work has been done in the Cartesian coordinate system with functions of the form $y = f(x)$. There are, however, alternative ways to generate curves and represent functions. We begin by introducing parametric equations, which are featured prominently in Chapter 12 to represent curves and trajectories in three-dimensional space. When working with objects that have circular, cylindrical, or spherical shapes, other coordinate systems are often advantageous. In this chapter, we introduce the polar coordinate system for circular geometries. Cylindrical and spherical coordinate systems appear in Chapter 14. After working with parametric equations and polar coordinates, the next step is to investigate calculus in these settings. How do we find slopes of tangent lines and rates of changes? How are areas of regions bounded by curves in polar coordinates computed? The chapter ends with the related topic of *conic sections*. Ellipses, parabolas, and hyperbolas (all of which are conic sections) can be represented in both Cartesian and polar coordinates. These important families of curves have many fascinating properties and appear throughout the remainder of the book.

11.1 Parametric Equations

So far, we have used functions of the form $y = f(x)$ to describe curves in the xy-plane. In this section we look at another way to define curves, known as *parametric equations*. As you will see, parametric curves enable us to describe both common and exotic curves; they are also indispensable for modeling the trajectories of moving objects.

Basic Ideas

A motor boat speeds counterclockwise around a circular course with a radius of 4 mi, completing one lap every hour at a constant speed. Suppose we wish to describe the points on the path of the boat $(x(t), y(t))$ at any time $t \geq 0$, where t is measured in hours. We assume that the boat starts on the positive x-axis at the point $(4, 0)$ (Figure 11.1). Note that the angle θ corresponding to the position of the boat increases by 2π radians every hour beginning with $\theta = 0$ when $t = 0$; therefore, $\theta = 2\pi t$, for $t \geq 0$. As we show in Example 2, the x- and y-coordinates of the boat are

$$x = 4 \cos \theta = 4 \cos 2\pi t \quad \text{and} \quad y = 4 \sin \theta = 4 \sin 2\pi t,$$

where $t \geq 0$. You can confirm that when $t = 0$, the boat is at the starting point $(4, 0)$; when $t = 1$, it returns to the starting point.

The equations $x = 4 \cos 2\pi t$ and $y = 4 \sin 2\pi t$ are examples of **parametric equations**. They specify x and y in terms of a third variable t called a **parameter**, which often represents time (Figure 11.2).

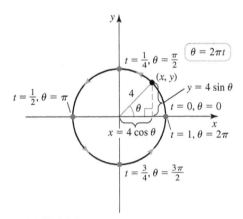

FIGURE 11.1

You can think of the parameter t as the independent variable. There are two dependent variables, x and y.

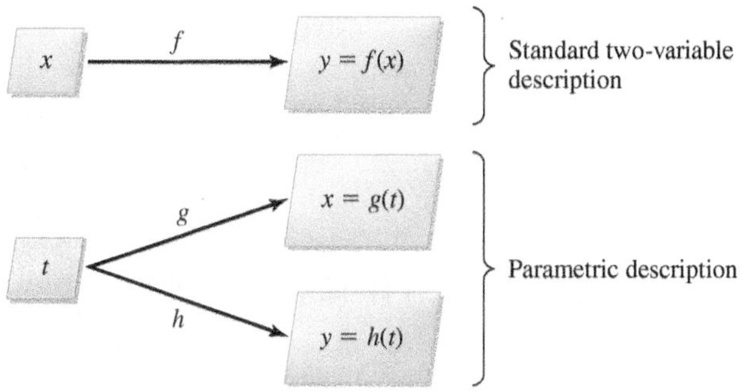

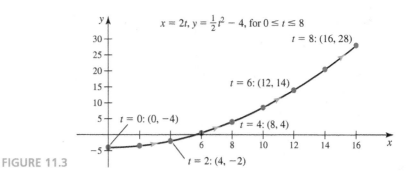

FIGURE 11.2

In general, parametric equations have the form

$$x = g(t), \quad y = h(t),$$

where g and h are given functions and the parameter t typically varies over a specified interval, such as $a \leq t \leq b$. The **parametric curve** described by these equations consists of the points in the plane that satisfy

$$(x, y) = (g(t), h(t)), \quad \text{for } a \leq t \leq b.$$

EXAMPLE 1 **Parametric parabola** Graph and analyze the parametric equations

$$x = g(t) = 2t, \quad y = h(t) = \frac{1}{2}t^2 - 4, \quad \text{for } 0 \leq t \leq 8.$$

SOLUTION Plotting individual points often helps visualize a parametric curve. Table 11.1 shows the values of x and y corresponding to several values of t on the interval $[0, 8]$. By plotting the (x, y) pairs in Table 11.1 and connecting them with a smooth curve, we obtain the graph shown in Figure 11.3. We see that as t increases from its initial value of $t = 0$ to its final value of $t = 8$, the curve is generated from the initial point $(0, -4)$ to the final point $(16, 28)$. Notice that the values of the parameter do not appear in the graph. The only signature of the parameter is the direction in which the curve is generated: In this case, it unfolds upward and to the right.

Table 11.1

t	x	y	(x, y)
0	0	-4	$(0, -4)$
1	2	$-\frac{7}{2}$	$(2, -\frac{7}{2})$
2	4	-2	$(4, -2)$
3	6	$\frac{1}{2}$	$(6, \frac{1}{2})$
4	8	4	$(8, 4)$
5	10	$\frac{17}{2}$	$(10, \frac{17}{2})$
6	12	14	$(12, 14)$
7	14	$\frac{41}{2}$	$(14, \frac{41}{2})$
8	16	28	$(16, 28)$

FIGURE 11.3

Occasionally, it is possible to eliminate the parameter from a set of parametric equations and obtain a description of the curve in terms of x and y. In this case, from the x-equation we have $t = x/2$, which may be substituted into the y-equation to give

$$y = \frac{1}{2}t^2 - 4 = \frac{1}{2}\left(\frac{x}{2}\right)^2 - 4 = \frac{x^2}{8} - 4.$$

Expressed in this form, we identify the graph as part of a parabola.

Related Exercises 7–16 ◄

QUICK CHECK 1 Identify the graph that is generated by the parametric equations $x = t^2$, $y = t$, for $-10 \leq t \leq 10$. ◄

Given a set of parametric equations, the preceding example shows that as the parameter increases, the corresponding curve unfolds in a particular direction. The following definition captures this fact and is important in upcoming work.

> **DEFINITION Forward or Positive Orientation**
>
> The direction in which a parametric curve is generated as the parameter increases is called the **forward**, or **positive**, **orientation** of the curve.

EXAMPLE 2   Parametric circle Graph and analyze the parametric equations

$$x = 4 \cos 2\pi t, \quad y = 4 \sin 2\pi t, \quad \text{for } 0 \le t \le 1$$

used to describe the path of the motor boat in the opening paragraphs.

SOLUTION For each value of t in Table 11.2, the corresponding ordered pairs (x, y) are recorded. Plotting these points as t increases from $t = 0$ to $t = 1$ results in a graph that appears to be a circle of radius 4; it is generated with positive orientation in the counterclockwise direction, beginning and ending at $(4, 0)$ (Figure 11.4). Letting t increase beyond $t = 1$ would simply retrace the same curve.

Table 11.2

t	(x, y)
0	$(4, 0)$
$\frac{1}{8}$	$(2\sqrt{2}, 2\sqrt{2})$
$\frac{1}{4}$	$(0, 4)$
$\frac{3}{8}$	$(-2\sqrt{2}, 2\sqrt{2})$
$\frac{1}{2}$	$(-4, 0)$
$\frac{3}{4}$	$(0, -4)$
1	$(4, 0)$

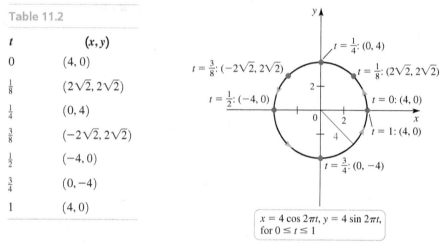

FIGURE 11.4

To identify the curve conclusively, the parameter t is eliminated by writing

$$x^2 + y^2 = (4 \cos 2\pi t)^2 + (4 \sin 2\pi t)^2$$
$$= 16\underbrace{(\cos^2 2\pi t + \sin^2 2\pi t)}_{1} = 16.$$

We see that the parametric equations are equivalent to $x^2 + y^2 = 16$, whose graph is a circle of radius 4.

Related Exercises 17–28 ◄

Generalizing Example 2 for nonzero real numbers a and b in the parametric equations $x = a \cos bt, \, y = a \sin bt$, notice that

$$x^2 + y^2 = (a \cos bt)^2 + (a \sin bt)^2$$
$$= a^2 \underbrace{(\cos^2 bt + \sin^2 bt)}_{1} = a^2.$$

Therefore, the parametric equations $x = a \cos bt, \, y = a \sin bt$ describe the circle $x^2 + y^2 = a^2$, centered at the origin with radius $|a|$, for any nonzero value of b. The circle

Recall that the functions $\sin bt$ and $\cos bt$ have period $2\pi/|b|$. The equations $x = a \cos bt$, $y = -a \sin bt$ also describe a circle of radius $|a|$, as do the equations $x = a \sin bt$, $y = \pm a \cos bt$.

is traversed once as t varies over any interval of length $2\pi/|b|$. If t represents time, the circle is traversed in $2\pi/|b|$ time units, which means we can vary the speed at which the curve unfolds by varying b. If $b > 0$, the curve is generated in the counterclockwise direction (positive orientation). If $b < 0$, the curve is generated in the clockwise direction.

More generally, the parametric equations

$$x = x_0 + a \cos bt, \quad y = y_0 + a \sin bt$$

describe the circle $(x - x_0)^2 + (y - y_0)^2 = a^2$, centered at (x_0, y_0) with radius $|a|$. If $b > 0$, then the circle is generated in the counterclockwise direction.

Example 3 shows that a single curve—for example, a circle of radius 4—may be parameterized in many different ways.

EXAMPLE 3   Circular path A turtle walks with constant speed in the counterclockwise direction on a circular track of radius 4 ft centered at the origin. Starting from the point $(4, 0)$, the turtle completes one lap in 30 minutes. Find a parametric description of the path of the turtle at any time $t \geq 0$.

SOLUTION Example 2 showed that a circle of radius of 4, generated in the counterclockwise direction, may be described by the parametric equations

$$x = 4 \cos bt, \quad y = 4 \sin bt.$$

The constant $|b|$ is called the *angular frequency* because it is the number of radians the object moves per unit time. The turtle travels 2π rad every 30 min, so the angular frequency is $2\pi/30 = \pi/15$ rad/min. Because radians have no units, the angular frequency in this case has units *per minute*, sometimes written min^{-1}.

The *angular frequency* b must be chosen so that, as t varies from 0 to 30, the product bt varies from 0 to 2π. Specifically, when $t = 30$, we must have $30b = 2\pi$, or $b = \pi/15$ rad/min. Therefore, the parametric equations for the turtle's motion are

$$x = 4 \cos\left(\frac{\pi t}{15}\right), \quad y = 4 \sin\left(\frac{\pi t}{15}\right), \quad \text{for } 0 \leq t \leq 30.$$

You should check that as t varies from 0 to 30, the points (x, y) make one complete circuit of a circle of radius 4 (Figure 11.5).

Related Exercises 29–32 ◀

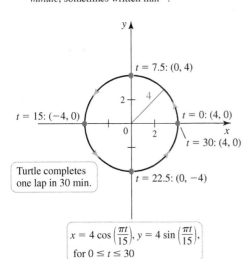

$t = 7.5$: $(0, 4)$

$t = 15$: $(-4, 0)$

$t = 0$: $(4, 0)$

$t = 30$: $(4, 0)$

Turtle completes one lap in 30 min.

$t = 22.5$: $(0, -4)$

$x = 4 \cos\left(\frac{\pi t}{15}\right), y = 4 \sin\left(\frac{\pi t}{15}\right)$, for $0 \leq t \leq 30$

FIGURE 11.5

QUICK CHECK 2 Give the center and radius of the circle generated by the equations $x = 3 \sin t$, $y = -3 \cos t$, for $0 \leq t \leq 2\pi$. Specify the direction of positive orientation. ◀

EXAMPLE 4   Parametric lines Express the curve described by the equations $x = x_0 + at$, $y = y_0 + bt$ in the form $y = f(x)$. Assume that x_0, y_0, a, and b are constants with $a \neq 0$, and $-\infty < t < \infty$.

SOLUTION The parameter t may be eliminated by solving the x-equation for t, resulting in $t = (x - x_0)/a$. Substituting t into the y-equation, we have

$$y = y_0 + bt = y_0 + b\left(\frac{x - x_0}{a}\right) \quad \text{or} \quad y - y_0 = \frac{b}{a}(x - x_0).$$

This equation describes the line with slope b/a passing through the point (x_0, y_0). Figure 11.6 illustrates the line $x = 2 + 3t$, $y = 1 + t$, which passes through the point $(2, 1)$ (when $t = 0$) with slope $\frac{1}{3}$.

We can also vary the point on the line that corresponds to $t = 0$. For example, the equations

$$x = -1 + 6t, \quad y = 2t$$

produce the same line shown in Figure 11.6. However, the point corresponding to $t = 0$ is $(-1, 0)$.

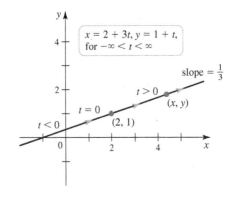

$x = 2 + 3t$, $y = 1 + t$, for $-\infty < t < \infty$

slope $= \frac{1}{3}$

$t > 0$

(x, y)

$t = 0$

$t < 0$

$(2, 1)$

FIGURE 11.6

QUICK CHECK 3 Describe the curve generated by $x = 3 + 2t$, $y = -12 - 6t$, for $-\infty < t < \infty$.

Notice that the parametric description of a given line is not unique: If k is any nonzero constant, the numbers a and b may be replaced by ka and kb, respectively, and the resulting equations describe the same line (although it is traversed at a different speed). If $b = 0$ and $a \neq 0$, the line has zero slope and is horizontal. If $a = 0$ and $b \neq 0$, the line is vertical.

Related Exercises 33–40◀

EXAMPLE 5   Parametric equations of curves A common task (particularly in upcoming chapters) is to parameterize curves given either by Cartesian equations or by graphs. Find a parametric representation of the following curves.

a. The segment of the parabola $y = 9 - x^2$, for $-1 \le x \le 3$

b. The complete curve $x = (y - 5)^2 + \sqrt{y}$

c. The piecewise linear path that connects $P(-2, 0)$ to $Q(0, 3)$ to $R(4, 0)$ (in that order), where the parameter varies over the interval $0 \le t \le 2$

SOLUTION

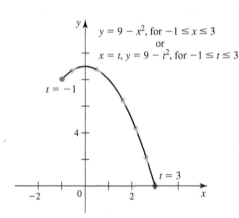

FIGURE 11.7

a. The simplest way to represent the curve $y = f(x)$ parametrically is to let $x = t$ and $y = f(t)$, where t is the parameter. We must then find the appropriate interval for the parameter. Using this approach, the curve $y = 9 - x^2$ has the parametric representation

$$x = t, \quad y = 9 - t^2, \quad \text{for} \quad -1 \le t \le 3.$$

This representation is not unique. You should check that the parametric equations

$$x = 1 - t, \quad y = 9 - (1 - t)^2, \quad \text{for} \quad -2 \le t \le 2$$

also do the job, although these equations trace the parabola from right to left, while the original equations trace the curve from left to right (Figure 11.7).

b. In this case, it is easier to let $y = t$. Then a parametric description of the curve is

$$x = (t - 5)^2 + \sqrt{t}, \quad y = t.$$

Notice that t can take values only in the interval $[0, \infty)$. As $t \to \infty$, we see that $x \to \infty$ and $y \to \infty$ (Figure 11.8).

c. The path consists of two line segments (Figure 11.9) that can be parameterized separately in the form $x = x_0 + at$ and $y = y_0 + bt$. The line segment PQ originates at $(-2, 0)$ and unfolds in the positive x-direction with slope $\frac{3}{2}$. It can be represented as

$$x = -2 + 2t, \quad y = 3t, \quad \text{for } 0 \le t \le 1.$$

In moving from P to Q, y increases as x increases. In moving from Q to R, y decreases as x increases. The parametric equations must reflect these changes. Recall that the line $x = x_0 + at$, $y = y_0 + bt$ has slope b/a.

The line segment QR originates at $(0, 3)$ and unfolds in the positive x-direction with slope $-\frac{3}{4}$. On the interval $1 \le t \le 2$, the point $(0, 3)$ corresponds to $t = 1$. Therefore, the line segment has the representation

$$x = -4 + 4t, \quad y = 6 - 3t, \quad \text{for } 1 \le t \le 2.$$

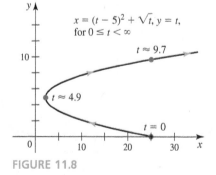

FIGURE 11.8

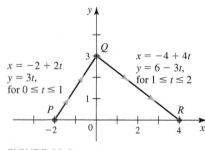

FIGURE 11.9

It is always wise to check the endpoints of the line segments for consistency. As before, this representation is not unique.

Related Exercises 41–44 ◄

QUICK CHECK 4 Find parametric equations for the line segment that goes from $Q(0, 3)$ to $P(-2, 0)$. ◄

EXAMPLE 6 **Rolling wheels** Many fascinating curves are generated by points on rolling wheels. The path of a light on the rim of a rolling wheel (Figure 11.10) is a **cycloid**, which has the parametric equations

$$x = a(t - \sin t), \quad y = a(1 - \cos t), \quad \text{for } t \geq 0,$$

where $a > 0$. Use a graphing utility to graph the cycloid with $a = 1$. On what interval does the parameter generate one arch of the cycloid?

SOLUTION The graph of the cycloid, for $0 \leq t \leq 3\pi$, is shown in Figure 11.11. The wheel completes one full revolution on the interval $0 \leq t \leq 2\pi$, which gives one arch of the cycloid.

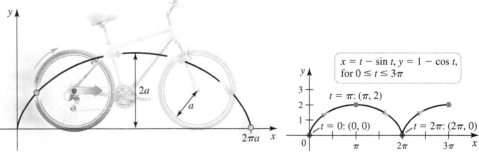

FIGURE 11.10

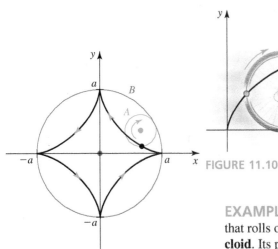

FIGURE 11.11

$$x = t - \sin t, y = 1 - \cos t,$$
for $0 \leq t \leq 3\pi$

$t = \pi: (\pi, 2)$

$t = 0: (0, 0)$ $t = 2\pi: (2\pi, 0)$

Related Exercises 45–54 ◄

FIGURE 11.12

EXAMPLE 7 **More rolling wheels** The path of a point on circle A with radius $a/4$ that rolls on the inside of circle B with radius a (Figure 11.12) is an **astroid** or **hypocycloid**. Its parametric equations are

$$x = a \cos^3 t, \quad y = a \sin^3 t, \quad \text{for } 0 \leq t \leq 2\pi.$$

Graph the astroid with $a = 1$ and find its equation in terms of x and y.

SOLUTION Because both $\cos^3 t$ and $\sin^3 t$ have a period of 2π, the complete curve is generated on the interval $0 \leq t \leq 2\pi$ (Figure 11.13). To eliminate t from the parametric equations, note that $x^{2/3} = \cos^2 t$ and $y^{2/3} = \sin^2 t$. Therefore,

$$x^{2/3} + y^{2/3} = \cos^2 t + \sin^2 t = 1,$$

where the Pythagorean identity has been used. We see that an alternative description of the astroid is $x^{2/3} + y^{2/3} = 1$.

Related Exercises 45–54 ◄

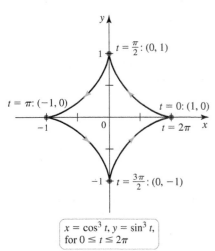

$t = \frac{\pi}{2}: (0, 1)$

$t = \pi: (-1, 0)$ $t = 0: (1, 0)$

$t = 2\pi$

$t = \frac{3\pi}{2}: (0, -1)$

$x = \cos^3 t, y = \sin^3 t,$
for $0 \leq t \leq 2\pi$

FIGURE 11.13

Derivatives and Parametric Equations

Parametric equations express a relationship between the variables x and y. Therefore, it makes sense to ask about dy/dx, the rate of change of y with respect to x at a point on a parametric curve. Once we know how to compute dy/dx, it can be used to determine slopes of lines tangent to parametric curves.

Consider the parametric equations $x = g(t)$, $y = h(t)$ on an interval on which both g and h are differentiable. The Chain Rule relates the derivatives dy/dt, dx/dt, and dy/dx:

$$\frac{dy}{dt} = \frac{dy}{dx}\frac{dx}{dt}.$$

Provided that $dx/dt \neq 0$, we divide both sides of this equation by dx/dt and solve for dy/dx to obtain the following result.

> We will soon interpret $x'(t)$ and $y'(t)$ as the horizontal and vertical velocities, respectively, of an object moving along a curve. The slope of the curve at a point is the ratio of the velocity components at that point.

THEOREM 11.1   Derivative for Parametric Curves

Let $x = g(t)$ and $y = h(t)$, where g and h are differentiable on an interval $[a, b]$. Then

$$\frac{dy}{dx} = \frac{dy/dt}{dx/dt} = \frac{y'(t)}{x'(t)},$$

provided $dx/dt \neq 0$.

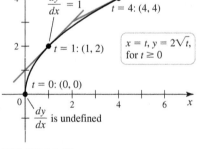

FIGURE 11.14

Figure 11.14 gives a geometric explanation of Theorem 11.1. The slope of the line tangent to a curve at a point is $\dfrac{dy}{dx} = \lim\limits_{\Delta x \to 0} \dfrac{\Delta y}{\Delta x}$. Using linear approximation (Section 4.5), we have $\Delta x \approx x'(t)\Delta t$ and $\Delta y \approx y'(t)\Delta t$, with these approximations improving as $\Delta t \to 0$. Notice also that $\Delta t \to 0$ as $\Delta x \to 0$. Therefore, the slope of the tangent line is

$$\frac{dy}{dx} = \lim_{\Delta x \to 0} \frac{\Delta y}{\Delta x} = \lim_{\Delta t \to 0} \frac{y'(t)\Delta t}{x'(t)\Delta t} = \frac{y'(t)}{x'(t)}.$$

EXAMPLE 8   Slopes of tangent lines Find dy/dx for the following curves. Interpret the result and determine the points (if any) at which the curve has a horizontal or a vertical tangent line.

a. $x = t$, $y = 2\sqrt{t}$, for $t \geq 0$

b. $x = 4\cos t$, $y = 16\sin t$, for $0 \leq t \leq 2\pi$

SOLUTION

a. We find that $x'(t) = 1$ and $y'(t) = 1/\sqrt{t}$. Therefore,

$$\frac{dy}{dx} = \frac{y'(t)}{x'(t)} = \frac{1/\sqrt{t}}{1} = \frac{1}{\sqrt{t}},$$

provided $t \neq 0$. Notice that $dy/dx \neq 0$ for $t > 0$, so the curve has no horizontal tangent lines. On the other hand, as $t \to 0^+$, we see that $dy/dx \to \infty$. Therefore, the curve has a vertical tangent line at the point $(0, 0)$. To eliminate t from the parametric equations, we substitute $t = x$ into the y-equation to find that $y = 2\sqrt{x}$, or $x = y^2/4$. Because $y \geq 0$, the curve is the upper half of a parabola (Figure 11.15). Slopes of tangent lines at other points on the curve are found by substituting the corresponding values of t. For example, the point $(4, 4)$ corresponds to $t = 4$ and the slope of the tangent line at that point is $1/\sqrt{4} = \frac{1}{2}$.

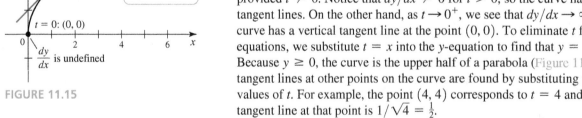

FIGURE 11.15

b. These parametric equations describe an **ellipse** with a long axis of length 32 on the y-axis and a short axis of length 8 on the x-axis (Figure 11.16). In this case, $x'(t) = -4\sin t$ and $y'(t) = 16\cos t$. Therefore,

$$\frac{dy}{dx} = \frac{y'(t)}{x'(t)} = \frac{16\cos t}{-4\sin t} = -4\cot t.$$

In general, the equations $x = a \cos t$, $y = b \sin t$, for $0 \le t \le 2\pi$, describe an ellipse. The constants a and b can be seen as horizontal and vertical scalings of the unit circle $x = \cos t, y = \sin t$. Ellipses are explored in Exercises 71–76 and in Section 11.4.

At $t = 0$ and $t = \pi$, $\cot t$ is undefined, and vertical tangent lines occur at the corresponding points $(\pm 4, 0)$. At $t = \pi/2$ and $t = 3\pi/2$, $\cot t = 0$ and the curve has horizontal tangent lines at the corresponding points $(0, \pm 16)$. Slopes of tangent lines at other points on the curve may be found. For example, the point $(2\sqrt{2}, 8\sqrt{2})$ corresponds to $t = \pi/4$; the slope of the tangent line at that point is $-4 \cot \pi/4 = -4$.

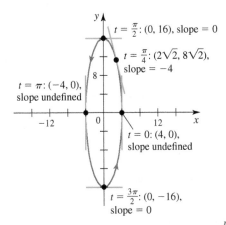

FIGURE 11.16

Related Exercises 55–60 ◀

SECTION 11.1 EXERCISES

Review Questions

1. Explain how a set of parametric equations generates a curve in the xy-plane.

2. Give two sets of parametric equations that generate a circle centered at the origin with radius 6.

3. Give a set of parametric equations that describes a full circle of radius R, where the parameter varies over the interval $[0, 10]$.

4. Give a set of parametric equations that generates the line with slope -2 passing through $(1, 3)$.

5. Find a set of parametric equations for the parabola $y = x^2$.

6. Describe the similarities and differences between the parametric equations $x = t, y = t^2$ and $x = -t, y = t^2$, where $t \ge 0$ in each case.

Basic Skills

7–10. Working with parametric equations *Consider the following parametric equations.*

a. *Make a brief table of values of t, x, and y.*
b. *Plot the points in the table and the full parametric curve, indicating the positive orientation (the direction of increasing t).*
c. *Eliminate the parameter to obtain an equation in x and y.*
d. *Describe the curve.*

7. $x = 2t, y = 3t - 4; -10 \le t \le 10$

8. $x = t^2 + 2, y = 4t; -4 \le t \le 4$

9. $x = -t + 6, y = 3t - 3; -5 \le t \le 5$

10. $x = t^3 - 1, y = 5t + 1; -3 \le t \le 3$

11–16. Working with parametric equations *Consider the following parametric equations.*

a. *Eliminate the parameter to obtain an equation in x and y.*
b. *Describe the curve and indicate the positive orientation.*

11. $x = \sqrt{t} + 4, y = 3\sqrt{t}; 0 \le t \le 16$

12. $x = (t + 1)^2, y = t + 2; -10 \le t \le 10$

13. $x = \cos t, y = \sin^2 t; 0 \le t \le \pi$

14. $x = 1 - \sin^2 t, y = \cos t; \pi \le t \le 2\pi$

15. $x = t - 1, y = t^3; -4 \le t \le 4$

16. $x = e^{2t}, y = e^t + 1; 0 \le t \le 25$

17–22. Circles and arcs *Eliminate the parameter to find a description of the following circles or circular arcs in terms of x and y. Give the center and radius, and indicate the positive orientation.*

17. $x = 3 \cos t, y = 3 \sin t; \pi \le t \le 2\pi$

18. $x = 3 \cos t, y = 3 \sin t; 0 \le t \le \pi/2$

19. $x = \cos t, y = 1 + \sin t; 0 \le t \le 2\pi$

20. $x = 2 \sin t - 3, y = 2 \cos t + 5; 0 \le t \le 2\pi$

21. $x = -7 \cos 2t, y = -7 \sin 2t; 0 \le t \le \pi$

22. $x = 1 - 3 \sin 4\pi t, y = 2 + 3 \cos 4\pi t; 0 \le t \le \frac{1}{2}$

23–28. Parametric equations of circles *Find parametric equations (not unique) for the following circles and give an interval for the parameter values. Graph the circle and find a description in terms of x and y.*

23. A circle centered at the origin with radius 4, generated counterclockwise

24. A circle centered at the origin with radius 12, generated clockwise with initial point $(0, 12)$

25. A circle centered at $(2, 3)$ with radius 1, generated counterclockwise

26. A circle centered at $(2, 0)$ with radius 3, generated clockwise

27. A circle centered at $(-2, -3)$ with radius 8, generated clockwise

28. A circle centered at $(2, -4)$ with radius $\frac{3}{2}$, generated counterclockwise with initial point $\left(\frac{7}{2}, -4\right)$

29–32. Circular motion *Find parametric equations that describe the circular path of the following objects. Assume (x, y) denotes the position of the object relative to the origin at the center of the circle. Use the units of time specified in the problem. There is more than one way to describe any circle.*

29. A go-cart moves counterclockwise with constant speed around a circular track of radius 400 m, completing a lap in 1.5 min.

30. The tip of the 15-inch second hand of a clock completes one revolution in 60 seconds.

31. A bicyclist rides counterclockwise with constant speed around a circular velodrome track with a radius of 50 m, completing one lap in 24 s.

32. A Ferris wheel has a radius of 20 m and completes a revolution in the clockwise direction at constant speed in 3 min. Assume that x and y measure the horizontal and vertical positions of a seat on the Ferris wheel relative to a coordinate system whose origin is at the low point of the wheel. Assume the seat begins moving at the origin.

33–36. Parametric lines *Find the slope of each line and a point on the line. Then graph the line.*

33. $x = 3 + t, y = 1 - t$

34. $x = 4 - 3t, y = -2 + 6t$

35. $x = 8 + 2t, y = 1$

36. $x = 1 + 2t/3, y = -4 - 5t/2$

37–40. Line segments *Find a parametric description of the line segment from the point P to the point Q. The solution is not unique.*

37. $P(0, 0), Q(2, 8)$ **38.** $P(1, 3), Q(-2, 6)$

39. $P(-1, -3), Q(6, -16)$ **40.** $P(-8, 2), Q(1, 2)$

41–44. Curves to parametric equations *Give a set of parametric equations that describes the following curves. Graph the curve and indicate the positive orientation. Be sure to specify the interval over which the parameter varies.*

41. The segment of the parabola $y = 2x^2 - 4$, where $-1 \le x \le 5$

42. The complete curve $x = y^3 - 3y$

43. The piecewise linear path from $P(-2, 3)$ to $Q(2, -3)$ to $R(3, 5)$

44. The path consisting of the line segment from $(-4, 4)$ to $(0, 8)$, followed by the segment of the parabola $y = 8 - 2x^2$ from $(0, 8)$ to $(2, 0)$

45–50. More parametric curves *Use a graphing utility to graph the following curves. Be sure to choose an interval for the parameter that generates all features of interest.*

45. Spiral $x = t \cos t, y = t \sin t; \ t \ge 0$

46. Witch of Agnesi $x = 2 \cot t, y = 1 - \cos 2t$

47. Folium of Descartes $x = \dfrac{3t}{1 + t^3}, y = \dfrac{3t^2}{1 + t^3}$

48. Involute of a circle $x = \cos t + t \sin t, y = \sin t - t \cos t$

49. Evolute of an ellipse $x = \dfrac{a^2 - b^2}{a} \cos^3 t, y = \dfrac{a^2 - b^2}{b} \sin^3 t$; $a = 4$ and $b = 3$

50. Cissoid of Diocles $x = 2 \sin 2t, y = \dfrac{2 \sin^3 t}{\cos t}$

51–54. Beautiful curves *Consider the family of curves*

$$x = \left(2 + \frac{1}{2} \sin at\right) \cos \left(t + \frac{\sin bt}{c}\right), y = \left(2 + \frac{1}{2} \sin at\right) \cdot$$

$$\sin \left(t + \frac{\sin bt}{c}\right). \textit{ Plot the curve for the given values of a, b, and c with}$$

$0 \le t \le 2\pi$. *(Source: Stan Wagon, Mathematica in Action, 3rd Ed., Springer; created by Norton Starr, Amherst College.)*

51. $a = b = 5, c = 2$ **52.** $a = 6, b = 12, c = 3$

53. $a = 18, b = 18, c = 7$ **54.** $a = 7, b = 4, c = 1$

55–60. Derivatives *Consider the following parametric curves.*

a. *Determine dy/dx in terms of t and evaluate it at the given value of t.*

b. *Make a sketch of the curve showing the tangent line at the point corresponding to the given value of t.*

55. $x = 2 + 4t, y = 4 - 8t; \ t = 2$

56. $x = 3 \sin t, y = 3 \cos t; \ t = \pi/2$

57. $x = \cos t, y = 8 \sin t; \ t = \pi/2$

58. $x = 2t, y = t^3; \ t = -1$

59. $x = t + 1/t, y = t - 1/t; \ t = 1$

60. $x = \sqrt{t}, y = 2t; \ t = 4$

Further Explorations

61. Explain why or why not Determine whether the following statements are true and give an explanation or counterexample.

a. The equations $x = -\cos t, y = -\sin t$, for $0 \le t \le 2\pi$, generate a circle in the clockwise direction.

b. An object following the parametric curve $x = 2 \cos 2\pi t$, $y = 2 \sin 2\pi t$ circles the origin once every 1 time unit.

c. The parametric equations $x = t$, $y = t^2$, for $t \geq 0$, describe the complete parabola $y = x^2$.

d. The parametric equations $x = \cos t$, $y = \sin t$, for $-\pi/2 \leq t \leq \pi/2$, describe a semicircle.

62–65. Tangent lines *Find an equation of the line tangent to the curve at the point corresponding to the given value of t.*

62. $x = \sin t$, $y = \cos t$; $t = \pi/4$

63. $x = t^2 - 1$, $y = t^3 + t$; $t = 2$

64. $x = e^t$, $y = \ln(t + 1)$; $t = 0$

65. $x = \cos t + t \sin t$, $y = \sin t - t \cos t$; $t = \pi/4$

66–69. Words to curves *Find parametric equations for the following curves. Include an interval for the parameter values.*

66. The left half of the parabola $y = x^2 + 1$, originating at $(0, 1)$

67. The line that passes through the points $(1, 1)$ and $(3, 5)$, oriented in the direction of increasing x

68. The lower half of the circle centered at $(-2, 2)$ with radius 6, oriented in the counterclockwise direction

69. The upper half of the parabola $x = y^2$, originating at $(0, 0)$

70. Matching curves and equations Match equations a–d with graphs A–D. Explain your reasoning.

a. $x = t^2 - 2$, $y = t^3 - t$
b. $x = \cos(t + \sin 50t)$, $y = \sin(t + \cos 50t)$
c. $x = t + \cos 2t$, $y = t - \sin 4t$
d. $x = 2\cos t + \cos 20t$, $y = 2\sin t + \sin 20t$

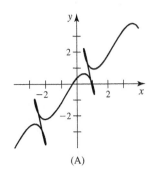

(A)

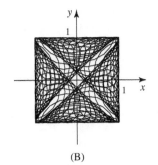

(B)

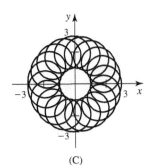

(C)

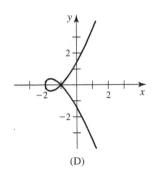

(D)

71–72. Ellipses *An **ellipse** (discussed in detail in Section 11.4) is generated by the parametric equations $x = a \cos t$, $y = b \sin t$. If $0 < a < b$, then the long axis (or **major axis**) lies on the y-axis and the short axis (or **minor axis**) lies on the x-axis. If $0 < b < a$, the axes are reversed. The lengths of the axes in the x- and y-directions are 2a and 2b, respectively. Sketch the graph of the following ellipses. Specify an interval in t over which the entire curve is generated.*

71. $x = 4 \cos t$, $y = 9 \sin t$

72. $x = 12 \sin 2t$, $y = 3 \cos 2t$

73–76. Parametric equations of ellipses *Find parametric equations (not unique) of the following ellipses (see Exercises 71–72). Graph the ellipse and find a description in terms of x and y.*

73. An ellipse centered at the origin with major axis of length 6 on the x-axis and minor axis of length 3 on the y-axis, generated counterclockwise

74. An ellipse centered at the origin with major and minor axes of lengths 12 and 2, on the x- and y-axes, respectively, generated clockwise

75. An ellipse centered at $(-2, -3)$ with major and minor axes of lengths 30 and 20, on the x- and y-axes, respectively, generated counterclockwise (*Hint:* Shift the parametric equations.)

76. An ellipse centered at $(0, -4)$ with major and minor axes of lengths 10 and 3, on the x- and y-axes, respectively, generated clockwise (*Hint:* Shift the parametric equations.)

77. Multiple descriptions Which of the following parametric equations describe the same line?

a. $x = 3 + t$, $y = 4 - 2t$; $-\infty < t < \infty$
b. $x = 3 + 4t$, $y = 4 - 8t$; $-\infty < t < \infty$
c. $x = 3 + t^3$, $y = 4 - t^3$; $-\infty < t < \infty$

78. Multiple descriptions Which of the following parametric equations describe the same curve?

a. $x = 2t^2$, $y = 4 + t$; $-4 \leq t \leq 4$
b. $x = 2t^4$, $y = 4 + t^2$; $-2 \leq t \leq 2$
c. $x = 2t^{2/3}$, $y = 4 + t^{1/3}$; $-64 \leq t \leq 64$

79–84. Eliminating the parameter *Eliminate the parameter to express the following parametric equations as a single equation in x and y.*

79. $x = 2 \sin 8t$, $y = 2 \cos 8t$ **80.** $x = 3 - t$, $y = 3 + t$

81. $x = t$, $y = \sqrt{4 - t^2}$ **82.** $x = \sqrt{t + 1}$, $y = \dfrac{1}{t + 1}$

83. $x = \tan t$, $y = \sec^2 t - 1$

84. $x = a \sin^n t$, $y = b \cos^n t$, where a and b are real numbers and n is a positive integer

85–88. Slopes of tangent lines *Find all the points on the following curves that have the given slope.*

85. $x = 4 \cos t$, $y = 4 \sin t$; slope $= \frac{1}{2}$

86. $x = 2 \cos t$, $y = 8 \sin t$; slope $= -1$

87. $x = t + 1/t, y = t - 1/t$; slope = 1

88. $x = 2 + \sqrt{t}, y = 2 - 4t$; slope = 0

89–90. Equivalent descriptions *Find real numbers a and b such that equations A and B describe the same curve.*

89. A: $x = 10 \sin t, y = 10 \cos t$; $0 \le t \le 2\pi$
B: $x = 10 \sin 3t, y = 10 \cos 3t$; $a \le t \le b$

90. A: $x = t + t^3, y = 3 + t^2$; $-2 \le t \le 2$
B: $x = t^{1/3} + t, y = 3 + t^{2/3}$; $a \le t \le b$

91–92. Lissajous curves *Consider the following Lissajous curves. Find all points on the curve at which there is (a) a horizontal tangent line and (b) a vertical tangent line. (See the Guided Project Parametric Art for more on Lissajous curves.)*

91. $x = \sin 2t, y = 2 \sin t$;
$0 \le t \le 2\pi$

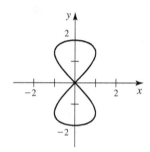

92. $x = \sin 4t, y = \sin 3t$;
$0 \le t \le 2\pi$

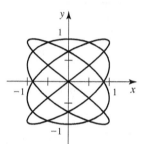

93. Lamé curves The *Lamé curve* described by $\left|\dfrac{x}{a}\right|^n + \left|\dfrac{y}{b}\right|^n = 1$, where a, b, and n are positive real numbers, is a generalization of an ellipse.

  a. Express this equation in parametric form (four sets of equations are needed).
  b. Graph the curve for $a = 4$ and $b = 2$, for various values of n.
  c. Describe how the curves change as n increases.

94. Hyperbolas A family of curves called *hyperbolas* (discussed in Section 11.4) has the parametric equations $x = a \tan t$, $y = b \sec t$, for $-\pi < t < \pi$ and $|t| \ne \pi/2$, where a and b are nonzero real numbers. Graph the hyperbola with $a = b = 1$. Indicate clearly the direction in which the curve is generated as t increases from $t = -\pi$ to $t = \pi$.

95. Trochoid explorations A *trochoid* is the path followed by a point b units from the center of a wheel of radius a as the wheel rolls along the x-axis. Its parametric description is $x = at - b \sin t$, $y = a - b \cos t$. Choose specific values of a and b, and use a graphing utility to plot different trochoids. In particular, explore the difference between the cases $a > b$ and $a < b$.

96. Epitrochoid An *epitrochoid* is the path of a point on a circle of radius b as it rolls on the outside of a circle of radius a. It is described by the equations

$$x = (a + b) \cos t - c \cos \left[\frac{(a + b)t}{b}\right]$$

$$y = (a + b) \sin t - c \sin \left[\frac{(a + b)t}{b}\right]$$

Use a graphing utility to explore the dependence of the curve on the parameters a, b, and c.

97. Hypocycloid A general *hypocycloid* is described by the equations

$$x = (a - b) \cos t + b \cos \left[\frac{(a - b)t}{b}\right]$$

$$y = (a - b) \sin t - b \sin \left[\frac{(a - b)t}{b}\right]$$

Use a graphing utility to explore the dependence of the curve on the parameters a and b.

Applications

98. Paths of moons An idealized model of the path of a moon (relative to the Sun) moving with constant speed in a circular orbit around a planet, where the planet in turn revolves around the Sun, is given by the parametric equations

$$x(\theta) = a \cos \theta + \cos n\theta, \quad y(\theta) = a \sin \theta + \sin n\theta.$$

The distance from the moon to the planet is taken to be 1, the distance from the planet to the Sun is a, and n is the number of times the moon orbits the planet for every 1 revolution of the planet around the Sun. Plot the graph of the path of a moon for the given constants, then conjecture which values of n produce loops for a fixed value of a.

  a. $a = 4, n = 3$ **b.** $a = 4, n = 4$ **c.** $a = 4, n = 5$

99. Paths of the moons of Earth and Jupiter Use the equations in Exercise 98 to plot the paths of the following moons in our solar system.

  a. Each year our moon revolves around Earth about $n = 13.4$ times and the distance from the Sun to Earth is approximately $a = 389.2$ times the distance from Earth to our moon.
  b. Plot a graph of the path of Callisto (one of Jupiter's moons) that corresponds to values of $a = 727.5$ and $n = 259.6$. Plot a small portion of the graph to see the behavior of the orbit.
  c. Plot a graph of the path of Io (another of Jupiter's moons) that corresponds to values of $a = 1846.2$ and $n = 2448.8$. Plot a small portion of the path of Io to see the loops in the orbits.

(Source for Exercises 98, 99: The Sun, the Moon, and Convexity, by Noah Samuel Brannen, The College Mathematics Journal, September 2001, Vol. 32, No. 4.)

100. Air drop A plane traveling horizontally at 80 m/s over flat ground at an elevation of 3000 m releases an emergency packet. The trajectory of the packet is given by

$$x = 80t, \quad y = -4.9t^2 + 3000, \quad \text{for } t \geq 0,$$

where the origin is the point on the ground directly beneath the plane at the moment of the release. Graph the trajectory of the packet and find the coordinates of the point where the packet lands.

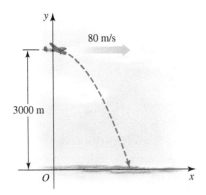

101. Air drop—inverse problem A plane traveling horizontally at 100 m/s over flat ground at an elevation of 4000 m must drop an emergency packet on a target on the ground. The trajectory of the packet is given by

$$x = 100t, \quad y = -4.9t^2 + 4000, \quad \text{for } t \geq 0,$$

where the origin is the point on the ground directly beneath the plane at the moment of the release. How many horizontal meters before the target should the packet be released in order to hit the target?

102. Projectile explorations A projectile launched from the ground with an initial speed of 20 m/s and a launch angle θ follows a trajectory approximated by

$$x = (20 \cos \theta)t, \quad y = -4.9t^2 + (20 \sin \theta)t,$$

where x and y are the horizontal and vertical positions of the projectile relative to the launch point $(0, 0)$.

a. Graph the trajectory for various values of θ in the range $0 < \theta < \pi/2$.

b. Based on your observations, what value of θ gives the greatest range (the horizontal distance between the launch and landing points)?

Additional Exercises

103. Implicit function graph Explain and carry out a method for graphing the curve $x = 1 + \cos^2 y - \sin^2 y$ using parametric equations and a graphing utility.

104. Second derivative Assume a curve is given by the parametric equations $x = g(t)$ and $y = h(t)$, where g and h are twice differentiable. Use the Chain Rule to show that

$$y''(x) = \frac{x'(t)y''(t) - y'(t)x''(t)}{(x'(t))^3}.$$

105. General equations for a circle Prove that the equations

$$x = a \cos t + b \sin t, \quad y = c \cos t + d \sin t,$$

where a, b, c, and d are real numbers, describe a circle of radius R provided $a^2 + c^2 = b^2 + d^2 = R^2$ and $ab + cd = 0$.

106. x^y versus y^x Consider positive real numbers x and y. Notice that $4^3 < 3^4$, while $3^2 > 2^3$, and $4^2 = 2^4$. Describe the regions in the first quadrant of the xy-plane in which $x^y > y^x$ and $x^y < y^x$. (*Hint:* Find a parametric description of the curve that separates the two regions.)

QUICK CHECK ANSWERS

1. A segment of the parabola $x = y^2$ opening to the right with vertex at the origin **2.** The circle has center $(0, 0)$ and radius 3; it is generated in the counterclockwise direction (positive orientation) starting at $(0, -3)$. **3.** The line $y = -3x - 3$ with slope -3 passing through $(3, -12)$ (when $t = 0$) **4.** One possibility is $x = -2t, y = 3 - 3t$, for $0 \leq t \leq 1$. ◄

11.2 Polar Coordinates

Suppose you work for a company that designs heat shields for space vehicles. The shields are thin plates that are either rectangular or circular in shape. To solve the heat transfer equations for these two shields, you must choose a coordinate system that best fits the geometry of the problem. A Cartesian (rectangular) coordinate system is a natural choice for the rectangular shields (Figure 11.17a). However, it does not provide a good fit for the circular shields (Figure 11.17b). On the other hand, a **polar coordinate** system, in which the coordinates are constant on circles and rays, is much better suited for the circular shields (Figure 11.17c).

> Recall that the terms *Cartesian* coordinate system and *rectangular* coordinate system both describe the usual xy-coordinate system.

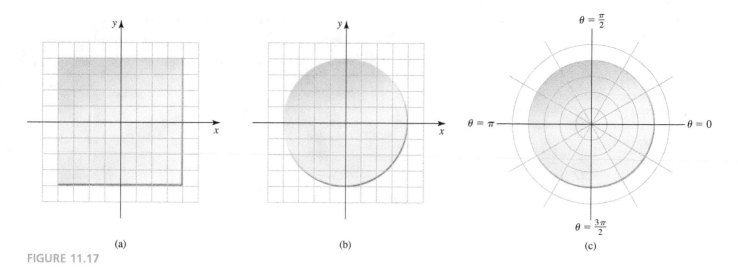

FIGURE 11.17

> Polar points and curves are plotted on a rectangular coordinate system, with standard "*x*" and "*y*" labels attached to the axes. However, plotting polar points and curves is often easier using polar graph paper, which has concentric circles centered at the origin and rays emanating from the origin (Figure 11.19).

QUICK CHECK 1 Which of the following coordinates represent the same point: $(3, \pi/2)$, $(3, 3\pi/2)$, $(3, 5\pi/2)$, $(-3, -\pi/2)$, and $(-3, 3\pi/2)$? ◄

Defining Polar Coordinates

Like Cartesian coordinates, polar coordinates are used to locate points in the plane. When working in polar coordinates, the origin of the coordinate system is also called the **pole**, and the positive *x*-axis is called the **polar axis**. The polar coordinates for a point *P* have the form (r, θ). **The radial coordinate** *r* describes the *signed*, or *directed*, distance from the origin to *P*. The **angular coordinate** θ describes an angle whose initial side is the positive *x*-axis and whose terminal side lies on the ray passing through the origin and *P* (Figure 11.18a). Positive angles are measured counterclockwise from the positive *x*-axis.

With polar coordinates, points have more than one representation for two reasons. First, angles are determined up to multiples of 2π radians, so the coordinates (r, θ) and $(r, \theta \pm 2\pi)$ refer to the same point (Figure 11.18b). Second, the radial coordinate may be negative, which is interpreted as follows: The points (r, θ) and $(-r, \theta)$ are reflections of each other through the origin (Figure 11.18c). This means that (r, θ), $(-r, \theta + \pi)$, and $(-r, \theta - \pi)$ all refer to the same point. The origin is specified as $(0, \theta)$ in polar coordinates, where θ is any angle.

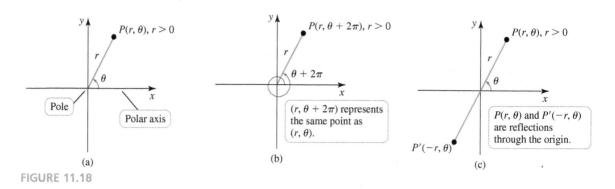

FIGURE 11.18

EXAMPLE 1   **Points in polar coordinates** Graph the following points in polar coordinates: $Q\left(1, \frac{5\pi}{4}\right)$, $R\left(-1, \frac{7\pi}{4}\right)$, and $S\left(2, -\frac{3\pi}{2}\right)$. Give two alternative representations for each point.

SOLUTION The point $Q\left(1, \frac{5\pi}{4}\right)$ is one unit from the origin on a line OQ that makes an angle of $\frac{5\pi}{4}$ with the positive *x*-axis (Figure 11.19a). Subtracting 2π from the angle, the point Q can be represented as $\left(1, -\frac{3\pi}{4}\right)$. Subtracting π from the angle and negating the radial coordinate means Q also has the coordinates $\left(-1, \frac{\pi}{4}\right)$.

To locate the point $R\left(-1, \frac{7\pi}{4}\right)$, it is easiest first to find the point $R'\left(1, \frac{7\pi}{4}\right)$ in the fourth quadrant. Then, $R\left(-1, \frac{7\pi}{4}\right)$ is the reflection of R' through the origin (Figure 11.19b). Other representations of R include $\left(-1, -\frac{\pi}{4}\right)$ and $\left(1, \frac{3\pi}{4}\right)$.

The point $S\left(2, -\frac{3\pi}{2}\right)$ is two units from the origin, found by rotating *clockwise* through an angle of $\frac{3\pi}{2}$ (Figure 11.19c). The point S can also be represented as $\left(2, \frac{\pi}{2}\right)$ or $\left(-2, -\frac{\pi}{2}\right)$.

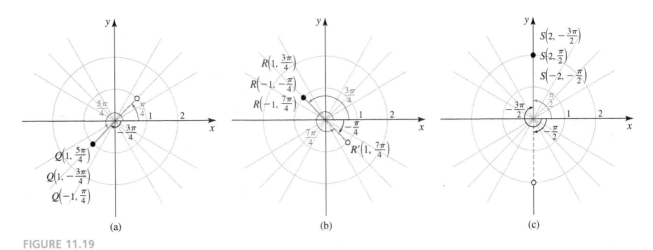

(a)   (b)   (c)

FIGURE 11.19

Related Exercises 9–14 ◄

Converting Between Cartesian and Polar Coordinates

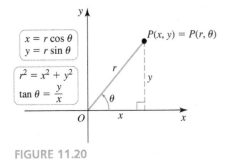

$$x = r\cos\theta$$
$$y = r\sin\theta$$

$$r^2 = x^2 + y^2$$
$$\tan\theta = \frac{y}{x}$$

FIGURE 11.20

We often need to convert between Cartesian and polar coordinates. The conversion equations emerge when we look at a right triangle (Figure 11.20) in which

$$\cos\theta = \frac{x}{r} \quad \text{and} \quad \sin\theta = \frac{y}{r}.$$

Given a point with polar coordinates (r, θ), we see that its Cartesian coordinates are $x = r\cos\theta$ and $y = r\sin\theta$. Conversely, given a point with Cartesian coordinates (x, y), its radial polar coordinate satisfies $r^2 = x^2 + y^2$. The coordinate θ is determined using the relation $\tan\theta = y/x$, where the quadrant in which θ lies is determined by the signs of x and y. Figure 11.20 illustrates the conversion formulas for a point P in the first quadrant. The same relationships hold if P is in any of the other three quadrants.

QUICK CHECK 2 Draw versions of Figure 11.20 with P in the second, third, and fourth quadrants. Verify that the same conversion formulas hold in all cases. ◄

> To determine θ, you may also use the relationships $\cos\theta = x/r$ and $\sin\theta = y/r$. Either method requires checking the signs of x and y to be sure that θ is in the correct quadrant.

PROCEDURE   Converting Coordinates

A point with polar coordinates (r, θ) has Cartesian coordinates (x, y), where

$$x = r\cos\theta \quad \text{and} \quad y = r\sin\theta.$$

A point with Cartesian coordinates (x, y) has polar coordinates (r, θ), where

$$r^2 = x^2 + y^2 \quad \text{and} \quad \tan\theta = y/x.$$

EXAMPLE 2   Converting coordinates

a. Express the point with polar coordinates $P\left(2, \frac{3\pi}{4}\right)$ in Cartesian coordinates.

b. Express the point with Cartesian coordinates $Q(1, -1)$ in polar coordinates.

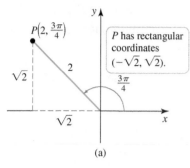

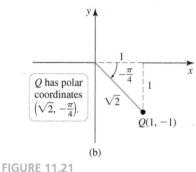

(a)

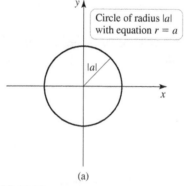

(b)

FIGURE 11.21

> If the equation $\theta = \theta_0$ is accompanied by the condition $r \geq 0$, the resulting set of points is a *ray* emanating from the origin.

SOLUTION

a. The point P has Cartesian coordinates

$$x = r \cos \theta = 2 \cos \left(\tfrac{3\pi}{4}\right) = -\sqrt{2}$$
$$y = r \sin \theta = 2 \sin \left(\tfrac{3\pi}{4}\right) = \sqrt{2}.$$

As shown in Figure 11.21a, P is in the second quadrant.

b. It's best to locate this point first to be sure that the angle θ is chosen correctly. As shown in Figure 11.21b, the point $Q(1, -1)$ is in the fourth quadrant at a distance $r = \sqrt{1^2 + (-1)^2} = \sqrt{2}$ from the origin. The coordinate θ satisfies

$$\tan \theta = \frac{y}{x} = \frac{-1}{1} = -1.$$

The angle in the fourth quadrant with $\tan \theta = -1$ is $\theta = -\frac{\pi}{4}$ or $\frac{7\pi}{4}$. Therefore, two (of infinitely many) polar representations of Q are $\left(\sqrt{2}, -\frac{\pi}{4}\right)$ and $\left(\sqrt{2}, \frac{7\pi}{4}\right)$.

Related Exercises 15–26◀

QUICK CHECK 3 Give two polar coordinate descriptions of the point with Cartesian coordinates $(1, 0)$. What are the Cartesian coordinates of the point with polar coordinates $\left(2, \frac{\pi}{2}\right)$? ◀

Basic Curves in Polar Coordinates

A curve in polar coordinates is the set of points that satisfy an equation in r and θ. Some sets of points are easier to describe in polar coordinates than in Cartesian coordinates. Let's begin with two simple curves.

The polar equation $r = 3$ is satisfied by the set of points whose distance from the origin is 3. The angle θ is arbitrary because it is not specified by the equation, so the graph of $r = 3$ is the circle of radius 3 centered at the origin. In general, the equation $r = a$ describes a circle of radius $|a|$ centered at the origin (Figure 11.22a).

The equation $\theta = \pi/3$ is satisfied by the points whose angle with respect to the positive x-axis is $\pi/3$. Because r is unspecified, it is arbitrary (and can be positive or negative). Therefore, $\theta = \pi/3$ describes the line through the origin making an angle of $\pi/3$ with the positive x-axis. More generally, $\theta = \theta_0$ describes the line through the origin making an angle of θ_0 with the positive x-axis (Figure 11.22b).

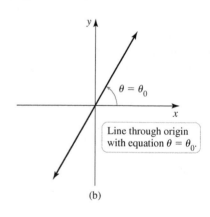

(a)

(b)

FIGURE 11.22

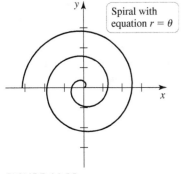

The simplest polar equation that involves both r and θ is $r = \theta$. Restricting θ to the interval $\theta \geq 0$, we see that as θ increases, r increases. Therefore, as θ increases, the points on the curve move away from the origin as they circle the origin in a counterclockwise direction, generating a spiral (Figure 11.23).

QUICK CHECK 4 Describe the polar curves $r = 12$, $r = 6\theta$, and $r\sin\theta = 10$. ◄

EXAMPLE 3   **Polar to Cartesian coordinates** Convert the polar equation $r = 6\sin\theta$ to Cartesian coordinates and describe the corresponding graph.

SOLUTION We first assume that $r \neq 0$ and multiply both sides of the equation by r, which produces the equation $r^2 = 6r\sin\theta$. Using the conversion relations $r^2 = x^2 + y^2$ and $y = r\sin\theta$, the equation

$$\underbrace{r^2}_{x^2+y^2} = \underbrace{6r\sin\theta}_{6y}$$

becomes $x^2 + y^2 - 6y = 0$. Completing the square gives the equation

$$x^2 + \underbrace{y^2 - 6y + 9}_{(y-3)^2} - 9 = x^2 + (y-3)^2 - 9 = 0.$$

We recognize $x^2 + (y-3)^2 = 9$ as the equation of a circle of radius 3 centered at $(0, 3)$ (Figure 11.24).

Related Exercises 27–36 ◄

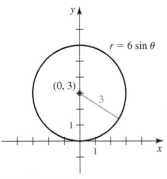

Calculations similar to those in Example 3 lead to the following equations of circles in polar coordinates.

SUMMARY   Circles in Polar Coordinates

The equation $r = a$ describes a circle of radius $|a|$ centered at $(0, 0)$.

The equation $r = 2a\sin\theta$ describes a circle of radius $|a|$ centered at $(0, a)$.

The equation $r = 2a\cos\theta$ describes a circle of radius $|a|$ centered at $(a, 0)$.

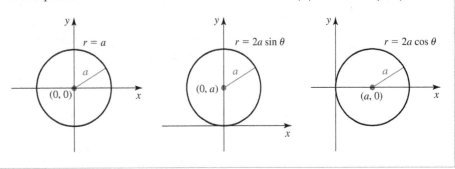

Graphing in Polar Coordinates

Equations in polar coordinates often describe curves that are difficult to represent in Cartesian coordinates. Partly for this reason, curve-sketching methods for polar coordinates differ from those used for curves in Cartesian coordinates. Conceptually, the easiest graphing method is to choose several values of θ, calculate the corresponding r-values, and tabulate the coordinates. The points are then plotted and connected with a smooth curve.

> When a curve is described as $r = f(\theta)$, it is natural to tabulate points in θ-r format, just as we list points in x-y format for $y = f(x)$. Despite this fact, the standard form for writing an ordered pair in polar coordinates is (r, θ).

EXAMPLE 4 **Plotting a polar curve** Graph the polar equation $r = f(\theta) = 1 + \sin\theta$.

SOLUTION The domain of f consists of all real values of θ; however, the complete curve is generated by letting θ vary over any interval of length 2π. Table 11.3 shows several (r, θ) pairs, which are plotted in Figure 11.25. The resulting curve, called a **cardioid**, is symmetric about the y-axis.

Table 11.3

θ	$r = 1 + \sin\theta$
0	1
$\pi/6$	3/2
$\pi/2$	2
$5\pi/6$	3/2
π	1
$7\pi/6$	1/2
$3\pi/2$	0
$11\pi/6$	1/2
2π	1

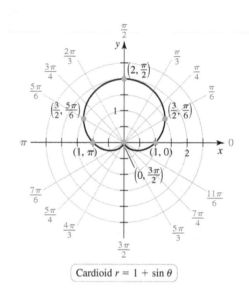

Cardioid $r = 1 + \sin\theta$

FIGURE 11.25

Related Exercises 37–48 ◄

Cartesian-to-Polar Method Plotting polar curves point by point is time consuming, and important details may not be revealed. Here is an alternative procedure for graphing polar curves that is usually quicker and more reliable.

> For some (but not all) curves, it suffices to graph $r = f(\theta)$ over any interval in θ whose length is the period of f. See Examples 6 and 9 for exceptions.

PROCEDURE   **Cartesian-to-Polar Method for Graphing $r = f(\theta)$**

1. Graph $r = f(\theta)$ *as if r and θ were Cartesian coordinates* with θ on the horizontal axis and r on the vertical axis. Be sure to choose an interval in θ on which the entire polar curve is produced.

2. Use the Cartesian graph in Step 1 as a guide to sketch the points (r, θ) on the final *polar* curve.

EXAMPLE 5 **Plotting polar graphs** Use the Cartesian-to-polar method to graph the polar equation $r = 1 + \sin\theta$ (Example 4).

SOLUTION Viewing r and θ as Cartesian coordinates, the graph of $r = 1 + \sin\theta$ on the interval $[0, 2\pi]$ is a standard sine curve with amplitude 1 shifted up 1 unit (Figure 11.26). Notice that the graph begins with $r = 1$ at $\theta = 0$, increases to $r = 2$ at $\theta = \pi/2$, decreases to $r = 0$ at $\theta = 3\pi/2$ (which indicates an intersection with the origin on the polar graph), and increases to $r = 1$ at $\theta = 2\pi$. The second row of Figure 11.26 shows the final polar curve (a cardioid) as it is transferred from the Cartesian curve.

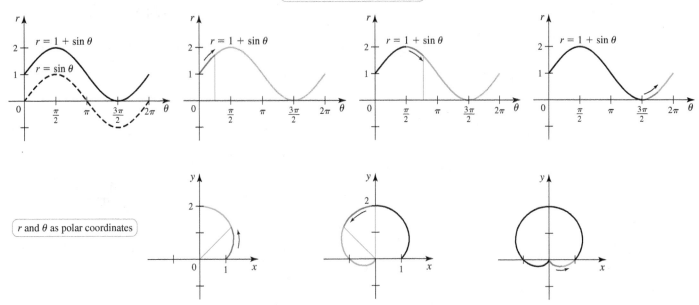

r and θ as Cartesian coordinates

r and θ as polar coordinates

FIGURE 11.26

Related Exercises 37–48 ◄

Symmetry   Given a polar equation in r and θ, three types of symmetry are easy to spot (Figure 11.27).

> Any two of these three symmetries implies the third. For example, if a graph is symmetric about both the x- and y-axes, then it must be symmetric about the origin.

SUMMARY   Symmetry in Polar Equations

Symmetry about the x-axis occurs if the point (r, θ) is on the graph whenever $(r, -\theta)$ is on the graph.

Symmetry about the y-axis occurs if the point (r, θ) is on the graph whenever $(r, \pi - \theta) = (-r, -\theta)$ is on the graph.

Symmetry about the origin occurs if the point (r, θ) is on the graph whenever $(-r, \theta) = (r, \theta + \pi)$ is on the graph.

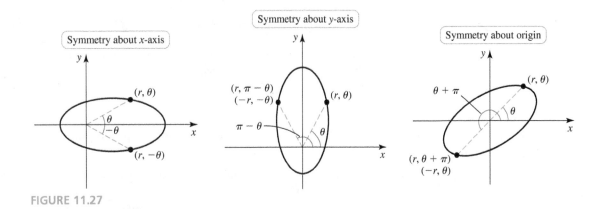

FIGURE 11.27

QUICK CHECK 5 Identify the symmetry in the graph of (a) $r = 4 + 4\cos\theta$ and (b) $r = 4\sin\theta$. ◄

For instance, consider the polar equation $r = 1 + \sin\theta$ in Example 5. If (r, θ) satisfies the equation, then $(r, \pi - \theta)$ also satisfies the equation because $\sin\theta = \sin(\pi - \theta)$. Therefore, the graph is symmetric about the y-axis, as shown in Figure 11.26. Testing for symmetry produces a more accurate graph and often simplifies the task of graphing polar equations.

EXAMPLE 6   Plotting polar graphs Graph the polar equation $r = 3 \sin 2\theta$.

SOLUTION The Cartesian graph of $r = 3 \sin 2\theta$ on the interval $[0, 2\pi]$ has amplitude 3 and period π (Figure 11.28). The θ-intercepts occur at $\theta = 0, \pi/2, \pi, 3\pi/2$, and 2π, which correspond to the intersections with the origin on the polar graph. Furthermore, the arches of the Cartesian curve between θ-intercepts correspond to loops in the polar curve. The resulting polar curve is a **four-leaf rose** (Figure 11.28).

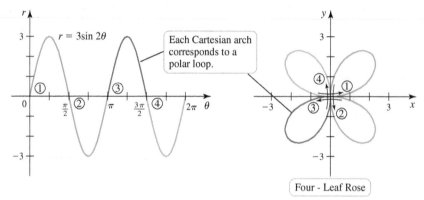

FIGURE 11.28

The graph is symmetric about the x-axis, the y-axis, and the origin. It is instructive to see how these symmetries are justified. To prove symmetry about the y-axis, notice that

$$\begin{aligned}
(r, \theta) \text{ on the graph} &\Rightarrow r = 3 \sin 2\theta \\
&\Rightarrow r = -3 \sin 2(-\theta) \qquad \sin(-\theta) = -\sin\theta \\
&\Rightarrow -r = 3 \sin 2(-\theta) \qquad \text{Simplify.} \\
&\Rightarrow (-r, -\theta) \text{ on the graph.}
\end{aligned}$$

We see that if (r, θ) is on the graph, then $(-r, -\theta)$ is also on the graph, which implies symmetry about the y-axis. Similarly, to prove symmetry about the origin, notice that

$$\begin{aligned}
(r, \theta) \text{ on the graph} &\Rightarrow r = 3 \sin 2\theta \\
&\Rightarrow r = 3 \sin(2\theta + 2\pi) \qquad \sin(\theta + 2\pi) = \sin\theta \\
&\Rightarrow r = 3 \sin[2(\theta + \pi)] \qquad \text{Simplify.} \\
&\Rightarrow (r, \theta + \pi) \text{ on the graph.}
\end{aligned}$$

We have shown that if (r, θ) is on the graph, then $(r, \theta + \pi)$ is also on the graph, which implies symmetry about the origin. Symmetry about the y-axis and the origin imply symmetry about the x-axis. Had we proved these symmetries in advance, we could have graphed the curve only in the first quadrant—reflections about the x- and y-axes would produce the full curve.

Related Exercises 37–48 ◄

> **Subtle Point**
>
> The fact that one point has several representations in polar coordinates presents potential pitfalls. In Example 6, you can show that $(-r, \theta)$ does *not* satisfy the equation $r = 3 \sin 2\theta$ when (r, θ) satisfies the equation. And yet, as shown, the graph is symmetric about the origin because $(r, \theta + \pi)$ satisfies the equation whenever (r, θ) satisfies the equation. Note that $(-r, \theta)$ and $(r, \theta + \pi)$ are the same point.

EXAMPLE 7   Plotting polar graphs Graph the polar equation $r^2 = 9 \cos \theta$. Use a graphing utility to check your work.

SOLUTION The graph of this equation has symmetry about the origin (because of the r^2) and about the x-axis (because of $\cos \theta$). These two symmetries imply symmetry about the y-axis.

A preliminary step is required before using the Cartesian-to-polar method for graphing the curve. Solving the given equation for r, we find that $r = \pm 3\sqrt{\cos \theta}$. Notice that $\cos \theta < 0$, for $\pi/2 < \theta < 3\pi/2$, so the curve does not exist on that interval. Therefore, we plot the curve on the intervals $0 \le \theta \le \pi/2$ and $3\pi/2 \le \theta \le 2\pi$ (the interval

$[-\pi/2, \pi/2]$ would also work). Both the positive and negative values of r are included in the Cartesian graph (Figure 11.29a).

Now we are ready to transfer points from the Cartesian graph to the final polar graph (Figure 11.29b). The resulting curve is called a **lemniscate**.

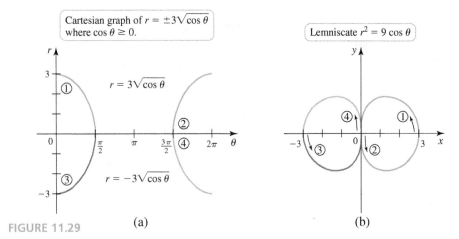

FIGURE 11.29 (a) (b)

Related Exercises 37–48 ◄

EXAMPLE 8 **Matching polar and Cartesian graphs** The butterfly curve

$$r = e^{\sin\theta} - 2\cos 4\theta, \quad \text{for } 0 \le \theta \le 2\pi,$$

is plotted in polar coordinates in Figure 11.30b. The same function, $r = e^{\sin\theta} - 2\cos 4\theta$, is plotted in a Cartesian coordinate system with θ on the horizontal axis and r on the vertical axis (Figure 11.30a). Follow the Cartesian graph through the points $A, B, C, \ldots, N, O$ and mark the corresponding points on the polar curve.

SOLUTION Point A in Figure 11.30a has the Cartesian coordinates $(\theta = 0, r = -1)$. The corresponding point in the polar plot (Figure 11.30b) with polar coordinates $(-1, 0)$ is marked A. Point B in the Cartesian plot is on the θ-axis; therefore, $r = 0$. The corresponding point in the polar plot is the origin. The same argument used to locate B applies to $F, H, J, L,$ and N, all of which appear at the origin in the polar plot. In general, the local and endpoint maxima and minima in the Cartesian graph $(A, C, D, E, G, I, K, M,$ and $O)$ correspond to the extreme points of the loops of the polar plot and are marked accordingly in Figure 11.30b.

> See Exercise 107 for a spectacular enhancement of the butterfly curve.

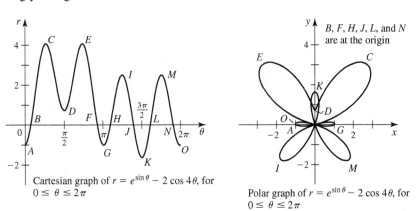

Cartesian graph of $r = e^{\sin\theta} - 2\cos 4\theta$, for $0 \le \theta \le 2\pi$

Polar graph of $r = e^{\sin\theta} - 2\cos 4\theta$, for $0 \le \theta \le 2\pi$

FIGURE 11.30

(*Source:* The butterfly curve is due to T. H. Fay, *Amer. Math. Monthly* **96** (1989), revived in Wagon and Packel, *Animating Calculus*, Freeman, 1994.)

Related Exercises 49–52 ◄

Using Graphing Utilities

With many graphing utilities, it is necessary to specify an interval in θ that generates the entire curve. In some cases, this problem is a challenge in itself.

> **Using a parametric equation plotter to graph polar curves**
>
> To graph $r = f(\theta)$, treat θ as a parameter and define the parametric equations
>
> $$x = r\cos\theta = \underbrace{f(\theta)}_{r}\cos\theta$$
>
> $$y = r\sin\theta = \underbrace{f(\theta)}_{r}\sin\theta$$
>
> Then graph $(x(\theta), y(\theta))$ as a parametric curve with θ as the parameter.

> Once P is found, the complete curve is generated as θ varies over any interval of length P. This choice of P described here ensures that the complete curve is generated. Smaller values of P work in some cases.

EXAMPLE 9 **Plotting complete curves** Consider the curve described by $r = \cos(2\theta/5)$. Give an interval in θ that generates the entire curve and then graph the curve.

SOLUTION Recall that $\cos\theta$ has a period of 2π. Therefore, $\cos(2\theta/5)$ completes one cycle when $2\theta/5$ varies from 0 to 2π, or when θ varies from 0 to 5π. Therefore, it is tempting to conclude that the complete curve $r = \cos(2\theta/5)$ is generated as θ varies from 0 to 5π. But you can check that the point corresponding to $\theta = 0$ is *not* the point corresponding to $\theta = 5\pi$, which means the curve does not close on itself over the interval $[0, 5\pi]$ (Figure 11.31a).

In general, an interval $[0, P]$ over which the complete curve $r = f(\theta)$ is guaranteed to be generated must satisfy two conditions: P is the smallest positive number such that

- P is a multiple of the period of f (so that $f(0) = f(P)$), and
- P is a multiple of 2π (so that the points $(0, f(0))$ and $(P, f(P))$ are the same).

To graph the *complete* curve $r = \cos(2\theta/5)$, we must find an interval $[0, P]$, where P is a multiple of 5π and a multiple of 2π. The smallest number satisfying these conditions is 10π. Graphing $r = \cos(2\theta/5)$ over the interval $[0, 10\pi]$ produces the complete curve (Figure 11.31b).

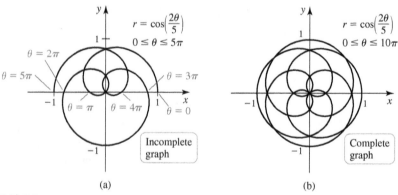

(a)   (b)

FIGURE 11.31

Related Exercises 53–60 ◄

SECTION 11.2 EXERCISES

Review Questions

1. Plot the points with polar coordinates $(2, \frac{\pi}{6})$ and $(-3, -\frac{\pi}{2})$. Give two alternative sets of coordinate pairs for both points.

2. Write the equations that are used to express a point with polar coordinates (r, θ) in Cartesian coordinates.

3. Write the equations that are used to express a point with Cartesian coordinates (x, y) in polar coordinates.

4. What is the polar equation of a circle of radius $|a|$ centered at the origin?

5. What is the polar equation of the vertical line $x = 5$?

6. What is the polar equation of the horizontal line $y = 5$?

7. Explain three symmetries in polar graphs and how they are detected in equations.

8. Explain the Cartesian-to-polar method for graphing polar curves.

Basic Skills

9–13. *Graph the points with the following polar coordinates. Give two alternative representations of the points in polar coordinates.*

9. $(2, \frac{\pi}{4})$ 10. $(3, \frac{2\pi}{3})$ 11. $(-1, -\frac{\pi}{3})$

12. $(2, \frac{7\pi}{4})$ 13. $(-4, \frac{3\pi}{2})$

14. Points in polar coordinates *Give two sets of polar coordinates for each of the points A–F in the figure.*

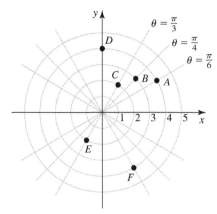

15–20. Converting coordinates *Express the following polar coordinates in Cartesian coordinates.*

15. $\left(3, \frac{\pi}{4}\right)$ **16.** $\left(1, \frac{2\pi}{3}\right)$ **17.** $\left(1, -\frac{\pi}{3}\right)$

18. $\left(2, \frac{7\pi}{4}\right)$ **19.** $\left(-4, \frac{3\pi}{4}\right)$ **20.** $(4, 5\pi)$

21–26. Converting coordinates *Express the following Cartesian coordinates in polar coordinates in at least two different ways.*

21. $(2, 2)$ **22.** $(-1, 0)$

23. $\left(1, \sqrt{3}\right)$ **24.** $(-9, 0)$

25. $\left(-4, 4\sqrt{3}\right)$ **26.** $\left(4, 4\sqrt{3}\right)$

27–36. Polar-to-Cartesian coordinates *Convert the following equations to Cartesian coordinates. Describe the resulting curve.*

27. $r\cos\theta = -4$ **28.** $r = \cot\theta\csc\theta$

29. $r = 2$ **30.** $r = 3\csc\theta$

31. $r = 2\sin\theta + 2\cos\theta$ **32.** $\sin\theta = |\cos\theta|$

33. $r\cos\theta = \sin 2\theta$ **34.** $r = \sin\theta\sec^2\theta$

35. $r = 8\sin\theta$ **36.** $r = \dfrac{1}{2\cos\theta + 3\sin\theta}$

37–40. Simple curves *Tabulate and plot enough points to sketch a graph of the following equations.*

37. $r = 8\cos\theta$ **38.** $r = 4 + 4\cos\theta$

39. $r(\sin\theta - 2\cos\theta) = 0$ **40.** $r = 1 - \cos\theta$

41–48. Graphing polar curves *Graph the following equations. Use a graphing utility to check your work and produce a final graph.*

41. $r = 1 - \sin\theta$ **42.** $r = 2 - 2\sin\theta$

43. $r = \sin^2(\theta/2)$ **44.** $r^2 = 4\sin\theta$

45. $r^2 = 16\cos\theta$ **46.** $r^2 = 16\sin 2\theta$

47. $r = \sin 3\theta$ **48.** $r = 2\sin 5\theta$

49–52. Matching polar and Cartesian curves *A Cartesian and a polar graph of $r = f(\theta)$ are given in the figures. Mark the points on the polar graph that correspond to the points shown on the Cartesian graph.*

49. $r = 1 - 2\sin 3\theta$

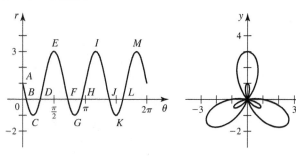

50. $r = \sin(1 + 3\cos\theta)$

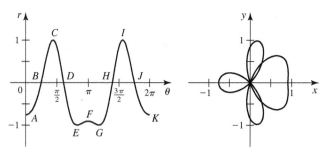

51. $r = \dfrac{1}{4} - \cos 4\theta$

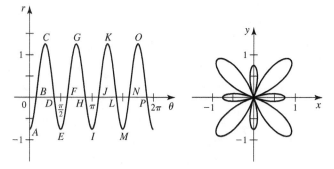

52. $r = \cos\theta + \sin 2\theta$

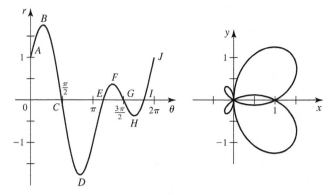

53–60. Using a graphing utility *Use a graphing utility to graph the following equations. In each case, give the smallest interval $[0, P]$ that generates the entire curve (if possible).*

53. $r = \theta\sin\theta$ **54.** $r = 2 - 4\cos 5\theta$

55. $r = \cos 3\theta + \cos^2 2\theta$ **56.** $r = \sin^2 2\theta + 2\sin 2\theta$

57. $r = \cos(3\theta/5)$ **58.** $r = \sin(3\theta/7)$

59. $r = 1 - 3\cos 2\theta$ **60.** $r = 1 - 2\sin 5\theta$

Further Explorations

61. Explain why or why not Determine whether the following statements are true and give an explanation or counterexample.

   a. The point with Cartesian coordinates $(-2, 2)$ has polar coordinates $(2\sqrt{2}, 3\pi/4)$, $(2\sqrt{2}, 11\pi/4)$, $(2\sqrt{2}, -5\pi/4)$, and $(-2\sqrt{2}, -\pi/4)$.

   b. The graphs of $r\cos\theta = 4$ and $r\sin\theta = -2$ intersect exactly once.

   c. The graphs of $r = 2$ and $\theta = \pi/4$ intersect exactly once.

   d. The point $(3, \pi/2)$ lies on the graph of $r = 3\cos 2\theta$.

   e. The graphs of $r = 2\sec\theta$ and $r = 3\csc\theta$ are lines.

62–65. Cartesian-to-polar coordinates *Convert the following equations to polar coordinates.*

62. $y = 3$ **63.** $y = x^2$

64. $(x - 1)^2 + y^2 = 1$ **65.** $y = 1/x$

66–73. Sets in polar coordinates *Sketch the following sets of points.*

66. $\{(r, \theta): r = 3\}$

67. $\{(r, \theta): \theta = 2\pi/3\}$

68. $\{(r, \theta): 2 \le r \le 8\}$

69. $\{(r, \theta): \pi/2 \le \theta \le 3\pi/4\}$

70. $\{(r, \theta): 1 < r < 2 \text{ and } \pi/6 \le \theta \le \pi/3\}$

71. $\{(r, \theta): |\theta| \le \pi/3\}$

72. $\{(r, \theta): |r| < 3 \text{ and } 0 \le \theta \le \pi\}$

73. $\{(r, \theta): r \ge 2\}$

74. Circles in general Show that the polar equation

$$r^2 - 2r(a\cos\theta + b\sin\theta) = R^2 - a^2 - b^2$$

describes a circle of radius R centered at (a, b).

75. Circles in general Show that the polar equation

$$r^2 - 2rr_0\cos(\theta - \theta_0) = R^2 - r_0^2$$

describes a circle of radius R whose center has polar coordinates (r_0, θ_0).

76–81. Equations of circles *Use the results of Exercises 74–75 to describe and graph the following circles.*

76. $r^2 - 6r\cos\theta = 16$

77. $r^2 - 4r\cos(\theta - \pi/3) = 12$

78. $r^2 - 8r\cos(\theta - \pi/2) = 9$

79. $r^2 - 2r(2\cos\theta + 3\sin\theta) = 3$

80. $r^2 + 2r(\cos\theta - 3\sin\theta) = 4$

81. $r^2 - 2r(-\cos\theta + 2\sin\theta) = 4$

82. Equations of circles Find equations of the circles in the figure. Determine whether the combined area of the circles is greater

than or less than the area of the region inside the square but outside the circles.

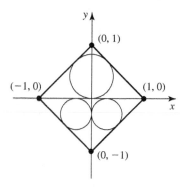

83. Vertical lines Consider the polar curve $r = 2\sec\theta$.

   a. Graph the curve on the intervals $(\pi/2, 3\pi/2)$, $(3\pi/2, 5\pi/2)$, and $(5\pi/2, 7\pi/2)$. In each case, state the direction in which the curve is generated as θ increases.

   b. Show that on any interval $(n\pi/2, (n + 2)\pi/2)$, where n is an odd integer, the graph is the vertical line $x = 2$.

84. Lines in polar coordinates

   a. Show that an equation of the line $y = mx + b$ in polar coordinates is $r = \dfrac{b}{\sin\theta - m\cos\theta}$.

   b. Use the figure to find an alternative polar equation of a line, $r\cos(\theta_0 - \theta) = r_0$. Note that $Q(r_0, \theta_0)$ is a fixed point on the line such that OQ is perpendicular to the line and $r_0 \ge 0$; $P(r, \theta)$ is an arbitrary point on the line.

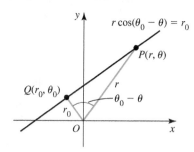

85–88. Equations of lines *Use the result of Exercise 84 to describe and graph the following lines.*

85. $r\cos\left(\theta - \frac{\pi}{3}\right) = 3$ **86.** $r\cos\left(\theta + \frac{\pi}{6}\right) = 4$

87. $r(\sin\theta - 4\cos\theta) - 3 = 0$ **88.** $r(4\sin\theta - 3\cos\theta) = 6$

89. The limaçon family The equations $r = a + b\cos\theta$ and $r = a + b\sin\theta$ describe curves known as *limaçons* (from Latin for *snail*). We have already encountered cardioids, which occur when $|a| = |b|$. The limaçon has an inner loop if $|a| < |b|$. The limaçon has a dent or dimple if $|b| < |a| < 2|b|$. And, the limaçon is oval-shaped if $|a| > 2|b|$. Match the limaçons in the figures A–F with equations a–f.

   a. $r = -1 + \sin\theta$ **b.** $r = -1 + 2\cos\theta$

   c. $r = 2 + \sin\theta$ **d.** $r = 1 - 2\cos\theta$

   e. $r = 1 + 2\sin\theta$ **f.** $r = 1 + \frac{2}{3}\sin\theta$

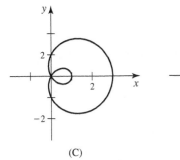

(A)

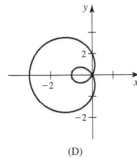

(B)

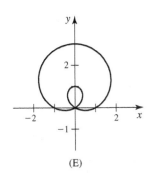

(C)

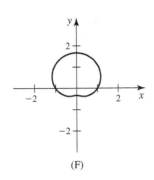

(D)

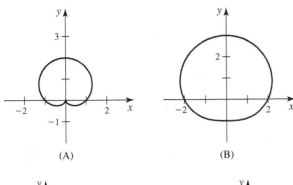

(E)

(F)

90. Limiting limaçon Consider the family of limaçons
$r = 1 + b \cos \theta$. Describe how the curves change as $b \to \infty$.

91–94. The lemniscate family *Equations of the form $r^2 = a \sin 2\theta$*
and $r^2 = a \cos 2\theta$ describe lemniscates (see Example 7). Graph the
following lemniscates.

91. $r^2 = \cos 2\theta$ **92.** $r^2 = 4 \sin 2\theta$

93. $r^2 = -2 \sin 2\theta$ **94.** $r^2 = -8 \cos 2\theta$

95–98. The rose family *Equations of the form $r = a \sin m\theta$ or*
$r = a \cos m\theta$, where a and b are real numbers and m is a positive
integer, have graphs known as roses (see Example 6). Graph the
following roses.

95. $r = \sin 2\theta$ **96.** $r = 4 \cos 3\theta$

97. $r = 2 \sin 4\theta$ **98.** $r = 6 \sin 5\theta$

99. Number of rose petals Show that the graph of $r = a \sin m\theta$ or
$r = a \cos m\theta$ is a rose with m leaves if m is an odd integer and a
rose with $2m$ leaves if m is an even integer.

100–102. Spirals *Graph the following spirals. Indicate the direction*
in which the spiral winds outward as θ increases, where $\theta > 0$. Let
$a = 1$ and $a = -1$.

100. Spiral of Archimedes: $r = a\theta$

101. Logarithmic spiral: $r = e^{a\theta}$

102. Hyperbolic spiral: $r = a/\theta$

103–106. Intersection points *Points at which the graphs of $r = f(\theta)$*
and $r = g(\theta)$ intersect must be determined carefully. Solving
$f(\theta) = g(\theta)$ identifies some—but perhaps not all—intersection points.
The reason is that the curves may pass through the same point for dif-
ferent values of θ. Use analytical methods and a graphing utility to find
all the intersection points of the following curves.

103. $r = 2 \cos \theta$ and $r = 1 + \cos \theta$

104. $r^2 = 4 \cos \theta$ and $r = 1 + \cos \theta$

105. $r = 1 - \sin \theta$ and $r = 1 + \cos \theta$

106. $r^2 = \cos 2\theta$ and $r^2 = \sin 2\theta$

107. Enhanced butterfly curve The butterfly curve of Example 8 may
be enhanced by adding a term:

$$r = e^{\sin \theta} - 2 \cos 4\theta + \sin^5 (\theta/12), \quad \text{for } 0 \le \theta \le 24\pi.$$

a. Graph the curve.
b. Explain why the new term produces the observed effect.

(*Source:* S. Wagon and E. Packel, *Animating Calculus*, Freeman, New
York, 1994.)

108. Finger curves Consider the curve $r = f(\theta) = \cos (a^{\theta}) - 1.5$,
where $a = (1 + 12\pi)^{1/2\pi} \approx 1.78933$ (see figure).

a. Show that $f(0) = f(2\pi)$ and find the point on the curve that
corresponds to $\theta = 0$ and $\theta = 2\pi$.
b. Is the same curve produced over the intervals $[-\pi, \pi]$ and
$[0, 2\pi]$?
c. Let $f(\theta) = \cos (a^{\theta}) - b$, where $a = (1 + 2k\pi)^{1/2\pi}$, k is an
integer, and b is a real number. Show that $f(0) = f(2\pi)$ and
that the curve closes on itself.
d. Plot the curve with various values of k. How many fingers can
you produce?

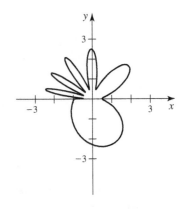

Applications

109. Earth–Mars system A simplified model assumes that the orbits
of Earth and Mars are circular with radii of 2 and 3, respectively,
and that Earth completes one orbit in one year while Mars takes
two years. The position of Mars as seen from Earth is given by the
parametric equations

$$x = (3 - 4 \cos \pi t) \cos \pi t + 2, \quad y = (3 - 4 \cos \pi t) \sin \pi t.$$

a. Graph the parametric equations, for $0 \le t \le 2$.

b. Letting $r = (3 - 4 \cos \pi t)$, explain why the path of Mars as seen from Earth is a limaçon.

110. Channel flow Water flows in a shallow semicircular channel with inner and outer radii of 1 m and 2 m (see figure). At a point $P(r, \theta)$ in the channel, the flow is in the tangential direction (counterclockwise along circles), and it depends only on r, the distance from the center of the semicircles.

a. Express the region formed by the channel as a set in polar coordinates.

b. Express the inflow and outflow regions of the channel as sets in polar coordinates.

c. Suppose the tangential velocity of the water in m/s is given by $v(r) = 10r$, for $1 \le r \le 2$. Is the velocity greater at $\left(1.5, \frac{\pi}{4}\right)$ or $\left(1.2, \frac{3\pi}{4}\right)$? Explain.

d. Suppose the tangential velocity of the water is given by
$$v(r) = \frac{20}{r}, \text{ for } 1 \le r \le 2.$$
Is the velocity greater at $\left(1.8, \frac{\pi}{6}\right)$ or $\left(1.3, \frac{2\pi}{3}\right)$? Explain.

e. The total amount of water that flows through the channel (across a cross section of the channel $\theta = \theta_0$) is proportional to $\int_1^2 v(r)\, dr$. Is the total flow through the channel greater for the flow in part (c) or (d)?

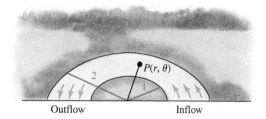

Outflow   Inflow

Additional Exercises

111. Special circles Show that the equation $r = a \cos \theta + b \sin \theta$, where a and b are real numbers, describes a circle. Find the center and radius of the circle.

112. Cartesian lemniscate Find the equation in Cartesian coordinates of the lemniscate $r^2 = a^2 \cos 2\theta$, where a is a real number.

113. Subtle symmetry Without using a graphing utility, determine the symmetries (if any) of the curve $r = 4 - \sin(\theta/2)$.

114. Complete curves Consider the polar curve $r = \cos(n\theta/m)$, where n and m are integers.

a. Graph the complete curve when $n = 2$ and $m = 3$.

b. Graph the complete curve when $n = 3$ and $m = 7$.

c. Find a general rule in terms of m and n for determining the least positive number P such that the complete curve is generated over the interval $[0, P]$.

QUICK CHECK ANSWERS

1. All the points are the same except $(3, 3\pi/2)$.   **3.** Polar coordinates: $(1, 0)$, $(1, 2\pi)$; Cartesian coordinates: $(0, 2)$ **4.** A circle centered at the origin with radius 12; a double spiral; the horizontal line $y = 10$ **5.** (a) Symmetric about the x-axis; (b) symmetric about the y-axis ◄

11.3 Calculus in Polar Coordinates

Having learned about the *geometry* of polar coordinates, we now have the groundwork needed to explore *calculus* in polar coordinates. Familiar topics, such as slopes of tangent lines and areas bounded by curves, are now revisited in a different setting.

Slopes of Tangent Lines

Given a function $y = f(x)$, the slope of the line tangent to the graph at a given point is dy/dx or $f'(x)$. So, it may be tempting to conclude that the slope of a curve described by the polar equation $r = f(\theta)$ is $dr/d\theta = f'(\theta)$. Unfortunately, it's not that simple.

> The slope is the change in the vertical coordinate divided by the change in the horizontal coordinate, independent of the coordinate system. In polar coordinates, neither r nor θ corresponds to a vertical or horizontal coordinate.

The key observation is that the slope of a tangent line—in any coordinate system—is the rate of change of the vertical coordinate y with respect to the horizontal coordinate x, which is dy/dx. We begin by writing the polar equation $r = f(\theta)$ in parametric form with θ as a parameter:

$$x = r \cos \theta = f(\theta) \cos \theta \quad \text{and} \quad y = r \sin \theta = f(\theta) \sin \theta. \tag{1}$$

From Section 11.1, when x and y are defined parametrically as differentiable functions of θ, the derivative is $\dfrac{dy}{dx} = \dfrac{y'(\theta)}{x'(\theta)}$. Using the Product Rule to compute $y'(\theta)$ and $x'(\theta)$ in equation (1), we have

$$\frac{dy}{dx} = \overbrace{\frac{f'(\theta) \sin \theta + f(\theta) \cos \theta}{\underbrace{f'(\theta) \cos \theta - f(\theta) \sin \theta}_{x'(\theta)}}}^{y'(\theta)}. \tag{2}$$

If the graph passes through the origin for some angle θ_0, then $f(\theta_0) = 0$, and equation (2) simplifies to

$$\frac{dy}{dx} = \frac{\sin \theta_0}{\cos \theta_0} = \tan \theta_0,$$

provided $f'(\theta_0) \neq 0$. However, $\tan \theta_0$ is the slope of the line $\theta = \theta_0$, which also passes through the origin. We conclude that if $f(\theta_0) = 0$, then the tangent line at $(0, \theta_0)$ is simply $\theta = \theta_0$ (Figure 11.32).

QUICK CHECK 1 Verify that if $y = f(\theta) \sin \theta$, then $y'(\theta) = f'(\theta) \sin \theta + f(\theta) \cos \theta$ (which was used earlier to find dy/dx). ◄

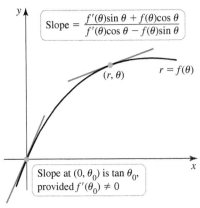

Slope $= \dfrac{f'(\theta)\sin \theta + f(\theta)\cos \theta}{f'(\theta)\cos \theta - f(\theta)\sin \theta}$

(r, θ)

$r = f(\theta)$

Slope at $(0, \theta_0)$ is $\tan \theta_0$, provided $f'(\theta_0) \neq 0$

FIGURE 11.32

THEOREM 11.2 Slope of a Tangent Line
Let f be a differentiable function at θ_0. The slope of the line tangent to the curve $r = f(\theta)$ at the point $(f(\theta_0), \theta_0)$ is

$$\frac{dy}{dx} = \frac{f'(\theta_0) \sin \theta_0 + f(\theta_0) \cos \theta_0}{f'(\theta_0) \cos \theta_0 - f(\theta_0) \sin \theta_0},$$

provided the denominator is nonzero at the point. At angles θ_0 for which $f(\theta_0) = 0$ and $f'(\theta_0) \neq 0$, the tangent line is $\theta = \theta_0$ with slope $\tan \theta_0$.

EXAMPLE 1 Slopes on a circle Find the slopes of the lines tangent to the circle $r = f(\theta) = 10$.

SOLUTION In this case, $f(\theta)$ is constant (independent of θ). Therefore, $f'(\theta) = 0$, $f(\theta) \neq 0$, and the slope formula becomes

$$\frac{dy}{dx} = \frac{f'(\theta) \sin \theta + f(\theta) \cos \theta}{f'(\theta) \cos \theta - f(\theta) \sin \theta} = -\frac{\cos \theta}{\sin \theta} = -\cot \theta.$$

We can check a few points to see that this result makes sense. With $\theta = 0$ and $\theta = \pi$, the slope $dy/dx = -\cot \theta$ is undefined, which is correct (Figure 11.33). With $\theta = \pi/2$ and $\theta = 3\pi/2$, the slope is zero; with $\theta = 3\pi/4$ and $\theta = 7\pi/4$, the slope is 1; and with $\theta = \pi/4$ and $\theta = 5\pi/4$, the slope is -1. At all points $P(r, \theta)$ on the circle, the slope of the line OP from the origin to P is $\tan \theta$, which is the negative reciprocal of $-\cot \theta$. Therefore, OP is perpendicular to the tangent line at all points P on the circle.

Related Exercises 5–14 ◄

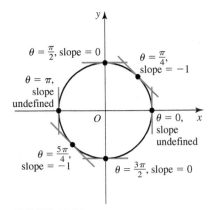

$\theta = \dfrac{\pi}{2}$, slope $= 0$

$\theta = \dfrac{\pi}{4}$, slope $= -1$

$\theta = \pi$, slope undefined

$\theta = 0$, slope undefined

$\theta = \dfrac{5\pi}{4}$, slope $= -1$

$\theta = \dfrac{3\pi}{2}$, slope $= 0$

FIGURE 11.33

EXAMPLE 2 Vertical and horizontal tangent lines Find the points on the interval $-\pi \leq \theta \leq \pi$ at which the cardioid $r = f(\theta) = 1 - \cos \theta$ has a vertical or horizontal tangent line.

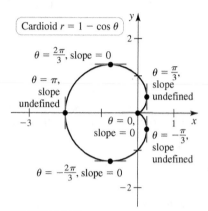

Cardioid $r = 1 - \cos\theta$

$\theta = \frac{2\pi}{3}$, slope $= 0$

$\theta = \pi$, slope undefined

$\theta = \frac{\pi}{3}$, slope undefined

$\theta = 0$, slope $= 0$

$\theta = -\frac{\pi}{3}$, slope undefined

$\theta = -\frac{2\pi}{3}$, slope $= 0$

FIGURE 11.34

SOLUTION Applying Theorem 11.2, we find that

$$\frac{dy}{dx} = \frac{f'(\theta)\sin\theta + f(\theta)\cos\theta}{f'(\theta)\cos\theta - f(\theta)\sin\theta}$$

$$\sin^2\theta = 1 - \cos^2\theta$$

$$= \frac{\sin\theta\sin\theta + (1 - \cos\theta)\cos\theta}{\sin\theta\cos\theta - (1 - \cos\theta)\sin\theta} \qquad \text{Substitute for } f(\theta) \text{ and } f'(\theta).$$

$$\underbrace{\qquad}_{\sin\theta\,(2\cos\theta - 1)}$$

$$= -\frac{(2\cos^2\theta - \cos\theta - 1)}{\sin\theta\,(2\cos\theta - 1)} \qquad \text{Simplify.}$$

$$= -\frac{(2\cos\theta + 1)(\cos\theta - 1)}{\sin\theta\,(2\cos\theta - 1)}. \qquad \text{Factor the numerator.}$$

The points with a horizontal tangent line satisfy $dy/dx = 0$ and occur where the numerator is zero and the denominator is nonzero. The numerator is zero when $\theta = 0$ and $\pm 2\pi/3$. Because the denominator is *not* zero when $\theta = \pm 2\pi/3$, horizontal tangent lines occur at $\theta = \pm 2\pi/3$ (Figure 11.34).

Vertical tangent lines occur where the numerator of dy/dx is nonzero and the denominator is zero. The denominator is zero when $\theta = 0, \pm\pi$, and $\pm\pi/3$, and the numerator is not zero at $\theta = \pm\pi$ and $\pm\pi/3$. Therefore, vertical tangent lines occur at $\theta = \pm\pi$ and $\pm\pi/3$.

The point $(0, 0)$ on the curve must be handled carefully because both the numerator and denominator of dy/dx equal 0 at $\theta = 0$. Notice that with $f(\theta) = 1 - \cos\theta$, we have $f(0) = f'(0) = 0$. Therefore, dy/dx may be computed as a limit using l'Hôpital's Rule. As $\theta \to 0^+$, we find that

$$\frac{dy}{dx} = \lim_{\theta\to 0^+}\left[-\frac{(2\cos\theta + 1)(\cos\theta - 1)}{\sin\theta\,(2\cos\theta - 1)}\right]$$

$$= \lim_{\theta\to 0^+}\frac{4\cos\theta\sin\theta - \sin\theta}{-2\sin^2\theta + 2\cos^2\theta - \cos\theta} \qquad \text{L'Hôpital's Rule}$$

$$= \frac{0}{1} = 0. \qquad \text{Evaluate the limit.}$$

A similar calculation using l'Hôpital's Rule shows that as $\theta \to 0^-$, $dy/dx \to 0$. Therefore, the curve has a slope of 0 at $(0, 0)$.

Related Exercises 15–20 ◀

QUICK CHECK 2 What is the slope of the line tangent to the cardioid in Example 2 at the point corresponding to $\theta = \pi/4$? ◀

Area of Regions Bounded by Polar Curves

The problem of finding the area of a region bounded by polar curves brings us back to the slice-and-sum strategy used extensively in Chapters 5 and 6. The objective is to find the area of the region R bounded by the graph of $r = f(\theta)$ between the two rays $\theta = \alpha$ and $\theta = \beta$ (Figure 11.35a). We assume that f is continuous and nonnegative on $[\alpha, \beta]$.

The area of R is found by slicing the region in the radial direction creating wedge-shaped slices. The interval $[\alpha, \beta]$ is partitioned into n subintervals by choosing the grid points

$$\alpha = \theta_0 < \theta_1 < \theta_2 < \cdots < \theta_k < \cdots < \theta_n = \beta.$$

We let $\Delta\theta_k = \theta_k - \theta_{k-1}$, for $k = 1, 2, \ldots, n$, and we let θ_k^* be any point of the interval $[\theta_{k-1}, \theta_k]$. The kth slice is approximated by the sector of a circle swept out by an angle $\Delta\theta_k$ with radius $f(\theta_k^*)$ (Figure 11.35b). Therefore, the area of the kth slice is

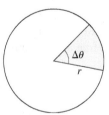

Area of circle $= \pi r^2$

Area of $\Delta\theta/(2\pi)$ of a circle

$= \left(\dfrac{\Delta\theta}{2\pi}\right)\pi r^2 = \dfrac{1}{2}r^2\Delta\theta$

approximately $\frac{1}{2}f(\theta_k^*)^2\Delta\theta_k$, for $k = 1, 2, \ldots, n$ (Figure 11.35c). To find the approximate area of R, we sum the areas of these slices:

$$\text{area} \approx \sum_{k=1}^{n}\frac{1}{2}f(\theta_k^*)^2\,\Delta\theta_k.$$

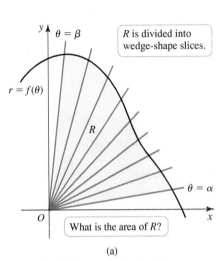

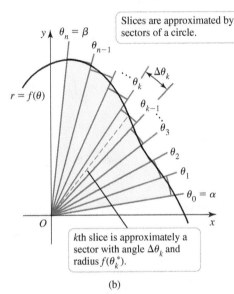

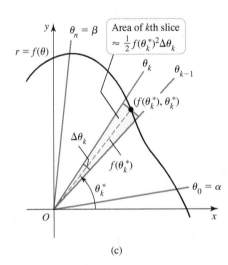

FIGURE 11.35

This approximation is a Riemann sum, and the approximation improves as we take more sectors $(n \to \infty)$ and let $\Delta\theta_k \to 0$, for all k. The exact area is given by $\displaystyle\lim_{n\to\infty}\sum_{k=1}^{n}\frac{1}{2}f(\theta_k^*)^2\,\Delta\theta_k$, which we identify as the definite integral $\displaystyle\int_{\alpha}^{\beta}\frac{1}{2}f(\theta)^2\,d\theta$.

With a slight modification, a more general result is obtained for the area of a region R bounded by two curves, $r = f(\theta)$ and $r = g(\theta)$, between the rays $\theta = \alpha$ and $\theta = \beta$ (Figure 11.36). We assume that f and g are continuous and $f(\theta) \geq g(\theta) \geq 0$ on $[\alpha, \beta]$. To find the area of R, we subtract the area of the region bounded by $r = g(\theta)$ from the area of the entire region bounded by $r = f(\theta)$ (all between $\theta = \alpha$ and $\theta = \beta$); that is,

$$\text{area} = \int_{\alpha}^{\beta}\frac{1}{2}f(\theta)^2\,d\theta - \int_{\alpha}^{\beta}\frac{1}{2}g(\theta)^2\,d\theta = \int_{\alpha}^{\beta}\frac{1}{2}\left(f(\theta)^2 - g(\theta)^2\right)d\theta.$$

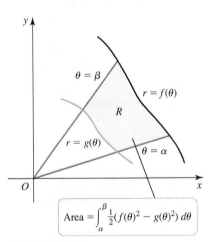

FIGURE 11.36

> If R is bounded by the graph of $r = f(\theta)$ between $\theta = \alpha$ and $\theta = \beta$, then $g(\theta) = 0$ and the area of R is $\int_{\alpha}^{\beta}\frac{1}{2}f(\theta)^2\,d\theta.$

DEFINITION Area of Regions in Polar Coordinates

Let R be the region bounded by the graphs of $r = f(\theta)$ and $r = g(\theta)$, between $\theta = \alpha$ and $\theta = \beta$, where f and g are continuous and $f(\theta) \geq g(\theta) \geq 0$ on $[\alpha, \beta]$. The area of R is

$$\int_{\alpha}^{\beta}\frac{1}{2}\left(f(\theta)^2 - g(\theta)^2\right)d\theta.$$

QUICK CHECK 3 Use integration to find the area of the circle $r = f(\theta) = 8$ (for $0 \leq \theta \leq 2\pi$). ◄

> The equation $r = 2\cos 2\theta$ is unchanged when θ is replaced by $-\theta$ (symmetry about the x-axis) and when θ is replaced by $\pi - \theta$ (symmetry about the y-axis).

EXAMPLE 3   Area of a polar region Find the area of the four-leaf rose $r = f(\theta) = 2\cos 2\theta$.

SOLUTION The graph of the rose (Figure 11.37) *appears* to be symmetric about the x- and y-axes; in fact, these symmetries can be proved. Appealing to this symmetry, we

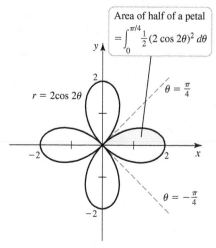

Area of half of a petal
$$= \int_0^{\pi/4} \frac{1}{2}(2 \cos 2\theta)^2 \, d\theta$$

$r = 2\cos 2\theta$

$\theta = \frac{\pi}{4}$

$\theta = -\frac{\pi}{4}$

FIGURE 11.37

find the area of one-half of a leaf and then multiply the result by 8 to obtain the area of the full rose. The upper half of the rightmost leaf is generated as θ increases from $\theta = 0$ (when $r = 2$) to $\theta = \pi/4$ (when $r = 0$). Therefore, the area of the entire rose is

$$8 \int_0^{\pi/4} \frac{1}{2} f(\theta)^2 \, d\theta = 4 \int_0^{\pi/4} (2 \cos 2\theta)^2 \, d\theta \qquad f(\theta) = 2 \cos 2\theta$$

$$= 16 \int_0^{\pi/4} \cos^2 2\theta \, d\theta \qquad \text{Simplify.}$$

$$= 16 \int_0^{\pi/4} \frac{1 + \cos 4\theta}{2} \, d\theta \qquad \text{Half-angle formula}$$

$$= (8\theta + 2 \sin 4\theta) \Big|_0^{\pi/4} \qquad \text{Fundamental Theorem}$$

$$= (2\pi + 0) - (0 + 0) = 2\pi. \qquad \text{Simplify.}$$

Related Exercises 21–36◀

QUICK CHECK 4 Give an interval over which you could integrate to find the area of one leaf of the rose $r = 2 \sin 3\theta$. ◀

EXAMPLE 4   Areas of polar regions Consider the circle $r = 1$ and the cardioid $r = 1 + \cos \theta$ (Figure 11.38).

a. Find the area of the region inside the circle and inside the cardioid.

b. Find the area of the region inside the circle and outside the cardioid.

SOLUTION

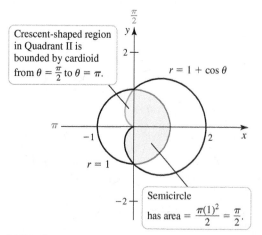

Crescent-shaped region in Quadrant II is bounded by cardioid from $\theta = \frac{\pi}{2}$ to $\theta = \pi$.

$r = 1 + \cos \theta$

$r = 1$

Semicircle has area $= \dfrac{\pi(1)^2}{2} = \dfrac{\pi}{2}$.

FIGURE 11.38

a. The points of intersection of the two curves can be found by solving $1 + \cos \theta = 1$, or $\cos \theta = 0$. The solutions are $\theta = \pm\pi/2$. The region inside the circle and inside the cardioid consists of two subregions.

• A semicircle with radius 1 in the first and fourth quadrants bounded by the circle $r = 1$

• Two crescent-shaped regions in the second and third quadrants bounded by the cardioid $r = 1 + \cos \theta$ and the y-axis

The area of the semicircle is $\pi/2$. To find the area of the upper crescent-shaped region in the second quadrant, notice that it is bounded by $r = 1 + \cos \theta$, as θ varies from $\pi/2$ to π. Therefore, its area is

$$\int_{\pi/2}^{\pi} \frac{1}{2}(1 + \cos \theta)^2 \, d\theta = \int_{\pi/2}^{\pi} \frac{1}{2}(1 + 2 \cos \theta + \cos^2 \theta) \, d\theta \qquad \text{Expand.}$$

$$= \frac{1}{2} \int_{\pi/2}^{\pi} \left(1 + 2 \cos \theta + \frac{1 + \cos 2\theta}{2}\right) d\theta \qquad \substack{\text{Half-angle} \\ \text{formula}}$$

$$= \frac{1}{2}\left(\theta + 2 \sin \theta + \frac{\theta}{2} + \frac{\sin 2\theta}{4}\right)\Big|_{\pi/2}^{\pi} \qquad \substack{\text{Fundamental} \\ \text{Theorem}}$$

$$= \frac{3\pi}{8} - 1. \qquad \text{Simplify.}$$

The area of the entire region (two crescents and a semicircle) is

$$2\left(\frac{3\pi}{8} - 1\right) + \frac{\pi}{2} = \frac{5\pi}{4} - 2.$$

b. The region inside the circle and outside the cardioid is bounded by the outer curve $r = 1$ and the inner curve $r = 1 + \cos\theta$ on the interval $[\pi/2, 3\pi/2]$ (Figure 11.38). Using the symmetry about the x-axis, the area of the region is

$$2\int_{\pi/2}^{\pi} \frac{1}{2}\left(1^2 - (1 + \cos\theta)^2\right) d\theta = \int_{\pi/2}^{\pi} (-2\cos\theta - \cos^2\theta)\, d\theta \quad \text{Simplify the integrand.}$$

$$= 2 - \frac{\pi}{4}. \quad \text{Evaluate the integral.}$$

Note that the regions in parts (a) and (b) comprise the interior of a circle of radius 1; indeed, their areas have a sum of π.

Related Exercises 21–36 ◀

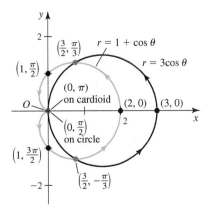

FIGURE 11.39

EXAMPLE 5 **Points of intersection** Find the points of intersection of the circle $r = 3\cos\theta$ and the cardioid $r = 1 + \cos\theta$ (Figure 11.39).

SOLUTION The fact that a point has multiple representations in polar coordinates may lead to subtle difficulties in finding intersection points. We first proceed algebraically. Equating the two expressions for r and solving for θ, we have

$$3\cos\theta = 1 + \cos\theta \quad \text{or} \quad \cos\theta = \frac{1}{2},$$

which has roots $\theta = \pm\pi/3$. Therefore, two intersection points are $(3/2, \pi/3)$ and $(3/2, -\pi/3)$ (Figure 11.39). Without graphs of the curves, we might be tempted to stop here. Yet, the figure shows another intersection point O that has not been detected. To find the third intersection point, we must investigate the way in which the two curves are generated. As θ increases from 0 to 2π, the cardioid is generated counterclockwise, beginning at $(2, 0)$. The cardioid passes through O when $\theta = \pi$. As θ increases from 0 to π, the circle is generated counterclockwise, beginning at $(3, 0)$. The circle passes through O when $\theta = \pi/2$. Therefore, the intersection point O is $(0, \pi)$ on the cardioid (and these coordinates do not satisfy the equation of the circle), while O is $(0, \pi/2)$ on the circle (and these coordinates do not satisfy the equation of the cardioid). There is no foolproof rule for detecting such "hidden" intersection points. Care must be used.

Related Exercises 37–40 ◀

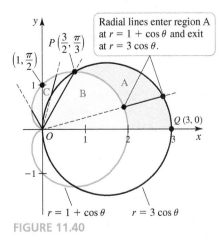

FIGURE 11.40

> One way to be sure the inner and outer boundaries of a region have been correctly identified is to draw a ray from the origin through the region—the ray should enter the region at the inner boundary and exit the region at the outer boundary. This is the case for every ray through region A, for $0 \leq \theta \leq \pi/3$.

EXAMPLE 6 **Computing areas** Example 5 discussed the points of intersection of the curves $r = 3\cos\theta$ (a circle) and $r = 1 + \cos\theta$ (a cardioid). Use those results to compute the areas of

a. region A in Figure 11.40   **b.** region B   **c.** region C.

SOLUTION

a. It is evident that region A is bounded on the inside by the cardioid and on the outside by the circle between the points $Q(\theta = 0)$ and $P(\theta = \pi/3)$. Therefore, the area of region A is

$$\frac{1}{2}\int_0^{\pi/3}\left((3\cos\theta)^2 - (1 + \cos\theta)^2\right) d\theta$$

$$= \frac{1}{2}\int_0^{\pi/3}(8\cos^2\theta - 1 - 2\cos\theta)\, d\theta \quad \text{Simplify.}$$

$$= \frac{1}{2}\int_0^{\pi/3}(3 + 4\cos 2\theta - 2\cos\theta)\, d\theta \quad \cos^2\theta = \frac{1 + \cos 2\theta}{2}$$

$$= \frac{1}{2}(3\theta + 2\sin 2\theta - 2\sin\theta)\Big|_0^{\pi/3} = \frac{\pi}{2}. \quad \text{Evaluate integral.}$$

b. Examining region B, notice that a ray drawn from the origin enters the region immediately. There is no inner boundary, and the outer boundary is $r = 1 + \cos\theta$ on $0 \le \theta \le \pi/3$ and $r = 3\cos\theta$ on $\pi/3 \le \theta \le \pi/2$ (recall from Example 5 that $\theta = \pi/2$ is the angle at which the circle intersects the origin). Therefore, we slice the region into two parts at $\theta = \pi/3$ and write two integrals for its area:

$$\text{area of region B} = \frac{1}{2}\int_0^{\pi/3} (1 + \cos\theta)^2 \, d\theta + \frac{1}{2}\int_{\pi/3}^{\pi/2} (3\cos\theta)^2 \, d\theta.$$

While these integrals may be evaluated directly, it's easier to notice that

$$\text{area of region B} = \text{area of semicircle } OPQ - \text{area of region A}.$$

Because $r = 3\cos\theta$ is a circle with a radius of $3/2$, we have

$$\text{area of region B} = \frac{1}{2}\cdot\pi\left(\frac{3}{2}\right)^2 - \frac{\pi}{2} = \frac{5\pi}{8}.$$

c. It's easy to *incorrectly* identify the inner boundary of region C as the circle and the outer boundary as the cardioid. While these identifications are true when $\pi/3 \le \theta \le \pi/2$ (notice again the radial lines in Figure 11.40), there is only one boundary curve (the cardioid) when $\pi/2 \le \theta \le \pi$. We conclude that the area of region C is

$$\frac{1}{2}\int_{\pi/3}^{\pi/2} \left((1 + \cos\theta)^2 - (3\cos\theta)^2\right) d\theta + \frac{1}{2}\int_{\pi/2}^{\pi} (1 + \cos\theta)^2 \, d\theta = \frac{\pi}{8}.$$

Related Exercises 41–44 ◀

SECTION 11.3 EXERCISES

Review Questions

1. Express the polar equation $r = f(\theta)$ in parametric form in Cartesian coordinates, where θ is the parameter.

2. How do you find the slope of the line tangent to the polar graph of $r = f(\theta)$ at a point?

3. Explain why the slope of the line tangent to the polar graph of $r = f(\theta)$ is not $dr/d\theta$.

4. What integral must be evaluated to find the area of the region bounded by the polar graphs of $r = f(\theta)$ and $r = g(\theta)$ on the interval $\alpha \le \theta \le \beta$, where $f(\theta) \ge g(\theta) \ge 0$?

Basic Skills

5–14. Slopes of tangent lines *Find the slope of the line tangent to the following polar curves at the given points. At the points where the curve intersects the origin (when this occurs), find the equation of the tangent line in polar coordinates.*

5. $r = 1 - \sin\theta$; $\left(\frac{1}{2}, \frac{\pi}{6}\right)$

6. $r = 4\cos\theta$; $\left(2, \frac{\pi}{3}\right)$

7. $r = 8\sin\theta$; $\left(4, \frac{5\pi}{6}\right)$

8. $r = 4 + \sin\theta$; $(4, 0)$ and $\left(3, \frac{3\pi}{2}\right)$

9. $r = 6 + 3\cos\theta$; $(3, \pi)$ and $(9, 0)$

10. $r = 2\sin 3\theta$; at the tips of the leaves

11. $r = 4\cos 2\theta$; at the tips of the leaves

12. $r = 1 + 2\sin 2\theta$; $\left(3, \frac{\pi}{4}\right)$

13. $r^2 = 4\cos 2\theta$; $\left(0, \pm\frac{\pi}{4}\right)$

14. $r = 2\theta$; $\left(\frac{\pi}{2}, \frac{\pi}{4}\right)$

15–20. Horizontal and vertical tangents *Find the points at which the following polar curves have a horizontal or a vertical tangent line.*

15. $r = 4\cos\theta$

16. $r = 2 + 2\sin\theta$

17. $r = \sin 2\theta$

18. $r = 3 + 6\sin\theta$

19. $r = 1 - \sin\theta$

20. $r = \sec\theta$

21–36. Areas of regions *Make a sketch of the region and its bounding curves. Find the area of the region.*

21. The region inside the curve $r = \sqrt{\cos\theta}$

22. The region inside the right lobe of $r = \sqrt{\cos 2\theta}$

23. The region inside the circle $r = 8\sin\theta$

24. The region inside the cardioid $r = 4 + 4\sin\theta$

25. The region inside the limaçon $r = 2 + \cos\theta$

26. The region inside all the leaves of the rose $r = 3\sin 2\theta$

27. The region inside one leaf of $r = \cos 3\theta$

28. The region inside the inner loop of $r = \cos\theta - \frac{1}{2}$

29. The region outside the circle $r = \frac{1}{2}$ and inside the circle $r = \cos\theta$

30. The region inside the curve $r = \sqrt{\cos\theta}$ and outside the circle $r = 1/\sqrt{2}$

31. The region inside the curve $r = \sqrt{\cos\theta}$ and inside the circle $r = 1/\sqrt{2}$ in the first quadrant

32. The region inside the right lobe of $r = \sqrt{\cos 2\theta}$ and inside the circle $r = 1/\sqrt{2}$ in the first quadrant

33. The region inside one leaf of the rose $r = \cos 5\theta$

34. The region inside the rose $r = 4\cos 2\theta$ and outside the circle $r = 2$

35. The region inside the rose $r = 4\sin 2\theta$ and inside the circle $r = 2$

36. The region inside the lemniscate $r^2 = 2\sin 2\theta$ and outside the circle $r = 1$

37–40. Intersection points *Use algebraic methods to find as many intersection points of the following curves as possible. Use graphical methods to identify the remaining intersection points.*

37. $r = 3\sin\theta$ and $r = 3\cos\theta$

38. $r = 2 + 2\sin\theta$ and $r = 2 - 2\sin\theta$

39. $r = 1 + \sin\theta$ and $r = 1 + \cos\theta$

40. $r = 1$ and $r = \sqrt{2}\cos 2\theta$

41–44. Finding areas *In Exercises 37–40, you found the intersection points of pairs of curves. Find the area of the entire region that lies within both of the following pairs of curves.*

41. $r = 3\sin\theta$ and $r = 3\cos\theta$

42. $r = 2 + 2\sin\theta$ and $r = 2 - 2\sin\theta$

43. $r = 1 + \sin\theta$ and $r = 1 + \cos\theta$

44. $r = 1$ and $r = \sqrt{2}\cos 2\theta$

Further Explorations

45. **Explain why or why not** Determine whether the following statements are true and give an explanation or counterexample.

   a. The area of the region bounded by the polar graph of $r = f(\theta)$ on the interval $[\alpha, \beta]$ is $\int_\alpha^\beta f(\theta)\, d\theta$.
   b. The slope of the line tangent to the polar curve $r = f(\theta)$ at a point (r, θ) is $f'(\theta)$.

46. **Multiple identities** Explain why the point $(-1, 3\pi/2)$ is on the polar graph of $r = 1 + \cos\theta$ even though it does not satisfy the equation $r = 1 + \cos\theta$.

47–50. Area of plane regions *Find the areas of the following regions.*

47. The region common to the circles $r = 2\sin\theta$ and $r = 1$

48. The region inside the inner loop of the limaçon $r = 2 + 4\cos\theta$

49. The region inside the outer loop but outside the inner loop of the limaçon $r = 3 - 6\sin\theta$

50. The region common to the circle $r = 3\cos\theta$ and the cardioid $r = 1 + \cos\theta$

51. **Spiral tangent lines** Use a graphing utility to determine the first three points with $\theta \geq 0$ at which the spiral $r = 2\theta$ has a horizontal tangent line. Find the first three points with $\theta \geq 0$ at which the spiral $r = 2\theta$ has a vertical tangent line.

52. **Area of roses**
   a. *Even number of leaves:* What is the relationship between the total area enclosed by the $4m$-leaf rose $r = \cos(2m\theta)$ and m?
   b. *Odd number of leaves:* What is the relationship between the total area enclosed by the $(2m + 1)$-leaf rose $r = \cos((2m + 1)\theta)$ and m?

53. **Regions bounded by a spiral** Let R_n be the region bounded by the nth turn and the $(n + 1)$st turn of the spiral $r = e^{-\theta}$ in the first and second quadrants, for $\theta \geq 0$ (see figure).
   a. Find the area A_n of R_n.
   b. Evaluate $\lim_{n\to\infty} A_n$.
   c. Evaluate $\lim_{n\to\infty} A_{n+1}/A_n$.

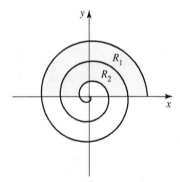

54–57. Area of polar regions *Find the area of the regions bounded by the following curves.*

54. The complete three-leaf rose $r = 2\cos 3\theta$

55. The lemniscate $r^2 = 6\sin 2\theta$

56. The limaçon $r = 2 - 4\sin\theta$

57. The limaçon $r = 4 - 2\cos\theta$

Applications

58. **Blood vessel flow** A blood vessel with a circular cross section of constant radius R carries blood that flows parallel to the axis of the vessel with a velocity of $v(r) = V(1 - r^2/R^2)$, where V is a constant and r is the distance from the axis of the vessel.

   a. Where is the velocity a maximum? A minimum?
   b. Find the average velocity of the blood over a cross section of the vessel.
   c. Suppose the velocity in the vessel is given by $v(r) = V(1 - r^2/R^2)^{1/p}$, where $p \geq 1$. Graph the velocity profiles for $p = 1, 2$, and 6 on the interval $0 \leq r \leq R$. Find the average velocity in the vessel as a function of p. How does the average velocity behave as $p \to \infty$?

59–61. Grazing goat problems *Consider the following sequence of problems related to grazing goats tied to a rope. (See the Guided Project Grazing Goat Problems.)*

59. A circular corral of unit radius is enclosed by a fence. A goat inside the corral is tied to the fence with a rope of length $0 \le a \le 2$ (see figure). What is the area of the region (inside the corral) that the goat can graze? Check your answer with the special cases $a = 0$ and $a = 2$.

60. A circular concrete slab of unit radius is surrounded by grass. A goat is tied to the edge of the slab with a rope of length $0 \le a \le 2$ (see figure). What is the area of the grassy region that the goat can graze? Note that the rope can extend over the concrete slab. Check your answer with the special cases $a = 0$ and $a = 2$.

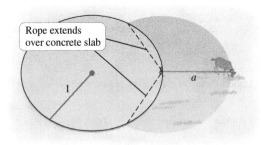

Rope extends over concrete slab

61. A circular corral of unit radius is enclosed by a fence. A goat is outside the corral and tied to the fence with a rope of length $a \ge 0$ (see figure). What is the area of the region (outside the corral) that the goat can reach?

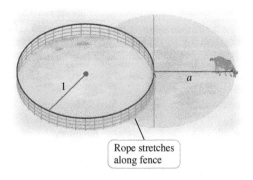

Rope stretches along fence

Additional Exercises

62. **Tangents and normals** Let a polar curve be described by $r = f(\theta)$ and let ℓ be the line tangent to the curve at the point $P(x, y) = P(r, \theta)$ (see figure).

    a. Explain why $\tan \alpha = dy/dx$.
    b. Explain why $\tan \theta = y/x$.
    c. Let φ be the angle between ℓ and OP. Prove that $\tan \varphi = f(\theta)/f'(\theta)$.
    d. Prove that the values of θ for which ℓ is parallel to the x-axis satisfy $\tan \theta = -f(\theta)/f'(\theta)$.
    e. Prove that the values of θ for which ℓ is parallel to the y-axis satisfy $\tan \theta = f'(\theta)/f(\theta)$.

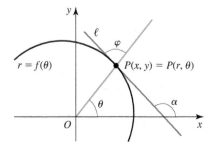

63. **Isogonal curves** Let a curve be described by $r = f(\theta)$, where $f(\theta) > 0$ on its domain. Referring to the figure of Exercise 62, a curve is **isogonal** provided the angle φ is constant for all θ.

    a. Prove that φ is constant for all θ provided $\cot \varphi = f'(\theta)/f(\theta)$ is constant, which implies that $\dfrac{d}{d\theta}[\ln f(\theta)] = k$, where k is a constant.
    b. Use part (a) to prove that the family of logarithmic spirals $r = Ce^{k\theta}$ consists of isogonal curves, where C and k are constants.
    c. Graph the curve $r = 2e^{2\theta}$ and confirm the result of part (b).

QUICK CHECK ANSWERS

1. Apply the Product Rule.   **2.** $\sqrt{2} + 1$
3. Area $= \displaystyle\int_0^{2\pi} \frac{1}{2}(8)^2 \, d\theta = 64\pi$
4. $\left[0, \frac{\pi}{3}\right]$ or $\left[\frac{\pi}{3}, \frac{2\pi}{3}\right]$ (among others)

11.4   Conic Sections

Conic sections are best visualized as the Greeks did over 2000 years ago by slicing a double cone with a plane (Figure 11.41). Three of the seven different sets of points that arise in this way are *ellipses, parabolas,* and *hyperbolas.* These curves have practical applications and broad theoretical importance. For example, celestial bodies travel in orbits that are modeled by ellipses and hyperbolas. Mirrors for telescopes are designed using the properties of conic sections. And architectural structures, such as domes and arches, are sometimes based on these curves.

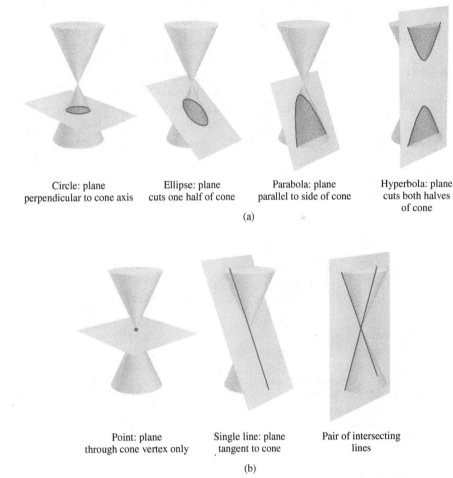

Circle: plane
perpendicular to cone axis

Ellipse: plane
cuts one half of cone

Parabola: plane
parallel to side of cone

Hyperbola: plane
cuts both halves
of cone

(a)

Point: plane
through cone vertex only

Single line: plane
tangent to cone

Pair of intersecting
lines

(b)

FIGURE 11.41 The standard conic sections (a) are the intersection sets of a double cone and a plane that does not pass through the vertex of the cone. Degenerate conic sections (lines and points) are produced when a plane passes through the vertex of the cone (b).

Parabolas

A **parabola** is the set of points in a plane that are equidistant from a fixed point F (called the **focus**) and a fixed line (called the **directrix**). In the four standard orientations, a parabola may open upward, downward, to the right, or to the left. We derive the equation of the parabola that opens upward.

Suppose the focus F is on the y-axis at $(0, p)$ and the directrix is the horizontal line $y = -p$, where $p > 0$. The parabola is the set of points P that satisfy the defining property $|PF| = |PL|$, where $L(x, -p)$ is the point on the directrix closest to P

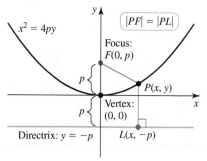

FIGURE 11.42

QUICK CHECK 1 Verify that $\sqrt{x^2 + (y - p)^2} = y + p$ is equivalent to $x^2 = 4py$. ◄

(Figure 11.42). Consider an arbitrary point $P(x, y)$ that satisfies this condition. Applying the distance formula, we have

$$\underbrace{\sqrt{x^2 + (y - p)^2}}_{|PF|} = \underbrace{y + p}_{|PL|}.$$

Squaring both sides of this equation and simplifying gives the equation $x^2 = 4py$. This is the equation of a parabola that is symmetric about the y-axis and opens upward. The **vertex** of the parabola is the point closest to the directrix; in this case it is $(0, 0)$ (which satisfies $|PF| = |PL| = p$).

The equations of the other three standard parabolas are derived in a similar way.

Equations of Four Standard Parabolas

Let p be a real number. The parabola with focus at $(0, p)$ and directrix $y = -p$ is symmetric about the y-axis and has the equation $x^2 = 4py$. If $p > 0$, then the parabola opens *upward*; if $p < 0$, then the parabola opens *downward*.

The parabola with focus at $(p, 0)$ and directrix $x = -p$ is symmetric about the x-axis and has the equation $y^2 = 4px$. If $p > 0$, then the parabola opens *to the right*; if $p < 0$, then the parabola opens *to the left*.

Each of these parabolas has its vertex at the origin (Figure 11.43).

> Recall that a curve is symmetric with respect to the x-axis if $(x, -y)$ is on the curve whenever (x, y) is on the curve. So, a y^2-term indicates symmetry with respect to the x-axis. Similarly, an x^2-term indicates symmetry with respect to the y-axis.

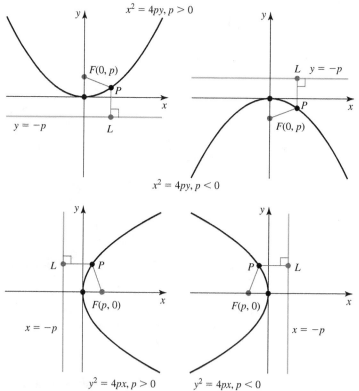

FIGURE 11.43

QUICK CHECK 2 In which direction do the following parabolas open?
a. $y^2 = -4x$ **b.** $x^2 = 4y$ ◄

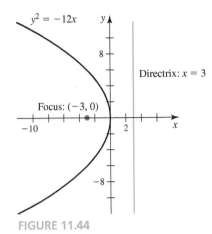

FIGURE 11.44

EXAMPLE 1 **Graphing parabolas** Find the focus and directrix of the parabola $y^2 = -12x$. Sketch its graph.

SOLUTION The y^2-term indicates that the parabola is symmetric with respect to the x-axis. Rewriting the equation as $x = -y^2/12$, we see that $x \le 0$ for all y, implying that the parabola opens to the left. Comparing $y^2 = -12x$ to the standard form $y^2 = 4px$, we see that $p = -3$; therefore, the focus is $(-3, 0)$, and the directrix is $x = 3$ (Figure 11.44).

Related Exercises 13–18 ◀

EXAMPLE 2 **Equations of parabolas** Find the equation of the parabola with vertex $(0, 0)$ that opens downward and passes through the point $(2, -3)$.

SOLUTION The standard parabola that opens downward has the equation $x^2 = 4py$. The point $(2, -3)$ must satisfy this equation. Substituting $x = 2$ and $y = -3$ into $x^2 = 4py$, we find that $p = -\frac{1}{3}$. Therefore, the focus is at $(0, -\frac{1}{3})$, the directrix is $y = \frac{1}{3}$, and the equation of the parabola is $x^2 = -4y/3$, or $y = -3x^2/4$ (Figure 11.45).

Related Exercises 19–26 ◀

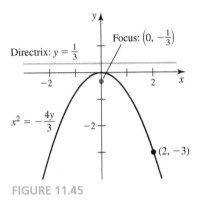

FIGURE 11.45

Reflection Property Parabolas have a property that makes them useful in the design of reflectors and transmitters. A particle approaching a parabola on any line parallel to the axis of the parabola is reflected on a line that passes through the focus (Figure 11.46); this property is used to focus incoming light by a parabolic mirror on a telescope. Alternatively, signals emanating from the focus are reflected on lines parallel to the axis, a property used to design radio transmitters and headlights (Exercise 83).

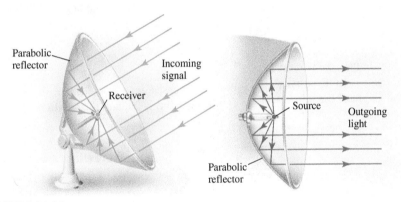

FIGURE 11.46

Ellipses

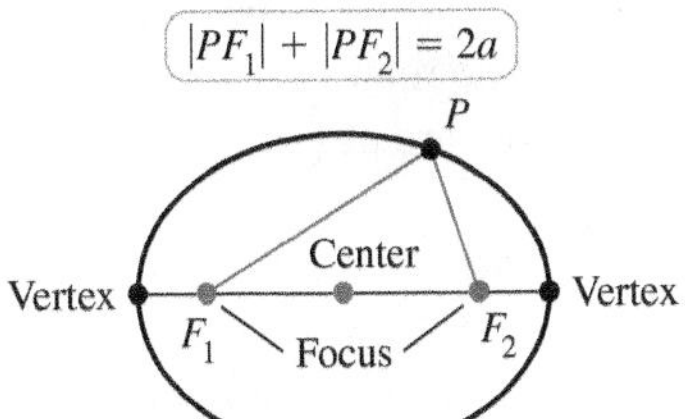

An **ellipse** is the set of points in a plane whose distances from two fixed points have a constant sum that we denote $2a$ (Figure 11.47). Each of the two fixed points is a **focus** (plural **foci**). The equation of an ellipse is simplest if the foci are on the x-axis at $(\pm c, 0)$ or on the y-axis at $(0, \pm c)$. In either case, the **center** of the ellipse is $(0, 0)$. If the foci are on the x-axis, the points $(\pm a, 0)$ lie on the ellipse and are called **vertices**. If the foci are on the y-axis, the vertices are $(0, \pm a)$ (Figure 11.48). A short calculation (Exercise 85) using the definition of the ellipse results in the following equations for an ellipse.

FIGURE 11.47

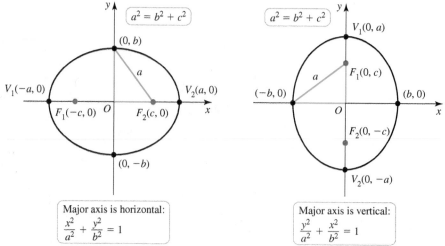

FIGURE 11.48

When necessary, we may distinguish between the *major-axis vertices* $(\pm a, 0)$ or $(0, \pm a)$, and the *minor-axis vertices* $(\pm b, 0)$ or $(0, \pm b)$. The word *vertices* (without further description) is understood to mean *major-axis vertices*.

QUICK CHECK 3 In the case that the vertices and foci are on the x-axis, show that the length of the minor axis of an ellipse is $2b$. ◄

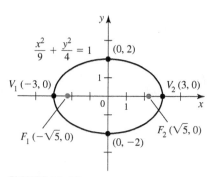

FIGURE 11.49

Equations of Standard Ellipses

An ellipse centered at the origin with foci at $(\pm c, 0)$ and vertices at $(\pm a, 0)$ has the equation

$$\frac{x^2}{a^2} + \frac{y^2}{b^2} = 1, \quad \text{where } a^2 = b^2 + c^2.$$

An ellipse centered at the origin with foci at $(0, \pm c)$ and vertices at $(0, \pm a)$ has the equation

$$\frac{y^2}{a^2} + \frac{x^2}{b^2} = 1, \quad \text{where } a^2 = b^2 + c^2.$$

In both cases, $a > b > 0$ and $a > c > 0$, the length of the long axis (called the **major axis**) is $2a$, and the length of the short axis (called the **minor axis**) is $2b$.

EXAMPLE 3   **Graphing ellipses**   Find the vertices, foci, and the length of the major and minor axes of the ellipse $\dfrac{x^2}{9} + \dfrac{y^2}{4} = 1$. Graph the ellipse.

SOLUTION   Because $9 > 4$, we identify $a^2 = 9$ and $b^2 = 4$. Therefore, $a = 3$ and $b = 2$. The lengths of the major and minor axes are $2a = 6$ and $2b = 4$, respectively. The vertices are at $(\pm 3, 0)$ and lie on the x-axis, as do the foci. The relationship $c^2 = a^2 - b^2$ implies that $c^2 = 5$, or $c = \sqrt{5}$. Therefore, the foci are at $(\pm \sqrt{5}, 0)$. The graph of the ellipse is shown in Figure 11.49.

Related Exercises 27–32 ◄

EXAMPLE 4   **Equation of an ellipse**   Find the equation of the ellipse centered at the origin with its foci on the y-axis, a major axis of length 8, and a minor axis of length 4. Graph the ellipse.

SOLUTION   Because the length of the major axis is 8, the vertices are located at $(0, \pm 4)$, and $a = 4$. Because the length of the minor axis is 4, we have $b = 2$. Therefore, the equation of the ellipse is

$$\frac{y^2}{16} + \frac{x^2}{4} = 1.$$

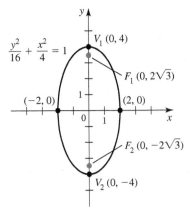

$$\frac{y^2}{16} + \frac{x^2}{4} = 1$$

$V_1\ (0, 4)$

$F_1\ (0, 2\sqrt{3})$

$(-2, 0)$ $(2, 0)$

$F_2\ (0, -2\sqrt{3})$

$V_2\ (0, -4)$

FIGURE 11.50

Using the relation $c^2 = a^2 - b^2$, we find that $c = 2\sqrt{3}$ and the foci are at $(0, \pm 2\sqrt{3})$. The ellipse is shown in Figure 11.50.

Related Exercises 33–38◀

Hyperbolas

A **hyperbola** is the set of points in a plane whose distances from two fixed points have a constant difference, either $2a$ or $-2a$ (Figure 11.51). As with ellipses, the two fixed points are called **foci**. The equation of a hyperbola is simplest if the foci are on either the x-axis at $(\pm c, 0)$ or on the y-axis at $(0, \pm c)$. If the foci are on the x-axis, the points $(\pm a, 0)$ on the hyperbola are called the **vertices**. In this case, the hyperbola has no y-intercepts, but it has the **asymptotes** $y = \pm bx/a$, where $b^2 = c^2 - a^2$. Similarly, if the foci are on the y-axis, the vertices are $(0, \pm a)$, the hyperbola has no x-intercepts, and it has the asymptotes $y = \pm ax/b$ (Figure 11.52). A short calculation (Exercise 86) using the definition of the hyperbola results in the following equations for standard hyperbolas.

> ➤ Asymptotes that are not parallel to one of the coordinate axes, as in the case of the standard hyperbolas, are called **oblique**, or **slant, asymptotes**.

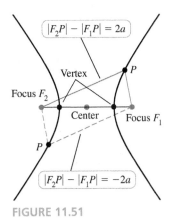

$|F_2P| - |F_1P| = 2a$

Vertex

Focus F_2

Center   Focus F_1

P

$|F_2P| - |F_1P| = -2a$

FIGURE 11.51

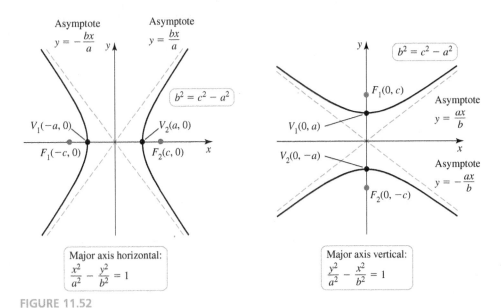

Asymptote $y = -\dfrac{bx}{a}$ Asymptote $y = \dfrac{bx}{a}$

$b^2 = c^2 - a^2$

$V_1(-a, 0)$ $V_2(a, 0)$

$F_1(-c, 0)$ $F_2(c, 0)$

Major axis horizontal:
$$\frac{x^2}{a^2} - \frac{y^2}{b^2} = 1$$

$b^2 = c^2 - a^2$

$F_1(0, c)$

Asymptote $y = \dfrac{ax}{b}$

$V_1(0, a)$

$V_2(0, -a)$

Asymptote $y = -\dfrac{ax}{b}$

$F_2(0, -c)$

Major axis vertical:
$$\frac{y^2}{a^2} - \frac{x^2}{b^2} = 1$$

FIGURE 11.52

> ➤ Notice that the asymptotes for hyperbolas are $y = \pm bx/a$ when the vertices are on the x-axis and $y = \pm ax/b$ when the vertices are on the y-axis (the roles of a and b are reversed).

Equations of Standard Hyperbolas

A hyperbola centered at the origin with foci at $(\pm c, 0)$ and vertices at $(\pm a, 0)$ has the equation

$$\frac{x^2}{a^2} - \frac{y^2}{b^2} = 1, \quad \text{where} \quad b^2 = c^2 - a^2.$$

The hyperbola has **asymptotes** $y = \pm bx/a$.

A hyperbola centered at the origin with foci at $(0, \pm c)$ and vertices at $(0, \pm a)$ has the equation

$$\frac{y^2}{a^2} - \frac{x^2}{b^2} = 1, \quad \text{where} \quad b^2 = c^2 - a^2.$$

The hyperbola has **asymptotes** $y = \pm ax/b$.

In both cases, $c > a > 0$ and $c > b > 0$.

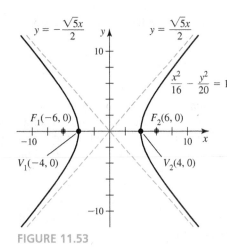

$y = -\dfrac{\sqrt{5}x}{2}$ $y = \dfrac{\sqrt{5}x}{2}$

$\dfrac{x^2}{16} - \dfrac{y^2}{20} = 1$

$F_1(-6, 0)$ $F_2(6, 0)$

$V_1(-4, 0)$ $V_2(4, 0)$

FIGURE 11.53

▷ The conic section lies in the plane formed by the directrix and the focus.

EXAMPLE 5   Graphing hyperbolas Find the equation of the hyperbola centered at the origin with vertices at $(\pm 4, 0)$ and foci at $(\pm 6, 0)$. Graph the hyperbola.

SOLUTION Because the foci are on the x-axis, the vertices are also on the x-axis, and there are no y-intercepts. With $a = 4$ and $c = 6$, we have $b^2 = c^2 - a^2 = 20$, or $b = 2\sqrt{5}$. Therefore, the equation of the hyperbola is

$$\frac{x^2}{16} - \frac{y^2}{20} = 1.$$

The asymptotes are $y = \pm bx/a = \pm\sqrt{5}x/2$ (Figure 11.53).

Related Exercises 39–50 ◀

QUICK CHECK 4 Identify the vertices and foci of the hyperbola $y^2 - x^2/4 = 1$. ◀

Eccentricity and Directrix

Parabolas, ellipses, and hyperbolas may also be developed in a single unified way called the *eccentricity-directrix* approach. We let ℓ be a line called the **directrix** and F be a point not on ℓ called a **focus**. The **eccentricity** is a real number $e > 0$. Consider the set C of points P in a plane with the property that the distance $|PF|$ equals e multiplied by the perpendicular distance $|PL|$ from P to ℓ (Figure 11.54); that is,

$$|PF| = e|PL| \quad \text{or} \quad \frac{|PF|}{|PL|} = e = \text{constant}.$$

Depending on the value of e, the set C is one of the three standard conic sections, as described in the following theorem.

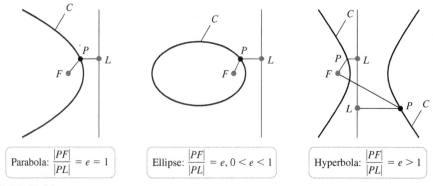

Parabola: $\dfrac{|PF|}{|PL|} = e = 1$ Ellipse: $\dfrac{|PF|}{|PL|} = e, 0 < e < 1$ Hyperbola: $\dfrac{|PF|}{|PL|} = e > 1$

FIGURE 11.54

▷ Theorem 11.3 for ellipses and hyperbolas describes how the entire curve is generated using just one focus and one directrix. Nevertheless, every ellipse or hyperbola has two foci and two directrices.

THEOREM 11.3   Eccentricity-Directrix Theorem

Let ℓ be a line, F a point not on ℓ, and $e > 0$ a real number. Let C be the set of points P in a plane with the property that $\dfrac{|PF|}{|PL|} = e$, where $|PL|$ is the perpendicular distance from P to ℓ.

1. If $e = 1$, C is a **parabola**.
2. If $0 < e < 1$, C is an **ellipse**.
3. If $e > 1$, C is a **hyperbola**.

The proof of the theorem is straightforward; it requires an algebraic calculation that can be found in Appendix B. The proof establishes relationships between five parameters a, b, c, d, and e that are characteristic of any ellipse or hyperbola. The relationships are given in the following summary.

> **SUMMARY** **Properties of Ellipses and Hyperbolas**
>
> An ellipse or hyperbola centered at the origin has the following properties.
>
> | | Foci on x-axis | Foci on y-axis |
> |---|---|---|
> | Major-axis vertices: | $(\pm a, 0)$ | $(0, \pm a)$ |
> | Minor-axis vertices (for ellipses): | $(0, \pm b)$ | $(\pm b, 0)$ |
> | Foci: | $(\pm c, 0)$ | $(0, \pm c)$ |
> | Directrices: | $x = \pm d$ | $y = \pm d$ |
> | Eccentricity: $0 < e < 1$ for ellipses, $e > 1$ for hyperbolas. | | |
>
> Given any two of the five parameters a, b, c, d, and e, the other three are found using the relations
>
> $$c = ae, \quad d = \frac{a}{e},$$
>
> $$b^2 = a^2 - c^2 \quad \text{(for ellipses)}, \qquad b^2 = c^2 - a^2 \quad \text{(for hyperbolas)}.$$

QUICK CHECK 5 Given an ellipse with $a = 3$ and $e = \frac{1}{2}$, what are the values of b, c, and d? ◄

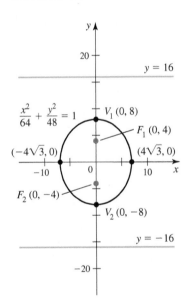

FIGURE 11.55

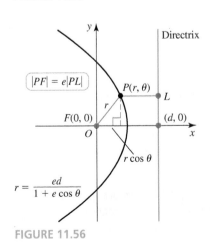

$$r = \frac{ed}{1 + e\cos\theta}$$

FIGURE 11.56

EXAMPLE 6 **Equations of ellipses** Find the equation of the ellipse centered at the origin with foci at $(0, \pm 4)$ and eccentricity $e = \frac{1}{2}$. Give the length of the major and minor axes, the location of the vertices, and the directrices. Graph the ellipse.

SOLUTION An ellipse with its major axis along the y-axis has the equation

$$\frac{y^2}{a^2} + \frac{x^2}{b^2} = 1,$$

where a and b must be determined (with $a > b$). Because the foci are at $(0, \pm 4)$, we have $c = 4$. Using $e = \frac{1}{2}$ and the relation $c = ae$, it follows that $a = c/e = 8$. So, the length of the major axis is $2a = 16$, and the major-axis vertices are $(0, \pm 8)$. Also $d = a/e = 16$, so the directrices are $y = \pm 16$. Finally, $b^2 = a^2 - c^2 = 48$, or $b = 4\sqrt{3}$. So, the length of the minor axis is $2b = 8\sqrt{3}$, and the minor-axis vertices are $(\pm 4\sqrt{3}, 0)$ (Figure 11.55). The equation of the ellipse is

$$\frac{y^2}{64} + \frac{x^2}{48} = 1.$$

Related Exercises 51–54 ◄

Polar Equations of Conic Sections

It turns out that conic sections have a natural representation in polar coordinates, provided we use the eccentricity-directrix approach given in Theorem 11.3. Furthermore, a single polar equation covers parabolas, ellipses, and hyperbolas.

When working in polar equations, the key is to place a focus of the conic section at the origin of the coordinate system. We begin by placing one focus F at the origin and taking a directrix perpendicular to the x-axis through $(d, 0)$, where $d > 0$ (Figure 11.56). We now use the definition $\dfrac{|PF|}{|PL|} = e$, where $P(r, \theta)$ is an arbitrary point on the conic. As shown in Figure 11.56, $|PF| = r$ and $|PL| = d - r\cos\theta$. The condition $\dfrac{|PF|}{|PL|} = e$ implies that $r = e(d - r\cos\theta)$. Solving for r, we have

$$r = \frac{ed}{1 + e\cos\theta}.$$

A similar derivation (Exercise 74) with the directrix at $x = -d$, where $d > 0$, results in the equation

$$r = \frac{ed}{1 - e \cos \theta}.$$

For horizontal directrices at $y = \pm d$ (Figure 11.57), a similar argument (Exercise 74) leads to the equations

$$r = \frac{ed}{1 \pm e \sin \theta}.$$

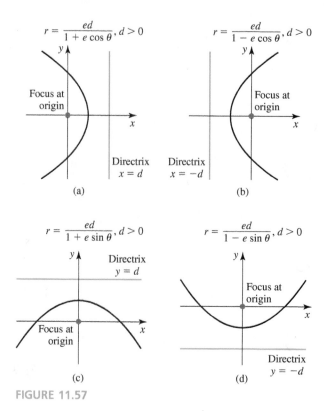

FIGURE 11.57

THEOREM 11.4   Polar Equations of Conic Sections

Let $d > 0$. The conic section with a focus at the origin and eccentricity e has the polar equation

$$r = \frac{ed}{1 + e \cos \theta} \quad \text{or} \quad r = \frac{ed}{1 - e \cos \theta}.$$

$$\underbrace{\phantom{r = \frac{ed}{1 + e \cos \theta}}}_{\text{if one directrix is } x = d} \qquad \underbrace{\phantom{r = \frac{ed}{1 - e \cos \theta}}}_{\text{if one directrix is } x = -d}$$

The conic section with a focus at the origin and eccentricity e has the polar equation

$$r = \frac{ed}{1 + e \sin \theta} \quad \text{or} \quad r = \frac{ed}{1 - e \sin \theta}.$$

$$\underbrace{\phantom{r = \frac{ed}{1 + e \sin \theta}}}_{\text{if one directrix is } y = d} \qquad \underbrace{\phantom{r = \frac{ed}{1 - e \sin \theta}}}_{\text{if one directrix is } y = -d}$$

If $0 < e < 1$, the conic section is an ellipse; if $e = 1$, it is a parabola; and if $e > 1$, it is a hyperbola. The curves are defined over any interval in θ of length 2π.

QUICK CHECK 6 On which axis do the vertices and foci of the conic section $r = 2/(1 - 2 \sin \theta)$ lie? ◄

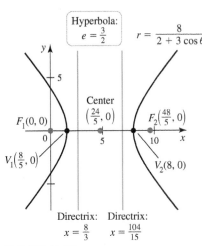

Hyperbola: $e = \frac{3}{2}$ $r = \frac{8}{2 + 3\cos\theta}$

$F_1(0, 0)$

$V_1\left(\frac{8}{5}, 0\right)$

Center $\left(\frac{24}{5}, 0\right)$ $F_2\left(\frac{48}{5}, 0\right)$

$V_2(8, 0)$

Directrix: $x = \frac{8}{3}$ Directrix: $x = \frac{104}{15}$

FIGURE 11.58

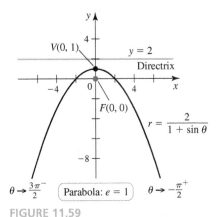

$V(0, 1)$ $y = 2$

Directrix

$F(0, 0)$

$r = \frac{2}{1 + \sin\theta}$

$\theta \to \frac{3\pi}{2}^-$ Parabola: $e = 1$ $\theta \to -\frac{\pi}{2}^+$

FIGURE 11.59

EXAMPLE 7 **Conic sections in polar coordinates** Find the vertices, foci, and directrices of the following conic sections. Graph each curve and then check your work with a graphing utility.

a. $r = \dfrac{8}{2 + 3\cos\theta}$ **b.** $r = \dfrac{2}{1 + \sin\theta}$

SOLUTION

a. The equation must be expressed in standard polar form for a conic section. Dividing numerator and denominator by 2, we have

$$r = \frac{4}{1 + \frac{3}{2}\cos\theta},$$

which allows us to identify $e = \frac{3}{2}$. Therefore, the equation describes a hyperbola (because $e > 1$) with one focus at the origin.

The directrices are vertical (because $\cos\theta$ appears in the equation). Knowing that $ed = 4$, we have $d = \frac{4}{e} = \frac{8}{3}$, and one directrix is $x = \frac{8}{3}$. Letting $\theta = 0$ and $\theta = \pi$, the polar coordinates of the vertices are $\left(\frac{8}{5}, 0\right)$ and $(-8, \pi)$; equivalently, the vertices are $\left(\frac{8}{5}, 0\right)$ and $(8, 0)$ in Cartesian coordinates (Figure 11.58). The center of the hyperbola is halfway between the vertices; therefore, its Cartesian coordinates are $\left(\frac{24}{5}, 0\right)$. The distance between the focus at $(0, 0)$ and the nearest vertex $\left(\frac{8}{5}, 0\right)$ is $\frac{8}{5}$. Therefore, the other focus is $\frac{8}{5}$ units to the right of the vertex $(8, 0)$. So, the Cartesian coordinates of the foci are $\left(\frac{48}{5}, 0\right)$ and $(0, 0)$. Because the directrices are symmetric about the center and the left directrix is $x = \frac{8}{3}$, the right directrix is $x = \frac{104}{15} \approx 6.9$. The graph of the hyperbola (Figure 11.58) is generated as θ varies from 0 to 2π $\Big($with $\theta \neq \pm\cos^{-1}\left(-\frac{2}{3}\right)\Big)$.

b. The equation is in standard form, and it describes a parabola because $e = 1$. The sole focus is at the origin. The directrix is horizontal (because of the $\sin\theta$ term); $ed = 2$ implies that $d = 2$, and the directrix is $y = 2$. The parabola opens downward because of the plus sign in the denominator. The vertex corresponds to $\theta = \frac{\pi}{2}$ and has polar coordinates $\left(1, \frac{\pi}{2}\right)$, or Cartesian coordinates $(0, 1)$. Setting $\theta = 0$ and $\theta = \pi$, the parabola crosses the x-axis at $(2, 0)$ and $(2, \pi)$ in polar coordinates, or $(\pm 2, 0)$ in Cartesian coordinates. As θ increases from $-\frac{\pi}{2}$ to $\frac{\pi}{2}$, the right branch of the parabola is generated and as θ increases from $\frac{\pi}{2}$ to $\frac{3\pi}{2}$, the left branch of the parabola is generated (Figure 11.59).

Related Exercises 55–64 ◄

EXAMPLE 8 **Conics in polar coordinates** Use a graphing utility to plot the curves $r = \dfrac{e}{1 + e\cos\theta}$, with $e = 0.2, 0.4, 0.6,$ and 0.8. Comment on the effect of varying the eccentricity, e.

SOLUTION Because $0 < e < 1$, all the curves are ellipses. Notice that the equation is in standard form with $d = 1$; therefore, the curves have the same directrix, $x = d = 1$. As the eccentricity increases, the ellipses becomes more elongated. Small values of e correspond to more circular ellipses (Figure 11.60).

Related Exercises 65–66 ◄

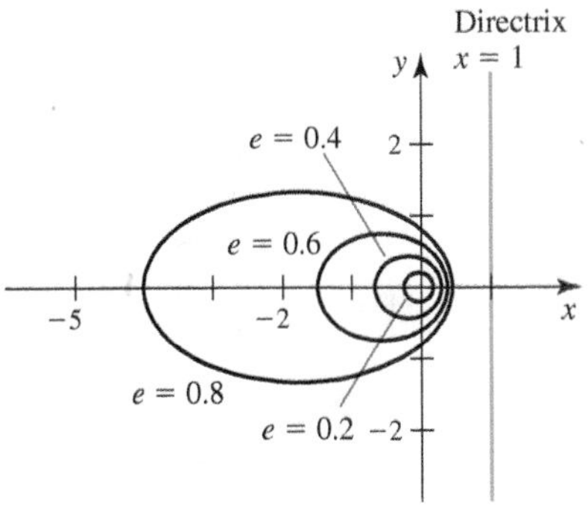

Directrix $x = 1$

$e = 0.4$

$e = 0.6$

$e = 0.8$

$e = 0.2$

FIGURE 11.60

SECTION 11.4 EXERCISES

Review Questions

1. Give the property that defines all parabolas.

2. Give the property that defines all ellipses.

3. Give the property that defines all hyperbolas.

4. Sketch the three basic conic sections in standard position with vertices and foci on the x-axis.

5. Sketch the three basic conic sections in standard position with vertices and foci on the y-axis.

6. What is the equation of the standard parabola with its vertex at the origin that opens downward?

7. What is the equation of the standard ellipse with vertices at $(\pm a, 0)$ and foci at $(\pm c, 0)$?

8. What is the equation of the standard hyperbola with vertices at $(0, \pm a)$ and foci at $(0, \pm c)$?

9. Given vertices $(\pm a, 0)$ and eccentricity e, what are the coordinates of the foci of an ellipse and a hyperbola?

10. Give the equation in polar coordinates of a conic section with a focus at the origin, eccentricity e, and a directrix $x = d$, where $d > 0$.

11. What are the equations of the asymptotes of a standard hyperbola with vertices on the x-axis?

12. How does the eccentricity determine the type of conic section?

Basic Skills

13–18. Graphing parabolas *Sketch the graph of the following parabolas. Specify the location of the focus and the equation of the directrix. Use a graphing utility to check your work.*

13. $x^2 = 12y$
14. $y^2 = 20x$
15. $x = -y^2/16$
16. $4x = -y^2$
17. $8y = -3x^2$
18. $12x = 5y^2$

19–24. Equations of parabolas *Find an equation of the following parabolas, assuming the vertex is at the origin.*

19. A parabola that opens to the right with directrix $x = -4$

20. A parabola that opens downward with directrix $y = 6$

21. A parabola with focus at $(3, 0)$

22. A parabola with focus at $(-4, 0)$

23. A parabola symmetric about the y-axis that passes through the point $(2, -6)$

24. A parabola symmetric about the x-axis that passes through the point $(1, -4)$

25–26. From graphs to equations *Write an equation of the following parabolas.*

25.
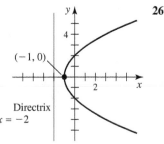

26.
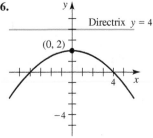

27–32. Graphing ellipses *Sketch the graph of the following ellipses. Plot and label the coordinates of the vertices and foci, and find the lengths of the major and minor axes. Use a graphing utility to check your work.*

27. $\dfrac{x^2}{4} + y^2 = 1$

28. $\dfrac{x^2}{9} + \dfrac{y^2}{4} = 1$

29. $\dfrac{x^2}{4} + \dfrac{y^2}{16} = 1$

30. $x^2 + \dfrac{y^2}{9} = 1$

31. $\dfrac{x^2}{5} + \dfrac{y^2}{7} = 1$

32. $12x^2 + 5y^2 = 60$

33–36. Equations of ellipses *Find an equation of the following ellipses, assuming the center is at the origin. Sketch a graph labeling the vertices and foci.*

33. An ellipse whose major axis is on the x-axis with length 8 and whose minor axis has length 6

34. An ellipse with vertices $(\pm 6, 0)$ and foci $(\pm 4, 0)$

35. An ellipse with vertices $(\pm 5, 0)$, passing through the point $\left(4, \frac{3}{5}\right)$

36. An ellipse with vertices $(0, \pm 10)$, passing through the point $\left(\sqrt{3}/2, 5\right)$

37–38. From graphs to equations *Write an equation of the following ellipses.*

37.
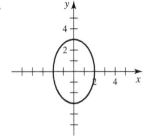

38.
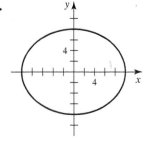

39–44. Graphing hyperbolas *Sketch the graph of the following hyperbolas. Specify the coordinates of the vertices and foci, and find the equations of the asymptotes. Use a graphing utility to check your work.*

39. $\dfrac{x^2}{4} - y^2 = 1$

40. $\dfrac{y^2}{16} - \dfrac{x^2}{9} = 1$

41. $4x^2 - y^2 = 16$

42. $25y^2 - 4x^2 = 100$

43. $\dfrac{x^2}{3} - \dfrac{y^2}{5} = 1$

44. $10x^2 - 7y^2 = 140$

45–48. Equations of hyperbolas *Find an equation of the following hyperbolas, assuming the center is at the origin. Sketch a graph labeling the vertices, foci, and asymptotes. Use a graphing utility to check your work.*

45. A hyperbola with vertices $(\pm 4, 0)$ and foci $(\pm 6, 0)$

46. A hyperbola with vertices $(\pm 1, 0)$ that passes through $(\frac{5}{3}, 8)$

47. A hyperbola with vertices $(\pm 2, 0)$ and asymptotes $y = \pm 3x/2$

48. A hyperbola with vertices $(0, \pm 4)$ and asymptotes $y = \pm 2x$

49–50. From graphs to equations *Write an equation of the following hyperbolas.*

49.

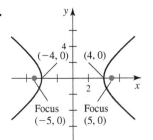

50.

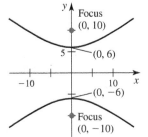

51–54. Eccentricity-directrix approach *Find an equation of the following curves, assuming the center is at the origin. Sketch a graph labeling the vertices, foci, asymptotes, and directrices. Use a graphing utility to check your work.*

51. An ellipse with vertices $(\pm 9, 0)$ and eccentricity $\frac{1}{3}$

52. An ellipse with vertices $(0, \pm 9)$ and eccentricity $\frac{1}{4}$

53. A hyperbola with vertices $(\pm 1, 0)$ and eccentricity 3

54. A hyperbola with vertices $(0, \pm 4)$ and eccentricity 2

55–60. Polar equations for conic sections *Graph the following conic sections, labeling the vertices, foci, directrices, and asymptotes (if they exist). Use a graphing utility to check your work.*

55. $r = \dfrac{4}{1 + \cos \theta}$

56. $r = \dfrac{4}{2 + \cos \theta}$

57. $r = \dfrac{1}{2 - \cos \theta}$

58. $r = \dfrac{6}{3 + 2 \sin \theta}$

59. $r = \dfrac{1}{2 - 2 \sin \theta}$

60. $r = \dfrac{12}{3 - \cos \theta}$

61–64. Tracing hyperbolas and parabolas *Graph the following equations. Then use arrows and labeled points to indicate how the curve is generated as θ increases from 0 to 2π.*

61. $r = \dfrac{1}{1 + \sin \theta}$

62. $r = \dfrac{1}{1 + 2 \cos \theta}$

63. $r = \dfrac{3}{1 - \cos \theta}$

64. $r = \dfrac{1}{1 - 2 \cos \theta}$

65. Parabolas with a graphing utility Use a graphing utility to graph the parabolas $y^2 = 4px$, for $p = -5, -2, -1, 1, 2,$ and 5 on the same set of axes. Explain how the shapes of the curves vary as p changes.

66. Hyperbolas with a graphing utility Use a graphing utility to graph the hyperbolas $r = \dfrac{e}{1 + e \cos \theta}$, for $e = 1.1, 1.3, 1.5, 1.7,$ and 2 on the same set of axes. Explain how the shapes of the curves vary as e changes.

Further Explorations

67. Explain why or why not Determine whether the following statements are true and give an explanation or counterexample.

  a. The hyperbola $x^2/4 - y^2/9 = 1$ has no y-intercepts.

  b. On every ellipse, there are exactly two points at which the curve has slope s, where s is any real number.

  c. Given the directrices and foci of a standard hyperbola, it is possible to find its vertices, eccentricity, and asymptotes.

  d. The point on a parabola closest to the focus is the vertex.

68–71. Tangent lines *Find an equation of the line tangent to the following curves at the given point.*

68. $y^2 = 8x$; $(8, -8)$

69. $x^2 = -6y$; $(-6, -6)$

70. $r = \dfrac{1}{1 + \sin \theta}$; $\left(\dfrac{2}{3}, \dfrac{\pi}{6}\right)$

71. $y^2 - \dfrac{x^2}{64} = 1$; $\left(6, -\dfrac{5}{4}\right)$

72–73. Graphs to polar equations *Find a polar equation for each conic section. Assume one focus is at the origin.*

72.

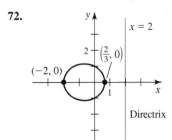

73.

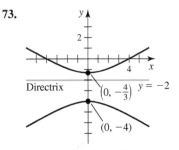

74. Deriving polar equations for conics Modify Figure 11.56 to derive the polar equation of a conic section with a focus at the origin in the following three cases.

  a. Vertical directrix at $x = -d$, where $d > 0$

  b. Horizontal directrix at $y = d$, where $d > 0$

  c. Horizontal directrix at $y = -d$, where $d > 0$

75. **Another construction for a hyperbola** Suppose two circles, whose centers are at least $2a$ units apart (see figure), are centered at F_1 and F_2, respectively. The radius of one circle is $2a + r$ and the radius of the other circle is r, where $r \geq 0$. Show that as r increases, the intersection point P of the two circles describes one branch of a hyperbola with foci at F_1 and F_2.

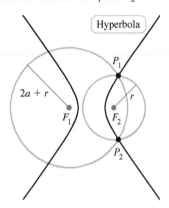

76. **The ellipse and the parabola** Let R be the region bounded by the upper half of the ellipse $x^2/2 + y^2 = 1$ and the parabola $y = x^2/\sqrt{2}$.

   a. Find the area of R.
   b. Which is greater, the volume of the solid generated when R is revolved about the x-axis or the volume of the solid generated when R is revolved about the y-axis?

77. **Tangent lines for an ellipse** Show that an equation of the line tangent to the ellipse $x^2/a^2 + y^2/b^2 = 1$ at the point (x_0, y_0) is

$$\frac{x x_0}{a^2} + \frac{y y_0}{b^2} = 1.$$

78. **Tangent lines for a hyperbola** Find an equation of the line tangent to the hyperbola $x^2/a^2 - y^2/b^2 = 1$ at the point (x_0, y_0).

79. **Volume of an ellipsoid** Suppose that the ellipse $x^2/a^2 + y^2/b^2 = 1$ is revolved about the x-axis. What is the volume of the solid enclosed by the *ellipsoid* that is generated? Is the volume different if the same ellipse is revolved about the y-axis?

80. **Area of a sector of a hyperbola** Consider the region R bounded by the right branch of the hyperbola $x^2/a^2 - y^2/b^2 = 1$ and the vertical line through the right focus.

   a. What is the area of R?
   b. Sketch a graph that shows how the area of R varies with the eccentricity e, for $e > 1$.

81. **Volume of a hyperbolic cap** Consider the region R bounded by the right branch of the hyperbola $x^2/a^2 - y^2/b^2 = 1$ and the vertical line through the right focus.

   a. What is the volume of the solid that is generated when R is revolved about the x-axis?
   b. What is the volume of the solid that is generated when R is revolved about the y-axis?

82. **Volume of a paraboloid (Archimedes)** The region bounded by the parabola $y = ax^2$ and the horizontal line $y = h$ is revolved about the y-axis to generate a solid bounded by a surface called a *paraboloid* (where $a > 0$ and $h > 0$). Show that the volume of the solid is $\frac{3}{2}$ the volume of the cone with the same base and vertex.

Applications

(See the Guided Project Properties of Conic Sections for additional applications of conic sections.)

83. **Reflection property of parabolas** Consider the parabola $y = x^2/4p$ with its focus at $F(0, p)$ (see figure). The goal is to show that the angle of incidence between the ray ℓ and the tangent line L (α in the figure) equals the angle of reflection between the line PF and L (β in the figure). If these two angles are equal, then the reflection property is proved because ℓ is reflected through F.

   a. Let $P(x_0, y_0)$ be a point on the parabola. Show that the slope of the line tangent to the curve at P is $\tan \theta = x_0/(2p)$.
   b. Show that $\tan \varphi = (p - y_0)/x_0$.
   c. Show that $\alpha = \pi/2 - \theta$; therefore, $\tan \alpha = \cot \theta$.
   d. Note that $\beta = \theta + \varphi$. Use the tangent addition formula

$$\tan(\theta + \varphi) = \frac{\tan \theta + \tan \varphi}{1 - \tan \theta \tan \varphi} \text{ to show that}$$

   $\tan \alpha = \tan \beta = 2p/x_0$.
   e. Conclude that because α and β are acute angles, $\alpha = \beta$.

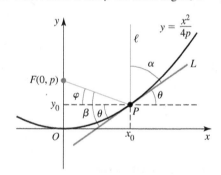

84. **Golden Gate Bridge** Completed in 1937, San Francisco's Golden Gate Bridge is 2.7 km long and weighs about 890,000 tons. The length of the span between the two central towers is 1280 m; the towers themselves extend 152 m above the roadway. The cables that support the deck of the bridge between the two towers hang in a parabola (see figure). Assuming the origin is midway between the towers on the deck of the bridge, find an equation that describes the cables. How long is a guy wire that hangs vertically from the cables to the roadway 500 m from the center of the bridge?

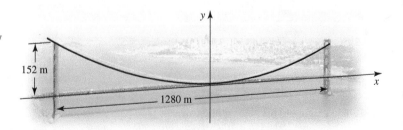

Additional Exercises

85. Equation of an ellipse Consider an ellipse to be the set of points in a plane whose distances from two fixed points have a constant sum $2a$. Derive the equation of an ellipse. Assume the two fixed points are on the x-axis equidistant from the origin.

86. Equation of a hyperbola Consider a hyperbola to be the set of points in a plane whose distances from two fixed points have a constant difference of $2a$ or $-2a$. Derive the equation of a hyperbola. Assume the two fixed points are on the x-axis equidistant from the origin.

87. Equidistant set Show that the set of points equidistant from a circle and a line not passing through the circle is a parabola. Assume the circle, line, and parabola lie in the same plane.

88. Polar equation of a conic Show that the polar equation of an ellipse or hyperbola with one focus at the origin, major axis of length $2a$ on the x-axis, and eccentricity e is

$$r = \frac{a(1 - e^2)}{1 + e \cos \theta}.$$

89. Shared asymptotes Suppose that two hyperbolas with eccentricities e and E have perpendicular major axes and share a set of asymptotes. Show that $e^{-2} + E^{-2} = 1$.

90–94. Focal chords *A **focal chord** of a conic section is a line through a focus joining two points of the curve. The **latus rectum** is the focal chord perpendicular to the major axis of the conic. Prove the following properties.*

90. The lines tangent to the endpoints of any focal chord of a parabola $y^2 = 4px$ intersect on the directrix and are perpendicular.

91. Let L be the latus rectum of the parabola $y^2 = 4px$, for $p > 0$. Let F be the focus of the parabola, P be any point on the parabola to the left of L, and D be the (shortest) distance between P and L. Show that for all P, $D + |FP|$ is a constant. Find the constant.

92. The length of the latus rectum of the parabola $y^2 = 4px$ or $x^2 = 4py$ is $4|p|$.

93. The length of the latus rectum of an ellipse centered at the origin is $2b^2/a = 2b\sqrt{1 - e^2}$.

94. The length of the latus rectum of a hyperbola centered at the origin is $2b^2/a = 2b\sqrt{e^2 - 1}$.

95. Confocal ellipse and hyperbola Show that an ellipse and a hyperbola that have the same two foci intersect at right angles.

96. Approach to asymptotes Show that the vertical distance between a hyperbola $x^2/a^2 - y^2/b^2 = 1$ and its asymptote $y = bx/a$ approaches zero as $x \to \infty$, where $0 < b < a$.

97. Sector of a hyperbola Let H be the right branch of the hyperbola $x^2 - y^2 = 1$ and let ℓ be the line $y = m(x - 2)$ that passes through the point $(2, 0)$ with slope m, where $-\infty < m < \infty$. Let R be the region in the first quadrant bounded by H and ℓ (see figure). Let $A(m)$ be the area of R. Note that for some values of m, $A(m)$ is not defined.

   a. Find the x-coordinates of the intersection points between H and ℓ as functions of m; call them $u(m)$ and $v(m)$, where $v(m) > u(m) > 1$. For what values of m are there two intersection points?

   b. Evaluate $\lim_{m \to 1^+} u(m)$ and $\lim_{m \to 1^+} v(m)$.

   c. Evaluate $\lim_{m \to \infty} u(m)$ and $\lim_{m \to \infty} v(m)$.

   d. Evaluate and interpret $\lim_{m \to \infty} A(m)$.

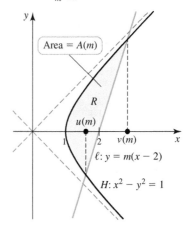

98. The anvil of a hyperbola Let H be the hyperbola $x^2 - y^2 = 1$ and let S be the 2-by-2 square bisected by the asymptotes of H. Let R be the anvil-shaped region bounded by the hyperbola and the horizontal lines $y = \pm p$ (see figure).

   a. For what value of p is the area of R equal to the area of S?
   b. For what value of p is the area of R twice the area of S?

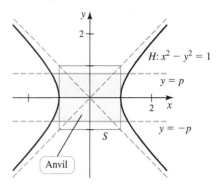

99. Parametric equations for an ellipse Consider the parametric equations

$$x = a \cos t + b \sin t, \quad y = c \cos t + d \sin t,$$

where a, b, c, and d are real numbers.

   a. Show that (apart from a set of special cases) the equations describe an ellipse of the form $Ax^2 + Bxy + Cy^2 = K$, where A, B, C, and K are constants.
   b. Show that (apart from a set of special cases), the equations describe an ellipse with its axes aligned with the x- and y-axes provided $ab + cd = 0$.
   c. Show that the equations describe a circle provided $ab + cd = 0$ and $c^2 + d^2 = a^2 + b^2 \neq 0$.

QUICK CHECK ANSWERS

2. a. Left   **b.** Up   **3.** The minor-axis vertices are $(0, \pm b)$. The distance between them is $2b$, which is the length of the minor axis.   **4.** Vertices: $(0, \pm 1)$; foci: $(0, \pm\sqrt{5})$ **5.** $b = 3\sqrt{3}/2, c = 3/2, d = 6$ **6.** y-axis ◄

CHAPTER 11   REVIEW EXERCISES

1. Explain why or why not Determine whether the following statements are true and give an explanation or counterexample.

    a. A set of parametric equations for a given curve is always unique.

    b. The equations $x = e^t$, $y = 2e^t$, for $-\infty < t < \infty$, describe a line passing through the origin with slope 2.

    c. The polar coordinates $(3, -3\pi/4)$ and $(-3, \pi/4)$ describe the same point in the plane.

    d. The limaçon $r = f(\theta) = 1 - 4\cos\theta$ has an outer and inner loop. The area of the region between the two loops is
$$\frac{1}{2}\int_0^{2\pi} (f(\theta))^2\, d\theta.$$

    e. The hyperbola $y^2/2 - x^2/4 = 1$ has no x-intercepts.

    f. The equation $x^2 + 4y^2 - 2x = 3$ describes an ellipse.

2–5. Parametric curves

a. Plot the following curves, indicating the positive orientation.

b. Eliminate the parameter to obtain an equation in x and y.

c. Identify or briefly describe the curve.

d. Evaluate dy/dx at the specified point.

2. $x = t^2 + 4$, $y = 6 - t$, for $-\infty < t < \infty$; evaluate dy/dx at $(5, 5)$.

3. $x = e^t$, $y = 3e^{-2t}$, for $-\infty < t < \infty$; evaluate dy/dx at $(1, 3)$.

4. $x = 10\sin 2t$, $y = 16\cos 2t$, for $0 \le t \le \pi$; evaluate dy/dx at $(5\sqrt{3}, 8)$.

5. $x = \ln t$, $y = 8\ln t^2$, for $1 \le t \le e^2$; evaluate dy/dx at $(1, 16)$.

6. Circles For what values of a, b, c, and d do the equations $x = a\cos t + b\sin t$, $y = c\cos t + d\sin t$ describe a circle? What is the radius of the circle?

7–9. Eliminating the parameter *Eliminate the parameter to find a description of the following curves in terms of x and y. Give a geometric description and the positive orientation of the curve.*

7. $x = 4\cos t$, $y = 3\sin t$; $0 \le t \le 2\pi$

8. $x = 4\cos t - 1$, $y = 4\sin t + 2$; $0 \le t \le 2\pi$

9. $x = \sin t - 3$, $y = \cos t + 6$; $0 \le t \le \pi$

10. Parametric to polar equations Find a description of the following curve in polar coordinates and describe the curve.

$$x = (1 + \cos t)\cos t, \quad y = (1 + \cos t)\sin t + 6; \quad 0 \le t \le 2\pi$$

11–16. Parametric description *Write parametric equations for the following curves. Solutions are not unique.*

11. The circle $x^2 + y^2 = 9$, generated clockwise

12. The upper half of the ellipse $\dfrac{x^2}{9} + \dfrac{y^2}{4} = 1$, generated counterclockwise

13. The right side of the ellipse $\dfrac{x^2}{9} + \dfrac{y^2}{4} = 1$, generated counterclockwise

14. The line $y - 3 = 4(x + 2)$

15. The line segment from $P(-1, 0)$ to $Q(1, 1)$ and the line segment from Q to P

16. The segment of the curve $f(x) = x^3 + 2x$ from $(0, 0)$ to $(2, 12)$

17. Tangent lines Find an equation of the line tangent to the cycloid $x = t - \sin t$, $y = 1 - \cos t$ at the points corresponding to $t = \pi/6$ and $t = 2\pi/3$.

18–19. Sets in polar coordinates *Sketch the following sets of points.*

18. $\{(r, \theta): 4 \le r^2 \le 9\}$

19. $\{(r, \theta): 0 \le r \le 4, -\pi/2 \le \theta \le -\pi/3\}$

20. Matching polar curves Match equations a–f with graphs A–F.

    a. $r = 3\sin 4\theta$ **b.** $r^2 = 4\cos\theta$

    c. $r = 2 - 3\sin\theta$ **d.** $r = 1 + 2\cos\theta$

    e. $r = 3\cos 3\theta$ **f.** $r = e^{-\theta/6}$

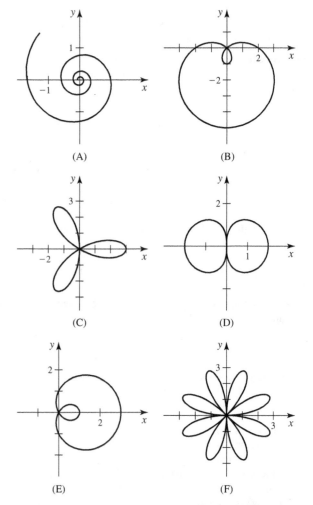

(A)   (B)

(C)   (D)

(E)   (F)

21. Polar valentine Liz wants to show her love for Jake by passing him a valentine on her graphing calculator. Sketch each of the following curves and determine which one Liz should use to get a heart-shaped curve.

a. $r = 5 \cos \theta$ **b.** $r = 1 - \sin \theta$ **c.** $r = \cos 3\theta$

22. Jake's response Jake responds to Liz (Exercise 21) with a graph that shows that his love for her is infinite. Sketch each of the following curves. Which one should Jake send to Liz to get a sideways, figure-8 curve (infinity symbol)?

a. $r = \theta$ **b.** $r = \frac{1}{2} + \sin \theta$ **c.** $r^2 = \cos 2\theta$

23. Polar conversion Write the equation $r^2 + r(2 \sin \theta - 6 \cos \theta) = 0$ in Cartesian coordinates and identify the corresponding curve.

24. Polar conversion Consider the equation $r = 4/(\sin \theta - 6 \cos \theta)$.

  a. Convert the equation to Cartesian coordinates and identify the curve it describes.

  b. Graph the curve and indicate the points that correspond to $\theta = 0, \pi/2$, and 2π.

  c. Give an interval in θ on which the entire curve is generated.

25. Cartesian conversion Write the circle $(x - 4)^2 + y^2 = 16$ in polar coordinates and state values of θ that produce the entire graph of the circle.

26. Cartesian conversion Write the parabola $x = y^2$ in polar coordinates and state values of θ that produce the entire graph of the parabola.

27. Intersection points Consider the polar equations $r = 1$ and $r = 2 - 4 \cos \theta$.

  a. Graph the curves. How many intersection points do you observe?

  b. Give the approximate polar coordinates of the intersection points.

28–31. Slopes of tangent lines

a. Find all points where the following curves have vertical and horizontal tangent lines.

b. Find the slope of the lines tangent to the curve at the origin (when relevant).

c. Sketch the curve and all the tangent lines identified in parts (a) and (b).

28. $r = 2 \cos 2\theta$ **29.** $r = 4 + 2 \sin \theta$

30. $r = 3 - 6 \cos \theta$ **31.** $r^2 = 2 \cos 2\theta$

32–37. Areas of regions Find the area of the following regions. In each case, graph the curve(s) and shade the region in question.

32. The region enclosed by all the leaves of the rose $r = 3 \sin 4\theta$

33. The region enclosed by the limaçon $r = 3 - \cos \theta$

34. The region inside the limaçon $r = 2 + \cos \theta$ and outside the circle $r = 2$

35. The region inside the lemniscate $r^2 = 4 \cos 2\theta$ and outside the circle $r = \frac{1}{2}$

36. The area that is inside both the cardioids $r = 1 - \cos \theta$ and $r = 1 + \cos \theta$

37. The area that is inside the cardioid $r = 1 + \cos \theta$ and outside the cardioid $r = 1 - \cos \theta$

38–43. Conic sections

a. Determine whether the following equations describe a parabola, an ellipse, or a hyperbola.

b. Use analytical methods to determine the location of the foci, vertices, and directrices.

c. Find the eccentricity of the curve.

d. Make an accurate graph of the curve.

38. $x = 16y^2$ **39.** $x^2 - y^2/2 = 1$

40. $x^2/4 + y^2/25 = 1$ **41.** $y^2 - 4x^2 = 16$

42. $y = 8x^2 + 16x + 8$ **43.** $4x^2 + 8y^2 = 16$

44. Matching equations and curves Match equations a–f with graphs A–F.

  a. $x^2 - y^2 = 4$ **b.** $x^2 + 4y^2 = 4$

  c. $y^2 - 3x = 0$ **d.** $x^2 + 3y = 1$

  e. $x^2/4 + y^2/8 = 1$ **f.** $y^2/8 - x^2/2 = 1$

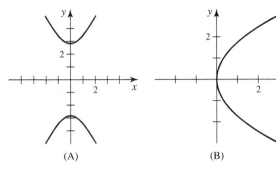

(A)   (B)

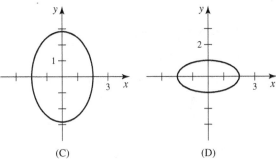

(C)   (D)

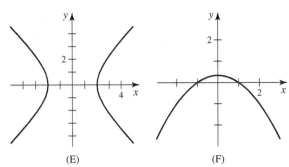

(E)   (F)

45–48. Tangent lines Find an equation of the line tangent to the following curves at the given point. Check your work with a graphing utility.

45. $y^2 = -12x;\ \left(-\dfrac{4}{3}, -4\right)$ **46.** $x^2 = 5y;\ \left(-2, \dfrac{4}{5}\right)$

47. $\dfrac{x^2}{100} + \dfrac{y^2}{64} = 1;\ \left(-6, -\dfrac{32}{5}\right)$ **48.** $\dfrac{x^2}{16} - \dfrac{y^2}{9} = 1;\ \left(\dfrac{20}{3}, -4\right)$

49–52. Polar equations for conic sections *Graph the following conic sections, labeling vertices, foci, directrices, and asymptotes (if they exist). Give the eccentricity of the curve. Use a graphing utility to check your work.*

49. $r = \dfrac{2}{1 + \sin \theta}$ **50.** $r = \dfrac{3}{1 - 2 \cos \theta}$

51. $r = \dfrac{4}{2 + \cos \theta}$ **52.** $r = \dfrac{10}{5 + 2 \cos \theta}$

53. A polar conic section Consider the equation $r^2 = \sec 2\theta$.

   a. Convert the equation to Cartesian coordinates and identify the curve.

   b. Find the vertices, foci, directrices, and eccentricity of the curve.

   c. Graph the curve. Explain why the polar equation does not have the form given in the text for conic sections in polar coordinates.

54–57. Eccentricity-directrix approach *Find an equation of the following curves, assuming the center is at the origin. Graph the curve, labeling vertices, foci, asymptotes (if they exist), and directrices.*

54. An ellipse with foci $(\pm 4, 0)$ and directrices $x = \pm 8$

55. An ellipse with vertices $(0, \pm 4)$ and directrices $y = \pm 10$

56. A hyperbola with vertices $(\pm 4, 0)$ and directrices $x = \pm 2$

57. A hyperbola with vertices $(0, \pm 2)$ and directrices $y = \pm 1$

58. Conic parameters A hyperbola has eccentricity $e = 2$ and foci $(0, \pm 2)$. Find the location of the vertices and directrices.

59. Conic parameters An ellipse has vertices $(0, \pm 6)$ and foci $(0, \pm 4)$. Find the eccentricity, the directrices, and the minor-axis vertices.

60–63. Intersection points *Use analytical methods to find as many intersection points of the following curves as possible. Use methods of your choice to find the remaining intersection points.*

60. $r = 1 - \cos \theta$ and $r = \theta$

61. $r^2 = \sin 2\theta$ and $r = \theta$

62. $r^2 = \sin 2\theta$ and $r = 1 - 2 \sin \theta$

63. $r = \theta/2$ and $r = -\theta$, for $\theta \geq 0$

64. Area of an ellipse Consider the polar equation of an ellipse $r = ed/(1 \pm e \cos \theta)$, where $0 < e < 1$. Evaluate an integral in polar coordinates to show that the area of the region enclosed by the ellipse is πab, where $2a$ and $2b$ are the lengths of the major and minor axes, respectively.

65. Maximizing area Among all rectangles centered at the origin with vertices on the ellipse $x^2/a^2 + y^2/b^2 = 1$, what are the dimensions of the rectangle with the maximum area (in terms of a and b)? What is that area?

66. Equidistant set Let S be the square centered at the origin with vertices $(\pm a, \pm a)$. Describe and sketch the set of points that are equidistant from the square and the origin.

67. Bisecting an ellipse Let R be the region in the first quadrant bounded by the ellipse $x^2/a^2 + y^2/b^2 = 1$. Find the value of m (in terms of a and b) such that the line $y = mx$ divides R into two subregions of equal area.

68. Parabola-hyperbola tangency Let P be the parabola $y = px^2$ and H be the right half of the hyperbola $x^2 - y^2 = 1$.

   a. For what value of p is P tangent to H?

   b. At what point does the tangency occur?

   c. Generalize your results for the hyperbola $x^2/a^2 - y^2/b^2 = 1$.

69. Another ellipse construction Start with two circles centered at the origin with radii $0 < a < b$ (see figure). Assume the line ℓ through the origin intersects the smaller circle at Q and the larger circle at R. Let $P(x, y)$ have the y-coordinate of Q and the x-coordinate of R. Show that the set of points $P(x, y)$ generated in this way for all lines ℓ through the origin is an ellipse.

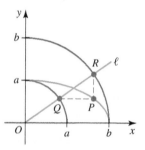

70–71. Graphs to polar equations *Find a polar equation for the conic sections in the figures.*

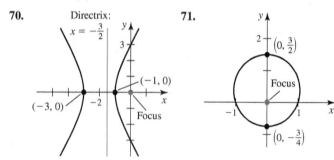

Chapter 11 Guided Projects

Applications of the material in this chapter and related topics can be found in the following Guided Projects. For additional information, see the Preface.

- The amazing cycloid
- Parametric art
- Polar art
- Grazing goat problems

- Translations and rotations of axes
- Celestial orbits
- Properties of conic sections

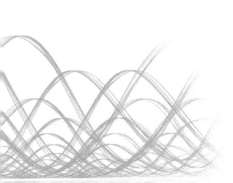

12

Vectors and Vector-Valued Functions

Chapter Preview We now make a significant departure from previous chapters by stepping out of the *xy*-plane into three-dimensional space. The fundamental concept of a *vector*—a quantity with magnitude and direction—is introduced in two and three dimensions. We then put vectors in motion by introducing *vector-valued functions*, or simply *vector functions*. The calculus of vector functions is a direct extension of everything you already know about limits, derivatives, and integrals. Also, with the calculus of vector functions, we can solve a wealth of practical problems involving the motion of objects in space. The chapter closes with an exploration of arc length, curvature, and tangent and normal vectors, all important features of space curves.

12.1 Vectors in the Plane

Imagine a raft drifting down a river, carried by the current. The speed and direction of the raft at a point may be represented by an arrow (Figure 12.1). The length of the arrow represents the speed of the raft at that point; longer arrows correspond to greater speeds. The orientation of the arrow gives the direction in which the raft is headed at that point. The arrows at points *A* and *C* in Figure 12.1 have the same length and direction, indicating that the raft has the same speed and heading at these locations. The arrow at *B* is shorter and points to the left of the rock, indicating that the raft slows down as it nears the rock.

FIGURE 12.1

Basic Vector Operations

The arrows that describe the raft's motion are examples of *vectors*—quantities that have both *length* (or *magnitude*) and *direction*. Vectors arise naturally in many situations. For example, electric and magnetic fields, the flow of air over an airplane wing, and the velocity and acceleration of elementary particles are described by vectors (Figure 12.2). In this section we examine vectors in the *xy*-plane and then extend the concept to three dimensions in Section 12.2.

The vector whose *tail* is at the point *P* and whose *head* is at the point *Q* is denoted $\vec{PQ}$ (Figure 12.3). The vector $\vec{QP}$ has its tail at *Q* and its head at *P*. We also label vectors with single, boldfaced characters such as **u** and **v**.

Two vectors **u** and **v** are *equal*, written **u** = **v**, if they have equal length and point in the same direction (Figure 12.4). An important fact is that equal vectors do not necessarily have the same location. *Any* two vectors with the same length and direction are equal.

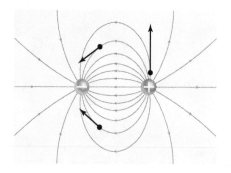

Electric field vectors due to two charges

FIGURE 12.2

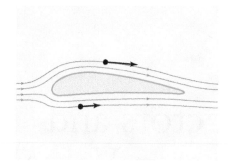

Velocity vectors of air flowing over an airplane wing

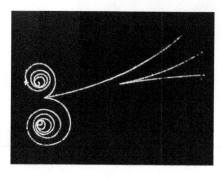

Tracks of elementary particles in a cloud chamber are aligned with the velocity vectors of the particles.

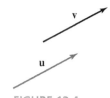

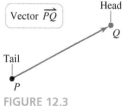

Vectors **u** and **v** are *equal* if they have the same length and direction.

FIGURE 12.3   **FIGURE 12.4**

> The vector **v** is commonly handwritten as $\vec{v}$.

Not all quantities are represented by vectors. For example, mass, temperature, and price have magnitude, but no direction. Such quantities are described by real numbers and are called *scalars*.

> In this book, *scalar* is another word for *real number*.

> The zero vector is handwritten $\vec{0}$.

Vectors, Equal Vectors, Scalars, Zero Vector

Vectors are quantities that have both **length** (or **magnitude**) and **direction**. Two vectors are **equal** if they have the same magnitude and direction. Quantities having magnitude but no direction are called **scalars**. One exception is the **zero vector**, denoted **0**: It has length 0 and no direction.

Scalar Multiplication

A scalar c and a vector **v** can be combined using scalar-vector multiplication, or simply *scalar multiplication*. The resulting vector, denoted $c\mathbf{v}$, is called a *scalar multiple* of **v**. The magnitude of $c\mathbf{v}$ is $|c|$ multiplied by the magnitude of **v**. The vector $c\mathbf{v}$ has the same direction as **v** if $c > 0$. If $c < 0$, then $c\mathbf{v}$ and **v** point in opposite directions. If $c = 0$, then $0 \cdot \mathbf{v} = \mathbf{0}$ (the zero vector).

For example, the vector $3\mathbf{v}$ is three times as long as **v** and has the same direction as **v**. The vector $-2\mathbf{v}$ is twice as long as **v**, but it points in the opposite direction. The vector $\frac{1}{2}\mathbf{v}$ points in the same direction as **v** and has half the length of **v** (Figure 12.5). The vectors **v**, $3\mathbf{v}$, $-2\mathbf{v}$, and $\mathbf{v}/2$ (that is, $\frac{1}{2}\mathbf{v}$) are examples of *parallel vectors*: each one is a scalar multiple of the others.

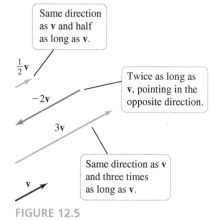

FIGURE 12.5

DEFINITION **Scalar Multiples and Parallel Vectors**

Given a scalar c and a vector **v**, the **scalar multiple** $c\mathbf{v}$ is a vector whose magnitude is $|c|$ multiplied by the magnitude of **v**. If $c > 0$, then $c\mathbf{v}$ has the same direction as **v**. If $c < 0$, then $c\mathbf{v}$ and **v** point in opposite directions. Two vectors are **parallel** if they are scalar multiples of each other.

> For convenience, we write $-\mathbf{u}$ for $(-1)\mathbf{u}$, $-c\mathbf{u}$ for $(-c)\mathbf{u}$, and $\mathbf{u}/c$ for $(1/c)\mathbf{u}$.

Notice that two vectors are parallel if they point in the same direction (for example, $\mathbf{v}$ and $12\mathbf{v}$) *or* if they point in opposite directions (for example, $\mathbf{v}$ and $-2\mathbf{v}$). Also, because $0\mathbf{v} = \mathbf{0}$ for all vectors $\mathbf{v}$, it follows that *the zero vector is parallel to all vectors*. While it may seem counterintuitive, this result turns out to be a useful convention.

QUICK CHECK 1 Describe the magnitude and direction of the vector $-5\mathbf{v}$ relative to $\mathbf{v}$. ◀

EXAMPLE 1 **Parallel vectors** Using Figure 12.6a, write the following vectors in terms of $\mathbf{u}$ or $\mathbf{v}$.

a. $\overrightarrow{PQ}$ **b.** $\overrightarrow{QP}$ **c.** $\overrightarrow{QR}$ **d.** $\overrightarrow{RS}$

SOLUTION

a. The vector $\overrightarrow{PQ}$ has the same direction and length as $\mathbf{u}$; therefore, $\overrightarrow{PQ} = \mathbf{u}$. These two vectors are equal even though they have different locations (Figure 12.6b).

b. Because $\overrightarrow{QP}$ and $\mathbf{u}$ have equal length, but opposite directions, $\overrightarrow{QP} = (-1)\mathbf{u} = -\mathbf{u}$.

c. $\overrightarrow{QR}$ points in the same direction as $\mathbf{v}$ and is twice as long as $\mathbf{v}$, so $\overrightarrow{QR} = 2\mathbf{v}$.

d. $\overrightarrow{RS}$ points in the direction opposite to that of $\mathbf{u}$ with three times the length of $\mathbf{u}$. Consequently, $\overrightarrow{RS} = -3\mathbf{u}$.

Related Exercises 17–20 ◀

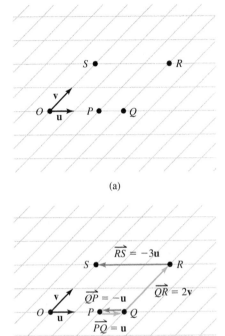

(a)

(b)

FIGURE 12.6

Vector Addition and Subtraction

To illustrate the idea of vector addition, consider a plane flying horizontally at a constant speed in a crosswind (Figure 12.7). The length of vector $\mathbf{v}_a$ represents the plane's *airspeed*, which is the speed the plane would have in still air; $\mathbf{v}_a$ points in the direction of the nose of the plane. The wind vector $\mathbf{w}$ points in the direction of the crosswind and has a length equal to the speed of the crosswind. The combined effect of the motion of the plane and the wind is the *vector sum* $\mathbf{v}_g = \mathbf{v}_a + \mathbf{w}$, which is the velocity of the plane relative to the ground.

QUICK CHECK 2 Sketch the sum $\mathbf{v}_a + \mathbf{w}$ in Figure 12.7 if the direction of $\mathbf{w}$ is reversed. ◀

Figure 12.8 illustrates two ways to form the vector sum of two nonzero vectors $\mathbf{u}$ and $\mathbf{v}$ geometrically. The first method, called the **Triangle Rule**, places the tail of $\mathbf{v}$ at the head of $\mathbf{u}$. The sum $\mathbf{u} + \mathbf{v}$ is the vector that extends from the tail of $\mathbf{u}$ to the head of $\mathbf{v}$ (Figure 12.8b).

When $\mathbf{u}$ and $\mathbf{v}$ are not parallel, another way to form $\mathbf{u} + \mathbf{v}$ is to use the **Parallelogram Rule**. The *tails* of $\mathbf{u}$ and $\mathbf{v}$ are connected to form adjacent sides of a parallelogram; then, the remaining two sides of the parallelogram are sketched. The sum $\mathbf{u} + \mathbf{v}$ is the vector that coincides with the diagonal of the parallelogram, beginning at the tails of $\mathbf{u}$ and $\mathbf{v}$ (Figure 12.8c). The Triangle Rule and Parallelogram Rule each produce the same vector sum $\mathbf{u} + \mathbf{v}$.

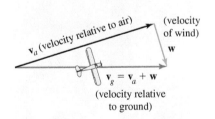

FIGURE 12.7

QUICK CHECK 3 Use the Triangle Rule to show that the vectors in Figure 12.8 satisfy $\mathbf{u} + \mathbf{v} = \mathbf{v} + \mathbf{u}$. ◀

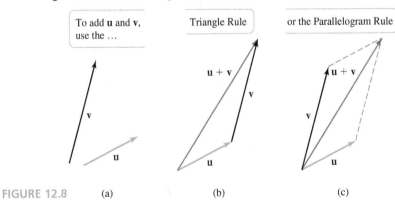

FIGURE 12.8   (a)   (b)   (c)

The difference $\mathbf{u} - \mathbf{v}$ is defined to be the sum $\mathbf{u} + (-\mathbf{v})$. By the Triangle Rule, the tail of $-\mathbf{v}$ is placed at the head of $\mathbf{u}$; then, $\mathbf{u} - \mathbf{v}$ extends from the tail of $\mathbf{u}$ to the head of $-\mathbf{v}$ (Figure 12.9a). Equivalently, when the tails of $\mathbf{u}$ and $\mathbf{v}$ coincide, $\mathbf{u} - \mathbf{v}$ has its tail at the head of $\mathbf{v}$ and its head at the head of $\mathbf{u}$ (Figure 12.9b).

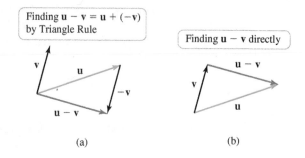

FIGURE 12.9   (a)   (b)

EXAMPLE 2   Vector operations Use Figure 12.10 to write the following vectors as sums of scalar multiples of $\mathbf{v}$ and $\mathbf{w}$.

a. $\overrightarrow{OP}$ **b.** $\overrightarrow{OQ}$ **c.** $\overrightarrow{QR}$

SOLUTION

a. Using the Triangle Rule, we start at O, move three lengths of $\mathbf{v}$ in the direction of $\mathbf{v}$ and then two lengths of $\mathbf{w}$ in the direction of $\mathbf{w}$ to reach P. Therefore, $\overrightarrow{OP} = 3\mathbf{v} + 2\mathbf{w}$ (Figure 12.11a).

b. The vector $\overrightarrow{OQ}$ coincides with the diagonal of a parallelogram having adjacent sides equal to $3\mathbf{v}$ and $-\mathbf{w}$. By the Parallelogram Rule, $\overrightarrow{OQ} = 3\mathbf{v} - \mathbf{w}$ (Figure 12.11b).

c. The vector $\overrightarrow{QR}$ lies on the diagonal of a parallelogram having adjacent sides equal to $\mathbf{v}$ and $2\mathbf{w}$. Therefore, $\overrightarrow{QR} = \mathbf{v} + 2\mathbf{w}$ (Figure 12.11c).

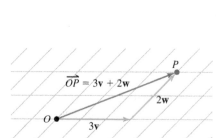

FIGURE 12.10

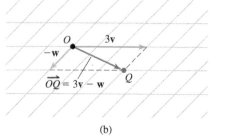

(a)   (b)

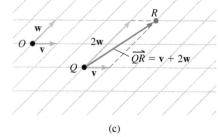

(c)

FIGURE 12.11

Related Exercises 21–22 ◄

Vector Components

So far, vectors have been examined from a geometric point of view. To do calculations with vectors, it is necessary to introduce a coordinate system. We begin by considering a vector $\mathbf{v}$ whose tail is at the origin in the Cartesian plane and whose head is at the point (v_1, v_2) (Figure 12.12a).

> Round brackets (a, b) enclose the *coordinates* of a point, while angle brackets $\langle a, b \rangle$ enclose the *components* of a vector. Note that in component form, the zero vector is $\mathbf{0} = \langle 0, 0 \rangle$.

DEFINITION Position Vectors and Vector Components

A vector $\mathbf{v}$ with its tail at the origin and head at the point (v_1, v_2) is called a **position vector** (or is said to be in **standard position**) and is written $\langle v_1, v_2 \rangle$. The real numbers v_1 and v_2 are the x- and y-**components** of $\mathbf{v}$, respectively. The position vectors $\mathbf{u} = \langle u_1, u_2 \rangle$ and $\mathbf{v} = \langle v_1, v_2 \rangle$ are **equal** if and only if $u_1 = v_1$ and $u_2 = v_2$.

There are infinitely many vectors equal to the position vector $\mathbf{v}$, all with the same length and direction (Figure 12.12b). It is important to abide by the convention that $\mathbf{v} = \langle v_1, v_2 \rangle$ refers to the position vector $\mathbf{v}$ *or to any other vector equal to* $\mathbf{v}$.

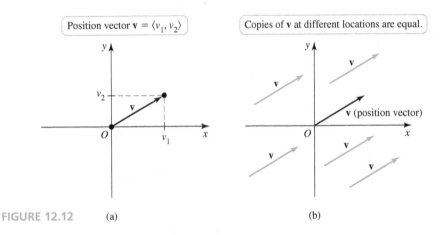

Position vector $\mathbf{v} = \langle v_1, v_2 \rangle$ Copies of $\mathbf{v}$ at different locations are equal.

FIGURE 12.12   (a)   (b)

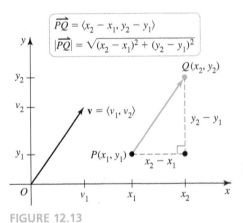

$$\overrightarrow{PQ} = \langle x_2 - x_1, y_2 - y_1 \rangle$$
$$|\overrightarrow{PQ}| = \sqrt{(x_2 - x_1)^2 + (y_2 - y_1)^2}$$

FIGURE 12.13

Now consider the vector $\overrightarrow{PQ}$, not in standard position, with its tail at the point $P(x_1, y_1)$ and its head at the point $Q(x_2, y_2)$. The x-component of $\overrightarrow{PQ}$ is the difference in the x-coordinates of Q and P, or $x_2 - x_1$. The y-component of $\overrightarrow{PQ}$ is the difference in the y-coordinates, $y_2 - y_1$ (Figure 12.13). Therefore, $\overrightarrow{PQ}$ has the same length and direction as the position vector $\langle v_1, v_2 \rangle = \langle x_2 - x_1, y_2 - y_1 \rangle$, and we write $\overrightarrow{PQ} = \langle x_2 - x_1, y_2 - y_1 \rangle$.

QUICK CHECK 4 Given the points $P(2, 3)$ and $Q(-4, 1)$, find the components of $\overrightarrow{PQ}$.

As already noted, there are infinitely many vectors equal to a given position vector. All these vectors have the same length and direction; therefore, they are all equal. In other words, two arbitrary vectors are **equal** if they are equal to the same position vector. For example, the vector $\overrightarrow{PQ}$ from $P(2, 5)$ to $Q(6, 3)$ and the vector $\overrightarrow{AB}$ from $A(7, 12)$ to $B(11, 10)$ are equal because they are both equal to the position vector $\langle 4, -2 \rangle$.

Magnitude

The magnitude of a vector is simply its length. By the Pythagorean Theorem and Figure 12.13, we have the following definition.

> Just as the absolute value $|p - q|$ gives the distance between two points on the number line, the magnitude $|\overrightarrow{PQ}|$ is the distance between the points P and Q. The magnitude of a vector is also called its **norm**.

DEFINITION Magnitude of a Vector

Given the points $P(x_1, y_1)$ and $Q(x_2, y_2)$, the **magnitude**, or **length**, of $\overrightarrow{PQ} = \langle x_2 - x_1, y_2 - y_1 \rangle$, denoted $|\overrightarrow{PQ}|$, is the distance between P and Q:

$$|\overrightarrow{PQ}| = \sqrt{(x_2 - x_1)^2 + (y_2 - y_1)^2}.$$

The magnitude of the position vector $\mathbf{v} = \langle v_1, v_2 \rangle$ is $|\mathbf{v}| = \sqrt{v_1^2 + v_2^2}$.

EXAMPLE 3 **Calculating components and magnitude** Given the points $O(0, 0)$, $P(-3, 4)$, and $Q(6, 5)$, find the components and magnitudes of the following vectors.

a. $\overrightarrow{OP}$ **b.** $\overrightarrow{PQ}$

SOLUTION

a. The vector $\overrightarrow{OP}$ is the position vector whose head is located at $P(-3, 4)$. Therefore, $\overrightarrow{OP} = \langle -3, 4 \rangle$ and $|\overrightarrow{OP}| = \sqrt{(-3)^2 + 4^2} = 5$.

b. $\overrightarrow{PQ} = \langle 6 - (-3), 5 - 4 \rangle = \langle 9, 1 \rangle$ and $|\overrightarrow{PQ}| = \sqrt{9^2 + 1^2} = \sqrt{82}$.

Related Exercises 23–27◄

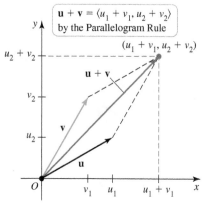

$\mathbf{u} + \mathbf{v} = \langle u_1 + v_1, u_2 + v_2 \rangle$ by the Parallelogram Rule

FIGURE 12.14

Vector Operations in Terms of Components

We now show how vector addition, vector subtraction, and scalar multiplication are performed using components. Suppose $\mathbf{u} = \langle u_1, u_2 \rangle$ and $\mathbf{v} = \langle v_1, v_2 \rangle$. The vector sum of $\mathbf{u}$ and $\mathbf{v}$ is $\mathbf{u} + \mathbf{v} = \langle u_1 + v_1, u_2 + v_2 \rangle$. This definition of a vector sum is consistent with the Parallelogram Rule given earlier (Figure 12.14).

For a scalar c and a vector $\mathbf{u}$, the scalar multiple $c\mathbf{u}$ is $c\mathbf{u} = \langle cu_1, cu_2 \rangle$; that is, the scalar c multiplies each component of $\mathbf{u}$. If $c > 0$, $\mathbf{u}$ and $c\mathbf{u}$ have the same direction (Figure 12.15a). If $c < 0$, $\mathbf{u}$ and $c\mathbf{u}$ have opposite directions (Figure 12.15b). In either case, $|c\mathbf{u}| = |c||\mathbf{u}|$ (Exercise 87).

Notice that $\mathbf{u} - \mathbf{v} = \mathbf{u} + (-\mathbf{v})$, where $-\mathbf{v} = \langle -v_1, -v_2 \rangle$. Therefore, the vector difference of $\mathbf{u}$ and $\mathbf{v}$ is $\mathbf{u} - \mathbf{v} = \langle u_1 - v_1, u_2 - v_2 \rangle$.

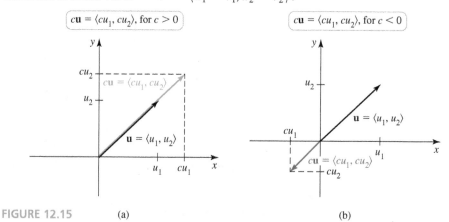

FIGURE 12.15   (a)   (b)

Vector Operations

Suppose c is a scalar, $\mathbf{u} = \langle u_1, u_2 \rangle$, and $\mathbf{v} = \langle v_1, v_2 \rangle$.

$$\mathbf{u} + \mathbf{v} = \langle u_1 + v_1, u_2 + v_2 \rangle \quad \text{Vector addition}$$
$$\mathbf{u} - \mathbf{v} = \langle u_1 - v_1, u_2 - v_2 \rangle \quad \text{Vector subtraction}$$
$$c\mathbf{u} = \langle cu_1, cu_2 \rangle \quad \text{Scalar multiplication}$$

EXAMPLE 4 **Vector operations** Let $\mathbf{u} = \langle -1, 2 \rangle$ and $\mathbf{v} = \langle 2, 3 \rangle$.

a. Evaluate $|\mathbf{u} + \mathbf{v}|$.   **b.** Simplify $2\mathbf{u} - 3\mathbf{v}$.

c. Find two vectors half as long as $\mathbf{u}$ and parallel to $\mathbf{u}$.

SOLUTION

a. Because $\mathbf{u} + \mathbf{v} = \langle -1, 2 \rangle + \langle 2, 3 \rangle = \langle 1, 5 \rangle$, we have $|\mathbf{u} + \mathbf{v}| = \sqrt{1^2 + 5^2} = \sqrt{26}$.

b. $2\mathbf{u} - 3\mathbf{v} = 2\langle -1, 2 \rangle - 3\langle 2, 3 \rangle = \langle -2, 4 \rangle - \langle 6, 9 \rangle = \langle -8, -5 \rangle$.

c. The vectors $\frac{1}{2}\mathbf{u} = \frac{1}{2}\langle -1, 2\rangle = \langle -\frac{1}{2}, 1\rangle$ and $-\frac{1}{2}\mathbf{u} = -\frac{1}{2}\langle -1, 2\rangle = \langle \frac{1}{2}, -1\rangle$ have half the length of $\mathbf{u}$ and are parallel to $\mathbf{u}$.

Related Exercises 28–41 ◄

Unit Vectors

A *unit vector* is any vector with length 1. Two useful unit vectors are the *coordinate unit vectors* $\mathbf{i} = \langle 1, 0\rangle$ and $\mathbf{j} = \langle 0, 1\rangle$ (Figure 12.16). These vectors are directed along the coordinate axes and allow us to express all vectors in an alternate form. For example, by the Triangle Rule (Figure 12.17a),

$$\langle 3, 4\rangle = 3\langle 1, 0\rangle + 4\langle 0, 1\rangle = 3\mathbf{i} + 4\mathbf{j}.$$

In general, the vector $\mathbf{v} = \langle v_1, v_2\rangle$ (Figure 12.17b) is also written

$$\mathbf{v} = v_1\langle 1, 0\rangle + v_2\langle 0, 1\rangle = v_1\mathbf{i} + v_2\mathbf{j}.$$

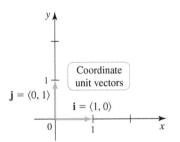

FIGURE 12.16

> Coordinate unit vectors are also called **standard basis vectors**.

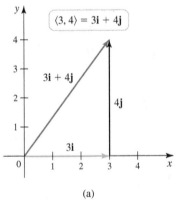

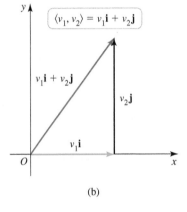

(a)   (b)

FIGURE 12.17

Given a nonzero vector $\mathbf{v}$, we sometimes need to construct a new vector parallel to $\mathbf{v}$ of a specified length. Dividing $\mathbf{v}$ by its length, we obtain the vector $\mathbf{u} = \dfrac{\mathbf{v}}{|\mathbf{v}|}$. Because $\mathbf{u}$ is a positive scalar multiple of $\mathbf{v}$, it follows that $\mathbf{u}$ has the same direction as $\mathbf{v}$. Furthermore, $\mathbf{u}$ is a unit vector because $|\mathbf{u}| = \dfrac{|\mathbf{v}|}{|\mathbf{v}|} = 1$. The vector $-\mathbf{u} = -\dfrac{\mathbf{v}}{|\mathbf{v}|}$ is also a unit vector (Figure 12.18). Therefore, $\pm\dfrac{\mathbf{v}}{|\mathbf{v}|}$ are unit vectors parallel to $\mathbf{v}$ that point in opposite directions.

To construct a vector that points in the direction of $\mathbf{v}$ and has a specified length $c > 0$, we form the vector $\dfrac{c\mathbf{v}}{|\mathbf{v}|}$. It is a positive scalar multiple of $\mathbf{v}$, so it points in the direction of $\mathbf{v}$, and its length is $\left|\dfrac{c\mathbf{v}}{|\mathbf{v}|}\right| = |c|\dfrac{|\mathbf{v}|}{|\mathbf{v}|} = c$. The vector $-\dfrac{c\mathbf{v}}{|\mathbf{v}|}$ points in the opposite direction and also has length c.

$\mathbf{u} = \dfrac{\mathbf{v}}{|\mathbf{v}|}$ and $-\mathbf{u} = -\dfrac{\mathbf{v}}{|\mathbf{v}|}$ have length 1.

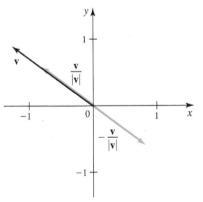

FIGURE 12.18

QUICK CHECK 5 Find vectors of length 10 parallel to the unit vector $\mathbf{u} = \left\langle \dfrac{3}{5}, \dfrac{4}{5}\right\rangle$. ◄

DEFINITION **Unit Vectors and Vectors of a Specified Length**

A **unit vector** is any vector with length 1. Given a nonzero vector $\mathbf{v}$, $\pm\dfrac{\mathbf{v}}{|\mathbf{v}|}$ are unit vectors parallel to $\mathbf{v}$. For a scalar $c > 0$, the vectors $\pm\dfrac{c\mathbf{v}}{|\mathbf{v}|}$ are vectors of length c parallel to $\mathbf{v}$.

EXAMPLE 5   **Magnitude and unit vectors** Consider the points $P(1, -2)$ and $Q(6, 10)$.

a. Find $\overrightarrow{PQ}$ and two unit vectors parallel to $\overrightarrow{PQ}$.

b. Find two vectors of length 2 parallel to $\overrightarrow{PQ}$.

SOLUTION

a. $\overrightarrow{PQ} = \langle 6 - 1, 10 - (-2) \rangle = \langle 5, 12 \rangle$, or $5\mathbf{i} + 12\mathbf{j}$. Because $|\overrightarrow{PQ}| = \sqrt{5^2 + 12^2} = \sqrt{169} = 13$, a unit vector parallel to $\overrightarrow{PQ}$ is

$$\frac{\overrightarrow{PQ}}{|\overrightarrow{PQ}|} = \frac{\langle 5, 12 \rangle}{13} = \left\langle \frac{5}{13}, \frac{12}{13} \right\rangle = \frac{5}{13}\mathbf{i} + \frac{12}{13}\mathbf{j}.$$

Another unit vector parallel to $\overrightarrow{PQ}$ but having the opposite direction is $\left\langle -\frac{5}{13}, -\frac{12}{13} \right\rangle$.

b. To obtain two vectors of length 2 that are parallel to $\overrightarrow{PQ}$, we multiply the unit vector $\frac{5}{13}\mathbf{i} + \frac{12}{13}\mathbf{j}$ by ± 2:

$$2\left(\frac{5}{13}\mathbf{i} + \frac{12}{13}\mathbf{j} \right) = \frac{10}{13}\mathbf{i} + \frac{24}{13}\mathbf{j} \quad \text{and} \quad -2\left(\frac{5}{13}\mathbf{i} + \frac{12}{13}\mathbf{j} \right) = -\frac{10}{13}\mathbf{i} - \frac{24}{13}\mathbf{j}.$$

Related Exercises 42–47 ◄

QUICK CHECK 6 Verify that the vector $\left\langle \frac{5}{13}, \frac{12}{13} \right\rangle$ has length 1. ◄

Properties of Vector Operations

> The Parallelogram Rule illustrates the commutative property $\mathbf{u} + \mathbf{v} = \mathbf{v} + \mathbf{u}$.

When we stand back and look at vector operations, ten general properties emerge. For example, the first property says that vector addition is commutative, which means $\mathbf{u} + \mathbf{v} = \mathbf{v} + \mathbf{u}$. This property is proved by letting $\mathbf{u} = \langle u_1, u_2 \rangle$ and $\mathbf{v} = \langle v_1, v_2 \rangle$. By the commutative property of addition for real numbers,

$$\mathbf{u} + \mathbf{v} = \langle u_1 + v_1, u_2 + v_2 \rangle = \langle v_1 + u_1, v_2 + u_2 \rangle = \mathbf{v} + \mathbf{u}.$$

The proofs of other properties are outlined in Exercises 82–85.

SUMMARY   **Properties of Vector Operations**

Suppose $\mathbf{u}$, $\mathbf{v}$, and $\mathbf{w}$ are vectors and a and c are scalars. Then the following properties hold (for vectors in any number of dimensions).

1. $\mathbf{u} + \mathbf{v} = \mathbf{v} + \mathbf{u}$ Commutative property of addition

2. $(\mathbf{u} + \mathbf{v}) + \mathbf{w} = \mathbf{u} + (\mathbf{v} + \mathbf{w})$ Associative property of addition

3. $\mathbf{v} + \mathbf{0} = \mathbf{v}$ Additive identity

4. $\mathbf{v} + (-\mathbf{v}) = \mathbf{0}$ Additive inverse

5. $c(\mathbf{u} + \mathbf{v}) = c\mathbf{u} + c\mathbf{v}$ Distributive property 1

6. $(a + c)\mathbf{v} = a\mathbf{v} + c\mathbf{v}$ Distributive property 2

7. $0\mathbf{v} = \mathbf{0}$ Multiplication by zero scalar

8. $c\mathbf{0} = \mathbf{0}$ Multiplication by zero vector

9. $1\mathbf{v} = \mathbf{v}$ Multiplicative identity

10. $a(c\mathbf{v}) = (ac)\mathbf{v}$ Associative property of scalar multiplication

---

These properties allow us to solve vector equations. For example, to solve the equation $\mathbf{u} + \mathbf{v} = \mathbf{w}$ for $\mathbf{u}$, we proceed as follows:

$$(\mathbf{u} + \mathbf{v}) + (-\mathbf{v}) = \mathbf{w} + (-\mathbf{v}) \quad \text{Add } -\mathbf{v} \text{ to both sides.}$$
$$\mathbf{u} + (\mathbf{v} + (-\mathbf{v})) = \mathbf{w} + (-\mathbf{v}) \quad \text{Property 2}$$
$$\underbrace{\phantom{\mathbf{v} + (-\mathbf{v})}}_{0}$$

$$\mathbf{u} + \mathbf{0} = \mathbf{w} - \mathbf{v} \quad \text{Property 4}$$
$$\mathbf{u} = \mathbf{w} - \mathbf{v}. \quad \text{Property 3}$$

> **QUICK CHECK 7** Solve $3\mathbf{u} + 4\mathbf{v} = 12\mathbf{w}$ for $\mathbf{u}$.

Applications of Vectors

Vectors have countless practical applications, particularly in the physical sciences and engineering. These applications are explored throughout the remainder of the book. For now we present two common uses of vectors: to describe velocities and forces.

Velocity Vectors Consider a motorboat crossing a river whose current is everywhere represented by the constant vector $\mathbf{w}$ (Figure 12.19); this means that $|\mathbf{w}|$ is the speed of the moving water and $\mathbf{w}$ points in the direction of the moving water. Assume that the vector $\mathbf{v}_w$ gives the direction and speed of the boat relative to the water. The combined effect of $\mathbf{w}$ and $\mathbf{v}_w$ is the sum $\mathbf{v}_g = \mathbf{v}_w + \mathbf{w}$, which gives the speed and direction of the boat that would be observed by someone on the shore (or on the ground).

> Speed of the boat relative to the water means the speed the boat would have in still water (or relative to someone traveling with the current).

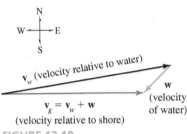

$\mathbf{v}_g = \mathbf{v}_w + \mathbf{w}$
(velocity relative to shore)

FIGURE 12.19

EXAMPLE 6 **Speed of a boat in a current** Assume the water in a river moves southwest (45° west of south) at 4 mi/hr. If a motorboat is traveling due east at 15 mi/hr relative to the shore, determine the speed of the boat and its heading relative to the moving water (Figure 12.19).

SOLUTION To solve this problem, the vectors are placed in a coordinate system (Figure 12.20). Because the boat is moving east at 15 mi/hr, $\mathbf{v}_g = \langle 15, 0 \rangle$. To obtain the components of $\mathbf{w} = \langle w_x, w_y \rangle$, observe that $|\mathbf{w}| = 4$ and the lengths of the sides of the 45–45–90 triangle in Figure 12.20 are

$$|w_x| = |w_y| = |\mathbf{w}| \cos 45° = \frac{4}{\sqrt{2}} = 2\sqrt{2}.$$

> Recall that the lengths of the legs of a 45–45–90 triangle are equal and are $(1/\sqrt{2})$ times the length of the hypotenuse.

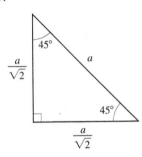

Given the orientation of $\mathbf{w}$ (southwest), $\mathbf{w} = \langle -2\sqrt{2}, -2\sqrt{2} \rangle$. Because $\mathbf{v}_g = \mathbf{v}_w + \mathbf{w}$ (Figure 12.19),

$$\mathbf{v}_w = \mathbf{v}_g - \mathbf{w} = \langle 15, 0 \rangle - \langle -2\sqrt{2}, -2\sqrt{2} \rangle$$
$$= \langle 15 + 2\sqrt{2}, 2\sqrt{2} \rangle.$$

The magnitude of $\mathbf{v}_w$ is

$$|\mathbf{v}_w| = \sqrt{(15 + 2\sqrt{2})^2 + (2\sqrt{2})^2} \approx 18.$$

Therefore, the speed of the boat relative to the water is approximately 18 mi/hr.

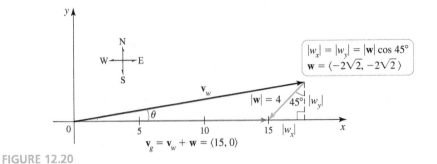

FIGURE 12.20

The heading of the boat is given by the angle θ between $\mathbf{v}_w$ and the positive x-axis. The x-component of $\mathbf{v}_w$ is $15 + 2\sqrt{2}$ and the y-component is $2\sqrt{2}$: therefore,

$$\theta = \tan^{-1}\left(\frac{2\sqrt{2}}{15 + 2\sqrt{2}}\right) \approx 9°.$$

The heading of the boat is approximately 9° north of east, and its speed relative to the water is approximately 18 mi/hr.

Related Exercises 48–53 ◄

> The magnitude of **F** is typically measured in pounds (lb) or newtons (N), where $1\,\text{N} = 1\,\text{kg} \cdot \text{m/s}^2$.

> The vector $\langle \cos\theta, \sin\theta \rangle$ is a unit vector. Therefore, any position vector **v** may be written $\mathbf{v} = \langle |\mathbf{v}| \cos\theta, |\mathbf{v}| \sin\theta \rangle$, where θ is the angle that **v** makes with the positive x-axis.

Force Vectors Suppose a child pulls on the handle of a wagon at an angle of θ with the horizontal (Figure 12.21a). The vector **F** represents the force exerted on the wagon; it has a magnitude $|\mathbf{F}|$ and a direction given by θ. We denote the horizontal and vertical components of **F** by F_x and F_y, respectively. Then, $F_x = |\mathbf{F}| \cos\theta$, $F_y = |\mathbf{F}| \sin\theta$, and the force vector is $\mathbf{F} = \langle |\mathbf{F}| \cos\theta, |\mathbf{F}| \sin\theta \rangle$ (Figure 12.21b).

(a)   (b)

FIGURE 12.21

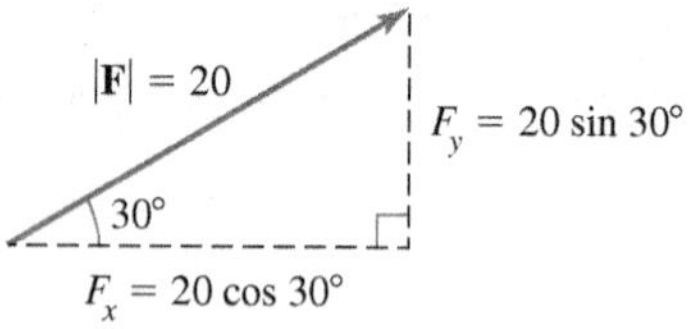

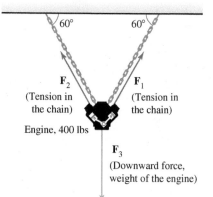

FIGURE 12.22

EXAMPLE 7   Finding force vectors A child pulls a wagon (Figure 12.21) with a force of $|\mathbf{F}| = 20$ lb at an angle of $\theta = 30°$ to the horizontal. Find the force vector **F**.

SOLUTION The force vector (Figure 12.22) is

$$\mathbf{F} = \langle |\mathbf{F}| \cos\theta, |\mathbf{F}| \sin\theta \rangle = \langle 20\cos 30°, 20\sin 30° \rangle = \langle 10\sqrt{3}, 10 \rangle.$$

Related Exercises 54–58 ◄

EXAMPLE 8   Balancing forces A 400-lb engine is suspended from two chains that form 60° angles with a horizontal ceiling (Figure 12.23). How much weight must each chain withstand?

SOLUTION Let $\mathbf{F}_1$ and $\mathbf{F}_2$ denote the forces exerted by the chains on the engine and let $\mathbf{F}_3$ be the downward force due to the weight of the engine (Figure 12.23). Placing the vectors in a standard coordinate system (Figure 12.24), we find that $\mathbf{F}_1 = \langle |\mathbf{F}_1| \cos 60°, |\mathbf{F}_1| \sin 60° \rangle$, $\mathbf{F}_2 = \langle -|\mathbf{F}_2| \cos 60°, |\mathbf{F}_2| \sin 60° \rangle$, and $\mathbf{F}_3 = \langle 0, -400 \rangle$.

FIGURE 12.23

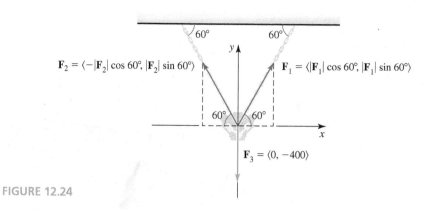

FIGURE 12.24

If the engine is in equilibrium (so the chains and engine are stationary), the sum of the forces must be zero; that is, $\mathbf{F}_1 + \mathbf{F}_2 + \mathbf{F}_3 = \mathbf{0}$ or $\mathbf{F}_1 + \mathbf{F}_2 = -\mathbf{F}_3$. Therefore,

$$\langle |\mathbf{F}_1| \cos 60° - |\mathbf{F}_2| \cos 60°, |\mathbf{F}_1| \sin 60° + |\mathbf{F}_2| \sin 60° \rangle = \langle 0, 400 \rangle.$$

Equating corresponding components, we obtain the following two equations to be solved for $|\mathbf{F}_1|$ and $|\mathbf{F}_2|$:

$$|\mathbf{F}_1| \cos 60° - |\mathbf{F}_2| \cos 60° = 0 \text{ and}$$
$$|\mathbf{F}_1| \sin 60° + |\mathbf{F}_2| \sin 60° = 400.$$

Factoring the first equation, we find that $(|\mathbf{F}_1| - |\mathbf{F}_2|) \cos 60° = 0$, which implies that $|\mathbf{F}_1| = |\mathbf{F}_2|$. Replacing $|\mathbf{F}_2|$ by $|\mathbf{F}_1|$ in the second equation gives $2|\mathbf{F}_1| \sin 60° = 400$. Noting that $\sin 60° = \sqrt{3}/2$ and solving for $|\mathbf{F}_1|$, we find that $|\mathbf{F}_1| = 400/\sqrt{3} \approx 231$. Each chain must be able to withstand a weight of approximately 231 lb.

Related Exercises 54–58 ◄

SECTION 12.1 EXERCISES

Review Questions

1. Interpret the following statement: Points have a location, but no size or direction; nonzero vectors have a size and direction, but no location.

2. What is a position vector?

3. Draw x- and y-axes on a page and mark two points P and Q. Then draw $\overrightarrow{PQ}$ and $\overrightarrow{QP}$.

4. On the diagram of Exercise 3, draw the position vector that is equal to $\overrightarrow{PQ}$.

5. Given a position vector $\mathbf{v}$, why are there infinitely many vectors equal to $\mathbf{v}$?

6. Explain how to add two vectors geometrically.

7. Explain how to find a scalar multiple of a vector geometrically.

8. Given two points P and Q, how are the components of $\overrightarrow{PQ}$ determined?

9. If $\mathbf{u} = \langle u_1, u_2 \rangle$ and $\mathbf{v} = \langle v_1, v_2 \rangle$, how do you find $\mathbf{u} + \mathbf{v}$?

10. If $\mathbf{v} = \langle v_1, v_2 \rangle$ and c is a scalar, how do you find $c\mathbf{v}$?

11. How do you compute the magnitude of $\mathbf{v} = \langle v_1, v_2 \rangle$?

12. Express the vector $\mathbf{v} = \langle v_1, v_2 \rangle$ in terms of the unit vectors $\mathbf{i}$ and $\mathbf{j}$.

13. How do you compute $|\overrightarrow{PQ}|$ from the coordinates of the points P and Q?

14. Explain how to find two unit vectors parallel to a vector $\mathbf{v}$.

15. How do you find a vector of length 10 in the direction of $\mathbf{v} = \langle 3, -2 \rangle$?

16. If a force has magnitude 100 and is directed 45° south of east, what are its components?

Basic Skills

17–22. Vector operations *Refer to the figure and carry out the following vector operations.*

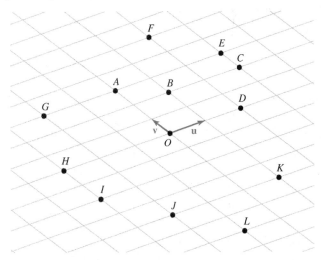

17. **Scalar multiples** Which of the following vectors equals $\overrightarrow{CE}$? (There may be more than one correct answer.)

   a. $\mathbf{v}$ **b.** $\frac{1}{2}\overrightarrow{HI}$ **c.** $\frac{1}{3}\overrightarrow{OA}$ **d.** $\mathbf{u}$ **e.** $\frac{1}{2}\overrightarrow{IH}$

18. **Scalar multiples** Which of the following vectors equals $\overrightarrow{BK}$? (There may be more than one correct answer.)

   a. $6\mathbf{v}$ **b.** $-6\mathbf{v}$ **c.** $3\overrightarrow{HI}$ **d.** $3\overrightarrow{IH}$ **e.** $2\overrightarrow{AO}$

19. **Scalar multiples** Write the following vectors as scalar multiples of $\mathbf{u}$ or $\mathbf{v}$.

   a. $\overrightarrow{OA}$ **b.** $\overrightarrow{OD}$ **c.** $\overrightarrow{OH}$ **d.** $\overrightarrow{AG}$ **e.** $\overrightarrow{CE}$

20. **Scalar multiples** Write the following vectors as scalar multiples of $\mathbf{u}$ or $\mathbf{v}$.

   a. $\overrightarrow{IH}$ **b.** $\overrightarrow{HI}$ **c.** $\overrightarrow{JK}$ **d.** $\overrightarrow{FD}$ **e.** $\overrightarrow{EA}$

21. Vector addition Write the following vectors as sums of scalar multiples of **u** and **v**.

    a. $\overrightarrow{OE}$ **b.** $\overrightarrow{OB}$ **c.** $\overrightarrow{OF}$ **d.** $\overrightarrow{OG}$ **e.** $\overrightarrow{OC}$

    f. $\overrightarrow{OI}$ **g.** $\overrightarrow{OJ}$ **h.** $\overrightarrow{OK}$ **i.** $\overrightarrow{OL}$

22. Vector addition Write the following vectors as sums of scalar multiples of **u** and **v**.

    a. $\overrightarrow{BF}$ **b.** $\overrightarrow{DE}$ **c.** $\overrightarrow{AF}$ **d.** $\overrightarrow{AD}$ **e.** $\overrightarrow{CD}$

    f. $\overrightarrow{JD}$ **g.** $\overrightarrow{JI}$ **h.** $\overrightarrow{DB}$ **i.** $\overrightarrow{IL}$

23. Components and magnitudes Define the points $O(0, 0)$, $P(3, 2)$, $Q(4, 2)$, and $R(-6, -1)$. For each vector, do the following.

    (i) Sketch the vector in an xy-coordinate system.

    (ii) Compute the magnitude of the vector.

    a. $\overrightarrow{OP}$ **b.** $\overrightarrow{QP}$ **c.** $\overrightarrow{RQ}$

24–27. Components and equality *Define the points* $P(-3, -1)$, $Q(-1, 2)$, $R(1, 2)$, $S(3, 5)$, $T(4, 2)$, *and* $U(6, 4)$.

24. Sketch $\overrightarrow{PU}$, $\overrightarrow{TR}$, and $\overrightarrow{SQ}$ and the corresponding position vectors.

25. Sketch $\overrightarrow{QU}$, $\overrightarrow{PT}$, and $\overrightarrow{RS}$ and the corresponding position vectors.

26. Find the equal vectors among $\overrightarrow{PQ}$, $\overrightarrow{RS}$, and $\overrightarrow{TU}$.

27. Which of the vectors $\overrightarrow{QT}$ or $\overrightarrow{SU}$ is equal to $\langle 5, 0 \rangle$?

28–33. Vector operations *Let* $\mathbf{u} = \langle 4, -2 \rangle$, $\mathbf{v} = \langle -4, 6 \rangle$, *and* $\mathbf{w} = \langle 0, 8 \rangle$. *Express the following vectors in the form* $\langle a, b \rangle$.

28. $\mathbf{u} + \mathbf{v}$ **29.** $\mathbf{w} - \mathbf{u}$ **30.** $2\mathbf{u} + 3\mathbf{v}$

31. $\mathbf{w} - 3\mathbf{v}$ **32.** $10\mathbf{u} - 3\mathbf{v} + \mathbf{w}$ **33.** $8\mathbf{w} + \mathbf{v} - 6\mathbf{u}$

34–41. Vector operations *Let* $\mathbf{u} = \langle 3, -4 \rangle$, $\mathbf{v} = \langle 1, 1 \rangle$, *and* $\mathbf{w} = \langle -1, 0 \rangle$. *Carry out the following computations.*

34. Find $|\mathbf{u} + \mathbf{v}|$.   **35.** Find $|-2\mathbf{v}|$.

36. Find $|\mathbf{u} + \mathbf{v} + \mathbf{w}|$.   **37.** Find $|2\mathbf{u} + 3\mathbf{v} - 4\mathbf{w}|$.

38. Find two vectors parallel to **u** with four times the magnitude of **u**.

39. Find two vectors parallel to **v** with three times the magnitude of **v**.

40. Which has the greater magnitude, $2\mathbf{u}$ or $7\mathbf{v}$?

41. Which has the greater magnitude, $\mathbf{u} - \mathbf{v}$ or $\mathbf{w} - \mathbf{u}$?

42–47. Unit vectors *Define the points* $P(-4, 1)$, $Q(3, -4)$, *and* $R(2, 6)$. *Carry out the following calculations.*

42. Express $\overrightarrow{PQ}$ in the form $a\mathbf{i} + b\mathbf{j}$.

43. Express $\overrightarrow{QR}$ in the form $a\mathbf{i} + b\mathbf{j}$.

44. Find the unit vector with the same direction as $\overrightarrow{QR}$.

45. Find two unit vectors parallel to $\overrightarrow{PR}$.

46. Find two vectors parallel to $\overrightarrow{RP}$ with length 4.

47. Find two vectors parallel to $\overrightarrow{QP}$ with length 4.

48. A boat in a current The water in a river moves south at 10 mi/hr. If a motorboat is traveling due east at a speed of 20 mi/hr relative to the shore, determine the speed and direction of the boat relative to the moving water.

49. Another boat in a current The water in a river moves south at 5 km/hr. If a motorboat is traveling due east at a speed of 40 km/hr relative to the water, determine the speed of the boat relative to the shore.

50. Parachute in the wind In still air, a parachute with a payload would fall vertically at a terminal speed of 4 m/s. Find the direction and magnitude of its terminal velocity relative to the ground if it falls in a steady wind blowing horizontally from west to east at 10 m/s.

51. Airplane in a wind An airplane flies horizontally from east to west at 320 mi/hr relative to the air. If it flies in a steady 40 mi/hr wind that blows horizontally toward the southwest (45° south of west), find the speed and direction of the airplane relative to the ground.

52. Canoe in a current A woman in a canoe paddles due west at 4 mi/hr relative to the water in a current that flows northwest at 2 mi/hr. Find the speed and direction of the canoe relative to the shore.

53. Boat in a wind A sailboat floats in a current that flows due east at 1 m/s. Due to a wind, the boat's actual speed relative to the shore is $\sqrt{3}$ m/s in a direction 30° north of east. Find the speed and direction of the wind.

54. Towing a boat A boat is towed with a force of 150 lb with a rope that makes an angle of 30° to the horizontal. Find the horizontal and vertical components of the force.

55. Pulling a suitcase Suppose you pull a suitcase with a strap that makes a 60° angle with the horizontal. The magnitude of the force you exert on the suitcase is 40 lb.

    a. Find the horizontal and vertical components of the force.

    b. Is the horizontal component of the force greater if the angle of the strap is 45° instead of 60°?

    c. Is the vertical component of the force greater if the angle of the strap is 45° instead of 60°?

56. Which is greater? Which has a greater horizontal component, a 100-N force directed at an angle of 60° above the horizontal or a 60-N force directed at an angle of 30° above the horizontal?

57. Suspended load If a 500-lb load is suspended by two chains (see figure), what is the magnitude of the force each chain must be able to withstand?

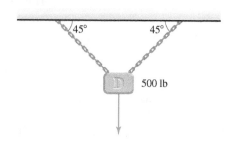

58. Net force Three forces are applied to an object, as shown in the figure. Find the magnitude and direction of the sum of the forces.

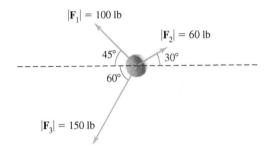

Further Explorations

59. Explain why or why not Determine whether the following statements are true and give an explanation or counterexample.

   a. José travels from point A to point B in the plane by following vector $\mathbf{u}$, then vector $\mathbf{v}$, and then vector $\mathbf{w}$. If he starts at A and follows $\mathbf{w}$, then $\mathbf{v}$, and then $\mathbf{u}$, he still arrives at B.
   b. Maria travels from A to B in the plane by following the vector $\mathbf{u}$. By following $-\mathbf{u}$, she returns from B to A.
   c. The magnitude of $\mathbf{u} + \mathbf{v}$ is at least the magnitude of $\mathbf{u}$.
   d. The magnitude of $\mathbf{u} + \mathbf{v}$ is at least the magnitude of $\mathbf{u}$ plus the magnitude of $\mathbf{v}$.
   e. Parallel vectors have the same length.
   f. If $\overrightarrow{AB} = \overrightarrow{CD}$, then $A = C$ and $B = D$.
   g. If $\mathbf{u}$ and $\mathbf{v}$ are perpendicular, then $|\mathbf{u} + \mathbf{v}| = |\mathbf{u}| + |\mathbf{v}|$.
   h. If $\mathbf{u}$ and $\mathbf{v}$ are parallel and have the same direction, then $|\mathbf{u} + \mathbf{v}| = |\mathbf{u}| + |\mathbf{v}|$.

60. Finding vectors from two points Given the points $A(-2, 0)$, $B(6, 16)$, $C(1, 4)$, $D(5, 4)$, $E(\sqrt{2}, \sqrt{2})$, and $F(3\sqrt{2}, -4\sqrt{2})$, find the position vector equal to the following vectors.

   a. $\overrightarrow{AB}$ **b.** $\overrightarrow{AC}$ **c.** $\overrightarrow{EF}$ **d.** $\overrightarrow{CD}$

61. Unit vectors

   a. Find two unit vectors parallel to $\mathbf{v} = 6\mathbf{i} - 8\mathbf{j}$.
   b. Find b if $\mathbf{v} = \langle \frac{1}{3}, b \rangle$ is a unit vector.
   c. Find all values of a such that $\mathbf{w} = a\mathbf{i} - \dfrac{a}{3}\mathbf{j}$ is a unit vector.

62. Equal vectors For the points $A(3, 4)$, $B(6, 10)$, $C(a + 2, b + 5)$, and $D(b + 4, a - 2)$, find the values of a and b such that $\overrightarrow{AB} = \overrightarrow{CD}$.

63–66. Vector equations *Use the properties of vectors to solve the following equations for the unknown vector* $\mathbf{x} = \langle a, b \rangle$. *Let* $\mathbf{u} = \langle 2, -3 \rangle$ *and* $\mathbf{v} = \langle -4, 1 \rangle$.

63. $10\mathbf{x} = \mathbf{u}$ **64.** $2\mathbf{x} + \mathbf{u} = \mathbf{v}$

65. $3\mathbf{x} - 4\mathbf{u} = \mathbf{v}$ **66.** $-4\mathbf{x} = \mathbf{u} - 8\mathbf{v}$

67–69. Linear combinations *A sum of scalar multiples of two or more vectors (such as* $c_1\mathbf{u} + c_2\mathbf{v} + c_3\mathbf{w}$, *where* c_i *are scalars) is called a **linear combination** of the vectors. Let* $\mathbf{i} = \langle 1, 0 \rangle$, $\mathbf{j} = \langle 0, 1 \rangle$, $\mathbf{u} = \langle 1, 1 \rangle$, *and* $\mathbf{v} = \langle -1, 1 \rangle$.

67. Express $\langle 4, -8 \rangle$ as a linear combination of $\mathbf{i}$ and $\mathbf{j}$ (that is, find scalars c_1 and c_2 such that $\langle 4, -8 \rangle = c_1\mathbf{i} + c_2\mathbf{j}$).

68. Express $\langle 4, -8 \rangle$ as a linear combination of $\mathbf{u}$ and $\mathbf{v}$.

69. For arbitrary real numbers a and b, express $\langle a, b \rangle$ as a linear combination of $\mathbf{u}$ and $\mathbf{v}$.

70–71. Solving vector equations *Solve the following pairs of equations for the vectors* $\mathbf{u}$ *and* $\mathbf{v}$. *Assume* $\mathbf{i} = \langle 1, 0 \rangle$ *and* $\mathbf{j} = \langle 0, 1 \rangle$.

70. $2\mathbf{u} = \mathbf{i}, \mathbf{u} - 4\mathbf{v} = \mathbf{j}$

71. $2\mathbf{u} + 3\mathbf{v} = \mathbf{i}, \mathbf{u} - \mathbf{v} = \mathbf{j}$

72–75. Designer vectors *Find the following vectors.*

72. The vector that is 3 times $\langle 3, -5 \rangle$ plus -9 times $\langle 6, 0 \rangle$

73. The vector in the direction of $\langle 5, -12 \rangle$ with length 3

74. The vector in the direction opposite to that of $\langle 6, -8 \rangle$ with length 10

75. The position vector for your final location if you start at the origin and walk along $\langle 4, -6 \rangle$ followed by $\langle 5, 9 \rangle$

Applications

76. Ant on a page An ant is walking due east at a constant speed of 2 mi/hr on a sheet of paper that rests on a table. Suddenly the sheet of paper starts moving southeast at $\sqrt{2}$ mi/hr. Describe the motion of the ant relative to the table.

77. Clock vectors Consider the 12 vectors that have their tails at the center of a (circular) clock and their heads at the numbers on the edge of the clock.

   a. What is the sum of these 12 vectors?
   b. If the 12:00 vector is removed, what is the sum of the remaining 11 vectors?
   c. By removing one or more of these 12 clock vectors, explain how to make the sum of the remaining vectors as large as possible in magnitude.
   d. If the clock vectors originate at 12:00 and point to the other 11 numbers, what is the sum of the vectors?
   (*Source: Calculus*, by Gilbert Strang. Wellesley-Cambridge Press, 1991.)

78. Three-way tug-of-war Three people located at A, B, and C pull on ropes tied to a ring. Find the magnitude and direction of the force with which C must pull so that no one moves (the system is in equilibrium).

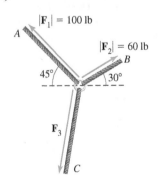

79. Net force Jack pulls east on a rope attached to a camel with a force of 40 lb. Jill pulls north on a rope attached to the same camel with a force of 30 lb. What is the magnitude and direction of the force on the camel? Assume the vectors lie in a horizontal plane.

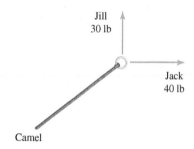

80. Mass on a plane A 100-kg object rests on an inclined plane at an angle of 30° to the floor. Find the components of the force perpendicular to and parallel to the plane. (The vertical component of the force exerted by an object of mass m is its weight, which is mg, where $g = 9.8 \text{ m/s}^2$ is the acceleration due to gravity.)

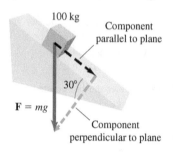

Additional Exercises

81–85. Vector properties *Prove the following vector properties using components. Then make a sketch to illustrate the property geometrically. Suppose* **u**, **v**, *and* **w** *are vectors in the xy-plane and a and c are scalars.*

81. $\mathbf{u} + \mathbf{v} = \mathbf{v} + \mathbf{u}$ Commutative property

82. $(\mathbf{u} + \mathbf{v}) + \mathbf{w} = \mathbf{u} + (\mathbf{v} + \mathbf{w})$ Associative property

83. $a(c\mathbf{v}) = (ac)\mathbf{v}$ Associative property

84. $a(\mathbf{u} + \mathbf{v}) = a\mathbf{u} + a\mathbf{v}$ Distributive property 1

85. $(a + c)\mathbf{v} = a\mathbf{v} + c\mathbf{v}$ Distributive property 2

86. Midpoint of a line segment Use vectors to show that the midpoint of the line segment joining $P(x_1, y_1)$ and $Q(x_2, y_2)$ is the point $((x_1 + x_2)/2, (y_1 + y_2)/2)$. (*Hint:* Let O be the origin and

let M be the midpoint of PQ. Draw a picture and show that $\overrightarrow{OM} = \overrightarrow{OP} + \frac{1}{2}\overrightarrow{PQ} = \overrightarrow{OP} + \frac{1}{2}(\overrightarrow{OQ} - \overrightarrow{OP})$.)

87. Magnitude of scalar multiple Prove that $|c\mathbf{v}| = |c||\mathbf{v}|$, where c is a scalar and **v** is a vector.

88. Equality of vectors Assume $\overrightarrow{PQ}$ equals $\overrightarrow{RS}$. Does it follow that $\overrightarrow{PR}$ is equal to $\overrightarrow{QS}$? Explain your answer.

89. Linear independence A pair of nonzero vectors in the plane is *linearly dependent* if one vector is a scalar multiple of the other. Otherwise, the pair is *linearly independent.*

    a. Which pairs of the following vectors are linearly dependent and which are linearly independent: $\mathbf{u} = \langle 2, -3 \rangle$, $\mathbf{v} = \langle -12, 18 \rangle$, and $\mathbf{w} = \langle 4, 6 \rangle$?

    b. Geometrically, what does it mean for a pair of nonzero vectors in the plane to be linearly dependent? Linearly independent?

    c. Prove that if a pair of vectors **u** and **v** is linearly independent, then given any vector **w**, there are constants c_1 and c_2 such that $\mathbf{w} = c_1\mathbf{u} + c_2\mathbf{v}$.

90. Perpendicular vectors Show that two nonzero vectors $\mathbf{u} = \langle u_1, u_2 \rangle$ and $\mathbf{v} = \langle v_1, v_2 \rangle$ are perpendicular to each other if $u_1 v_1 + u_2 v_2 = 0$.

91. Parallel and perpendicular vectors Let $\mathbf{u} = \langle a, 5 \rangle$ and $\mathbf{v} = \langle 2, 6 \rangle$.

    a. Find the value of a such that **u** is parallel to **v**.

    b. Find the value of a such that **u** is perpendicular to **v**.

92. The Triangle Inequality Suppose **u** and **v** are vectors in the plane.

    a. Use the Triangle Rule for adding vectors to explain why $|\mathbf{u} + \mathbf{v}| \le |\mathbf{u}| + |\mathbf{v}|$. This result is known as the *Triangle Inequality.*

    b. Under what conditions is $|\mathbf{u} + \mathbf{v}| = |\mathbf{u}| + |\mathbf{v}|$?

QUICK CHECK ANSWERS

1. The vector $-5\mathbf{v}$ is five times as long as **v** and points in the opposite direction.   **2.** $\mathbf{v}_a + \mathbf{w}$ points in a northeasterly direction.
3. Constructing $\mathbf{u} + \mathbf{v}$ and $\mathbf{v} + \mathbf{u}$ using the Triangle Rule produces vectors having the same direction and magnitude.
4. $\overrightarrow{PQ} = \langle -6, -2 \rangle$ **5.** $10\mathbf{u} = \langle 6, 8 \rangle$ and $-10\mathbf{u} = \langle -6, -8 \rangle$
6. $\left| \left\langle \dfrac{5}{13}, \dfrac{12}{13} \right\rangle \right| = \sqrt{\dfrac{25 + 144}{169}} = \sqrt{\dfrac{169}{169}} = 1$
7. $\mathbf{u} = -\frac{4}{3}\mathbf{v} + 4\mathbf{w}$

12.2 Vectors in Three Dimensions

Up to this point, our study of calculus has been limited to functions, curves, and vectors that can be plotted in the two-dimensional xy-plane. However, a two-dimensional coordinate system is insufficient for modeling many physical phenomena. For example, to describe the trajectory of a jet gaining altitude, we need two coordinates, say x and y, to measure east–west and north–south distances. In addition, another coordinate, say z, is needed to measure the altitude of the jet. By adding a third coordinate and creating an ordered triple (x, y, z), the location of the jet can be described. The set of all points described by the triples (x, y, z) is called *three-dimensional space, xyz-space,* or $\mathbb{R}^3$. Many of the properties of xyz-space are extensions of familiar ideas you have seen in the xy-plane.

The *xyz*-Coordinate System

> Recall that ℝ is the notation for the real numbers and $\mathbb{R}^2$ (pronounced *R-two*) stands for all ordered pairs of real numbers. The notation $\mathbb{R}^3$ (pronounced *R-three*) stands for the set of all ordered triples of real numbers.

A three-dimensional coordinate system is created by adding a new axis, called the **z-axis**, to the familiar *xy*-coordinate system. The new *z*-axis is inserted through the origin perpendicular to the *x*- and *y*-axes (Figure 12.25). The result is a new coordinate system called the **three-dimensional rectangular coordinate system** or the **xyz-coordinate system**.

The coordinate system described here is a conventional **right-handed coordinate system**: If the curled fingers of the right hand are rotated from the positive *x*-axis to the positive *y*-axis, the thumb points in the direction of the positive *z*-axis (Figure 12.25).

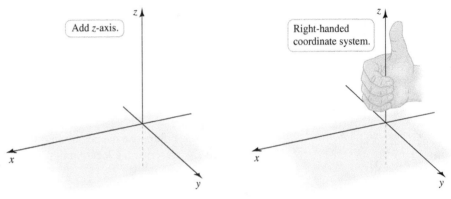

Add *z*-axis.

Right-handed coordinate system.

FIGURE 12.25

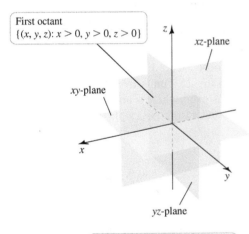

First octant
$\{(x, y, z): x > 0, y > 0, z > 0\}$

xz-plane

xy-plane

yz-plane

xyz-space is divided into octants.

FIGURE 12.26

The coordinate plane containing the *x*-axis and *y*-axis is still called the *xy*-plane. We now have two new coordinate planes: the **xz-plane** containing the *x*-axis and the *z*-axis, and the **yz-plane** containing the *y*-axis and the *z*-axis. Taken together, these three coordinate planes divide *xyz*-space into eight regions called **octants** (Figure 12.26).

The point where all three axes intersect is the **origin**, which has coordinates $(0, 0, 0)$. An ordered triple (a, b, c) refers to a point in *xyz*-space that is found by starting at the origin, moving *a* units in the *x*-direction, *b* units in the *y*-direction, and *c* units in the *z*-direction. With a negative coordinate, you move in the negative direction along the corresponding coordinate axis. To visualize this point, it's helpful to construct a rectangular box with one vertex at the origin and the opposite vertex at the point (a, b, c) (Figure 12.27).

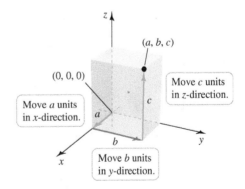

(a, b, c)

$(0, 0, 0)$

Move *c* units in *z*-direction.

Move *a* units in *x*-direction.

Move *b* units in *y*-direction.

FIGURE 12.27

EXAMPLE 1 **Plotting points in xyz-space** Plot the following points.

a. $(3, 4, 5)$ **b.** $(-2, -3, 5)$

SOLUTION

a. Starting at $(0, 0, 0)$, we move 3 units in the *x*-direction to the point $(3, 0, 0)$, then 4 units in the *y*-direction to the point $(3, 4, 0)$, and finally, 5 units in the *z*-direction to reach the point $(3, 4, 5)$ (Figure 12.28).

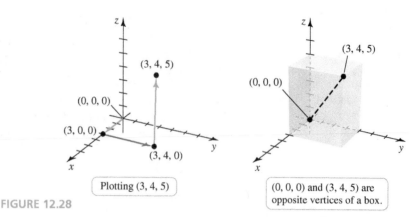

Plotting (3, 4, 5)

(0, 0, 0) and (3, 4, 5) are opposite vertices of a box.

FIGURE 12.28

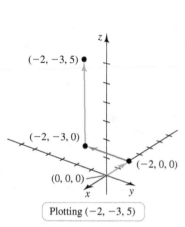

Plotting (−2, −3, 5)

FIGURE 12.29

b. We move −2 units in the x-direction to $(-2, 0, 0)$, −3 units in the y-direction to $(-2, -3, 0)$, and 5 units in the z-direction to reach $(-2, -3, 5)$ (Figure 12.29).

Related Exercises 9–14 ◄

QUICK CHECK 1 Suppose the positive x-, y-, and z-axes point east, north, and upward, respectively. Describe the location of the points $(-1, -1, 0)$, $(1, 0, 1)$, and $(-1, -1, -1)$ relative to the origin. ◄

Equations of Simple Planes

The xy-plane consists of all points in xyz-space that have a z-coordinate of 0. Therefore, the xy-plane is the set $\{(x, y, z): z = 0\}$; it is represented by the equation $z = 0$. Similarly, the xz-plane has the equation $y = 0$, and the yz-plane has the equation $x = 0$.

> Planes that are not parallel to the coordinate planes are extremely important in three-dimensional calculus. They are discussed in Section 13.1.

Planes parallel to one of the coordinate planes are easy to describe. For example, the equation $x = 2$ describes the set of all points whose x-coordinate is 2 and whose y- and z-coordinates are arbitrary; this plane is parallel to and 2 units from the yz-plane. Similarly, the equation $y = a$ describes a plane that is everywhere a units from the xz-plane, and $z = a$ is the equation of a horizontal plane a units from the xy-plane (Figure 12.30).

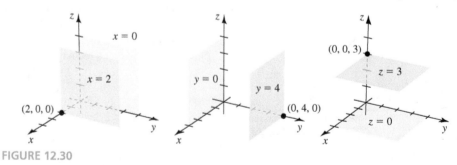

FIGURE 12.30

Plane is parallel to the xz-plane and passes through $(2, -3, 7)$.

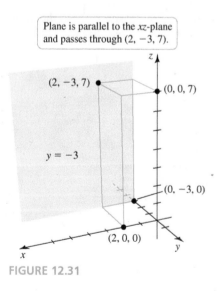

FIGURE 12.31

QUICK CHECK 2 To which coordinate planes are the planes $x = -2$ and $z = 16$ parallel? ◄

EXAMPLE 2   **Parallel planes** Determine the equation of the plane parallel to the xz-plane passing through the point $(2, -3, 7)$.

SOLUTION Points on a plane parallel to the xz-plane have the same y-coordinate. Therefore, the plane passing through the point $(2, -3, 7)$ with a y-coordinate of -3 has the equation $y = -3$ (Figure 12.31).

Related Exercises 15–22 ◄

Distances in xyz-Space

Recall that the distance between two points (x_1, y_1) and (x_2, y_2) in the xy-plane is $\sqrt{(x_2 - x_1)^2 + (y_2 - y_1)^2}$. This distance formula is useful in deriving a similar formula for the distance between two points $P(x_1, y_1, z_1)$ and $Q(x_2, y_2, z_2)$ in xyz-space.

Figure 12.32 shows the points P and Q, together with the auxiliary point $R(x_2, y_2, z_1)$, which has the same z-coordinate as P and the same x- and y-coordinates as Q. The line segment PR has length $|PR| = \sqrt{(x_2 - x_1)^2 + (y_2 - y_1)^2}$ and is one leg of the right triangle $\triangle PRQ$. The hypotenuse of that triangle is the distance between P and Q:

$$\sqrt{|PR|^2 + |RQ|^2} = \sqrt{\underbrace{(x_2 - x_1)^2 + (y_2 - y_1)^2}_{|PR|^2} + \underbrace{(z_2 - z_1)^2}_{|RQ|^2}}.$$

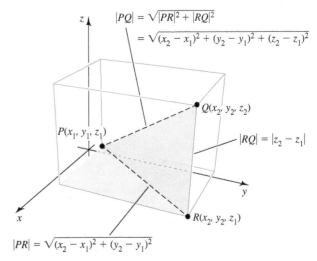

$|PQ| = \sqrt{|PR|^2 + |RQ|^2}$
$= \sqrt{(x_2 - x_1)^2 + (y_2 - y_1)^2 + (z_2 - z_1)^2}$

$Q(x_2, y_2, z_2)$

$P(x_1, y_1, z_1)$

$|RQ| = |z_2 - z_1|$

$R(x_2, y_2, z_1)$

$|PR| = \sqrt{(x_2 - x_1)^2 + (y_2 - y_1)^2}$

FIGURE 12.32

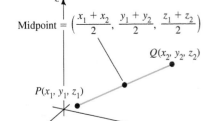

Midpoint $= \left(\dfrac{x_1 + x_2}{2}, \dfrac{y_1 + y_2}{2}, \dfrac{z_1 + z_2}{2} \right)$

$Q(x_2, y_2, z_2)$

$P(x_1, y_1, z_1)$

FIGURE 12.33

> Just as a circle is the boundary of a disk in two dimensions, a *sphere* is the boundary of a *ball* in three dimensions. We have defined a *closed ball*, which includes its boundary. An *open ball* does not contain its boundary.

Distance Formula in xyz-Space

The distance between the points $P(x_1, y_1, z_1)$ and $Q(x_2, y_2, z_2)$ is

$$\sqrt{(x_2 - x_1)^2 + (y_2 - y_1)^2 + (z_2 - z_1)^2}.$$

By using the distance formula, we can derive the formula (Exercise 79) for the **midpoint** of the line segment joining $P(x_1, y_1, z_1)$ and $Q(x_2, y_2, z_2)$, which is found by averaging the x-, y-, and z-coordinates (Figure 12.33):

$$\left(\frac{x_1 + x_2}{2}, \frac{y_1 + y_2}{2}, \frac{z_1 + z_2}{2} \right).$$

Equation of a Sphere

A *sphere* is the set of all points that are a fixed distance r from a point (a, b, c); r is the *radius* of the sphere and (a, b, c) is the *center* of the sphere. A *ball* centered at (a, b, c) with radius r consists of all the points inside and on the sphere centered at (a, b, c) with radius r (Figure 12.34). We now use the distance formula to translate these statements.

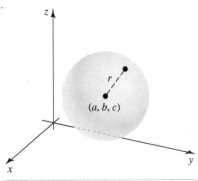

r

(a, b, c)

Sphere: $(x - a)^2 + (y - b)^2 + (z - c)^2 = r^2$
Ball: $(x - a)^2 + (y - b)^2 + (z - c)^2 \le r^2$

FIGURE 12.34

Spheres and Balls

A **sphere** centered at (a, b, c) with radius r is the set of points satisfying the equation

$$(x - a)^2 + (y - b)^2 + (z - c)^2 = r^2.$$

A **ball** centered at (a, b, c) with radius r is the set of points satisfying the inequality

$$(x - a)^2 + (y - b)^2 + (z - c)^2 \le r^2.$$

EXAMPLE 3 Equation of a sphere Consider the points $P(1, -2, 5)$ and $Q(3, 4, -6)$. Find an equation of the sphere for which the line segment PQ is a diameter.

SOLUTION The center of the sphere is the midpoint of PQ:

$$\left(\frac{1+3}{2}, \frac{-2+4}{2}, \frac{5-6}{2} \right) = \left(2, 1, -\frac{1}{2} \right).$$

The diameter of the sphere is the distance $|PQ|$, which is

$$\sqrt{(3-1)^2 + (4+2)^2 + (-6-5)^2} = \sqrt{161}.$$

Therefore, the sphere's radius is $\frac{1}{2}\sqrt{161}$, its center is $\left(2, 1, -\frac{1}{2} \right)$, and it is described by the equation

$$(x-2)^2 + (y-1)^2 + \left(z + \frac{1}{2} \right)^2 = \left(\frac{1}{2}\sqrt{161} \right)^2 = \frac{161}{4}.$$

Related Exercises 23–28◄

EXAMPLE 4 Identifying equations Describe the set of points that satisfy the equation $x^2 + y^2 + z^2 - 2x + 6y - 8z = -1$.

SOLUTION We simplify the equation by completing the square and factoring:

$$\begin{aligned}
(x^2 - 2x) + (y^2 + 6y) + (z^2 - 8z) &= -1 \quad &\text{Group terms.} \\
(x^2 - 2x + 1) + (y^2 + 6y + 9) + (z^2 - 8z + 16) &= 25 \quad &\text{Complete the square.} \\
(x-1)^2 + (y+3)^2 + (z-4)^2 &= 25. \quad &\text{Factor.}
\end{aligned}$$

The equation describes a sphere of radius 5 with center $(1, -3, 4)$.

Related Exercises 29–38◄

QUICK CHECK 3 Describe the solution set of the equation

$$(x-1)^2 + y^2 + (z+1)^2 + 4 = 0.$$

Vectors in $\mathbb{R}^3$

Vectors in $\mathbb{R}^3$ are straightforward extensions of vectors in the xy-plane; we simply include a third component. The position vector $\mathbf{v} = \langle v_1, v_2, v_3 \rangle$ has its tail at the origin and its head at the point (v_1, v_2, v_3). Vectors having the same magnitude and direction are equal. Therefore, the vector from $P(x_1, y_1, z_1)$ to $Q(x_2, y_2, z_2)$ is denoted $\overrightarrow{PQ}$ and is equal to the position vector $\langle x_2 - x_1, y_2 - y_1, z_2 - z_1 \rangle$. It is also equal to all vectors such as $\overrightarrow{RS}$ that have the same length and direction as $\mathbf{v}$ (Figure 12.35).

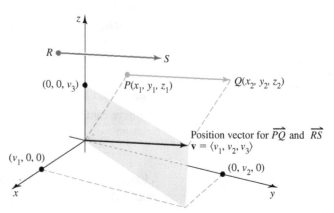

FIGURE 12.35

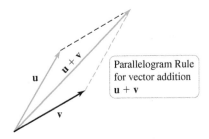

Parallelogram Rule for vector addition $\mathbf{u} + \mathbf{v}$

The operations of vector addition and scalar multiplication in $\mathbb{R}^2$ generalize in a natural way to three dimensions. For example, the sum of two vectors is found geometrically using the Triangle Rule or the Parallelogram Rule (Section 12.1). The sum is found analytically by adding the respective components of the two vectors. As with two-dimensional vectors, scalar multiplication corresponds to stretching or compressing a vector, possibly with a reversal of direction. Two nonzero vectors are parallel if one is a scalar multiple of the other (Figure 12.36).

QUICK CHECK 4 Which of the following vectors are parallel to each other?

a. $\mathbf{u} = \langle -2, 4, -6 \rangle$ **b.** $\mathbf{v} = \langle 4, -8, 12 \rangle$ **c.** $\mathbf{w} = \langle -1, 2, 3 \rangle$ ◄

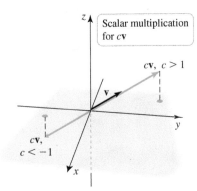

Scalar multiplication for $c\mathbf{v}$

$c\mathbf{v}, c > 1$

$c\mathbf{v}, c < -1$

FIGURE 12.36

DEFINITION Vector Operations in $\mathbb{R}^3$

Let c be a scalar, $\mathbf{u} = \langle u_1, u_2, u_3 \rangle$, and $\mathbf{v} = \langle v_1, v_2, v_3 \rangle$.

$$\mathbf{u} + \mathbf{v} = \langle u_1 + v_1, u_2 + v_2, u_3 + v_3 \rangle \quad \text{Vector addition}$$
$$\mathbf{u} - \mathbf{v} = \langle u_1 - v_1, u_2 - v_2, u_3 - v_3 \rangle \quad \text{Vector subtraction}$$
$$c\mathbf{u} = \langle cu_1, cu_2, cu_3 \rangle \quad \text{Scalar multiplication}$$

EXAMPLE 5 Vectors in $\mathbb{R}^3$ Let $\mathbf{u} = \langle 2, -4, 1 \rangle$ and $\mathbf{v} = \langle 3, 0, -1 \rangle$. Find the components of the following vectors and draw them in $\mathbb{R}^3$.

a. $2\mathbf{u}$ **b.** $-2\mathbf{v}$ **c.** $\mathbf{u} + 2\mathbf{v}$

SOLUTION

a. Using the definition of scalar multiplication, $2\mathbf{u} = 2\langle 2, -4, 1 \rangle = \langle 4, -8, 2 \rangle$. The vector $2\mathbf{u}$ has the same direction as $\mathbf{u}$ with twice the magnitude of $\mathbf{u}$ (Figure 12.37).

b. Using scalar multiplication, $-2\mathbf{v} = -2\langle 3, 0, -1 \rangle = \langle -6, 0, 2 \rangle$. The vector $-2\mathbf{v}$ has the opposite direction as $\mathbf{v}$ and twice the magnitude of $\mathbf{v}$ (Figure 12.38).

c. Using vector addition and scalar multiplication,

$$\mathbf{u} + 2\mathbf{v} = \langle 2, -4, 1 \rangle + 2\langle 3, 0, -1 \rangle = \langle 8, -4, -1 \rangle.$$

The vector $\mathbf{u} + 2\mathbf{v}$ is drawn by applying the Parallelogram Rule to $\mathbf{u}$ and $2\mathbf{v}$ (Figure 12.39).

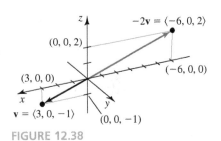

$2\mathbf{u} = \langle 4, -8, 2 \rangle$ $\mathbf{u} = \langle 2, -4, 1 \rangle$

$(0, 0, 1)$

$(0, -4, 0)$ $(2, 0, 0)$

FIGURE 12.37

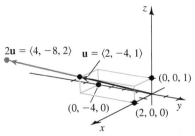

$-2\mathbf{v} = \langle -6, 0, 2 \rangle$

$(0, 0, 2)$

$(3, 0, 0)$

$(-6, 0, 0)$

$\mathbf{v} = \langle 3, 0, -1 \rangle$ $(0, 0, -1)$

FIGURE 12.38

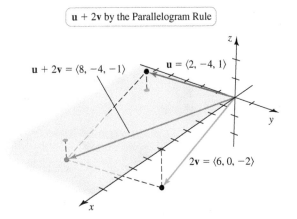

$\mathbf{u} + 2\mathbf{v}$ by the Parallelogram Rule

$\mathbf{u} + 2\mathbf{v} = \langle 8, -4, -1 \rangle$ $\mathbf{u} = \langle 2, -4, 1 \rangle$

$2\mathbf{v} = \langle 6, 0, -2 \rangle$

FIGURE 12.39

Related Exercises 39–44 ◄

Magnitude and Unit Vectors

The magnitude of the vector $\overrightarrow{PQ}$ from $P(x_1, y_1, z_1)$ to $Q(x_2, y_2, z_2)$ is denoted $|\overrightarrow{PQ}|$; it is the distance between P and Q and is given by the distance formula (Figure 12.40).

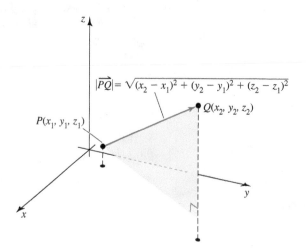

FIGURE 12.40

DEFINITION **Magnitude of a Vector**

The **magnitude** (or **length**) of the vector $\overrightarrow{PQ} = \langle x_2 - x_1, y_2 - y_1, z_2 - z_1 \rangle$ is the distance from $P(x_1, y_1, z_1)$ to $Q(x_2, y_2, z_2)$:

$$|\overrightarrow{PQ}| = \sqrt{(x_2 - x_1)^2 + (y_2 - y_1)^2 + (z_2 - z_1)^2}.$$

The coordinate unit vectors introduced in Section 12.1 extend naturally to three dimensions. The three coordinate unit vectors in $\mathbb{R}^3$ (Figure 12.41) are

$$\mathbf{i} = \langle 1, 0, 0 \rangle, \quad \mathbf{j} = \langle 0, 1, 0 \rangle, \quad \text{and} \quad \mathbf{k} = \langle 0, 0, 1 \rangle.$$

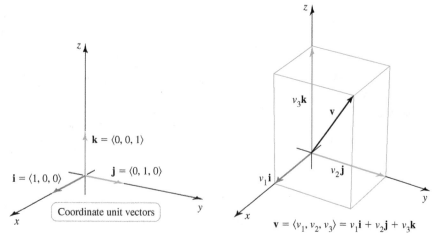

FIGURE 12.41

These unit vectors give an alternative way of expressing position vectors. If $\mathbf{v} = \langle v_1, v_2, v_3 \rangle$, then we have

$$\mathbf{v} = v_1 \langle 1, 0, 0 \rangle + v_2 \langle 0, 1, 0 \rangle + v_3 \langle 0, 0, 1 \rangle = v_1 \mathbf{i} + v_2 \mathbf{j} + v_3 \mathbf{k}.$$

EXAMPLE 6   **Magnitudes and unit vectors** Consider the points $P(5, 3, 1)$ and $Q(-7, 8, 1)$.

a. Express $\vec{PQ}$ in terms of the unit vectors **i**, **j**, and **k**.

b. Find the magnitude of $\vec{PQ}$.

c. Find the position vector of magnitude 10 in the direction of $\vec{PQ}$.

SOLUTION

a. $\vec{PQ}$ is equal to the position vector $\langle -7 - 5, 8 - 3, 1 - 1 \rangle = \langle -12, 5, 0 \rangle$. Thus,
$\vec{PQ} = -12\mathbf{i} + 5\mathbf{j}$.

b. $|\vec{PQ}| = |-12\mathbf{i} + 5\mathbf{j}| = \sqrt{12^2 + 5^2} = \sqrt{169} = 13$

c. The unit vector in the direction of $\vec{PQ}$ is $\mathbf{u} = \dfrac{\vec{PQ}}{|\vec{PQ}|} = \dfrac{1}{13} \langle -12, 5, 0 \rangle$. Therefore, a

vector in the direction of **u** with a magnitude of 10 is $10\mathbf{u} = \dfrac{10}{13} \langle -12, 5, 0 \rangle$.

Related Exercises 45–50 ◄

QUICK CHECK 5 Which vector has the smaller magnitude: $\mathbf{u} = 3\mathbf{i} - \mathbf{j} - \mathbf{k}$ or $\mathbf{v} = 2(\mathbf{i} + \mathbf{j} + \mathbf{k})$? ◄

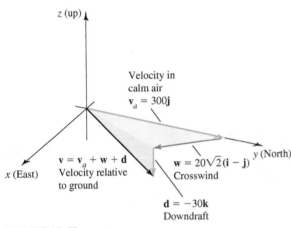

FIGURE 12.42

EXAMPLE 7   **Flight in crosswinds** A plane is flying horizontally due north in calm air at 300 mi/hr when it encounters a horizontal crosswind blowing southeast at 40 mi/hr and a downdraft blowing vertically downward at 30 mi/hr. What are the resulting speed and direction of the plane relative to the ground?

SOLUTION Let the unit vectors **i**, **j**, and **k** point east, north, and upward, respectively (Figure 12.42). The velocity of the plane relative to the air (300 mi/hr due north) is $\mathbf{v}_a = 300\mathbf{j}$. The crosswind blows 45° south of east, so its component to the east is $40 \cos 45° = 20\sqrt{2}$ (in the **i** direction) and its component to the south is $40 \cos 45° = 20\sqrt{2}$ (in the $-\mathbf{j}$ direction). Therefore, the crosswind may be expressed as $\mathbf{w} = 20\sqrt{2}\mathbf{i} - 20\sqrt{2}\mathbf{j}$. Finally, the downdraft in the negative **k** direction is $\mathbf{d} = -30\mathbf{k}$. The velocity of the plane relative to the ground is the sum of $\mathbf{v}_a$, **w**, and **d**:

$$\begin{aligned}
\mathbf{v} &= \mathbf{v}_a + \mathbf{w} + \mathbf{d} \\
&= 300\mathbf{j} + (20\sqrt{2}\mathbf{i} - 20\sqrt{2}\mathbf{j}) - 30\mathbf{k} \\
&= 20\sqrt{2}\mathbf{i} + (300 - 20\sqrt{2})\mathbf{j} - 30\mathbf{k}.
\end{aligned}$$

Figure 12.42 shows the velocity vector of the plane. A quick calculation shows that the speed is $|\mathbf{v}| \approx 275$ mi/hr. The direction of the plane is slightly east of north and downward. (In the next section, we present methods for precisely determining the direction of the vector.)

Related Exercises 51–56 ◄

SECTION 12.2 EXERCISES

Review Questions

1. Explain how to plot the point $(3, -2, 1)$ in $\mathbb{R}^3$.

2. What is the y-coordinate of all points in the xz-plane?

3. Describe the plane $x = 4$.

4. What position vector is equal to the vector from $(3, 5, -2)$ to $(0, -6, 3)$?

5. Let $\mathbf{u} = \langle 3, 5, -7 \rangle$ and $\mathbf{v} = \langle 6, -5, 1 \rangle$. Evaluate $\mathbf{u} + \mathbf{v}$ and $3\mathbf{u} - \mathbf{v}$.

6. What is the magnitude of a vector joining two points $P(x_1, y_1, z_1)$ and $Q(x_2, y_2, z_2)$?

7. Which point is farther from the origin, $(3, -1, 2)$ or $(0, 0, -4)$?

8. Express the vector from $P(-1, -4, 6)$ to $Q(1, 3, -6)$ as a position vector in terms of **i**, **j**, and **k**.

Basic Skills

9–12. Points in $\mathbb{R}^3$ *Find the coordinates of the vertices A, B, and C of the following rectangular boxes.*

9.

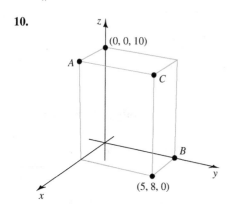

10.

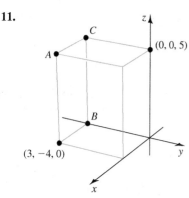

11.

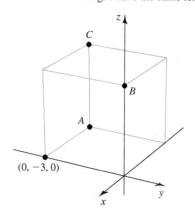

12. Assume all the edges have the same length.

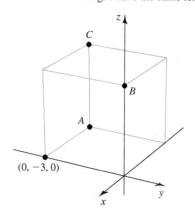

13–14. Plotting points in $\mathbb{R}^3$ *For each point $P(x, y, z)$ given below, let $A(x, y, 0)$, $B(x, 0, z)$, and $C(0, y, z)$ be points in the xy-, xz-, and yz-planes, respectively. Plot and label the points A, B, C, and P in $\mathbb{R}^3$.*

13. a. $P(2, 2, 4)$ **b.** $P(1, 2, 5)$ **c.** $P(-2, 0, 5)$

14. a. $P(-3, 2, 4)$ **b.** $P(4, -2, -3)$ **c.** $P(-2, -4, -3)$

15–20. Sketching planes *Sketch the following planes in the window* $[0, 5] \times [0, 5] \times [0, 5]$.

15. $x = 2$ **16.** $z = 3$ **17.** $y = 2$ **18.** $z = y$

19. The plane that passes through $(2, 0, 0)$, $(0, 3, 0)$, and $(0, 0, 4)$

20. The plane parallel to the xz-plane containing the point $(1, 2, 3)$

21. Planes Sketch the plane parallel to the xy-plane through $(2, 4, 2)$ and find its equation.

22. Planes Sketch the plane parallel to the yz-plane through $(2, 4, 2)$ and find its equation.

23–26. Spheres and balls *Find an equation or inequality that describes the following objects.*

23. A sphere with center $(1, 2, 3)$ and radius 4

24. A sphere with center $(1, 2, 0)$ passing through the point $(3, 4, 5)$

25. A ball with center $(-2, 0, 4)$ and radius 1

26. A ball with center $(0, -2, 6)$ with the point $(1, 4, 8)$ on its boundary

27. Midpoints and spheres Find an equation of the sphere passing through $P(1, 0, 5)$ and $Q(2, 3, 9)$ with its center at the midpoint of PQ.

28. Midpoints and spheres Find an equation of the sphere passing through $P(-4, 2, 3)$ and $Q(0, 2, 7)$ with its center at the midpoint of PQ.

29–38. Identifying sets *Give a geometric description of the following sets of points.*

29. $(x - 1)^2 + y^2 + z^2 - 9 = 0$

30. $(x + 1)^2 + y^2 + z^2 - 2y - 24 = 0$

31. $x^2 + y^2 + z^2 - 2y - 4z - 4 = 0$

32. $x^2 + y^2 + z^2 - 6x + 6y - 8z - 2 = 0$

33. $x^2 + y^2 - 14y + z^2 \geq -13$

34. $x^2 + y^2 - 14y + z^2 \leq -13$

35. $x^2 + y^2 + z^2 - 8x - 14y - 18z \leq 79$

36. $x^2 + y^2 + z^2 - 8x + 14y - 18z \geq 65$

37. $x^2 - 2x + y^2 + 6y + z^2 + 10 = 0$

38. $x^2 - 4x + y^2 + 6y + z^2 + 14 = 0$

39–44. Vector operations *For the given vectors $\mathbf{u}$ and $\mathbf{v}$, evaluate the following expressions.*

a. $3\mathbf{u} + 2\mathbf{v}$ **b.** $4\mathbf{u} - \mathbf{v}$ **c.** $|\mathbf{u} + 3\mathbf{v}|$

39. $\mathbf{u} = \langle 4, -3, 0 \rangle, \mathbf{v} = \langle 0, 1, 1 \rangle$

40. $\mathbf{u} = \langle -2, -3, 0 \rangle, \mathbf{v} = \langle 1, 2, 1 \rangle$

41. $u = \langle -2, 1, -2 \rangle, v = \langle 1, 1, 1 \rangle$

42. $u = \langle -5, 0, 2 \rangle, v = \langle 3, 1, 1 \rangle$

43. $u = \langle -7, 11, 8 \rangle, v = \langle 3, -5, -1 \rangle$

44. $u = \langle -4, -8\sqrt{3}, 2\sqrt{2} \rangle, v = \langle 2, 3\sqrt{3}, -\sqrt{2} \rangle$

45–50. Unit vectors and magnitude *Consider the following points P and Q.*

a. Find $\overrightarrow{PQ}$ and state your answer in two forms: $\langle a, b, c \rangle$ and $a\mathbf{i} + b\mathbf{j} + c\mathbf{k}$.

b. Find the magnitude of $\overrightarrow{PQ}$.

c. Find two unit vectors parallel to $\overrightarrow{PQ}$.

45. $P(1, 5, 0), Q(3, 11, 2)$

46. $P(5, 11, 12), Q(1, 14, 13)$

47. $P(-3, 1, 0), Q(-3, -4, 1)$

48. $P(3, 8, 12), Q(3, 9, 11)$

49. $P(0, 0, 2), Q(-2, 4, 0)$

50. $P(a, b, c), Q(1, 1, -1)$ $(a, b,$ and c are real numbers)

51. Flight in crosswinds A model airplane is flying horizontally due north at 20 mi/hr when it encounters a horizontal crosswind blowing east at 20 mi/hr and a downdraft blowing vertically downward at 10 mi/hr.

    a. Find the position vector that represents the velocity of the plane relative to the ground.

    b. Find the speed of the plane relative to the ground.

52. Another crosswind flight A model airplane is flying horizontally due east at 10 mi/hr when it encounters a horizontal crosswind blowing south at 5 mi/hr and an updraft blowing vertically upward at 5 mi/hr.

    a. Find the position vector that represents the velocity of the plane relative to the ground.

    b. Find the speed of the plane relative to the ground.

53. Crosswinds A small plane is flying horizontally due east in calm air at 250 mi/hr when it is hit by a horizontal crosswind blowing southwest at 50 mi/hr and a 30-mi/hr updraft. Find the resulting speed of the plane and describe with a sketch the approximate direction of the velocity relative to the ground.

54. Combined force An object at the origin is acted on by the forces $\mathbf{F}_1 = 20\mathbf{i} - 10\mathbf{j}, \mathbf{F}_2 = 30\mathbf{j} + 10\mathbf{k},$ and $\mathbf{F}_3 = 40\mathbf{i} + 20\mathbf{k}$. Find the magnitude of the combined force and describe the approximate direction of the force.

55. Submarine course A submarine climbs at an angle of 30° above the horizontal with a heading to the northeast. If its speed is 20 knots, find the components of the velocity in the east, north, and vertical directions.

56. Maintaining equilibrium An object is acted upon by the forces $\mathbf{F}_1 = \langle 10, 6, 3 \rangle$ and $\mathbf{F}_2 = \langle 0, 4, 9 \rangle$. Find the force $\mathbf{F}_3$ that must act on the object so that the sum of the forces is zero.

Further Explorations

57. Explain why or why not Determine whether the following statements are true and give an explanation or counterexample.

    a. Suppose $\mathbf{u}$ and $\mathbf{v}$ both make a 45° angle with $\mathbf{w}$ in $\mathbb{R}^3$. Then $\mathbf{u} + \mathbf{v}$ makes a 45° angle with $\mathbf{w}$.

    b. Suppose $\mathbf{u}$ and $\mathbf{v}$ both make a 90° angle with $\mathbf{w}$ in $\mathbb{R}^3$. Then $\mathbf{u} + \mathbf{v}$ can never make a 90° angle with $\mathbf{w}$.

    c. $\mathbf{i} + \mathbf{j} + \mathbf{k} = \mathbf{0}$.

    d. The intersection of the planes $x = 1, y = 1,$ and $z = 1$ is a point.

58–60. Sets of points *Describe with a sketch the sets of points (x, y, z) satisfying the following equations.*

58. $(x + 1)(y - 3) = 0$ **59.** $x^2y^2z^2 > 0$

60. $y - z = 0$

61. Sets of points Give a geometric description of the set of points (x, y, z) satisfying the pair of equations $z = 0$ and $x^2 + y^2 = 1$. Sketch a figure of this set of points.

62. Sets of points Give a geometric description of the set of points (x, y, z) satisfying the pair of equations $z = x^2$ and $y = 0$. Sketch a figure of this set of points.

63. Sets of points Give a geometric description of the set of points (x, y, z) that lie on the intersection of the sphere $x^2 + y^2 + z^2 = 5$ and the plane $z = 1$.

64. Sets of points Give a geometric description of the set of points (x, y, z) that lie on the intersection of the sphere $x^2 + y^2 + z^2 = 36$ and the plane $z = 6$.

65. Describing a circle Find a pair of equations describing a circle of radius 3 centered at $(2, 4, 1)$ that lies in a plane parallel to the xz-plane.

66. Describing a line Find a pair of equations describing a line passing through the point $(-2, -5, 1)$ that is parallel to the x-axis.

67–70. Parallel vectors of varying lengths *Find vectors parallel to $\mathbf{v}$ of the given length.*

67. $\mathbf{v} = \langle 6, -8, 0 \rangle$; length $= 20$

68. $\mathbf{v} = \langle 3, -2, 6 \rangle$; length $= 10$

69. $\mathbf{v} = \overrightarrow{PQ}$ with $P(3, 4, 0)$ and $Q(2, 3, 1)$; length $= 3$

70. $\mathbf{v} = \overrightarrow{PQ}$ with $P(1, 0, 1)$ and $Q(2, -1, 1)$; length $= 3$

71. Collinear points Determine whether the points $P, Q,$ and R are collinear (lie on a line) by comparing $\overrightarrow{PQ}$ and $\overrightarrow{PR}$. If the points are collinear, determine which point lies between the other two points.

    a. $P(1, 6, -5), Q(2, 5, -3), R(4, 3, 1)$

    b. $P(1, 5, 7), Q(5, 13, -1), R(0, 3, 9)$

    c. $P(1, 2, 3), Q(2, -3, 6), R(3, -1, 9)$

    d. $P(9, 5, 1), Q(11, 18, 4), R(6, 3, 0)$

72. Collinear points Determine the values of x and y such that the points $(1, 2, 3), (4, 7, 1),$ and $(x, y, 2)$ are collinear (lie on a line).

73. Lengths of the diagonals of a box A fisherman wants to know if his fly rod will fit in a rectangular 2 ft × 3 ft × 4 ft packing box. What is the longest rod that fits in this box?

Applications

74. Forces on an inclined plane An object on an inclined plane does not slide provided the component of the object's weight parallel to the plane $|\mathbf{W}_{par}|$ is less than or equal to the magnitude of the opposing frictional force $|\mathbf{F}_f|$. The magnitude of the frictional force, in turn, is proportional to the component of the object's weight perpendicular to the plane $|\mathbf{W}_{perp}|$ (see figure). The constant of proportionality is the coefficient of static friction, μ.

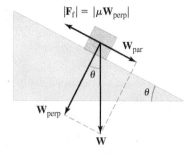

a. Suppose a 100-lb block rests on a plane that is tilted at an angle of $\theta = 20°$ to the horizontal. Find $|\mathbf{W}_{par}|$ and $|\mathbf{W}_{perp}|$.
b. The condition for the block not sliding is $|\mathbf{W}_{par}| \le \mu|\mathbf{W}_{perp}|$. If $\mu = 0.65$, does the block slide?
c. What is the critical angle above which the block slides with $\mu = 0.65$?

75. Three-cable load A 500-kg load hangs from three cables of equal length that are anchored at the points $(-2, 0, 0)$, $(1, \sqrt{3}, 0)$, and $(1, -\sqrt{3}, 0)$. The load is located at $(0, 0, -2\sqrt{3})$. Find the vectors describing the forces on the cables due to the load.

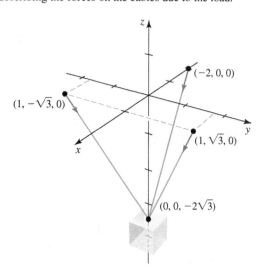

76. Four-cable load A 500-lb load hangs from four cables of equal length that are anchored at the points $(\pm 2, 0, 0)$ and $(0, \pm 2, 0)$.

The load is located at $(0, 0, -4)$. Find the vectors describing the forces on the cables due to the load.

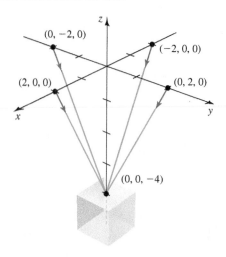

Additional Exercises

77. Possible parallelograms The points $O(0, 0, 0)$, $P(1, 4, 6)$, and $Q(2, 4, 3)$ lie at three vertices of a parallelogram. Find all possible locations of the fourth vertex.

78. Diagonals of parallelograms Two sides of a parallelogram are formed by the vectors $\mathbf{u}$ and $\mathbf{v}$. Prove that the diagonals of the parallelogram are $\mathbf{u} + \mathbf{v}$ and $\mathbf{u} - \mathbf{v}$.

79. Midpoint formula Prove that the midpoint of the line segment joining $P(x_1, y_1, z_1)$ and $Q(x_2, y_2, z_2)$ is

$$\left(\frac{x_1 + x_2}{2}, \frac{y_1 + y_2}{2}, \frac{z_1 + z_2}{2} \right).$$

80. Equation of a sphere For constants a, b, c, and d, show that the equation

$$x^2 + y^2 + z^2 - 2ax - 2by - 2cz = d$$

describes a sphere centered at (a, b, c) with radius r, where $r^2 = d + a^2 + b^2 + c^2$, provided $d + a^2 + b^2 + c^2 > 0$.

81. Medians of a triangle—coordinate free Assume that $\mathbf{u}$, $\mathbf{v}$, and $\mathbf{w}$ are vectors in $\mathbb{R}^3$ that form the sides of a triangle (see figure). Use the following steps to prove that the medians intersect at a point that divides each median in a 2:1 ratio. The proof does not use a coordinate system.

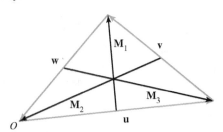

a. Show that $\mathbf{u} + \mathbf{v} + \mathbf{w} = \mathbf{0}$.

b. Let $\mathbf{M}_1$ be the median vector from the midpoint of $\mathbf{u}$ to the opposite vertex. Define $\mathbf{M}_2$ and $\mathbf{M}_3$ similarly. Using the geometry of vector addition show that $\mathbf{M}_1 = \mathbf{u}/2 + \mathbf{v}$. Find analogous expressions for $\mathbf{M}_2$ and $\mathbf{M}_3$.

c. Let $\mathbf{a}$, $\mathbf{b}$, and $\mathbf{c}$ be the vectors from O to the points one-third of the way along $\mathbf{M}_1, \mathbf{M}_2$, and $\mathbf{M}_3$, respectively. Show that $\mathbf{a} = \mathbf{b} = \mathbf{c} = (\mathbf{u} - \mathbf{w})/3$.

d. Conclude that the medians intersect at a point that divides each median in a 2:1 ratio.

82. Medians of a triangle—with coordinates In contrast to the proof in Exercise 81, we now use coordinates and position vectors to prove the same result. Without loss of generality, let $P(x_1, y_1, 0)$ and $Q(x_2, y_2, 0)$ be two points in the xy-plane and let $R(x_3, y_3, z_3)$ be a third point, such that P, Q, and R do not lie on a line. Consider $\triangle PQR$.

a. Let M_1 be the midpoint of the side PQ. Find the coordinates of M_1 and the components of the vector $\overrightarrow{RM_1}$.

b. Find the vector $\overrightarrow{OZ_1}$ from the origin to the point Z_1 two-thirds of the way along $\overrightarrow{RM_1}$.

c. Repeat the calculation of part (b) with the midpoint M_2 of RQ and the vector $\overrightarrow{PM_2}$ to obtain the vector $\overrightarrow{OZ_2}$.

d. Repeat the calculation of part (b) with the midpoint M_3 of PR and the vector $\overrightarrow{QM_3}$ to obtain the vector $\overrightarrow{OZ_3}$.

e. Conclude that the medians of $\triangle PQR$ intersect at a point. Give the coordinates of the point.

f. With $P(2, 4, 0)$, $Q(4, 1, 0)$, and $R(6, 3, 4)$, find the point at which the medians of $\triangle PQR$ intersect.

83. The amazing quadrilateral property—coordinate free The points P, Q, R, and S, joined by the vectors $\mathbf{u}$, $\mathbf{v}$, $\mathbf{w}$, and $\mathbf{x}$, are the vertices of a quadrilateral in $\mathbb{R}^3$. *The four points needn't lie in a plane* (see figure). Use the following steps to prove that the line segments joining the midpoints of the sides of the quadrilateral form a parallelogram. The proof does not use a coordinate system.

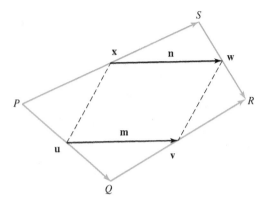

a. Use vector addition to show that $\mathbf{u} + \mathbf{v} = \mathbf{w} + \mathbf{x}$.

b. Let $\mathbf{m}$ be the vector that joins the midpoints of PQ and QR. Show that $\mathbf{m} = (\mathbf{u} + \mathbf{v})/2$.

c. Let $\mathbf{n}$ be the vector that joins the midpoints of PS and SR. Show that $\mathbf{n} = (\mathbf{x} + \mathbf{w})/2$.

d. Combine parts (a), (b), and (c) to conclude that $\mathbf{m} = \mathbf{n}$.

e. Explain why part (d) implies that the line segments joining the midpoints of the sides of the quadrilateral form a parallelogram.

84. The amazing quadrilateral property—with coordinates Prove the quadrilateral property in Exercise 83, assuming the coordinates of P, Q, R, and S are $P(x_1, y_1, 0)$, $Q(x_2, y_2, 0)$, $R(x_3, y_3, 0)$, and $S(x_4, y_4, z_4)$, where we assume that P, Q, and R lie in the xy-plane without loss of generality.

QUICK CHECK ANSWERS

1. Southwest; due east and upward; southwest and downward
2. yz-plane; xy-plane **3.** No solution **4.** $\mathbf{u}$ and $\mathbf{v}$ are parallel. **5.** $|\mathbf{u}| = \sqrt{11}$ and $|\mathbf{v}| = \sqrt{12} = 2\sqrt{3}$; $\mathbf{u}$ has the smaller magnitude.

12.3 Dot Products

> The dot product is also called the *scalar product*, a term we do not use in order to avoid confusion with *scalar multiplication*.

The *dot product* is used to determine the angle between two vectors. It is also a tool for calculating *projections*—the measure of how much of a given vector lies in the direction of another vector.

To see the usefulness of the dot product, consider an example. Recall that the work done by a constant force F in moving an object a distance d is $W = Fd$ (Section 6.7). This rule applies provided the force acts in the direction of motion (Figure 12.43a). Now assume the force is a vector $\mathbf{F}$ applied at an angle θ to the direction of motion; the resulting displacement of the object is a vector $\mathbf{d}$. In this case, the work done by the force is the component of the force in the direction of motion multiplied by the distance moved by the object, which is $W = (|\mathbf{F}| \cos\theta)|\mathbf{d}|$ (Figure 12.43b). We call this product of the magnitudes of two vectors and the cosine of the angle between them the dot product.

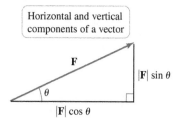

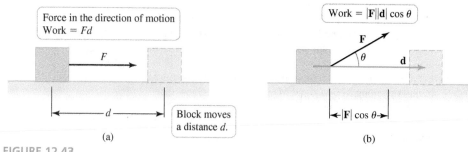

FIGURE 12.43

Two Forms of the Dot Product

Guided by the example of work done by a force, we give one definition of the dot product. Then an equivalent definition is derived that is often better suited for computation.

DEFINITION   Dot Product

Given two nonzero vectors **u** and **v** in two or three dimensions, their **dot product** is

$$\mathbf{u} \cdot \mathbf{v} = |\mathbf{u}||\mathbf{v}| \cos \theta,$$

where θ is the angle between **u** and **v** with $0 \le \theta \le \pi$ (Figure 12.44). If $\mathbf{u} = \mathbf{0}$ or $\mathbf{v} = \mathbf{0}$, then $\mathbf{u} \cdot \mathbf{v} = 0$, and θ is undefined.

The dot product of two vectors is itself a scalar. Two special cases immediately arise:

• **u** and **v** are parallel ($\theta = 0$ or $\theta = \pi$) if and only if $\mathbf{u} \cdot \mathbf{v} = \pm|\mathbf{u}||\mathbf{v}|$.

• **u** and **v** are perpendicular ($\theta = \pi/2$) if and only if $\mathbf{u} \cdot \mathbf{v} = 0$.

The second case gives rise to the important property of *orthogonality*.

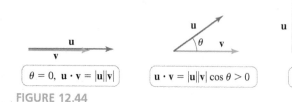

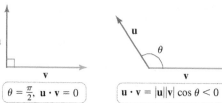

FIGURE 12.44

> In two and three dimensions, *orthogonal* and *perpendicular* are used interchangeably. *Orthogonal* is a more general term that also applies in more than three dimensions.

DEFINITION   Orthogonal Vectors

Two vectors **u** and **v** are **orthogonal** if and only if $\mathbf{u} \cdot \mathbf{v} = 0$. The zero vector is orthogonal to all vectors. In two or three dimensions, two nonzero orthogonal vectors are perpendicular to each other.

QUICK CHECK 1 Sketch two nonzero vectors **u** and **v** with $\theta = 0$. Sketch two nonzero vectors **u** and **v** with $\theta = \pi$. ◄

EXAMPLE 1   Dot products   Compute the dot products of the following vectors.

a. $\mathbf{u} = 2\mathbf{i} - 6\mathbf{j}$ and $\mathbf{v} = 12\mathbf{k}$

b. $\mathbf{u} = \langle \sqrt{3}, 1 \rangle$ and $\mathbf{v} = \langle 0, 1 \rangle$

SOLUTION

a. The vector **u** lies in the xy-plane and the vector **v** is perpendicular to the xy-plane. Therefore, $\theta = \dfrac{\pi}{2}$, **u** and **v** are orthogonal, and $\mathbf{u} \cdot \mathbf{v} = 0$ (Figure 12.45a).

b. As shown in Figure 12.45b, **u** and **v** form two sides of a 30–60–90 triangle in the xy-plane, with an angle of $\pi/3$ between them. Because $|\mathbf{u}| = 2$, $|\mathbf{v}| = 1$, and $\cos \pi/3 = 1/2$, the dot product is

$$\mathbf{u} \cdot \mathbf{v} = |\mathbf{u}||\mathbf{v}| \cos \theta = 2 \cdot 1 \cdot \tfrac{1}{2} = 1.$$

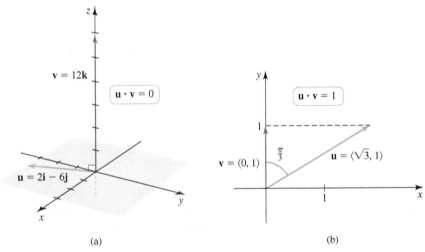

FIGURE 12.45

(a)   (b)

Related Exercises 9–14 ◄

The definition of the dot product requires knowing the angle θ between the vectors. Often the angle is not known; in fact, it may be exactly what we seek. For this reason, we present another method for computing the dot product that does not require knowing θ.

▷ In $\mathbb{R}^2$ with $\mathbf{u} = \langle u_1, u_2 \rangle$ and $\mathbf{v} = \langle v_1, v_2 \rangle$, $\mathbf{u} \cdot \mathbf{v} = u_1 v_1 + u_2 v_2$.

THEOREM 12.1 Dot Product
Given two vectors $\mathbf{u} = \langle u_1, u_2, u_3 \rangle$ and $\mathbf{v} = \langle v_1, v_2, v_3 \rangle$,

$$\mathbf{u} \cdot \mathbf{v} = u_1 v_1 + u_2 v_2 + u_3 v_3.$$

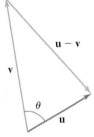

FIGURE 12.46

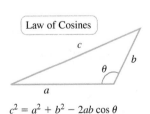

Law of Cosines

$c^2 = a^2 + b^2 - 2ab \cos \theta$

Proof: Consider two position vectors $\mathbf{u} = \langle u_1, u_2, u_3 \rangle$ and $\mathbf{v} = \langle v_1, v_2, v_3 \rangle$, and suppose θ is the angle between them. The vector $\mathbf{u} - \mathbf{v}$ forms the third side of a triangle (Figure 12.46). By the Law of Cosines,

$$|\mathbf{u} - \mathbf{v}|^2 = |\mathbf{u}|^2 + |\mathbf{v}|^2 - 2\underbrace{|\mathbf{u}||\mathbf{v}| \cos \theta}_{\mathbf{u} \cdot \mathbf{v}}.$$

The definition of the dot product, $\mathbf{u} \cdot \mathbf{v} = |\mathbf{u}||\mathbf{v}| \cos \theta$, allows us to write

$$\mathbf{u} \cdot \mathbf{v} = |\mathbf{u}||\mathbf{v}| \cos \theta = \frac{1}{2} \left(|\mathbf{u}|^2 + |\mathbf{v}|^2 - |\mathbf{u} - \mathbf{v}|^2 \right). \tag{1}$$

Using the definition of magnitude, we find that

$$|\mathbf{u}|^2 = u_1^2 + u_2^2 + u_3^2, \quad |\mathbf{v}|^2 = v_1^2 + v_2^2 + v_3^2,$$

and

$$|\mathbf{u} - \mathbf{v}|^2 = (u_1 - v_1)^2 + (u_2 - v_2)^2 + (u_3 - v_3)^2.$$

Expanding the terms in $|\mathbf{u} - \mathbf{v}|^2$ and simplifying yields

$$|\mathbf{u}|^2 + |\mathbf{v}|^2 - |\mathbf{u} - \mathbf{v}|^2 = 2(u_1 v_1 + u_2 v_2 + u_3 v_3).$$

Substituting into expression (1) gives a compact expression for the dot product:

$$\mathbf{u} \cdot \mathbf{v} = u_1 v_1 + u_2 v_2 + u_3 v_3.$$

This new representation of $\mathbf{u} \cdot \mathbf{v}$ has two immediate consequences.

1. Combining it with the definition of dot product gives

$$\mathbf{u} \cdot \mathbf{v} = u_1 v_1 + u_2 v_2 + u_3 v_3 = |\mathbf{u}||\mathbf{v}| \cos \theta.$$

If $\mathbf{u}$ and $\mathbf{v}$ are both nonzero, then

> **QUICK CHECK 2** Use Theorem 12.1 to compute the dot products $\mathbf{i} \cdot \mathbf{j}$, $\mathbf{i} \cdot \mathbf{k}$, and $\mathbf{j} \cdot \mathbf{k}$ for the unit coordinate vectors. What do you conclude about the angles between these vectors?

$$\cos \theta = \frac{u_1 v_1 + u_2 v_2 + u_3 v_3}{|\mathbf{u}||\mathbf{v}|} = \frac{\mathbf{u} \cdot \mathbf{v}}{|\mathbf{u}||\mathbf{v}|},$$

and we have a way to compute θ.

2. Notice that $\mathbf{u} \cdot \mathbf{u} = u_1^2 + u_2^2 + u_3^2 = |\mathbf{u}|^2$. Therefore, we have a relationship between the dot product and the magnitude of a vector: $|\mathbf{u}| = \sqrt{\mathbf{u} \cdot \mathbf{u}}$ or $|\mathbf{u}|^2 = \mathbf{u} \cdot \mathbf{u}$.

EXAMPLE 2 Dot products and angles Let $\mathbf{u} = \langle \sqrt{3}, 1, 0 \rangle$, $\mathbf{v} = \langle 1, \sqrt{3}, 0 \rangle$, and $\mathbf{w} = \langle 1, \sqrt{3}, 2\sqrt{3} \rangle$.

a. Compute $\mathbf{u} \cdot \mathbf{v}$.

b. Find the angle between $\mathbf{u}$ and $\mathbf{v}$.

c. Find the angle between $\mathbf{u}$ and $\mathbf{w}$.

SOLUTION

a. $\mathbf{u} \cdot \mathbf{v} = \langle \sqrt{3}, 1, 0 \rangle \cdot \langle 1, \sqrt{3}, 0 \rangle = \sqrt{3} + \sqrt{3} + 0 = 2\sqrt{3}$

b. Note that $|\mathbf{u}| = \sqrt{\mathbf{u} \cdot \mathbf{u}} = \sqrt{\langle \sqrt{3}, 1, 0 \rangle \cdot \langle \sqrt{3}, 1, 0 \rangle} = 2$ and similarly $|\mathbf{v}| = 2$. Therefore,

$$\cos \theta = \frac{\mathbf{u} \cdot \mathbf{v}}{|\mathbf{u}||\mathbf{v}|} = \frac{2\sqrt{3}}{2 \cdot 2} = \frac{\sqrt{3}}{2}.$$

Because $0 \le \theta \le \pi$, it follows that $\theta = \cos^{-1}\left(\dfrac{\sqrt{3}}{2}\right) = \pi/6$.

c. $\cos \theta = \dfrac{\mathbf{u} \cdot \mathbf{w}}{|\mathbf{u}||\mathbf{w}|} = \dfrac{\langle \sqrt{3}, 1, 0 \rangle \cdot \langle 1, \sqrt{3}, 2\sqrt{3} \rangle}{|\langle \sqrt{3}, 1, 0 \rangle||\langle 1, \sqrt{3}, 2\sqrt{3} \rangle|} = \dfrac{2\sqrt{3}}{2 \cdot 4} = \dfrac{\sqrt{3}}{4}$

It follows that

$$\theta = \cos^{-1}\left(\frac{\sqrt{3}}{4}\right) \approx 1.12 \text{ rad} \approx 64.3°.$$

Related Exercises 15–24 ◄

Properties of Dot Products The properties of the dot product in the following theorem are easily proved using vector components (Exercises 76–80).

> Theorem 12.1 extends to vectors with any number of components. If $\mathbf{u} = \langle u_1, \ldots, u_n \rangle$ and $\mathbf{v} = \langle v_1, \ldots, v_n \rangle$, then
>
> $$\mathbf{u} \cdot \mathbf{v} = u_1 v_1 + \cdots + u_n v_n.$$
>
> The properties in Theorem 12.2 also apply in two or more dimensions.

THEOREM 12.2 Properties of the Dot Product

Suppose $\mathbf{u}$, $\mathbf{v}$, and $\mathbf{w}$ are vectors and let c be a scalar.

1. $\mathbf{u} \cdot \mathbf{v} = \mathbf{v} \cdot \mathbf{u}$ Commutative property

2. $c(\mathbf{u} \cdot \mathbf{v}) = (c\mathbf{u}) \cdot \mathbf{v} = \mathbf{u} \cdot (c\mathbf{v})$ Associative property

3. $\mathbf{u} \cdot (\mathbf{v} + \mathbf{w}) = \mathbf{u} \cdot \mathbf{v} + \mathbf{u} \cdot \mathbf{w}$ Distributive property

Orthogonal Projections

Given vectors **u** and **v**, how closely aligned are they? That is, how much of **u** points in the direction of **v**? This question is answered using *projections*. As shown in Figure 12.47a, the projection of the vector **u** onto a nonzero vector **v**, denoted proj$_\mathbf{v}$**u**, is the "shadow" cast by **u** onto the line through **v**. The projection of **u** onto **v** is itself a vector; it points in the same direction as **v** if the angle between **u** and **v** lies in the interval $0 \le \theta < \pi/2$ (Figure 12.47b); it points in the direction opposite to that of **v** if the angle between **u** and **v** lies in the interval $\pi/2 < \theta \le \pi$ (Figure 12.47c). If $\theta = \dfrac{\pi}{2}$, **u** and **v** are orthogonal, and there is no shadow.

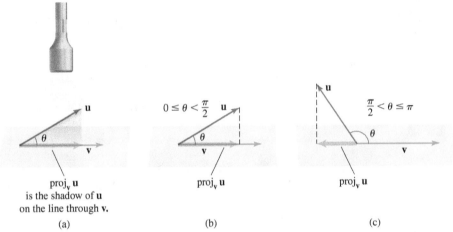

proj$_\mathbf{v}$ **u**
is the shadow of **u**
on the line through **v**.

(a)   (b)   (c)

FIGURE 12.47

To find the projection of **u** onto **v**, we proceed as follows: With the tails of **u** and **v** together, we drop a perpendicular line segment from the head of **u** to the point P on the line through **v** (Figure 12.48). The vector $\overrightarrow{OP}$ is the *orthogonal projection of* **u** *onto* **v**. An expression for proj$_\mathbf{v}$**u** is found using two observations.

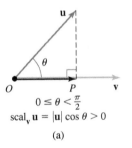

$0 \le \theta < \dfrac{\pi}{2}$
scal$_\mathbf{v}$ **u** $= |\mathbf{u}| \cos \theta > 0$

(a)

- If $0 \le \theta < \pi/2$, then proj$_\mathbf{v}$**u** has length $|\mathbf{u}| \cos \theta$ and points in the direction of the unit vector $\mathbf{v}/|\mathbf{v}|$ (Figure 12.48a). Therefore,

$$\text{proj}_\mathbf{v}\mathbf{u} = \underbrace{|\mathbf{u}| \cos \theta}_{\text{length}} \underbrace{\left(\frac{\mathbf{v}}{|\mathbf{v}|} \right)}_{\text{direction}}.$$

We define the *scalar component of* **u** *in the direction of* **v** to be scal$_\mathbf{v}$**u** $= |\mathbf{u}| \cos \theta$. In this case, scal$_\mathbf{v}$**u** is the length of proj$_\mathbf{v}$**u**.

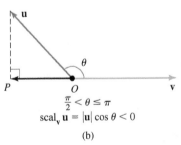

$\dfrac{\pi}{2} < \theta \le \pi$
scal$_\mathbf{v}$ **u** $= |\mathbf{u}| \cos \theta < 0$

(b)

FIGURE 12.48

> Notice that scal$_\mathbf{v}$**u** may be positive, negative, or zero. However, $|$scal$_\mathbf{v}$**u**$|$ is the length of proj$_\mathbf{v}$**u**. The projection proj$_\mathbf{v}$**u** is defined for all vectors **u**, but only for nonzero vectors **v**.

- If $\pi/2 < \theta \le \pi$, then proj$_\mathbf{v}$**u** has length $-|\mathbf{u}| \cos \theta$ (which is positive) and points in the direction of $-\mathbf{v}/|\mathbf{v}|$ (Figure 12.48b). Therefore,

$$\text{proj}_\mathbf{v}\mathbf{u} = \underbrace{-|\mathbf{u}| \cos \theta}_{\text{length}} \underbrace{\left(-\frac{\mathbf{v}}{|\mathbf{v}|} \right)}_{\text{direction}} = |\mathbf{u}| \cos \theta \left(\frac{\mathbf{v}}{|\mathbf{v}|} \right).$$

In this case, scal$_\mathbf{v}$**u** $= |\mathbf{u}| \cos \theta < 0$.

We see that in both cases, the expression for proj$_\mathbf{v}$**u** is the same:

$$\text{proj}_\mathbf{v}\mathbf{u} = \underbrace{|\mathbf{u}| \cos \theta}_{\text{scal}_\mathbf{v}\mathbf{u}} \left(\frac{\mathbf{v}}{|\mathbf{v}|} \right) = \text{scal}_\mathbf{v}\mathbf{u} \left(\frac{\mathbf{v}}{|\mathbf{v}|} \right).$$

Note that if $\theta = \dfrac{\pi}{2}$, proj$_\mathbf{v}$**u** $= \mathbf{0}$ and scal$_\mathbf{v}$**u** $= 0$.

Using properties of the dot product, $\text{proj}_\mathbf{v}\mathbf{u}$ may be written in different ways:

$$\text{proj}_\mathbf{v}\mathbf{u} = |\mathbf{u}| \cos \theta \left(\frac{\mathbf{v}}{|\mathbf{v}|} \right)$$

$$= \frac{\mathbf{u} \cdot \mathbf{v}}{|\mathbf{v}|} \left(\frac{\mathbf{v}}{|\mathbf{v}|} \right) \qquad |\mathbf{u}| \cos \theta = \frac{|\mathbf{u}||\mathbf{v}| \cos \theta}{|\mathbf{v}|} = \frac{\mathbf{u} \cdot \mathbf{v}}{|\mathbf{v}|}$$

$$= \underbrace{\left(\frac{\mathbf{u} \cdot \mathbf{v}}{\mathbf{v} \cdot \mathbf{v}} \right)}_{\text{scalar}} \mathbf{v}. \qquad \text{Regroup terms; } |\mathbf{v}|^2 = \mathbf{v} \cdot \mathbf{v}$$

QUICK CHECK 3 Let $\mathbf{u} = 4\mathbf{i} - 3\mathbf{j}$. By inspection (not calculations), find the orthogonal projection of $\mathbf{u}$ onto $\mathbf{i}$ and onto $\mathbf{j}$. Find the scalar component of $\mathbf{u}$ in the direction of $\mathbf{i}$ and in the direction of $\mathbf{j}$. ◂

The first two expressions show that $\text{proj}_\mathbf{v}\mathbf{u}$ is a scalar multiple of the unit vector $\dfrac{\mathbf{v}}{|\mathbf{v}|}$, whereas the last expression shows that $\text{proj}_\mathbf{v}\mathbf{u}$ is a scalar multiple of $\mathbf{v}$.

DEFINITION (Orthogonal) Projection of u onto v

The **orthogonal projection of u onto v**, denoted $\text{proj}_\mathbf{v}\mathbf{u}$, where $\mathbf{v} \neq \mathbf{0}$, is

$$\text{proj}_\mathbf{v}\mathbf{u} = |\mathbf{u}| \cos \theta \left(\frac{\mathbf{v}}{|\mathbf{v}|} \right).$$

The orthogonal projection may also be computed with the formulas

$$\text{proj}_\mathbf{v}\mathbf{u} = \text{scal}_\mathbf{v}\mathbf{u} \left(\frac{\mathbf{v}}{|\mathbf{v}|} \right) = \left(\frac{\mathbf{u} \cdot \mathbf{v}}{\mathbf{v} \cdot \mathbf{v}} \right)\mathbf{v},$$

where the **scalar component of u in the direction of v** is

$$\text{scal}_\mathbf{v}\mathbf{u} = |\mathbf{u}| \cos \theta = \frac{\mathbf{u} \cdot \mathbf{v}}{|\mathbf{v}|}.$$

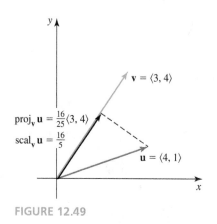

FIGURE 12.49

EXAMPLE 3   Orthogonal projections Find $\text{proj}_\mathbf{v}\mathbf{u}$ and $\text{scal}_\mathbf{v}\mathbf{u}$ for the following vectors and illustrate each result.

a. $\mathbf{u} = \langle 4, 1 \rangle, \mathbf{v} = \langle 3, 4 \rangle$ **b.** $\mathbf{u} = \langle -4, -3 \rangle, \mathbf{v} = \langle 1, -1 \rangle$

SOLUTION

a. The scalar component of $\mathbf{u}$ in the direction of $\mathbf{v}$ (Figure 12.49) is

$$\text{scal}_\mathbf{v}\mathbf{u} = \frac{\mathbf{u} \cdot \mathbf{v}}{|\mathbf{v}|} = \frac{\langle 4, 1 \rangle \cdot \langle 3, 4 \rangle}{|\langle 3, 4 \rangle|} = \frac{16}{5}.$$

Because $\dfrac{\mathbf{v}}{|\mathbf{v}|} = \left\langle \dfrac{3}{5}, \dfrac{4}{5} \right\rangle$, we have

$$\text{proj}_\mathbf{v}\mathbf{u} = \text{scal}_\mathbf{v}\mathbf{u} \left(\frac{\mathbf{v}}{|\mathbf{v}|} \right) = \frac{16}{5} \left\langle \frac{3}{5}, \frac{4}{5} \right\rangle = \frac{16}{25} \langle 3, 4 \rangle.$$

b. Using another formula for $\text{proj}_\mathbf{v}\mathbf{u}$, we have

$$\text{proj}_\mathbf{v}\mathbf{u} = \left(\frac{\mathbf{u} \cdot \mathbf{v}}{\mathbf{v} \cdot \mathbf{v}} \right)\mathbf{v} = \left(\frac{\langle -4, -3 \rangle \cdot \langle 1, -1 \rangle}{\langle 1, -1 \rangle \cdot \langle 1, -1 \rangle} \right) \langle 1, -1 \rangle = -\frac{1}{2} \langle 1, -1 \rangle.$$

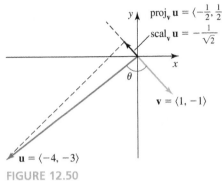

$$\text{proj}_\mathbf{v}\,\mathbf{u} = \langle -\tfrac{1}{2}, \tfrac{1}{2} \rangle$$
$$\text{scal}_\mathbf{v}\,\mathbf{u} = -\tfrac{1}{\sqrt{2}}$$

$$\mathbf{v} = \langle 1, -1 \rangle$$

$$\mathbf{u} = \langle -4, -3 \rangle$$

FIGURE 12.50

The vectors $\mathbf{v}$ and $\text{proj}_\mathbf{v}\mathbf{u}$ point in opposite directions because $\pi/2 < \theta \le \pi$ (Figure 12.50). This fact is reflected in the scalar component of $\mathbf{u}$ in the direction of $\mathbf{v}$, which is negative:

$$\text{scal}_\mathbf{v}\mathbf{u} = \frac{\langle -4, -3 \rangle \cdot \langle 1, -1 \rangle}{|\langle 1, -1 \rangle|} = -\frac{1}{\sqrt{2}}.$$

Related Exercises 25–36 ◄

Applications of Dot Products

Work and Force In the opening of this section, we observed that if a constant force $\mathbf{F}$ acts at an angle θ to the direction of motion of an object (Figure 12.51), the work done by the force is

$$W = |\mathbf{F}| \cos \theta\, |\mathbf{d}| = \mathbf{F} \cdot \mathbf{d}.$$

Notice that the work is a scalar, and if the force acts in a direction orthogonal to the motion, then $\theta = \pi/2$, $\mathbf{F} \cdot \mathbf{d} = 0$, and no work is done by the force.

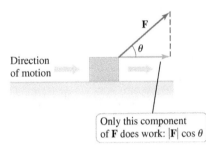

$$\mathbf{F}$$
$$\theta$$

Direction of motion

Only this component of $\mathbf{F}$ does work: $|\mathbf{F}| \cos \theta$

FIGURE 12.51

> If the unit of force is newtons (N) and the distance is measured in meters, then the unit of work is joules (J), where $1\,\text{J} = 1\,\text{N} \cdot \text{m}$. If force is measured in lb and distance is measured in ft, then work has units of ft-lb.

> **DEFINITION Work**
>
> Let a constant force $\mathbf{F}$ be applied to an object, producing a displacement $\mathbf{d}$. If the angle between $\mathbf{F}$ and $\mathbf{d}$ is θ, then the **work** done by the force is
>
> $$W = |\mathbf{F}||\mathbf{d}| \cos \theta = \mathbf{F} \cdot \mathbf{d}.$$

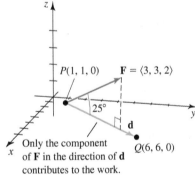

$$P(1, 1, 0) \quad \mathbf{F} = \langle 3, 3, 2 \rangle$$
$$25°$$
$$\mathbf{d}$$
$$Q(6, 6, 0)$$

Only the component of $\mathbf{F}$ in the direction of $\mathbf{d}$ contributes to the work.

FIGURE 12.52

EXAMPLE 4 Calculating work A force $\mathbf{F} = \langle 3, 3, 2 \rangle$ (in newtons) moves an object from $P(1, 1, 0)$ to $Q(6, 6, 0)$ (in meters). What is the work done by the force? Interpret the result.

SOLUTION The displacement of the object is $\mathbf{d} = \overrightarrow{PQ} = \langle 6 - 1, 6 - 1, 0 - 0 \rangle = \langle 5, 5, 0 \rangle$. Therefore, the work done by the force is

$$W = \mathbf{F} \cdot \mathbf{d} = \langle 3, 3, 2 \rangle \cdot \langle 5, 5, 0 \rangle = 30\,\text{J}.$$

To interpret this result, notice that the angle between the force and the displacement vector satisfies

$$\cos \theta = \frac{\mathbf{F} \cdot \mathbf{d}}{|\mathbf{F}||\mathbf{d}|} = \frac{\langle 3, 3, 2 \rangle \cdot \langle 5, 5, 0 \rangle}{|\langle 3, 3, 2 \rangle||\langle 5, 5, 0 \rangle|} = \frac{30}{\sqrt{22}\sqrt{50}} \approx 0.905.$$

Therefore, $\theta \approx 0.44$ rad $\approx 25°$. The magnitude of the force is $|\mathbf{F}| = \sqrt{22} \approx 4.7\,\text{N}$, but only the component of that force in the direction of motion, $|\mathbf{F}|\cos \theta \approx \sqrt{22} \cos 0.44 \approx 4.2\,\text{N}$, contributes to the work (Figure 12.52).

Related Exercises 37–42 ◄

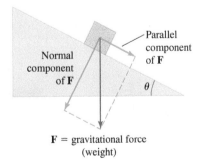

Normal component of $\mathbf{F}$

Parallel component of $\mathbf{F}$

$$\theta$$

$$\mathbf{F} = \text{gravitational force (weight)}$$

FIGURE 12.53

Parallel and Normal Forces Projections find frequent use in expressing a force in terms of orthogonal components. A common situation arises when an object rests on an inclined plane (Figure 12.53). The gravitational force on the object equals its weight, which is directed vertically downward. The projection of the force in the directions **parallel** to and **normal** (or perpendicular) to the plane are of interest. Specifically, the projection of the force parallel to the plane determines the tendency of the object to slide down the plane, while the projection of the force normal to the plane determines its tendency to "stick" to the plane.

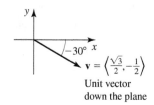

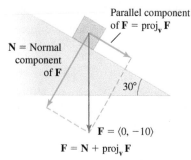

Unit vector
down the plane

Parallel component
of $\mathbf{F}$ = proj$_\mathbf{v}$ $\mathbf{F}$

$\mathbf{N}$ = Normal
component
of $\mathbf{F}$

$30°$

$\mathbf{F} = \langle 0, -10 \rangle$

$\mathbf{F} = \mathbf{N} + \text{proj}_\mathbf{v}\, \mathbf{F}$

FIGURE 12.54

EXAMPLE 5   Components of a force A 10-lb block rests on a plane that is inclined at 30° below the horizontal. Find the components of the gravitational force parallel and normal (perpendicular) to the plane.

SOLUTION The gravitational force $\mathbf{F}$ acting on the block equals the weight of the block (10 lb), which we regard as a point mass. Using the coordinate system shown in Figure 12.54, the force acts in the negative y-direction; therefore, $\mathbf{F} = \langle 0, -10 \rangle$. The direction *down* the plane is given by the unit vector $\mathbf{v} = \langle \cos(-30°), \sin(-30°) \rangle = \langle \frac{\sqrt{3}}{2}, -\frac{1}{2} \rangle$ (check that $|\mathbf{v}| = 1$). The component of the force parallel to the plane is

$$\text{proj}_\mathbf{v}\mathbf{F} = \left(\frac{\mathbf{F} \cdot \mathbf{v}}{\underbrace{\mathbf{v} \cdot \mathbf{v}}_{\mathbf{v}\cdot\mathbf{v} = 1}} \right)\mathbf{v} = \left(\underbrace{\langle 0, -10 \rangle}_{\mathbf{F}} \cdot \underbrace{\left\langle \frac{\sqrt{3}}{2}, -\frac{1}{2} \right\rangle}_{\mathbf{v}} \right)\underbrace{\left\langle \frac{\sqrt{3}}{2}, -\frac{1}{2} \right\rangle}_{\mathbf{v}} = 5\left\langle \frac{\sqrt{3}}{2}, -\frac{1}{2} \right\rangle.$$

Let the component of $\mathbf{F}$ normal to the plane be $\mathbf{N}$. Note that $\mathbf{F} = \text{proj}_\mathbf{v}\mathbf{F} + \mathbf{N}$ so that

$$\mathbf{N} = \mathbf{F} - \text{proj}_\mathbf{v}\mathbf{F} = \langle 0, -10 \rangle - 5\left\langle \frac{\sqrt{3}}{2}, -\frac{1}{2} \right\rangle = \left\langle -\frac{5\sqrt{3}}{2}, -\frac{15}{2} \right\rangle.$$

Figure 12.54 shows how the components of $\mathbf{F}$ parallel and normal to the plane combine to form the total force $\mathbf{F}$.

Related Exercises 43–46 ◄

SECTION 12.3 EXERCISES

Review Questions

1. Define the dot product of $\mathbf{u}$ and $\mathbf{v}$ in terms of their magnitudes and the angle between them.

2. Define the dot product of $\mathbf{u}$ and $\mathbf{v}$ in terms of the components of the vectors.

3. Compute $\langle 2, 3, -6 \rangle \cdot \langle 1, -8, 3 \rangle$.

4. What is the dot product of two orthogonal vectors?

5. Explain how to find the angle between two nonzero vectors.

6. Use a sketch to illustrate the projection of $\mathbf{u}$ onto $\mathbf{v}$.

7. Use a sketch to illustrate the scalar component of $\mathbf{u}$ in the direction of $\mathbf{v}$.

8. Explain how the work done by a force in moving an object is computed using dot products.

Basic Skills

9–12. Dot product from the definition *Consider the following vectors* $\mathbf{u}$ *and* $\mathbf{v}$. *Sketch the vectors, find the angle between the vectors, and compute the dot product using the definition* $\mathbf{u} \cdot \mathbf{v} = |\mathbf{u}||\mathbf{v}| \cos \theta$.

9. $\mathbf{u} = 4\mathbf{i}$ and $\mathbf{v} = 6\mathbf{j}$

10. $\mathbf{u} = \langle -3, 2, 0 \rangle$ and $\mathbf{v} = \langle 0, 0, 6 \rangle$

11. $\mathbf{u} = \langle 10, 0 \rangle$ and $\mathbf{v} = \langle 10, 10 \rangle$

12. $\mathbf{u} = \langle -\sqrt{3}, 1 \rangle$ and $\mathbf{v} = \langle \sqrt{3}, 1 \rangle$

13. **Dot product from the definition** Compute $\mathbf{u} \cdot \mathbf{v}$ if $\mathbf{u}$ and $\mathbf{v}$ are unit vectors and the angle between them is $\pi/3$.

14. **Dot product from the definition** Compute $\mathbf{u} \cdot \mathbf{v}$ if $\mathbf{u}$ is a unit vector, $|\mathbf{v}| = 2$, and the angle between them is $3\pi/4$.

⊞ 15–24. Dot products and angles *Compute the dot product of the vectors* $\mathbf{u}$ *and* $\mathbf{v}$, *and find the angle between the vectors.*

15. $\mathbf{u} = \mathbf{i} + \mathbf{j}$ and $\mathbf{v} = \mathbf{i} - \mathbf{j}$

16. $\mathbf{u} = \langle 10, 0 \rangle$ and $\mathbf{v} = \langle -5, 5 \rangle$

17. $\mathbf{u} = \mathbf{i}$ and $\mathbf{v} = \mathbf{i} + \sqrt{3}\mathbf{j}$

18. $\mathbf{u} = \sqrt{2}\mathbf{i} + \sqrt{2}\mathbf{j}$ and $\mathbf{v} = -\sqrt{2}\mathbf{i} - \sqrt{2}\mathbf{j}$

19. $\mathbf{u} = 4\mathbf{i} + 3\mathbf{j}$ and $\mathbf{v} = 4\mathbf{i} - 6\mathbf{j}$

20. $\mathbf{u} = \langle 3, 4, 0 \rangle$ and $\mathbf{v} = \langle 0, 4, 5 \rangle$

21. $\mathbf{u} = \langle -10, 0, 4 \rangle$ and $\mathbf{v} = \langle 1, 2, 3 \rangle$

22. $\mathbf{u} = \langle 3, -5, 2 \rangle$ and $\mathbf{v} = \langle -9, 5, 1 \rangle$

23. $\mathbf{u} = 2\mathbf{i} - 3\mathbf{k}$ and $\mathbf{v} = \mathbf{i} + 4\mathbf{j} + 2\mathbf{k}$

24. $\mathbf{u} = \mathbf{i} - 4\mathbf{j} - 6\mathbf{k}$ and $\mathbf{v} = 2\mathbf{i} - 4\mathbf{j} + 2\mathbf{k}$

25–28. Sketching orthogonal projections *Find* proj$_\mathbf{v}\mathbf{u}$ *and* scal$_\mathbf{v}\mathbf{u}$ *by inspection without using formulas.*

25.

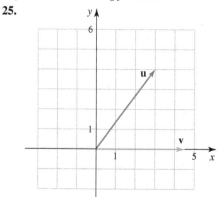

26.

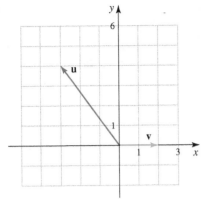

27.

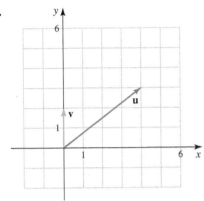

28.

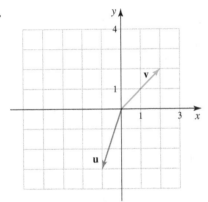

29–36. Calculating orthogonal projections *For the given vectors* **u** *and* **v**, *calculate* proj$_\mathbf{v}$**u** *and* scal$_\mathbf{v}$**u**.

29. $\mathbf{u} = \langle -1, 4 \rangle$ and $\mathbf{v} = \langle -4, 2 \rangle$

30. $\mathbf{u} = \langle 10, 5 \rangle$ and $\mathbf{v} = \langle 2, 6 \rangle$

31. $\mathbf{u} = \langle 3, 3, -3 \rangle$ and $\mathbf{v} = \langle 1, -1, 2 \rangle$

32. $\mathbf{u} = \langle 13, 0, 26 \rangle$ and $\mathbf{v} = \langle 4, -1, -3 \rangle$

33. $\mathbf{u} = \langle -8, 0, 2 \rangle$ and $\mathbf{v} = \langle 1, 3, -3 \rangle$

34. $\mathbf{u} = \langle 5, 0, 15 \rangle$ and $\mathbf{v} = \langle 0, 4, -2 \rangle$

35. $\mathbf{u} = 5\mathbf{i} + \mathbf{j} - 5\mathbf{k}$ and $\mathbf{v} = -\mathbf{i} + \mathbf{j} - 2\mathbf{k}$

36. $\mathbf{u} = \mathbf{i} + 4\mathbf{j} + 7\mathbf{k}$ and $\mathbf{v} = 2\mathbf{i} - 4\mathbf{j} + 2\mathbf{k}$

37–42. Computing work *Calculate the work done in the following situations.*

37. A suitcase is pulled 50 ft along a flat sidewalk with a constant force of 30 lb at an angle of 30° above the horizontal.

38. A stroller is pushed 20 m with a constant force of 10 N at an angle of 15° below the horizontal.

39. A sled is pulled 10 m along flat ground with a constant force of 5 N at an angle of 45° above the horizontal.

40. A constant force $\mathbf{F} = \langle 4, 3, 2 \rangle$ (in newtons) moves an object from $(0, 0, 0)$ to $(8, 6, 0)$. (Distance is measured in meters.)

41. A constant force $\mathbf{F} = \langle 40, 30 \rangle$ (in newtons) is used to move a sled horizontally 10 m.

42. A constant force $\mathbf{F} = \langle 2, 4, 1 \rangle$ (in newtons) moves an object from $(0, 0, 0)$ to $(2, 4, 6)$. (Distance is measured in meters.)

43–46. Parallel and normal forces *Find the components of the vertical force* $\mathbf{F} = \langle 0, -10 \rangle$ *in the directions parallel to and normal to the following planes. Show that the total force is the sum of the two component forces.*

43. A plane that makes an angle of $\pi/4$ with the positive x-axis

44. A plane that makes an angle of $\pi/6$ with the positive x-axis

45. A plane that makes an angle of $\pi/3$ with the positive x-axis

46. A plane that makes an angle of $\theta = \tan^{-1}\left(\frac{4}{5}\right)$ with the positive x-axis

Further Explorations

47. Explain why or why not Determine whether the following statements are true and give an explanation or counterexample.

    a. proj$_\mathbf{v}$**u** = proj$_\mathbf{u}$**v**

    b. If nonzero vectors **u** and **v** have the same magnitude they make equal angles with **u** + **v**.

    c. $(\mathbf{u} \cdot \mathbf{i})^2 + (\mathbf{u} \cdot \mathbf{j})^2 + (\mathbf{u} \cdot \mathbf{k})^2 = |\mathbf{u}|^2$.

    d. If **u** is orthogonal to **v** and **v** is orthogonal to **w**, then **u** is orthogonal to **w**.

    e. The vectors orthogonal to $\langle 1, 1, 1 \rangle$ lie on the same line.

    f. If proj$_\mathbf{v}$**u** = **0**, then vectors **u** and **v** (both nonzero) are orthogonal.

48–52. Orthogonal vectors *Let a and b be real numbers.*

48. Find all unit vectors orthogonal to $\mathbf{v} = \langle 3, 4, 0 \rangle$.

49. Find all vectors $\langle 1, a, b \rangle$ orthogonal to $\langle 4, -8, 2 \rangle$.

50. Describe all unit vectors orthogonal to $\mathbf{v} = \mathbf{i} + \mathbf{j} + \mathbf{k}$.

51. Find three mutually orthogonal unit vectors in $\mathbb{R}^3$ besides $\pm\mathbf{i}$, $\pm\mathbf{j}$, and $\pm\mathbf{k}$.

52. Find two vectors that are orthogonal to $\langle 0, 1, 1 \rangle$ and to each other.

53. Equal angles Consider the set of all unit position vectors $\mathbf{u}$ in $\mathbb{R}^3$ that make a 60° angle with the unit vector $\mathbf{k}$ in $\mathbb{R}^3$.

    a. Prove that $\text{proj}_{\mathbf{k}}\mathbf{u}$ is the same for all vectors in this set.

    b. Is $\text{scal}_{\mathbf{k}}\mathbf{u}$ the same for all vectors in this set?

54–57. Vectors with equal projections *Given a fixed vector* $\mathbf{v}$, *there is an infinite set of vectors* $\mathbf{u}$ *with the same value of* $\text{proj}_{\mathbf{v}}\mathbf{u}$.

54. Find another vector that has the same projection onto $\mathbf{v} = \langle 1, 1 \rangle$ as $\mathbf{u} = \langle 1, 2 \rangle$. Draw a picture.

55. Let $\mathbf{v} = \langle 1, 1 \rangle$. Give a description of the position vectors $\mathbf{u}$ such that $\text{proj}_{\mathbf{v}}\mathbf{u} = \text{proj}_{\mathbf{v}}\langle 1, 2 \rangle$.

56. Find another vector that has the same projection onto $\mathbf{v} = \langle 1, 1, 1 \rangle$ as $\mathbf{u} = \langle 1, 2, 3 \rangle$.

57. Let $\mathbf{v} = \langle 0, 0, 1 \rangle$. Give a description of all position vectors $\mathbf{u}$ such that $\text{proj}_{\mathbf{v}}\mathbf{u} = \text{proj}_{\mathbf{v}}\langle 1, 2, 3 \rangle$.

58–61. Decomposing vectors *For the following vectors* $\mathbf{u}$ *and* $\mathbf{v}$, *express* $\mathbf{u}$ *as the sum* $\mathbf{u} = \mathbf{p} + \mathbf{n}$, *where* $\mathbf{p}$ *is parallel to* $\mathbf{v}$ *and* $\mathbf{n}$ *is orthogonal to* $\mathbf{v}$.

58. $\mathbf{u} = \langle 4, 3 \rangle, \mathbf{v} = \langle 1, 1 \rangle$

59. $\mathbf{u} = \langle -2, 2 \rangle, \mathbf{v} = \langle 2, 1 \rangle$

60. $\mathbf{u} = \langle 4, 3, 0 \rangle, \mathbf{v} = \langle 1, 1, 1 \rangle$

61. $\mathbf{u} = \langle -1, 2, 3 \rangle, \mathbf{v} = \langle 2, 1, 1 \rangle$

62–65. Distance between a point and a line *Carry out the following steps to determine the (smallest) distance between the point* P *and the line* ℓ *through the origin.*

    a. *Find any vector* $\mathbf{v}$ *in the direction of* ℓ.

    b. *Find the position vector* $\mathbf{u}$ *corresponding to* P.

    c. *Find* $\text{proj}_{\mathbf{v}}\mathbf{u}$.

    d. *Show that* $\mathbf{w} = \mathbf{u} - \text{proj}_{\mathbf{v}}\mathbf{u}$ *is a vector orthogonal to* $\mathbf{v}$ *whose length is the distance between* P *and the line* ℓ.

    e. *Find* $\mathbf{w}$ *and* $|\mathbf{w}|$. *Explain why* $|\mathbf{w}|$ *is the distance between* P *and* ℓ.

62. $P(2, -5)$; $\ell: y = 3x$

63. $P(-12, 4)$; $\ell: y = 2x$

64. $P(0, 2, 6)$; ℓ has the direction of $\langle 3, 0, -4 \rangle$.

65. $P(1, 1, -1)$; ℓ has the direction of $\langle -6, 8, 3 \rangle$.

66–68. Orthogonal unit vectors in $\mathbb{R}^2$ *Consider the vectors* $\mathbf{I} = \langle 1/\sqrt{2}, 1/\sqrt{2} \rangle$ *and* $\mathbf{J} = \langle -1/\sqrt{2}, 1/\sqrt{2} \rangle$.

66. Show that $\mathbf{I}$ and $\mathbf{J}$ are orthogonal unit vectors.

67. Express $\mathbf{I}$ and $\mathbf{J}$ in terms of the usual unit coordinate vectors $\mathbf{i}$ and $\mathbf{j}$. Then, write $\mathbf{i}$ and $\mathbf{j}$ in terms of $\mathbf{I}$ and $\mathbf{J}$.

68. Write the vector $\langle 2, -6 \rangle$ in terms of $\mathbf{I}$ and $\mathbf{J}$.

69. Orthogonal unit vectors in $\mathbb{R}^3$ Consider the vectors $\mathbf{I} = \langle 1/2, 1/2, 1/\sqrt{2} \rangle$, $\mathbf{J} = \langle -1/\sqrt{2}, 1/\sqrt{2}, 0 \rangle$, and $\mathbf{K} = \langle 1/2, 1/2, -1/\sqrt{2} \rangle$.

    a. Sketch $\mathbf{I}$, $\mathbf{J}$, and $\mathbf{K}$ and show that they are unit vectors.

    b. Show that $\mathbf{I}$, $\mathbf{J}$, and $\mathbf{K}$ are pairwise orthogonal.

    c. Express the vector $\langle 1, 0, 0 \rangle$ in terms of $\mathbf{I}$, $\mathbf{J}$, and $\mathbf{K}$.

70–71. Angles of a triangle *For the given points P, Q, and R, find the approximate measurements of the angles of* $\triangle PQR$.

70. $P(1, -4), Q(2, 7), R(-2, 2)$

71. $P(0, -1, 3), Q(2, 2, 1), R(-2, 2, 4)$

Applications

72. Flow through a circle Suppose water flows in a thin sheet over the xy-plane with a uniform velocity given by the vector $\mathbf{v} = \langle 1, 2 \rangle$; this means that at all points of the plane, the velocity of the water has components 1 m/s in the x-direction and 2 m/s in the y-direction (see figure). Let C be an imaginary unit circle (that does not interfere with the flow).

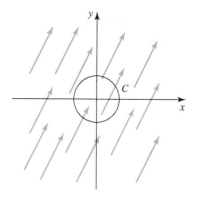

    a. Show that at the point (x, y) on the circle C the outward-pointing unit vector normal to C is $\mathbf{n} = \langle x, y \rangle$.

    b. Show that at the point $(\cos \theta, \sin \theta)$ on the circle C the outward-pointing unit vector normal to C is also $\mathbf{n} = \langle \cos \theta, \sin \theta \rangle$.

    c. Find all points on C at which the velocity is normal to C.

    d. Find all points on C at which the velocity is tangential to C.

    e. At each point on C find the component of $\mathbf{v}$ normal to C. Express the answer as a function of (x, y) and as a function of θ.

    f. What is the net flow through the circle? That is, does water accumulate inside the circle?

73. Heat flux Let D be a solid heat-conducting cube formed by the planes $x = 0$, $x = 1$, $y = 0$, $y = 1$, $z = 0$, and $z = 1$. The heat flow at every point of D is given by the constant vector $\mathbf{Q} = \langle 0, 2, 1 \rangle$.

    a. Through which faces of D does $\mathbf{Q}$ point into D?

    b. Through which faces of D does $\mathbf{Q}$ point out of D?

    c. On which faces of D is $\mathbf{Q}$ tangential to D (pointing neither in nor out of D)?

    d. Find the scalar component of $\mathbf{Q}$ normal to the face $x = 0$.

    e. Find the scalar component of $\mathbf{Q}$ normal to the face $z = 1$.

    f. Find the scalar component of $\mathbf{Q}$ normal to the face $y = 0$.

74. Hexagonal circle packing The German mathematician Gauss proved that the densest way to pack circles with the same radius in the plane is to place the centers of the circles on a hexagonal grid (see figure). Some molecular structures use this packing or its three-dimensional analog. Assume all circles have a radius of 1 and let $\mathbf{r}_{ij}$ be the vector that extends from the center of circle i to the center of circle j, for $i, j = 0, 1, \ldots, 6$.

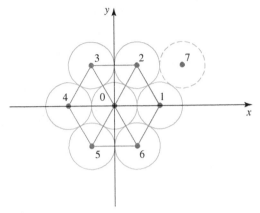

a. Find $\mathbf{r}_{0j}$, for $j = 1, 2, \ldots, 6$.

b. Find $\mathbf{r}_{12}$, $\mathbf{r}_{34}$, and $\mathbf{r}_{61}$.

c. Imagine circle 7 is added to the arrangement as shown in the figure. Find $\mathbf{r}_{07}$, $\mathbf{r}_{17}$, $\mathbf{r}_{47}$, and $\mathbf{r}_{75}$.

75. Hexagonal sphere packing Imagine three unit spheres (radius equal to 1) with centers at $O(0, 0, 0)$, $P(\sqrt{3}, -1, 0)$, and $Q(\sqrt{3}, 1, 0)$. Now place another unit sphere symmetrically on top of these spheres with its center at R (see figure).

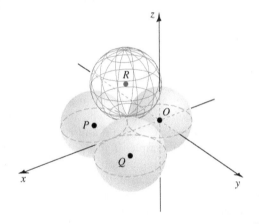

a. Find the coordinates of R. (*Hint:* The distance between the centers of any two spheres is 2.)

b. Let $\mathbf{r}_{ij}$ be the vector from the center of sphere i to the center of sphere j. Find $\mathbf{r}_{OP}$, $\mathbf{r}_{OQ}$, $\mathbf{r}_{PQ}$, $\mathbf{r}_{OR}$, and $\mathbf{r}_{PR}$.

Additional Exercises

76–80. Properties of dot products *Let* $\mathbf{u} = \langle u_1, u_2, u_3 \rangle$, $\mathbf{v} = \langle v_1, v_2, v_3 \rangle$, *and* $\mathbf{w} = \langle w_1, w_2, w_3 \rangle$. *Let c be a scalar. Prove the following vector properties.*

76. $|\mathbf{u} \cdot \mathbf{v}| \le |\mathbf{u}||\mathbf{v}|$

77. $\mathbf{u} \cdot \mathbf{v} = \mathbf{v} \cdot \mathbf{u}$ Commutative property

78. $c(\mathbf{u} \cdot \mathbf{v}) = (c\mathbf{u}) \cdot \mathbf{v} = \mathbf{u} \cdot (c\mathbf{v})$ Associative property

79. $\mathbf{u} \cdot (\mathbf{v} + \mathbf{w}) = \mathbf{u} \cdot \mathbf{v} + \mathbf{u} \cdot \mathbf{w}$ Distributive property

80. Distributive properties

a. Show that $(\mathbf{u} + \mathbf{v}) \cdot (\mathbf{u} + \mathbf{v}) = |\mathbf{u}|^2 + 2\mathbf{u} \cdot \mathbf{v} + |\mathbf{v}|^2$.

b. Show that $(\mathbf{u} + \mathbf{v}) \cdot (\mathbf{u} + \mathbf{v}) = |\mathbf{u}|^2 + |\mathbf{v}|^2$ if $\mathbf{u}$ is perpendicular to $\mathbf{v}$.

c. Show that $(\mathbf{u} + \mathbf{v}) \cdot (\mathbf{u} - \mathbf{v}) = |\mathbf{u}|^2 - |\mathbf{v}|^2$.

81. Prove or disprove For fixed values of a, b, c, and d, the value of $\text{proj}_{\langle ka, kb \rangle} \langle c, d \rangle$ is constant for all nonzero values of k, for $\langle a, b \rangle \neq \langle 0, 0 \rangle$.

82. Orthogonal lines Recall that two lines $y = mx + b$ and $y = nx + c$ are orthogonal provided $mn = -1$ (the slopes are negative reciprocals of each other). Prove that the condition $mn = -1$ is equivalent to the orthogonality condition $\mathbf{u} \cdot \mathbf{v} = 0$, where $\mathbf{u}$ points in the direction of one line and $\mathbf{v}$ points in the direction of the other line.

83. Direction angles and cosines Let $\mathbf{v} = \langle a, b, c \rangle$ and let α, β, and γ be the angles between $\mathbf{v}$ and the positive x-axis, the positive y-axis, and the positive z-axis, respectively (see figure).

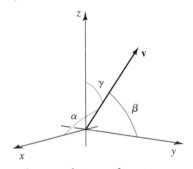

a. Prove that $\cos^2 \alpha + \cos^2 \beta + \cos^2 \gamma = 1$.

b. Find a vector that makes a $45°$ angle with $\mathbf{i}$ and $\mathbf{j}$. What angle does it make with $\mathbf{k}$?

c. Find a vector that makes a $60°$ angle with $\mathbf{i}$ and $\mathbf{j}$. What angle does it make with $\mathbf{k}$?

d. Is there a vector that makes a $30°$ angle with $\mathbf{i}$ and $\mathbf{j}$? Explain.

e. Find a vector $\mathbf{v}$ such that $\alpha = \beta = \gamma$. What is the angle?

84–88. Cauchy–Schwarz Inequality *The definition* $\mathbf{u} \cdot \mathbf{v} = |\mathbf{u}||\mathbf{v}| \cos \theta$ *implies that* $|\mathbf{u} \cdot \mathbf{v}| \le |\mathbf{u}||\mathbf{v}|$ *(because* $|\cos \theta| \le 1$*). This inequality, known as the Cauchy–Schwarz Inequality, holds in any number of dimensions and has many consequences.*

84. What conditions on $\mathbf{u}$ and $\mathbf{v}$ lead to equality in the Cauchy–Schwarz Inequality?

85. Verify that the Cauchy–Schwarz Inequality holds for $\mathbf{u} = \langle 3, -5, 6 \rangle$ and $\mathbf{v} = \langle -8, 3, 1 \rangle$.

86. Geometric-arithmetic mean Use the vectors $\mathbf{u} = \langle \sqrt{a}, \sqrt{b} \rangle$ and $\mathbf{v} = \langle \sqrt{b}, \sqrt{a} \rangle$ to show that $\sqrt{ab} \le (a + b)/2$, where $a \ge 0$ and $b \ge 0$.

87. Triangle Inequality Consider the vectors $\mathbf{u}$, $\mathbf{v}$, and $\mathbf{u} + \mathbf{v}$ (in any number of dimensions). Use the following steps to prove that $|\mathbf{u} + \mathbf{v}| \le |\mathbf{u}| + |\mathbf{v}|$.

a. Show that $|\mathbf{u} + \mathbf{v}|^2 = (\mathbf{u} + \mathbf{v}) \cdot (\mathbf{u} + \mathbf{v}) = |\mathbf{u}|^2 + 2\mathbf{u} \cdot \mathbf{v} + |\mathbf{v}|^2$.

b. Use the Cauchy–Schwarz Inequality to show that $|\mathbf{u} + \mathbf{v}|^2 \le (|\mathbf{u}| + |\mathbf{v}|)^2$.

c. Conclude that $|\mathbf{u} + \mathbf{v}| \le |\mathbf{u}| + |\mathbf{v}|$.

d. Interpret the Triangle Inequality geometrically in $\mathbb{R}^2$ or $\mathbb{R}^3$.

88. Algebra inequality Show that for real numbers u_1, u_2, and u_3, it is true that

$$(u_1 + u_2 + u_3)^2 \le 3(u_1^2 + u_2^2 + u_3^2).$$

(*Hint:* Use the Cauchy–Schwarz Inequality in three dimensions with $\mathbf{u} = \langle u_1, u_2, u_3 \rangle$ and choose $\mathbf{v}$ in the right way.)

89. Diagonals of a parallelogram Consider the parallelogram with adjacent sides $\mathbf{u}$ and $\mathbf{v}$.

a. Show that the diagonals of the parallelogram are $\mathbf{u} + \mathbf{v}$ and $\mathbf{u} - \mathbf{v}$.

b. Prove that the diagonals have the same length if and only if $\mathbf{u} \cdot \mathbf{v} = 0$.

c. Show that the sum of the squares of the lengths of the diagonals equals the sum of the squares of the lengths of the sides.

90. Distance between a point and a line in the plane Use projections to find a general formula for the (smallest) distance between the point $P(x_0, y_0)$ and the line $ax + by = c$. (See Exercises 62–65.)

QUICK CHECK ANSWERS

1. If $\theta = 0$, $\mathbf{u}$ and $\mathbf{v}$ are parallel and point in the same direction. If $\theta = \pi$, $\mathbf{u}$ and $\mathbf{v}$ are parallel and point in opposite directions.   **2.** All these dot products are zero, and the unit vectors are mutually orthogonal. The angle between two different unit vectors is $\pi/2$.   **3.** $\text{proj}_\mathbf{i}\mathbf{u} = 4\mathbf{i}$, $\text{proj}_\mathbf{j}\mathbf{u} = -3\mathbf{j}$, $\text{scal}_\mathbf{i}\mathbf{u} = 4$, $\text{scal}_\mathbf{j}\mathbf{u} = -3$. ◄

12.4 Cross Products

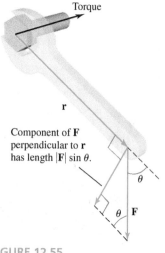

FIGURE 12.55

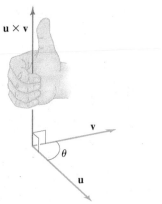

FIGURE 12.56

The dot product combines two vectors to produce a *scalar* result. There is an equally fundamental way to combine two vectors in $\mathbb{R}^3$ and obtain a *vector* result. This operation, known as the *cross product* (or *vector product*) may be motivated by a physical application.

Suppose you want to loosen a bolt with a wrench. As you apply force to the end of the wrench in the plane perpendicular to the bolt, the "twisting power" you generate depends on three variables:

• the magnitude of the force $\mathbf{F}$ applied to the wrench;

• the length $|\mathbf{r}|$ of the wrench;

• the angle at which the force is applied to the wrench.

The twisting generated by a force acting at a distance from a pivot point is called **torque** (from the Latin *to twist*). The torque is a vector whose magnitude is proportional to $|\mathbf{F}|$, $|\mathbf{r}|$, and $\sin\theta$, where θ is the angle between $\mathbf{F}$ and $\mathbf{r}$ (Figure 12.55). If the force is applied parallel to the wrench—for example, if you pull the wrench ($\theta = 0$) or push the wrench ($\theta = \pi$)—there is no twisting effect; if the force is applied perpendicular to the wrench ($\theta = \pi/2$), the twisting effect is maximized. The direction of the torque vector is defined to be orthogonal to both $\mathbf{F}$ and $\mathbf{r}$. As we will see shortly, the torque is expressed in terms of the cross product of $\mathbf{F}$ and $\mathbf{r}$.

The Cross Product

The preceding physical example leads to the following definition of the cross product.

DEFINITION Cross Product

Given two nonzero vectors $\mathbf{u}$ and $\mathbf{v}$ in $\mathbb{R}^3$, the **cross product** $\mathbf{u} \times \mathbf{v}$ is a vector with magnitude

$$|\mathbf{u} \times \mathbf{v}| = |\mathbf{u}||\mathbf{v}| \sin\theta,$$

where $0 \le \theta \le \pi$ is the angle between $\mathbf{u}$ and $\mathbf{v}$. The direction of $\mathbf{u} \times \mathbf{v}$ is given by the **right-hand rule**: When you put the vectors tail to tail and let the fingers of your right hand curl from $\mathbf{u}$ to $\mathbf{v}$, the direction of $\mathbf{u} \times \mathbf{v}$ is the direction of your thumb, orthogonal to both $\mathbf{u}$ and $\mathbf{v}$ (Figure 12.56). When $\mathbf{u} \times \mathbf{v} = \mathbf{0}$, the direction of $\mathbf{u} \times \mathbf{v}$ is undefined.

Sketch the vectors $\mathbf{u} = \langle 1, 2, 0 \rangle$ and $\mathbf{v} = \langle -1, 2, 0 \rangle$. Which way does $\mathbf{u} \times \mathbf{v}$ point? Which way does $\mathbf{v} \times \mathbf{u}$ point?

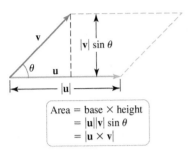

Area = base × height
$= |\mathbf{u}||\mathbf{v}| \sin \theta$
$= |\mathbf{u} \times \mathbf{v}|$

FIGURE 12.57

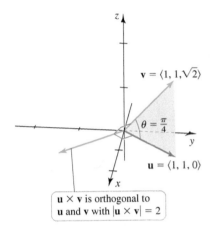

$\mathbf{u} \times \mathbf{v}$ is orthogonal to $\mathbf{u}$ and $\mathbf{v}$ with $|\mathbf{u} \times \mathbf{v}| = 2$

FIGURE 12.58

Explain why the vector $2\mathbf{u} \times 3\mathbf{v}$ points in the same direction as $\mathbf{u} \times \mathbf{v}$.

The following theorem is a consequence of the definition of the cross product.

> **THEOREM 12.3   Geometry of the Cross Product**
> Let $\mathbf{u}$ and $\mathbf{v}$ be two nonzero vectors in $\mathbb{R}^3$.
>
> 1. The vectors $\mathbf{u}$ and $\mathbf{v}$ are parallel ($\theta = 0$ or $\theta = \pi$) if and only if $\mathbf{u} \times \mathbf{v} = \mathbf{0}$.
>
> 2. If $\mathbf{u}$ and $\mathbf{v}$ are two sides of a parallelogram (Figure 12.57), then the area of the parallelogram is
> $$|\mathbf{u} \times \mathbf{v}| = |\mathbf{u}||\mathbf{v}| \sin \theta.$$

EXAMPLE 1   A cross product Find the magnitude and direction of $\mathbf{u} \times \mathbf{v}$, where $\mathbf{u} = \langle 1, 1, 0 \rangle$ and $\mathbf{v} = \langle 1, 1, \sqrt{2} \rangle$.

SOLUTION Because $\mathbf{u}$ is one side of a 45–45–90 triangle and $\mathbf{v}$ is the hypotenuse (Figure 12.58), we have $\theta = \pi/4$ and $\sin \theta = \frac{1}{\sqrt{2}}$. Also, $|\mathbf{u}| = \sqrt{2}$ and $|\mathbf{v}| = 2$, so the magnitude of $\mathbf{u} \times \mathbf{v}$ is

$$|\mathbf{u} \times \mathbf{v}| = |\mathbf{u}||\mathbf{v}| \sin \theta = \sqrt{2} \cdot 2 \cdot \frac{1}{\sqrt{2}} = 2.$$

The direction of $\mathbf{u} \times \mathbf{v}$ is given by the right-hand rule: $\mathbf{u} \times \mathbf{v}$ is orthogonal to $\mathbf{u}$ and $\mathbf{v}$ (Figure 12.58).

Related Exercises 7–14 ◄

Properties of the Cross Product

The cross product has several algebraic properties that simplify calculations. For example, scalars factor out of a cross product; that is, if a and b are scalars, then (Exercise 69)

$$(a\mathbf{u}) \times (b\mathbf{v}) = ab(\mathbf{u} \times \mathbf{v}).$$

The order in which the cross product is performed is important. The magnitudes of $\mathbf{u} \times \mathbf{v}$ and $\mathbf{v} \times \mathbf{u}$ are equal. However, applying the right-hand rule shows that $\mathbf{u} \times \mathbf{v}$ and $\mathbf{v} \times \mathbf{u}$ point in opposite directions. Therefore, $\mathbf{u} \times \mathbf{v} = -(\mathbf{v} \times \mathbf{u})$. There are two distributive properties for the cross product, whose proofs are omitted.

> **THEOREM 12.4   Properties of the Cross Product**
> Let $\mathbf{u}$, $\mathbf{v}$, and $\mathbf{w}$ be nonzero vectors in $\mathbb{R}^3$, and let a and b be scalars.
>
> 1. $\mathbf{u} \times \mathbf{v} = -(\mathbf{v} \times \mathbf{u})$ Anticommutative property
> 2. $(a\mathbf{u}) \times (b\mathbf{v}) = ab(\mathbf{u} \times \mathbf{v})$ Associative property
> 3. $\mathbf{u} \times (\mathbf{v} + \mathbf{w}) = (\mathbf{u} \times \mathbf{v}) + (\mathbf{u} \times \mathbf{w})$ Distributive property
> 4. $(\mathbf{u} + \mathbf{v}) \times \mathbf{w} = (\mathbf{u} \times \mathbf{w}) + (\mathbf{v} \times \mathbf{w})$ Distributive property

EXAMPLE 2   Cross products of unit vectors Evaluate all the cross products among the coordinate unit vectors $\mathbf{i}$, $\mathbf{j}$, and $\mathbf{k}$.

SOLUTION These vectors are mutually orthogonal, which means the angle between any two distinct vectors is $\theta = \pi/2$ and $\sin \theta = 1$. Furthermore, $|\mathbf{i}| = |\mathbf{j}| = |\mathbf{k}| = 1$. Therefore, the cross product of any two distinct vectors has magnitude 1. By the right-hand rule, when the fingers of the right hand curl from $\mathbf{i}$ to $\mathbf{j}$, the thumb points in the direction of the positive z-axis (Figure 12.59). The unit vector in the positive z-direction is $\mathbf{k}$, so $\mathbf{i} \times \mathbf{j} = \mathbf{k}$. Similar calculations show that $\mathbf{j} \times \mathbf{k} = \mathbf{i}$ and $\mathbf{k} \times \mathbf{i} = \mathbf{j}$.

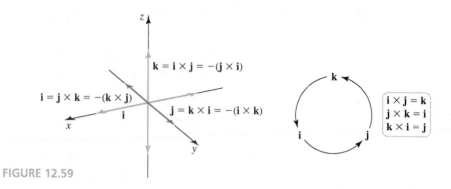

FIGURE 12.59

By property 1 of Theorem 12.4, $\mathbf{j} \times \mathbf{i} = -(\mathbf{i} \times \mathbf{j}) = -\mathbf{k}$, so $\mathbf{j} \times \mathbf{i}$ and $\mathbf{i} \times \mathbf{j}$ point in opposite directions. Similarly, $\mathbf{k} \times \mathbf{j} = -\mathbf{i}$ and $\mathbf{i} \times \mathbf{k} = -\mathbf{j}$. These relationships are easily remembered with a circle diagram (Figure 12.59). Finally, the angle between any unit vector and itself is $\theta = 0$. Therefore, $\mathbf{i} \times \mathbf{i} = \mathbf{j} \times \mathbf{j} = \mathbf{k} \times \mathbf{k} = \mathbf{0}$.

Related Exercises 15–20 ◀

THEOREM 12.5   Cross Products of Coordinate Unit Vectors

$$\mathbf{i} \times \mathbf{j} = -(\mathbf{j} \times \mathbf{i}) = \mathbf{k} \qquad \mathbf{j} \times \mathbf{k} = -(\mathbf{k} \times \mathbf{j}) = \mathbf{i}$$
$$\mathbf{k} \times \mathbf{i} = -(\mathbf{i} \times \mathbf{k}) = \mathbf{j} \qquad \mathbf{i} \times \mathbf{i} = \mathbf{j} \times \mathbf{j} = \mathbf{k} \times \mathbf{k} = \mathbf{0}$$

What is missing so far is a method for finding the components of the cross product of two vectors in $\mathbb{R}^3$. Let $\mathbf{u} = u_1\mathbf{i} + u_2\mathbf{j} + u_3\mathbf{k}$ and $\mathbf{v} = v_1\mathbf{i} + v_2\mathbf{j} + v_3\mathbf{k}$. Using the distributive properties of the cross product (Theorem 12.4) we have

$$\mathbf{u} \times \mathbf{v} = (u_1\mathbf{i} + u_2\mathbf{j} + u_3\mathbf{k}) \times (v_1\mathbf{i} + v_2\mathbf{j} + v_3\mathbf{k})$$
$$= u_1v_1\underbrace{(\mathbf{i} \times \mathbf{i})}_{\mathbf{0}} + u_1v_2\underbrace{(\mathbf{i} \times \mathbf{j})}_{\mathbf{k}} + u_1v_3\underbrace{(\mathbf{i} \times \mathbf{k})}_{-\mathbf{j}}$$
$$+ u_2v_1\underbrace{(\mathbf{j} \times \mathbf{i})}_{-\mathbf{k}} + u_2v_2\underbrace{(\mathbf{j} \times \mathbf{j})}_{\mathbf{0}} + u_2v_3\underbrace{(\mathbf{j} \times \mathbf{k})}_{\mathbf{i}}$$
$$+ u_3v_1\underbrace{(\mathbf{k} \times \mathbf{i})}_{\mathbf{j}} + u_3v_2\underbrace{(\mathbf{k} \times \mathbf{j})}_{-\mathbf{i}} + u_3v_3\underbrace{(\mathbf{k} \times \mathbf{k})}_{\mathbf{0}}.$$

> The determinant of the matrix A is denoted both $|A|$ and det A. The formula for the determinant of A is
>
> $$\begin{vmatrix} a_1\, a_2\, a_3 \\ b_1\, b_2\, b_3 \\ c_1\, c_2\, c_3 \end{vmatrix} = a_1\begin{vmatrix} b_2\, b_3 \\ c_2\, c_3 \end{vmatrix} - a_2\begin{vmatrix} b_1\, b_3 \\ c_1\, c_3 \end{vmatrix}$$
> $$+ a_3\begin{vmatrix} b_1\, b_2 \\ c_1\, c_2 \end{vmatrix},$$
>
> where
>
> $$\begin{vmatrix} a & b \\ c & d \end{vmatrix} = ad - bc.$$

This formula looks impossible to remember until we see that it fits the pattern used to evaluate 3×3 determinants. Specifically, if we compute the determinant of the matrix

$$\begin{matrix} \text{Unit vectors} & \to \\ \text{Components of } \mathbf{u} & \to \\ \text{Components of } \mathbf{v} & \to \end{matrix} \begin{pmatrix} \mathbf{i} & \mathbf{j} & \mathbf{k} \\ u_1 & u_2 & u_3 \\ v_1 & v_2 & v_3 \end{pmatrix}$$

(expanding about the first row), the following formula for the cross product emerges (see margin note).

THEOREM 12.6   Evaluating the Cross Product

Let $\mathbf{u} = u_1\mathbf{i} + u_2\mathbf{j} + u_3\mathbf{k}$ and $\mathbf{v} = v_1\mathbf{i} + v_2\mathbf{j} + v_3\mathbf{k}$. Then

$$\mathbf{u} \times \mathbf{v} = \begin{vmatrix} \mathbf{i} & \mathbf{j} & \mathbf{k} \\ u_1 & u_2 & u_3 \\ v_1 & v_2 & v_3 \end{vmatrix} = \begin{vmatrix} u_2 & u_3 \\ v_2 & v_3 \end{vmatrix}\mathbf{i} - \begin{vmatrix} u_1 & u_3 \\ v_1 & v_3 \end{vmatrix}\mathbf{j} + \begin{vmatrix} u_1 & u_2 \\ v_1 & v_2 \end{vmatrix}\mathbf{k}.$$

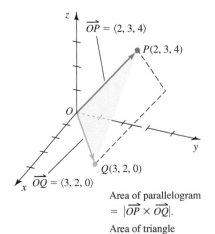

Area of parallelogram
= $|\overrightarrow{OP} \times \overrightarrow{OQ}|$.

Area of triangle
= $\frac{1}{2}|\overrightarrow{OP} \times \overrightarrow{OQ}|$.

FIGURE 12.60

EXAMPLE 3 **Area of a triangle** Find the area of the triangle with vertices $O(0, 0, 0)$, $P(2, 3, 4)$, and $Q(3, 2, 0)$ (Figure 12.60).

SOLUTION First consider the parallelogram, two of whose sides are the vectors $\overrightarrow{OP}$ and $\overrightarrow{OQ}$. By Theorem 12.3, the area of this parallelogram is $|\overrightarrow{OP} \times \overrightarrow{OQ}|$. Computing the cross product, we find that

$$\overrightarrow{OP} \times \overrightarrow{OQ} = \begin{vmatrix} \mathbf{i} & \mathbf{j} & \mathbf{k} \\ 2 & 3 & 4 \\ 3 & 2 & 0 \end{vmatrix} = \begin{vmatrix} 3 & 4 \\ 2 & 0 \end{vmatrix}\mathbf{i} - \begin{vmatrix} 2 & 4 \\ 3 & 0 \end{vmatrix}\mathbf{j} + \begin{vmatrix} 2 & 3 \\ 3 & 2 \end{vmatrix}\mathbf{k}$$

$$= -8\mathbf{i} + 12\mathbf{j} - 5\mathbf{k}.$$

Therefore, the area of the parallelogram is

$$|\overrightarrow{OP} \times \overrightarrow{OQ}| = |-8\mathbf{i} + 12\mathbf{j} - 5\mathbf{k}| = \sqrt{233} \approx 15.26.$$

The triangle with vertices O, P, and Q comprises half of the parallelogram, so its area is $\sqrt{233}/2 \approx 7.63$.

Related Exercises 21–34 ◄

EXAMPLE 4 **Vector normal to two vectors** Find a vector normal (or orthogonal) to the two vectors $\mathbf{u} = -\mathbf{i} + 6\mathbf{k}$ and $\mathbf{v} = 2\mathbf{i} - 5\mathbf{j} - 3\mathbf{k}$.

SOLUTION A vector normal to $\mathbf{u}$ and $\mathbf{v}$ is parallel to $\mathbf{u} \times \mathbf{v}$ (Figure 12.61). One normal vector is

$$\mathbf{u} \times \mathbf{v} = \begin{vmatrix} \mathbf{i} & \mathbf{j} & \mathbf{k} \\ -1 & 0 & 6 \\ 2 & -5 & -3 \end{vmatrix}$$

$$= (0 + 30)\mathbf{i} - (3 - 12)\mathbf{j} + (5 - 0)\mathbf{k}$$

$$= 30\mathbf{i} + 9\mathbf{j} + 5\mathbf{k}.$$

Any scalar multiple of this vector is also orthogonal to $\mathbf{u}$ and $\mathbf{v}$.

Related Exercises 35–38 ◄

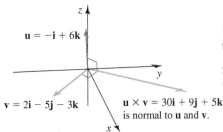

FIGURE 12.61

QUICK CHECK 3 A good check on a cross product calculation is to verify that $\mathbf{u}$ and $\mathbf{v}$ are orthogonal to the computed $\mathbf{u} \times \mathbf{v}$. In Example 4, verify that $\mathbf{u} \cdot (\mathbf{u} \times \mathbf{v}) = 0$ and $\mathbf{v} \cdot (\mathbf{u} \times \mathbf{v}) = 0$. ◄

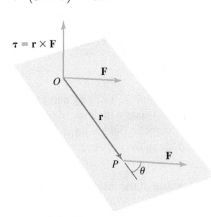

FIGURE 12.62

Applications of the Cross Product

We now investigate two physical applications of the cross product.

Torque Returning to the example of applying a force to a wrench, suppose a force $\mathbf{F}$ is applied to the point P at the head of a vector $\mathbf{r} = \overrightarrow{OP}$ (Figure 12.62). The **torque**, or twisting effect, produced by the force about the point O is given by $\boldsymbol{\tau} = \mathbf{r} \times \mathbf{F}$. The torque vector has a magnitude of

$$|\boldsymbol{\tau}| = |\mathbf{r} \times \mathbf{F}| = |\mathbf{r}||\mathbf{F}| \sin \theta,$$

where θ is the angle between $\mathbf{r}$ and $\mathbf{F}$. The direction of the torque is given by the right-hand rule; it is orthogonal to both $\mathbf{r}$ and $\mathbf{F}$. As noted earlier, if $\mathbf{r}$ and $\mathbf{F}$ are parallel then $\sin \theta = 0$ and the torque is zero. For a given $\mathbf{r}$ and $\mathbf{F}$, the maximum torque occurs when $\mathbf{F}$ is applied in a direction orthogonal to $\mathbf{r}$ ($\theta = \pi/2$).

EXAMPLE 5 **Tightening a bolt** Suppose you apply a force of 20 N to a wrench attached to a bolt in a direction perpendicular to the bolt (Figure 12.63). Which produces more torque: applying the force at an angle of 60° on a wrench that is 0.15 m long or applying the force at an angle of 135° on a wrench that is 0.25 m long? In each case, what is the direction of the torque?

When standard threads are added to the bolt in Figure 12.63, the forces used in Example 5 cause the bolt to move upward into a nut—in the direction of the torque.

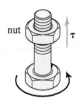

nut

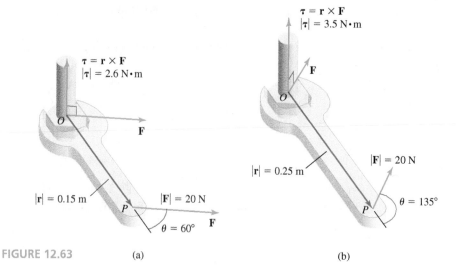

$\boldsymbol{\tau} = \mathbf{r} \times \mathbf{F}$
$|\boldsymbol{\tau}| = 2.6 \text{ N} \cdot \text{m}$

O

$\mathbf{F}$

$|\mathbf{r}| = 0.15 \text{ m}$

$|\mathbf{F}| = 20 \text{ N}$

P

$\theta = 60°$ $\mathbf{F}$

$\boldsymbol{\tau} = \mathbf{r} \times \mathbf{F}$
$|\boldsymbol{\tau}| = 3.5 \text{ N} \cdot \text{m}$

$\mathbf{F}$

O

$|\mathbf{F}| = 20 \text{ N}$

$|\mathbf{r}| = 0.25 \text{ m}$

$\theta = 135°$

P

FIGURE 12.63   (a)   (b)

SOLUTION The magnitude of the torque in the first case is

$$|\boldsymbol{\tau}| = |\mathbf{r}||\mathbf{F}| \sin \theta = (0.15 \text{ m})(20 \text{ N}) \sin 60° \approx 2.6 \text{ N} \cdot \text{m}.$$

In the second case, the magnitude of the torque is

$$|\boldsymbol{\tau}| = |\mathbf{r}||\mathbf{F}| \sin \theta = (0.25 \text{ m})(20 \text{ N}) \sin 135° \approx 3.5 \text{ N} \cdot \text{m}.$$

The second instance gives the greater torque. In both cases, the torque is orthogonal to $\mathbf{r}$ and $\mathbf{F}$, parallel to the shaft of the bolt (Figure 12.63).

Related Exercises 39–44 ◄

Magnetic Force on a Moving Charge   Moving electric charges (either isolated charges or a current in a wire) experience a force when they pass through a magnetic field. For an isolated charge q, the force is given by $\mathbf{F} = q(\mathbf{v} \times \mathbf{B})$, where $\mathbf{v}$ is the velocity of the charge and $\mathbf{B}$ is the magnetic field. The magnitude of the force is

$$|\mathbf{F}| = |q||\mathbf{v} \times \mathbf{B}| = |q||\mathbf{v}||\mathbf{B}| \sin \theta,$$

where θ is the angle between $\mathbf{v}$ and $\mathbf{B}$ (Figure 12.64). Note that the sign of the charge also determines the direction of the force. If the velocity vector is parallel to the magnetic field, the charge experiences no force. The maximum force occurs when the velocity is orthogonal to the magnetic field.

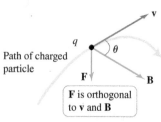

Path of charged particle

q θ $\mathbf{v}$

$\mathbf{F}$ $\mathbf{B}$

F is orthogonal to **v** and **B**

FIGURE 12.64

The standard unit of magnetic field strength is the tesla (T, named after Nicola Tesla). A strong bar magnet has a strength of 1 T. In terms of other units, $1 \text{ T} = 1 \text{ kg}/(\text{C} \cdot \text{s})$, where C is the unit of charge called the *coulomb*.

EXAMPLE 6   Force on a proton A proton with a mass of 1.7×10^{-27} kg and a charge of $q = +1.6 \times 10^{-19}$ coulombs (C) moves along the x-axis with a speed of $|\mathbf{v}| = 9 \times 10^5$ m/s. When it reaches $(0, 0, 0)$ a uniform magnetic field is turned on. The field has a constant strength of 1 tesla and is directed along the negative z-axis (Figure 12.65).

a. Find the magnitude and direction of the force on the proton at the instant it enters the magnetic field.

b. Assume that the proton loses no energy and the force in part (a) acts as a *centripetal force* with magnitude $|\mathbf{F}| = m|\mathbf{v}|^2/R$ that keeps the proton in a circular orbit of radius R. Find the radius of the orbit.

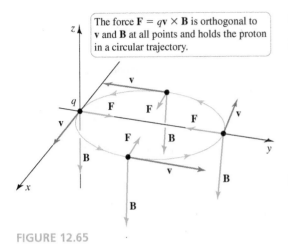

The force $\mathbf{F} = q\mathbf{v} \times \mathbf{B}$ is orthogonal to $\mathbf{v}$ and $\mathbf{B}$ at all points and holds the proton in a circular trajectory.

FIGURE 12.65

SOLUTION

a. Expressed as vectors, we have $\mathbf{v} = 9 \times 10^5\,\mathbf{i}$ and $\mathbf{B} = -\mathbf{k}$. Therefore, the force on the proton in newtons is

$$\mathbf{F} = q(\mathbf{v} \times \mathbf{B}) = 1.6 \times 10^{-19}((9 \times 10^5\,\mathbf{i}) \times (-\mathbf{k}))$$
$$= 1.44 \times 10^{-13}\mathbf{j}.$$

As shown in Figure 12.65, when the proton enters the magnetic field in the positive x-direction, the force acts in the positive y-direction, which changes the path of the proton.

b. The magnitude of the force acting on the proton remains 1.44×10^{-13} N at all times (from part (a)). Equating this force to the centripetal force $|\mathbf{F}| = m|\mathbf{v}|^2/R$, we find that

$$R = \frac{m|\mathbf{v}|^2}{|\mathbf{F}|} = \frac{(1.7 \times 10^{-27}\,\text{kg})(9 \times 10^5\,\text{m/s})^2}{1.44 \times 10^{-13}\,\text{N}} \approx 0.01\,\text{m}.$$

Assuming no energy loss, the proton moves in a circular orbit of radius 0.01 m.

Related Exercises 45–48 ◄

SECTION 12.4 EXERCISES

Review Questions

1. Explain how to find the magnitude of the cross product $\mathbf{u} \times \mathbf{v}$.

2. Explain how to find the direction of the cross product $\mathbf{u} \times \mathbf{v}$.

3. What is the magnitude of the cross product of two parallel vectors?

4. If $\mathbf{u}$ and $\mathbf{v}$ are orthogonal, what is the magnitude of $\mathbf{u} \times \mathbf{v}$?

5. Explain how to use a determinant to compute $\mathbf{u} \times \mathbf{v}$.

6. Explain how to find the torque produced by a force using cross products.

Basic Skills

7–8. Cross products from the definition *Find the cross product* $\mathbf{u} \times \mathbf{v}$ *in each figure.*

7.

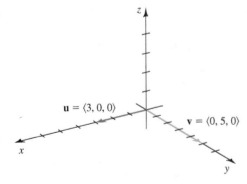

8.

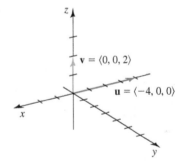

9–12. Cross products from the definition *Sketch the following vectors* $\mathbf{u}$ *and* $\mathbf{v}$. *Then compute* $|\mathbf{u} \times \mathbf{v}|$ *and show the cross product on your sketch.*

9. $\mathbf{u} = \langle 0, -2, 0 \rangle, \mathbf{v} = \langle 0, 1, 0 \rangle$

10. $\mathbf{u} = \langle 0, 4, 0 \rangle, \mathbf{v} = \langle 0, 0, -8 \rangle$

11. $\mathbf{u} = \langle 3, 3, 0 \rangle, \mathbf{v} = \langle 3, 3, 3\sqrt{2} \rangle$

12. $\mathbf{u} = \langle 0, -2, -2 \rangle, \mathbf{v} = \langle 0, 2, -2 \rangle$

13. **Magnitude of a cross product** Compute $|\mathbf{u} \times \mathbf{v}|$ if $\mathbf{u}$ and $\mathbf{v}$ are unit vectors and the angle between $\mathbf{u}$ and $\mathbf{v}$ is $\pi/4$.

14. **Magnitude of a cross product** Compute $|\mathbf{u} \times \mathbf{v}|$ if $|\mathbf{u}| = 3$ and $|\mathbf{v}| = 4$ and the angle between $\mathbf{u}$ and $\mathbf{v}$ is $2\pi/3$.

15–20. Coordinate unit vectors *Compute the following cross products. Then make a sketch showing the two vectors and their cross product.*

15. $\mathbf{j} \times \mathbf{k}$ **16.** $\mathbf{i} \times \mathbf{k}$ **17.** $-\mathbf{j} \times \mathbf{k}$

18. $3\mathbf{j} \times \mathbf{i}$ **19.** $-2\mathbf{i} \times 3\mathbf{k}$ **20.** $2\mathbf{j} \times (-5)\mathbf{i}$

21–24. Area of a parallelogram *Find the area of the parallelogram that has two adjacent sides **u** and **v**.*

21. $\mathbf{u} = 3\mathbf{i} - \mathbf{j}, \mathbf{v} = 3\mathbf{j} + 2\mathbf{k}$

22. $\mathbf{u} = -3\mathbf{i} + 2\mathbf{k}, \mathbf{v} = \mathbf{i} + \mathbf{j} + \mathbf{k}$

23. $\mathbf{u} = 2\mathbf{i} - \mathbf{j} - 2\mathbf{k}, \mathbf{v} = 3\mathbf{i} + 2\mathbf{j} - \mathbf{k}$

24. $\mathbf{u} = 8\mathbf{i} + 2\mathbf{j} - 3\mathbf{k}, \mathbf{v} = 2\mathbf{i} + 4\mathbf{j} - 4\mathbf{k}$

25–28. Area of a triangle *For the given points A, B, and C, find the area of the triangle with vertices A, B, and C.*

25. $A(0, 0, 0), B(3, 0, 1), C(1, 1, 0)$

26. $A(1, 2, 3), B(5, 1, 5), C(2, 3, 3)$

27. $A(5, 6, 2), B(7, 16, 4), C(6, 7, 3)$

28. $A(-1, -5, -3), B(-3, -2, -1), C(0, -5, -1)$

29–34. Computing cross products *Find the cross products* $\mathbf{u} \times \mathbf{v}$ *and* $\mathbf{v} \times \mathbf{u}$ *for the following vectors* **u** *and* **v**.

29. $\mathbf{u} = \langle 3, 5, 0 \rangle, \mathbf{v} = \langle 0, 3, -6 \rangle$

30. $\mathbf{u} = \langle -4, 1, 1 \rangle, \mathbf{v} = \langle 0, 1, -1 \rangle$

31. $\mathbf{u} = \langle 2, 3, -9 \rangle, \mathbf{v} = \langle -1, 1, -1 \rangle$

32. $\mathbf{u} = \langle 3, -4, 6 \rangle, \mathbf{v} = \langle 1, 2, -1 \rangle$

33. $\mathbf{u} = 3\mathbf{i} - \mathbf{j} - 2\mathbf{k}, \mathbf{v} = \mathbf{i} + 3\mathbf{j} - 2\mathbf{k}$

34. $\mathbf{u} = 2\mathbf{i} - 10\mathbf{j} + 15\mathbf{k}, \mathbf{v} = 0.5\mathbf{i} + \mathbf{j} - 0.6\mathbf{k}$

35–38. Normal vectors *Find a vector normal to the given vectors.*

35. $\langle 0, 1, 2 \rangle$ and $\langle -2, 0, 3 \rangle$ **36.** $\langle 1, 2, 3 \rangle$ and $\langle -2, 4, -1 \rangle$

37. $\langle 8, 0, 4 \rangle$ and $\langle -8, 2, 1 \rangle$ **38.** $\langle 6, -2, 4 \rangle$ and $\langle 1, 2, 3 \rangle$

39. Tightening a bolt Suppose you apply a force of 20 N to a 0.25-meter-long wrench attached to a bolt in a direction perpendicular to the bolt. Determine the magnitude of the torque when the force is applied at an angle of 45° to the wrench.

40. Opening a laptop Suppose you apply a force of 1.5 lb in a direction perpendicular to the screen of a laptop at a distance of 10 in from the hinge of the screen. Find the magnitude of torque (in ft · lb) that you apply.

41–44. Computing torque *Answer the following questions about torque.*

41. Let $\mathbf{r} = \overrightarrow{OP} = \mathbf{i} + \mathbf{j} + \mathbf{k}$. A force $\mathbf{F} = \langle 20, 0, 0 \rangle$ is applied at P. Find the torque about O that is produced.

42. Let $\mathbf{r} = \overrightarrow{OP} = \mathbf{i} - \mathbf{j} + 2\mathbf{k}$. A force $\mathbf{F} = \langle 10, 10, 0 \rangle$ is applied at P. Find the torque about O that is produced.

43. Let $\mathbf{r} = \overrightarrow{OP} = 10\mathbf{i}$. Which is greater (in magnitude): the torque about O when a force $\mathbf{F} = 5\mathbf{i} - 5\mathbf{k}$ is applied at P or the torque about O when a force $\mathbf{F} = 4\mathbf{i} - 3\mathbf{j}$ is applied at P?

44. A pump handle has a pivot at $(0, 0, 0)$ and extends to $P(5, 0, -5)$. A force $\mathbf{F} = \langle 1, 0, -10 \rangle$ is applied at P. Find the magnitude and direction of the torque about the pivot.

45–48. Force on a moving charge *Answer the following questions about force on a moving charge.*

45. A particle with a positive unit charge ($q = 1$) enters a constant magnetic field $\mathbf{B} = \mathbf{i} + \mathbf{j}$ with a velocity $\mathbf{v} = 20\mathbf{k}$. Find the magnitude and direction of the force on the particle. Make a sketch of the magnetic field, the velocity, and the force.

46. A particle with a unit negative charge ($q = -1$) enters a constant magnetic field $\mathbf{B} = 5\mathbf{k}$ with a velocity $\mathbf{v} = \mathbf{i} + 2\mathbf{j}$. Find the magnitude and direction of the force on the particle. Make a sketch of the magnetic field, the velocity, and the force.

47. An electron ($q = -1.6 \times 10^{-19}$ C) enters a constant 2-T magnetic field at an angle of 45° to the field with a speed of 2×10^5 m/s. Find the magnitude of the force on the electron.

48. A proton ($q = 1.6 \times 10^{-19}$ C) with velocity $2 \times 10^6 \mathbf{j}$ m/s experiences a force in newtons of $\mathbf{F} = 5 \times 10^{-12} \mathbf{k}$ as it passes through the origin. Find the magnitude and direction of the magnetic field at that instant.

Further Explorations

49. Explain why or why not Determine whether the following statements are true and give an explanation or counterexample.

   a. The cross product of two nonzero vectors is a nonzero vector.
   b. $|\mathbf{u} \times \mathbf{v}|$ is less than both $|\mathbf{u}|$ and $|\mathbf{v}|$.
   c. If **u** points east and **v** points south, then $\mathbf{u} \times \mathbf{v}$ points west.
   d. If $\mathbf{u} \times \mathbf{v} = \mathbf{0}$ and $\mathbf{u} \cdot \mathbf{v} = 0$, then either $\mathbf{u} = \mathbf{0}$ or $\mathbf{v} = \mathbf{0}$ (or both).
   e. Law of Cancellation? If $\mathbf{u} \times \mathbf{v} = \mathbf{u} \times \mathbf{w}$, then $\mathbf{v} = \mathbf{w}$.

50–51. Collinear points *Use cross products to determine whether the points A, B, and C are collinear.*

50. $A(3, 2, 1), B(5, 4, 7)$, and $C(9, 8, 19)$

51. $A(-3, -2, 1), B(1, 4, 7)$, and $C(4, 10, 14)$

52. Finding an unknown Find the value of a such that $\langle a, a, 2 \rangle \times \langle 1, a, 3 \rangle = \langle 2, -4, 2 \rangle$.

53. Parallel vectors Evaluate $\langle a, b, a \rangle \times \langle b, a, b \rangle$. For what nonzero values of a and b are the vectors $\langle a, b, a \rangle$ and $\langle b, a, b \rangle$ parallel?

54–57. Areas of triangles *Find the area of the following triangles T. (The area of a triangle is half the area of the corresponding parallelogram.)*

54. The sides of T are $\mathbf{u} = \langle 0, 6, 0 \rangle$, $\mathbf{v} = \langle 4, 4, 4 \rangle$, and $\mathbf{u} - \mathbf{v}$.

55. The sides of T are $\mathbf{u} = \langle 3, 3, 3 \rangle$, $\mathbf{v} = \langle 6, 0, 6 \rangle$, and $\mathbf{u} - \mathbf{v}$.

56. The vertices of T are $O(0, 0, 0)$, $P(2, 4, 6)$, and $Q(3, 5, 7)$.

57. The vertices of T are $O(0, 0, 0)$, $P(1, 2, 3)$, and $Q(6, 5, 4)$.

58. A unit cross product Under what conditions is $\mathbf{u} \times \mathbf{v}$ a unit vector?

59. Vector equation Find all vectors **u** that satisfy the equation

$$\langle 1, 1, 1 \rangle \times \mathbf{u} = \langle -1, -1, 2 \rangle.$$

60. Vector equation Find all vectors $\mathbf{u}$ that satisfy the equation

$$\langle 1, 1, 1 \rangle \times \mathbf{u} = \langle 0, 0, 1 \rangle.$$

61. Area of a triangle Find the area of the triangle with vertices on the coordinate axes at the points $(a, 0, 0)$, $(0, b, 0)$, and $(0, 0, c)$, in terms of a, b, and c.

62–64. Scalar triple product *Another operation with vectors is the* **scalar triple product**, *defined to be* $\mathbf{u} \cdot (\mathbf{v} \times \mathbf{w})$, *for vectors* $\mathbf{u}$, $\mathbf{v}$, *and* $\mathbf{w}$ *in* $\mathbb{R}^3$.

62. Express $\mathbf{u}$, $\mathbf{v}$, and $\mathbf{w}$ in terms of their components and show that $\mathbf{u} \cdot (\mathbf{v} \times \mathbf{w})$ equals the determinant

$$\begin{vmatrix} u_1 & u_2 & u_3 \\ v_1 & v_2 & v_3 \\ w_1 & w_2 & w_3 \end{vmatrix}.$$

63. Consider the *parallelepiped* (slanted box) determined by the position vectors $\mathbf{u}$, $\mathbf{v}$, and $\mathbf{w}$ (see figure). Show that the volume of the parallelepiped is $|\mathbf{u} \cdot (\mathbf{v} \times \mathbf{w})|$.

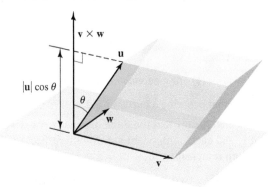

64. Prove that $\mathbf{u} \cdot (\mathbf{v} \times \mathbf{w}) = (\mathbf{u} \times \mathbf{v}) \cdot \mathbf{w}$.

Applications

65. Bicycle brakes A set of caliper brakes exerts a force on the rim of a bicycle wheel that creates a frictional force $\mathbf{F}$ of 40 N (see figure). Assuming the wheel has a radius of 66 cm, find the magnitude and direction of the torque about the axle of the wheel.

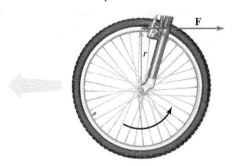

66. Arm torque A horizontally outstretched arm supports a weight of 20 lb in a hand (see figure). If the distance from the shoulder to the elbow is 1 ft and the distance from the elbow to the hand is 1 ft, find the magnitude and describe the direction of the torque about (a) the shoulder and (b) the elbow. (The units of torque in this case are ft-lb.)

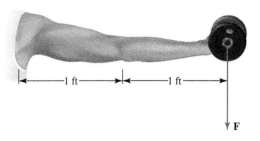

67. Electron speed An electron with a mass of 9.1×10^{-31} kg and a charge of -1.6×10^{-19} C travels in a circular path with no loss of energy in a magnetic field of 0.05 T that is orthogonal to the path of the electron (see figure). If the radius of the path is 0.002 m, what is the speed of the electron?

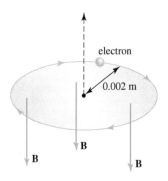

Additional Exercises

68. Three proofs Prove that $\mathbf{u} \times \mathbf{u} = \mathbf{0}$ in three ways.

    a. Use the definition of the cross product.
    b. Use the determinant formulation of the cross product.
    c. Use the property that $\mathbf{u} \times \mathbf{v} = -(\mathbf{v} \times \mathbf{u})$.

69. Associative property Prove in two ways that for scalars a and b, $(a\mathbf{u}) \times (b\mathbf{v}) = ab(\mathbf{u} \times \mathbf{v})$. Use the definition of the cross product and the determinant formula.

70–72. Possible identities *Determine whether the following statements are true using a proof or counterexample. Assume that* $\mathbf{u}$, $\mathbf{v}$, *and* $\mathbf{w}$ *are nonzero vectors in* $\mathbb{R}^3$.

70. $\mathbf{u} \times (\mathbf{u} \times \mathbf{v}) = \mathbf{0}$

71. $(\mathbf{u} - \mathbf{v}) \times (\mathbf{u} + \mathbf{v}) = 2\mathbf{u} \times \mathbf{v}$

72. $\mathbf{u} \cdot (\mathbf{v} \times \mathbf{w}) = \mathbf{w} \cdot (\mathbf{u} \times \mathbf{v})$

73–74. Identities *Prove the following identities. Assume that* $\mathbf{u}$, $\mathbf{v}$, $\mathbf{w}$, *and* $\mathbf{x}$ *are nonzero vectors in* $\mathbb{R}^3$.

73. $\mathbf{u} \times (\mathbf{v} \times \mathbf{w}) = (\mathbf{u} \cdot \mathbf{w})\mathbf{v} - (\mathbf{u} \cdot \mathbf{v})\mathbf{w}$ Vector triple product

74. $(\mathbf{u} \times \mathbf{v}) \cdot (\mathbf{w} \times \mathbf{x}) = (\mathbf{u} \cdot \mathbf{w})(\mathbf{v} \cdot \mathbf{x}) - (\mathbf{u} \cdot \mathbf{x})(\mathbf{v} \cdot \mathbf{w})$

75. Cross product equations Suppose **u** and **v** are nonzero vectors in $\mathbb{R}^3$.

    a. Prove that the equation $\mathbf{u} \times \mathbf{z} = \mathbf{v}$ has a nonzero solution **z** if and only if $\mathbf{u} \cdot \mathbf{v} = 0$. (*Hint:* Take the dot product of both sides with **v**.)

    b. Explain this result geometrically.

QUICK CHECK ANSWERS

1. $\mathbf{u} \times \mathbf{v}$ points in the positive z-direction; $\mathbf{v} \times \mathbf{u}$ points in the negative z-direction.   **2.** The vector $2\mathbf{u}$ points in the same direction as **u** and the vector $3\mathbf{v}$ points in the same direction as **v**. So, the right-hand rule gives the same direction for $2\mathbf{u} \times 3\mathbf{v}$ as it does for $\mathbf{u} \times \mathbf{v}$.
3. $\mathbf{u} \cdot (\mathbf{u} \times \mathbf{v}) = \langle -1, 0, 6 \rangle \cdot \langle 30, 9, 5 \rangle = -30 + 0 + 30 = 0$. A similar calculation shows that $\mathbf{v} \cdot (\mathbf{u} \times \mathbf{v}) = 0.$ ◀

12.5   Lines and Curves in Space

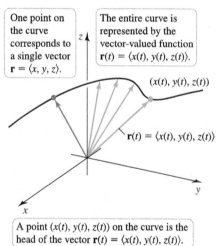

One point on the curve corresponds to a single vector $\mathbf{r} = \langle x, y, z \rangle$.

The entire curve is represented by the vector-valued function $\mathbf{r}(t) = \langle x(t), y(t), z(t) \rangle$.

$(x(t), y(t), z(t))$

$\mathbf{r}(t) = \langle x(t), y(t), z(t) \rangle$

A point $(x(t), y(t), z(t))$ on the curve is the head of the vector $\mathbf{r}(t) = \langle x(t), y(t), z(t) \rangle$.

FIGURE 12.66

Imagine a projectile moving along a path in three-dimensional space; it could be an electron or a comet, a soccer ball or a rocket. If you take a snapshot of the object, its position is described by a static position vector $\mathbf{r} = \langle x, y, z \rangle$. However, if you want to describe the full trajectory of the object as it unfolds in time, you must use a position vector such as $\mathbf{r}(t) = \langle x(t), y(t), z(t) \rangle$ whose components change in time (Figure 12.66). The goal of this section is to describe continuous motion by using vector-valued functions.

Vector-Valued Functions

A function of the form $\mathbf{r}(t) = \langle x(t), y(t), z(t) \rangle$ may be viewed in two ways.

- It is a set of three parametric equations that describe a curve in space.

- It is also a **vector-valued function**, which means that the three dependent variables (x, y, and z) are the components of **r**, and each component varies with respect to a single independent variable t (that often represents time).

    Here is the connection between these two perspectives: As t varies, a point $(x(t), y(t), z(t))$ on a parametric curve is also the head of the position vector $\mathbf{r}(t) = \langle x(t), y(t), z(t) \rangle$. It is useful to keep both of these interpretations in mind as you work with vector-valued functions.

Lines in Space

Two distinct points in $\mathbb{R}^3$ determine a unique line. Alternatively, one point and a direction also determine a unique line. We use both of these properties to derive parametric equations for lines in space. The result is an example of a vector-valued function in $\mathbb{R}^3$.

    Let ℓ be the line passing through the point $P_0(x_0, y_0, z_0)$ parallel to the nonzero vector $\mathbf{v} = \langle a, b, c \rangle$, where P_0 and **v** are given. The fixed point P_0 is associated with the position vector $\mathbf{r}_0 = \overrightarrow{OP_0} = \langle x_0, y_0, z_0 \rangle$. We let $P(x, y, z)$ be a variable point on ℓ with $\mathbf{r} = \overrightarrow{OP} = \langle x, y, z \rangle$ the position vector associated with P (Figure 12.67). Because ℓ is parallel to **v**, the vector $\overrightarrow{P_0P}$ is also parallel to **v**; therefore, $\overrightarrow{P_0P} = t\mathbf{v}$, where t is a real number. By vector addition, we see that $\overrightarrow{OP} = \overrightarrow{OP_0} + \overrightarrow{P_0P}$, or $\overrightarrow{OP} = \overrightarrow{OP_0} + t\mathbf{v}$. It follows that

$$\underbrace{\langle x, y, z \rangle}_{\mathbf{r} = \overrightarrow{OP}} = \underbrace{\langle x_0, y_0, z_0 \rangle}_{\mathbf{r}_0 = \overrightarrow{OP_0}} + t\underbrace{\langle a, b, c \rangle}_{\mathbf{v}} \quad \text{or} \quad \mathbf{r} = \mathbf{r}_0 + t\mathbf{v}.$$

Equating the components, the line is described by the parametric equations

$$x = x_0 + at, \quad y = y_0 + bt, \quad z = z_0 + ct, \quad \text{for} -\infty < t < \infty.$$

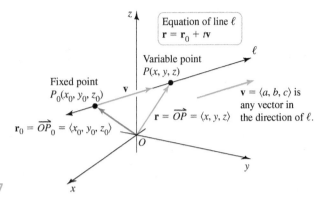

FIGURE 12.67

The parameter t determines the location of points on the line, where $t = 0$ corresponds to P_0. If t increases from 0, we move along the line in the direction of $\mathbf{v}$, and if t decreases from 0, we move along the line in the direction of $-\mathbf{v}$. As t varies over all real numbers ($-\infty < t < \infty$), the vector $\mathbf{r}$ sweeps out the entire line ℓ. If, instead of knowing the direction $\mathbf{v}$ of the line, we are given two points $P_0(x_0, y_0, z_0)$ and $P_1(x_1, y_1, z_1)$, then the direction of the line is $\mathbf{v} = \overrightarrow{P_0 P_1} = \langle x_1 - x_0, y_1 - y_0, z_1 - z_0 \rangle$.

QUICK CHECK 1 Describe the line $\mathbf{r}(t) = t\mathbf{k}$, for $-\infty < t < \infty$. Describe the line $\mathbf{r}(t) = t(\mathbf{i} + \mathbf{j} + 0\mathbf{k})$, for $-\infty < t < \infty$.

▶ Although we may refer to *the* equation of a line, there are infinitely many equations for the same line. The direction vector is determined only up to a scalar multiple.

Equation of a Line

An **equation of the line** passing through the point $P_0(x_0, y_0, z_0)$ in the direction of the vector $\mathbf{v} = \langle a, b, c \rangle$ is $\mathbf{r} = \mathbf{r}_0 + t\mathbf{v}$, or

$$\langle x, y, z \rangle = \langle x_0, y_0, z_0 \rangle + t\langle a, b, c \rangle, \quad \text{for} \quad -\infty < t < \infty.$$

Equivalently, the parametric equations of the line are

$$x = x_0 + at, \quad y = y_0 + bt, \quad z = z_0 + ct, \quad \text{for} \quad -\infty < t < \infty.$$

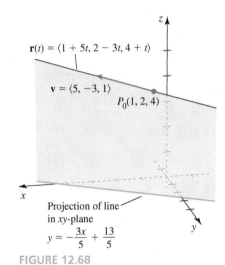

FIGURE 12.68

EXAMPLE 1 **Equations of lines** Find an equation of the line that passes through the point $P_0(1, 2, 4)$ in the direction of $\mathbf{v} = \langle 5, -3, 1 \rangle$.

SOLUTION We are given $\mathbf{r}_0 = \langle 1, 2, 4 \rangle$. Therefore, an equation of the line is

$$\mathbf{r}(t) = \mathbf{r}_0 + t\mathbf{v} = \langle 1, 2, 4 \rangle + t\langle 5, -3, 1 \rangle = \langle 1 + 5t, 2 - 3t, 4 + t \rangle,$$

for $-\infty < t < \infty$ (Figure 12.68). The corresponding parametric equations are

$$x = 1 + 5t, \quad y = 2 - 3t, \quad z = 4 + t, \quad \text{for} \quad -\infty < t < \infty.$$

The line is easier to visualize if it is plotted with its projection in the xy-plane. Setting $z = 0$ (the equation of the xy-plane), the parametric equations of the projection line are $x = 1 + 5t, y = 2 - 3t$, and $z = 0$. Eliminating t from these equations, an equation of the projection line is $y = -\frac{3}{5}x + \frac{13}{5}$ (Figure 12.68).

Related Exercises 9–24 ◀

EXAMPLE 2 **Equations of lines** Let ℓ be the line that passes through the points $P_0(-3, 5, 8)$ and $P_1(4, 2, -1)$.

a. Find an equation of ℓ.

b. Find equations of the projections of ℓ on the xy- and xz-planes. Then graph those projection lines.

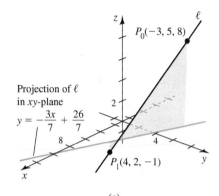

Projection of ℓ
in xy-plane

$y = -\dfrac{3x}{7} + \dfrac{26}{7}$

(a)

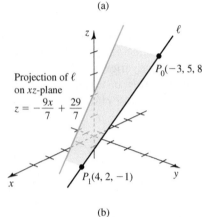

Projection of ℓ
on xz-plane

$z = -\dfrac{9x}{7} + \dfrac{29}{7}$

(b)

FIGURE 12.69

▷ A related problem: To find the point at which the line in Example 2 intersects the xy-plane, we set $z = 0$, solve for t, and find the corresponding x- and y-coordinates: $z = 0$ implies $t = \frac{8}{9}$, which implies $x = \frac{29}{9}$ and $y = \frac{7}{3}$.

SOLUTION

a. The direction of the line is

$$\mathbf{v} = \overrightarrow{P_0 P_1} = \langle 4 - (-3), 2 - 5, -1 - 8 \rangle = \langle 7, -3, -9 \rangle.$$

Therefore, with $\mathbf{r}_0 = \langle -3, 5, 8 \rangle$, the equation of ℓ is

$$\mathbf{r}(t) = \mathbf{r}_0 + t\mathbf{v}$$
$$= \langle -3, 5, 8 \rangle + t\langle 7, -3, -9 \rangle$$
$$= \langle -3 + 7t, 5 - 3t, 8 - 9t \rangle.$$

b. Setting the z-component of the equation of ℓ equal to zero, the parametric equations of the projection of ℓ on the xy-plane are $x = -3 + 7t$, $y = 5 - 3t$. Eliminating t from these equations gives the equation $y = -\frac{3}{7}x + \frac{26}{7}$ (Figure 12.69a). The projection of ℓ on the xz-plane (setting $y = 0$) is $x = -3 + 7t$, $z = 8 - 9t$. Eliminating t gives the equation $z = -\frac{9}{7}x + \frac{29}{7}$ (Figure 12.69b).

Related Exercises 9–24 ◀

QUICK CHECK 2 In the equation of the line

$$\mathbf{r}(t) = \langle x_0, y_0, z_0 \rangle + t\langle x_1 - x_0, y_1 - y_0, z_1 - z_0 \rangle,$$

what value of t corresponds to the point $P_0(x_0, y_0, z_0)$? What value of t corresponds to the point $P_1(x_1, y_1, z_1)$? ◀

EXAMPLE 3   Equation of a line segment Find the equation of the line segment between $P_0(3, -1, 4)$ and $P_1(0, 5, 2)$.

SOLUTION The same ideas used to find an equation of an entire line work here. We just restrict the values of the parameter t, so that only the given line segment is generated. The direction of the line segment is

$$\mathbf{v} = \overrightarrow{P_0 P_1} = \langle 0 - 3, 5 - (-1), 2 - 4 \rangle = \langle -3, 6, -2 \rangle.$$

Letting $\mathbf{r}_0 = \langle 3, -1, 4 \rangle$, the equation of the line through P_0 and P_1 is

$$\mathbf{r}(t) = \mathbf{r}_0 + t\mathbf{v} = \langle 3 - 3t, -1 + 6t, 4 - 2t \rangle.$$

Notice that if $t = 0$, then $\mathbf{r}(0) = \langle 3, -1, 4 \rangle$, which is a vector with endpoint P_0. If $t = 1$, then $\mathbf{r}(1) = \langle 0, 5, 2 \rangle$, which is a vector with endpoint P_1. Letting t vary from 0 to 1 generates the line segment between P_0 and P_1 (Figure 12.70). Therefore, the equation of the line segment is

$$\mathbf{r}(t) = \langle 3 - 3t, -1 + 6t, 4 - 2t \rangle, \quad \text{for } 0 \leq t \leq 1.$$

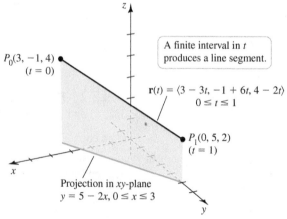

FIGURE 12.70

Related Exercises 25–28 ◀

Curves in Space

We now explore general vector-valued functions of the form

$$\mathbf{r}(t) = \langle f(t), g(t), h(t) \rangle = f(t)\mathbf{i} + g(t)\mathbf{j} + h(t)\mathbf{k},$$

where f, g, and h are defined on an interval $a \le t \le b$. The **domain** of $\mathbf{r}$ is the largest set of values of t on which all of f, g, and h are defined.

Figure 12.71 illustrates how a parameterized curve is generated by such a function. As the parameter t varies over the interval $a \le t \le b$, each value of t produces a position vector that corresponds to a point on the curve, starting at the initial vector $\mathbf{r}(a)$ and ending at the terminal vector $\mathbf{r}(b)$. The resulting parameterized curve can either have finite length or extend indefinitely. The curve may also cross itself or close and retrace itself.

> When f, g, and h are linear functions of t, the resulting curve is a line or line segment.

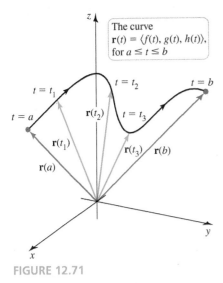

The curve
$\mathbf{r}(t) = \langle f(t), g(t), h(t) \rangle$,
for $a \le t \le b$

FIGURE 12.71

Orientation of Curves   If a smooth curve C is viewed only as a set of points, then at any point of C it is possible to draw tangent vectors in two directions (Figure 12.72a). On the other hand, a parameterized curve described by the function $\mathbf{r}(t)$, where $a \le t \le b$, has a natural direction, or **orientation**. The *positive* or *forward* direction is the direction in which the curve is generated as the parameter increases from a to b. For example, the positive direction of the circle $\mathbf{r}(t) = \langle \cos t, \sin t \rangle$, for $0 \le t \le 2\pi$, is counterclockwise (Figure 12.72b). The orientation of a parameterized curve and its tangent vectors are consistent: The positive direction of the curve is also the direction in which the tangent vectors point along the curve. A precise definition of the tangent vector is given in Section 12.6.

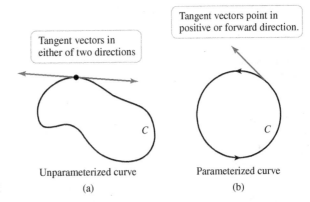

Tangent vectors in
either of two directions

Tangent vectors point in
positive or forward direction.

Unparameterized curve   Parameterized curve

FIGURE 12.72   (a)   (b)

EXAMPLE 4   **A helix**   Graph the curve described by the equation

$$\mathbf{r}(t) = 4 \cos t\,\mathbf{i} + \sin t\,\mathbf{j} + \frac{t}{2\pi}\mathbf{k},$$

where (a) $0 \le t \le 2\pi$ and (b) $-\infty < t < \infty$.

SOLUTION

a. We begin by setting $z = 0$ to determine the projection of the curve in the xy-plane. The resulting function $\mathbf{r}(t) = 4 \cos t\,\mathbf{i} + \sin t\,\mathbf{j}$ implies that $x = 4 \cos t$ and $y = \sin t$; these equations describe an ellipse in the xy-plane whose positive direction is counterclockwise (Figure 12.73a). Because $z = \frac{t}{2\pi}$, the value of z increases from 0 to 1 as t increases from 0 to 2π. Therefore, the curve rises out of the xy-plane to create a helix (or coil). Over the interval $[0, 2\pi]$, the helix begins at $(4, 0, 0)$, circles the z-axis once, and ends at $(4, 0, 1)$ (Figure 12.73b).

b. Letting the parameter vary over the interval $-\infty < t < \infty$ generates a helix that winds around the z-axis endlessly in both directions (Figure 12.73c). The forward direction is upward on the z-axis.

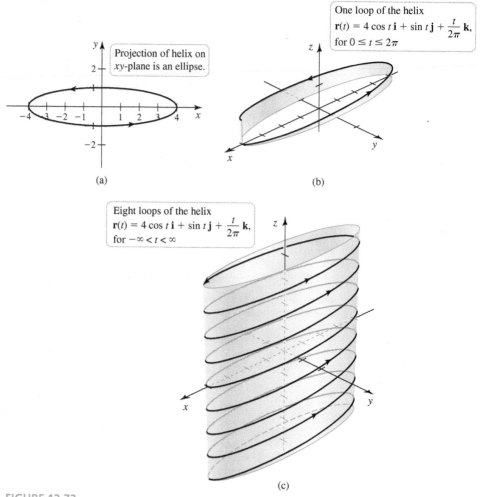

Projection of helix on xy-plane is an ellipse.

(a)

One loop of the helix
$\mathbf{r}(t) = 4\cos t\,\mathbf{i} + \sin t\,\mathbf{j} + \dfrac{t}{2\pi}\,\mathbf{k}$,
for $0 \le t \le 2\pi$

(b)

Eight loops of the helix
$\mathbf{r}(t) = 4\cos t\,\mathbf{i} + \sin t\,\mathbf{j} + \dfrac{t}{2\pi}\,\mathbf{k}$,
for $-\infty < t < \infty$

(c)

FIGURE 12.73

> Recall that the functions $\sin at$ and $\cos at$ oscillate a times over the interval $[0, 2\pi]$. Therefore, their period is $2\pi/a$.

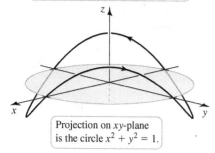

Roller coaster curve
$\mathbf{r}(t) = \cos t\,\mathbf{i} + \sin t\,\mathbf{j} + 0.4\sin 2t\,\mathbf{k}$,
for $0 \le t \le 2\pi$

Projection on xy-plane is the circle $x^2 + y^2 = 1$.

FIGURE 12.74

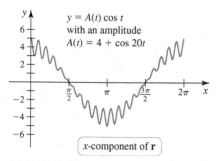

$y = A(t)\cos t$ with an amplitude $A(t) = 4 + \cos 20t$

x-component of $\mathbf{r}$

FIGURE 12.75

Related Exercises 29–36 ◄

EXAMPLE 5   Roller coaster curve Graph the curve

$$\mathbf{r}(t) = \cos t\,\mathbf{i} + \sin t\,\mathbf{j} + 0.4\sin 2t\,\mathbf{k}, \quad \text{for } 0 \le t \le 2\pi.$$

SOLUTION Without the z-component, the resulting function $\mathbf{r}(t) = \cos t\,\mathbf{i} + \sin t\,\mathbf{j}$ describes a circle of radius 1 in the xy-plane. The z-component of the function varies between -0.4 and 0.4 with a period of π units. Therefore, on the interval $[0, 2\pi]$ the z-coordinates of points on the curve oscillate twice between -0.4 and 0.4, while the x- and y-coordinates describe a circle. The result is a curve that circles the z-axis once in the counterclockwise direction with two peaks and two valleys (Figure 12.74).

Related Exercises 37–40 ◄

EXAMPLE 6   Slinky curve Graph the curve

$$\mathbf{r}(t) = (4 + \cos 20t)\cos t\,\mathbf{i} + (4 + \cos 20t)\sin t\,\mathbf{j} + 0.4\sin 20t\,\mathbf{k},$$

for $0 \le t \le 2\pi$.

SOLUTION The factor $A(t) = 4 + \cos 20t$ that appears in the x- and y-components is a varying amplitude for $\cos t\,\mathbf{i}$ and $\sin t\,\mathbf{j}$. Its effect is seen in the graph of the x-component $A(t)\cos t$ (Figure 12.75). For $0 \le t \le 2\pi$, the curve consists of one period of $4\cos t$

with 20 small oscillations superimposed on it. As a result, the x-component of $\mathbf{r}$ varies from -5 to 5 with 20 small oscillations along the way. A similar behavior is seen in the y-component of $\mathbf{r}$. Finally, the z-component of $\mathbf{r}$, which is $0.4 \sin 20t$, oscillates between -0.4 and 0.4 twenty times over $[0, 2\pi]$. Combining these effects, we discover a coil-shaped curve that circles the z-axis in the counterclockwise direction and closes on itself. Figure 12.76 shows two views, one looking along the xy-plane and the other from overhead on the z-axis.

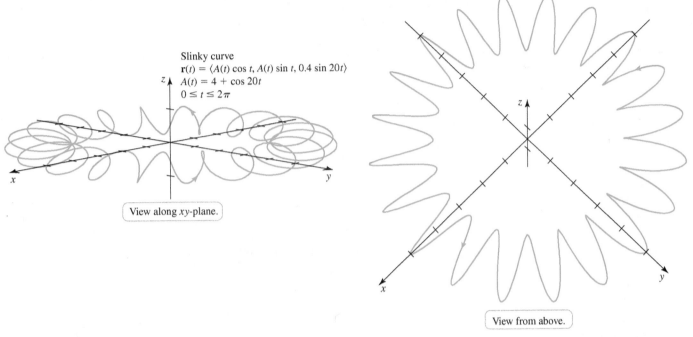

Slinky curve
$\mathbf{r}(t) = \langle A(t) \cos t, A(t) \sin t, 0.4 \sin 20t \rangle$
$A(t) = 4 + \cos 20t$
$0 \le t \le 2\pi$

View along xy-plane.

View from above.

FIGURE 12.76

Related Exercises 37–40 ◄

Limits and Continuity for Vector-Valued Functions

The limit of a vector-valued function $\mathbf{r}(t) = f(t)\mathbf{i} + g(t)\mathbf{j} + h(t)\mathbf{k}$ is defined much as it is for scalar-valued functions. If there is a vector $\mathbf{L}$ such that $|\mathbf{r}(t) - \mathbf{L}|$ can be made arbitrarily small by taking t sufficiently close to a, then we write $\lim_{t \to a} \mathbf{r}(t) = \mathbf{L}$ and say that the limit of $\mathbf{r}$ as t approaches a is $\mathbf{L}$.

> **DEFINITION Limit of a Vector-Valued Function**
>
> A vector-valued function $\mathbf{r}$ approaches the limit $\mathbf{L}$ as t approaches a, written $\lim_{t \to a} \mathbf{r}(t) = \mathbf{L}$, provided $\lim_{t \to a} |\mathbf{r}(t) - \mathbf{L}| = 0$.

This definition, together with a short calculation (Exercise 78), leads to a straightforward method for computing limits of the vector-valued function $\mathbf{r} = \langle f, g, h \rangle$. Suppose that

$$\lim_{t \to a} f(t) = L_1, \qquad \lim_{t \to a} g(t) = L_2, \qquad \text{and} \qquad \lim_{t \to a} h(t) = L_3.$$

Then

$$\lim_{t \to a} \mathbf{r}(t) = \left\langle \lim_{t \to a} f(t), \lim_{t \to a} g(t), \lim_{t \to a} h(t) \right\rangle = \langle L_1, L_2, L_3 \rangle.$$

In other words, the limit of $\mathbf{r}$ is determined by computing the limits of its components.

The limits laws in Chapter 2 have analogs for vector-valued functions. For example, if $\lim_{t \to a} \mathbf{r}(t)$ and $\lim_{t \to a} \mathbf{s}(t)$ exist and c is a scalar, then

$$\lim_{t \to a} (\mathbf{r}(t) + \mathbf{s}(t)) = \lim_{t \to a} \mathbf{r}(t) + \lim_{t \to a} \mathbf{s}(t) \quad \text{and} \quad \lim_{t \to a} c\mathbf{r}(t) = c \lim_{t \to a} \mathbf{r}(t).$$

The idea of continuity also extends directly to vector-valued functions. A function $\mathbf{r}(t) = f(t)\mathbf{i} + g(t)\mathbf{j} + h(t)\mathbf{k}$ is continuous at a provided $\lim_{t \to a} \mathbf{r}(t) = \mathbf{r}(a)$. Specifically, if the component functions f, g, and h are continuous at a, then $\mathbf{r}$ is also continuous at a and vice versa. The function $\mathbf{r}$ is continuous on an interval I if it is continuous for all t in I.

➤ Continuity is often taken as part of the definition of a parameterized curve.

Continuity has the same intuitive meaning in this setting as it does for scalar-valued functions. If $\mathbf{r}$ is a continuous function, the curve it describes has no breaks or gaps, which is an important property when $\mathbf{r}$ describes the trajectory of an object.

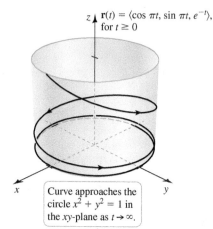

$\mathbf{r}(t) = \langle \cos \pi t, \sin \pi t, e^{-t} \rangle$, for $t \geq 0$

Curve approaches the circle $x^2 + y^2 = 1$ in the xy-plane as $t \to \infty$.

FIGURE 12.77

EXAMPLE 7   **Limits and continuity**   Consider the function

$$\mathbf{r}(t) = \cos \pi t\, \mathbf{i} + \sin \pi t\, \mathbf{j} + e^{-t}\mathbf{k}, \quad \text{for } t \geq 0.$$

a. Evaluate $\lim_{t \to 2} \mathbf{r}(t)$.

b. Evaluate $\lim_{t \to \infty} \mathbf{r}(t)$.

c. At what points is $\mathbf{r}$ continuous?

SOLUTION

a. We evaluate the limit of each component of $\mathbf{r}$:

$$\lim_{t \to 2} \mathbf{r}(t) = \lim_{t \to 2} (\underbrace{\cos \pi t}_{\to 1}\, \mathbf{i} + \underbrace{\sin \pi t}_{\to 0}\, \mathbf{j} + \underbrace{e^{-t}}_{\to e^{-2}}\mathbf{k}) = \mathbf{i} + e^{-2}\mathbf{k}.$$

b. Note that although $\lim_{t \to \infty} e^{-t} = 0$ exists, $\lim_{t \to \infty} \cos t$ and $\lim_{t \to \infty} \sin t$ do not exist. Therefore, $\lim_{t \to \infty} \mathbf{r}(t)$ does not exist. As shown in Figure 12.77, the curve is a coil that approaches the unit circle in the xy-plane.

c. Because the components of $\mathbf{r}$ are continuous for all t, $\mathbf{r}$ is also continuous for all t.

Related Exercises 41–46 ◄

SECTION 12.5 EXERCISES

Review Questions

1. How many independent variables does the function $\mathbf{r}(t) = \langle f(t), g(t), h(t) \rangle$ have?

2. How many dependent scalar variables does the function $\mathbf{r}(t) = \langle f(t), g(t), h(t) \rangle$ have?

3. Why is $\mathbf{r}(t) = \langle f(t), g(t), h(t) \rangle$ called a vector-valued function?

4. Explain how to find a vector in the direction of the line segment from $P_0(x_0, y_0, z_0)$ to $P_1(x_1, y_1, z_1)$.

5. How do you find an equation for the line through the points $P_0(x_0, y_0, z_0)$ and $P_1(x_1, y_1, z_1)$?

6. In what plane does the curve $\mathbf{r}(t) = t\mathbf{i} + t^2\mathbf{k}$ lie?

7. How do you evaluate $\lim_{t \to a} \mathbf{r}(t)$, where $\mathbf{r}(t) = \langle f(t), g(t), h(t) \rangle$?

8. How do you determine whether $\mathbf{r}(t) = f(t)\mathbf{i} + g(t)\mathbf{j} + h(t)\mathbf{k}$ is continuous at $t = a$?

Basic Skills

9–24. Equations of lines *Find equations of the following lines.*

9. The line through $(0, 0, 1)$ in the direction of the vector $\mathbf{v} = \langle 4, 7, 0 \rangle$

10. The line through $(-3, 2, -1)$ in the direction of the vector $\mathbf{v} = \langle 1, -2, 0 \rangle$

11. The line through $(0, 0, 1)$ parallel to the y-axis

12. The line through $(0, 0, 1)$ parallel to the x-axis

13. The line through $(0, 0, 0)$ and $(1, 2, 3)$

14. The line through $(1, 0, 1)$ and $(3, -3, 3)$

15. The line through $(-3, 4, 6)$ and $(5, -1, 0)$

16. The line through $(0, 4, 8)$ and $(10, -5, -4)$

17. The line through $(0, 0, 0)$ that is parallel to the line $\mathbf{r}(t) = \langle 3 - 2t, 5 + 8t, 7 - 4t \rangle$

18. The line through $(1, -3, 4)$ that is parallel to the line
$\mathbf{r}(t) = \langle 3 + 4t, 5 - t, 7 \rangle$

19. The line through $(0, 0, 0)$ that is perpendicular to both
$\mathbf{u} = \langle 1, 0, 2 \rangle$ and $\mathbf{v} = \langle 0, 1, 1 \rangle$

20. The line through $(-3, 4, 2)$ that is perpendicular to both
$\mathbf{u} = \langle 1, 1, -5 \rangle$ and $\mathbf{v} = \langle 0, 4, 0 \rangle$

21. The line through $(-2, 5, 3)$ that is perpendicular to both
$\mathbf{u} = \langle 1, 1, 2 \rangle$ and the x-axis

22. The line through $(0, 2, 1)$ that is perpendicular to both
$\mathbf{u} = \langle 4, 3, -5 \rangle$ and the z-axis

23. The line through $(1, 2, 3)$ that is perpendicular
to the lines $\mathbf{r}_1(t) = \langle 3 - 2t, 5 + 8t, 7 - 4t \rangle$ and
$\mathbf{r}_2(t) = \langle -2t, 5 + t, 7 - t \rangle$

24. The line through $(1, 0, -1)$ that is perpendicular to the lines
$\mathbf{r}_1(t) = \langle 3 + 2t, 3t, -4t \rangle$ and $\mathbf{r}_2(t) = \langle t, t, -t \rangle$

25–28. Line segments *Find an equation of the line segment joining the first point to the second point.*

25. $(0, 0, 0)$ and $(1, 2, 3)$ **26.** $(1, 0, 1)$ and $(0, -2, 1)$

27. $(2, 4, 8)$ and $(7, 5, 3)$ **28.** $(-1, -8, 4)$ and $(-9, 5, -3)$

29–36. Curves in space *Graph the curves described by the following functions, indicating the direction of positive orientation. Try to anticipate the shape of the curve before using a graphing utility.*

29. $\mathbf{r}(t) = \cos t\,\mathbf{i} + \sin t\,\mathbf{k}$, for $0 \leq t \leq 2\pi$

30. $\mathbf{r}(t) = 4 \cos t\,\mathbf{j} + 16 \sin t\,\mathbf{k}$, for $0 \leq t \leq 2\pi$

31. $\mathbf{r}(t) = \cos t\,\mathbf{i} + \mathbf{j} + \sin t\,\mathbf{k}$, for $0 \leq t \leq 2\pi$

32. $\mathbf{r}(t) = 2 \cos t\,\mathbf{i} + 2 \sin t\,\mathbf{j} + 2\mathbf{k}$, for $0 \leq t \leq 2\pi$

33. $\mathbf{r}(t) = t \cos t\,\mathbf{i} + t \sin t\,\mathbf{j} + t\mathbf{k}$, for $0 \leq t \leq 6\pi$

34. $\mathbf{r}(t) = 4 \sin t\,\mathbf{i} + 4 \cos t\,\mathbf{j} + e^{-t/10}\mathbf{k}$, for $0 \leq t < \infty$

35. $\mathbf{r}(t) = e^{-t/20} \sin t\,\mathbf{i} + e^{-t/20} \cos t\,\mathbf{j} + t\mathbf{k}$, for $0 \leq t < \infty$

36. $\mathbf{r}(t) = e^{-t/10}\mathbf{i} + 3 \cos t\,\mathbf{j} + 3 \sin t\,\mathbf{k}$, for $0 \leq t < \infty$

37–40. Exotic curves *Graph the curves described by the following functions. Use analysis to anticipate the shape of the curve before using a graphing utility.*

37. $\mathbf{r}(t) = 0.5 \cos 15t\,\mathbf{i} + (8 + \sin 15t) \cos t\,\mathbf{j} + (8 + \sin 15t) \sin t\,\mathbf{k}$,
for $0 \leq t \leq 2\pi$

38. $\mathbf{r}(t) = 2 \cos t\,\mathbf{i} + 4 \sin t\,\mathbf{j} + \cos 10t\,\mathbf{k}$, for $0 \leq t \leq 2\pi$

39. $\mathbf{r}(t) = \sin t\,\mathbf{i} + \sin^2 t\,\mathbf{j} + t/(5\pi)\mathbf{k}$, for $0 \leq t \leq 10\pi$

40. $\mathbf{r}(t) = \cos t \sin 3t\,\mathbf{i} + \sin t \sin 3t\,\mathbf{j} + \sqrt{t}\,\mathbf{k}$, for $0 \leq t \leq 9$

41–46. Limits *Evaluate the following limits.*

41. $\lim\limits_{t \to \pi/2} \left(\cos 2t\,\mathbf{i} - 4 \sin t\,\mathbf{j} + \dfrac{2t}{\pi}\mathbf{k} \right)$

42. $\lim\limits_{t \to \ln 2} (2e^t\mathbf{i} + 6e^{-t}\mathbf{j} - 4e^{-2t}\mathbf{k})$

43. $\lim\limits_{t \to \infty} \left(e^{-t}\mathbf{i} - \dfrac{2t}{t + 1}\mathbf{j} + \tan^{-1}t\,\mathbf{k} \right)$

44. $\lim\limits_{t \to 2} \left(\dfrac{t}{t^2 + 1}\mathbf{i} - 4e^{-t} \sin \pi t\,\mathbf{j} + \dfrac{1}{\sqrt{4t + 1}}\mathbf{k} \right)$

45. $\lim\limits_{t \to 0} \left(\dfrac{\sin t}{t}\mathbf{i} - \dfrac{e^t - t - 1}{t}\mathbf{j} + \dfrac{\cos t + t^2/2 - 1}{t^2}\mathbf{k} \right)$

46. $\lim\limits_{t \to 0} \left(\dfrac{\tan t}{t}\mathbf{i} - \dfrac{3t}{\sin t}\mathbf{j} + \sqrt{t + 1}\,\mathbf{k} \right)$

Further Explorations

47. Explain why or why not Determine whether the following statements are true and give an explanation or counterexample.
  a. The line $\mathbf{r}(t) = \langle 3, -1, 4 \rangle + t\langle 6, -2, 8 \rangle$ passes through the origin.
  b. Any two nonparallel lines in $\mathbb{R}^3$ intersect.
  c. The curve $\mathbf{r}(t) = \langle e^{-t}, \sin t, -\cos t \rangle$ approaches a circle as $t \to \infty$.
  d. If $\mathbf{r}(t) = e^{-t^2}\langle 1, 1, 1 \rangle$ then $\lim\limits_{t \to \infty} \mathbf{r}(t) = \lim\limits_{t \to -\infty} \mathbf{r}(t)$.

48. Point of intersection Determine the equation of the line that is perpendicular to the lines $\mathbf{r}(t) = \langle -2 + 3t, 2t, 3t \rangle$ and $\mathbf{R}(s) = \langle -6 + s, -8 + 2s, -12 + 3s \rangle$ and passes through the point of intersection of the lines $\mathbf{r}$ and $\mathbf{R}$.

49. Point of intersection Determine the equation of the line that is perpendicular to the lines $\mathbf{r}(t) = \langle 4t, 1 + 2t, 3t \rangle$ and $\mathbf{R}(s) = \langle -1 + s, -7 + 2s, -12 + 3s \rangle$ and passes through the point of intersection of the lines $\mathbf{r}$ and $\mathbf{R}$.

50–55. Skew lines *A pair of lines in $\mathbb{R}^3$ are said to be skew if they are neither parallel nor intersecting. Determine whether the following pairs of lines are parallel, intersecting, or skew. If the lines intersect, determine the point(s) of intersection.*

50. $\mathbf{r}(t) = \langle 3 + 4t, 1 - 6t, 4t \rangle$;
     $\mathbf{R}(s) = \langle -2s, 5 + 3s, 4 - 2s \rangle$

51. $\mathbf{r}(t) = \langle 1 + 6t, 3 - 7t, 2 + t \rangle$;
     $\mathbf{R}(s) = \langle 10 + 3s, 6 + s, 14 + 4s \rangle$

52. $\mathbf{r}(t) = \langle 4 + 5t, -2t, 1 + 3t \rangle$;
     $\mathbf{R}(s) = \langle 10s, 6 + 4s, 4 + 6s \rangle$

53. $\mathbf{r}(t) = \langle 4, 6 - t, 1 + t \rangle$;
     $\mathbf{R}(s) = \langle -3 - 7s, 1 + 4s, 4 - s \rangle$

54. $\mathbf{r}(t) = \langle 4 + t, -2t, 1 + 3t \rangle$;
     $\mathbf{R}(s) = \langle 1 - 7s, 6 + 14s, 4 - 21s \rangle$

55. $\mathbf{r}(t) = \langle 1 + 2t, 7 - 3t, 6 + t \rangle$;
     $\mathbf{R}(s) = \langle -9 + 6s, 22 - 9s, 1 + 3s \rangle$

56–59. Domains *Find the domains of the following vector-valued functions.*

56. $\mathbf{r}(t) = \dfrac{2}{t - 1}\mathbf{i} + \dfrac{3}{t + 2}\mathbf{j}$

57. $\mathbf{r}(t) = \sqrt{t + 2}\,\mathbf{i} + \sqrt{2 - t}\,\mathbf{j}$

58. $\mathbf{r}(t) = \cos 2t\,\mathbf{i} + e^{\sqrt{t}}\mathbf{j} + \dfrac{12}{t}\mathbf{k}$

59. $\mathbf{r}(t) = \sqrt{4 - t^2}\,\mathbf{i} + \sqrt{t}\,\mathbf{j} - \dfrac{2}{\sqrt{1 + t}}\mathbf{k}$

60–63. Line-plane intersections *Find the point (if it exists) at which the following planes and lines intersect.*

60. $x = 3$; $\mathbf{r}(t) = \langle t, t, t \rangle$

61. $z = 4$; $\mathbf{r}(t) = \langle 2t + 1, -t + 4, t - 6 \rangle$

62. $y = -2$; $\mathbf{r}(t) = \langle 2t + 1, -t + 4, t - 6 \rangle$

63. $z = -8$; $\mathbf{r}(t) = \langle 3t - 2, t - 6, -2t + 4 \rangle$

64–66. Curve-plane intersections *Find the points (if they exist) at which the following planes and curves intersect.*

64. $y = 1$; $\mathbf{r}(t) = \langle 10 \cos t, 2 \sin t, 1 \rangle$, for $0 \le t \le 2\pi$

65. $z = 16$; $\mathbf{r}(t) = \langle t, 2t, 4 + 3t \rangle$, for $-\infty < t < \infty$

66. $y + x = 0$; $\mathbf{r}(t) = \langle \cos t, \sin t, t \rangle$, for $0 \le t \le 4\pi$

67. Matching functions with graphs Match functions a–f with the appropriate graphs A–F.

a. $\mathbf{r}(t) = \langle t, -t, t \rangle$ **b.** $\mathbf{r}(t) = \langle t^2, t, t \rangle$

c. $\mathbf{r}(t) = \langle 4 \cos t, 4 \sin t, 2 \rangle$ **d.** $\mathbf{r}(t) = \langle 2t, \sin t, \cos t \rangle$

e. $\mathbf{r}(t) = \langle \sin t, \cos t, \sin 2t \rangle$ **f.** $\mathbf{r}(t) = \langle \sin t, 2t, \cos t \rangle$

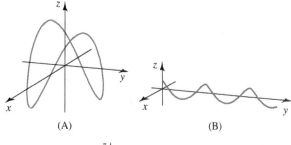

(A)   (B)

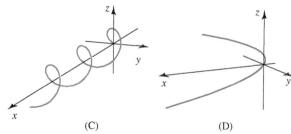

(C)   (D)

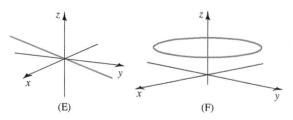

(E)   (F)

68. Intersecting lines and colliding particles Consider the lines

$$\mathbf{r}(t) = \langle 2 + 2t, 8 + t, 10 + 3t \rangle \text{ and}$$
$$\mathbf{R}(s) = \langle 6 + s, 10 - 2s, 16 - s \rangle.$$

a. Determine whether the lines intersect (have a common point) and if so, find the coordinates of that point.

b. If $\mathbf{r}$ and $\mathbf{R}$ describe the paths of two particles, do the particles collide? Assume $t \ge 0$ and $s \ge 0$ measure time in seconds, and that motion starts at $s = t = 0$.

69. Upward path Consider the curve described by the vector function $\mathbf{r}(t) = (50e^{-t} \cos t)\mathbf{i} + (50e^{-t} \sin t)\mathbf{j} + (5 - 5e^{-t})\mathbf{k}$, for $t \ge 0$.

a. What is the initial point of the path corresponding to $\mathbf{r}(0)$?

b. What is $\lim\limits_{t \to \infty} \mathbf{r}(t)$?

c. Sketch the curve.

d. Eliminate the parameter t to show that $z = 5 - r/10$, where $r^2 = x^2 + y^2$.

70–73. Closed plane curves *Consider the curve*
$\mathbf{r}(t) = (a \cos t + b \sin t)\mathbf{i} + (c \cos t + d \sin t)\mathbf{j} + (e \cos t + f \sin t)\mathbf{k}$, *where a, b, c, d, e, and f are real numbers. It can be shown that this curve lies in a plane.*

70. Assuming the curve lies in a plane, show that it is a circle centered at the origin with radius R provided $a^2 + c^2 + e^2 = b^2 + d^2 + f^2 = R^2$ and $ab + cd + ef = 0$.

71. Graph the following curve and describe it.

$$\mathbf{r}(t) = \left(\frac{1}{\sqrt{2}} \cos t + \frac{1}{\sqrt{3}} \sin t\right)\mathbf{i} + \left(-\frac{1}{\sqrt{2}} \cos t + \frac{1}{\sqrt{3}} \sin t\right)\mathbf{j} + \left(\frac{1}{\sqrt{3}} \sin t\right)\mathbf{k}$$

72. Graph the following curve and describe it.

$$\mathbf{r}(t) = (2 \cos t + 2 \sin t)\mathbf{i} + (-\cos t + 2 \sin t)\mathbf{j} + (\cos t - 2 \sin t)\mathbf{k}$$

73. Find a general expression for a nonzero vector orthogonal to the plane containing the curve.

$$\mathbf{r}(t) = (a \cos t + b \sin t)\mathbf{i} + (c \cos t + d \sin t)\mathbf{j} + (e \cos t + f \sin t)\mathbf{k},$$

where $\langle a, c, e \rangle \times \langle b, d, f \rangle \ne \mathbf{0}$.

Applications

Applications of parametric curves are considered in detail in Section 12.7.

74. Golf slice A golfer launches a tee shot down a horizontal fairway and it follows a path given by $\mathbf{r}(t) = \langle at, (75 - 0.1a)t, -5t^2 + 80t \rangle$, where $t \ge 0$ measures time in seconds and $\mathbf{r}$ has units of feet. The y-axis points straight down the fairway and the z-axis points vertically upward. The parameter a is the slice factor that determines how much the shot deviates from a straight path down the fairway.

a. With no slice ($a = 0$), sketch and describe the shot. How far does the ball travel horizontally (the distance between the point the ball leaves the ground and the point where it first strikes the ground)?

b. With a slice ($a = 0.2$), sketch and describe the shot. How far does the ball travel horizontally?

c. How far does the ball travel horizontally with $a = 2.5$?

Additional Exercises

75–77. Curves on spheres

75. Graph the curve $\mathbf{r}(t) = \langle \frac{1}{2} \sin 2t, \frac{1}{2}(1 - \cos 2t), \cos t \rangle$ and prove that it lies on the surface of a sphere centered at the origin.

76. Prove that for integers m and n, the curve

$$\mathbf{r}(t) = \langle a \sin mt \cos nt, b \sin mt \sin nt, c \cos mt \rangle$$

lies on the surface of a sphere provided $a^2 + b^2 = c^2$.

77. Find the period of the function in Exercise 76; that is, find the smallest positive real number T such that $\mathbf{r}(t + T) = \mathbf{r}(t)$ for all t.

78. Limits of vector functions Let $\mathbf{r}(t) = \langle f(t), g(t), h(t) \rangle$.

a. Assume that $\lim_{t \to a} \mathbf{r}(t) = \mathbf{L} = \langle L_1, L_2, L_3 \rangle$, which means that

$\lim_{t \to a} |\mathbf{r}(t) - \mathbf{L}| = 0$. Prove that

$$\lim_{t \to a} f(t) = L_1, \qquad \lim_{t \to a} g(t) = L_2, \quad \text{and} \quad \lim_{t \to a} h(t) = L_3.$$

b. Assume that $\lim_{t \to a} f(t) = L_1, \lim_{t \to a} g(t) = L_2$, and

$\lim_{t \to a} h(t) = L_3$. Prove that $\lim_{t \to a} \mathbf{r}(t) = \mathbf{L} = \langle L_1, L_2, L_3 \rangle$,

which means that $\lim_{t \to a} |\mathbf{r}(t) - \mathbf{L}| = 0$.

QUICK CHECK ANSWERS

1. The z-axis; the line $y = x$ in the xy-plane   **2.** When $t = 0$, the point on the line is P_0; when $t = 1$, the point on the line is P_1. ◄

12.6 Calculus of Vector-Valued Functions

We now turn to the topic of ultimate interest in this chapter: the calculus of vector-valued functions. Everything you learned about differentiating and integrating functions of the form $y = f(x)$ carries over to vector-valued functions $\mathbf{r}(t)$; you simply apply the rules of differentiation and integration to the individual components of $\mathbf{r}$.

The Derivative and Tangent Vector

Consider the function $\mathbf{r}(t) = f(t)\mathbf{i} + g(t)\mathbf{j} + h(t)\mathbf{k}$, where f, g, and h are differentiable functions on an interval $a < t < b$. The first task is to explain the meaning of the *derivative* of a vector-valued function and to show how to compute it. We begin with the definition of the derivative—now with a vector perspective:

$$\mathbf{r}'(t) = \lim_{\Delta t \to 0} \frac{\Delta \mathbf{r}}{\Delta t} = \lim_{\Delta t \to 0} \frac{\mathbf{r}(t + \Delta t) - \mathbf{r}(t)}{\Delta t}.$$

Before computing this limit, we look at its geometry. The function $\mathbf{r}(t) = f(t)\mathbf{i} + g(t)\mathbf{j} + h(t)\mathbf{k}$ describes a parameterized curve in space. Let P be a point on that curve associated with the position vector $\mathbf{r}(t)$ and let Q be a nearby point associated with the position vector $\mathbf{r}(t + \Delta t)$, where $\Delta t > 0$ is a small increment in t (Figure 12.78a). The difference $\Delta \mathbf{r} = \mathbf{r}(t + \Delta t) - \mathbf{r}(t)$ is the vector $\vec{PQ}$, where we assume $\Delta \mathbf{r} \neq \mathbf{0}$. Because Δt is a scalar, the direction of $\Delta \mathbf{r}/\Delta t$ is the same as the direction of $\vec{PQ}$.

> An analogous interpretation can be given for $\Delta t < 0$.

As Δt approaches 0, Q approaches P and the vector $\Delta \mathbf{r}/\Delta t$ approaches a limiting vector that we denote $\mathbf{r}'(t)$ (Figure 12.78b). This new vector $\mathbf{r}'(t)$ has two important interpretations.

- The vector $\mathbf{r}'(t)$ points in the direction of the curve at P. For this reason $\mathbf{r}'(t)$ is a *tangent vector* at P (provided it is not the zero vector).

- The vector $\mathbf{r}'(t)$ is the *derivative* of $\mathbf{r}$ with respect to t; it gives the rate of change of the function $\mathbf{r}(t)$ at the point P. In fact, if $\mathbf{r}(t)$ is the position function of a moving object, then $\mathbf{r}'(t)$ is the velocity vector of the object, which always points in the direction of motion, and $|\mathbf{r}'(t)|$ is the speed of the object.

> Section 12.7 is devoted to problems of motion in two and three dimensions.

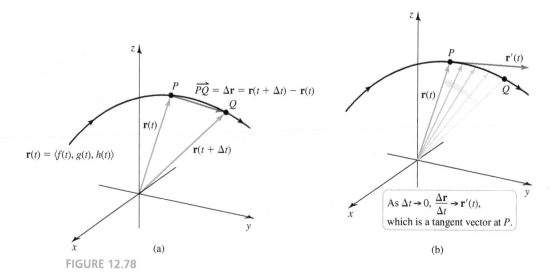

FIGURE 12.78

We now evaluate the limit that defines $\mathbf{r}'(t)$ by expressing $\mathbf{r}$ in terms of its components and using the properties of limits.

$$\mathbf{r}'(t) = \lim_{\Delta t \to 0} \frac{\mathbf{r}(t + \Delta t) - \mathbf{r}(t)}{\Delta t}$$

$$= \lim_{\Delta t \to 0} \frac{(f(t + \Delta t)\mathbf{i} + g(t + \Delta t)\mathbf{j} + h(t + \Delta t)\mathbf{k}) - (f(t)\mathbf{i} + g(t)\mathbf{j} + h(t)\mathbf{k})}{\Delta t}$$

Substitute components of $\mathbf{r}$.

$$= \lim_{\Delta t \to 0} \left[\frac{f(t + \Delta t) - f(t)}{\Delta t}\mathbf{i} + \frac{g(t + \Delta t) - g(t)}{\Delta t}\mathbf{j} + \frac{h(t + \Delta t) - h(t)}{\Delta t}\mathbf{k} \right]$$

Rearrange terms inside of limit.

$$= \underbrace{\lim_{\Delta t \to 0} \frac{f(t + \Delta t) - f(t)}{\Delta t}}_{f'(t)}\mathbf{i} + \underbrace{\lim_{\Delta t \to 0} \frac{g(t + \Delta t) - g(t)}{\Delta t}}_{g'(t)}\mathbf{j} + \underbrace{\lim_{\Delta t \to 0} \frac{h(t + \Delta t) - h(t)}{\Delta t}}_{h'(t)}\mathbf{k}$$

Limit of sum equals sum of limits.

Because f, g, and h are differentiable scalar-valued functions of the variable t, the three limits in the last step are identified as the derivatives of f, g, and h, respectively. Therefore, there are no surprises:

$$\mathbf{r}'(t) = f'(t)\mathbf{i} + g'(t)\mathbf{j} + h'(t)\mathbf{k}.$$

In other words, to differentiate the vector-valued function $\mathbf{r}(t)$, we simply differentiate each of its components with respect to t.

DEFINITION **Derivative and Tangent Vector**

Let $\mathbf{r}(t) = f(t)\mathbf{i} + g(t)\mathbf{j} + h(t)\mathbf{k}$, where f, g, and h are differentiable functions on (a, b). Then $\mathbf{r}$ has a **derivative** (or is **differentiable**) on (a, b) and

$$\mathbf{r}'(t) = f'(t)\mathbf{i} + g'(t)\mathbf{j} + h'(t)\mathbf{k}.$$

Provided $\mathbf{r}'(t) \neq \mathbf{0}$, $\mathbf{r}'(t)$ is a **tangent vector** (or velocity vector) at the point corresponding to $\mathbf{r}(t)$.

EXAMPLE 1 Derivative of vector functions Compute the derivative of the following functions.

a. $\mathbf{r}(t) = \langle t^3, 3t^2, t^3/6 \rangle$ **b.** $\mathbf{r}(t) = e^{-t}\mathbf{i} + 10\sqrt{t}\,\mathbf{j} + 2\cos 3t\,\mathbf{k}$

SOLUTION

a. $\mathbf{r}'(t) = \langle 3t^2, 6t, t^2/2 \rangle$; note that $\mathbf{r}$ is differentiable for all t and $\mathbf{r}'(0) = \mathbf{0}$.

b. $\mathbf{r}'(t) = -e^{-t}\mathbf{i} + \dfrac{5}{\sqrt{t}}\mathbf{j} - 6\sin 3t\,\mathbf{k}$; the function $\mathbf{r}$ is differentiable for $t > 0$.

Related Exercises 7–20 ◀

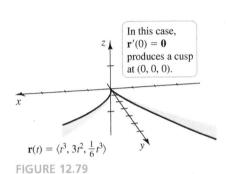

In this case, $\mathbf{r}'(0) = \mathbf{0}$ produces a cusp at $(0, 0, 0)$.

$\mathbf{r}(t) = \langle t^3, 3t^2, \frac{1}{6}t^3 \rangle$

FIGURE 12.79

> If a curve has a cusp at a point, then $\mathbf{r}'(t) = \mathbf{0}$ at that point. However, the converse is not true; it may happen that $\mathbf{r}'(t) = \mathbf{0}$ at a point that is not a cusp (Exercise 89).

QUICK CHECK 1 Let $\mathbf{r}(t) = \langle t, t, t \rangle$. Compute $\mathbf{r}'(t)$ and interpret the result. ◀

The condition that $\mathbf{r}'(t) \neq \mathbf{0}$ in order for the tangent vector to be defined requires explanation. Consider the function $\mathbf{r}(t) = \langle t^3, 3t^2, t^3/6 \rangle$. As shown in Example 1a, $\mathbf{r}'(0) = \mathbf{0}$; that is, all three components of $\mathbf{r}'(t)$ are zero simultaneously when $t = 0$. We see in Figure 12.79 that an otherwise smooth curve has a *cusp* or a sharp point at the origin. If $\mathbf{r}$ describes the motion of an object, then $\mathbf{r}'(t) = \mathbf{0}$ means that the velocity (and speed) of the object is zero at a point. At such a stationary point the object *may* change direction abruptly creating a cusp in its trajectory. For this reason, we say a function $\mathbf{r}(t) = \langle f(t), g(t), h(t) \rangle$ is **smooth** on an interval if f, g, and h are differentiable *and* $\mathbf{r}'(t) \neq \mathbf{0}$ on that interval. Smooth curves have no cusps or corners.

Unit Tangent Vector In situations in which only the direction (but not the length) of the tangent vector is of interest, we work with the *unit tangent vector*. It is the vector with magnitude 1, formed by dividing $\mathbf{r}'(t)$ by its length.

QUICK CHECK 2 Suppose $\mathbf{r}'(t)$ has units m/s. Explain why $\mathbf{T}(t) = \mathbf{r}'(t)/|\mathbf{r}'(t)|$ is dimensionless (has no units) and carries information only about direction. ◀

DEFINITION Unit Tangent Vector

Let $\mathbf{r} = f(t)\mathbf{i} + g(t)\mathbf{j} + h(t)\mathbf{k}$ be a smooth parameterized curve, for $a \le t \le b$. The **unit tangent vector** for a particular value of t is

$$\mathbf{T}(t) = \frac{\mathbf{r}'(t)}{|\mathbf{r}'(t)|}.$$

EXAMPLE 2 Unit tangent vectors Find the unit tangent vectors for the following parameterized curves.

a. $\mathbf{r}(t) = \langle t^2, 4t, 4\ln t \rangle$,   for $t > 0$
b. $\mathbf{r}(t) = \langle 10, 3\cos t, 3\sin t \rangle$,   for $0 \le t \le 2\pi$

SOLUTION

a. A tangent vector is $\mathbf{r}'(t) = \langle 2t, 4, 4/t \rangle$, which has a magnitude of

$$
\begin{aligned}
|\mathbf{r}'(t)| &= \sqrt{(2t)^2 + 4^2 + \left(\frac{4}{t}\right)^2} && \text{Definition of magnitude} \\
&= \sqrt{4t^2 + 16 + \frac{16}{t^2}} && \text{Expand.} \\
&= \sqrt{\left(2t + \frac{4}{t}\right)^2} && \text{Factor.} \\
&= 2t + \frac{4}{t}. && \text{Simplify.}
\end{aligned}
$$

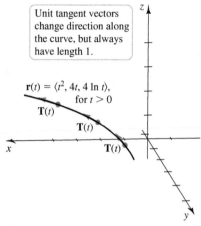

Unit tangent vectors change direction along the curve, but always have length 1.

$\mathbf{r}(t) = \langle t^2, 4t, 4 \ln t \rangle$, for $t > 0$

FIGURE 12.80

Therefore, the unit tangent vector for a particular value of t is

$$\mathbf{T}(t) = \frac{\langle 2t, 4, 4/t \rangle}{2t + 4/t}.$$

As shown in Figure 12.80, the unit tangent vectors change direction along the curve but maintain unit length.

b. In this case, $\mathbf{r}'(t) = \langle 0, -3 \sin t, 3 \cos t \rangle$ and

$$|\mathbf{r}'(t)| = \sqrt{0^2 + (-3 \sin t)^2 + (3 \cos t)^2} = \sqrt{9(\underbrace{\sin^2 t + \cos^2 t}_{1})} = 3.$$

Therefore, the unit tangent vector for a particular value of t is

$$\mathbf{T}(t) = \frac{1}{3} \langle 0, -3 \sin t, 3 \cos t \rangle = \langle 0, -\sin t, \cos t \rangle.$$

The direction of $\mathbf{T}$ changes along the curve, but its length remains 1.

Related Exercises 21–30◄

Derivative Rules   The rules for derivatives for single-variable functions either carry over directly to vector-valued functions or have close analogs. These rules are generally proved by working on the individual components of the vector function.

> **THEOREM 12.7**   **Derivative Rules**
>
> Let $\mathbf{u}$ and $\mathbf{v}$ be differentiable vector-valued functions and let f be a differentiable scalar-valued function, all at a point t. Let $\mathbf{c}$ be a constant vector. The following rules apply.
>
> **1.** $\dfrac{d}{dt}(\mathbf{c}) = \mathbf{0}$ Constant Rule
>
> **2.** $\dfrac{d}{dt}(\mathbf{u}(t) + \mathbf{v}(t)) = \mathbf{u}'(t) + \mathbf{v}'(t)$ Sum Rule
>
> **3.** $\dfrac{d}{dt}(f(t)\mathbf{u}(t)) = f'(t)\mathbf{u}(t) + f(t)\mathbf{u}'(t)$ Product Rule
>
> **4.** $\dfrac{d}{dt}(\mathbf{u}(f(t))) = \mathbf{u}'(f(t))f'(t)$ Chain Rule
>
> **5.** $\dfrac{d}{dt}(\mathbf{u}(t) \cdot \mathbf{v}(t)) = \mathbf{u}'(t) \cdot \mathbf{v}(t) + \mathbf{u}(t) \cdot \mathbf{v}'(t)$ Dot Product Rule
>
> **6.** $\dfrac{d}{dt}(\mathbf{u}(t) \times \mathbf{v}(t)) = \mathbf{u}'(t) \times \mathbf{v}(t) + \mathbf{u}(t) \times \mathbf{v}'(t)$ Cross Product Rule

> With the exception of the Cross Product Rule, these rules apply to vector-valued functions with any number of components. Notice that we have three new product rules, all of which mimic the original Product Rule. In Rule 4, $\mathbf{u}$ must be differentiable at $f(t)$.

QUICK CHECK 3   Let $\mathbf{u}(t) = \langle t, t, t \rangle$ and $\mathbf{v}(t) = \langle 1, 1, 1 \rangle$. Compute $\dfrac{d}{dt}[\mathbf{u}(t) \cdot \mathbf{v}(t)]$ using Derivative Rule 5 and show that it agrees with the result obtained by first computing the dot product and differentiating directly. ◄

The proofs of these rules are assigned in Exercises 86–88 with the exception of the following representative proofs.

Proof of the Chain Rule: Let $\mathbf{u}(t) = \langle u_1(t), u_2(t), u_3(t) \rangle$, which implies that

$$\mathbf{u}(f(t)) = u_1(f(t))\,\mathbf{i} + u_2(f(t))\,\mathbf{j} + u_3(f(t))\,\mathbf{k}.$$

We now apply the ordinary Chain Rule componentwise:

$$\frac{d}{dt}\big(\mathbf{u}(f(t))\big) = \frac{d}{dt}\big(u_1(f(t))\mathbf{i} + u_2(f(t))\mathbf{j} + u_3(f(t))\mathbf{k}\big) \qquad \text{Components of } \mathbf{u}$$

$$= \frac{d}{dt}\big(u_1(f(t))\big)\mathbf{i} + \frac{d}{dt}\big(u_2(f(t))\big)\mathbf{j} + \frac{d}{dt}\big(u_3(f(t))\big)\mathbf{k} \qquad \text{Derivative of a sum}$$

$$= u_1{'}(f(t))f'(t)\mathbf{i} + u_2{'}(f(t))f'(t)\mathbf{j} + u_3{'}(f(t))f'(t)\mathbf{k} \qquad \text{Chain Rule}$$

$$= \big(u_1{'}(f(t))\mathbf{i} + u_2{'}(f(t))\mathbf{j} + u_3{'}(f(t))\mathbf{k}\big)f'(t) \qquad \text{Factor } f'(t).$$

$$= \mathbf{u}'(f(t))f'(t). \qquad \text{Definition of } \mathbf{u}'$$

◄

Proof of the Dot Product Rule: One proof of the Dot Product Rule uses the standard Product Rule on each component. Let $\mathbf{u}(t) = \langle u_1(t), u_2(t), u_3(t) \rangle$ and $\mathbf{v}(t) = \langle v_1(t), v_2(t), v_3(t) \rangle$. Then

$$\frac{d}{dt}(\mathbf{u} \cdot \mathbf{v}) = \frac{d}{dt}(u_1 v_1 + u_2 v_2 + u_3 v_3) \qquad \text{Definition of dot product}$$

$$= u_1{'} v_1 + u_1 v_1{'} + u_2{'} v_2 + u_2 v_2{'} + u_3{'} v_3 + u_3 v_3{'} \qquad \text{Product Rule}$$

$$= \underbrace{u_1{'} v_1 + u_2{'} v_2 + u_3{'} v_3}_{\mathbf{u}' \cdot \mathbf{v}} + \underbrace{u_1 v_1{'} + u_2 v_2{'} + u_3 v_3{'}}_{\mathbf{u} \cdot \mathbf{v}'} \qquad \text{Rearrange.}$$

$$= \mathbf{u}' \cdot \mathbf{v} + \mathbf{u} \cdot \mathbf{v}'.$$

◄

EXAMPLE 3   **Derivative rules** Compute the following derivatives, where

$$\mathbf{u}(t) = t\mathbf{i} + t^2\mathbf{j} - t^3\mathbf{k} \quad \text{and} \quad \mathbf{v}(t) = \sin t\,\mathbf{i} + 2\cos t\,\mathbf{j} + \cos t\,\mathbf{k}.$$

a. $\dfrac{d}{dt}(\mathbf{v}(t^2))$ **b.** $\dfrac{d}{dt}(t^2\,\mathbf{v}(t))$ **c.** $\dfrac{d}{dt}(\mathbf{u}(t) \cdot \mathbf{v}(t))$

SOLUTION

a. Note that $\mathbf{v}'(t) = \cos t\,\mathbf{i} - 2\sin t\,\mathbf{j} - \sin t\,\mathbf{k}$. Using the Chain Rule, we have

$$\frac{d}{dt}(\mathbf{v}(t^2)) = \mathbf{v}'(t^2)\frac{d}{dt}(t^2) = \underbrace{(\cos t^2\mathbf{i} - 2\sin t^2\mathbf{j} - \sin t^2\mathbf{k})}_{\mathbf{v}'(t^2)}(2t).$$

b. $\dfrac{d}{dt}(t^2\,\mathbf{v}(t)) = \dfrac{d}{dt}(t^2)\mathbf{v}(t) + t^2\dfrac{d}{dt}(\mathbf{v}(t))$ \hspace{2cm} Product Rule

$$= 2t\,\mathbf{v}(t) + t^2\,\mathbf{v}'(t)$$

$$= 2t\underbrace{(\sin t\,\mathbf{i} + 2\cos t\,\mathbf{j} + \cos t\,\mathbf{k})}_{\mathbf{v}(t)} + t^2\underbrace{(\cos t\,\mathbf{i} - 2\sin t\,\mathbf{j} - \sin t\,\mathbf{k})}_{\mathbf{v}'(t)}$$

Differentiate.

$$= (2t\sin t + t^2\cos t)\mathbf{i} + (4t\cos t - 2t^2\sin t)\mathbf{j} + (2t\cos t - t^2\sin t)\mathbf{k}$$

Collect terms.

c. $\dfrac{d}{dt}(\mathbf{u}(t) \cdot \mathbf{v}(t)) = \mathbf{u}'(t) \cdot \mathbf{v}(t) + \mathbf{u}(t) \cdot \mathbf{v}'(t)$ \hspace{2cm} Dot Product Rule

$$= (\mathbf{i} + 2t\mathbf{j} - 3t^2\mathbf{k}) \cdot (\sin t\,\mathbf{i} + 2\cos t\,\mathbf{j} + \cos t\,\mathbf{k})$$
$$+ (t\mathbf{i} + t^2\mathbf{j} - t^3\mathbf{k}) \cdot (\cos t\,\mathbf{i} - 2\sin t\,\mathbf{j} - \sin t\,\mathbf{k}) \qquad \text{Differentiate.}$$

$$= (\sin t + 4t\cos t - 3t^2\cos t) + (t\cos t - 2t^2\sin t + t^3\sin t) \qquad \text{Dot products}$$

$$= (1 - 2t^2 + t^3)\sin t + (5t - 3t^2)\cos t \qquad \text{Simplify.}$$

Note that the result is a scalar. The same result is obtained if you first compute $\mathbf{u} \cdot \mathbf{v}$ and then differentiate.

Related Exercises 31–40◄

Higher Derivatives Higher derivatives of vector-valued functions are computed in the expected way: We simply differentiate each component multiple times. Second derivatives feature prominently in the next section, playing the role of acceleration.

EXAMPLE 4 **Higher derivatives** Compute the first, second, and third derivative of $\mathbf{r}(t) = \langle t^2, 8 \ln t, 3e^{-2t} \rangle$.

SOLUTION Differentiating once, we have $\mathbf{r}'(t) = \langle 2t, 8/t, -6e^{-2t} \rangle$. Differentiating again produces $\mathbf{r}''(t) = \langle 2, -8/t^2, 12e^{-2t} \rangle$. Differentiating once more we have $\mathbf{r}'''(t) = \langle 0, 16/t^3, -24e^{-2t} \rangle$.

Related Exercises 41–46 ◀

Integrals of Vector-Valued Functions

An **antiderivative** of the vector function $\mathbf{r}$ is a function $\mathbf{R}$ such that $\mathbf{R}' = \mathbf{r}$. If

$$\mathbf{r} = f\mathbf{i} + g\mathbf{j} + h\mathbf{k},$$

then an antiderivative of $\mathbf{r}$ is

$$\mathbf{R} = F\mathbf{i} + G\mathbf{j} + H\mathbf{k},$$

where F, G, and H are antiderivatives of f, g, and h, respectively. This fact follows by differentiating the components of $\mathbf{R}$ and verifying that $\mathbf{R}' = \mathbf{r}$. The collection of all antiderivatives of $\mathbf{r}$ is the *indefinite integral* of $\mathbf{r}$.

> **DEFINITION** **Indefinite Integral of a Vector-Valued Function**
>
> Let $\mathbf{r} = f\mathbf{i} + g\mathbf{j} + h\mathbf{k}$ be a vector function and let $\mathbf{R} = F\mathbf{i} + G\mathbf{j} + H\mathbf{k}$, where F, G, and H are antiderivatives of f, g, and h, respectively. The **indefinite integral** of $\mathbf{r}$ is
>
> $$\int \mathbf{r}(t) \, dt = \mathbf{R}(t) + \mathbf{C},$$
>
> where $\mathbf{C}$ is an arbitrary constant vector.

EXAMPLE 5 **Indefinite integrals** Compute

$$\int \left[\frac{t}{\sqrt{t^2 + 2}}\mathbf{i} + e^{-3t}\mathbf{j} + (\sin 4t + 1)\mathbf{k} \right] dt.$$

> The substitution $u = t^2 + 2$ is used to evaluate the **i**-component of the integral.

SOLUTION We compute the indefinite integral of each component:

$$\int \left[\frac{t}{\sqrt{t^2 + 2}}\mathbf{i} + e^{-3t}\mathbf{j} + (\sin 4t + 1)\mathbf{k} \right] dt$$

$$= \left(\sqrt{t^2 + 2} + C_1 \right)\mathbf{i} + \left(-\frac{1}{3}e^{-3t} + C_2 \right)\mathbf{j} + \left(-\frac{1}{4}\cos 4t + t + C_3 \right)\mathbf{k}$$

$$= \sqrt{t^2 + 2}\,\mathbf{i} - \frac{1}{3}e^{-3t}\mathbf{j} + \left(t - \frac{1}{4}\cos 4t \right)\mathbf{k} + \mathbf{C}. \quad \text{Let } \mathbf{C} = C_1\mathbf{i} + C_2\mathbf{j} + C_3\mathbf{k}.$$

In the last step, we combine the arbitrary constants for each component and use one constant vector $\mathbf{C}$. You may suppress C_1, C_2, and C_3 and append the vector constant $\mathbf{C}$ at the end of the calculation.

Related Exercises 47–52 ◀

QUICK CHECK 4 Let $\mathbf{r}(t) = \langle 1, 2t, 3t^2 \rangle$. Compute $\int \mathbf{r}(t) \, dt$. ◀

EXAMPLE 6 **Finding one antiderivative** Find $\mathbf{r}(t)$ such that $\mathbf{r}'(t) = \langle e^2, \sin t, t \rangle$ and $\mathbf{r}(0) = \mathbf{j}$.

SOLUTION The required function $\mathbf{r}$ is an antiderivative of $\langle e^2, \sin t, t \rangle$:

$$\mathbf{r}(t) = \int \langle e^2, \sin t, t \rangle \, dt = \left\langle e^2 t, -\cos t, \frac{t^2}{2} \right\rangle + \mathbf{C},$$

where $\mathbf{C}$ is an arbitrary constant vector. The condition $\mathbf{r}(0) = \mathbf{j}$ allows us to determine $\mathbf{C}$; substituting $t = 0$ implies that $\mathbf{r}(0) = \langle 0, -1, 0 \rangle + \mathbf{C} = \mathbf{j}$, where $\mathbf{j} = \langle 0, 1, 0 \rangle$. Solving for $\mathbf{C}$, we have $\mathbf{C} = \langle 0, 1, 0 \rangle - \langle 0, -1, 0 \rangle = \langle 0, 2, 0 \rangle$. Therefore,

$$\mathbf{r}(t) = \left\langle e^2 t, 2 - \cos t, \frac{t^2}{2} \right\rangle.$$

Related Exercises 53–58 ◄

Definite integrals are evaluated by applying the Fundamental Theorem of Calculus to each component of a vector-valued function.

DEFINITION **Definite Integral of a Vector-Valued Function**

Let $\mathbf{r}(t) = f(t)\,\mathbf{i} + g(t)\,\mathbf{j} + h(t)\,\mathbf{k}$, where f, g, and h are integrable on the interval $[a, b]$.

$$\int_a^b \mathbf{r}(t) \, dt = \left[\int_a^b f(t) \, dt \right] \mathbf{i} + \left[\int_a^b g(t) \, dt \right] \mathbf{j} + \left[\int_a^b h(t) \, dt \right] \mathbf{k}$$

EXAMPLE 7 **Definite integrals** Evaluate

$$\int_0^\pi \left[\mathbf{i} + 3 \cos \frac{t}{2} \mathbf{j} - 4t\,\mathbf{k} \right] dt.$$

SOLUTION

$$\int_0^\pi \left[\mathbf{i} + 3 \cos \frac{t}{2} \mathbf{j} - 4t\,\mathbf{k} \right] dt = t\mathbf{i} \Big|_0^\pi + 6 \sin \frac{t}{2} \mathbf{j} \Big|_0^\pi - 2t^2 \mathbf{k} \Big|_0^\pi \quad \text{Evaluate integrals for each component.}$$

$$= \pi\,\mathbf{i} + 6\mathbf{j} - 2\pi^2\,\mathbf{k} \quad \text{Simplify.}$$

Related Exercises 59–66 ◄

With the tools of differentiation and integration in hand, we are prepared to tackle some practical problems, notably the motion of objects in space.

SECTION 12.6 EXERCISES

Review Questions

1. Explain how to compute the derivative of $\mathbf{r}(t) = \langle f(t), g(t), h(t) \rangle$.

2. Explain the geometric meaning of $\mathbf{r}'(t)$.

3. Given a tangent vector on an oriented curve, how do you find the unit tangent vector?

4. Compute $\mathbf{r}''(t)$ when $\mathbf{r}(t) = \langle t^{10}, 8t, \cos t \rangle$.

5. How do you find the indefinite integral of $\mathbf{r}(t) = \langle f(t), g(t), h(t) \rangle$?

6. How do you evaluate $\int_a^b \mathbf{r}(t) \, dt$?

Basic Skills

7–14. Derivatives of vector-valued functions *Differentiate the following functions.*

7. $\mathbf{r}(t) = \langle \cos t, t^2, \sin t \rangle$

8. $\mathbf{r}(t) = \langle 4e^t, 5, \ln t \rangle$

9. $\mathbf{r}(t) = \langle 2t^3, 6\sqrt{t}, 3/t \rangle$

10. $\mathbf{r}(t) = \langle 4, 3 \cos 2t, 2 \sin 3t \rangle$

11. $\mathbf{r}(t) = \langle e^t, 2e^{-t}, -4e^{2t} \rangle$

12. $\mathbf{r}(t) = \langle \tan t, \sec t, \cos^2 t \rangle$

13. $\mathbf{r}(t) = \langle te^{-t}, t \ln t, t \cos t \rangle$

14. $\mathbf{r}(t) = \langle (t + 1)^{-1}, \tan^{-1} t, \ln (t + 1) \rangle$

15–20. Tangent vectors *Find a tangent vector at the given value of t for the following curves.*

15. $\mathbf{r}(t) = \langle t, 3t^2, t^3 \rangle, t = 1$

16. $\mathbf{r}(t) = \langle e^t, e^{3t}, e^{5t} \rangle, t = 0$

17. $\mathbf{r}(t) = \langle t, \cos 2t, 2 \sin t \rangle, t = \pi/2$

18. $\mathbf{r}(t) = \langle 2 \sin t, 3 \cos t, \sin (t/2) \rangle, t = \pi$

19. $\mathbf{r}(t) = \langle 2t^4, 6t^{3/2}, 10/t \rangle, t = 1$

20. $\mathbf{r}(t) = \langle 2e^t, e^{-2t}, 4e^{2t} \rangle, t = \ln 3$

21–26. Unit tangent vectors *Find the unit tangent vector for the following parameterized curves.*

21. $\mathbf{r}(t) = \langle 2t, 2t, t \rangle$, for $0 \le t \le 1$

22. $\mathbf{r}(t) = \langle \cos t, \sin t, 2 \rangle$, for $0 \le t \le 2\pi$

23. $\mathbf{r}(t) = \langle 8, \cos 2t, 2 \sin 2t \rangle$, for $0 \le t \le 2\pi$

24. $\mathbf{r}(t) = \langle \sin t, \cos t, \cos t \rangle$, for $0 \le t \le 2\pi$

25. $\mathbf{r}(t) = \langle t, 2, 2/t \rangle$, for $t \ge 1$

26. $\mathbf{r}(t) = \langle e^{2t}, 2e^{2t}, 2e^{-3t} \rangle$, for $t \ge 0$

27–30. Unit tangent vectors at a point *Find the unit tangent vector at the given value of t for the following parameterized curves.*

27. $\mathbf{r}(t) = \langle \cos 2t, 4, 3 \sin 2t \rangle$, for $0 \le t \le \pi; t = \pi/2$

28. $\mathbf{r}(t) = \langle \sin t, \cos t, e^{-t} \rangle$, for $0 \le t \le \pi; t = 0$

29. $\mathbf{r}(t) = \langle 6t, 6, 3/t \rangle$, for $0 < t < 2; t = 1$

30. $\mathbf{r}(t) = \langle \sqrt{7}e^t, 3e^t, 3e^t \rangle$, for $0 \le t \le 1; t = \ln 2$

31–36. Derivative rules *Let*

$$\mathbf{u}(t) = 2t^3\mathbf{i} + (t^2 - 1)\mathbf{j} - 8\mathbf{k} \text{ and } \mathbf{v}(t) = e^t\mathbf{i} + 2e^{-t}\mathbf{j} - e^{2t}\mathbf{k}.$$

Compute the derivative of the following functions.

31. $(t^{12} + 3t)\mathbf{u}(t)$

32. $(4t^8 - 6t^3)\mathbf{v}(t)$

33. $\mathbf{u}(t^4 - 2t)$

34. $\mathbf{v}(\sqrt{t})$

35. $\mathbf{u}(t) \cdot \mathbf{v}(t)$

36. $\mathbf{u}(t) \times \mathbf{v}(t)$

37–40. Derivative rules *Compute the following derivatives.*

37. $\dfrac{d}{dt}[t^2(\mathbf{i} + 2\mathbf{j} - 2t\mathbf{k}) \cdot (e^t\mathbf{i} + 2e^t\mathbf{j} - 3e^{-t}\mathbf{k})]$

38. $\dfrac{d}{dt}[(t^3\mathbf{i} - 2t\mathbf{j} - 2\mathbf{k}) \times (t\mathbf{i} - t^2\mathbf{j} - t^3\mathbf{k})]$

39. $\dfrac{d}{dt}[(3t^2\mathbf{i} + \sqrt{t}\mathbf{j} - 2t^{-1}\mathbf{k}) \cdot (\cos t\mathbf{i} + \sin 2t\mathbf{j} - 3t\mathbf{k})]$

40. $\dfrac{d}{dt}[(t^3\mathbf{i} + 6\mathbf{j} - 2\sqrt{t}\mathbf{k}) \times (3t\mathbf{i} - 12t^2\mathbf{j} - 6t^{-2}\mathbf{k})]$

41–46. Higher derivatives *Compute $\mathbf{r}''(t)$ and $\mathbf{r}'''(t)$ for the following functions.*

41. $\mathbf{r}(t) = \langle t^2 + 1, t + 1, 1 \rangle$

42. $\mathbf{r}(t) = \langle 3t^{12} - t^2, t^8 + t^3, t^{-4} - 2 \rangle$

43. $\mathbf{r}(t) = \langle \cos 3t, \sin 4t, \cos 6t \rangle$

44. $\mathbf{r}(t) = \langle e^{4t}, 2e^{-4t} + 1, 2e^{-t} \rangle$

45. $\mathbf{r}(t) = \sqrt{t+4}\mathbf{i} + \dfrac{t}{t+1}\mathbf{j} - e^{-t^2}\mathbf{k}$

46. $\mathbf{r}(t) = \tan t\mathbf{i} + \left(t + \dfrac{1}{t}\right)\mathbf{j} - \ln (t + 1)\mathbf{k}$

47–52. Indefinite integrals *Compute the indefinite integral of the following functions.*

47. $\mathbf{r}(t) = \langle t^3 - 3t, 2t - 1, 10 \rangle$

48. $\mathbf{r}(t) = \langle 5t^{-4} - t^2, t^6 - 4t^3, 2/t \rangle$

49. $\mathbf{r}(t) = \langle 2 \cos t, 2 \sin 3t, 4 \cos 8t \rangle$

50. $\mathbf{r}(t) = te^t\mathbf{i} + t \sin t^2\mathbf{j} - \dfrac{2t}{\sqrt{t^2 + 4}}\mathbf{k}$

51. $\mathbf{r}(t) = e^{3t}\mathbf{i} + \dfrac{1}{1 + t^2}\mathbf{j} - \dfrac{1}{\sqrt{2t}}\mathbf{k}$

52. $\mathbf{r}(t) = 2^t\mathbf{i} + \dfrac{1}{1 + 2t}\mathbf{j} + \ln t\mathbf{k}$

53–58. Finding r from r′ *Find the function $\mathbf{r}$ that satisfies the given condition.*

53. $\mathbf{r}'(t) = \langle e^t, \sin t, \sec^2 t \rangle; \ \mathbf{r}(0) = \langle 2, 2, 2 \rangle$

54. $\mathbf{r}'(t) = \langle 0, 2, 2t \rangle; \ \mathbf{r}(1) = \langle 4, 3, -5 \rangle$

55. $\mathbf{r}'(t) = \langle 1, 2t, 3t^2 \rangle; \ \mathbf{r}(1) = \langle 4, 3, -5 \rangle$

56. $\mathbf{r}'(t) = \langle \sqrt{t}, \cos \pi t, 4/t \rangle; \ \mathbf{r}(1) = \langle 2, 3, 4 \rangle$

57. $\mathbf{r}'(t) = \langle e^{2t}, 1 - 2e^{-t}, 1 - 2e^t \rangle; \ \mathbf{r}(0) = \langle 1, 1, 1 \rangle$

58. $\mathbf{r}'(t) = \dfrac{t}{t^2 + 1}\mathbf{i} + te^{-t^2}\mathbf{j} - \dfrac{2t}{\sqrt{t^2 + 4}}\mathbf{k}; \ \mathbf{r}(0) = \mathbf{i} + \dfrac{3}{2}\mathbf{j} - 3\mathbf{k}$

59–66. Definite integrals *Evaluate the following definite integrals.*

59. $\displaystyle\int_{-1}^{1} (\mathbf{i} + t\mathbf{j} + 3t^2\mathbf{k})\, dt$

60. $\displaystyle\int_{1}^{4} (6t^2\mathbf{i} + 8t^3\mathbf{j} + 9t^2\mathbf{k})\, dt$

61. $\displaystyle\int_{0}^{\ln 2} (e^t\mathbf{i} + e^t \cos(\pi e^t)\mathbf{j})\, dt$

62. $\displaystyle\int_{1/2}^{1} \left(\dfrac{3}{1 + 2t}\mathbf{i} - \pi \csc^2\left(\dfrac{\pi}{2}t\right)\mathbf{k}\right)\, dt$

63. $\displaystyle\int_{-\pi}^{\pi} (\sin t\mathbf{i} + \cos t\mathbf{j} + 2t\mathbf{k})\, dt$

64. $\displaystyle\int_{0}^{\ln 2} (e^{-t}\mathbf{i} + 2e^{2t}\mathbf{j} - 4e^t\mathbf{k})\, dt$

65. $\displaystyle\int_{0}^{2} te^t(\mathbf{i} + 2\mathbf{j} - \mathbf{k})\, dt$

66. $\displaystyle\int_{0}^{\pi/4} (\sec^2 t\mathbf{i} - 2 \cos t\mathbf{j} - \mathbf{k})\, dt$

Further Explorations

67. Explain why or why not Determine whether the following statements are true and give an explanation or counterexample.

a. The vectors $\mathbf{r}(t)$ and $\mathbf{r}'(t)$ are parallel for all values of t in the domain.

b. The curve described by the function $\mathbf{r}(t) = \langle t, t^2 - 2t, \cos \pi t \rangle$ is smooth, for $-\infty < t < \infty$.

c. If f, g, and h are odd integrable functions and a is a real number, then

$$\int_{-a}^{a} (f(t)\mathbf{i} + g(t)\mathbf{j} + h(t)\mathbf{k})\, dt = \mathbf{0}.$$

68–71. Tangent lines *Suppose the vector-valued function $\mathbf{r}(t) = \langle f(t), g(t), h(t) \rangle$ is smooth on an interval containing the point $(f(t_0), g(t_0), h(t_0))$. The line tangent to $\mathbf{r}(t)$ at $t = t_0$ is the line parallel to the tangent vector $\mathbf{r}'(t_0)$ that passes through $(f(t_0), g(t_0), h(t_0))$. For each of the following functions, find the line tangent to the curve at $t = t_0$.*

68. $\mathbf{r}(t) = \langle e^t, e^{2t}, e^{3t} \rangle$; $t_0 = 0$

69. $\mathbf{r}(t) = \langle 2 + \cos t, 3 + \sin 2t, t \rangle$; $t_0 = \pi/2$

70. $\mathbf{r}(t) = \langle \sqrt{2t + 1}, \sin \pi t, 4 \rangle$; $t_0 = 4$

71. $\mathbf{r}(t) = \langle 3t - 1, 7t + 2, t^2 \rangle$; $t_0 = 1$

72–77. Derivative rules *Let $\mathbf{u}(t) = \langle 1, t, t^2 \rangle$, $\mathbf{v}(t) = \langle t^2, -2t, 1 \rangle$, and $g(t) = 2\sqrt{t}$. Compute the derivatives of the following functions.*

72. $\mathbf{u}(t^3)$ **73.** $\mathbf{v}(e^t)$ **74.** $g(t)\mathbf{v}(t)$

75. $\mathbf{v}(g(t))$ **76.** $\mathbf{u}(t) \cdot \mathbf{v}(t)$ **77.** $\mathbf{u}(t) \times \mathbf{v}(t)$

78–83. Relationship between r and r′

78. Consider the circle $\mathbf{r}(t) = \langle a \cos t, a \sin t \rangle$, for $0 \le t \le 2\pi$, where a is a positive real number. Compute $\mathbf{r}'$ and show that it is orthogonal to $\mathbf{r}$ for all t.

79. Consider the parabola $\mathbf{r}(t) = \langle at^2 + 1, t \rangle$, for $-\infty < t < \infty$, where a is a positive real number. Find all points on the parabola at which $\mathbf{r}$ and $\mathbf{r}'$ are orthogonal.

80. Consider the curve $\mathbf{r}(t) = \langle \sqrt{t}, 1, t \rangle$, for $t > 0$. Find all points on the curve at which $\mathbf{r}$ and $\mathbf{r}'$ are orthogonal.

81. Consider the helix $\mathbf{r}(t) = \langle \cos t, \sin t, t \rangle$, for $-\infty < t < \infty$. Find all points on the helix at which $\mathbf{r}$ and $\mathbf{r}'$ are orthogonal.

82. Consider the ellipse $\mathbf{r}(t) = \langle 2 \cos t, 8 \sin t, 0 \rangle$, for $0 \le t \le 2\pi$. Find all points on the ellipse at which $\mathbf{r}$ and $\mathbf{r}'$ are orthogonal.

83. Give two families of curves in $\mathbb{R}^3$ where $\mathbf{r}$ and $\mathbf{r}'$ are parallel for all t in the domain.

84. Derivative rules Suppose $\mathbf{u}$ and $\mathbf{v}$ are differentiable functions at $t = 0$ with $\mathbf{u}(0) = \langle 0, 1, 1 \rangle$, $\mathbf{u}'(0) = \langle 0, 7, 1 \rangle$, $\mathbf{v}(0) = \langle 0, 1, 1 \rangle$, and $\mathbf{v}'(0) = \langle 1, 1, 2 \rangle$. Evaluate the following expressions.

a. $\dfrac{d}{dt}(\mathbf{u} \cdot \mathbf{v})\Big|_{t=0}$

b. $\dfrac{d}{dt}(\mathbf{u} \times \mathbf{v})\Big|_{t=0}$

c. $\dfrac{d}{dt}(\cos t\, \mathbf{u}(t))\Big|_{t=0}$

Additional Exercises

85. Vectors r and r′ for lines

a. If $\mathbf{r}(t) = \langle at, bt, ct \rangle$ with $\langle a, b, c \rangle \ne \langle 0, 0, 0 \rangle$, show that the angle between $\mathbf{r}$ and $\mathbf{r}'$ is constant for all $t > 0$.

b. If $\mathbf{r}(t) = \langle x_0 + at, y_0 + bt, z_0 + ct \rangle$, where x_0, y_0, and z_0 are not all zero, show that the angle between $\mathbf{r}$ and $\mathbf{r}'$ varies with t.

c. Explain the results of parts (a) and (b) geometrically.

86. Proof of Sum Rule By expressing $\mathbf{u}$ and $\mathbf{v}$ in terms of their components, prove that

$$\frac{d}{dt}(\mathbf{u}(t) + \mathbf{v}(t)) = \mathbf{u}'(t) + \mathbf{v}'(t).$$

87. Proof of Product Rule By expressing $\mathbf{u}$ in terms of its components, prove that

$$\frac{d}{dt}(f(t)\mathbf{u}(t)) = f'(t)\mathbf{u}(t) + f(t)\mathbf{u}'(t).$$

88. Proof of Cross Product Rule Prove that

$$\frac{d}{dt}(\mathbf{u}(t) \times \mathbf{v}(t)) = \mathbf{u}'(t) \times \mathbf{v}(t) + \mathbf{u}(t) \times \mathbf{v}'(t).$$

There are two ways to proceed: Either express $\mathbf{u}$ and $\mathbf{v}$ in terms of their three components or use the definition of the derivative.

89. Cusps and noncusps

a. Graph the curve $\mathbf{r}(t) = \langle t^3, t^3 \rangle$. Show that $\mathbf{r}'(0) = \mathbf{0}$ and the curve does not have a cusp at $t = 0$. Explain.

b. Graph the curve $\mathbf{r}(t) = \langle t^3, t^2 \rangle$. Show that $\mathbf{r}'(0) = \mathbf{0}$ and the curve has a cusp at $t = 0$. Explain.

c. The functions $\mathbf{r}(t) = \langle t, t^2 \rangle$ and $\mathbf{p}(t) = \langle t^2, t^4 \rangle$ both satisfy $y = x^2$. Explain how the curves they parameterize are different.

d. Consider the curve $\mathbf{r}(t) = \langle t^m, t^n \rangle$, where $m > 1$ and $n > 1$ are integers with no common factors. Is it true that the curve has a cusp at $t = 0$ if one (not both) of m and n is even? Explain.

90. Motion on a sphere Prove that $\mathbf{r}$ describes a curve that lies on the surface of a sphere centered at the origin ($x^2 + y^2 + z^2 = a^2$ with $a \ge 0$) if and only if $\mathbf{r}$ and $\mathbf{r}'$ are orthogonal at all points of the curve.

QUICK CHECK ANSWERS

1. $\mathbf{r}(t)$ describes a line, so its tangent vector $\mathbf{r}'(t) = \langle 1, 1, 1 \rangle$ has constant direction and magnitude.
2. Both $\mathbf{r}'$ and $|\mathbf{r}'|$ have units of m/s. In forming $\mathbf{r}'/|\mathbf{r}'|$, the units cancel and $\mathbf{T}(t)$ is without units. **3.** $\dfrac{d}{dt}[\mathbf{u}(t) \cdot \mathbf{v}(t)] =$
$\langle 1, 1, 1 \rangle \cdot \langle 1, 1, 1 \rangle + \langle t, t, t \rangle \cdot \langle 0, 0, 0 \rangle = 3$.
$\dfrac{d}{dt}[\langle t, t, t \rangle \cdot \langle 1, 1, 1 \rangle] = \dfrac{d}{dt}[3t] = 3$. **4.** $\langle t, t^2, t^3 \rangle + \mathbf{C}$, where $\mathbf{C} = \langle a, b, c \rangle$ and a, b, and c are real numbers.

12.7 Motion in Space

It is a remarkable fact that given the forces acting on an object and its initial position and velocity, the motion of the object in three-dimensional space can be modeled for all future times. To be sure, the accuracy of the results depends on how well the various forces on the object are described. For example, it may be more difficult to predict the trajectory of a spinning soccer ball than the path of a space station orbiting Earth. Nevertheless, as shown in this section, by combining Newton's Second Law of Motion with everything we have learned about vectors, it is possible to solve a variety of moving body problems.

Position, Velocity, Speed, Acceleration

Until now we have studied objects that move in one dimension (along a line). The next step is to consider the motion of objects in two dimensions (in a plane) and three dimensions (in space).

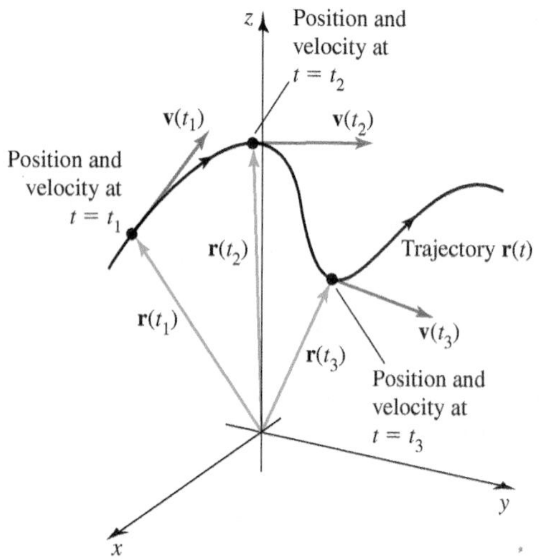

We work in a three-dimensional coordinate system and let the vector-valued function $\mathbf{r}(t) = \langle x(t), y(t), z(t) \rangle$ describe the *position* of a moving object at times $t \geq 0$. The curve described by $\mathbf{r}$ is the *path* or *trajectory* of the object (Figure 12.81). Just as with one-dimensional motion, the rate of change of the position function with respect to time is the *instantaneous velocity* of the object—a vector with three components corresponding to the velocity in the x-, y-, and z-directions:

$$\mathbf{v}(t) = \mathbf{r}'(t) = \langle x'(t), y'(t), z'(t) \rangle.$$

This expression should look familiar. The velocity vectors of a moving object are simply tangent vectors; that is, at any point the velocity vector is tangent to the trajectory (Figure 12.81).

As with one-dimensional motion, the *speed* of an object moving in three dimensions is the magnitude of its velocity vector:

$$|\mathbf{v}(t)| = |\langle x'(t), y'(t), z'(t) \rangle| = \sqrt{x'(t)^2 + y'(t)^2 + z'(t)^2}.$$

The speed is a nonnegative scalar-valued function.

Finally, the *acceleration* of a moving object is the rate of change of the velocity:

$$\mathbf{a}(t) = \mathbf{v}'(t) = \mathbf{r}''(t).$$

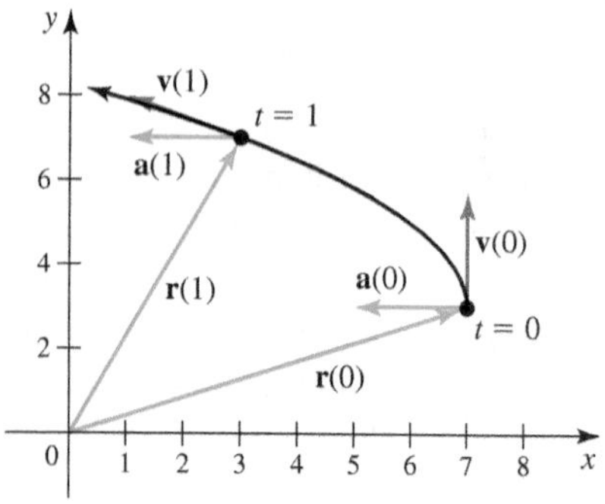

While the position vector gives the path of a moving object and the velocity vector is always tangent to the path, the acceleration vector is more difficult to visualize. Figure 12.82 shows one particular instance of two-dimensional motion. The trajectory is a segment of a parabola and is traced out by the position vectors (shown at $t = 0$ and 1). As expected, the velocity vectors are tangent to the trajectory. In this case, the acceleration is $\mathbf{a} = \langle -2, 0 \rangle$; it is constant in magnitude and direction for all times. The relationships among $\mathbf{r}$, $\mathbf{v}$, and $\mathbf{a}$ are explored in the coming examples.

FIGURE 12.81

FIGURE 12.82

In the case of two-dimensional motion, $\mathbf{r}(t) = \langle x(t), y(t) \rangle$, $\mathbf{v}(t) = \mathbf{r}'(t)$, and $\mathbf{a}(t) = \mathbf{r}''(t)$.

QUICK CHECK 1 Given $\mathbf{r}(t) = \langle t, t^2, t^3 \rangle$, find $\mathbf{v}(t)$ and $\mathbf{a}(t)$.

DEFINITION **Position, Velocity, Speed, Acceleration**

Let the **position** of an object moving in three-dimensional space be given by $\mathbf{r}(t) = \langle x(t), y(t), z(t) \rangle$, for $t \geq 0$. The **velocity** of the object is

$$\mathbf{v}(t) = \mathbf{r}'(t) = \langle x'(t), y'(t), z'(t) \rangle.$$

The **speed** of the object is the scalar function

$$|\mathbf{v}(t)| = \sqrt{x'(t)^2 + y'(t)^2 + z'(t)^2}.$$

The **acceleration** of the object is $\mathbf{a}(t) = \mathbf{v}'(t) = \mathbf{r}''(t)$.

EXAMPLE 1   Velocity and acceleration from position Consider the two-dimensional motion given by the position vector

$$\mathbf{r}(t) = \langle x(t), y(t) \rangle = \langle 3\cos t, 3\sin t \rangle, \quad \text{for } 0 \le t \le 2\pi.$$

a. Sketch the trajectory of the object.

b. Find the velocity and speed of the object.

c. Find the acceleration of the object.

d. Sketch the position, velocity, and acceleration vectors, for $t = 0, \pi/2, \pi,$ and $3\pi/2$.

SOLUTION

a. Notice that

$$x(t)^2 + y(t)^2 = 9(\cos^2 t + \sin^2 t) = 9,$$

which is the equation of a circle centered at the origin with radius 3. The object moves on this circle in the counterclockwise direction (Figure 12.83).

b. $\mathbf{v}(t) = \langle x'(t), y'(t) \rangle = \langle -3\sin t, 3\cos t \rangle$ Velocity vector

$\qquad |\mathbf{v}(t)| = \sqrt{x'(t)^2 + y'(t)^2}$ Definition of speed

$\qquad\qquad = \sqrt{(-3\sin t)^2 + (3\cos t)^2}$

$\qquad\qquad = \sqrt{9\underbrace{(\sin^2 t + \cos^2 t)}_{1}} = 3$

The velocity vector has a constant magnitude and a continuously changing direction.

c. $\mathbf{a}(t) = \mathbf{v}'(t) = \langle -3\cos t, -3\sin t \rangle = -\mathbf{r}(t)$

In this case, the acceleration vector is the negative of the position vector at all times.

d. The relationships among $\mathbf{r}, \mathbf{v},$ and $\mathbf{a}$ at four points in time are shown in Figure 12.83. The velocity vector is always tangent to the trajectory and has length 3, while the acceleration vector and position vector each have length 3 and point in opposite directions. At all times, $\mathbf{v}$ is orthogonal to $\mathbf{r}$ and $\mathbf{a}$.

Related Exercises 7–18 ◄

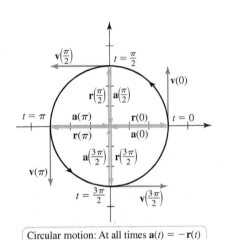

Circular motion: At all times $\mathbf{a}(t) = -\mathbf{r}(t)$ and $\mathbf{v}(t)$ is orthogonal to $\mathbf{r}(t)$ and $\mathbf{a}(t)$.

FIGURE 12.83

EXAMPLE 2   Comparing trajectories Consider the trajectories described by the position functions

$$\mathbf{r}(t) = \left\langle t, t^2 - 4, \frac{t^3}{4} - 8 \right\rangle, \quad \text{for } t \ge 0, \text{ and}$$

$$\mathbf{R}(t) = \left\langle t^2, t^4 - 4, \frac{t^6}{4} - 8 \right\rangle, \quad \text{for } t \ge 0,$$

where t is measured in the same time units for both functions.

a. Graph and compare the trajectories using a graphing utility.

b. Find the velocity vectors associated with the position functions.

SOLUTION

a. Plotting the position functions at selected values of t results in the trajectories shown in Figure 12.84. Because $\mathbf{r}(0) = \mathbf{R}(0) = \langle 0, -4, -8 \rangle$, both curves have the same initial point. For $t \ge 0$, the two curves consist of the same points, but they are traced out differently. For example, both curves pass through the point $(4, 12, 8)$, but that point corresponds to $\mathbf{r}(4)$ on the first curve and $\mathbf{R}(2)$ on the second curve. In general, $\mathbf{r}(t^2) = \mathbf{R}(t)$, for $t \ge 0$.

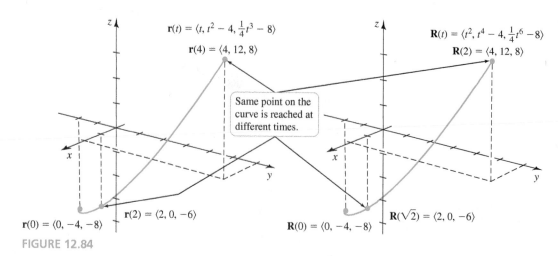

FIGURE 12.84

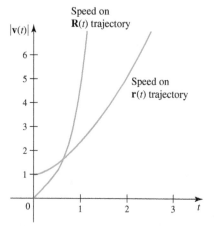

FIGURE 12.85

> See Exercise 61 for a discussion of nonuniform straight-line motion.

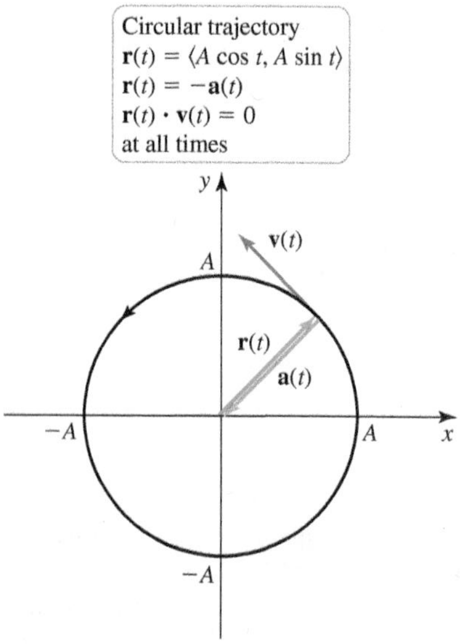

Circular trajectory
$\mathbf{r}(t) = \langle A \cos t, A \sin t \rangle$
$\mathbf{r}(t) = -\mathbf{a}(t)$
$\mathbf{r}(t) \cdot \mathbf{v}(t) = 0$
at all times

FIGURE 12.86

b. The velocity vectors are

$$\mathbf{r}'(t) = \left\langle 1, 2t, \frac{3t^2}{4} \right\rangle \quad \text{and} \quad \mathbf{R}'(t) = \left\langle 2t, 4t^3, \frac{3}{2}t^5 \right\rangle.$$

The difference in the motion on the two curves is revealed by the graphs of the speeds associated with the trajectories (Figure 12.85). The object on the first trajectory reaches the point $(4, 12, 8)$ at $t = 4$ where its speed is $|\mathbf{r}'(4)| = |\langle 1, 8, 12 \rangle| \approx 14.5$. The object on the second trajectory reaches the same point $(4, 12, 8)$ at $t = 2$, where its speed is $|\mathbf{R}'(2)| = |\langle 4, 32, 48 \rangle| \approx 57.8$.

Related Exercises 19–24◄

QUICK CHECK 2 Find the functions that give the speed of the two objects in Example 2, for $t \geq 0$ (corresponding to the graphs in Figure 12.85). ◄

Straight-Line and Circular Motion

Two types of motion in space arise frequently and deserve to be singled out. First consider a trajectory described by the vector function

$$\mathbf{r}(t) = \langle x_0 + at, y_0 + bt, z_0 + ct \rangle, \quad \text{for } t \geq 0,$$

where x_0, y_0, z_0, a, b, and c are constants. This function describes a straight-line trajectory with an initial point $\langle x_0, y_0, z_0 \rangle$ and a direction given by the vector $\langle a, b, c \rangle$ (Section 12.5). The velocity on this trajectory is the constant $\mathbf{v}(t) = \mathbf{r}'(t) = \langle a, b, c \rangle$ in the direction of the trajectory, and the acceleration is $\mathbf{a} = \langle 0, 0, 0 \rangle$. The motion associated with this function is **uniform** (constant velocity) **straight-line motion**.

A different situation is **circular motion** (Example 1). Consider the two-dimensional circular path

$$\mathbf{r}(t) = \langle A \cos t, A \sin t \rangle, \quad \text{for } 0 \leq t \leq 2\pi,$$

where A is a nonzero constant (Figure 12.86). The velocity and acceleration vectors are

$$\mathbf{v}(t) = \langle -A \sin t, A \cos t \rangle \quad \text{and}$$
$$\mathbf{a}(t) = \langle -A \cos t, -A \sin t \rangle = -\mathbf{r}(t).$$

Notice that $\mathbf{r}$ and $\mathbf{a}$ are parallel, but point in opposite directions. Furthermore, $\mathbf{r} \cdot \mathbf{v} = \mathbf{a} \cdot \mathbf{v} = 0$; thus, the position and acceleration vectors are both orthogonal to the velocity vectors at any given point (Figure 12.86). Finally, $\mathbf{r}$, $\mathbf{v}$, and $\mathbf{a}$ have constant magnitude A and variable directions. The conclusion that $\mathbf{r} \cdot \mathbf{v} = 0$ applies to any motion for which $|\mathbf{r}|$ is constant; that is, motion on a circle or a sphere (Figure 12.87).

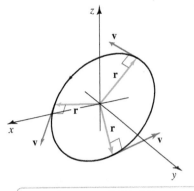

On a trajectory on which $|\mathbf{r}(t)|$ is constant, $\mathbf{v}$ is orthogonal to $\mathbf{r}$ at all points.

FIGURE 12.87

> **THEOREM 12.8   Motion with Constant $|\mathbf{r}|$**
> Let $\mathbf{r}$ describe a path on which $|\mathbf{r}|$ is constant (motion on a circle or sphere centered at the origin). Then, $\mathbf{r} \cdot \mathbf{v} = 0$, which means the position vector and the velocity vector are orthogonal at all times for which the functions are defined.

Proof: If $\mathbf{r}$ has constant magnitude, then $|\mathbf{r}(t)|^2 = \mathbf{r}(t) \cdot \mathbf{r}(t) = c$ for some constant c. Differentiating the equation $\mathbf{r}(t) \cdot \mathbf{r}(t) = c$, we have

$$
\begin{aligned}
0 &= \frac{d}{dt}(\mathbf{r}(t) \cdot \mathbf{r}(t)) && \text{Differentiate both sides of } |\mathbf{r}(t)|^2 = c \\
&= \mathbf{r}'(t) \cdot \mathbf{r}(t) + \mathbf{r}(t) \cdot \mathbf{r}'(t) && \text{Derivative of dot product (Theorem 12.7)} \\
&= 2\mathbf{r}'(t) \cdot \mathbf{r}(t) && \text{Simplify.} \\
&= 2\mathbf{v}(t) \cdot \mathbf{r}(t). && \mathbf{r}'(t) = \mathbf{v}(t)
\end{aligned}
$$

Because $\mathbf{r}(t) \cdot \mathbf{v}(t) = 0$ for all t, it follows that $\mathbf{r}$ and $\mathbf{v}$ are orthogonal for all t. ◄

EXAMPLE 3   Path on a sphere An object moves on a trajectory described by

$$\mathbf{r}(t) = \langle x(t), y(t), z(t) \rangle = \langle 3 \cos t, 5 \sin t, 4 \cos t \rangle, \quad \text{for } 0 \le t \le 2\pi.$$

a. Show that the object moves on a sphere and find the radius of the sphere.

b. Find the velocity and speed of the object.

SOLUTION

> For generalizations of this example and explorations of trajectories that lie on spheres and ellipses, see Exercises 79, 82, and 83.

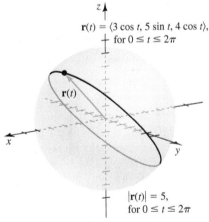

$\mathbf{r}(t) = \langle 3 \cos t, 5 \sin t, 4 \cos t \rangle$, for $0 \le t \le 2\pi$

$\mathbf{r}(t)$

$|\mathbf{r}(t)| = 5$, for $0 \le t \le 2\pi$

FIGURE 12.88

a.
$$
\begin{aligned}
|\mathbf{r}(t)|^2 &= x(t)^2 + y(t)^2 + z(t)^2 && \text{Square of the distance from the origin} \\
&= (3 \cos t)^2 + (5 \sin t)^2 + (4 \cos t)^2 && \text{Substitute.} \\
&= 25 \cos^2 t + 25 \sin^2 t && \text{Simplify.} \\
&= 25\underbrace{(\cos^2 t + \sin^2 t)}_{1} = 25 && \text{Factor.}
\end{aligned}
$$

Therefore, $|\mathbf{r}(t)| = 5$, for $0 \le t \le 2\pi$, and the curve lies on a sphere of radius 5 centered at the origin (Figure 12.88).

b.
$$
\begin{aligned}
\mathbf{v}(t) = \mathbf{r}'(t) &= \langle -3 \sin t, 5 \cos t, -4 \sin t \rangle && \text{Velocity vector} \\
|\mathbf{v}(t)| &= \sqrt{\mathbf{v}(t) \cdot \mathbf{v}(t)} && \text{Speed of the object} \\
&= \sqrt{9 \sin^2 t + 25 \cos^2 t + 16 \sin^2 t} && \text{Evaluate the dot product.} \\
&= \sqrt{25\underbrace{(\sin^2 t + \cos^2 t)}_{1}} && \text{Simplify.} \\
&= 5 && \text{Simplify.}
\end{aligned}
$$

The speed of the object is always 5. You should verify that $\mathbf{r}(t) \cdot \mathbf{v}(t) = 0$, for all t, implying that $\mathbf{r}$ and $\mathbf{v}$ are always orthogonal.

Related Exercises 25–30 ◄

QUICK CHECK 3 Verify that $\mathbf{r}(t) \cdot \mathbf{v}(t) = 0$ in Example 3. ◄

Two-Dimensional Motion in a Gravitational Field

Newton's Second Law of Motion, which is used to model the motion of most objects, states that

$$\underbrace{\text{Mass}}_{m} \cdot \underbrace{\text{acceleration}}_{\mathbf{a}(t) = \mathbf{r}''(t)} = \underbrace{\text{sum of all forces.}}_{\sum \mathbf{F}_i}$$

In other words, the governing law says something about the *acceleration* of an object, and in order to describe the motion fully, we must find the velocity and position from the acceleration.

Finding Velocity and Position from Acceleration
We begin with the case of two-dimensional projectile motion in which the only force acting on the object is the gravitational force; for the moment, air resistance and other possible external forces are neglected.

A convenient coordinate system uses a y-axis that points vertically upward and an x-axis that points in the direction of horizontal motion. The gravitational force is in the negative y-direction and is given by $\mathbf{F} = \langle 0, -mg \rangle$, where m is the mass of the object and $g \approx 9.8 \text{ m/s}^2 \approx 32 \text{ ft/s}^2$ is the acceleration due to gravity (Figure 12.89).

With these observations, Newton's Second Law takes the form

$$m\mathbf{a}(t) = \mathbf{F} = \langle 0, -mg \rangle.$$

Significantly, the mass of the object cancels, leaving the vector equation

$$\mathbf{a}(t) = \langle 0, -g \rangle. \tag{1}$$

In order to find the velocity $\mathbf{v}(t) = \langle x'(t), y'(t) \rangle$ and the position $\mathbf{r}(t) = \langle x(t), y(t) \rangle$ from this equation, we must be given the following **initial conditions**:

$$\text{Initial velocity at } t = 0: \mathbf{v}(0) = \langle u_0, v_0 \rangle \text{ and}$$
$$\text{Initial position at } t = 0: \mathbf{r}(0) = \langle x_0, y_0 \rangle.$$

We now proceed in two steps.

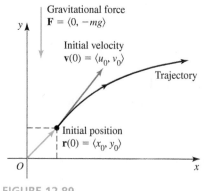

Gravitational force
$\mathbf{F} = \langle 0, -mg \rangle$

Initial velocity
$\mathbf{v}(0) = \langle u_0, v_0 \rangle$

Trajectory

Initial position
$\mathbf{r}(0) = \langle x_0, y_0 \rangle$

FIGURE 12.89

> Recall that an antiderivative of 0 is a constant C and an antiderivative of $-g$ is $-gt + C$.

1. **Solve for the velocity** The velocity is an antiderivative of the acceleration in equation (1). Integrating the acceleration, we have

$$\mathbf{v}(t) = \int \mathbf{a}(t)\, dt = \int \langle 0, -g \rangle\, dt = \langle 0, -gt \rangle + \mathbf{C},$$

where $\mathbf{C}$ is an arbitrary constant vector. The arbitrary constant is determined by substituting $t = 0$ and using the initial condition $\mathbf{v}(0) = \langle u_0, v_0 \rangle$. We find that $\mathbf{v}(0) = \langle 0, 0 \rangle + \mathbf{C} = \langle u_0, v_0 \rangle$, or $\mathbf{C} = \langle u_0, v_0 \rangle$. Therefore, the velocity is

$$\mathbf{v}(t) = \langle 0, -gt \rangle + \langle u_0, v_0 \rangle = \langle u_0, -gt + v_0 \rangle. \tag{2}$$

> You have a choice. You may do these calculations in vector notation as we have done here, or you may work with individual components.

Notice that the horizontal component of velocity is simply the initial horizontal velocity u_0 for all time. The vertical component of velocity decreases linearly from its initial value of v_0.

2. **Solve for the position** The position is an antiderivative of the velocity given by equation (2):

$$\mathbf{r}(t) = \int \mathbf{v}(t)\, dt = \int \langle u_0, -gt + v_0 \rangle\, dt = \left\langle u_0\, t, -\frac{1}{2} g t^2 + v_0\, t \right\rangle + \mathbf{C},$$

where $\mathbf{C}$ is an arbitrary constant vector. Substituting $t = 0$, we have $\mathbf{r}(0) = \langle 0, 0 \rangle + \mathbf{C} = \langle x_0, y_0 \rangle$, which implies that $\mathbf{C} = \langle x_0, y_0 \rangle$. Therefore, the position of the object, for $t \geq 0$, is

$$\mathbf{r}(t) = \left\langle u_0 t, -\frac{1}{2} g t^2 + v_0 t \right\rangle + \langle x_0, y_0 \rangle = \left\langle \underbrace{u_0 t + x_0}_{x(t)}, \underbrace{-\frac{1}{2} g t^2 + v_0 t + y_0}_{y(t)} \right\rangle.$$

SUMMARY **Two-Dimensional Motion in a Gravitational Field**

Consider an object moving in a plane with a horizontal x-axis and a vertical y-axis, subject only to the force of gravity. Given the initial velocity $\mathbf{v}(0) = \langle u_0, v_0 \rangle$ and the initial position $\mathbf{r}(0) = \langle x_0, y_0 \rangle$, the velocity of the object, for $t \geq 0$, is

$$\mathbf{v}(t) = \langle x'(t), y'(t) \rangle = \langle u_0, -gt + v_0 \rangle$$

and the position is

$$\mathbf{r}(t) = \langle x(t), y(t) \rangle = \left\langle u_0 t + x_0, -\frac{1}{2} g t^2 + v_0 t + y_0 \right\rangle.$$

EXAMPLE 4   **Flight of a baseball**   A baseball is hit from 3 ft above home plate with an initial velocity in ft/s of $\mathbf{v}(0) = \langle u_0, v_0 \rangle = \langle 80, 80 \rangle$. Neglect all forces other than gravity.

a. Find the position and velocity of the ball between the time it is hit and the time it first hits the ground.

b. Show that the trajectory of the ball is a segment of a parabola.

c. Assuming a flat playing field, how far does the ball travel horizontally? Plot the trajectory of the ball.

d. What is the maximum height of the ball?

e. Does the ball clear a 20-ft fence that is 380 ft from home plate (directly under the path of the ball)?

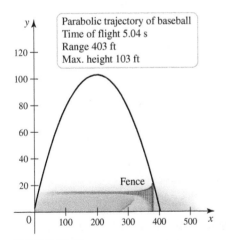

Parabolic trajectory of baseball
Time of flight 5.04 s
Range 403 ft
Max. height 103 ft

Fence

FIGURE 12.90

▷ The equation in part (c) can be solved using the quadratic formula or a root-finder on a calculator.

SOLUTION   Assume the origin is located at home plate. Because distances are measured in feet, we use $g = 32 \text{ ft/s}^2$.

a. Substituting $x_0 = 0$ and $y_0 = 3$ into the equation for $\mathbf{r}$, the position of the ball is

$$\mathbf{r}(t) = \langle x(t), y(t) \rangle = \langle 80t, -16t^2 + 80t + 3 \rangle, \quad \text{for } t \geq 0. \tag{3}$$

We then compute $\mathbf{v}(t) = \mathbf{r}'(t) = \langle 80, -32t + 80 \rangle$.

b. Equation (3) says that $x = 80t$ and $y = -16t^2 + 80t + 3$. Substituting $t = x/80$ into the equation for y gives

$$y = -16 \left(\frac{x}{80} \right)^2 + x + 3 = -\frac{x^2}{400} + x + 3,$$

which is the equation of a parabola.

c. The ball lands on the ground at the value of $t > 0$ at which $y = 0$. Solving $y(t) = -16t^2 + 80t + 3 = 0$, we find that $t \approx -0.04$ and $t \approx 5.04$ s. The first root is not relevant for the problem at hand, so we conclude that the ball lands when $t \approx 5.04$ s. The horizontal distance traveled by the ball is $x(5.04) \approx 403$ ft. The path of the ball in the xy-coordinate system on the time interval $[0, 5.04]$ is shown in Figure 12.90.

d. The ball reaches its maximum height at the time its vertical velocity is zero. Solving $y'(t) = -32t + 80 = 0$, we find that $t = 2.5$ s. The height at that time is $y(2.5) = 103$ ft.

e. The ball reaches a horizontal distance of 380 ft (the distance to the fence) when $x(t) = 80t = 380$. Solving for t, we find that $t = 4.75$ s. The height of the ball at that time is $y(4.75) = 22$ ft. So, indeed, the ball clears a 20-ft fence.

Related Exercises 31–36 ◄

QUICK CHECK 4 Write the functions $x(t)$ and $y(t)$ in Example 4 in the case that $x_0 = 0$, $y_0 = 2$, $u_0 = 100$, and $v_0 = 60$. ◄

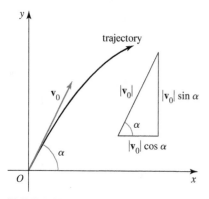

FIGURE 12.91

Range, Time of Flight, Maximum Height Having solved one specific motion problem, we can now make some general observations about two-dimensional projectile motion in a gravitational field. Assume that the motion of an object begins at the origin; that is, $x_0 = y_0 = 0$. Assume also that the object is launched at an angle of α $(0 \le \alpha \le \pi/2)$ above the horizontal with an initial speed $|\mathbf{v}_0|$ (Figure 12.91). This means that the initial velocity is

$$\langle u_0, v_0 \rangle = \langle |\mathbf{v}_0| \cos \alpha, |\mathbf{v}_0| \sin \alpha \rangle.$$

Substituting these values into the general expressions for the velocity and position, we find that the velocity of the object is

$$\mathbf{v}(t) = \langle u_0, -gt + v_0 \rangle = \langle |\mathbf{v}_0| \cos \alpha, -gt + |\mathbf{v}_0| \sin \alpha \rangle.$$

The position of the object (with $x_0 = y_0 = 0$) is

$$\mathbf{r}(t) = \langle x(t), y(t) \rangle = \langle (|\mathbf{v}_0| \cos \alpha)t, -gt^2/2 + (|\mathbf{v}_0| \sin \alpha)t \rangle.$$

Notice that the motion is determined entirely by the parameters $|\mathbf{v}_0|$ and α. Several general conclusions now follow.

> ➤ The other root of the equation $y(t) = 0$ is $t = 0$, the time the object leaves the ground.

1. Assuming the object is launched from the origin over horizontal ground, it returns to the ground when $y(t) = -gt^2/2 + (|\mathbf{v}_0| \sin \alpha)t = 0$. Solving for t, the **time of flight** is $T = 2|\mathbf{v}_0| \sin \alpha/g$.

2. The **range** of the object, which is the horizontal distance it travels, is the x-coordinate of the trajectory at the time of flight:

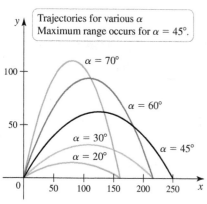

FIGURE 12.92

$$x(T) = (|\mathbf{v}_0| \cos \alpha)T$$

$$= (|\mathbf{v}_0| \cos \alpha) \frac{2|\mathbf{v}_0| \sin \alpha}{g} \qquad \text{Substitute for } T.$$

$$= \frac{2|\mathbf{v}_0|^2 \sin \alpha \cos \alpha}{g} \qquad \text{Simplify.}$$

$$= \frac{|\mathbf{v}_0|^2 \sin 2\alpha}{g}. \qquad 2 \sin \alpha \cos \alpha = \sin 2\alpha$$

Note that on the interval $0 \le \alpha \le \pi/2$, $\sin 2\alpha$ has a maximum value of 1 when $\alpha = \pi/4$, so the maximum range is $|\mathbf{v}_0|^2/g$. In other words, in an ideal world, firing an object from the ground at a 45° angle maximizes its range. Notice that the ranges obtained with the angles α and $\pi/2 - \alpha$ are equal (Figure 12.92).

QUICK CHECK 5 Show that the range attained with an angle α equals the range attained with the angle $\pi/2 - \alpha$. ◄

3. The maximum height of the object is reached when the vertical velocity is zero, or when $y'(t) = -gt + |\mathbf{v}_0| \sin \alpha = 0$. Solving for t, the maximum height is reached at $t = |\mathbf{v}_0|(\sin \alpha)/g = T/2$, which is half of the time of flight. The object spends equal amounts of time ascending and descending. The maximum height is

$$y\left(\frac{T}{2}\right) = \frac{(|\mathbf{v}_0| \sin \alpha)^2}{2g}.$$

4. Finally, by eliminating t from the equations for $x(t)$ and $y(t)$, it can be shown (Exercise 78) that the trajectory of the object is a segment of a parabola.

SUMMARY   Two-Dimensional Motion

Assume an object traveling over horizontal ground, acted on only by the gravitational force, has an initial position $\langle x_0, y_0 \rangle = \langle 0, 0 \rangle$ and initial velocity $\langle u_0, v_0 \rangle = \langle |\mathbf{v}_0| \cos \alpha, |\mathbf{v}_0| \sin \alpha \rangle$. The trajectory, which is a segment of a parabola, has the following properties.

$$\text{time of flight} = T = \frac{2|\mathbf{v}_0| \sin \alpha}{g}$$

$$\text{range} = \frac{|\mathbf{v}_0|^2 \sin 2\alpha}{g}$$

$$\text{maximum height} = y\left(\frac{T}{2}\right) = \frac{(|\mathbf{v}_0| \sin \alpha)^2}{2g}$$

EXAMPLE 5   Flight of a golf ball A golf ball is driven down a horizontal fairway with an initial speed of 55 m/s at an initial angle of 25° (from a tee with negligible height). Neglect all forces except gravity and assume that the ball's trajectory lies in a plane.

a. How far does the ball travel horizontally and when does it land?

b. What is the maximum height of the ball?

c. At what angles should the ball be hit to reach a green that is 300 m from the tee?

SOLUTION

a. Using the range formula with $\alpha = 25°$ and $|\mathbf{v}_0| = 55$ m/s, the ball travels

$$\frac{|\mathbf{v}_0|^2 \sin 2\alpha}{g} = \frac{(55 \text{ m/s})^2 \sin (50°)}{9.8 \text{ m/s}^2} \approx 236 \text{ m}.$$

The time of the flight is

$$T = \frac{2|\mathbf{v}_0| \sin \alpha}{g} = \frac{2(55 \text{ m/s}) \sin 25°}{9.8 \text{ m/s}^2} \approx 4.7 \text{ s}.$$

b. The maximum height of the ball is

$$\frac{(|\mathbf{v}_0| \sin \alpha)^2}{2g} = \frac{((55 \text{ m/s}) (\sin 25°))^2}{2(9.8 \text{ m/s}^2)} \approx 27.6 \text{ m}.$$

c. Letting R denote the range and solving the range formula for $\sin 2\alpha$, we find that $\sin 2\alpha = Rg/|\mathbf{v}_0|^2$. For a range of $R = 300$ m and an initial speed of $|\mathbf{v}_0| = 55$ m/s, the required angle satisfies

$$\sin 2\alpha = \frac{Rg}{|\mathbf{v}_0|^2} = \frac{(300 \text{ m}) (9.8 \text{ m/s}^2)}{(55 \text{ m/s})^2} \approx 0.972.$$

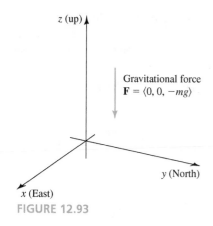

z (up)

Gravitational force
$\mathbf{F} = \langle 0, 0, -mg \rangle$

y (North)

x (East)

FIGURE 12.93

To travel a horizontal distance of exactly 300 m, the required angles are
$\alpha = \frac{1}{2}\sin^{-1}(0.972) \approx 38.2°$ or $51.8°$.

Related Exercises 37–42 ◄

Three-Dimensional Motion

To solve three-dimensional motion problems, we adopt a coordinate system in which the *x*- and *y*-axes point in two perpendicular horizontal directions (for example, east and north), while the positive *z*-axis points vertically upward (Figure 12.93). Newton's Second Law now has three components and appears in the form

$$m\mathbf{a}(t) = \langle mx''(t), my''(t), mz''(t) \rangle = \mathbf{F}.$$

If only the gravitational force is present (now in the negative *z*-direction), then the force vector is $\mathbf{F} = \langle 0, 0, -mg \rangle$; the equation of motion is then $\mathbf{a}(t) = \langle 0, 0, -g \rangle$. Other effects, such as crosswinds, spins, or slices, can be modeled by including other force components.

EXAMPLE 6   Projectile motion A small projectile is fired over horizontal ground in an easterly direction with an initial speed of $|\mathbf{v}_0| = 300$ m/s at an angle of $\alpha = 30°$ above the horizontal. A crosswind blows from south to north producing an acceleration of the projectile of 0.36 m/s^2 to the north.

a. Where does the projectile land?

b. In order to correct for the crosswind and make the projectile land due east of the launch site, at what angle from due east must the projectile be fired? Assume the initial speed $|\mathbf{v}_0| = 300$ m/s and the angle of elevation $\alpha = 30°$ are the same as in part (a).

SOLUTION

a. Letting $g = 9.8$ m/s^2, the equations of motion are $\mathbf{a}(t) = \mathbf{v}'(t) = \langle 0, 0.36, -9.8 \rangle$. Proceeding as in the two-dimensional case, the indefinite integral of the acceleration is the velocity function

$$\mathbf{v}(t) = \langle 0, 0.36t, -9.8t \rangle + \mathbf{C},$$

where **C** is an arbitrary constant. With an initial speed $|\mathbf{v}_0| = 300$ m/s and an angle of elevation of $\alpha = 30°$ (Figure 12.94a), the initial velocity is

$$\mathbf{v}(0) = \langle 300\cos 30°, 0, 300\sin 30° \rangle = \langle 150\sqrt{3}, 0, 150 \rangle.$$

Substituting $t = 0$ and using the initial condition, we find that $\mathbf{C} = \langle 150\sqrt{3}, 0, 150 \rangle$. Therefore, the velocity function is

$$\mathbf{v}(t) = \langle 150\sqrt{3}, 0.36t, -9.8t + 150 \rangle.$$

Integrating the velocity function produces the position function

$$\mathbf{r}(t) = \langle 150\sqrt{3}t, 0.18t^2, -4.9t^2 + 150t \rangle + \mathbf{C}.$$

Using the initial condition $\mathbf{r}(0) = \langle 0, 0, 0 \rangle$, we find that $\mathbf{C} = \langle 0, 0, 0 \rangle$, and the position function is

$$\mathbf{r}(t) = \langle x(t), y(t), z(t) \rangle = \langle 150\sqrt{3}t, 0.18t^2, -4.9t^2 + 150t \rangle.$$

The projectile lands when $z(t) = -4.9t^2 + 150t = 0$. Solving for *t*, the positive root, which gives the time of flight, is $T = 150/4.9 \approx 30.6$ s. The *x*- and *y*-coordinates at that time are

$$x(T) \approx 7953 \text{ m} \quad \text{and} \quad y(T) \approx 169 \text{ m}.$$

Thus, the projectile lands approximately 7953 m east and 169 m north of the firing site (Figure 12.94a).

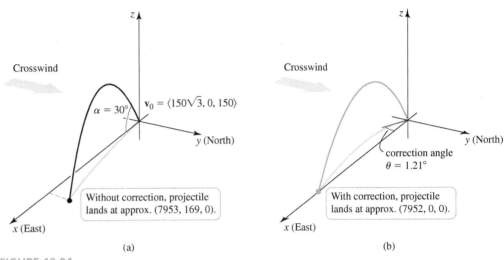

FIGURE 12.94

b. Keeping the initial speed of the projectile equal to $|\mathbf{v}_0| = 300$ m/s, we decompose the horizontal component of the speed, $150\sqrt{3}$ m/s, into an east component, $u_0 = 150\sqrt{3}\cos\theta$, and a north component, $v_0 = 150\sqrt{3}\sin\theta$, where θ is the angle relative to due east; we must determine the correction angle θ (Figure 12.94b). The x- and y-components of the position are

$$x(t) = (150\sqrt{3}\cos\theta)t \quad \text{and} \quad y(t) = 0.18t^2 + (150\sqrt{3}\sin\theta)t.$$

These changes in the initial velocity affect the x- and y-equations, but not the z-equation. Thus, the time of flight is still $T = 150/4.9 \approx 30.6$ s. The aim is to choose θ so that the projectile lands on the x-axis (due east from the launch site), which means $y(T) = 0$. Solving

$$y(T) = 0.18T^2 + (150\sqrt{3}\sin\theta)T = 0,$$

with $T = 150/4.9$, we find that $\sin\theta \approx -0.0212$; therefore, $\theta \approx -0.0212$ rad $\approx -1.21°$. In other words, the projectile must be fired at a horizontal angle of $1.21°$ to the *south* of east to correct for the northerly crosswind (Figure 12.94b). The landing location of the projectile is $x(T) \approx 7952$ m and $y(T) = 0$.

Related Exercises 43–52 ◀

SECTION 12.7 EXERCISES

Review Questions

1. Given the position function $\mathbf{r}$ of a moving object, explain how to find the velocity, speed, and acceleration of the object.

2. What is the relationship between the position and velocity vectors for motion on a circle?

3. State Newton's Second Law of Motion in vector form.

4. Write Newton's Second Law of Motion for three-dimensional motion with only the gravitational force (acting in the z-direction).

5. Given the acceleration of an object and its initial velocity, how do you find the velocity of the object, for $t \geq 0$?

6. Given the velocity of an object and its initial position, how do you find the position of the object, for $t \geq 0$?

Basic Skills

7–18. Velocity and acceleration from position *Consider the following position functions.*

a. *Find the velocity and speed of the object.*
b. *Find the acceleration of the object.*

7. $\mathbf{r}(t) = \langle 3t^2 + 1, 4t^2 + 3 \rangle$, for $t \geq 0$

8. $\mathbf{r}(t) = \left\langle \frac{5}{2}t^2 + 3, 6t^2 + 10 \right\rangle$, for $t \geq 0$

9. $\mathbf{r}(t) = \langle 2 + 2t, 1 - 4t \rangle$, for $t \geq 0$

10. $\mathbf{r}(t) = \langle 1 - t^2, 3 + 2t^3 \rangle$, for $t \geq 0$

11. $\mathbf{r}(t) = \langle 8\sin t, 8\cos t \rangle$, for $0 \leq t \leq 2\pi$

12. $\mathbf{r}(t) = \langle 3 \cos t, 4 \sin t \rangle$, for $0 \le t \le 2\pi$

13. $\mathbf{r}(t) = \left\langle t^2 + 3, t^2 + 10, \frac{1}{2} t^2 \right\rangle$, for $t \ge 0$

14. $\mathbf{r}(t) = \langle 2e^{2t} + 1, e^{2t} - 1, 2e^{2t} - 10 \rangle$, for $t \ge 0$

15. $\mathbf{r}(t) = \langle 3 + t, 2 - 4t, 1 + 6t \rangle$, for $t \ge 0$

16. $\mathbf{r}(t) = \langle 3 \sin t, 5 \cos t, 4 \sin t \rangle$, for $0 \le t \le 2\pi$

17. $\mathbf{r}(t) = \langle 1, t^2, e^{-t} \rangle$, for $t \ge 0$

18. $\mathbf{r}(t) = \langle 13 \cos 2t, 12 \sin 2t, 5 \sin 2t \rangle$, for $0 \le t \le \pi$

19–24. Comparing trajectories *Consider the following position functions* $\mathbf{r}$ *and* $\mathbf{R}$ *for two objects.*

a. *Find the interval* $[c, d]$ *over which the* $\mathbf{R}$ *trajectory is the same as the* $\mathbf{r}$ *trajectory over* $[a, b]$.
b. *Find the velocity for both objects.*
c. *Graph the speed of the two objects over the intervals* $[a, b]$ *and* $[c, d]$, *respectively.*

19. $\mathbf{r}(t) = \langle t, t^2 \rangle, [a, b] = [0, 2]$,
$\mathbf{R}(t) = \langle 2t, 4t^2 \rangle$ on $[c, d]$

20. $\mathbf{r}(t) = \langle 1 + 3t, 2 + 4t \rangle, [a, b] = [0, 6]$,
$\mathbf{R}(t) = \langle 1 + 9t, 2 + 12t \rangle$ on $[c, d]$

21. $\mathbf{r}(t) = \langle \cos t, 4 \sin t \rangle, [a, b] = [0, 2\pi]$,
$\mathbf{R}(t) = \langle \cos 3t, 4 \sin 3t \rangle$ on $[c, d]$

22. $\mathbf{r}(t) = \langle 2 - e^t, 4 - e^{-t} \rangle, [a, b] = [0, \ln 10]$,
$\mathbf{R}(t) = \langle 2 - t, 4 - 1/t \rangle$ on $[c, d]$

23. $\mathbf{r}(t) = \langle 4 + t^2, 3 - 2t^4, 1 + 3t^6 \rangle, [a, b] = [0, 6]$,
$\mathbf{R}(t) = \langle 4 + \ln t, 3 - 2 \ln^2 t, 1 + 3 \ln^3 t \rangle$ on $[c, d]$.
For graphing, let $c = 1$ and $d = 20$.

24. $\mathbf{r}(t) = \langle 2 \cos 2t, \sqrt{2} \sin 2t, \sqrt{2} \sin 2t \rangle, [a, b] = [0, \pi]$,
$\mathbf{R}(t) = \langle 2 \cos 4t, \sqrt{2} \sin 4t, \sqrt{2} \sin 4t \rangle$ on $[c, d]$

25–30. Trajectories on circles and spheres *Determine whether the following trajectories lie on a circle in* $\mathbb{R}^2$ *or sphere in* $\mathbb{R}^3$ *centered at the origin. If so, find the radius of the circle or sphere and show that the position vector and the velocity vector are everywhere orthogonal.*

25. $\mathbf{r}(t) = \langle 8 \cos 2t, 8 \sin 2t \rangle$, for $0 \le t \le \pi$

26. $\mathbf{r}(t) = \langle 4 \sin t, 2 \cos t \rangle$, for $0 \le t \le 2\pi$

27. $\mathbf{r}(t) = \langle \sin t + \sqrt{3} \cos t, \sqrt{3} \sin t - \cos t \rangle$, for $0 \le t \le 2\pi$

28. $\mathbf{r}(t) = \langle 3 \sin t, 5 \cos t, 4 \sin t \rangle$, for $0 \le t \le 2\pi$

29. $\mathbf{r}(t) = \langle \sin t, \cos t, \cos t \rangle$, for $0 \le t \le 2\pi$

30. $\mathbf{r}(t) = \langle \sqrt{3} \cos t + \sqrt{2} \sin t, -\sqrt{3} \cos t + \sqrt{2} \sin t, \sqrt{2} \sin t \rangle$,
for $0 \le t \le 2\pi$

31–36. Solving equations of motion *Given an acceleration vector, initial velocity* $\langle u_0, v_0 \rangle$, *and initial position* $\langle x_0, y_0 \rangle$, *find the velocity and position vectors, for* $t \ge 0$.

31. $\mathbf{a}(t) = \langle 0, 1 \rangle, \langle u_0, v_0 \rangle = \langle 2, 3 \rangle, \langle x_0, y_0 \rangle = \langle 0, 0 \rangle$

32. $\mathbf{a}(t) = \langle 1, 2 \rangle, \langle u_0, v_0 \rangle = \langle 1, 1 \rangle, \langle x_0, y_0 \rangle = \langle 2, 3 \rangle$

33. $\mathbf{a}(t) = \langle 0, 10 \rangle, \langle u_0, v_0 \rangle = \langle 0, 5 \rangle, \langle x_0, y_0 \rangle = \langle 1, -1 \rangle$

34. $\mathbf{a}(t) = \langle 1, t \rangle, \langle u_0, v_0 \rangle = \langle 2, -1 \rangle, \langle x_0, y_0 \rangle = \langle 0, 8 \rangle$

35. $\mathbf{a}(t) = \langle \cos t, 2 \sin t \rangle, \langle u_0, v_0 \rangle = \langle 0, 1 \rangle, \langle x_0, y_0 \rangle = \langle 1, 0 \rangle$

36. $\mathbf{a}(t) = \langle e^{-t}, 1 \rangle, \langle u_0, v_0 \rangle = \langle 1, 0 \rangle, \langle x_0, y_0 \rangle = \langle 0, 0 \rangle$

37–42. Two-dimensional motion *Consider the motion of the following objects. Assume the x-axis is horizontal, the positive y-axis is vertical and opposite g, the ground is horizontal, and only the gravitational force acts on the object.*

a. *Find the velocity and position vectors, for* $t \ge 0$.
b. *Graph the trajectory.*
c. *Determine the time of flight and range of the object.*
d. *Determine the maximum height of the object.*

37. A soccer ball has an initial position $\langle x_0, y_0 \rangle = \langle 0, 0 \rangle$ when it is kicked with an initial velocity of $\langle u_0, v_0 \rangle = \langle 30, 6 \rangle$ m/s.

38. A golf ball has an initial position $\langle x_0, y_0 \rangle = \langle 0, 0 \rangle$ when it is hit at an angle of $30°$ with an initial speed of 150 ft/s.

39. A baseball has an initial position (in feet) of $\langle x_0, y_0 \rangle = \langle 0, 6 \rangle$ when it is thrown with an initial velocity of $\langle u_0, v_0 \rangle = \langle 80, 10 \rangle$ ft/s.

40. A baseball is thrown horizontally from a height of 10 ft above the ground with a speed of 132 ft/s.

41. A projectile is launched from a platform 20 ft above the ground at an angle of $60°$ with a speed of 250 ft/s. Assume the origin is at the base of the platform.

42. A rock is thrown from the edge of a vertical cliff 40 m above the ground at an angle of $45°$ with a speed of $10\sqrt{2}$ m/s. Assume the origin is at the foot of the cliff.

43–46. Solving equations of motion *Given an acceleration vector, initial velocity* $\langle u_0, v_0, w_0 \rangle$, *and initial position* $\langle x_0, y_0, z_0 \rangle$, *find the velocity and position vectors, for* $t \ge 0$.

43. $\mathbf{a}(t) = \langle 0, 0, 10 \rangle, \langle u_0, v_0, w_0 \rangle = \langle 1, 5, 0 \rangle$,
$\langle x_0, y_0, z_0 \rangle = \langle 0, 5, 0 \rangle$

44. $\mathbf{a}(t) = \langle 1, t, 4t \rangle, \langle u_0, v_0, w_0 \rangle = \langle 20, 0, 0 \rangle$,
$\langle x_0, y_0, z_0 \rangle = \langle 0, 0, 0 \rangle$

45. $\mathbf{a}(t) = \langle \sin t, \cos t, 1 \rangle, \langle u_0, v_0, w_0 \rangle = \langle 0, 2, 0 \rangle$,
$\langle x_0, y_0, z_0 \rangle = \langle 0, 0, 0 \rangle$

46. $\mathbf{a}(t) = \langle t, e^{-t}, 1 \rangle, \langle u_0, v_0, w_0 \rangle = \langle 0, 0, 1 \rangle$,
$\langle x_0, y_0, z_0 \rangle = \langle 4, 0, 0 \rangle$

47–52. Three-dimensional motion *Consider the motion of the following objects. Assume the x-axis points east, the y-axis points north, the positive z-axis is vertical and opposite g, the ground is horizontal, and only the gravitational force acts on the object unless otherwise stated.*

a. *Find the velocity and position vectors for,* $t \ge 0$.
b. *Make a sketch of the trajectory.*
c. *Determine the time of flight and range of the object.*
d. *Determine the maximum height of the object.*

47. A bullet is fired from a rifle 1 m above the ground in a northeast direction. The initial velocity of the bullet is $\langle 200, 200, 0 \rangle$ m/s.

48. A golf ball is hit east down a fairway with an initial velocity of $\langle 50, 0, 30 \rangle$ m/s. A crosswind blowing to the south produces an acceleration of the ball of -0.8 m/s^2.

49. A baseball is hit 3 ft above home plate with an initial velocity of $\langle 60, 80, 80 \rangle$ ft/s. The spin on the baseball produces a horizontal acceleration of the ball of 10 ft/s^2 in the eastward direction.

50. A baseball is hit 3 ft above home plate with an initial velocity of $\langle 30, 30, 80 \rangle$ ft/s. The spin on the baseball produces a horizontal acceleration of the ball of 5 ft/s^2 in the northward direction.

51. A small rocket is fired from a launch pad 10 m above the ground with an initial velocity, in m/s, of $\langle 300, 400, 500 \rangle$. A crosswind blowing to the north produces an acceleration of the rocket of 2.5 m/s^2.

52. A soccer ball is kicked from the point $\langle 0, 0, 0 \rangle$ with an initial velocity of $\langle 0, \ 80, \ 80 \rangle$ ft/s. The spin on the ball produces an acceleration of $\langle 1.2, 0, 0 \rangle$ ft/s^2.

Further Explorations

53. Explain why or why not Determine whether the following statements are true and give an explanation or counterexample.

    a. If the speed of an object is constant, then its velocity components are constant.

    b. The functions $\mathbf{r}(t) = \langle \cos t, \sin t \rangle$ and $\mathbf{R}(t) = \langle \sin t^2, \cos t^2 \rangle$ generate the same set of points, for $t \geq 0$.

    c. It is not possible for a velocity vector to have a constant direction but a variable magnitude, for all $t \geq 0$.

    d. If the acceleration of an object is zero, for all $t \geq 0$ ($\mathbf{a}(t) = \mathbf{0}$), then the velocity of the object is constant.

    e. If you double the initial speed of a projectile, its range also doubles (assume no forces other than gravity act on the projectile).

    f. If you double the initial speed of a projectile, its time of flight also doubles (assume no forces other than gravity).

    g. A trajectory with $\mathbf{v}(t) = \mathbf{a}(t) \neq \mathbf{0}$, for all t, is possible.

54–57. Trajectory properties *Find the time of flight, range, and maximum height of the following two-dimensional trajectories, assuming no forces other than gravity. In each case the initial position is $\langle 0, 0 \rangle$ and the initial velocity is $\mathbf{v}_0 = \langle u_0, v_0 \rangle$.*

54. $\langle u_0, v_0 \rangle = \langle 10, 20 \rangle$ ft/s

55. Initial speed $|\mathbf{v}_0| = 150$ m/s, launch angle $\alpha = 30°$

56. $\langle u_0, v_0 \rangle = \langle 40, 80 \rangle$ m/s

57. Initial speed $|\mathbf{v}_0| = 400$ ft/s, launch angle $\alpha = 60°$

58. Motion on the moon The acceleration due to gravity on the moon is approximately $g/6$ (one-sixth its value on Earth). Compare the time of flight, range, and maximum height of a projectile on the moon with the corresponding values on Earth.

59. Firing angles A projectile is fired over horizontal ground from the origin with an initial speed of 60 m/s. What firing angles will produce a range of 300 m?

60. Firing strategies Suppose you wish to fire a projectile over horizontal ground from the origin and attain a range of 1000 m.

    a. Make a graph of the initial speed required for all firing angles $0 < \alpha < \pi/2$.

    b. What firing angle requires the least initial speed?

    c. What firing angle requires the least flight time?

61. Nonuniform straight-line motion Consider the motion of an object given by the position function

$$\mathbf{r}(t) = f(t)\langle a, b, c \rangle + \langle x_0, y_0, z_0 \rangle, \quad \text{for } t \geq 0,$$

where a, b, c, x_0, y_0, and z_0 are constants and f is a differentiable scalar function, for $t \geq 0$.

    a. Explain why this function describes motion along a line.

    b. Find the velocity function. In general, is the velocity constant in magnitude or direction along the path?

62. A race Two people travel from $P(4, 0)$ to $Q(-4, 0)$ along the paths given by

$$\mathbf{r}(t) = \langle 4 \cos{(\pi t/8)}, 4 \sin{(\pi t/8)} \rangle \quad \text{and}$$
$$\mathbf{R}(t) = \langle 4 - t, (4 - t)^2 - 16 \rangle.$$

    a. Graph both paths between P and Q.

    b. Graph the speeds of both people between P and Q.

    c. Who arrives at Q first?

63. Circular motion Consider an object moving along the circular trajectory $\mathbf{r}(t) = \langle A \cos \omega t, A \sin \omega t \rangle$, where A and ω are constants.

    a. Over what time interval $[0, T]$ does the object traverse the circle once?

    b. Find the velocity and speed of the object. Is the velocity constant in either direction or magnitude? Is the speed constant?

    c. Find the acceleration of the object.

    d. How are the position and velocity related? How are the position and acceleration related?

    e. Sketch the position, velocity, and acceleration vectors at four different points on the trajectory with $A = \omega = 1$.

64. A linear trajectory An object moves along a straight line from the point $P(1, 2, 4)$ to the point $Q(-6, 8, 10)$.

    a. Find a position function $\mathbf{r}$ that describes the motion if it occurs with a constant speed over the time interval $[0, 5]$.

    b. Find a position function $\mathbf{r}$ that describes the motion if it occurs with speed e^t.

65. A circular trajectory An object moves clockwise around a circle centered at the origin with radius 5 m beginning at the point $(0, 5)$.

    a. Find a position function $\mathbf{r}$ that describes the motion if the object moves with a constant speed, completing 1 lap every 12 s.

    b. Find a position function $\mathbf{r}$ that describes the motion if it occurs with speed e^{-t}.

66. A helical trajectory An object moves on the helix $\langle \cos t, \sin t, t \rangle$, for $t \geq 0$.

    a. Find a position function $\mathbf{r}$ that describes the motion if it occurs with a constant speed of 10.

    b. Find a position function $\mathbf{r}$ that describes the motion if it occurs with speed t.

67. Speed on an ellipse An object moves along an ellipse given by the function $\mathbf{r}(t) = \langle a \cos t, b \sin t \rangle$, for $0 \leq t \leq 2\pi$, where $a > 0$ and $b > 0$.

    a. Find the velocity and speed of the object in terms of a and b, for $0 \leq t \leq 2\pi$.

b. With $a = 1$ and $b = 6$, graph the speed function, for $0 \le t \le 2\pi$. Mark the points on the trajectory at which the speed is a minimum and a maximum.

c. Is it true that the object speeds up along the flattest (straightest) parts of the trajectory and slows down where the curves are sharpest?

d. For general a and b, find the ratio of the maximum speed to the minimum speed on the ellipse (in terms of a and b).

68. Travel on a cycloid Consider an object moving on the cycloid $\mathbf{r}(t) = \langle t - \sin t, 1 - \cos t \rangle$, for $0 \le t \le 4\pi$.

a. Graph the trajectory.

b. Find the velocity and speed of the object. At what point(s) on the trajectory does the object move fastest? Slowest?

c. Find the acceleration of the object and show that $|\mathbf{a}(t)|$ is constant.

d. Explain why the trajectory has a cusp at $t = 2\pi$.

69. Analyzing a trajectory Consider the trajectory given by the position function

$$\mathbf{r}(t) = \langle 50e^{-t}\cos t, 50e^{-t}\sin t, 5(1 - e^{-t}) \rangle, \quad \text{for } t \ge 0.$$

a. Find the initial point ($t = 0$) and the "terminal" point ($\lim_{t \to \infty} \mathbf{r}(t)$) of the trajectory.

b. At what point on the trajectory is the speed the greatest?

c. Graph the trajectory.

Applications

70. Golf shot A golfer stands 390 ft (130 yd) horizontally from the hole and 40 ft below the hole (see figure). Assuming the ball is hit with an initial speed of 150 ft/s, at what angle should it be hit to land in the hole? Assume that the path of the ball lies in a plane.

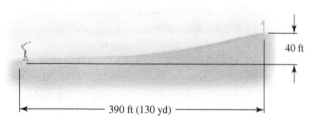

390 ft (130 yd)

40 ft

71. Another golf shot A golfer stands 420 ft (140 yd) horizontally from the hole and 50 ft above the hole (see figure). Assuming the ball is hit with an initial speed of 120 ft/s, at what angle should it be hit to land in the hole? Assume that the path of the ball lies in a plane.

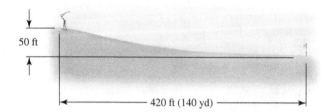

50 ft

420 ft (140 yd)

72. Initial velocity of a golf shot A golfer stands 390 ft horizontally from the hole and 40 ft below the hole (see figure for Exercise 70). If the ball is struck and leaves the ground at an initial angle of 45° with the horizontal, then with what initial velocity should it be hit to land in the hole?

73. Initial velocity of a golf shot A golfer stands 420 ft horizontally from the hole and 50 ft above the hole (see figure for Exercise 71). If the ball is struck and leaves the ground at an initial angle of 30° with the horizontal, then with what initial velocity should it be hit to land in the hole?

74. Ski jump The lip of a ski jump is 8 m above the outrun that is sloped at an angle of 30° to the horizontal (see figure).

a. If the initial velocity of a ski jumper at the lip of the jump is $\langle 40, 0 \rangle$ m/s, how far down the outrun does he land? Assume only gravity affects the motion.

b. Assume that air resistance produces a constant horizontal acceleration of 0.15 m/s² opposing the motion. How far down the outrun does the ski jumper land?

c. Suppose that the takeoff ramp is tilted upward at an angle of θ°, so that the skier's initial velocity is $40\langle \cos \theta, \sin \theta \rangle$ m/s. What value of θ maximizes the length of the jump? Express your answer in degrees and neglect air resistance.

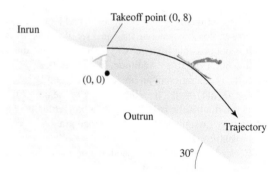

Inrun

Takeoff point (0, 8)

(0, 0)

Outrun

Trajectory

30°

75. Designing a baseball pitch A baseball leaves the hand of a pitcher 6 vertical feet above home plate and 60 ft from home plate. Assume that the coordinate axes are oriented as shown in the figure.

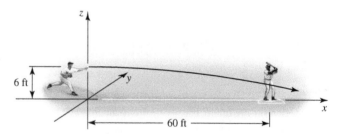

6 ft

60 ft

a. In the absence of all forces except gravity, assume that a pitch is thrown with an initial velocity of $\langle 130, 0, -3 \rangle$ ft/s (about 90 mi/hr). How far above the ground is the ball when it crosses home plate and how long does it take for the pitch to arrive?

b. What vertical velocity component should the pitcher use so that the pitch crosses home plate exactly 3 ft above the ground?

c. A simple model to describe the curve of a baseball assumes that the spin of the ball produces a constant sideways acceleration (in the y-direction) of c ft/s². Assume a pitcher throws a curve ball with $c = 8$ ft/s² (one-fourth the acceleration of gravity). How far does the ball move in the y-direction by the time it reaches home plate, assuming an initial velocity of $\langle 130, 0, -3 \rangle$ ft/s?

d. In part (c), does the ball curve more in the first half of its trip to the plate or in the second half? How does this fact affect the batter?

e. Suppose the pitcher releases the ball from an initial position of $\langle 0, -3, 6 \rangle$ with initial velocity $\langle 130, 0, -3 \rangle$. What value of the spin parameter c is needed to put the ball over home plate passing through the point $(60, 0, 3)$?

76. **Trajectory with a sloped landing** Assume an object is launched from the origin with an initial speed $|v_0|$ at an angle α to the horizontal, where $0 < \alpha < \dfrac{\pi}{2}$.

a. Find the time of flight, range, and maximum height (relative to the launch point) of the trajectory if the ground slopes *downward* at a constant angle of θ from the launch site, where $0 < \theta < \dfrac{\pi}{2}$.

b. Find the time of flight, range, and maximum height of the trajectory if the ground slopes *upward* at a constant angle of θ from the launch site.

77. **Time of flight, range, height** Derive the formulas for time of flight, range, and maximum height in the case that an object is launched from the initial position $\langle 0, y_0 \rangle$ with initial velocity $|v_0|\langle \cos \alpha, \sin \alpha \rangle$.

Additional Exercises

78. **Parabolic trajectories** Show that the two-dimensional trajectory

$$x(t) = u_0 t + x_0 \quad \text{and} \quad y(t) = -\dfrac{gt^2}{2} + v_0 t + y_0, \quad \text{for } 0 \le t \le T,$$

of an object moving in a gravitational field is a segment of a parabola for some value of $T > 0$. Find T such that $y(T) = 0$.

79. **Tilted ellipse** Consider the curve $\mathbf{r}(t) = \langle \cos t, \sin t, c \sin t \rangle$, for $0 \le t \le 2\pi$, where c is a real number. It can be shown that the curve lies in a plane. Prove that the curve is an ellipse in that plane.

80. **Equal area property** Consider the ellipse $\mathbf{r}(t) = \langle a \cos t, b \sin t \rangle$, for $0 \le t \le 2\pi$, where a and b are real numbers. Let θ be the angle between the position vector and the x-axis.

a. Show that $\tan \theta = (b/a) \tan t$.

b. Find $\theta'(t)$.

c. Recall that the area bounded by the polar curve $r = f(\theta)$ on the interval $[0, \theta]$ is $A(\theta) = \dfrac{1}{2} \displaystyle\int_0^\theta (f(u))^2 \, du$. Letting $f(\theta(t)) = |\mathbf{r}(\theta(t))|$, show that $A'(t) = \dfrac{1}{2} ab$.

d. Conclude that as an object moves around the ellipse, it sweeps out equal areas in equal times.

81. **Another property of constant $|\mathbf{r}|$ motion** Suppose an object moves on the surface of a sphere with $|\mathbf{r}(t)|$ constant for all t. Show that $\mathbf{r}(t)$ and $\mathbf{a}(t) = \mathbf{r}''(t)$ satisfy $\mathbf{r}(t) \cdot \mathbf{a}(t) = -|\mathbf{v}(t)|^2$.

82. **Conditions for a circular/elliptical trajectory in the plane** An object moves along a path given by

$$\mathbf{r}(t) = \langle a \cos t + b \sin t, c \cos t + d \sin t \rangle, \quad \text{for } 0 \le t \le 2\pi.$$

a. What conditions on a, b, c, and d guarantee that the path is a circle?

b. What conditions on a, b, c, and d guarantee that the path is an ellipse?

83. **Conditions for a circular/elliptical trajectory in space** An object moves along a path given by

$$\mathbf{r}(t) = \langle a \cos t + b \sin t, c \cos t + d \sin t, e \cos t + f \sin t \rangle,$$

for $0 \le t \le 2\pi$.

a. What conditions on a, b, c, d, e, and f guarantee that the path is a circle (in a plane)?

b. What conditions on a, b, c, d, e, and f guarantee that the path is an ellipse (in a plane)?

QUICK CHECK ANSWERS

1. $\mathbf{v}(t) = \langle 1, 2t, 3t^2 \rangle$, $\mathbf{a}(t) = \langle 0, 2, 6t \rangle$
2. $|\mathbf{r}'(t)| = \sqrt{1 + 4t^2 + 9t^4/16}$
   $|\mathbf{R}'(t)| = \sqrt{4t^2 + 16t^6 + 9t^{10}/4}$
3. $\mathbf{r} \cdot \mathbf{v} = \langle 3 \cos t, 5 \sin t, 4 \cos t \rangle$
   $\cdot \langle -3 \sin t, 5 \cos t, -4 \sin t \rangle = 0$
4. $x(t) = 100t, y(t) = -16t^2 + 60t + 2$
5. $\sin[2(\pi/2 - \alpha)] = \sin(\pi - 2\alpha) = \sin 2\alpha$

12.8 Length of Curves

With the methods of Section 12.7, it is possible to model the trajectory of an object moving in three-dimensional space. Although we can predict the position of the object at all times, we still don't have the tools needed to answer a simple question: How far does the object travel along its flight path over a given interval of time? In this section we answer this question of *arc length*.

Arc Length

▷ Arc length for curves of the form $y = f(x)$ was discussed in Section 6.5. You should look for the parallels between that discussion and the one in this section.

Suppose that a parameterized curve C is given by the vector-valued function $\mathbf{r}(t) = \langle f(t), g(t), h(t) \rangle$, for $a \leq t \leq b$, where f', g', and h' are continuous on $[a, b]$. We first show how to find the length of the two-dimensional curve $\mathbf{r}(t) = \langle f(t), g(t) \rangle$, for $a \leq t \leq b$. The modification for three-dimensional curves then follows.

To find the length of the curve between $(f(a), g(a))$ and $(f(b), g(b))$, we first subdivide the interval $[a, b]$ into n subintervals using the grid points

$$a = t_0 < t_1 < t_2 < \cdots < t_n = b.$$

We connect the corresponding points on the curve,

$$(f(t_0), g(t_0)), \ldots, (f(t_k), g(t_k)), \ldots, (f(t_n), g(t_n)),$$

with line segments (Figure 12.95a).

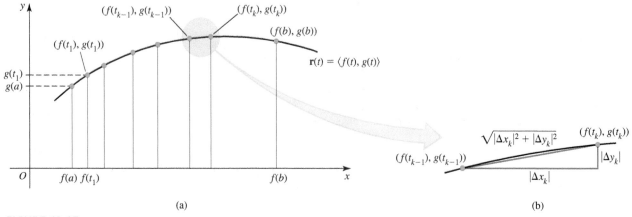

(a)

(b)

FIGURE 12.95

The kth line segment is the hypotenuse of a right triangle, whose legs have lengths $|\Delta x_k|$ and $|\Delta y_k|$, where

$$\Delta x_k = f(t_k) - f(t_{k-1}) \quad \text{and} \quad \Delta y_k = g(t_k) - g(t_{k-1}),$$

for $k = 1, 2, \ldots, n$ (Figure 12.95b). Therefore, the length of the kth line segment is

$$\sqrt{|\Delta x_k|^2 + |\Delta y_k|^2}.$$

The length of the entire curve L is approximated by the sum of the lengths of the line segments:

$$L \approx \sum_{k=1}^{n} \sqrt{|\Delta x_k|^2 + |\Delta y_k|^2} = \sum_{k=1}^{n} \sqrt{(\Delta x_k)^2 + (\Delta y_k)^2}. \tag{1}$$

The goal is to express this sum as a Riemann sum.

The change in $x = f(t)$ over the kth subinterval is $\Delta x_k = f(t_k) - f(t_{k-1})$. By the Mean Value Theorem, there is a point t_k^* in (t_{k-1}, t_k) such that

$$\underbrace{\overbrace{\frac{f(t_k) - f(t_{k-1})}{t_k - t_{k-1}}}^{\Delta x_k}}_{\Delta t_k} = f'(t_k^*).$$

So, the change in x as t changes by $\Delta t_k = t_k - t_{k-1}$ is

$$\Delta x_k = f(t_k) - f(t_{k-1}) = f'(t_k^*)\Delta t_k.$$

Similarly, the change in y over the kth subinterval is

$$\Delta y_k = g(t_k) - g(t_{k-1}) = g'(\hat{t}_k)\Delta t_k,$$

where $\hat{t}_k$ is also a point in (t_{k-1}, t_k). We now substitute these expressions for Δx_k and Δy_k into equation (1):

$$L \approx \sum_{k=1}^{n} \sqrt{(\Delta x_k)^2 + (\Delta y_k)^2}$$

$$= \sum_{k=1}^{n} \sqrt{(f'(t_k^*)\Delta t_k)^2 + (g'(\hat{t}_k)\Delta t_k)^2} \quad \text{Substitute for } \Delta x_k \text{ and } \Delta y_k.$$

$$= \sum_{k=1}^{n} \sqrt{f'(t_k^*)^2 + g'(\hat{t}_k)^2}\,\Delta t_k. \quad \text{Factor } \Delta t_k \text{ out of square root.}$$

The intermediate points t_k^* and $\hat{t}_k$ both approach t_k as n increases and as Δt_k approaches zero. Therefore, given the conditions on f' and g', the limit of this sum as $n \to \infty$ and $\Delta t_k \to 0$, for all k, exists and equals a definite integral:

$$L = \lim_{n \to \infty} \sum_{k=1}^{n} \sqrt{f'(t_k^*)^2 + g'(\hat{t}_k)^2}\,\Delta t_k = \int_a^b \sqrt{f'(t)^2 + g'(t)^2}\,dt.$$

QUICK CHECK 1 Use the arc length formula to find the length of the line $\mathbf{r}(t) = \langle t, t \rangle$, for $0 \le t \le 1$.

An analogous arc length formula for three-dimensional curves follows using a similar argument. The length of the curve $\mathbf{r}(t) = \langle f(t), g(t), h(t) \rangle$ on the interval $[a, b]$ is

$$L = \int_a^b \sqrt{f'(t)^2 + g'(t)^2 + h'(t)^2}\,dt.$$

Noting that $\mathbf{r}'(t) = \langle f'(t), g'(t), h'(t) \rangle$, we state the following definition.

> Arc length integrals are usually difficult to evaluate exactly. The few easily evaluated integrals appear in the examples and exercises. Often numerical methods must be used to approximate the more challenging integrals (see Example 4).

DEFINITION Arc Length for Vector Functions

Consider the parameterized curve $\mathbf{r}(t) = \langle f(t), g(t), h(t) \rangle$, where f', g', and h' are continuous, and the curve is traversed once for $a \le t \le b$. The **arc length** of the curve between $(f(a), g(a), h(a))$ and $(f(b), g(b), h(b))$ is

$$L = \int_a^b \sqrt{f'(t)^2 + g'(t)^2 + h'(t)^2}\,dt = \int_a^b |\mathbf{r}'(t)|\,dt.$$

QUICK CHECK 2 What does the arc length formula give for the length of the line $\mathbf{r}(t) = \langle t, t, t \rangle$, for $0 \le t \le 1$?

EXAMPLE 1   Circumference of a circle Prove that the circumference of a circle of radius a is $2\pi a$.

SOLUTION A circle of radius a is described by

$$\mathbf{r}(t) = \langle f(t), g(t) \rangle = \langle a \cos t, a \sin t \rangle,$$

➤ An important fact is that the arc length of a smooth parameterized curve is independent of the choice of parameter (Exercise 70).

for $0 \le t \le 2\pi$. For curves in the xy-plane we set $h(t) = 0$ in the definition of arc length. Note that $f'(t) = -a \sin t$ and $g'(t) = a \cos t$. The circumference is

$$L = \int_0^{2\pi} \sqrt{f'(t)^2 + g'(t)^2}\, dt \qquad \text{Arc length formula}$$

$$= \int_0^{2\pi} \sqrt{(-a \sin t)^2 + (a \cos t)^2}\, dt \quad \text{Substitute for } f' \text{ and } g'.$$

$$= a \int_0^{2\pi} \sqrt{\sin^2 t + \cos^2 t}\, dt \qquad \text{Factor } a > 0 \text{ out of square root.}$$

$$= a \int_0^{2\pi} 1\, dt \qquad \sin^2 t + \cos^2 t = 1$$

$$= 2\pi a. \qquad \text{Integrate a constant.}$$

Related Exercises 9–22◄

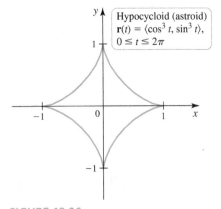

Hypocycloid (astroid)
$\mathbf{r}(t) = \langle \cos^3 t, \sin^3 t \rangle$,
$0 \le t \le 2\pi$

FIGURE 12.96

EXAMPLE 2 **Length of a hypocycloid (or astroid)** Find the length of the complete hypocycloid given by $\mathbf{r}(t) = \langle \cos^3 t, \sin^3 t \rangle$, where $0 \le t \le 2\pi$ (Figure 12.96).

SOLUTION The length of the entire curve is four times the length of the curve in the first quadrant. You should verify that the curve in the first quadrant is generated as the parameter varies from $t = 0$ (corresponding to $(1, 0)$) to $t = \pi/2$ (corresponding to $(0, 1)$). Letting $f(t) = \cos^3 t$ and $g(t) = \sin^3 t$, we have

$$f'(t) = -3 \cos^2 t \sin t \quad \text{and} \quad g'(t) = 3 \sin^2 t \cos t.$$

The arc length of the full curve is

$$L = 4 \int_0^{\pi/2} \sqrt{f'(t)^2 + g'(t)^2}\, dt \qquad \text{Factor of 4 by symmetry}$$

$$= 4 \int_0^{\pi/2} \sqrt{(-3 \cos^2 t \sin t)^2 + (3 \sin^2 t \cos t)^2}\, dt \quad \text{Substitute for } f' \text{ and } g'.$$

$$= 4 \int_0^{\pi/2} \sqrt{9 \cos^4 t \sin^2 t + 9 \cos^2 t \sin^4 t}\, dt \qquad \text{Simplify terms.}$$

$$= 4 \int_0^{\pi/2} 3 \sqrt{\cos^2 t \sin^2 t \underbrace{(\cos^2 t + \sin^2 t)}_{1}}\, dt \qquad \text{Factor.}$$

$$= 12 \int_0^{\pi/2} \cos t \sin t\, dt. \qquad \cos t \sin t \ge 0, \text{ for } 0 \le t \le \frac{\pi}{2}$$

Letting $u = \sin t$ with $du = \cos t\, dt$, we have

$$L = 12 \int_0^{\pi/2} \cos t \sin t\, dt = 12 \int_0^1 u\, du = 6.$$

The length of the entire hypocycloid is 6 units.

Related Exercises 9–22◄

▷ Recall from Chapter 6 that the distance traveled by an object in one dimension is $\int_a^b |v(t)|\, dt$. The arc length formula generalizes this formula to three dimensions.

Paths and Trajectories If the function $\mathbf{r}(t) = \langle x(t), y(t), z(t) \rangle$ is the position function for a moving object, then the arc length formula has a natural interpretation. Recall that $\mathbf{v}(t) = \mathbf{r}'(t)$ is the velocity of the object and $|\mathbf{v}(t)| = |\mathbf{r}'(t)|$ is the speed of the object. Therefore, the arc length formula becomes

$$L = \int_a^b |\mathbf{r}'(t)|\, dt = \int_a^b |\mathbf{v}(t)|\, dt.$$

This formula is the analog of the familiar *distance = speed × elapsed time* formula.

EXAMPLE 3 **Flight of an eagle** An eagle rises at a rate of 100 vertical ft/min on a helical path given by

$$\mathbf{r}(t) = \langle 250 \cos t, 250 \sin t, 100t \rangle$$

(Figure 12.97), where $\mathbf{r}$ is measured in feet and t is measured in minutes. How far does it travel in 10 min?

SOLUTION The speed of the eagle is

$$
\begin{aligned}
|\mathbf{v}(t)| &= \sqrt{x'(t)^2 + y'(t)^2 + z'(t)^2} \\
&= \sqrt{(-250 \sin t)^2 + (250 \cos t)^2 + 100^2} \quad \text{Substitute derivatives.} \\
&= \sqrt{250^2 (\sin^2 t + \cos^2 t) + 100^2} \quad \text{Combine terms.} \\
&= \sqrt{250^2 + 100^2} \approx 269. \quad \sin^2 t + \cos^2 t = 1
\end{aligned}
$$

The constant speed makes the arc length integral easy to evaluate:

$$L = \int_0^{10} |\mathbf{v}(t)|\, dt \approx \int_0^{10} 269\, dt = 2690.$$

The eagle travels approximately 2690 ft in 10 min.

Related Exercises 23–26 ◀

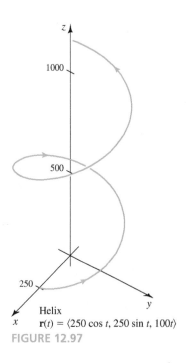

Helix
$\mathbf{r}(t) = \langle 250 \cos t, 250 \sin t, 100t \rangle$

FIGURE 12.97

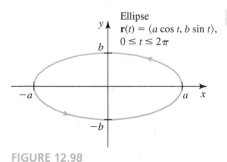

Ellipse
$\mathbf{r}(t) = \langle a \cos t, b \sin t \rangle$,
$0 \le t \le 2\pi$

FIGURE 12.98

QUICK CHECK 3 If the speed of an object is a constant S (as in Example 3), explain why the arc length on the interval $[a, b]$ is $S(b - a)$. ◀

EXAMPLE 4 **Lengths of planetary orbits** According to Kepler's first law, the planets revolve about the sun in elliptical orbits. A vector function that describes an ellipse in the xy-plane is

$$\mathbf{r}(t) = \langle a \cos t, b \sin t \rangle, \quad \text{where } 0 \le t \le 2\pi.$$

If $a > b > 0$, then $2a$ is the length of the major axis and $2b$ is the length of the minor axis (Figure 12.98). Verify the lengths of the planetary orbits given in Table 12.1. Distances are given in terms of the astronomical unit (AU), which is the length of the semimajor axis of Earth's orbit, or about 93 million miles.

▷ The German astronomer and mathematician Johannes Kepler (1571–1630) worked with the meticulously gathered data of Tycho Brahe to formulate three empirical laws obeyed by planets and comets orbiting the sun. The work of Kepler formed the foundation for Newton's laws of gravitation developed 50 years later.

▷ In September 2006, Pluto joined the ranks of Ceres, Haumea, Makemake, and Eris as one of five dwarf planets in our solar system.

Table 12.1

Planet	Semimajor axis, a (AU)	Semiminor axis, b (AU)	$\alpha = b/a$	Orbit length (AU)
Mercury	0.387	0.379	0.979	2.41
Venus	0.723	0.723	1.000	4.54
Earth	1.000	0.999	0.999	6.28
Mars	1.524	1.517	0.995	9.57
Jupiter	5.203	5.179	0.995	32.68
Saturn	9.539	9.524	0.998	59.88
Uranus	19.182	19.161	0.999	120.46
Neptune	30.058	30.057	1.000	189.86

SOLUTION Using the arc length formula, the length of a general elliptical orbit is

$$L = \int_0^{2\pi} \sqrt{(x'(t))^2 + (y'(t))^2}\, dt$$

$$= \int_0^{2\pi} \sqrt{(-a\sin t)^2 + (b\cos t)^2}\, dt \quad \text{Substitute for } x'(t) \text{ and } y'(t).$$

$$= \int_0^{2\pi} \sqrt{a^2\sin^2 t + b^2\cos^2 t}\, dt. \quad \text{Simplify.}$$

Factoring a^2 out of the square root and letting $\alpha = b/a$, we have

$$L = \int_0^{2\pi} \sqrt{a^2\left(\sin^2 t + (b/a)^2\cos^2 t\right)}\, dt \quad \text{Factor out } a^2.$$

$$= a\int_0^{2\pi} \sqrt{\sin^2 t + \alpha^2\cos^2 t}\, dt \quad \text{Let } \alpha = b/a.$$

$$= 4a\int_0^{\pi/2} \sqrt{\sin^2 t + \alpha^2\cos^2 t}\, dt. \quad \text{Use symmetry.}$$

> ▷ The integral that gives the length of the ellipse is a *complete elliptic integral of the second kind*. Many reference books and software packages provide approximate values of this integral.

In the last step we used the fact that the length of the full orbit is four times the length of a quarter of the orbit.

Unfortunately, an antiderivative for this integrand cannot be found in terms of elementary functions, so we have two options: This integral is well known and values have been tabulated for various values of α. Alternatively, we may use a calculator to approximate the integral numerically (see Section 7.7). Using numerical integration, the orbit lengths in Table 12.1 are obtained. For example, the length of Mercury's orbit with $a = 0.387$ and $\alpha = 0.979$ is

$$L = 4a\int_0^{\pi/2} \sqrt{\sin^2 t + \alpha^2\cos^2 t}\, dt$$

$$= 1.548\int_0^{\pi/2} \sqrt{\sin^2 t + 0.958\cos^2 t}\, dt \quad \text{Simplify.}$$

$$\approx 2.41. \quad \text{Approximate using calculator.}$$

The fact that α is so close to 1 for all of the planets means that their orbits are very nearly circular. For this reason, the lengths of the orbits shown in the table are nearly equal to $2\pi a$, which is the length of a circular orbit with radius a.

Related Exercises 27–30 ◄

Arc Length of a Polar Curve

> ▷ Recall from Section 11.2 that to convert from polar to Cartesian coordinates we use the relations
> $$x = r\cos\theta \quad \text{and} \quad y = r\sin\theta.$$

We now return to polar coordinates and answer the arc length question for polar curves: Given the polar equation $r = f(\theta)$, what is the length of the corresponding curve for $\alpha \leq \theta \leq \beta$? The key idea is to express the polar equation as a set of parametric equations in Cartesian coordinates and then use the arc length formula derived above. Letting θ play the role of a parameter and using $r = f(\theta)$, the parametric equations for the polar curve are

$$x = r\cos\theta = f(\theta)\cos\theta \quad \text{and} \quad y = r\sin\theta = f(\theta)\sin\theta,$$

where $\alpha \leq \theta \leq \beta$. The arc length formula in terms of the parameter θ is

$$L = \int_{\alpha}^{\beta} \sqrt{\left(\frac{dx}{d\theta}\right)^2 + \left(\frac{dy}{d\theta}\right)^2} \, d\theta,$$

where

$$\frac{dx}{d\theta} = f'(\theta) \cos \theta - f(\theta) \sin \theta \quad \text{and} \quad \frac{dy}{d\theta} = f'(\theta) \sin \theta + f(\theta) \cos \theta.$$

When substituted into the arc length formula and simplified, the result is a new arc length integral (Exercise 68).

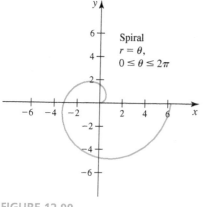

FIGURE 12.99

Arc Length of a Polar Curve

Let f have a continuous derivative on the interval $[\alpha, \beta]$. The **arc length** of the polar curve $r = f(\theta)$ on $[\alpha, \beta]$ is

$$L = \int_{\alpha}^{\beta} \sqrt{f(\theta)^2 + f'(\theta)^2} \, d\theta.$$

QUICK CHECK 4 Find the arc length of the circle $r = f(\theta) = 1$, for $0 \leq \theta \leq 2\pi$.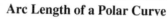

EXAMPLE 5 **Arc length of polar curves**

a. Find the arc length of the spiral $r = f(\theta) = \theta$, for $0 \leq \theta \leq 2\pi$ (Figure 12.99).
b. Find the arc length of the cardioid $r = 1 + \cos \theta$ (Figure 12.100).

SOLUTION

a. $\displaystyle L = \int_0^{2\pi} \sqrt{\theta^2 + 1} \, d\theta$ $\qquad$ $f(\theta) = \theta$ and $f'(\theta) = 1$

$$= \left[\frac{\theta}{2}\sqrt{\theta^2 + 1} + \frac{1}{2}\ln(\theta + \sqrt{\theta^2 + 1})\right]\Big|_0^{2\pi} \quad \text{Table of integrals or trigonometric substitution}$$

$$= \pi\sqrt{4\pi^2 + 1} + \frac{1}{2}\ln(2\pi + \sqrt{4\pi^2 + 1}) \quad \text{Substitute limits of integration.}$$

$$\approx 21.26 \qquad \text{Evaluate.}$$

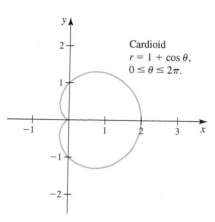

FIGURE 12.100

b. The cardioid is symmetric about the x-axis and its upper half is generated for $0 \leq \theta \leq \pi$. The length of the full curve is twice the length of its upper half:

$$L = 2\int_0^{\pi} \sqrt{(1 + \cos \theta)^2 + (-\sin \theta)^2} \, d\theta \quad f(\theta) = 1 + \cos \theta; f'(\theta) = -\sin \theta$$

$$= 2\int_0^{\pi} \sqrt{2 + 2\cos \theta} \, d\theta \qquad \text{Simplify.}$$

$$= 2\int_0^{\pi} \sqrt{4\cos^2(\theta/2)} \, d\theta \qquad 1 + \cos \theta = 2\cos^2(\theta/2)$$

$$= 4\int_0^{\pi} \cos(\theta/2) \, d\theta \qquad \cos(\theta/2) \geq 0, \text{ for } 0 \leq \theta \leq \pi$$

$$= 8\sin(\theta/2)\Big|_0^{\pi} = 8. \qquad \text{Integrate and simplify.}$$

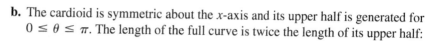

Related Exercises 31–40 ◄

Arc Length as a Parameter

Until now the parameter t used to describe a curve $\mathbf{r}(t) = \langle f(t), g(t), h(t) \rangle$ has been chosen either for convenience or because it represents time in some specified unit. We now introduce the most natural parameter for describing curves; that parameter is *arc length*. Let's see what it means for a curve to be *parameterized by arc length*.

Consider the following two characterizations of the unit circle centered at the origin:

- $\langle \cos t, \sin t \rangle$, for $0 \leq t \leq 2\pi$
- $\langle \cos 2t, \sin 2t \rangle$, for $0 \leq t \leq \pi$

In the first description, as the parameter t increases from $t = 0$ to $t = 2\pi$, the full circle is generated and the arc length s of the curve also increases from $s = 0$ to $s = 2\pi$. In other words, as the parameter t increases, it measures the arc length of the curve that is generated (Figure 12.101a).

In the second description, as t varies from $t = 0$ to $t = \pi$, the full circle is generated and the arc length increases from $s = 0$ to $s = 2\pi$. In this case, the length of the interval in t does not equal the length of the curve generated; therefore, the parameter t does not correspond to arc length (Figure 12.101b). In general, there are infinitely many ways to parameterize a given curve; however, for a given initial point and orientation, arc length is the parameter for only one of them.

> **QUICK CHECK 5** Consider the portion of a circle $\mathbf{r}(t) = \langle \cos t, \sin t \rangle$, for $a \leq t \leq b$. Show that the arc length of the curve is $b - a$.

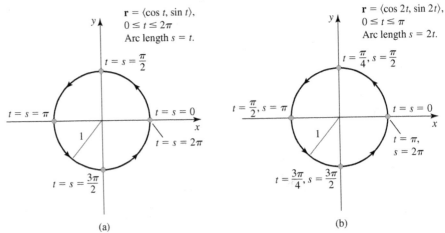

FIGURE 12.101

The Arc Length Function Suppose that a smooth curve is represented by the function $\mathbf{r}(t) = \langle x(t), y(t), z(t) \rangle$, for $t \geq a$, where t is a parameter. Notice that as t increases, the length of the curve also increases. Using the arc length formula, the length of the curve from $\mathbf{r}(a)$ to $\mathbf{r}(t)$ is

> Notice that t is the independent variable of the function $s(t)$, so a different symbol u is used for the variable of integration. It is common to use s as the arc length function.

$$s(t) = \int_a^t \sqrt{x'(u)^2 + y'(u)^2 + z'(u)^2}\, du = \int_a^t |\mathbf{v}(u)|\, du.$$

This equation gives the relationship between the arc length of a curve and any parameter t used to describe the curve.

An important consequence of this relationship arises if we differentiate both sides with respect to t using the Fundamental Theorem of Calculus:

$$\frac{ds}{dt} = \frac{d}{dt}\left(\int_a^t |\mathbf{v}(u)|\, du \right) = |\mathbf{v}(t)|.$$

Specifically, if t represents time and $\mathbf{r}$ is the position of an object moving on the curve, then the rate of change of the arc length with respect to time is the speed of the object. Notice that if $\mathbf{r}(t)$ describes a smooth curve, then $|\mathbf{v}(t)| \neq 0$; hence $ds/dt > 0$, and s is an increasing function of t—as t increases, the arc length also increases. If $\mathbf{r}(t)$ is a curve on which $|\mathbf{v}(t)| = 1$, then

$$s(t) = \int_a^t |\mathbf{v}(u)| \, du = \int_a^t 1 \, du = t - a,$$

which means the parameter t corresponds to arc length.

THEOREM 12.9   Arc Length as a Function of a Parameter

Let $\mathbf{r}(t)$ describe a smooth curve, for $t \geq a$. The arc length is given by

$$s(t) = \int_a^t |\mathbf{v}(u)| \, du,$$

where $|\mathbf{v}| = |\mathbf{r}'|$. Equivalently, $\dfrac{ds}{dt} = |\mathbf{v}(t)| > 0$. If $|\mathbf{v}(t)| = 1$, for all $t \geq a$, then the parameter t corresponds to arc length.

EXAMPLE 6   Arc length parameterization Consider the helix $\mathbf{r}(t) = \langle 2 \cos t, 2 \sin t, 4t \rangle$, for $t \geq 0$.

a. Find the arc length function $s(t)$.

b. Find another description of the helix that uses arc length as the parameter.

SOLUTION

a. Note that $\mathbf{r}'(t) = \langle -2 \sin t, 2 \cos t, 4 \rangle$ and

$$\begin{aligned}
|\mathbf{v}(t)| = |\mathbf{r}'(t)| &= \sqrt{(-2 \sin t)^2 + (2 \cos t)^2 + 4^2} \\
&= \sqrt{4(\sin^2 t + \cos^2 t) + 4^2} \qquad \text{Simplify.}\\
&= \sqrt{4 + 4^2} \qquad\qquad\qquad \sin^2 t + \cos^2 t = 1\\
&= \sqrt{20} = 2\sqrt{5}. \qquad\qquad \text{Simplify.}
\end{aligned}$$

Therefore, the relationship between the arc length s and the parameter t is

$$s(t) = \int_a^t |\mathbf{v}(u)| \, du = \int_0^t 2\sqrt{5} \, du = 2\sqrt{5}\,t.$$

b. Substituting $t = s/(2\sqrt{5})$ into the original parametric description of the helix, we find that the description with arc length as a parameter is (using a different function name)

$$\mathbf{r}_1(s) = \left\langle 2 \cos\left(\frac{s}{2\sqrt{5}}\right), 2 \sin\left(\frac{s}{2\sqrt{5}}\right), \frac{2s}{\sqrt{5}} \right\rangle, \quad \text{for } s \geq 0.$$

This description has the property that an increment of Δs in the parameter corresponds to an increment of exactly Δs in the arc length.

Related Exercises 41–50◄

QUICK CHECK 6 Does the line $\mathbf{r}(t) = \langle t, t, t \rangle$ have arc length as a parameter? Explain.

SECTION 12.8 EXERCISES

Review Questions

1. Find the length of the line given by $\mathbf{r}(t) = \langle t, 2t \rangle$, for $a \le t \le b$.

2. Explain how to find the length of the curve $\mathbf{r}(t) = \langle f(t), g(t), h(t) \rangle$, for $a \le t \le b$.

3. Express the arc length of a curve in terms of the speed of an object moving along the curve.

4. Suppose an object moves in space with the position function $\mathbf{r}(t) = \langle x(t), y(t), z(t) \rangle$. Write the integral that gives the distance it travels between $t = a$ and $t = b$.

5. An object moves on a trajectory given by $\mathbf{r}(t) = \langle 10 \cos 2t, 10 \sin 2t \rangle$, for $0 \le t \le \pi$. How far does it travel?

6. How do you find the arc length of the polar curve $r = f(\theta)$, for $\alpha \le \theta \le \beta$?

7. Explain what it means for a curve to be parameterized by its arc length.

8. Is the curve $\mathbf{r}(t) = \langle \cos t, \sin t \rangle$ parameterized by its arc length? Explain.

Basic Skills

9–22. Arc length calculations *Find the length of the following two- and three-dimensional curves.*

9. $\mathbf{r}(t) = \langle 3t^2 - 1, 4t^2 + 5 \rangle$, for $0 \le t \le 1$

10. $\mathbf{r}(t) = \langle 3t - 1, 4t + 5, t \rangle$, for $0 \le t \le 1$

11. $\mathbf{r}(t) = \langle 3 \cos t, 3 \sin t \rangle$, for $0 \le t \le \pi$

12. $\mathbf{r}(t) = \langle 4 \cos 3t, 4 \sin 3t \rangle$, for $0 \le t \le 2\pi/3$

13. $\mathbf{r}(t) = \langle \cos t + t \sin t, \sin t - t \cos t \rangle$, for $0 \le t \le \pi/2$

14. $\mathbf{r}(t) = \langle \cos t + \sin t, \cos t - \sin t \rangle$, for $0 \le t \le 2\pi$

15. $\mathbf{r}(t) = \langle 2 + 3t, 1 - 4t, -4 + 3t \rangle$, for $1 \le t \le 6$

16. $\mathbf{r}(t) = \langle 4 \cos t, 4 \sin t, 3t \rangle$, for $0 \le t \le 6\pi$

17. $\mathbf{r}(t) = \langle t, 8 \sin t, 8 \cos t \rangle$, for $0 \le t \le 4\pi$

18. $\mathbf{r}(t) = \langle t^2/2, (2t + 1)^{3/2}/3 \rangle$, for $0 \le t \le 2$

19. $\mathbf{r}(t) = \langle e^{2t}, 2e^{2t} + 5, 2e^{2t} - 20 \rangle$, for $0 \le t \le \ln 2$

20. $\mathbf{r}(t) = \langle t^2, t^3 \rangle$, for $0 \le t \le 4$

21. $\mathbf{r}(t) = \langle \cos^3 t, \sin^3 t \rangle$, for $0 \le t \le \pi/2$

22. $\mathbf{r}(t) = \langle 3 \cos t, 4 \cos t, 5 \sin t \rangle$, for $0 \le t \le 2\pi$

23–26. Speed and arc length *For the following trajectories, find the speed associated with the trajectory and then find the length of the trajectory on the given interval.*

23. $\mathbf{r}(t) = \langle 2t^3, -t^3, 5t^3 \rangle$, for $0 \le t \le 4$

24. $\mathbf{r}(t) = \langle 5 \cos t^2, 5 \sin t^2, 12t^2 \rangle$, for $0 \le t \le 2$

25. $\mathbf{r}(t) = \langle 13 \sin 2t, 12 \cos 2t, 5 \cos 2t \rangle$, for $0 \le t \le \pi$

26. $\mathbf{r}(t) = \langle e^t \sin t, e^t \cos t, e^t \rangle$, for $0 \le t \le \ln 2$

27–30. Arc length approximations *Use a calculator to approximate the length of the following curves. In each case, simplify the arc length integral as much as possible before finding an approximation.*

27. $\mathbf{r}(t) = \langle 2 \cos t, 4 \sin t \rangle$, for $0 \le t \le 2\pi$

28. $\mathbf{r}(t) = \langle 2 \cos t, 4 \sin t, 6 \cos t \rangle$, for $0 \le t \le 2\pi$

29. $\mathbf{r}(t) = \langle t, 4t^2, 10 \rangle$, for $-2 \le t \le 2$

30. $\mathbf{r}(t) = \langle e^t, 2e^{-t}, t \rangle$, for $0 \le t \le \ln 3$

31–40. Arc length of polar curves *Find the length of the following polar curves.*

31. The complete circle $r = a \sin \theta$, where $a > 0$

32. The complete cardioid $r = 2 - 2 \sin \theta$

33. The spiral $r = \theta^2$, where $0 \le \theta \le 2\pi$

34. The spiral $r = e^\theta$, where $0 \le \theta \le 2\pi n$, for a positive integer n

35. The complete cardioid $r = 4 + 4 \sin \theta$

36. The spiral $r = 4\theta^2$, for $0 \le \theta \le 6$

37. The spiral $r = 2e^{2\theta}$, for $0 \le \theta \le \ln 8$

38. The curve $r = \sin^2 (\theta/2)$, for $0 \le \theta \le \pi$

39. The curve $r = \sin^3 (\theta/3)$, for $0 \le \theta \le \pi/2$

40. The parabola $r = \sqrt{2}/(1 + \cos \theta)$, for $0 \le \theta \le \pi/2$

41–50. Arc length parameterization *Determine whether the following curves use arc length as a parameter. If not, find a description that uses arc length as a parameter.*

41. $\mathbf{r}(t) = \langle 1, \sin t, \cos t \rangle$, for $t \ge 1$

42. $\mathbf{r}(t) = \left\langle \dfrac{t}{\sqrt{3}}, \dfrac{t}{\sqrt{3}}, \dfrac{t}{\sqrt{3}} \right\rangle$, for $0 \le t \le 10$

43. $\mathbf{r}(t) = \langle t, 2t \rangle$, for $0 \le t \le 3$

44. $\mathbf{r}(t) = \langle t + 1, 2t - 3, 6t \rangle$, for $0 \le t \le 10$

45. $\mathbf{r}(t) = \langle 2 \cos t, 2 \sin t \rangle$, for $0 \le t \le 2\pi$

46. $\mathbf{r}(t) = \langle 5 \cos t, 3 \sin t, 4 \sin t \rangle$, for $0 \le t \le \pi$

47. $\mathbf{r}(t) = \langle \cos t^2, \sin t^2 \rangle$, for $0 \le t \le \sqrt{\pi}$

48. $\mathbf{r}(t) = \langle t^2, 2t^2, 4t^2 \rangle$, for $1 \le t \le 4$

49. $\mathbf{r}(t) = \langle e^t, e^t, e^t \rangle$, for $t \ge 0$

50. $\mathbf{r}(t) = \left\langle \dfrac{\cos t}{\sqrt{2}}, \dfrac{\cos t}{\sqrt{2}}, \sin t \right\rangle$, for $0 \le t \le 10$

Further Explorations

51. **Explain why or why not** Determine whether the following statements are true and give an explanation or counterexample.

a. If an object moves on a trajectory with constant speed S over a time interval $a \le t \le b$, then the length of the trajectory is $S(b - a)$.

b. The curves defined by $\mathbf{r}(t) = \langle f(t), g(t) \rangle$ and $\mathbf{R}(t) = \langle g(t), f(t) \rangle$ have the same length over the interval $[a, b]$.

c. The curve $\mathbf{r}(t) = \langle f(t), g(t) \rangle$, for $0 \leq a \leq t \leq b$, and the curve $\mathbf{R}(t) = \langle f(t^2), g(t^2) \rangle$, for $\sqrt{a} \leq t \leq \sqrt{b}$, have the same length.

d. The curve $\mathbf{r}(t) = \langle t, t^2, 3t^2 \rangle$, for $1 \leq t \leq 4$, is parameterized by arc length.

52. **Length of a line segment** Consider the line segment joining the points $P(x_0, y_0, z_0)$ and $Q(x_1, y_1, z_1)$.

   a. Find a parametric description of the line segment PQ.
   b. Use the arc length formula to find the length of PQ.
   c. Use geometry (distance formula) to verify the result of part (b).

53. **Tilted circles** Let the curve C be described by $\mathbf{r}(t) = \langle a \cos t, b \sin t, c \sin t \rangle$, where a, b, and c are real positive numbers.

   a. Assume that C lies in a plane. Show that C is a circle centered at the origin provided $a^2 = b^2 + c^2$.
   b. Find the arc length of the circle.
   c. Assuming that the curve lies in a plane, find the conditions under which $\mathbf{r}(t) = \langle a \cos t + b \sin t, c \cos t + d \sin t, e \cos t + f \sin t \rangle$ describes a circle. Then find its arc length.

54. **A family of arc length integrals** Find the length of the curve $\mathbf{r}(t) = \langle t^m, t^m, t^{3m/2} \rangle$, for $0 \leq a \leq t \leq b$, where m is a real number. Express the result in terms of m, a, and b.

55. **A special case** Suppose a curve is described by $\mathbf{r}(t) = \langle A h(t), B h(t) \rangle$, for $a \leq t \leq b$, where A and B are constants and h has a continuous derivative.

   a. Show that the length of the curve is
   $$\sqrt{A^2 + B^2} \int_a^b |h'(t)| \, dt.$$

   b. Use part (a) to find the length of the curve $x = 2t^3$, $y = 5t^3$, for $0 \leq t \leq 4$.
   c. Use part (a) to find the length of the curve $x = 4/t$, $y = 10/t$, for $1 \leq t \leq 8$.

56. **Spiral arc length** Consider the spiral $r = 4\theta$, for $\theta \geq 0$.

   a. Use a trigonometric substitution to find the length of the spiral, for $0 \leq \theta \leq \sqrt{8}$.
   b. Find $L(\theta)$, the length of the spiral on the interval $[0, \theta]$, for any $\theta \geq 0$.
   c. Show that $L'(\theta) > 0$. Is $L''(\theta)$ positive or negative? Interpret your answers.

57. **Spiral arc length** Find the length of the entire spiral $r = e^{-a\theta}$, for $\theta \geq 0$ and $a > 0$.

58–61. **Arc length using technology** *Use a calculator to find the approximate length of the following curves.*

58. The three-leaf rose $r = 2 \cos 3\theta$

59. The lemniscate $r^2 = 6 \sin 2\theta$

60. The limaçon $r = 2 - 4 \sin \theta$

61. The limaçon $r = 4 - 2 \cos \theta$

Applications

62. **A cycloid** A cycloid is the path traced by a point on a rolling circle (think of a light on the rim of a moving bicycle wheel). The cycloid generated by a circle of radius a is given by the parametric equations

$$x = a(t - \sin t), \quad y = a(1 - \cos t);$$

the parameter range $0 \leq t \leq 2\pi$ produces one arch of the cycloid (see figure). Show that the length of one arch of a cycloid is $8a$.

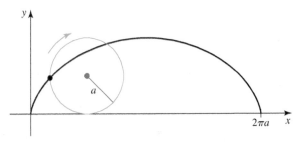

63. **Projectile trajectories** A projectile (such as a baseball or a cannonball) launched from the origin with an initial horizontal velocity u_0 and an initial vertical velocity v_0 moves in a parabolic trajectory given by

$$x = u_0 t, \quad y = -\tfrac{1}{2}gt^2 + v_0 t, \quad \text{for } t \geq 0,$$

where air resistance is neglected and $g \approx 9.8 \text{ m/s}^2$ is the acceleration due to gravity.

   a. Let $u_0 = 20$ m/s and $v_0 = 25$ m/s. Assuming the projectile is launched over horizontal ground, at what time does it return to Earth?
   b. Find the integral that gives the length of the trajectory from launch to landing.
   c. Evaluate the integral in part (b) by first making the change of variables $u = -gt + v_0$. The resulting integral is evaluated either by making a second change of variables or by using a calculator. What is the length of the trajectory?
   d. How far does the projectile land from its launch site?

64. **Variable speed on a circle** Consider a particle that moves in a plane according to the equations $x = \sin t^2$ and $y = \cos t^2$ with a starting position $(0, 1)$ at $t = 0$.

   a. Describe the path of the particle, including the time required to return to the starting position.
   b. What is the length of the path in part (a)?
   c. Describe how the motion of this particle differs from the motion described by the equations $x = \sin t$ and $y = \cos t$.
   d. Now consider the motion described by $x = \sin t^n$ and $y = \cos t^n$, where n is a positive integer. Describe the path of the particle, including the time required to return to the starting position.
   e. What is the length of the path in part (d) for any positive integer n?
   f. If you were watching a race on a circular path between two runners, one moving according to $x = \sin t$ and $y = \cos t$ and one according to $x = \sin t^2$ and $y = \cos t^2$, who would win and when would one runner pass the other?

Additional Exercises

65. **Arc length parameterization** Prove that the line $\mathbf{r}(t) = \langle x_0 + at, y_0 + bt, z_0 + ct \rangle$ is parameterized by arc length provided $a^2 + b^2 + c^2 = 1$.

66. Arc length parameterization Prove that the curve
$\mathbf{r}(t) = \langle a \cos t, b \sin t, c \sin t \rangle$ is parameterized by arc length
provided $a^2 = b^2 + c^2 = 1$.

67. Lengths of related curves Suppose a curve is given by
$\mathbf{r}(t) = \langle f(t), g(t) \rangle$, where f' and g' are continuous, for
$a \leq t \leq b$. Assume the curve is traversed once, for $a \leq t \leq b$,
and the length of the curve between $(f(a), g(a))$ and $(f(b), g(b))$
is L. Prove that for any nonzero constant c the length of the curve
defined by $\mathbf{r}(t) = \langle cf(t), cg(t) \rangle$, for $a \leq t \leq b$, is $|c| L$.

68. Arc length for polar curves Prove that the length of the curve
$r = f(\theta)$, for $\alpha \leq \theta \leq \beta$, is

$$L = \int_\alpha^\beta \sqrt{f(\theta)^2 + f'(\theta)^2} \, d\theta.$$

69. Arc length for $y = f(x)$ The arc length formula for functions of
the form $y = f(x)$ on $[a, b]$ found in Section 6.5 is

$$L = \int_a^b \sqrt{1 + f'(x)^2} \, dx.$$

Derive this formula from the arc length formula for vector curves.
(*Hint*: Let $x = t$ be the parameter.)

70. Change of variables Consider the parameterized curves $\mathbf{r}(t) = \langle f(t), g(t), h(t) \rangle$ and $\mathbf{R}(t) = \langle f(u(t)), g(u(t)), h(u(t)) \rangle$, where
f, g, h, and u are continuously differentiable functions and u has an
inverse on $[a, b]$.

a. Show that the curve generated by $\mathbf{r}$ on the interval
$a \leq t \leq b$ is the same as the curve generated by $\mathbf{R}$ on
$u^{-1}(a) \leq t \leq u^{-1}(b)$ (or $u^{-1}(b) \leq t \leq u^{-1}(a)$).
b. Show that the lengths of the two curves are equal. (*Hint*: Use
the Chain Rule and a change of variables in the arc length integral for the curve generated by $\mathbf{R}$.)

QUICK CHECK ANSWERS

1. $\sqrt{2}$ 2. $\sqrt{3}$

3. $L = \int_a^b |\mathbf{v}(t)| \, dt = \int_a^b S \, dt = S(b - a)$ 4. 2π

5. For $a \leq t \leq b$, the curve C generated is $(b - a)/2\pi$ of
a full circle. Because the full circle has a length of 2π, the
curve C has a length of $b - a$.   6. No. If t increases by one
unit, the length of the curve increases by $\sqrt{3}$ units.

12.9 Curvature and Normal Vectors

We know how to find tangent vectors and lengths of curves in space, but much more can be
said about the shape of such curves. In this section, we introduce several new concepts. *Curvature* measures how *fast* a curve turns at a point, the *normal vector* gives the *direction* in
which a curve turns, and the *binormal vector* and the *torsion* describe the twisting of a curve.

Curvature

Imagine driving a car along a winding mountain road. There are two ways to change the
velocity of the car (that is, to accelerate). You can change the *speed* of the car or you can
change the *direction* of the car. A change of speed is relatively easy to describe, so we
postpone that discussion and focus on the change of direction. The rate at which the car
changes direction is related to the notion of *curvature*.

Unit Tangent Vector   Recall from Section 12.6 that if $\mathbf{r}(t) = \langle x(t), y(t), z(t) \rangle$ is a
smooth oriented curve, then the unit tangent vector at a point is the unit vector that points in
the direction of the tangent vector $\mathbf{r}'(t)$; that is,

$$\mathbf{T}(t) = \frac{\mathbf{r}'(t)}{|\mathbf{r}'(t)|} = \frac{\mathbf{v}(t)}{|\mathbf{v}(t)|}.$$

Because $\mathbf{T}$ is a unit vector, its length does not change along the curve. The only way $\mathbf{T}$ can
change is through a change in direction.

How quickly does $\mathbf{T}$ change (in direction) as we move along the curve? If a small
increment in arc length Δs along the curve results in a large change in the direction of
$\mathbf{T}$, the curve is turning quickly over that interval and we say it has a large *curvature*
(Figure 12.102a). If a small increment Δs in arc length results in a small change in
the direction of $\mathbf{T}$, the curve is turning slowly over that interval and it has a small curvature (Figure 12.102b). The magnitude of the rate at which the direction of $\mathbf{T}$ changes with
respect to arc length is the curvature of the curve.

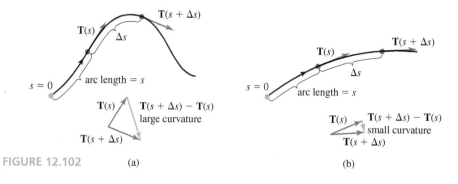

FIGURE 12.102   (a)   (b)

> Recall that the unit tangent vector at a point depends on the orientation of the curve. The curvature does not depend on the orientation of the curve, but it does depend on the shape of the curve. The Greek letter *kappa*, κ is used to denote curvature.

DEFINITION Curvature

Let $\mathbf{r}$ describe a smooth parameterized curve. If s denotes arc length and $\mathbf{T} = \mathbf{r}'/|\mathbf{r}'|$ is the unit tangent vector, the **curvature** is $\kappa(s) = \left|\dfrac{d\mathbf{T}}{ds}\right|$.

Note that κ is a nonnegative scalar-valued function. A large value of κ at a point indicates a tight curve that changes direction quickly. If κ is small, then the curve is relatively flat and its direction changes slowly. The minimum curvature (zero) occurs on a straight line where the tangent never changes direction along the curve.

In order to evaluate $d\mathbf{T}/ds$, a description of the curve in terms of the arc length appears to be needed, but it may be difficult to obtain. A short calculation leads to the first of two practical curvature formulas.

Letting t be an arbitrary parameter, we begin with the Chain Rule and write $\dfrac{d\mathbf{T}}{dt} = \dfrac{d\mathbf{T}}{ds} \cdot \dfrac{ds}{dt}$. Dividing by $ds/dt = |\mathbf{v}|$ and taking absolute values leads to

$$\kappa = \left|\frac{d\mathbf{T}}{ds}\right| = \frac{|d\mathbf{T}/dt|}{|ds/dt|} = \frac{1}{|\mathbf{v}|}\left|\frac{d\mathbf{T}}{dt}\right|.$$

This calculation is a proof of the following theorem.

THEOREM 12.10   Curvature Formula

Let $\mathbf{r}(t)$ describe a smooth parameterized curve, where t is any parameter. If $\mathbf{v} = \mathbf{r}'$ is the velocity and $\mathbf{T}$ is the unit tangent vector, then the curvature is

$$\kappa(t) = \frac{1}{|\mathbf{v}|}\left|\frac{d\mathbf{T}}{dt}\right| = \frac{|\mathbf{T}'(t)|}{|\mathbf{r}'(t)|}.$$

EXAMPLE 1   Lines have zero curvature Consider the line $\mathbf{r}(t) = \langle x_0 + at, y_0 + bt, z_0 + ct \rangle$, for $-\infty < t < \infty$. Show that $\kappa = 0$ at all points on the line.

SOLUTION Note that $\mathbf{r}'(t) = \langle a, b, c \rangle$ and $|\mathbf{r}'(t)| = |\mathbf{v}(t)| = \sqrt{a^2 + b^2 + c^2}$. Therefore,

$$\mathbf{T}(t) = \frac{\mathbf{r}'(t)}{|\mathbf{r}'(t)|} = \frac{\langle a, b, c \rangle}{\sqrt{a^2 + b^2 + c^2}}.$$

Because $\mathbf{T}$ is a constant, $\dfrac{d\mathbf{T}}{dt} = \mathbf{0}$ and $\kappa = 0$ at all points of the line.

Related Exercises 11–20 ◄

EXAMPLE 2   Circles have constant curvature Consider the circle $\mathbf{r}(t) = \langle R \cos t, R \sin t \rangle$, for $0 \le t \le 2\pi$, where $R > 0$. Show that $\kappa = 1/R$.

SOLUTION We compute $\mathbf{r}'(t) = \langle -R \sin t, R \cos t \rangle$ and

$$
\begin{aligned}
|\mathbf{v}(t)| = |\mathbf{r}'(t)| &= \sqrt{(-R \sin t)^2 + (R \cos t)^2} \\
&= \sqrt{R^2 (\sin^2 t + \cos^2 t)} \qquad \text{Simplify.} \\
&= R. \qquad\qquad\qquad \sin^2 t + \cos^2 t = 1, R > 0
\end{aligned}
$$

Therefore,

$$
\mathbf{T}(t) = \frac{\mathbf{r}'(t)}{|\mathbf{r}'(t)|} = \frac{\langle -R \sin t, R \cos t \rangle}{R} = \langle -\sin t, \cos t \rangle, \text{ and}
$$

$$
\frac{d\mathbf{T}}{dt} = \langle -\cos t, -\sin t \rangle.
$$

> The curvature of a curve at a point can also be visualized in terms of a **circle of curvature**, which is a circle of radius R that is tangent to the curve at that point. The curvature at the point is $\kappa = 1/R$. See Exercises 70–74.

Combining these observations, the curvature is

$$
\kappa = \frac{1}{|\mathbf{v}|} \left| \frac{d\mathbf{T}}{dt} \right| = \frac{1}{R} |\langle -\cos t, -\sin t \rangle| = \frac{1}{R} \underbrace{\sqrt{\cos^2 t + \sin^2 t}}_{1} = \frac{1}{R}.
$$

The curvature of a circle is constant; a circle with a small radius has a large curvature and vice versa.

Related Exercises 11–20 ◄

QUICK CHECK 1 What is the curvature of the circle $\mathbf{r}(t) = \langle 3 \sin t, 3 \cos t \rangle$? ◄

An Alternative Curvature Formula A second curvature formula, which pertains specifically to trajectories of moving objects, is easier to use in some cases. The calculation is instructive because it relies on many properties of vector functions. In the end, a remarkably simple formula emerges.

Again consider a smooth curve $\mathbf{r}(t) = \langle x(t), y(t), z(t) \rangle$, where $\mathbf{v}(t) = \mathbf{r}'(t)$ and $\mathbf{a}(t) = \mathbf{v}'(t)$ are the velocity and acceleration of an object moving along that curve, respectively. We assume that $\mathbf{v}(t) \ne \mathbf{0}$ and $\mathbf{a}(t) \ne \mathbf{0}$. Because $\mathbf{T} = \mathbf{v}/|\mathbf{v}|$, we begin by writing $\mathbf{v} = |\mathbf{v}|\,\mathbf{T}$ and differentiating both sides with respect to t:

$$
\mathbf{a} = \frac{d\mathbf{v}}{dt} = \frac{d}{dt}(|\mathbf{v}(t)|\,\mathbf{T}(t)) = \frac{d}{dt}(|\mathbf{v}(t)|)\mathbf{T}(t) + |\mathbf{v}(t)|\frac{d\mathbf{T}}{dt}. \quad \text{Product Rule} \quad (1)
$$

We now form $\mathbf{v} \times \mathbf{a}$:

> Distributive law for cross products:
>
> $\mathbf{w} \times (\mathbf{u} + \mathbf{v}) = (\mathbf{w} \times \mathbf{u}) + (\mathbf{w} \times \mathbf{v})$
>
> $(\mathbf{u} + \mathbf{v}) \times \mathbf{w} = (\mathbf{u} \times \mathbf{w}) + (\mathbf{v} \times \mathbf{w})$

$$
\mathbf{v} \times \mathbf{a} = \underbrace{|\mathbf{v}|\mathbf{T}}_{\mathbf{v}} \times \underbrace{\left[\frac{d}{dt}(|\mathbf{v}(t)|)\mathbf{T} + |\mathbf{v}|\frac{d\mathbf{T}}{dt} \right]}_{\mathbf{a}}
$$

$$
= \underbrace{|\mathbf{v}|\mathbf{T} \times \left(\frac{d}{dt}(|\mathbf{v}(t)|) \right)\mathbf{T}}_{0} + |\mathbf{v}|\mathbf{T} \times |\mathbf{v}|\frac{d\mathbf{T}}{dt} \quad \text{Distributive law for cross products}
$$

The first term in this expression has the form $a\mathbf{T} \times b\mathbf{T}$, where a and b are scalars. Therefore, $a\mathbf{T}$ and $b\mathbf{T}$ are parallel vectors and $a\mathbf{T} \times b\mathbf{T} = \mathbf{0}$. To simplify the second term, recall that a vector $\mathbf{u}(t)$ of constant length has the property that $\mathbf{u}$ and $d\mathbf{u}/dt$ are orthogonal (Section 12.7). Because $\mathbf{T}$ is a unit vector, it has constant length, and $\mathbf{T}$ and $d\mathbf{T}/dt$ are orthogonal. Furthermore, scalar multiples of $\mathbf{T}$ and $d\mathbf{T}/dt$ are also orthogonal. Therefore, the magnitude of the second term simplifies as follows:

> Recall that the magnitude of the cross product of nonzero vectors is $|\mathbf{u} \times \mathbf{v}| = |\mathbf{u}||\mathbf{v}| \sin \theta$, where θ is the angle between the vectors. If the vectors are orthogonal, $\sin \theta = 1$ and $|\mathbf{u} \times \mathbf{v}| = |\mathbf{u}||\mathbf{v}|$.

$$\left| |\mathbf{v}|\mathbf{T} \times |\mathbf{v}|\frac{d\mathbf{T}}{dt} \right| = |\mathbf{v}||\mathbf{T}|\left| |\mathbf{v}|\frac{d\mathbf{T}}{dt} \right| \underbrace{\sin \theta}_{1} \qquad |\mathbf{u} \times \mathbf{v}| = |\mathbf{u}||\mathbf{v}| \sin \theta$$

$$= |\mathbf{v}|^2 \left|\frac{d\mathbf{T}}{dt}\right| \underbrace{|\mathbf{T}|}_{1} \qquad \text{Simplify, } \theta = \pi/2.$$

$$= |\mathbf{v}|^2 \left|\frac{d\mathbf{T}}{dt}\right|. \qquad |\mathbf{T}| = 1$$

The final step is to use Theorem 12.10 and substitute $\left|\dfrac{d\mathbf{T}}{dt}\right| = \kappa|\mathbf{v}|$. Putting these results together, we find that

$$|\mathbf{v} \times \mathbf{a}| = |\mathbf{v}|^2 \left|\frac{d\mathbf{T}}{dt}\right| = |\mathbf{v}|^2 \kappa|\mathbf{v}| = \kappa|\mathbf{v}|^3.$$

> Note that $\mathbf{a}(t) = \mathbf{0}$ corresponds to straight-line motion and $\kappa = 0$. If $\mathbf{v}(t) = \mathbf{0}$, the object is at rest and κ is undefined.

Solving for the curvature gives $\kappa = \dfrac{|\mathbf{v} \times \mathbf{a}|}{|\mathbf{v}|^3}$.

THEOREM 12.11   Alternative Curvature Formula

Let $\mathbf{r}$ be the position of an object moving on a smooth curve. The **curvature** at a point on the curve is

$$\kappa = \frac{|\mathbf{v} \times \mathbf{a}|}{|\mathbf{v}|^3},$$

where $\mathbf{v} = \mathbf{r}'$ is the velocity and $\mathbf{a} = \mathbf{v}'$ is the acceleration.

QUICK CHECK 2 Use the alternative curvature formula to compute the curvature of the curve $\mathbf{r}(t) = \langle t^2, 10, -10 \rangle$.◄

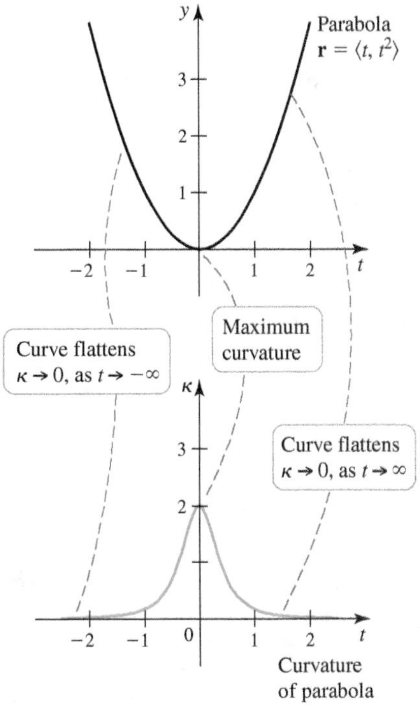

EXAMPLE 3   Curvature of a parabola Find the curvature of the parabola $\mathbf{r}(t) = \langle t, at^2 \rangle$, for $-\infty < t < \infty$, where $a > 0$ is a real number.

SOLUTION The alternative formula works well in this case. We find that $\mathbf{v}(t) = \mathbf{r}'(t) = \langle 1, 2at \rangle$ and $\mathbf{a}(t) = \mathbf{v}'(t) = \langle 0, 2a \rangle$. To compute the cross product $\mathbf{v} \times \mathbf{a}$, we append a third component of 0 to each vector:

$$\mathbf{v} \times \mathbf{a} = \begin{vmatrix} \mathbf{i} & \mathbf{j} & \mathbf{k} \\ 1 & 2at & 0 \\ 0 & 2a & 0 \end{vmatrix} = 2a\mathbf{k}.$$

Therefore, the curvature is

$$\kappa(t) = \frac{|\mathbf{v} \times \mathbf{a}|}{|\mathbf{v}|^3} = \frac{|2a\mathbf{k}|}{|\langle 1, 2at \rangle|^3} = \frac{2a}{(1 + 4a^2 t^2)^{3/2}}.$$

The curvature is a maximum at the vertex of the parabola where $t = 0$ and $\kappa = 2a$. The curvature decreases as one moves along the curve away from the vertex, as shown in Figure 12.103 with $a = 1$.

Related Exercises 21–26◄

EXAMPLE 4   Curvature of a helix Find the curvature of the helix $\mathbf{r}(t) = \langle a \cos t, a \sin t, bt \rangle$, for $-\infty < t < \infty$, where $a > 0$ and $b > 0$ are real numbers.

Parabola $\mathbf{r} = \langle t, t^2 \rangle$

Curve flattens $\kappa \to 0$, as $t \to -\infty$

Maximum curvature

Curve flattens $\kappa \to 0$, as $t \to \infty$

Curvature of parabola

FIGURE 12.103

SOLUTION We use the alternative curvature formula, with

$$\mathbf{v}(t) = \mathbf{r}'(t) = \langle -a\sin t, a\cos t, b \rangle \quad \text{and}$$
$$\mathbf{a}(t) = \mathbf{v}'(t) = \langle -a\cos t, -a\sin t, 0 \rangle.$$

The cross product $\mathbf{v} \times \mathbf{a}$ is

$$\mathbf{v} \times \mathbf{a} = \begin{vmatrix} \mathbf{i} & \mathbf{j} & \mathbf{k} \\ -a\sin t & a\cos t & b \\ -a\cos t & -a\sin t & 0 \end{vmatrix} = ab\sin t\,\mathbf{i} - ab\cos t\,\mathbf{j} + a^2\mathbf{k}.$$

Therefore,

$$|\mathbf{v} \times \mathbf{a}| = |ab\sin t\,\mathbf{i} - ab\cos t\,\mathbf{j} + a^2\mathbf{k}|$$
$$= \sqrt{a^2 b^2 \underbrace{(\sin^2 t + \cos^2 t)}_{1} + a^4}$$
$$= a\sqrt{a^2 + b^2}.$$

> In the curvature formula for the helix, if $b = 0$, the helix becomes a circle of radius a with $\kappa = \dfrac{1}{a}$. At the other extreme, holding a fixed and letting $b \to \infty$ stretches and straightens the helix so that $\kappa \to 0$.

By a familiar calculation, $|\mathbf{v}| = |\langle -a\sin t, a\cos t, b \rangle| = \sqrt{a^2 + b^2}$. Therefore,

$$\kappa = \frac{|\mathbf{v} \times \mathbf{a}|}{|\mathbf{v}|^3} = \frac{a\sqrt{a^2 + b^2}}{(\sqrt{a^2 + b^2})^3} = \frac{a}{a^2 + b^2}.$$

A similar calculation shows that all helices of this form have constant curvature.

Related Exercises 21–26 ◄

Principal Unit Normal Vector

The curvature answers the question of how *fast* a curve turns. The *principal unit normal* vector determines the *direction* in which a curve turns. Specifically, the magnitude of $d\mathbf{T}/ds$ is the curvature: $\kappa = |d\mathbf{T}/ds|$. What about the direction of $d\mathbf{T}/ds$? If only the direction, but not the magnitude, of a vector is of interest, it is convenient to work with a unit vector that has the same direction as the original vector. We apply this idea to $d\mathbf{T}/ds$. The unit vector that points in the direction of $d\mathbf{T}/ds$ is the *principal unit normal vector*.

> The principal unit normal vector depends on the shape of the curve but not on the orientation of the curve.

DEFINITION **Principal Unit Normal Vector**

Let $\mathbf{r}$ describe a smooth parameterized curve. The **principal unit normal vector** at a point P on the curve at which $\kappa \neq 0$ is

$$\mathbf{N}(s) = \frac{d\mathbf{T}/ds}{|d\mathbf{T}/ds|} = \frac{1}{\kappa}\frac{d\mathbf{T}}{ds}.$$

In practice, we use the equivalent formula

$$\mathbf{N}(t) = \frac{d\mathbf{T}/dt}{|d\mathbf{T}/dt|},$$

evaluated at the value of t corresponding to P.

The practical formula $\mathbf{N} = \dfrac{d\mathbf{T}/dt}{|d\mathbf{T}/dt|}$ follows from the definition by using the Chain Rule to write $\dfrac{d\mathbf{T}}{ds} = \dfrac{d\mathbf{T}}{dt} \cdot \dfrac{dt}{ds}$ (Exercise 80). Two important properties of the principal unit normal vector follow from the definition.

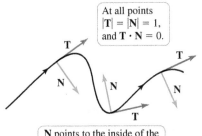

At all points
$|\mathbf{T}| = |\mathbf{N}| = 1$,
and $\mathbf{T} \cdot \mathbf{N} = 0$.

N points to the inside of the
curve—in the direction the
curve is turning.

FIGURE 12.104

> **THEOREM 12.12   Properties of the Principal Unit Normal Vector**
> Let $\mathbf{r}$ describe a smooth parameterized curve with unit tangent vector $\mathbf{T}$ and principal unit normal vector $\mathbf{N}$.
>
> 1. $\mathbf{T}$ and $\mathbf{N}$ are orthogonal at all points of the curve; that is, $\mathbf{T}(t) \cdot \mathbf{N}(t) = 0$ at all points where $\mathbf{N}$ is defined.
>
> 2. The principal unit normal vector points to the inside of the curve—in the direction that the curve is turning.

Proof:

1. As a unit vector, $\mathbf{T}$ has constant length. Therefore, by Theorem 12.8, $\mathbf{T}$ and $d\mathbf{T}/dt$ (or $\mathbf{T}$ and $d\mathbf{T}/ds$) are orthogonal. Because $\mathbf{N}$ is a scalar multiple of $d\mathbf{T}/ds$, $\mathbf{T}$ and $\mathbf{N}$ are orthogonal (Figure 12.104).

2. We motivate—but do not prove—this fact, by recalling that

$$\frac{d\mathbf{T}}{ds} = \lim_{\Delta s \to 0} \frac{\mathbf{T}(s + \Delta s) - \mathbf{T}(s)}{\Delta s}.$$

Therefore, $d\mathbf{T}/ds$ points in the approximate direction of $\mathbf{T}(s + \Delta s) - \mathbf{T}(s)$ when Δs is small. As shown in Figure 12.105, this difference points in the direction in which the curve is turning. Because $\mathbf{N}$ is a positive scalar multiple of $d\mathbf{T}/ds$, it points in the same direction. ◀

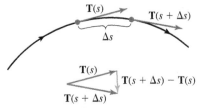

For small Δs
$\mathbf{T}(s + \Delta s) - \mathbf{T}(s)$
points to the inside of
the curve, as does $d\mathbf{T}/ds$.

FIGURE 12.105

QUICK CHECK 3 Consider the parabola $\mathbf{r}(t) = \langle t, -t^2 \rangle$. Does the principal unit normal vector point in the positive y-direction or negative y-direction along the curve? ◀

EXAMPLE 5   Principal unit normal vector for a helix Find the principal unit normal vector for the helix $\mathbf{r}(t) = \langle a \cos t, a \sin t, bt \rangle$, for $-\infty < t < \infty$, where $a > 0$ and $b > 0$ are real numbers.

SOLUTION Several preliminary calculations are needed. First, we have $\mathbf{v}(t) = \mathbf{r}'(t) = \langle -a \sin t, a \cos t, b \rangle$. Therefore,

$$\begin{aligned}
|\mathbf{v}(t)| = |\mathbf{r}'(t)| &= \sqrt{(-a \sin t)^2 + (a \cos t)^2 + b^2} \\
&= \sqrt{a^2 (\sin^2 t + \cos^2 t) + b^2} \qquad \text{Simplify.} \\
&= \sqrt{a^2 + b^2}. \qquad\qquad \sin^2 t + \cos^2 t = 1
\end{aligned}$$

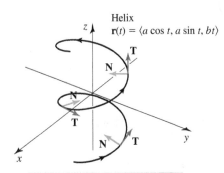

Helix
$\mathbf{r}(t) = \langle a \cos t, a \sin t, bt \rangle$

$\mathbf{T} \cdot \mathbf{N} = 0$ at all points of the curve.
$\mathbf{T}$ points in the direction of the curve.
$\mathbf{N}$ points to the inside of the curve.

FIGURE 12.106

The unit tangent vector is

$$\mathbf{T}(t) = \frac{\mathbf{r}'(t)}{|\mathbf{r}'(t)|} = \frac{\langle -a \sin t, a \cos t, b \rangle}{\sqrt{a^2 + b^2}}.$$

Notice that $\mathbf{T}$ points along the curve in an upward direction (at an angle to the horizontal that satisfies $\tan \theta = b/a$) (Figure 12.106). We can now calculate the principal unit normal vector. First, we determine that

$$\frac{d\mathbf{T}}{dt} = \frac{d}{dt} \left(\frac{\langle -a \sin t, a \cos t, b \rangle}{\sqrt{a^2 + b^2}} \right) = \frac{\langle -a \cos t, -a \sin t, 0 \rangle}{\sqrt{a^2 + b^2}}$$

and

$$\left| \frac{d\mathbf{T}}{dt} \right| = \frac{a}{\sqrt{a^2 + b^2}}.$$

The principal unit normal vector now follows:

$$\mathbf{N} = \frac{d\mathbf{T}/dt}{|d\mathbf{T}/dt|} = \frac{\dfrac{\langle -a\cos t, -a\sin t, 0\rangle}{\sqrt{a^2+b^2}}}{\dfrac{a}{\sqrt{a^2+b^2}}} = \langle -\cos t, -\sin t, 0\rangle.$$

Several important checks should be made. First note that $\mathbf{N}$ is a unit vector; that is, $|\mathbf{N}| = 1$. It should also be confirmed that $\mathbf{T}\cdot\mathbf{N} = 0$; that is, the unit tangent vector and the principal unit normal vector are everywhere orthogonal. Finally, $\mathbf{N}$ is parallel to the xy-plane and points inward toward the z-axis, in the direction the curve turns (Figure 12.106). Notice that in the special case $b = 0$, the trajectory is a circle, but the normal vector is still $\mathbf{N} = \langle -\cos t, -\sin t, 0\rangle$.

Related Exercises 27–34 ◀

> **QUICK CHECK 4** Explain why the principal unit vector for a straight line is undefined. ◀

Components of the Acceleration

We now use the vectors $\mathbf{T}$ and $\mathbf{N}$ to gain insight into how moving objects accelerate. Recall the observation made earlier that the two ways to change the velocity of an object (to accelerate) are to change its *speed* and change its *direction* of motion. We now show that changing the speed produces acceleration in the direction of $\mathbf{T}$ and changing the direction produces acceleration in the direction of $\mathbf{N}$.

We begin with the fact that

$$\mathbf{T} = \frac{\mathbf{v}}{|\mathbf{v}|} \quad \text{or} \quad \mathbf{v} = \mathbf{T}|\mathbf{v}| = \mathbf{T}\frac{ds}{dt}.$$

> Recall that the speed is $|\mathbf{v}| = ds/dt$, where s is arc length.

Differentiating both sides of $\mathbf{v} = \mathbf{T}\dfrac{ds}{dt}$ with respect to t gives

$$\begin{aligned}
\mathbf{a} = \frac{d\mathbf{v}}{dt} &= \frac{d}{dt}\left(\mathbf{T}\frac{ds}{dt}\right) \\
&= \frac{d\mathbf{T}}{dt}\frac{ds}{dt} + \mathbf{T}\frac{d^2s}{dt^2} \qquad \text{Product Rule} \\
&= \frac{d\mathbf{T}}{ds}\frac{ds}{dt}\frac{ds}{dt} + \mathbf{T}\frac{d^2s}{dt^2}. \qquad \text{Chain Rule: } \frac{d\mathbf{T}}{dt} = \frac{d\mathbf{T}}{ds}\frac{ds}{dt}
\end{aligned}$$

We now substitute $|\mathbf{v}| = ds/dt$ and $\kappa\mathbf{N} = d\mathbf{T}/ds$ to obtain the following useful result.

> Note that a_N and a_T are defined even at points where $\kappa = 0$ and $\mathbf{N}$ is undefined.

THEOREM 12.13 Tangential and Normal Components of the Acceleration

The acceleration vector of an object moving in space along a smooth curve has the following representation in terms of its **tangential component** a_T (in the direction of $\mathbf{T}$) and its **normal component** a_N (in the direction of $\mathbf{N}$):

$$\mathbf{a} = a_N\mathbf{N} + a_T\mathbf{T},$$

where $a_N = \kappa|\mathbf{v}|^2 = \dfrac{|\mathbf{v}\times\mathbf{a}|}{|\mathbf{v}|}$ and $a_T = \dfrac{d^2s}{dt^2}$.

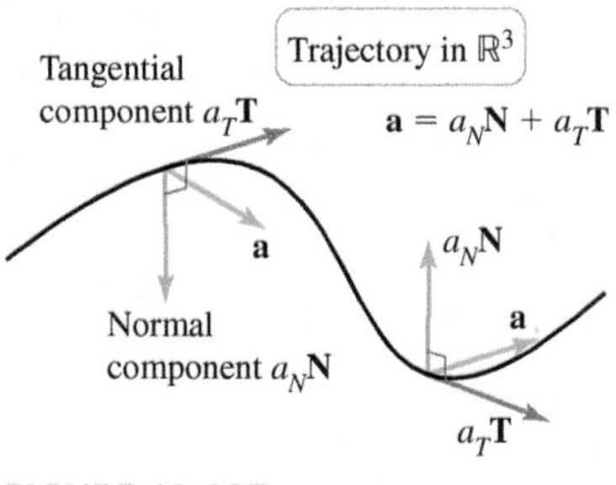

Tangential component $a_T\mathbf{T}$

Trajectory in $\mathbb{R}^3$

$\mathbf{a} = a_N\mathbf{N} + a_T\mathbf{T}$

$a_N\mathbf{N}$

$\mathbf{a}$

Normal component $a_N\mathbf{N}$

$\mathbf{a}$

$a_T\mathbf{T}$

FIGURE 12.107

The tangential component of the acceleration, in the direction of $\mathbf{T}$, is the usual acceleration $a_T = d^2s/dt^2$ of an object moving along a straight line (Figure 12.107). The normal component, in the direction of $\mathbf{N}$, increases with the speed $|\mathbf{v}|$ and with the curvature. Higher speeds on tighter curves produce greater normal accelerations.

EXAMPLE 6 **Acceleration on a circular path** Find the components of the acceleration on the circular trajectory

$$\mathbf{r}(t) = \langle R\cos\omega t, R\sin\omega t\rangle,$$

where R and ω are positive real numbers.

SOLUTION We find that $\mathbf{r}'(t) = \langle -R\omega\sin\omega t, R\omega\cos\omega t\rangle$, $|\mathbf{v}(t)| = |\mathbf{r}'(t)| = R\omega$, and, by Example 2, $\kappa = 1/R$. Recall that $ds/dt = |\mathbf{v}(t)|$, which is constant; therefore, $d^2s/dt^2 = 0$ and the tangential component of the acceleration is zero. The acceleration is

$$\mathbf{a} = \kappa|\mathbf{v}|^2\mathbf{N} + \underbrace{\frac{d^2s}{dt^2}}_{0}\mathbf{T} = \frac{1}{R}(R\omega)^2\mathbf{N} = R\omega^2\mathbf{N}.$$

On a circular path (traversed at constant speed), the acceleration is entirely in the normal direction, orthogonal to the tangent vectors. The acceleration increases with the radius of the circle R and with the frequency of the motion ω.

Related Exercises 35–40 ◄

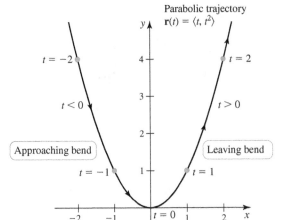

Parabolic trajectory
$\mathbf{r}(t) = \langle t, t^2\rangle$

$t = -2$ $t = 2$

$t < 0$ $t > 0$

Approaching bend   Leaving bend

$t = -1$ $t = 1$

$t = 0$

FIGURE 12.108

➤ Using the fact that $|\mathbf{T}| = |\mathbf{N}| = 1$, we have, from Section 12.3, that

$$a_N = \text{scal}_\mathbf{N}\mathbf{a} = \frac{\mathbf{a}\cdot\mathbf{N}}{|\mathbf{N}|} = \mathbf{a}\cdot\mathbf{N}$$

and

$$a_T = \text{scal}_\mathbf{T}\mathbf{a} = \frac{\mathbf{a}\cdot\mathbf{T}}{|\mathbf{T}|} = \mathbf{a}\cdot\mathbf{T} = \frac{\mathbf{v}\cdot\mathbf{a}}{|\mathbf{v}|}.$$

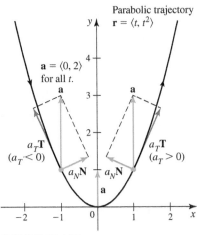

Parabolic trajectory
$\mathbf{r} = \langle t, t^2\rangle$

$\mathbf{a} = \langle 0, 2\rangle$
for all t.

$a_T\mathbf{T}$
$(a_T < 0)$ $a_T\mathbf{T}$
$(a_T > 0)$

$a_N\mathbf{N}$ $a_N\mathbf{N}$

$\mathbf{a}$

FIGURE 12.109

EXAMPLE 7 **A bend in the road** The driver of a car follows the parabolic trajectory $\mathbf{r}(t) = \langle t, t^2\rangle$, for $-2 \le t \le 2$, through a sharp bend (Figure 12.108). Find the tangential and normal components of the acceleration of the car.

SOLUTION The velocity and acceleration vectors are easily computed: $\mathbf{v}(t) = \mathbf{r}'(t) = \langle 1, 2t\rangle$ and $\mathbf{a}(t) = \mathbf{r}''(t) = \langle 0, 2\rangle$. The goal is to express $\mathbf{a} = \langle 0, 2\rangle$ in terms of $\mathbf{T}$ and $\mathbf{N}$. A short calculation reveals that

$$\mathbf{T} = \frac{\mathbf{v}}{|\mathbf{v}|} = \frac{\langle 1, 2t\rangle}{\sqrt{1 + 4t^2}} \quad \text{and} \quad \mathbf{N} = \frac{d\mathbf{T}/dt}{|d\mathbf{T}/dt|} = \frac{\langle -2t, 1\rangle}{\sqrt{1 + 4t^2}}.$$

We now have two ways to proceed. One is to compute the normal and tangential components of the acceleration directly using the definitions. More efficient is to note that $\mathbf{T}$ and $\mathbf{N}$ are orthogonal unit vectors, and then to compute the scalar projections of $\mathbf{a} = \langle 0, 2\rangle$ in the directions of $\mathbf{T}$ and $\mathbf{N}$. We find that

$$a_N = \mathbf{a}\cdot\mathbf{N} = \langle 0, 2\rangle\cdot\frac{\langle -2t, 1\rangle}{\sqrt{1 + 4t^2}} = \frac{2}{\sqrt{1 + 4t^2}}$$

and

$$a_T = \mathbf{a}\cdot\mathbf{T} = \langle 0, 2\rangle\cdot\frac{\langle 1, 2t\rangle}{\sqrt{1 + 4t^2}} = \frac{4t}{\sqrt{1 + 4t^2}}.$$

You should verify that at all times (Exercise 76),

$$\mathbf{a} = a_N\mathbf{N} + a_T\mathbf{T} = \frac{2}{\sqrt{1 + 4t^2}}(\mathbf{N} + 2t\mathbf{T}) = \langle 0, 2\rangle.$$

Let's interpret these results. First, notice that the driver negotiates the curve in a sensible way: The speed $|\mathbf{v}| = \sqrt{1 + 4t^2}$ decreases as the car approaches the origin (the tightest part of the curve) and increases as it moves away from the origin (Figure 12.109). As the car approaches the origin ($t < 0$), $\mathbf{T}$ points in the direction of the trajectory and $\mathbf{N}$ points to the inside of the curve. However, $a_T = \frac{d^2s}{dt^2} < 0$ when $t < 0$, so $a_T\mathbf{T}$ points in the direction opposite to that of $\mathbf{T}$ (corresponding to a deceleration). As the car leaves the origin ($t > 0$), $a_T > 0$ (corresponding to an acceleration) and $a_T\mathbf{T}$ and $\mathbf{T}$ point in the direction of the trajectory, while $\mathbf{N}$ still points to the inside of the curve (Figure 12.109; Exercise 78).

Related Exercises 35–40 ◄

QUICK CHECK 5 Verify that $\mathbf{T}$ and $\mathbf{N}$ given in Example 7 satisfy $|\mathbf{T}| = |\mathbf{N}| = 1$ and that $\mathbf{T} \cdot \mathbf{N} = 0$.

The Binormal Vector and Torsion

We have seen that the curvature function and the principal unit normal vector tell us how quickly and in what direction a curve turns. For curves in two dimensions, these quantities give a fairly complete description of motion along the curve. However, in three dimensions, a curve has more "room" in which to change its course, and another descriptive function is often useful. Figure 12.110 shows a smooth parameterized curve C with its unit tangent vector $\mathbf{T}$ and its principal unit normal vector $\mathbf{N}$ at two different points. These two vectors determine a plane called the *osculating plane* (Figure 12.110b). The question we now ask is, How quickly does the curve C move out of the plane determined by $\mathbf{T}$ and $\mathbf{N}$?

To answer this question, we begin by defining the *unit binormal vector* $\mathbf{B} = \mathbf{T} \times \mathbf{N}$. By the definition of the cross product, $\mathbf{B}$ is orthogonal to $\mathbf{T}$ and $\mathbf{N}$. Because $\mathbf{T}$ and $\mathbf{N}$ are unit vector, $\mathbf{B}$ is also a unit vector. Notice that $\mathbf{T}$, $\mathbf{N}$, and $\mathbf{B}$ form a right-handed coordinate system (like the xyz-coordinate system) that changes its orientation as we move along the curve. This coordinate system is often called the **TNB frame** (Figure 12.110).

> The TNB frame is also called the Frenet-Serret frame, after two 19th-century French mathematicians, Jean Frenet and Joseph Serret.

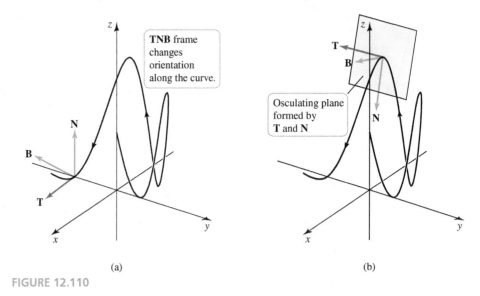

TNB frame changes orientation along the curve.

Osculating plane formed by $\mathbf{T}$ and $\mathbf{N}$

(a)   (b)

FIGURE 12.110

QUICK CHECK 6 Explain why $\mathbf{B} = \mathbf{T} \times \mathbf{N}$ is a unit vector.

The rate at which the curve C twists out of the plane determined by $\mathbf{T}$ and $\mathbf{N}$ is the rate at which $\mathbf{B}$ changes as we move along C, which is $\dfrac{d\mathbf{B}}{ds}$. A short calculation leads to a practical formula for the twisting of the curve. Differentiating the cross product $\mathbf{T} \times \mathbf{N}$, we find that

$$\frac{d\mathbf{B}}{ds} = \frac{d}{ds}(\mathbf{T} \times \mathbf{N})$$

$$= \underbrace{\frac{d\mathbf{T}}{ds} \times \mathbf{N}}_{\text{parallel vectors}} + \mathbf{T} \times \frac{d\mathbf{N}}{ds} \qquad \text{Rule for differentiating a cross product}$$

$$= \mathbf{T} \times \frac{d\mathbf{N}}{ds}. \qquad \frac{d\mathbf{T}}{ds} \text{ and } \mathbf{N} \text{ are parallel; } \frac{d\mathbf{T}}{ds} \times \mathbf{N} = \mathbf{0}.$$

Notice that by definition, $\mathbf{N} = \dfrac{1}{\kappa} \dfrac{d\mathbf{T}}{ds}$, which implies that $\mathbf{N}$ and $\dfrac{d\mathbf{T}}{ds}$ are scalar multiples of each other. Therefore, their cross product is the zero vector.

The properties of $\dfrac{d\mathbf{B}}{ds}$ become clear with the following observations.

- $\dfrac{d\mathbf{B}}{ds}$ is orthogonal to both $\mathbf{T}$ and $\dfrac{d\mathbf{N}}{ds}$, because it is the cross product of $\mathbf{T}$ and $\dfrac{d\mathbf{N}}{ds}$.

> Note that $\mathbf{B}$ is a unit vector (of constant length). Therefore, by Theorem 12.8, $\mathbf{B}$ and $\mathbf{B}'(t)$ are orthogonal. Because $\mathbf{B}'(t)$ and $\mathbf{B}'(s)$ are parallel, it follows that $\mathbf{B}$ and $\mathbf{B}'(s)$ are orthogonal.

- Applying Theorem 12.8 to the unit vector $\mathbf{B}$, it follows that $\dfrac{d\mathbf{B}}{ds}$ is also orthogonal to $\mathbf{B}$.

- By the previous two observations, $\dfrac{d\mathbf{B}}{ds}$ is orthogonal to both $\mathbf{B}$ and $\mathbf{T}$, so it must be parallel to $\mathbf{N}$.

Because $\dfrac{d\mathbf{B}}{ds}$ is parallel to (a scalar multiple of) $\mathbf{N}$, we write

$$\frac{d\mathbf{B}}{ds} = -\tau\mathbf{N},$$

where the scalar τ is the *torsion*. Notice that $\left|\dfrac{d\mathbf{B}}{ds}\right| = |-\tau\mathbf{N}| = |-\tau|$, so the magnitude

> The negative sign in the definition of the torsion is conventional. However, τ may be positive or negative (or zero), and in general, it varies along the curve.

of the torsion equals the magnitude of $\dfrac{d\mathbf{B}}{ds}$, which is the rate at which the curve twists out of the $\mathbf{TN}$-plane.

A short calculation gives a method for computing the torsion. We take the dot product of both sides of the equation defining the torsion with $\mathbf{N}$:

$$\frac{d\mathbf{B}}{ds}\cdot\mathbf{N} = -\tau\underbrace{\mathbf{N}\cdot\mathbf{N}}_{1}$$

$$\frac{d\mathbf{B}}{ds}\cdot\mathbf{N} = -\tau. \qquad \text{N is a unit vector.}$$

QUICK CHECK 7 Explain why $\mathbf{N}\cdot\mathbf{N} = 1$.

> Notice that $\mathbf{B}$ and τ depend on the orientation of the curve.

FIGURE 12.111

> The third plane formed by the vectors $\mathbf{T}$ and $\mathbf{B}$ is called the *rectifying plane*.

DEFINITION   Unit Binormal Vector and Torsion

Let C be a smooth parameterized curve with unit tangent and principal unit normal vectors $\mathbf{T}$ and $\mathbf{N}$, respectively. Then, at each point of the curve at which the curvature is nonzero, the **unit binormal vector** is

$$\mathbf{B} = \mathbf{T} \times \mathbf{N},$$

and the **torsion** is

$$\tau = -\frac{d\mathbf{B}}{ds}\cdot\mathbf{N}.$$

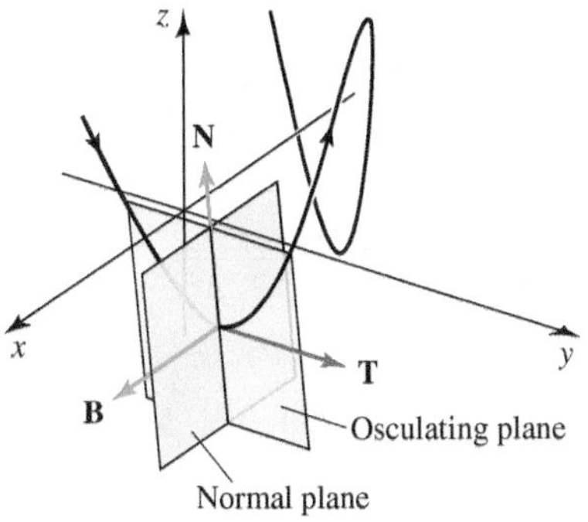

Figure 12.111 provides some interpretation of the curvature and the torsion. First, we see a smooth curve C passing through a point P, where the mutually orthogonal vectors $\mathbf{T}$, $\mathbf{N}$, and $\mathbf{B}$ are defined. The **osculating plane** is defined by the vectors $\mathbf{T}$ and $\mathbf{N}$. The plane orthogonal to the osculating plane containing $\mathbf{N}$ is called the **normal plane**. Because $\mathbf{N}$ and $\dfrac{d\mathbf{B}}{ds}$ are parallel, $\dfrac{d\mathbf{B}}{ds}$ also lies in the normal plane. The torsion, which is equal in magnitude to $\left|\dfrac{d\mathbf{B}}{ds}\right|$, gives the rate at which the curve moves *out of* the osculating plane. In a complementary way, the curvature, which is equal to $\left|\dfrac{d\mathbf{T}}{ds}\right|$, gives the rate at which the curve turns *within* the osculating plane. Two examples will clarify these concepts.

EXAMPLE 8   Unit binormal vector Consider the circle C defined by

$$\mathbf{r}(t) = \langle R \cos t, R \sin t \rangle, \text{ for } 0 \leq t \leq 2\pi, \text{ with } R > 0.$$

a. Without doing any calculations, find the unit binormal vector $\mathbf{B}$ and determine the torsion.

b. Use the definition of $\mathbf{B}$ to calculate $\mathbf{B}$ and confirm your answer in part (a).

SOLUTION

a. The circle C lies in the xy-plane, so at all points on the circle, $\mathbf{T}$ and $\mathbf{N}$ are in the xy-plane. Therefore, at all points of the circle, $\mathbf{B} = \mathbf{T} \times \mathbf{N}$ is the unit vector in the positive z-direction (by the right-hand rule); that is, $\mathbf{B} = \mathbf{k}$. Because $\mathbf{B}$ changes neither in length nor direction, $\dfrac{d\mathbf{B}}{ds} = \mathbf{0}$ and $\tau = 0$ (Figure 12.112).

b. Building on the calculations of Example 2, we find that

$$\mathbf{T} = \langle -\sin t, \cos t \rangle \quad \text{and} \quad \mathbf{N} = \langle -\cos t, -\sin t \rangle.$$

Therefore, the unit binormal vector is

$$\mathbf{B} = \mathbf{T} \times \mathbf{N} = \begin{vmatrix} \mathbf{i} & \mathbf{j} & \mathbf{k} \\ -\sin t & \cos t & 0 \\ -\cos t & -\sin t & 0 \end{vmatrix} = 0 \cdot \mathbf{i} - 0 \cdot \mathbf{j} + 1 \cdot \mathbf{k} = \mathbf{k}.$$

As in part (a), it follows that the torsion is zero.

Related Exercises 41–48 ◄

Generalizing Example 8, it can be shown that the binormal vector of any curve that lies in the xy-plane is always parallel to the z-axis; therefore, the torsion of the curve is everywhere zero.

EXAMPLE 9   Torsion of a helix Compute the torsion of the helix $\mathbf{r}(t) = \langle a \cos t, a \sin t, bt \rangle$, for $t \geq 0$, with $a > 0$ and $b > 0$.

SOLUTION In Example 5, we found that

$$\mathbf{T} = \frac{\langle -a \sin t, a \cos t, b \rangle}{\sqrt{a^2 + b^2}} \quad \text{and} \quad \mathbf{N} = \langle -\cos t, -\sin t, 0 \rangle.$$

Therefore,

$$\mathbf{B} = \mathbf{T} \times \mathbf{N} = \frac{1}{\sqrt{a^2 + b^2}} \begin{vmatrix} \mathbf{i} & \mathbf{j} & \mathbf{k} \\ -a \sin t & a \cos t & b \\ -\cos t & -\sin t & 0 \end{vmatrix} = \frac{\langle b \sin t, -b \cos t, a \rangle}{\sqrt{a^2 + b^2}}.$$

The next step is to determine $\dfrac{d\mathbf{B}}{ds}$, which we do in the same way we computed $\dfrac{d\mathbf{T}}{ds}$, by writing

$$\frac{d\mathbf{B}}{dt} = \frac{d\mathbf{B}}{ds} \cdot \frac{ds}{dt} \quad \text{or} \quad \frac{d\mathbf{B}}{ds} = \frac{d\mathbf{B}/dt}{ds/dt}.$$

In this case,

$$\frac{ds}{dt} = |\mathbf{r}'(t)| = \sqrt{a^2 \sin^2 t + a^2 \cos^2 t + b^2} = \sqrt{a^2 + b^2}.$$

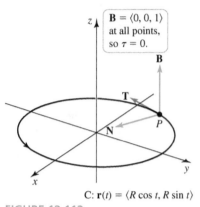

$\mathbf{B} = \langle 0, 0, 1 \rangle$ at all points, so $\tau = 0$.

$C: \mathbf{r}(t) = \langle R \cos t, R \sin t \rangle$

FIGURE 12.112

Computing $\dfrac{d\mathbf{B}}{dt}$, we have

$$\frac{d\mathbf{B}}{ds} = \frac{d\mathbf{B}/dt}{ds/dt} = \frac{\langle b\cos t, b\sin t, 0\rangle}{a^2 + b^2}.$$

The final step is to compute the torsion:

$$\tau = -\frac{d\mathbf{B}}{ds}\cdot\mathbf{N} = -\frac{\langle b\cos t, b\sin t, 0\rangle}{a^2 + b^2}\cdot\langle -\cos t, -\sin t, 0\rangle = \frac{b}{a^2 + b^2}.$$

We see that the torsion is constant over the helix. In Example 4, we found that the curvature of a helix is also constant. This special property of circular helices means that the curve turns about its axis at a constant rate and rises vertically at a constant rate (Figure 12.113).

Related Exercises 41–48◄

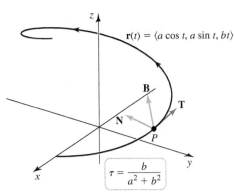

$\mathbf{r}(t) = \langle a\cos t, a\sin t, bt\rangle$

$\tau = \dfrac{b}{a^2 + b^2}$

FIGURE 12.113

Example 9 suggests that the computation of the binormal vector and the torsion can be involved. We close by stating some alternative formulas for $\mathbf{B}$ and τ that *may* simplify calculations in some cases. Letting $\mathbf{v} = \mathbf{r}'(t)$ and $\mathbf{a} = \mathbf{v}'(t) = \mathbf{r}''(t)$, the binormal vector can be written compactly as (Exercise 83)

$$\mathbf{B} = \mathbf{T}\times\mathbf{N} = \frac{\mathbf{v}\times\mathbf{a}}{|\mathbf{v}\times\mathbf{a}|}.$$

We also state without proof that the torsion may be expressed in either of the forms

$$\tau = \frac{(\mathbf{v}\times\mathbf{a})\cdot\mathbf{a}'}{|\mathbf{v}\times\mathbf{a}|^2} \quad\text{or}\quad \tau = \frac{(\mathbf{r}'\times\mathbf{r}'')\cdot\mathbf{r}'''}{|\mathbf{r}'\times\mathbf{r}''|^2}.$$

SUMMARY   Formulas for Curves in Space

Position function: $\mathbf{r}(t) = \langle x(t), y(t), z(t)\rangle$

Velocity: $\mathbf{v} = \mathbf{r}'$

Acceleration: $\mathbf{a} = \mathbf{v}'$

Unit tangent vector: $\mathbf{T} = \dfrac{\mathbf{v}}{|\mathbf{v}|}$

Principal unit normal vector: $\mathbf{N} = \dfrac{d\mathbf{T}/dt}{|d\mathbf{T}/dt|}$ (provided $d\mathbf{T}/dt \neq \mathbf{0}$)

Curvature: $\kappa = \left|\dfrac{d\mathbf{T}}{ds}\right| = \dfrac{1}{|\mathbf{v}|}\left|\dfrac{d\mathbf{T}}{dt}\right| = \dfrac{|\mathbf{v}\times\mathbf{a}|}{|\mathbf{v}|^3}$

Components of acceleration: $\mathbf{a} = a_N\mathbf{N} + a_T\mathbf{T}$, where $a_N = \kappa|\mathbf{v}|^2 = \dfrac{|\mathbf{v}\times\mathbf{a}|}{|\mathbf{v}|}$

and $a_T = \dfrac{d^2s}{dt^2} = \dfrac{\mathbf{v}\cdot\mathbf{a}}{|\mathbf{v}|}$

Unit binormal vector: $\mathbf{B} = \mathbf{T}\times\mathbf{N} = \dfrac{\mathbf{v}\times\mathbf{a}}{|\mathbf{v}\times\mathbf{a}|}$

Torsion: $\tau = -\dfrac{d\mathbf{B}}{ds}\cdot\mathbf{N} = \dfrac{(\mathbf{v}\times\mathbf{a})\cdot\mathbf{a}'}{|\mathbf{v}\times\mathbf{a}|^2} = \dfrac{(\mathbf{r}'\times\mathbf{r}'')\cdot\mathbf{r}'''}{|\mathbf{r}'\times\mathbf{r}''|^2}$

SECTION 12.9 EXERCISES

Review Questions

1. What is the curvature of a straight line?

2. Explain the meaning of *the curvature of a curve*. Is it a scalar function or a vector function?

3. Give a practical formula for computing the curvature.

4. Interpret *the principal unit normal vector of a curve*. Is it a scalar function or a vector function?

5. Give a practical formula for computing the principal unit normal vector.

6. Explain how to decompose the acceleration vector of a moving object into its tangential and normal components.

7. Explain how the vectors **T**, **N**, and **B** are related geometrically.

8. How do you compute **B**?

9. Give a geometrical interpretation of the torsion.

10. How do you compute the torsion?

Basic Skills

11–20. Curvature *Find the unit tangent vector* **T** *and the curvature* κ *for the following parameterized curves.*

11. $\mathbf{r}(t) = \langle 2t + 1, 4t - 5, 6t + 12 \rangle$

12. $\mathbf{r}(t) = \langle 2 \cos t, -2 \sin t \rangle$

13. $\mathbf{r}(t) = \langle 2t, 4 \sin t, 4 \cos t \rangle$

14. $\mathbf{r}(t) = \langle \cos t^2, \sin t^2 \rangle$

15. $\mathbf{r}(t) = \langle \sqrt{3} \sin t, \sin t, 2 \cos t \rangle$

16. $\mathbf{r}(t) = \langle t, \ln (\cos t) \rangle$

17. $\mathbf{r}(t) = \langle t, 2t^2 \rangle$

18. $\mathbf{r}(t) = \langle \cos^3 t, \sin^3 t \rangle$

19. $\mathbf{r}(t) = \left\langle \int_0^t \cos (\pi u^2/2) \, du, \int_0^t \sin (\pi u^2/2) \, du \right\rangle, t > 0$

20. $\mathbf{r}(t) = \left\langle \int_0^t \cos u^2 \, du, \int_0^t \sin u^2 \, du \right\rangle, t > 0$

21–26. Alternative curvature formula *Use the alternative curvature formula* $\kappa = |\mathbf{v} \times \mathbf{a}|/|\mathbf{v}|^3$ *to find the curvature of the following parameterized curves.*

21. $\mathbf{r}(t) = \langle -3 \cos t, 3 \sin t, 0 \rangle$

22. $\mathbf{r}(t) = \langle 4t, 3 \sin t, 3 \cos t \rangle$

23. $\mathbf{r}(t) = \langle 4 + t^2, t, 0 \rangle$

24. $\mathbf{r}(t) = \langle \sqrt{3} \sin t, \sin t, 2 \cos t \rangle$

25. $\mathbf{r}(t) = \langle 4 \cos t, \sin t, 2 \cos t \rangle$

26. $\mathbf{r}(t) = \langle e^t \cos t, e^t \sin t, e^t \rangle$

27–34. Principal unit normal vector *Find the unit tangent vector* **T** *and the principal unit normal vector* **N** *for the following parameterized curves. In each case, verify that* $|\mathbf{T}| = |\mathbf{N}| = 1$ *and* $\mathbf{T} \cdot \mathbf{N} = 0$.

27. $\mathbf{r}(t) = \langle 2 \sin t, 2 \cos t \rangle$

28. $\mathbf{r}(t) = \langle 4 \sin t, 4 \cos t, 10t \rangle$

29. $\mathbf{r}(t) = \langle t^2/2, 4 - 3t, 1 \rangle$

30. $\mathbf{r}(t) = \langle t^2/2, t^3/3 \rangle, t > 0$

31. $\mathbf{r}(t) = \langle \cos t^2, \sin t^2 \rangle$

32. $\mathbf{r}(t) = \langle \cos^3 t, \sin^3 t \rangle$

33. $\mathbf{r}(t) = \langle t^2, t \rangle$

34. $\mathbf{r}(t) = \langle t, \ln \cos t \rangle$

35–40. Components of the acceleration *Consider the following trajectories of moving objects. Find the tangential and normal components of the acceleration.*

35. $\mathbf{r}(t) = \langle t, 1 + 4t, 2 - 6t \rangle$

36. $\mathbf{r}(t) = \langle 10 \cos t, -10 \sin t \rangle$

37. $\mathbf{r}(t) = \langle e^t \cos t, e^t \sin t, e^t \rangle$

38. $\mathbf{r}(t) = \langle t, t^2 + 1 \rangle$

39. $\mathbf{r}(t) = \langle t^3, t^2 \rangle$

40. $\mathbf{r}(t) = \langle 20 \cos t, 20 \sin t, 30t \rangle$

41–44. Computing the binormal vector and torsion *In Exercises 27–30, the unit tangent vector* **T** *and the principal unit normal vector* **N** *were computed for the following parameterized curves. Use the definitions to compute their unit binormal vector and torsion.*

41. $\mathbf{r}(t) = \langle 2 \sin t, 2 \cos t \rangle$.

42. $\mathbf{r}(t) = \langle 4 \sin t, 4 \cos t, 10t \rangle$

43. $\mathbf{r}(t) = \langle t^2/2, 4 - 3t, 1 \rangle$

44. $\mathbf{r}(t) = \langle t^2/2, t^3/3 \rangle, t > 0$

45–48. Computing the binormal vector and torsion *Use the definitions to compute the unit binormal vector and torsion of the following curves.*

45. $\mathbf{r}(t) = \langle 2 \cos t, 2 \sin t, -t \rangle$

46. $\mathbf{r}(t) = \langle t, \cosh t, -\sinh t \rangle$

47. $\mathbf{r}(t) = \langle 12t, 5 \cos t, 5 \sin t \rangle$

48. $\mathbf{r}(t) = \langle \sin t - t \cos t, \cos t + t \sin t, t \rangle$

Further Explorations

49. **Explain why or why not** Determine whether the following statements are true and give an explanation or counterexample.

   a. The position, unit tangent, and principal unit normal vectors (**r**, **T**, and **N**) at a point lie in the same plane.
   b. The vectors **T** and **N** at a point depend on the orientation of a curve.
   c. The curvature at a point depends on the orientation of a curve.
   d. An object with unit speed ($|\mathbf{v}| = 1$) on a circle of radius R has an acceleration of $\mathbf{a} = \mathbf{N}/R$.
   e. If the speedometer of a car reads a constant 60 mi/hr, the car is not accelerating.
   f. A curve in the *xy*-plane that is concave up at all points has positive torsion.
   g. A curve with large curvature also has large torsion.

50. Special formula: Curvature for $y = f(x)$ Assume that f is twice differentiable. Prove that the curve $y = f(x)$ has curvature

$$\kappa(x) = \frac{|f''(x)|}{(1 + f'(x)^2)^{3/2}}.$$

(*Hint:* Use the parametric description $x = t$, $y = f(t)$.)

51–54. Curvature for $y = f(x)$ *Use the result of Exercise 50 to find the curvature function of the following curves.*

51. $f(x) = x^2$ **52.** $f(x) = \sqrt{a^2 - x^2}$

53. $f(x) = \ln x$ **54.** $f(x) = \ln \cos x$

55. Special formula: Curvature for plane curves Show that the curve $\mathbf{r}(t) = \langle f(t), g(t) \rangle$, where f and g are twice differentiable, has curvature

$$\kappa(t) = \frac{|f'g'' - f''g'|}{((f')^2 + (g')^2)^{3/2}},$$

where all derivatives are taken with respect to t.

56–59. Curvature for plane curves *Use the result of Exercise 55 to find the curvature function of the following curves.*

56. $\mathbf{r}(t) = \langle a \sin t, a \cos t \rangle$ (circle)

57. $\mathbf{r}(t) = \langle a \sin t, b \cos t \rangle$ (ellipse)

58. $\mathbf{r}(t) = \langle a \cos^3 t, a \sin^3 t \rangle$ (astroid)

59. $\mathbf{r}(t) = \langle t, at^2 \rangle$ (parabola)

When appropriate, consider using the special formulas derived in Exercises 50 and 55 in the remaining exercises.

60–63. Same paths, different velocity *The position functions of objects A and B describe different motion along the same path, for $t \geq 0$.*

a. *Sketch the path followed by both A and B.*

b. *Find the velocity and acceleration of A and B and discuss the differences.*

c. *Express the acceleration of A and B in terms of the tangential and normal components and discuss the differences.*

60. $A: \mathbf{r}(t) = \langle 1 + 2t, 2 - 3t, 4t \rangle$, $B: \mathbf{r}(t) = \langle 1 + 6t, 2 - 9t, 12t \rangle$

61. $A: \mathbf{r}(t) = \langle t, 2t, 3t \rangle$, $B: \mathbf{r}(t) = \langle t^2, 2t^2, 3t^2 \rangle$

62. $A: \mathbf{r}(t) = \langle \cos t, \sin t \rangle$, $B: \mathbf{r}(t) = \langle \cos 3t, \sin 3t \rangle$

63. $A: \mathbf{r}(t) = \langle \cos t, \sin t \rangle$, $B: \mathbf{r}(t) = \langle \cos t^2, \sin t^2 \rangle$

64–67. Graphs of the curvature *Consider the following curves.*

a. *Graph the curve.*

b. *Compute the curvature.*

c. *Graph the curvature as a function of the parameter.*

d. *Identify the points (if any) at which the curve has a maximum or minimum curvature.*

e. *Verify that the graph of the curvature is consistent with the graph of the curve.*

64. $\mathbf{r}(t) = \langle t, t^2 \rangle$, for $-2 \leq t \leq 2$ (parabola)

65. $\mathbf{r}(t) = \langle t - \sin t, 1 - \cos t \rangle$, for $0 \leq t \leq 2\pi$ (cycloid)

66. $\mathbf{r}(t) = \langle t, \sin t \rangle$, for $0 \leq t \leq \pi$ (sine curve)

67. $\mathbf{r}(t) = \langle t^2/2, t^3/3 \rangle$, for $t > 0$

68. Curvature of $\ln x$ Find the curvature of $f(x) = \ln x$, for $x > 0$, and find the point at which it is a maximum. What is the value of the maximum curvature?

69. Curvature of e^x Find the curvature of $f(x) = e^x$ and find the point at which it is a maximum. What is the value of the maximum curvature?

70. Circle and radius of curvature Choose a point P on a smooth curve C in the plane. The **circle of curvature** (or **osculating circle**) at the point P is the circle that (a) is tangent to C at P, (b) has the same curvature as C at P, and (c) lies on the same side of C as the principal unit normal $\mathbf{N}$ (see figure). The **radius of curvature** is the radius of the circle of curvature. Show that the radius of curvature is $1/\kappa$, where κ is the curvature of C at P.

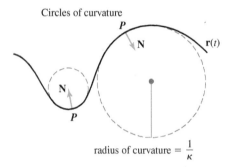

Circles of curvature

radius of curvature $= \dfrac{1}{\kappa}$

71–74. Finding radii of curvature *Find the radius of curvature (see Exercise 70) of the following curves at the given point. Then write the equation of the circle of curvature at the point.*

71. $\mathbf{r}(t) = \langle t, t^2 \rangle$ (parabola) at $t = 0$

72. $y = \ln x$ at $x = 1$

73. $\mathbf{r}(t) = \langle t - \sin t, 1 - \cos t \rangle$ (cycloid) at $t = \pi$

74. $y = \sin x$ at $x = \pi/2$

75. Curvature of the sine curve The function $f(x) = \sin nx$, where n is a positive real number, has a local maximum at $x = \pi/(2n)$. Compute the curvature κ of f at this point. How does κ vary (if at all) as n varies?

Applications

76. Parabolic trajectory In Example 7 it was shown that for the parabolic trajectory $\mathbf{r}(t) = \langle t, t^2 \rangle$, $\mathbf{a} = \langle 0, 2 \rangle$ and

$$\mathbf{a} = \frac{2}{\sqrt{1 + 4t^2}} (\mathbf{N} + 2t\mathbf{T}).$$ Show that the second expression for $\mathbf{a}$ reduces to the first expression.

77. Parabolic trajectory Consider the parabolic trajectory

$$x = (V_0 \cos \alpha)\, t, \quad y = (V_0 \sin \alpha)\, t - \tfrac{1}{2} g t^2,$$

where V_0 is the initial speed, α is the angle of launch, and g is the acceleration due to gravity. Consider all times $[0, T]$ for which $y \geq 0$.

a. Find and graph the speed, for $0 \leq t \leq T$.

b. Find and graph the curvature, for $0 \leq t \leq T$.

c. At what times (if any) do the speed and curvature have maximum and minimum values?

78. Relationship between T, N, and a Show that if an object accelerates in the sense that $d^2s/dt^2 > 0$ and $\kappa \neq 0$, then the acceleration vector lies between **T** and **N** in the plane of **T** and **N**. If an object decelerates in the sense that $d^2s/dt^2 < 0$, then the acceleration vector lies in the plane of **T** and **N**, but not between **T** and **N**.

Additional Exercises

79. Zero curvature Prove that the curve

$$\mathbf{r}(t) = \langle a + bt^p, c + dt^p, e + ft^p \rangle,$$

where $a, b, c, d, e,$ and f are real numbers and p is a positive integer, has zero curvature. Give an explanation.

80. Practical formula for N Show that the definition of the principal unit normal vector $\mathbf{N} = \dfrac{d\mathbf{T}/ds}{|d\mathbf{T}/ds|}$ implies the practical formula $\mathbf{N} = \dfrac{d\mathbf{T}/dt}{|d\mathbf{T}/dt|}$. Use the Chain Rule and recall that $|\mathbf{v}| = ds/dt > 0$.

81. Maximum curvature Consider the "superparabolas" $f_n(x) = x^{2n}$, where n is a positive integer.

  a. Find the curvature function of f_n, for $n = 1, 2,$ and 3.

  b. Plot f_n and their curvature functions, for $n = 1, 2,$ and 3, and check for consistency.

  c. At what points does the maximum curvature occur, for $n = 1, 2, 3$?

  d. Let the maximum curvature for f_n occur at $x = \pm z_n$. Using either analytical methods or a calculator determine $\lim\limits_{n \to \infty} z_n$. Interpret your result.

82. Alternative derivation of the curvature Derive the computational formula for curvature using the following steps.

  a. Use the tangential and normal components of the acceleration to show that $\mathbf{v} \times \mathbf{a} = \kappa |\mathbf{v}|^3 \mathbf{B}$. (Note that $\mathbf{T} \times \mathbf{T} = \mathbf{0}$.)

  b. Solve the equation in part (a) for κ and conclude that $\kappa = \dfrac{|\mathbf{v} \times \mathbf{a}|}{|\mathbf{v}^3|}$, as shown in the text.

83. Computational formula for B Use the result of part (a) of Exercise 82 and the formula for κ to show that

$$\mathbf{B} = \frac{\mathbf{v} \times \mathbf{a}}{|\mathbf{v} \times \mathbf{a}|}.$$

84. Torsion formula Show that the formula defining the torsion, $\tau = -\dfrac{d\mathbf{B}}{ds} \cdot \mathbf{N}$, is equivalent to $\tau = -\dfrac{1}{|\mathbf{v}|}\dfrac{d\mathbf{B}}{dt} \cdot \mathbf{N}$. The second formula is generally easier to use.

85. Descartes' four-circle solution Consider the four mutually tangent circles shown in the figure that have radii $a, b, c,$ and d, and curvatures $A = 1/a, B = 1/b, C = 1/c,$ and $D = 1/d$. Prove Descartes' result (1643) that

$$(A + B + C + D)^2 = 2(A^2 + B^2 + C^2 + D^2).$$

QUICK CHECK ANSWERS

1. $\kappa = \frac{1}{3}$ **2.** $\kappa = 0$ **3.** Negative y-direction   **4.** $\kappa = 0$, so **N** is undefined.   **6.** $|\mathbf{T}| = |\mathbf{N}| = 1$, so $|\mathbf{B}| = 1$ **7.** For any vector, $\mathbf{u} \cdot \mathbf{u} = |\mathbf{u}|^2$. Because $|\mathbf{N}| = 1, \mathbf{N} \cdot \mathbf{N} = 1$. ◄

CHAPTER 12   REVIEW EXERCISES

1. Explain why or why not Determine whether the following statements are true and give an explanation or counterexample.

  a. Given two vectors **u** and **v**, it is always true that $2\mathbf{u} + \mathbf{v} = \mathbf{v} + 2\mathbf{u}$.

  b. The vector in the direction of **u** with the length of **v** equals the vector in the direction of **v** with the length of **u**.

  c. If $\mathbf{u} \neq \mathbf{0}$ and $\mathbf{u} + \mathbf{v} = \mathbf{0}$, then **u** and **v** are parallel.

  d. If $\mathbf{r}'(t) = \mathbf{0}$, then $\mathbf{r}(t) = \langle a, b, c \rangle$, where $a, b,$ and c are real numbers.

  e. The curve $\mathbf{r}(t) = \langle 5 \cos t, 12 \cos t, 13 \sin t \rangle$ has arc length as a parameter.

  f. The position vector and the principal unit normal are always parallel on a smooth curve.

2–5. Drawing vectors Let $\mathbf{u} = \langle 3, -4 \rangle$ and $\mathbf{v} = \langle -1, 2 \rangle$. Use geometry to sketch **u**, **v**, and the following vectors.

2. $\mathbf{u} - \mathbf{v}$

3. $-3\mathbf{v}$

4. $\mathbf{u} + 2\mathbf{v}$

5. $2\mathbf{v} - \mathbf{u}$

6–11. Working with vectors Let $\mathbf{u} = \langle 2, 4, -5 \rangle$ and $\mathbf{v} = \langle -6, 10, 2 \rangle$.

6. Compute $\mathbf{u} - 3\mathbf{v}$.

7. Compute $|\mathbf{u} + \mathbf{v}|$.

8. Find the unit vector with the same direction as **u**.

9. Find a vector parallel to **v** with length 20.

10. Compute **u · v** and the angle between **u** and **v**.

11. Compute **u × v**, **v × u**, and the area of the triangle with vertices $(0, 0, 0), (2, 4, -5)$, and $(-6, 10, 2)$.

12. Scalar multiples Find scalars a, b, and c such that

$$\langle 2, 2, 2 \rangle = a\langle 1, 1, 0 \rangle + b\langle 0, 1, 1 \rangle + c\langle 1, 0, 1 \rangle.$$

13. Velocity vectors Assume the positive x-axis points east and the positive y-axis points north.

  a. An airliner flies northwest at a constant altitude at 550 mi/hr in calm air. Find a and b such that its velocity may be expressed in the form $\mathbf{v} = a\mathbf{i} + b\mathbf{j}$.

  b. An airliner flies northwest at a constant altitude at 550 mi/hr relative to the air in a southerly crosswind $\mathbf{w} = \langle 0, 40 \rangle$. Find the velocity of the airliner relative to the ground.

14. Position vectors Let $\overrightarrow{PQ}$ extend from $P(2, 0, 6)$ to $Q(2, -8, 5)$.

  a. Find the position vector equal to $\overrightarrow{PQ}$.

  b. Find the midpoint M of the line segment PQ. Then find the magnitude of $\overrightarrow{PM}$.

  c. Find a vector of length 8 with direction opposite to that of $\overrightarrow{PQ}$.

15–17. Spheres and balls *Use set notation to describe the following sets.*

15. The sphere of radius 4 centered at $(1, 0, -1)$

16. The points inside the sphere of radius 10 centered at $(2, 4, -3)$

17. The points outside the sphere of radius 2 centered at $(0, 1, 0)$

18–21. Identifying sets. *Give a geometric description of the following sets of points.*

18. $x^2 - 6x + y^2 + 8y + z^2 - 2z - 23 = 0$

19. $x^2 - x + y^2 + 4y + z^2 - 6z + 11 \le 0$

20. $x^2 + y^2 - 10y + z^2 - 6z = -34$

21. $x^2 - 6x + y^2 + z^2 - 20z + 9 > 0$

22. Combined force An object at the origin is acted on by the forces $\mathbf{F}_1 = -10\mathbf{i} + 20\mathbf{k}, \mathbf{F}_2 = 40\mathbf{j} + 10\mathbf{k}$, and $\mathbf{F}_3 = -50\mathbf{i} + 20\mathbf{j}$. Find the magnitude of the combined force and describe with a sketch the direction of the force.

23. Falling probe A remote sensing probe falls vertically with a terminal velocity of 60 m/s when it encounters a horizontal crosswind blowing north at 4 m/s and an updraft blowing vertically at 10 m/s. Find the magnitude and direction of the resulting velocity relative to the ground.

24. Crosswinds A small plane is flying north in calm air at 250 mi/hr when it is hit by a horizontal crosswind blowing northeast at 40 mi/hr and a 25 mi/hr downdraft. Find the resulting velocity and speed of the plane.

25. Sets of points Describe the set of points satisfying both the equation $x^2 + z^2 = 1$ and $y = 2$.

26–27. Angles and projections

  a. Find the angle between **u** and **v**.
  b. Compute $\text{proj}_\mathbf{v}\mathbf{u}$ and $\text{scal}_\mathbf{v}\mathbf{u}$.
  c. Compute $\text{proj}_\mathbf{u}\mathbf{v}$ and $\text{scal}_\mathbf{u}\mathbf{v}$.

26. $\mathbf{u} = -3\mathbf{j} + 4\mathbf{k}, \mathbf{v} = -4\mathbf{i} + \mathbf{j} + 5\mathbf{k}$

27. $\mathbf{u} = -\mathbf{i} + 2\mathbf{j} + 2\mathbf{k}, \mathbf{v} = 3\mathbf{i} + 6\mathbf{j} + 6\mathbf{k}$

28. Work A 180-lb man stands on a hillside that makes an angle of $30°$ with the horizontal, producing a force of $\mathbf{W} = \langle 0, -180 \rangle$.

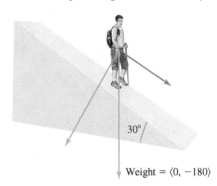

Weight = $\langle 0, -180 \rangle$

  a. Find the component of his weight in the downward direction perpendicular to the hillside and in the downward direction parallel to the hillside.

  b. How much work is done when the man moves 10 ft up the hillside?

29. Vectors normal to a plane Find a unit vector normal to the vectors $\langle 2, -6, 9 \rangle$ and $\langle -1, 0, 6 \rangle$.

30. Angle in two ways Find the angle between $\langle 2, 0, -2 \rangle$ and $\langle 2, 2, 0 \rangle$ using (a) the dot product and (b) the cross product.

31. Knee torque Jan does leg lifts with a 10-kg weight attached to her foot, so the resulting force is $mg \approx 98$ N directed vertically downward. If the distance from her knee to the weight is 0.4 m and her lower leg makes an angle of θ to the vertical, find the magnitude of the torque about her knee as her leg is lifted (as a function of θ). What is the minimum and maximum magnitude of the torque? Does the direction of the torque change as her leg is lifted?

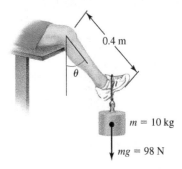

0.4 m

θ

$m = 10$ kg

$mg = 98$ N

32–36. Lines in space *Find an equation of the following lines or line segments.*

32. The line that passes through the points $(2, 6, -1)$ and $(-6, 4, 0)$

33. The line segment that joins the points $(0, -3, 9)$ and $(2, -8, 1)$

34. The line through the point $(0, 1, 1)$ and parallel to the line $\mathbf{R}(t) = \langle 1 + 2t, 3 - 5t, 7 + 6t \rangle$

35. The line through the point $(0, 1, 1)$ that is normal to both $\langle 0, -1, 3 \rangle$ and $\langle 2, -1, 2 \rangle$

36. The line through the point (0, 1, 4) and normal to the vector $\langle -2, 1, 7 \rangle$ and the y-axis

37. Area of a parallelogram Find the area of the parallelogram with vertices (1, 2, 3), (1, 0, 6), and (4, 2, 4).

38. Area of a triangle Find the area of the triangle with vertices (1, 0, 3), (5, 0, −1), and (0, 2, −2).

39–41. Curves in space *Sketch the curves described by the following functions, indicating the orientation of the curve. Use analysis and describe the shape of the curve before using a graphing utility.*

39. $\mathbf{r}(t) = 4 \cos t\, \mathbf{i} + \mathbf{j} + 4 \sin t\, \mathbf{k}$, for $0 \le t \le 2\pi$

40. $\mathbf{r}(t) = e^t \mathbf{i} + 2e^t \mathbf{j} + \mathbf{k}$, for $t \ge 0$

41. $\mathbf{r}(t) = \sin t\, \mathbf{i} + \sqrt{2} \cos t\, \mathbf{j} + \sin t\, \mathbf{k}$, for $0 \le t \le 2\pi$

42. Orthogonal r and r′ Find all points on the ellipse $\mathbf{r}(t) = \langle 1, 8 \sin t, \cos t \rangle$, for $0 \le t \le 2\pi$, at which $\mathbf{r}(t)$ and $\mathbf{r}'(t)$ are orthogonal. Sketch the curve and the tangent vectors to verify your conclusion.

43. Projectile motion A projectile is launched from the origin, which is a point 50 ft from a 30-ft vertical cliff (see figure). It is launched at a speed of $50\sqrt{2}$ ft/s at an angle of 45° to the horizontal. Assume that the ground is horizontal on top of the cliff and that only the gravitational force affects the motion of the object.

a. Give the coordinates of the landing spot of the projectile on the top of the cliff.
b. What is the maximum height reached by the projectile?
c. What is the time of flight?
d. Write an integral that gives the length of the trajectory.
e. Approximate the length of the trajectory.
f. What is the range of launch angles needed to clear the edge of the cliff?

44. Baseball motion A toddler on level ground throws a baseball into the air at an angle of 30° with the ground from a height of 2 ft. If the ball lands 10 ft from the child, determine the initial speed of the ball.

45. Shooting a basket A basketball player tosses a basketball into the air at an angle of 45° with the ground from a height of 6 ft above the ground. If the ball goes through the basket 15 ft away and 10 ft above the ground, determine the initial velocity of the ball.

46–48. Arc length *Find the arc length of the following curves.*

46. $\mathbf{r}(t) = \langle 2t^{9/2}, t^3 \rangle$, for $0 \le t \le 2$

47. $\mathbf{r}(t) = \left\langle t^2, \dfrac{4\sqrt{2}}{3}t^{3/2}, 2t \right\rangle$, for $1 \le t \le 3$

48. $\mathbf{r}(t) = \langle t, \ln(\sec t), \ln(\sec t + \tan t) \rangle$, for $0 \le t \le \pi/4$

49. Velocity and trajectory length The acceleration of a wayward firework is given by $\mathbf{a}(t) = \sqrt{2}\mathbf{j} + 2t\mathbf{k}$, for $0 \le t \le 3$. Suppose the initial velocity of the firework is $\mathbf{v}(0) = \mathbf{i}$.

a. Find the velocity of the firework, for $0 \le t \le 3$.
b. Find the length of the trajectory of the firework over the interval $0 \le t \le 3$.

50–51. Arc length of polar curves *Find the approximate length of the following curves.*

50. The limaçon $r = 3 + 2 \cos \theta$

51. The limaçon $r = 3 - 6 \cos \theta$

52–53. Arc length parameterization *Find a description of the following curves that uses arc length as a parameter.*

52. $\mathbf{r}(t) = (1 + 4t)\mathbf{i} - 3t\mathbf{j}$, for $t \ge 1$

53. $\mathbf{r}(t) = \left\langle t^2, \dfrac{4\sqrt{2}}{3}t^{3/2}, 2t \right\rangle$, for $t \ge 0$

54. Tangents and normals for an ellipse Consider the ellipse $\mathbf{r}(t) = \langle 3 \cos t, 4 \sin t \rangle$, for $0 \le t \le 2\pi$.

a. Find the tangent vector $\mathbf{r}'$, the unit tangent vector $\mathbf{T}$, and the principal unit normal vector $\mathbf{N}$ at all points on the curve.
b. At what points does $|\mathbf{r}'|$ have maximum and minimum values?
c. At what points does the curvature have maximum and minimum values? Interpret this result in light of part (b).
d. Find the points (if any) at which $\mathbf{r}$ and $\mathbf{N}$ are parallel.

55–58. Properties of space curves *Do the following calculations for all values of t for which the given curve is defined.*

a. Find the tangent vector and the unit tangent vector.
b. Find the curvature.
c. Find the principal unit normal vector.
d. Verify that $|\mathbf{N}| = 1$ and $\mathbf{T} \cdot \mathbf{N} = 0$.
e. Graph the curve and sketch $\mathbf{T}$ and $\mathbf{N}$ at two points.

55. $\mathbf{r}(t) = \langle 6 \cos t, 3 \sin t \rangle$, for $0 \le t \le 2\pi$

56. $\mathbf{r}(t) = \cos t\, \mathbf{i} + 2 \sin t\, \mathbf{j} + \mathbf{k}$, for $0 \le t \le 2\pi$

57. $\mathbf{r}(t) = \cos t\, \mathbf{i} + 2 \cos t\, \mathbf{j} + \sqrt{5} \sin t\, \mathbf{k}$, for $0 \le t \le 2\pi$

58. $\mathbf{r}(t) = t\mathbf{i} + 2 \cos t\, \mathbf{j} + 2 \sin t\, \mathbf{k}$, for $0 \le t \le 2\pi$

59–62. Analyzing motion *Consider the position vector of the following moving objects.*

a. Find the normal and tangential components of the acceleration.
b. Graph the trajectory and sketch the normal and tangential components of the acceleration at two points on the trajectory. Show that their sum gives the total acceleration.

59. $\mathbf{r}(t) = 2 \cos t\, \mathbf{i} + 2 \sin t\, \mathbf{j}$, for $0 \le t \le 2\pi$

60. $\mathbf{r}(t) = 3t\mathbf{i} + (4 - t)\mathbf{j} + t\mathbf{k}$, for $t \ge 0$

61. $\mathbf{r}(t) = (t^2 + 1)\mathbf{i} + 2t\mathbf{j}$, for $t \ge 0$

62. $\mathbf{r}(t) = 2 \cos t\, \mathbf{i} + 2 \sin t\, \mathbf{j} + 10t\mathbf{k}$, for $0 \le t \le 2\pi$

63. Lines in the plane

   a. Use a dot product to find the equation of the line in the xy-plane passing through the point (x_0, y_0) perpendicular to the vector $\langle a, b \rangle$.

   b. Given a point $(x_0, y_0, 0)$ and a vector $\mathbf{v} = \langle a, b, 0 \rangle$ in $\mathbb{R}^3$, describe the set of points that satisfy the equation $\langle a, b, 0 \rangle \times \langle x - x_0, y - y_0, 0 \rangle = \mathbf{0}$. Use this result to determine an equation of a line in $\mathbb{R}^2$ passing through (x_0, y_0) parallel to the vector $\langle a, b \rangle$.

64. Length of a DVD groove The capacity of a single-sided, single-layer digital versatile disc (DVD) is approximately 4.7 billion bytes—enough to store a two-hour movie. (Newer double-sided, double-layer DVDs have about four times that capacity, and Blu-ray discs are in the range of 50 gigabytes.) A DVD consists of a single "groove" that spirals outward from the inner edge to the outer edge of the storage region.

   a. First consider the spiral given in polar coordinates by $r = t\theta/(2\pi)$, where $0 \leq \theta \leq 2\pi N$ and successive loops of the spiral are t units apart. Explain why this spiral has N loops and why the entire spiral has a radius of $R = Nt$ units. Sketch three loops of the spiral.

   b. Write an integral for the length L of the spiral with N loops.

   c. The integral in part (b) can be evaluated exactly, but a good approximation can also be made. Assuming N is large, explain why $\theta^2 + 1 \approx \theta^2$. Use this approximation to simplify the integral in part (b) and show that $L \approx t\pi N^2 = \dfrac{\pi R^2}{t}$.

   d. Now consider a DVD with an inner radius of $r = 2.5$ cm and an outer radius of $R = 5.9$ cm. Model the groove by a spiral with a thickness of $t = 1.5$ microns $= 1.5 \times 10^{-6}$ m. Because of the hole in the DVD, the lower limit in the arc length integral is not $\theta = 0$. What are the limits of integration?

   e. Use the approximation in part (c) to find the length of the DVD groove. Express your answer in centimeters and miles.

65. Computing the binormal vector and torsion Compute the unit binormal vector $\mathbf{B}$ and the torsion of the curve $\mathbf{r}(t) = \langle t, t^2, t^3 \rangle$ at $t = 1$.

66–67. Curve analysis *Carry out the following steps for the given curves C.*

a. Find $\mathbf{T}(t)$ at all points of C.

b. Find $\mathbf{N}(t)$ and the curvature at all points of C.

c. Sketch the curve and show $\mathbf{T}(t)$ and $\mathbf{N}(t)$ at the points of C corresponding to $t = 0$ and $t = \pi/2$.

d. Do the results of parts (a) and (b) appear to be consistent with the graph?

e. Find $\mathbf{B}(t)$ at all points of C.

f. On the graph of part (c), plot $\mathbf{B}(t)$ at the points of C corresponding to $t = 0$ and $t = \pi/2$.

g. Describe three calculations that serve to check the accuracy of your results in part (a)–(f).

h. Compute the torsion at all points of C. Interpret this result.

66. $C: \mathbf{r}(t) = \langle 3 \sin t, 4 \sin t, 5 \cos t \rangle$, for $0 \leq t \leq 2\pi$.

67. $C: \mathbf{r}(t) = \langle 3 \sin t, 3 \cos t, 4t \rangle$, for $0 \leq t \leq 2\pi$.

68. Torsion of a plane curve Suppose $\mathbf{r}(t) = \langle f(t), g(t), h(t) \rangle$, where f, g, and h are the quadratic functions $f(t) = a_1 t^2 + b_1 t + c_1$, $g(t) = a_2 t^2 + b_2 t + c_2$, and $h(t) = a_3 t^2 + b_3 t + c_3$, and where at least one of the leading coefficients a_1, a_2, or a_3 is nonzero. Apart from a set of degenerate cases (for example, $\mathbf{r}(t) = \langle t^2, t^2, t^2 \rangle$, whose graph is a line), it can be shown that the graph of $\mathbf{r}(t)$ is a parabola that lies in a plane (Exercise 69).

   a. Show by direct computation that $\mathbf{v} \times \mathbf{a}$ is constant. Then explain why the unit binormal vector is constant at all points on the curve. What does this result say about the torsion of the curve?

   b. Compute $\mathbf{a}'(t)$ and explain why the torsion is zero at all points on the curve for which the torsion is defined.

69. Families of plane curves Let f and g be continuous on an interval I. Consider the curve

$$C: \mathbf{r}(t) = \langle a_1 f(t) + a_2 g(t) + a_3, b_1 f(t) + b_2 g(t) + b_3, c_1 f(t) + c_2 g(t) + c_3 \rangle,$$

for t in I, and where a_i, b_i, and c_i, for $i = 1, 2$, and 3, are real numbers.

   a. Show that, in general, apart from a set of special cases, C lies in a plane.

   b. Explain why the torsion is zero at all points of C for which the torsion is defined.

   c. Find the plane in which $C: \mathbf{r}(t) = \langle t^2 - 2, -t^2 + t + 2, t - 4 \rangle$ lies.

Chapter 12 Guided Projects

Applications of the material in this chapter and related topics can be found in the following Guided Projects. For additional information, see the Preface.

- Designing a trajectory
- Intercepting a UFO
- CORDIC algorithms: How your calculator works
- Bezier curves for graphic design
- Kepler's laws

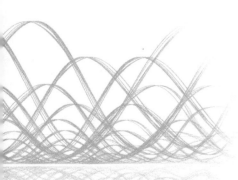

13

Functions of Several Variables

Chapter Preview Chapter 12 was devoted to vector-valued functions, which generally have one independent variable and two or more dependent variables. In this chapter, we step into three-dimensional space along a different path by considering functions with several independent variables and one dependent variable. All the familiar properties of single-variable functions—domains, graphs, limits, continuity, and derivatives—have generalizations for multivariable functions, although there are often subtle differences when compared to single-variable functions. With functions of several independent variables, we work with *partial derivatives*, which, in turn, give rise to directional derivatives and the *gradient*, a fundamental concept in calculus. Partial derivatives allow us to find maximum and minimum values of multivariable functions. We define tangent planes, rather than tangent lines, that allow us to make linear approximations. The chapter ends with a survey of optimization problems in several variables.

13.1 Planes and Surfaces

Functions with one independent variable, such as $f(x) = xe^{-x}$, or *equations* in two variables, such as $x^2 + y^2 = 4$, describe curves in $\mathbb{R}^2$. We now add a third variable to the picture and consider functions of two independent variables (for example, $f(x, y) = x^2 + 2y^2$) and equations in three variables (for example, $x^2 + y^2 + 2z^2 = 4$). We see in this chapter that such functions and equations describe *surfaces* that may be displayed in $\mathbb{R}^3$. Just as a line is the simplest curve in $\mathbb{R}^2$, a plane is the simplest surface in $\mathbb{R}^3$.

Equations of Planes

Intuitively, a plane is a flat surface with infinite extent in all directions. Three noncollinear points (not all on the same line) determine a unique plane in $\mathbb{R}^3$. A plane in $\mathbb{R}^3$ is also uniquely determined by one point in the plane and any nonzero vector orthogonal (perpendicular) to the plane. Such a vector, called a *normal vector*, specifies the orientation of the plane.

> Just as the slope determines the orientation of a line, a normal vector determines the orientation of a plane.

> **DEFINITION** **Plane in** $\mathbb{R}^3$
>
> Given a fixed point P_0 and a nonzero **normal vector n**, the set of points P in $\mathbb{R}^3$ for which $\overrightarrow{P_0P}$ is orthogonal to **n** is called a **plane** (Figure 13.1).

QUICK CHECK 1 Describe the plane that is orthogonal to the unit vector $\mathbf{i} = \langle 1, 0, 0 \rangle$ and passes through the point $(1, 2, 3)$. ◄

We now derive an equation of the plane passing through the point $P_0(x_0, y_0, z_0)$ with nonzero normal vector $\mathbf{n} = \langle a, b, c \rangle$. Notice that for any point $P(x, y, z)$ in the plane, the vector $\overrightarrow{P_0P} = \langle x - x_0, y - y_0, z - z_0 \rangle$ lies in the plane and is orthogonal to $\mathbf{n}$. This orthogonality relationship is written and simplified as follows:

$$\mathbf{n} \cdot \overrightarrow{P_0P} = 0 \qquad \text{Dot product of orthogonal vectors}$$
$$\langle a, b, c \rangle \cdot \langle x - x_0, y - y_0, z - z_0 \rangle = 0 \qquad \text{Substitute vector components.}$$
$$a(x - x_0) + b(y - y_0) + c(z - z_0) = 0 \qquad \text{Expand the dot product.}$$
$$ax + by + cz = d. \qquad d = ax_0 + by_0 + cz_0$$

This important result states that the most general linear equation in three variables, $ax + by + cz = d$, describes a plane in $\mathbb{R}^3$.

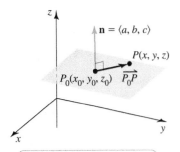

The orientation of a plane is specified by a normal vector $\mathbf{n}$. All vectors $\overrightarrow{P_0P}$ in the plane are orthogonal to $\mathbf{n}$.

FIGURE 13.1

▷ A vector $\mathbf{n} = \langle a, b, c \rangle$ is used to describe a *plane* by specifying a direction *orthogonal* to the plane. By contrast, a vector $\mathbf{v} = \langle a, b, c \rangle$ is used to describe a *line* by specifying a direction *parallel* to the line (Section 12.5).

General Equation of a Plane in $\mathbb{R}^3$

The plane passing through the point $P_0(x_0, y_0, z_0)$ with a nonzero normal vector $\mathbf{n} = \langle a, b, c \rangle$ is described by the equation

$$a(x - x_0) + b(y - y_0) + c(z - z_0) = 0 \quad \text{or} \quad ax + by + cz = d,$$

where $d = ax_0 + by_0 + cz_0$.

The coefficients a, b, and c in the equation of a plane determine the *orientation* of the plane, while the constant term d determines the *location* of the plane. If a, b, and c are held constant and d is varied, a family of parallel planes is generated, all with the same orientation (Figure 13.2).

QUICK CHECK 2 Consider the equation of a plane in the form $\mathbf{n} \cdot \overrightarrow{P_0P} = 0$. Explain why the equation of the plane depends only on the direction, but not the length, of the normal vector $\mathbf{n}$. ◁

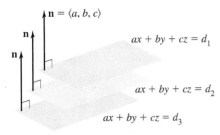

The normal vectors of parallel planes have the same direction.

FIGURE 13.2

EXAMPLE 1 Equation of a plane Find an equation of the plane passing through $P_0(2, -3, 4)$ with a normal vector $\mathbf{n} = \langle -1, 2, 3 \rangle$.

SOLUTION Substituting the components of $\mathbf{n}$ ($a = -1$, $b = 2$, and $c = 3$) and the coordinates of P_0 ($x_0 = 2$, $y_0 = -3$, and $z_0 = 4$) into the equation of a plane, we have

$$a(x - x_0) + b(y - y_0) + c(z - z_0) = 0 \qquad \text{General equation of a plane}$$
$$(-1)(x - 2) + 2(y - (-3)) + 3(z - 4) = 0 \qquad \text{Substitute.}$$
$$-x + 2y + 3z = 4. \qquad \text{Simplify.}$$

The plane is shown in Figure 13.3.

Related Exercises 11–16 ◀

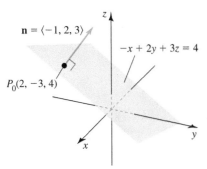

FIGURE 13.3

▷ Three points P, Q, and R determine a plane provided they are not collinear. If P, Q, and R *are* collinear, then the vectors $\overrightarrow{PQ}$ and $\overrightarrow{PR}$ are parallel, which implies that $\overrightarrow{PQ} \times \overrightarrow{PR} = \mathbf{0}$.

EXAMPLE 2 A plane through three points Find an equation of the plane that passes through the (noncollinear) points $P(2, -1, 3)$, $Q(1, 4, 0)$, and $R(0, -1, 5)$.

SOLUTION To write an equation of the plane, we must find a normal vector. Because P, Q, and R lie in the plane, the vectors $\overrightarrow{PQ} = \langle -1, 5, -3 \rangle$ and $\overrightarrow{PR} = \langle -2, 0, 2 \rangle$ also lie in the plane. The cross product $\overrightarrow{PQ} \times \overrightarrow{PR}$ is perpendicular to both $\overrightarrow{PQ}$ and $\overrightarrow{PR}$; therefore a vector normal to the plane is

$$\mathbf{n} = \overrightarrow{PQ} \times \overrightarrow{PR} = \begin{vmatrix} \mathbf{i} & \mathbf{j} & \mathbf{k} \\ -1 & 5 & -3 \\ -2 & 0 & 2 \end{vmatrix} = 10\,\mathbf{i} + 8\,\mathbf{j} + 10\,\mathbf{k}.$$

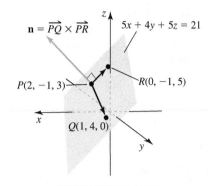

$\overrightarrow{PQ}$ and $\overrightarrow{PR}$ lie in the same plane.
$\overrightarrow{PQ} \times \overrightarrow{PR}$ is orthogonal to the plane.

FIGURE 13.4

Any scalar multiple of **n** may be used as the normal vector. Choosing $\mathbf{n} = \langle 5, 4, 5 \rangle$ and $P_0(2, -1, 3)$ as the fixed point in the plane (Figure 13.4), an equation of the plane is

$$5(x - 2) + 4(y - (-1)) + 5(z - 3) = 0 \quad \text{or} \quad 5x + 4y + 5z = 21.$$

Using either Q or R as the fixed point in the plane leads to an equivalent equation of the plane.

Related Exercises 17–20 ◄

QUICK CHECK 3 Verify in Example 2 that the same equation for the plane results if either Q or R is used as the fixed point in the plane. ◄

EXAMPLE 3   Properties of a plane Let Q be the plane described by the equation $2x - 3y - z = 6$.

a. Find a vector normal to Q.

b. Find the points at which Q intersects the coordinate axes and plot Q.

c. Describe the sets of points at which Q intersects the yz-plane, the xz-plane, and the xy-plane.

SOLUTION

a. The coefficients of x, y, and z in the equation of Q are the components of a vector normal to Q. Therefore, a normal vector is $\mathbf{n} = \langle 2, -3, -1 \rangle$ (or any nonzero multiple of **n**).

b. The point (x, y, z) at which Q intersects the x-axis must have $y = z = 0$. Substituting $y = z = 0$ into the equation of Q gives $x = 3$, so Q intersects the x-axis at $(3, 0, 0)$. Similarly, Q intersects the y-axis at $(0, -2, 0)$, and Q intersects the z-axis at $(0, 0, -6)$. Connecting the three intercepts with straight lines allows us to visualize the plane (Figure 13.5).

> There is a possibility for confusion here. Working in $\mathbb{R}^3$ with no other restrictions, the equation $-3y - z = 6$ describes a plane that is parallel to the x-axis (because x is unspecified). To make it clear that $-3y - z = 6$ is a line in the yz-plane, the condition $x = 0$ is included.

c. All points in the yz-plane have $x = 0$. Setting $x = 0$ in the equation of Q gives the equation $-3y - z = 6$, which, with the condition $x = 0$, describes a line in the yz-plane. If we set $y = 0$, Q intersects the xz-plane in the line $2x - z = 6$, where $y = 0$. If $z = 0$, Q intersects the xy-plane in the line $2x - 3y = 6$, where $z = 0$ (Figure 13.5).

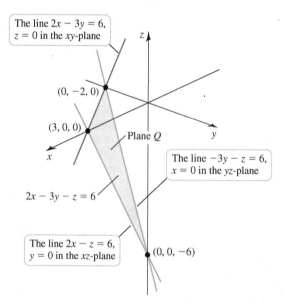

FIGURE 13.5

Related Exercises 21–24 ◄

Two distinct planes are parallel if $\mathbf{n}_1$ and $\mathbf{n}_2$ are parallel.

(a)

Two planes are orthogonal if $\mathbf{n}_1 \cdot \mathbf{n}_2 = 0$.

(b)

FIGURE 13.6

QUICK CHECK 4 Verify in Example 4 that $\mathbf{n}_R \cdot \mathbf{n}_S = 0$ and $\mathbf{n}_R \cdot \mathbf{n}_T = 0$. ◄

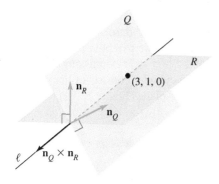

$\mathbf{n}_Q \times \mathbf{n}_R$ is a vector perpendicular to $\mathbf{n}_Q$ and $\mathbf{n}_R$.
Line ℓ is perpendicular to $\mathbf{n}_Q$ and $\mathbf{n}_R$.
Thus, ℓ and $\mathbf{n}_Q \times \mathbf{n}_R$ are parallel to each other.

FIGURE 13.7

➤ By setting $z = 0$ and solving these two equations, we find the point that lies on both planes *and* lies in the xy-plane ($z = 0$).

Parallel and Orthogonal Planes

The normal vectors of distinct planes tell us about the relative orientation of the planes. Two cases are of particular interest: Two distinct planes may be *parallel* (Figure 13.6a) and two intersecting planes may be *orthogonal* (Figure 13.6b).

DEFINITION Parallel and Orthogonal Planes

Two distinct planes are **parallel** if their respective normal vectors are parallel (that is, the normal vectors are scalar multiples of each other). Two planes are **orthogonal** if their respective normal vectors are orthogonal (that is, the dot product of the normal vectors is zero).

EXAMPLE 4 Parallel and orthogonal planes Which of the following distinct planes are parallel and which are orthogonal?

$$Q:\ 2x - 3y + 6z = 12 \qquad R:\ -x + \tfrac{3}{2}y - 3z = 14$$
$$S:\ 6x + 8y + 2z = 1 \qquad T:\ -9x - 12y - 3z = 7$$

SOLUTION Let $\mathbf{n}_Q$, $\mathbf{n}_R$, $\mathbf{n}_S$, and $\mathbf{n}_T$ be vectors normal to $Q, R, S,$ and T, respectively. Normal vectors may be read from the coefficients of $x, y,$ and z in the equations of the planes.

$$\mathbf{n}_Q = \langle 2, -3, 6 \rangle \qquad \mathbf{n}_R = \langle -1, \tfrac{3}{2}, -3 \rangle$$
$$\mathbf{n}_S = \langle 6, 8, 2 \rangle \qquad \mathbf{n}_T = \langle -9, -12, -3 \rangle$$

Notice that $\mathbf{n}_Q = -2\mathbf{n}_R$, which implies that Q and R are parallel. Similarly, $\mathbf{n}_T = -\tfrac{3}{2}\mathbf{n}_S$, so S and T are parallel. Furthermore, $\mathbf{n}_Q \cdot \mathbf{n}_S = 0$ and $\mathbf{n}_Q \cdot \mathbf{n}_T = 0$, which implies that Q is orthogonal to both S and T. Because Q and R are parallel, it follows that R is also orthogonal to both S and T.

Related Exercises 25–30 ◄

EXAMPLE 5 Parallel planes Find an equation of the plane Q that passes through the point $(-2, 4, 1)$ and is parallel to the plane $R: 3x - 2y + z = 4$.

SOLUTION The vector $\mathbf{n} = \langle 3, -2, 1 \rangle$ is normal to R. Because Q and R are parallel, $\mathbf{n}$ is also normal to Q. Therefore, an equation of Q, passing through $(-2, 4, 1)$ with normal vector $\langle 3, -2, 1 \rangle$, is

$$3(x + 2) - 2(y - 4) + (z - 1) = 0 \quad \text{or} \quad 3x - 2y + z = -13.$$

Related Exercises 31–34 ◄

EXAMPLE 6 Intersecting planes Find an equation of the line of intersection of the planes $Q: x + 2y + z = 5$ and $R: 2x + y - z = 7$.

SOLUTION First note that the vectors normal to the planes, $\mathbf{n}_Q = \langle 1, 2, 1 \rangle$ and $\mathbf{n}_R = \langle 2, 1, -1 \rangle$, are *not* multiples of each other. Therefore, the planes are not parallel and they must intersect in a line; call it ℓ. To find an equation of ℓ, we need two pieces of information: a point on ℓ and a vector pointing in the direction of ℓ. Here is one of several ways to find a point on ℓ. Setting $z = 0$ in the equations of the planes gives equations of the lines in which the planes intersect the xy-plane:

$$x + 2y = 5$$
$$2x + y = 7.$$

Solving these equations simultaneously, we find that $x = 3$ and $y = 1$. Combining this result with $z = 0$, we see that $(3, 1, 0)$ is a point on ℓ (Figure 13.7).

We next find a vector parallel to ℓ. Because ℓ lies in Q and R, it is orthogonal to the normal vectors $\mathbf{n}_Q$ and $\mathbf{n}_R$. Therefore, the cross product of $\mathbf{n}_Q$ and $\mathbf{n}_R$ is a vector parallel to ℓ (Figure 13.7). In this case, the cross product is

$$\mathbf{n}_Q \times \mathbf{n}_R = \begin{vmatrix} \mathbf{i} & \mathbf{j} & \mathbf{k} \\ 1 & 2 & 1 \\ 2 & 1 & -1 \end{vmatrix} = -3\mathbf{i} + 3\mathbf{j} - 3\mathbf{k} = \langle -3, 3, -3 \rangle.$$

> Another question related to Example 6 concerns the angle between two planes. See Exercise 95 for an example.

An equation of the line ℓ in the direction of the vector $\langle -3, 3, -3 \rangle$ passing through the point $(3, 1, 0)$ is

$$\begin{aligned} \mathbf{r}(t) &= \langle x_0, y_0, z_0 \rangle + t\langle a, b, c \rangle \quad \text{Equation of a line (Section 12.5)} \\ &= \langle 3, 1, 0 \rangle + t\langle -3, 3, -3 \rangle \quad \text{Substitute.} \\ &= \langle 3 - 3t, 1 + 3t, -3t \rangle, \quad \text{Simplify.} \end{aligned}$$

> Any nonzero scalar multiple of $\langle -3, 3, -3 \rangle$ can be used for the direction of ℓ. For example, another equation of ℓ is $\mathbf{r}(t) = \langle 3 + t, 1 - t, t \rangle$.

where $-\infty < t < \infty$. You can check that any point (x, y, z) with $x = 3 - 3t$, $y = 1 + 3t$, and $z = -3t$ satisfies the equations of both planes.   *Related Exercises 35–38* ◄

Cylinders and Traces

In the context of three-dimensional surfaces, the term *cylinder* has a more general meaning than it does in everyday usage.

DEFINITION Cylinder

Given a curve C in a plane P and a line ℓ not in P, a **cylinder** is the surface consisting of all lines parallel to ℓ that pass through C (Figure 13.8).

A common situation arises when ℓ is parallel to one of the coordinate axes. In these cases, the cylinder is also parallel to one of the coordinate axes. Equations for such cylinders are easy to identify: The variable corresponding to the coordinate axis parallel to ℓ is missing.

For example, working in $\mathbb{R}^3$, the equation $y = x^2$ does not include z, which means that z is arbitrary and can take on all values. Therefore, $y = x^2$ describes the cylinder consisting of all lines parallel to the z-axis that pass through the parabola $y = x^2$ in the xy-plane (Figure 13.9a). In a similar way, the equation $z^2 = y$ in $\mathbb{R}^3$ is missing the variable x, so it describes a cylinder parallel to the x-axis. The cylinder consists of lines parallel to the x-axis that pass through the curve $z^2 = y$ in the yz-plane (Figure 13.9b).

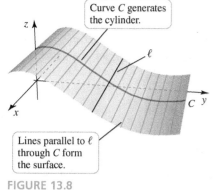

Curve C generates the cylinder.

Lines parallel to ℓ through C form the surface.

FIGURE 13.8

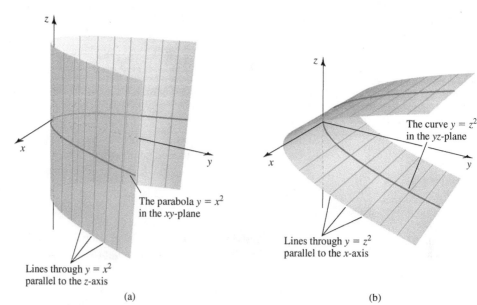

The parabola $y = x^2$ in the xy-plane

Lines through $y = x^2$ parallel to the z-axis

(a)

The curve $y = z^2$ in the yz-plane

Lines through $y = z^2$ parallel to the x-axis

(b)

FIGURE 13.9

QUICK CHECK 5 To which coordinate axis in $\mathbb{R}^3$ is the cylinder $z - 2 \ln x = 0$ parallel? To which coordinate axis in $\mathbb{R}^3$ is the cylinder $y = 4z^2 - 1$ parallel?

Graphing surfaces—and cylinders in particular—is facilitated by identifying the *traces* of the surface.

DEFINITION Trace

A **trace** of a surface is the set of points at which the surface intersects a plane that is parallel to one of the coordinate planes. The traces in the coordinate planes are called the **xy-trace**, the **xz-trace**, and the **yz-trace** (Figure 13.10).

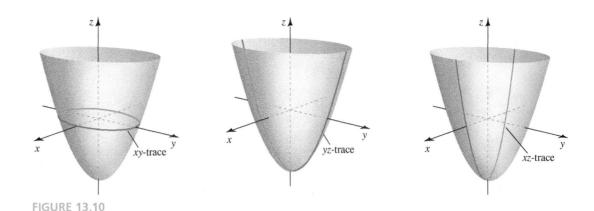

FIGURE 13.10

EXAMPLE 7   Graphing cylinders Sketch the graphs of the following cylinders in $\mathbb{R}^3$. Identify the axis to which each cylinder is parallel.

a. $x^2 + 4y^2 = 16$ **b.** $x - \sin z = 0$

SOLUTION

a. As an equation in $\mathbb{R}^3$, the variable z is absent. Therefore, z assumes all real values and the graph is a cylinder consisting of lines parallel to the z-axis passing through the curve $x^2 + 4y^2 = 16$ in the xy-plane. You can sketch the cylinder in the following steps.

  1. Rewriting the given equation as $\dfrac{x^2}{4^2} + \dfrac{y^2}{2^2} = 1$, we see that the trace of the cylinder in the xy-plane (the xy-trace) is an ellipse. We begin by drawing this ellipse.

  2. Next draw a second trace (a copy of the ellipse in Step 1) in a plane parallel to the xy-plane.

  3. Now draw lines parallel to the z-axis through the two traces to fill out the cylinder (Figure 13.11a).

The resulting surface, called an *elliptic cylinder*, runs parallel to the z-axis (Figure 13.11b).

b. As an equation in $\mathbb{R}^3$, $x - \sin z = 0$ is missing the variable y. Therefore, y assumes all real values and the graph is a cylinder consisting of lines parallel to the y-axis passing through the curve $x = \sin z$ in the xz-plane. You can sketch the cylinder in the following steps.

  1. Graph the curve $x = \sin z$ in the xz-plane, which is the xz-trace of the surface.

  2. Draw a second trace (a copy of the curve in Step 1) in a plane parallel to the xz-plane.

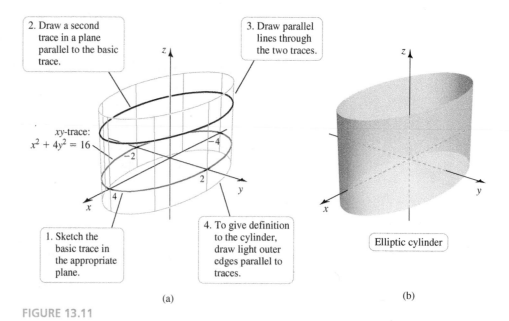

2. Draw a second trace in a plane parallel to the basic trace.

3. Draw parallel lines through the two traces.

xy-trace: $x^2 + 4y^2 = 16$

1. Sketch the basic trace in the appropriate plane.

4. To give definition to the cylinder, draw light outer edges parallel to traces.

Elliptic cylinder

(a)   (b)

FIGURE 13.11

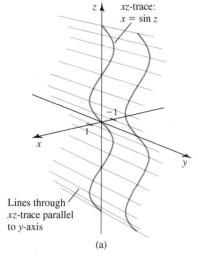

xz-trace: $x = \sin z$

Lines through xz-trace parallel to y-axis

(a)

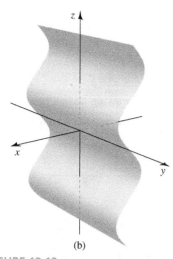

(b)

FIGURE 13.12

> Working with quadric surfaces requires familiarity with conic sections (Section 11.4).

3. Draw lines parallel to the y-axis passing through the two traces. (Figure 13.12a).

The result is a cylinder, running parallel to the y-axis, consisting of copies of the curve $x = \sin z$ (Figure 13.12b).

Related Exercises 39–46 ◄

Quadric Surfaces

Quadric surfaces are described by the general quadratic (second-degree) equation in three variables,

$$Ax^2 + By^2 + Cz^2 + Dxy + Exz + Fyz + Gx + Hy + Iz + J = 0,$$

where the coefficients $A, \ldots, J$ are constants and not all of A, B, C, D, E, and F are zero. We do not attempt a detailed study of this large family of surfaces. However, a few standard surfaces are worth investigating.

Apart from their mathematical interest, quadric surfaces have a variety of practical uses. Paraboloids (defined in Example 9) share the reflective properties of their two-dimensional counterparts (Section 11.4) and are used to design satellite dishes, headlamps, and mirrors in telescopes. Cooling towers for nuclear power plants have the shape of hyperboloids of one sheet. Ellipsoids appear in the design of water tanks and gears.

Making hand sketches of quadric surfaces can be challenging. Here are a few general ideas to keep in mind as you sketch their graphs.

1. **Intercepts** Determine the points, if any, where the surface intersects the coordinate axes. To find these intercepts, set x, y, and z equal to zero in pairs in the equation of the surface and solve for the third coordinate.

2. **Traces** As illustrated in the following examples, finding traces of the surface helps visualize the surface. For example, setting $z = 0$ or $z = z_0$ (a constant) gives the traces in planes parallel to the xy-plane.

3. Sketch at least two traces in parallel planes (for example, traces with $z = 0$ and $z = \pm 1$). Then draw smooth curves that pass through the traces to fill out the surface.

QUICK CHECK 6 Explain why the elliptic cylinder discussed in Example 7a is a quadric surface. ◄

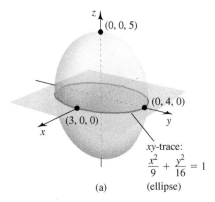

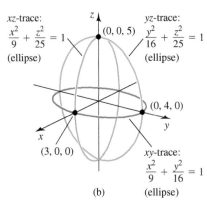

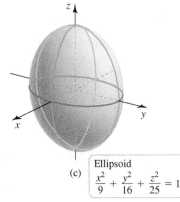

Ellipsoid
$$\frac{x^2}{9} + \frac{y^2}{16} + \frac{z^2}{25} = 1$$

(a)

z (0, 0, 5)

(0, 4, 0)

(3, 0, 0) y

x

xy-trace:
$\frac{x^2}{9} + \frac{y^2}{16} = 1$

(ellipse)

xz-trace:
$\frac{x^2}{9} + \frac{z^2}{25} = 1$
(ellipse)

z (0, 0, 5)

yz-trace:
$\frac{y^2}{16} + \frac{z^2}{25} = 1$
(ellipse)

(0, 4, 0)

x y

(3, 0, 0)

xy-trace:
$\frac{x^2}{9} + \frac{y^2}{16} = 1$

(b)   (ellipse)

(c)

FIGURE 13.13

> The name *ellipsoid* is used because all traces of this surface, when they exist, are ellipses.

EXAMPLE 8   **An ellipsoid**   The surface defined by the equation $\frac{x^2}{a^2} + \frac{y^2}{b^2} + \frac{z^2}{c^2} = 1$ is an *ellipsoid*. Graph the ellipsoid with $a = 3$, $b = 4$, and $c = 5$.

SOLUTION   Setting x, y, and z equal to zero in pairs gives the intercepts $(\pm 3, 0, 0)$, $(0, \pm 4, 0)$, and $(0, 0, \pm 5)$. Note that points in $\mathbb{R}^3$ with $|x| > 3$ or $|y| > 4$ or $|z| > 5$ do not satisfy the equation of the surface (because the left side of the equation is the sum of nonnegative terms, which cannot exceed 1). Therefore, the entire surface is contained in the rectangular box defined by $|x| \leq 3$, $|y| \leq 4$, and $|z| \leq 5$.

The trace in the horizontal plane $z = z_0$ is found by substituting $z = z_0$ into the equation of the ellipsoid, which gives

$$\frac{x^2}{9} + \frac{y^2}{16} + \frac{z_0^2}{25} = 1 \quad \text{or} \quad \frac{x^2}{9} + \frac{y^2}{16} = 1 - \frac{z_0^2}{25}.$$

If $|z_0| < 5$, then $1 - \frac{z_0^2}{25} > 0$, and the equation describes an ellipse in the horizontal plane $z = z_0$. The largest ellipse parallel to the xy-plane occurs with $z_0 = 0$; it is the xy-trace, which is the ellipse $\frac{x^2}{9} + \frac{y^2}{16} = 1$ with axes of length 6 and 8 (Figure 13.13a).

You can check that the yz-trace, found by setting $x = 0$, is the ellipse $\frac{y^2}{16} + \frac{z^2}{25} = 1$.

The xz-trace (set $y = 0$) is the ellipse $\frac{x^2}{9} + \frac{z^2}{25} = 1$ (Figure 13.13b). By sketching the xy-, xz-, and yz-traces, an outline of the ellipsoid emerges (Figure 13.13c).

Related Exercises 47–50 ◀

QUICK CHECK 7   Assume that $0 < c < b < a$ in the general equation of an ellipsoid. Along which coordinate axis does the ellipsoid have its longest axis? Its shortest axis? ◀

EXAMPLE 9   **An elliptic paraboloid**   The surface defined by the equation $z = \frac{x^2}{a^2} + \frac{y^2}{b^2}$ is an *elliptic paraboloid*. Graph the elliptic paraboloid with $a = 4$ and $b = 2$.

SOLUTION   Note that the only intercept of the coordinate axes is $(0, 0, 0)$, which is the *vertex* of the paraboloid. The trace in the horizontal plane $z = z_0$, where $z_0 > 0$, satisfies the equation $\frac{x^2}{16} + \frac{y^2}{4} = z_0$, which describes an ellipse; there are no horizontal traces when $z_0 < 0$ (Figure 13.14a). The trace in the vertical plane $x = x_0$ is the parabola $z = \frac{x_0^2}{16} + \frac{y^2}{4}$ (Figure 13.14b); the trace in the vertical plane $y = y_0$ is the parabola $z = \frac{x^2}{16} + \frac{y_0^2}{4}$ (Figure 13.14c).

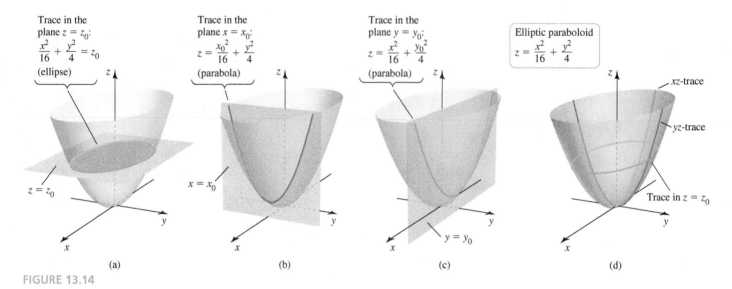

FIGURE 13.14

To graph the surface, we sketch the xz-trace $z = \dfrac{x^2}{16}$ (setting $y = 0$) and the

yz-trace $z = \dfrac{y^2}{4}$ (setting $x = 0$). When these traces are combined with an elliptical trace

$\dfrac{x^2}{16} + \dfrac{y^2}{4} = z_0$ in a plane $z = z_0$, an outline of the surface appears (Figure 13.14d).

Related Exercises 51–54 ◄

> The name *elliptic paraboloid* says that the traces of this surface are parabolas and ellipses. Two of the three traces in the coordinate planes are parabolas, so it is called a paraboloid rather than an ellipsoid.

QUICK CHECK 8 The elliptic paraboloid $x = \dfrac{y^2}{3} + \dfrac{z^2}{7}$ is a bowl-shaped surface. Along which axis does the bowl open? ◄

EXAMPLE 10 **A hyperboloid of one sheet** Graph the surface defined by the equation $\dfrac{x^2}{4} + \dfrac{y^2}{9} - z^2 = 1$.

> To be completely accurate, this surface should be called an *elliptic hyperboloid of one sheet* because the traces are ellipses and hyperbolas.

SOLUTION The intercepts of the coordinate axes are $(0, \pm 3, 0)$ and $(\pm 2, 0, 0)$. Setting $z = z_0$, the traces in horizontal planes are ellipses of the form $\dfrac{x^2}{4} + \dfrac{y^2}{9} = 1 + z_0{}^2$. This equation has solutions for all choices of z_0, so the surface has traces in all horizontal planes. These elliptical traces increase in size as $|z_0|$ increases (Figure 13.15a), with the smallest trace being the ellipse $\dfrac{x^2}{4} + \dfrac{y^2}{9} = 1$ in the xy-plane. Setting $x = 0$, the yz-trace is the hyperbola $\dfrac{y^2}{9} - z^2 = 1$; with $y = 0$, the xz-trace is the hyperbola $\dfrac{x^2}{4} - z^2 = 1$ (Figure 13.15b,c). In fact, the intersection of the surface with any vertical plane is a hyperbola. The resulting surface is a *hyperboloid of one sheet* (Figure 13.15d).

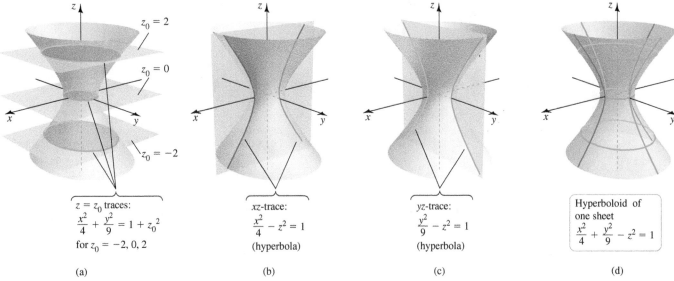

$z = z_0$ traces:
$$\frac{x^2}{4} + \frac{y^2}{9} = 1 + z_0{}^2$$
for $z_0 = -2, 0, 2$

(a)

xz-trace:
$$\frac{x^2}{4} - z^2 = 1$$
(hyperbola)

(b)

yz-trace:
$$\frac{y^2}{9} - z^2 = 1$$
(hyperbola)

(c)

Hyperboloid of
one sheet
$$\frac{x^2}{4} + \frac{y^2}{9} - z^2 = 1$$

(d)

FIGURE 13.15

Related Exercises 55–58 ◄

QUICK CHECK 9 Which coordinate axis is the axis of the hyperboloid
$$\frac{y^2}{a^2} + \frac{z^2}{b^2} - \frac{x^2}{c^2} = 1?$$ ◄

➤ The name *hyperbolic paraboloid* tells us that the traces are hyperbolas and parabolas. Two of the three traces in the coordinate planes are parabolas, so it is a paraboloid rather than a hyperboloid.

➤ The hyperbolic paraboloid has a feature called a *saddle point*. For the surface in Example 11, if you walk from the saddle point at the origin in the direction of the *x*-axis, you move uphill. If you walk from the saddle point in the direction of the *y*-axis, you move downhill. Saddle points are examined in detail in Section 13.8.

EXAMPLE 11   A hyperbolic paraboloid Graph the surface defined by the equation
$$z = x^2 - \frac{y^2}{4}.$$

SOLUTION Setting $z = 0$ in the equation of the surface, we see that the *xy*-trace consists of the two lines $y = \pm 2x$. However, slicing the surface with any other horizontal plane $z = z_0$ produces a hyperbola $x^2 - \frac{y^2}{4} = z_0$. If $z_0 > 0$, then the axis of the hyperbola is parallel to the *x*-axis. On the other hand, if $z_0 < 0$, then the axis of the hyperbola is parallel to the *y*-axis (Figure 13.16a). Setting $x = x_0$ produces the trace $z = x_0{}^2 - \frac{y^2}{4}$, which

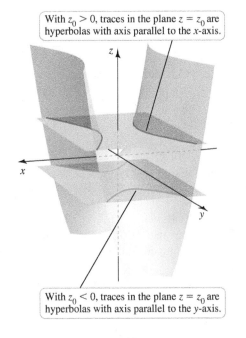

With $z_0 > 0$, traces in the plane $z = z_0$ are hyperbolas with axis parallel to the *x*-axis.

With $z_0 < 0$, traces in the plane $z = z_0$ are hyperbolas with axis parallel to the *y*-axis.

(a)

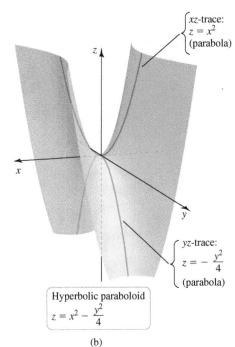

xz-trace:
$z = x^2$
(parabola)

yz-trace:
$z = -\frac{y^2}{4}$
(parabola)

Hyperbolic paraboloid
$z = x^2 - \frac{y^2}{4}$

(b)

FIGURE 13.16

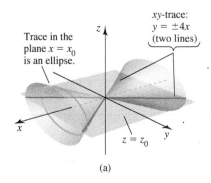

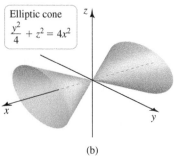

FIGURE 13.17

is the equation of a parabola that opens downward in a plane parallel to the yz-plane. You can check that traces in planes parallel to the xz-plane are parabolas that open upward. The resulting surface is a *hyperbolic paraboloid* (Figure 13.16b).

Related Exercises 59–62 ◄

EXAMPLE 12   Elliptic cones   Graph the surface defined by the equation
$$\frac{y^2}{4} + z^2 = 4x^2.$$

SOLUTION   The only intercept of the coordinate axes is $(0, 0, 0)$. Traces in the planes $x = x_0$ are ellipses of the form $\frac{y^2}{4} + z^2 = 4x_0^2$ that shrink in size as x_0 approaches 0.

Setting $y = 0$, the xz-trace satisfies the equation $z^2 = 4x^2$ or $z = \pm 2x$, which are equations of two lines in the xz-plane that intersect at the origin. Setting $z = 0$, the xy-trace satisfies $y^2 = 16x^2$ or $y = \pm 4x$, which describe two lines in the xy-plane that intersect at the origin (Figure 13.17a). The complete surface consists of two *cones* opening in opposite directions along the x-axis with a common vertex at the origin (Figure 13.17b).

Related Exercises 63–66 ◄

EXAMPLE 13   A hyperboloid of two sheets   Graph the surface defined by the equation
$$-16x^2 - 4y^2 + z^2 + 64x - 80 = 0.$$

SOLUTION   We first regroup terms, giving
$$-16\underbrace{(x^2 - 4x)}_{\substack{\text{complete the}\\\text{square}}} - 4y^2 + z^2 - 80 = 0,$$

and then complete the square in x:
$$-16(\underbrace{x^2 - 4x + 4}_{(x-2)^2} - 4) - 4y^2 + z^2 - 80 = 0.$$

> The equation $-x^2 - \dfrac{y^2}{4} + \dfrac{z^2}{16} = 1$ describes a hyperboloid of two sheets with its axis on the z-axis. Therefore, the equation in Example 13 describes the same surface shifted 2 units in the positive x-direction.

Collecting terms and dividing by 16 gives the equation
$$-(x - 2)^2 - \frac{y^2}{4} + \frac{z^2}{16} = 1.$$

Notice that if $z = 0$, the equation has no solutions, so the surface does not intersect the xy-plane. The traces in planes parallel to the xz- and yz-planes are hyperbolas. If $|z_0| \geq 4$, the trace in the plane $z = z_0$ is an ellipse. This equation describes a *hyperboloid of two sheets*, with its axis parallel to the z-axis and shifted 2 units in the positive x-direction (Figure 13.18).

Related Exercises 67–70 ◄

QUICK CHECK 10   In which variable(s) should you complete the square to identify the surface $x = y^2 + 2y + z^2 - 4z + 16$? Name and describe the surface. ◄

Table 13.1 summarizes the standard quadric surfaces. It is important to note that the same surfaces with different orientations are obtained when the roles of the variables are interchanged. For this reason, Table 13.1 summarizes many more surfaces than those listed.

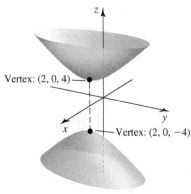

FIGURE 13.18

Table 13.1

Name	Standard Equation	Features	Graph
Ellipsoid	$\dfrac{x^2}{a^2} + \dfrac{y^2}{b^2} + \dfrac{z^2}{c^2} = 1$	All traces are ellipses.	
Elliptic paraboloid	$z = \dfrac{x^2}{a^2} + \dfrac{y^2}{b^2}$	Traces with $z = z_0 > 0$ are ellipses. Traces with $x = x_0$ or $y = y_0$ are parabolas.	
Hyperboloid of one sheet	$\dfrac{x^2}{a^2} + \dfrac{y^2}{b^2} - \dfrac{z^2}{c^2} = 1$	Traces with $z = z_0$ are ellipses for all z_0. Traces with $x = x_0$ or $y = y_0$ are hyperbolas.	
Hyperboloid of two sheets	$-\dfrac{x^2}{a^2} - \dfrac{y^2}{b^2} + \dfrac{z^2}{c^2} = 1$	Traces with $z = z_0$ with $|z_0| > |c|$ are ellipses. Traces with $x = x_0$ and $y = y_0$ are hyperbolas.	
Elliptic cone	$\dfrac{x^2}{a^2} + \dfrac{y^2}{b^2} = \dfrac{z^2}{c^2}$	Traces with $z = z_0 \neq 0$ are ellipses. Traces with $x = x_0$ or $y = y_0$ are hyperbolas or intersecting lines.	
Hyperbolic paraboloid	$z = \dfrac{x^2}{a^2} - \dfrac{y^2}{b^2}$	Traces with $z = z_0 \neq 0$ are hyperbolas. Traces with $x = x_0$ or $y = y_0$ are parabolas.	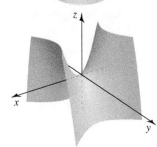

SECTION 13.1 EXERCISES

Review Questions

1. Give two pieces of information which, taken together, uniquely determine a plane.

2. Find a vector normal to the plane $-2x - 3y + 4z = 12$.

3. Where does the plane $-2x - 3y + 4z = 12$ intersect the coordinate axes?

4. Give an equation of the plane with a normal vector $\mathbf{n} = \langle 1, 1, 1 \rangle$ that passes through the point $(1, 0, 0)$.

5. To which coordinate axes are the following cylinders in $\mathbb{R}^3$ parallel: $x^2 + 2y^2 = 8$, $z^2 + 2y^2 = 8$, and $x^2 + 2z^2 = 8$?

6. Describe the graph of $x = z^2$ in $\mathbb{R}^3$.

7. What are the traces of a surface?

8. What is the name of the surface defined by the equation $y = \dfrac{x^2}{4} + \dfrac{z^2}{8}$?

9. What is the name of the surface defined by the equation $x^2 + \dfrac{y^2}{3} + 2z^2 = 1$?

10. What is the name of the surface defined by the equation $-y^2 - \dfrac{z^2}{2} + x^2 = 1$?

Basic Skills

11–16. Equations of planes *Find an equation of the plane that passes through the point P_0 with a normal vector $\mathbf{n}$.*

11. $P_0(0, 2, -2)$; $\mathbf{n} = \langle 1, 1, -1 \rangle$

12. $P_0(1, 0, -3)$; $\mathbf{n} = \langle 1, -1, 2 \rangle$

13. $P_0(2, 3, 0)$; $\mathbf{n} = \langle -1, 2, -3 \rangle$

14. $P_0(1, 2, -3)$; $\mathbf{n} = \langle -1, 4, -3 \rangle$

15. **Equation of a plane** Find the equation of the plane that is parallel to the vectors $\langle 1, 0, 1 \rangle$ and $\langle 0, 2, 1 \rangle$, passing through the point $(1, 2, 3)$.

16. **Equation of a plane** Find the equation of the plane that is parallel to the vectors $\langle 1, -3, 1 \rangle$ and $\langle 4, 2, 0 \rangle$, passing through the point $(3, 0, -2)$.

17–20. Equations of planes *Find an equation of the following planes.*

17. The plane passing through the points $(1, 0, 3)$, $(0, 4, 2)$, and $(1, 1, 1)$

18. The plane passing through the points $(-1, 1, 1)$, $(0, 0, 2)$, and $(3, -1, -2)$

19. The plane passing through the points $(2, -1, 4)$, $(1, 1, -1)$, and $(-4, 1, 1)$

20. The plane passing through the points $(5, 3, 1)$, $(1, 3, -5)$, and $(-1, 3, 1)$

21–24. Properties of planes *Find the points at which the following planes intersect the coordinate axes and find equations of the lines where the planes intersect the coordinate planes. Sketch a graph of the plane.*

21. $3x - 2y + z = 6$

22. $-4x + 8z = 16$

23. $x + 3y - 5z - 30 = 0$

24. $12x - 9y + 4z + 72 = 0$

25–28. Pairs of planes *Determine if the following pairs of planes are parallel, orthogonal, or neither parallel nor orthogonal.*

25. $x + y + 4z = 10$ and $-x - 3y + z = 10$

26. $2x + 2y - 3z = 10$ and $-10x - 10y + 15z = 10$

27. $3x + 2y - 3z = 10$ and $-6x - 10y + z = 10$

28. $3x + 2y + 2z = 10$ and $-6x - 10y + 19z = 10$

29–30. Equations of planes *For the following sets of planes, determine which pairs of planes in the set are parallel, orthogonal, or identical.*

29. $Q: 3x - 2y + z = 12$; $R: -x + 2y/3 - z/3 = 0$; $S: -x + 2y + 7z = 1$; $T: 3x/2 - y + z/2 = 6$

30. $Q: x + y - z = 0$; $R: y + z = 0$; $S: x - y = 0$; $T: x + y + z = 0$

31–34. Parallel planes *Find an equation of the plane parallel to the plane Q passing through the point P_0.*

31. $Q: -x + 2y - 4z = 1$; $P_0(1, 0, 4)$

32. $Q: 2x + y - z = 1$; $P_0(0, 2, -2)$

33. $Q: 4x + 3y - 2z = 12$; $P_0(1, -1, 3)$

34. $Q: x - 5y - 2z = 1$; $P_0(1, 2, 0)$

35–38. Intersecting planes *Find an equation of the line of intersection of the planes Q and R.*

35. $Q: -x + 2y + z = 1$; $R: x + y + z = 0$

36. $Q: x + 2y - z = 1$; $R: x + y + z = 1$

37. $Q: 2x - y + 3z - 1 = 0$; $R: -x + 3y + z - 4 = 0$

38. $Q: x - y - 2z = 1$; $R: x + y + z = -1$

39–46. Cylinders in $\mathbb{R}^3$ *Consider the following cylinders in $\mathbb{R}^3$.*

a. *Identify the coordinate axis to which the cylinder is parallel.*
b. *Sketch the cylinder.*

39. $z = y^2$

40. $x^2 + 4y^2 = 4$

41. $x^2 + z^2 = 4$

42. $x = z^2 - 4$

43. $y - x^3 = 0$

44. $x - 2z^2 = 0$

45. $z - \ln y = 0$

46. $x - 1/y = 0$

47–70. Quadric surfaces *Consider the following equations of quadric surfaces.*

a. *Find the intercepts with the three coordinate axes, when they exist.*
b. *Find the equations of the xy-, xz-, and yz-traces, when they exist.*
c. *Sketch a graph of the surface.*

Ellipsoids

47. $x^2 + \dfrac{y^2}{4} + \dfrac{z^2}{9} = 1$

48. $4x^2 + y^2 + \dfrac{z^2}{2} = 1$

49. $\dfrac{x^2}{3} + 3y^2 + \dfrac{z^2}{12} = 3$

50. $\dfrac{x^2}{6} + 24y^2 + \dfrac{z^2}{24} - 6 = 0$

Elliptic paraboloids

51. $x = y^2 + z^2$

52. $z = \dfrac{x^2}{4} + \dfrac{y^2}{9}$

53. $9x - 81y^2 - \dfrac{z^2}{4} = 0$

54. $2y - \dfrac{x^2}{8} - \dfrac{z^2}{18} = 0$

Hyperboloids of one sheet

55. $\dfrac{x^2}{25} + \dfrac{y^2}{9} - z^2 = 1$

56. $\dfrac{y^2}{4} + \dfrac{z^2}{9} - \dfrac{x^2}{16} = 1$

57. $\dfrac{y^2}{16} + 36z^2 - \dfrac{x^2}{4} - 9 = 0$

58. $9z^2 + x^2 - \dfrac{y^2}{3} - 1 = 0$

Hyperbolic paraboloids

59. $z = \dfrac{x^2}{9} - y^2$

60. $y = \dfrac{x^2}{16} - 4z^2$

61. $5x - \dfrac{y^2}{5} + \dfrac{z^2}{20} = 0$

62. $6y + \dfrac{x^2}{6} - \dfrac{z^2}{24} = 0$

Elliptic cones

63. $x^2 + \dfrac{y^2}{4} = z^2$

64. $4y^2 + z^2 = x^2$

65. $\dfrac{z^2}{32} + \dfrac{y^2}{18} = 2x^2$

66. $\dfrac{x^2}{3} + \dfrac{z^2}{12} = 3y^2$

Hyperboloids of two sheets

67. $-x^2 + \dfrac{y^2}{4} - \dfrac{z^2}{9} = 1$

68. $1 - 4x^2 + y^2 + \dfrac{z^2}{2} = 0$

69. $-\dfrac{x^2}{3} + 3y^2 - \dfrac{z^2}{12} = 1$

70. $-\dfrac{x^2}{6} - 24y^2 + \dfrac{z^2}{24} - 6 = 0$

Further Explorations

71. Explain why or why not Determine whether the following statements are true and give an explanation or counterexample.

a. The plane passing through the point $(1, 1, 1)$ with a normal vector $\mathbf{n} = \langle 1, 2, -3 \rangle$ is the same as the plane passing through the point $(3, 0, 1)$ with a normal vector $\mathbf{n} = \langle -2, -4, 6 \rangle$.

b. The equations $x + y - z = 1$ and $-x - y + z = 1$ describe the same plane.

c. Given a plane Q, there is exactly one plane orthogonal to Q.

d. Given a line ℓ and a point P_0 not on ℓ, there is exactly one plane that contains ℓ and passes through P_0.

e. Given a plane R and a point P_0, there is exactly one plane that is orthogonal to R and passes through P_0.

f. Any two distinct lines in $\mathbb{R}^3$ determine a unique plane.

g. If plane Q is orthogonal to plane R and plane R is orthogonal to plane S, then plane Q is orthogonal to plane S.

72. Plane containing a line and a point Find an equation of the plane that passes through the point P_0 and contains the line ℓ.

a. $P_0(1, -2, 3)$; ℓ: $\mathbf{r} = \langle t, -t, 2t \rangle$
b. $P_0(-4, 1, 2)$; ℓ: $\mathbf{r} = \langle 2t, -2t, -4t \rangle$

73–74. Lines normal to planes *Find an equation of the line passing through P_0 and normal to the plane P.*

73. $P_0(2, 1, 3)$; P: $2x - 4y + z = 10$

74. $P_0(0, -10, -3)$; P: $x + 4z = 2$

75. A family of orthogonal planes Find an equation for a family of planes that are orthogonal to the planes $2x + 3y = 4$ and $-x - y + 2z = 8$.

76. Orthogonal plane Find an equation of the plane passing through $(0, -2, 4)$ that is orthogonal to the planes $2x + 5y - 3z = 0$ and $-x + 5y + 2z = 8$.

77. Three intersecting planes Describe the set of all points at which all three planes $x + 3z = 3$, $y + 4z = 6$, and $x + y + 6z = 9$ intersect.

78. Three intersecting planes Describe the set of all points at which all three planes $x + 2y + 2z = 3$, $y + 4z = 6$, and $x + 2y + 8z = 9$ intersect.

79. Matching graphs with equations Match equations a–f with surfaces A–F.

a. $y - z^2 = 0$

b. $2x + 3y - z = 5$

c. $4x^2 + \dfrac{y^2}{9} + z^2 = 1$

d. $x^2 + \dfrac{y^2}{9} - z^2 = 1$

e. $x^2 + \dfrac{y^2}{9} = z^2$

f. $y = |x|$

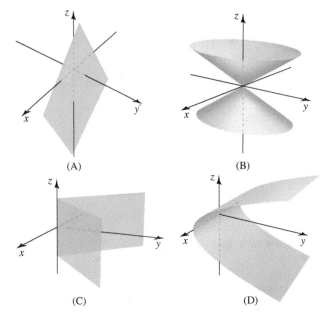

(A)   (B)

(C)   (D)

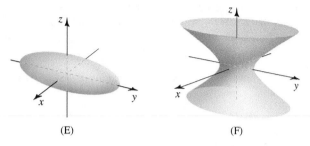

(E)   (F)

80–89. Identifying surfaces *Identify and briefly describe the surfaces defined by the following equations.*

80. $z^2 + 4y^2 - x^2 = 1$ **81.** $y = 4z^2 - x^2$

82. $-y^2 - 9z^2 + x^2/4 = 1$ **83.** $y = x^2/6 + z^2/16$

84. $x^2 + y^2 + 4z^2 + 2x = 0$ **85.** $9x^2 + y^2 - 4z^2 + 2y = 0$

86. $x^2 + 4y^2 = 1$ **87.** $y^2 - z^2 = 2$

88. $-x^2 - y^2 + z^2/9 + 6x - 8y = 26$

89. $x^2/4 + y^2 - 2x - 10y - z^2 + 41 = 0$

90–93. Curve–plane intersections *Find the points (if they exist) at which the following planes and curves intersect.*

90. $y = 2x + 1$; $\mathbf{r}(t) = \langle 10\cos t, 2\sin t, 1 \rangle$, for $0 \le t \le 2\pi$

91. $8x + y + z = 60$; $\mathbf{r}(t) = \langle t, t^2, 3t^2 \rangle$, for $-\infty < t < \infty$

92. $8x + 15y + 3z = 20$; $\mathbf{r}(t) = \langle 1, \sqrt{t}, -t \rangle$, for $t > 0$

93. $2x + 3y - 12z = 0$; $\mathbf{r}(t) = \langle 4\cos t, 4\sin t, \cos t \rangle$, for $0 \le t \le 2\pi$

94. Intercepts Let $a, b, c,$ and d be constants. Find the points at which the plane $ax + by + cz = d$ intersects the x-, y-, and z-axes.

95. Angle between planes The angle between two planes is the angle θ between the normal vectors of the planes, where the directions of the normal vectors are chosen so that $0 \le \theta < \pi$. Find the angle between the planes $5x + 2y - z = 0$ and $-3x + y + 2z = 0$.

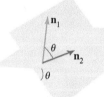

96. Solids of revolution Consider the ellipse $x^2 + 4y^2 = 1$ in the xy-plane.

   a. If this ellipse is revolved about the x-axis, what is the equation of the resulting ellipsoid?

   b. If this ellipse is revolved about the y-axis, what is the equation of the resulting ellipsoid?

97. Solids of revolution Which of the quadric surfaces in Table 13.1 can be generated by revolving a curve in one of the coordinate planes about a coordinate axis, assuming $a = b = c \ne 0$?

98. Light cones The idea of a *light cone* appears in the Special Theory of Relativity. The xy-plane (see figure) represents all of three-dimensional space, and the z-axis is the time axis (t-axis). If an event E occurs at the origin, the interior of the future light cone ($t > 0$) represents all events in the future that could be affected by E, assuming that no signal travels faster than the speed of light. The interior of the past light cone ($t < 0$) represents all events in the past that could have affected E, again assuming that no signal travels faster than the speed of light.

   a. If time is measured in seconds and distance (x and y) is measured in light-seconds (the distance light travels in 1 s), the light cone makes a 45° angle with the xy-plane. Write the equation of the light cone in this case.

   b. Suppose distance is measured in meters and time is measured in seconds. Write the equation of the light cone in this case given that the speed of light is 3×10^8 m/s.

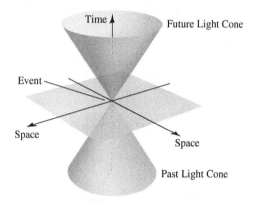

99. T-shirt profits A clothing company makes a profit of $10 on its long-sleeved T-shirts and $5 on its short-sleeved T-shirts. Assuming there is a $200 setup cost, the profit on T-shirt sales is $z = 10x + 5y - 200$, where x is the number of long-sleeved T-shirts sold and y is the number of short-sleeved T-shirts sold. Assume x and y are nonnegative.

   a. Graph the plane that gives the profit using the window $[0, 40] \times [0, 40] \times [-400, 400]$.

   b. If $x = 20$ and $y = 10$, is the profit positive or negative?

   c. Describe the values of x and y for which the company breaks even (for which the profit is zero). Mark this set on your graph.

100. Parallel line and plane Show that the plane $ax + by + cz = d$ and the line $\mathbf{r}(t) = \mathbf{r}_0 + \mathbf{v}t$, not in the plane, have no points of intersection if and only if $\mathbf{v} \cdot \langle a, b, c \rangle = 0$. Give a geometric explanation of the result.

101. Tilted ellipse Consider the curve $\mathbf{r}(t) = \langle \cos t, \sin t, c\sin t \rangle$, for $0 \le t \le 2\pi$, where c is a real number.

   a. What is the equation of the plane P in which the curve lies?

   b. What is the angle between P and the xy-plane?

   c. Prove that the curve is an ellipse in P.

102. Distance from a point to a plane

   a. Show that the point in the plane $ax + by + cz = d$ nearest the origin is $P(ad/D^2, bd/D^2, cd/D^2)$, where $D^2 = a^2 + b^2 + c^2$. Conclude that the least distance from the plane to the origin is $|d|/D$. (*Hint:* The least distance is along a normal to the plane.)

b. Show that the least distance from the point $P_0(x_0, y_0, z_0)$ to the plane $ax + by + cz = d$ is $|ax_0 + by_0 + cz_0 - d|/D$. (*Hint:* Find the point P on the plane closest to P_0.)

103. Another distance formula. Suppose P is a point in the plane $ax + by + cz = d$. Then the least distance from any point Q to the plane equals the length of the orthogonal projections of $\vec{PQ}$ onto the normal vector $\mathbf{n} = \langle a, b. c \rangle$.

a. Use this information to show that the least distance from Q to the plane is $\dfrac{|\vec{PQ} \cdot \mathbf{n}|}{|\mathbf{n}|}$.

b. Find the least distance from the point $(1, 2, -4)$ to the plane $2x - y + 3z = 1$.

104. Ellipsoid–plane intersection Let E be the ellipsoid $x^2/9 + y^2/4 + z^2 = 1$, P be the plane $z = Ax + By$, and C be the intersection of E and P.

a. Is C an ellipse for all values of A and B? Explain.

b. Sketch and interpret the situation in which $A = 0$ and $B \neq 0$.

c. Find an equation of the projection of C on the xy-plane.

d. Assume $A = \frac{1}{6}$ and $B = \frac{1}{2}$. Find a parametric description of C as a curve in $\mathbb{R}^3$. (*Hint:* Assume C is described by $\langle a \cos t + b \sin t, c \cos t + d \sin t, e \cos t + f \sin t \rangle$ and find $a, b, c, d, e,$ and f.)

QUICK CHECK **ANSWERS**

1. The plane passes through $(1, 2, 3)$ and is parallel to the yz-plane; its equation is $x = 1$. **2.** Because the right side of the equation is 0, the equation can be multiplied by any nonzero constant (changing the length of $\mathbf{n}$) without changing the graph. **5.** y-axis; x-axis **6.** The equation $x^2 + 4y^2 = 16$ is a special case of the general equation for quadric surfaces; all the coefficients except A, B, and J are zero. **7.** x-axis; z-axis **8.** Positive x-axis **9.** x-axis **10.** Complete the square in y and z; elliptic paraboloid with its axis parallel to the x-axis. ◄

13.2 Graphs and Level Curves

In Chapter 12 we discussed vector-valued functions with one independent variable and several dependent variables. We now reverse the situation and consider functions with several independent variables and one dependent variable. Such functions are aptly called *functions of several variables* or *multivariable functions*.

To set the stage, consider the following practical questions that illustrate a few of the many applications of functions of several variables.

- What is the probability that one man selected randomly from a large group of men weighs more than 200 pounds and is over 6 feet tall?

- Where on the wing of an airliner flying at a speed of 550 mi/hr is the pressure greatest?

- A physician knows the optimal blood concentration of an antibiotic needed by a patient. What dosage of antibiotic is needed and how often should it be given to reach this optimal level?

Although we don't answer these questions immediately, they provide an idea of the scope and importance of the topic. First, we must introduce the idea of a function of several variables.

Functions of Two Variables

The key concepts related to functions of several variables are most easily presented in the case of two independent variables; the extension to three or more variables is then straightforward. In general, functions of two variables are written *explicitly* in the form

$$z = f(x, y)$$

or in the form

$$F(x, y, z) = 0.$$

Both forms are important, but for now we consider explicitly defined functions.

The concepts of domain and range carry over directly from functions of a single variable.

> **DEFINITION Function, Domain, and Range with Two Independent Variables**
>
> A **function** $z = f(x, y)$ assigns to each point (x, y) in a set D in $\mathbb{R}^2$ a unique real number z in a subset of $\mathbb{R}$. The set D is the **domain** of f. The **range** of f is the set of real numbers z that are assumed as the points (x, y) vary over the domain (Figure 13.19).

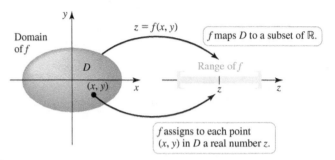

FIGURE 13.19

As with functions of one variable, a function of several variables may have a domain that is restricted by the context of the problem. For example, if the independent variables correspond to price or length or population, they take only nonnegative values, even though the associated function may be defined for negative values of the variables. If not stated otherwise, D is the set of points for which the function is defined.

A polynomial in x and y consists of sums and products of polynomials in x and polynomials in y; for example, $f(x, y) = x^2y - 2xy - xy^2$. Such polynomials are defined for all values of x and y, so their domain is $\mathbb{R}^2$. A quotient of two polynomials in x and y, such as $h(x, y) = \dfrac{xy}{x - y}$, is a rational function in x and y. The domain of a rational function must exclude points at which the denominator is zero, so the domain of h is $\{(x, y): x \neq y\}$.

EXAMPLE 1   Finding domains Find the domain of the function $g(x, y) = \sqrt{4 - x^2 - y^2}$.

SOLUTION Because g involves a square root, its domain consists of ordered pairs (x, y) for which $4 - x^2 - y^2 \geq 0$ or $x^2 + y^2 \leq 4$. Therefore, the domain of g is $\{(x, y): x^2 + y^2 \leq 4\}$, which is the set of points on or within the circle of radius 2 centered at the origin in the xy-plane (a *disk* of radius 2) (Figure 13.20).

Related Exercises 11–20 ◀

QUICK CHECK 1 Find the domains of $f(x, y) = \sin xy$ and $g(x, y) = \sqrt{(x^2 + 1)y}$. ◀

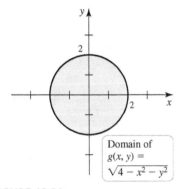

Domain of
$g(x, y) = \sqrt{4 - x^2 - y^2}$

FIGURE 13.20

Graphs of Functions of Two Variables

The **graph** of a function f of two variables is the set of points (x, y, z) that satisfy the equation $z = f(x, y)$. More specifically, for each point (x, y) in the domain of f, the point $(x, y, f(x, y))$ lies on the graph of f (Figure 13.21). A similar definition applies to relations of the form $F(x, y, z) = 0$.

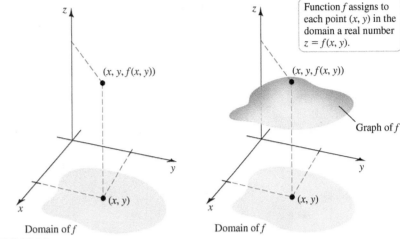

FIGURE 13.21

Like functions of one variable, functions of two variables must pass a **vertical line test**. A relation of the form $F(x, y, z) = 0$ is a function provided every line parallel to the z-axis intersects the graph of F at most once. For example, an ellipsoid (discussed in Section 13.1) is not the graph of a function because some vertical lines intersect the surface twice. On the other hand, an elliptic paraboloid of the form $z = ax^2 + by^2$ does represent a function (Figure 13.22).

QUICK CHECK 2 Does the graph of a hyperboloid of one sheet represent a function? Does the graph of a cone with its axis parallel to the x-axis represent a function? ◂

EXAMPLE 2 **Graphing two-variable functions** Find the domain and range of the following functions. Then sketch a graph.

a. $f(x, y) = 2x + 3y - 12$ **b.** $g(x, y) = x^2 + y^2$
c. $h(x, y) = \sqrt{1 + x^2 + y^2}$

SOLUTION

a. Letting $z = f(x, y)$, we have the equation $z = 2x + 3y - 12$, or $2x + 3y - z = 12$, which describes a plane with a normal vector $\langle 2, 3, -1 \rangle$ (Section 13.1). The domain consists of all points in $\mathbb{R}^2$, and the range is $\mathbb{R}$. We sketch the surface by noting that the x-intercept is $(6, 0, 0)$ (setting $y = z = 0$); the y-intercept is $(0, 4, 0)$ and the z-intercept is $(0, 0, -12)$ (Figure 13.23).

An ellipsoid does not pass the vertical line test: not the graph of a function.

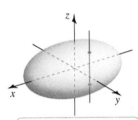

This elliptic paraboloid passes the vertical line test: graph of a function.

FIGURE 13.22

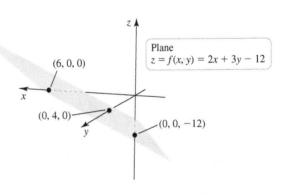

FIGURE 13.23

Paraboloid
$z = f(x, y) = x^2 + y^2$

FIGURE 13.24

b. Letting $z = g(x, y)$, we have the equation $z = x^2 + y^2$, which describes an elliptic paraboloid that opens upward with vertex $(0, 0, 0)$. The domain is $\mathbb{R}^2$ and the range consists of all nonnegative real numbers (Figure 13.24).

c. The domain of the function is $\mathbb{R}^2$ because the quantity under the square root is always positive. Note that $1 + x^2 + y^2 \geq 1$, so the range is $\{z: z \geq 1\}$. Squaring both sides of $z = \sqrt{1 + x^2 + y^2}$, we obtain $z^2 = 1 + x^2 + y^2$, or $-x^2 - y^2 + z^2 = 1$. This is the equation of a hyperboloid of two sheets that opens along the z-axis. Because the range is $\{z: z \geq 1\}$, the given function represents only the upper sheet of the hyperboloid (Figure 13.25; the lower sheet was introduced when we squared the original equation).

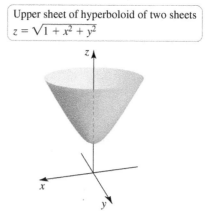

Upper sheet of hyperboloid of two sheets
$z = \sqrt{1 + x^2 + y^2}$

FIGURE 13.25

Related Exercises 21–29◄

QUICK CHECK 3 Find a function whose graph is the lower half of the hyperboloid $-x^2 - y^2 + z^2 = 1$. ◄

> To anticipate results that appear later in the chapter, notice how the streams in the topographic map—which flow downhill—cross the level curves roughly at right angles.

Level Curves   Functions of two variables are represented by surfaces in $\mathbb{R}^3$. However, such functions can be represented in another illuminating way, which is used to make topographic maps (Figure 13.26).

Closely spaced contours: rapid changes in elevation

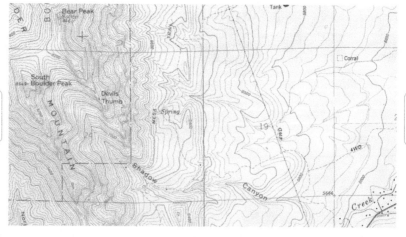

Widely spaced contours: slow changes in elevation

FIGURE 13.26

> A contour curve is a trace in the plane $z = z_0$.

> A level curve may not always be a single curve. It might consist of a point ($x^2 + y^2 = 0$) or it might consist of several lines or curves ($xy = 0$).

Consider a surface defined by the function $z = f(x, y)$ (Figure 13.27). Now imagine stepping onto the surface and walking along a path on which your elevation has the constant value $z = z_0$. The path you walk on the surface is part of a **contour curve**; the complete contour curve is the intersection of the surface and the horizontal plane $z = z_0$. When the contour curve is projected onto the xy-plane, the result is the curve $f(x, y) = z_0$. This curve in the xy-plane is called a **level curve**.

Imagine repeating this process with a different constant value of z, say, $z = z_1$. The path you walk this time when projected onto the xy-plane is part of another level curve $f(x, y) = z_1$. A collection of such level curves, corresponding to different values of z, provides a useful two-dimensional representation of the surface (Figure 13.28).

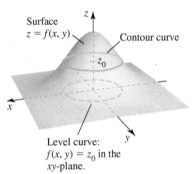

FIGURE 13.27

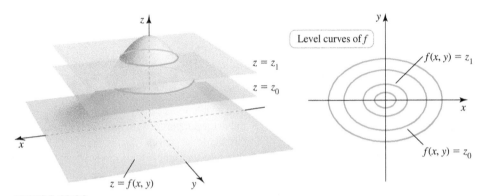

FIGURE 13.28

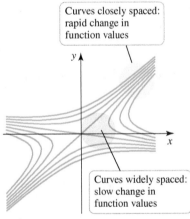

FIGURE 13.29

QUICK CHECK 4 Can two level curves of a function intersect? Explain. ◄

Assuming that two adjacent level curves always correspond to the same change in z, widely spaced level curves indicate gradual changes in z-values, while closely spaced level curves indicate rapid changes in some directions (Figure 13.29). Concentric closed level curves indicate either a peak or a depression on the surface.

QUICK CHECK 5 Describe in words the level curves of the top half of the sphere $x^2 + y^2 + z^2 = 1$. ◄

EXAMPLE 3   **Level curves** Find and sketch the level curves of the following surfaces.

a. $f(x, y) = y - x^2 - 1$ **b.** $f(x, y) = e^{-x^2 - y^2}$

SOLUTION

a. The level curves are described by the equation $y - x^2 - 1 = z_0$, where z_0 is a constant in the range of f. For all values of z_0, these curves are parabolas in the xy-plane, as seen by writing the equation in the form $y = x^2 + z_0 + 1$. For example:

- With $z_0 = 0$, the level curve is the parabola $y = x^2 + 1$; along this curve, the surface has an elevation (z-coordinate) of 0.
- With $z_0 = -1$, the level curve is $y = x^2$; along this curve, the surface has an elevation of -1.
- With $z_0 = 1$, the level curve is $y = x^2 + 2$, along which the surface has an elevation of 1.

As shown in Figure 13.30a, the level curves form a family of shifted parabolas. When these level curves are labeled with their z-coordinates, the graph of the surface $z = f(x, y)$ can be visualized (Figure 13.30b).

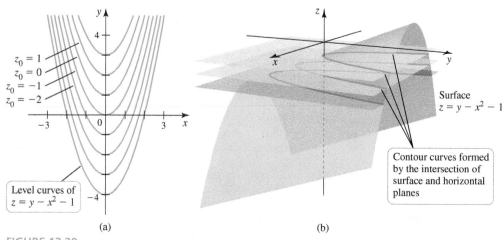

FIGURE 13.30

b. The level curves satisfy the equation $e^{-x^2-y^2} = z_0$, where z_0 is a positive constant. Taking the natural logarithm of both sides gives the equation $x^2 + y^2 = -\ln z_0$, which describes circular level curves. These curves can be sketched for all values of z_0 with $0 < z_0 \leq 1$ (because the right side of $x^2 + y^2 = -\ln z_0$ must be nonnegative). For example:

- With $z_0 = 1$, the level curve satisfies the equation $x^2 + y^2 = 0$, whose solution is the single point $(0, 0)$; at this point, the surface has an elevation of 1.

- With $z_0 = e^{-1}$, the level curve is $x^2 + y^2 = -\ln e^{-1} = 1$, which is a circle centered at $(0, 0)$ with a radius of 1; along this curve the surface has an elevation of $e^{-1} \approx 0.37$.

In general, the level curves are circles centered at $(0, 0)$; as the radii of the circles increase, the corresponding z-values decrease. Figure 13.31a shows the level curves, with larger z-values corresponding to darker shades. From these labeled level curves, we can reconstruct the graph of the surface (Figure 13.31b).

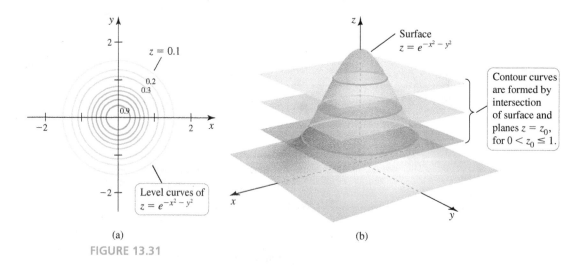

FIGURE 13.31

Related Exercises 30–38◄

QUICK CHECK 6 Does the surface in Example 3b have a level curve for $z_0 = 0$? Explain.

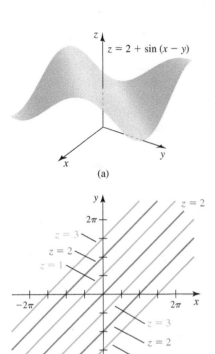

$z = 2 + \sin(x - y)$

(a)

$z = 2$

2π

$z = 3$
$z = 2$
$z = 1$

-2π 2π x

$z = 3$
$z = 2$
$z = 1$
-2π

Level curves of
$z = 2 + \sin(x - y)$

(b)

FIGURE 13.32

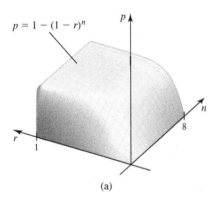

$p = 1 - (1 - r)^n$

p

n

8

r

1

(a)

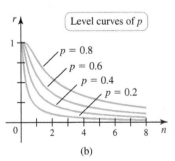

r

Level curves of p

1

$p = 0.8$
$p = 0.6$
$p = 0.4$
$p = 0.2$

0   2   4   6   8 n

(b)

FIGURE 13.33

EXAMPLE 4 Level curves The graph of the function

$$f(x, y) = 2 + \sin(x - y)$$

is shown in Figure 13.32a. Sketch several level curves of the function.

SOLUTION The level curves are $f(x, y) = 2 + \sin(x - y) = z_0$, or
$\sin(x - y) = z_0 - 2$. Because $-1 \le \sin(x - y) \le 1$, the admissible values of z_0
satisfy $-1 \le z_0 - 2 \le 1$, or, equivalently, $1 \le z_0 \le 3$. For example, when $z_0 = 2$,
the level curves satisfy $\sin(x - y) = 0$. The solutions of this equation are $x - y = k\pi$,
or $y = x - k\pi$, where k is an integer. Therefore, the surface has an elevation of 2
on this set of lines. With $z_0 = 1$ (the minimum value of z), the level curves satisfy
$\sin(x - y) = -1$. The solutions are $x - y = -\pi/2 + 2k\pi$, where k is an integer;
along these lines, the surface has an elevation of 1. Here we have an example in which
each level curve is an infinite collection of lines of slope 1 (Figure 13.32b).

Related Exercises 30–38◄

Applications of Functions of Two Variables

The following examples offer two of many applications of functions of two variables.

EXAMPLE 5   A probability function of two variables Suppose that on a particular
day, the fraction of students on campus infected with flu is r, where $0 \le r \le 1$. If you
have n random (possibly repeated) encounters with students during the day, the probability of meeting *at least* one infected person is $p(n, r) = 1 - (1 - r)^n$ (Figure 13.33a).
Discuss this probability function.

SOLUTION The independent variable r is restricted to the interval $[0, 1]$ because it is a
fraction of the population. The other independent variable n is any nonnegative integer;
for the purposes of graphing, we treat n as a real number in the interval $[0, 8]$. With
$0 \le r \le 1$, note that $0 \le 1 - r \le 1$. If n is nonnegative, then $0 \le (1 - r)^n \le 1$, and
it follows that $0 \le p(n, r) \le 1$. Therefore, the range of the function is $[0, 1]$, which is
consistent with the fact that p is a probability.

The level curves (Figure 13.33b) show that for a fixed value of n, the probability
of at least one encounter increases with r; and for a fixed value of r, the probability increases with n. Therefore, as r increases or as n increases, the probability approaches
1 (surprisingly quickly). If 10% of the population is infected ($r = 0.1$) and you have
$n = 10$ encounters, then the probability of at least one encounter with an infected person
is $p(0.1, 10) \approx 0.651$, which is about 2 in 3.

A numerical view of this function is given in Table 13.2, where we see probabilities
tabulated for various values of n and r (rounded to two digits). The numerical values confirm the preceding observations.

Related Exercises 39–45◄

QUICK CHECK 7 In Example 5, if 50% of the population is infected, what is the probability
of meeting at least one infected person in five encounters? ◄

EXAMPLE 6   Electric potential function in two variables The electric field at
points in the xy-plane due to two point charges located at $(0, 0)$ and $(1, 0)$ is related to
the electric potential function

$$\varphi(x, y) = \frac{2}{\sqrt{x^2 + y^2}} + \frac{2}{\sqrt{(x - 1)^2 + y^2}}.$$

Discuss the electric potential function.

Table 13.2

| | \multicolumn{5}{c}{n} |
r	2	5	10	15	20
0.05	0.10	0.23	0.40	0.54	0.64
0.1	0.19	0.41	0.65	0.79	0.88
0.3	0.51	0.83	0.97	1	1
0.5	0.75	0.97	1	1	1
0.7	0.91	1	1	1	1

> The electric potential function, often denoted φ (pronounced *fee* or *fie*), is a scalar-valued function from which the electric field can be computed. Potential functions are discussed in detail in Chapter 15.

> A function that grows without bound near a point, as in the case of the electric potential function, is said to have a *singularity* at that point. A singularity is analogous to a vertical asymptote in a function of one variable.

SOLUTION The domain of the function contains all points of $\mathbb{R}^2$ except $(0, 0)$ and $(1, 0)$ where the charges are located. As these points are approached, the potential function becomes arbitrarily large (Figure 13.34a). The potential approaches zero as x or y increases in magnitude. These observations imply that the range of the potential function is all positive real numbers. The level curves of φ are closed curves, encircling either a single charge (at small distances) or both charges (at larger distances; Figure 13.34b).

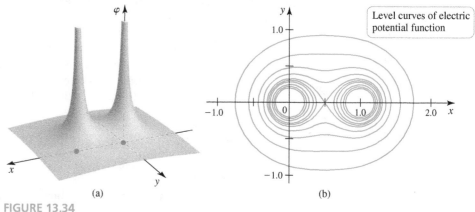

(a)

(b)

FIGURE 13.34

Related Exercises 39–45 ◄

QUICK CHECK 8 In Example 6, what is the electric potential at the point $\left(\frac{1}{2}, 0\right)$? ◄

Functions of More Than Two Variables

The characteristics of functions of two independent variables extend naturally to functions of three or more variables. A function of three variables is defined explicitly in the form $w = f(x, y, z)$ and implicitly in the form $F(w, x, y, z) = 0$. With more than three independent variables, the variables are usually written $x_1, \ldots, x_n$. Table 13.3 shows the progression of functions of several variables.

Table 13.3

Number of Independent Variables	Explicit Form	Implicit Form	Graph Resides In...
1	$y = f(x)$	$F(x, y) = 0$	$\mathbb{R}^2$ (xy-plane)
2	$z = f(x, y)$	$F(x, y, z) = 0$	$\mathbb{R}^3$ (xyz-space)
3	$w = f(x, y, z)$	$F(w, x, y, z) = 0$	$\mathbb{R}^4$
n	$y = f(x_1, x_2, \ldots, x_n)$	$F(x_1, x_2, \ldots, x_n, x_{n+1}) = 0$	$\mathbb{R}^{n+1}$

The concepts of domain and range extend from the one- and two-variable cases in an obvious way.

DEFINITION Function, Domain, and Range with n Independent Variables

The **function** $y = f(x_1, x_2, \ldots, x_n)$ assigns a unique real number y to each point $(x_1, x_2, \ldots, x_n)$ in a set D in $\mathbb{R}^n$. The set D is the **domain** of f. The **range** is the set of real numbers y that are assumed as the points $(x_1, x_2, \ldots, x_n)$ vary over the domain.

EXAMPLE 7 **Finding domains** Find the domain of the following functions.

a. $g(x, y, z) = \sqrt{16 - x^2 - y^2 - z^2}$ **b.** $h(x, y, z) = \dfrac{12y^2}{z - y}$

SOLUTION

> Recall that a closed ball of radius r is the set of all points on or within a sphere of radius r.

a. Values of the variables that make the argument of a square root negative must be excluded from the domain. In this case, the quantity under the square root is nonnegative provided

$$16 - x^2 - y^2 - z^2 \geq 0, \quad \text{or} \quad x^2 + y^2 + z^2 \leq 16.$$

Therefore, the domain of g is a closed ball in $\mathbb{R}^3$ of radius 4 centered at the origin.

b. Values of the variables that make a denominator zero must be excluded from the domain. In this case, the denominator vanishes for all points in $\mathbb{R}^3$ that satisfy $z - y = 0$, or $y = z$. Therefore, the domain of h is the set $\{(x, y, z): y \neq z\}$. This set is $\mathbb{R}^3$ excluding the points on the plane $y = z$.

Related Exercises 46–52 ◄

QUICK CHECK 9 What is the domain of the function $w = f(x, y, z) = 1/xyz$? ◄

Graphs of Functions of More Than Two Variables

Graphing functions of *two* independent variables requires a three-dimensional coordinate system, which is the limit of ordinary graphing methods. Clearly, difficulties arise in graphing functions with three or more independent variables. For example, the graph of the function $w = f(x, y, z)$ resides in four dimensions. Here are two approaches to representing functions of three independent variables.

The idea of level curves can be extended. With the function $w = f(x, y, z)$, level curves become **level surfaces**, which are surfaces in $\mathbb{R}^3$ on which w is constant. For example, the level surfaces of the function

$$w = f(x, y, z) = \sqrt{z - x^2 - 2y^2}$$

satisfy $w = \sqrt{z - x^2 - 2y^2} = C$, where C is a nonnegative constant. This equation is satisfied when $z = x^2 + 2y^2 + C^2$. Therefore, the level surfaces are elliptic paraboloids, stacked one inside another (Figure 13.35).

Another approach to displaying functions of three variables is to use colors to gain access to the fourth dimension. Figure 13.36a shows the electrical activity of the heart at one snapshot in time. The three independent variables correspond to locations in the heart. At each point, the value of the electrical activity, which is the dependent variable, is coded by colors.

In Figure 13.36b, the dependent variable is the switching speed in an integrated circuit, again represented by colors, as it varies over points of the domain. Software to produce such images, once expensive and inefficient, has become much more accessible.

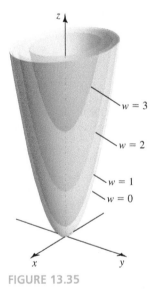

FIGURE 13.35

$w = 3$
$w = 2$
$w = 1$
$w = 0$

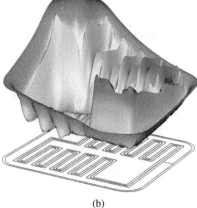

FIGURE 13.36   (a)   (b)

SECTION 13.2 EXERCISES

Review Questions

1. A function is defined by $z = x^2y - xy^2$. Identify the independent and dependent variables.

2. What is the domain of $f(x, y) = x^2y - xy^2$?

3. What is the domain of $g(x, y) = 1/(xy)$?

4. What is the domain of $h(x, y) = \sqrt{x - y}$?

5. How many axes (or how many dimensions) are needed to graph the function $z = f(x, y)$? Explain.

6. Explain how to graph the level curves of a surface $z = f(x, y)$.

7. Describe in words the level curves of the paraboloid $z = x^2 + y^2$.

8. How many axes (or how many dimensions) are needed to graph the level surfaces of $w = f(x, y, z)$? Explain.

9. The domain of $Q = f(u, v, w, x, y, z)$ lies in $\mathbb{R}^n$ for what value of n? Explain.

10. Give two methods for graphically representing a function with three independent variables.

Basic Skills

11–20. Domains *Find the domain of the following functions.*

11. $f(x, y) = 2xy - 3x + 4y$ 12. $f(x, y) = \cos(x^2 - y^2)$

13. $f(x, y) = \sqrt{25 - x^2 - y^2}$ 14. $f(x, y) = \dfrac{1}{\sqrt{x^2 + y^2 - 25}}$

15. $f(x, y) = \sin\dfrac{x}{y}$ 16. $f(x, y) = \dfrac{12}{y^2 - x^2}$

17. $g(x, y) = \ln(x^2 - y)$ 18. $f(x, y) = \sin^{-1}(y - x^2)$

19. $g(x, y) = \sqrt{\dfrac{xy}{x^2 + y^2}}$ 20. $h(x, y) = \sqrt{x - 2y + 4}$

21–28. Graphs of familiar functions *Use what you learned about surfaces in Section 13.1 to sketch a graph of the following functions. In each case identify the surface, and state the domain and range of the function.*

21. $f(x, y) = 3x - 6y + 18$ 22. $h(x, y) = 2x^2 + 3y^2$

23. $p(x, y) = x^2 - y^2$ 24. $F(x, y) = \sqrt{1 - x^2 - y^2}$

25. $G(x, y) = -\sqrt{1 + x^2 + y^2}$ 26. $H(x, y) = \sqrt{x^2 + y^2}$

27. $P(x, y) = \sqrt{x^2 + y^2 - 1}$ 28. $g(x, y) = y^3 + 1$

29. **Matching surfaces** Match functions a–d with surfaces A–D in the figure.

   a. $f(x, y) = \cos xy$
   b. $g(x, y) = \ln(x^2 + y^2)$
   c. $h(x, y) = 1/(x - y)$
   d. $p(x, y) = 1/(1 + x^2 + y^2)$

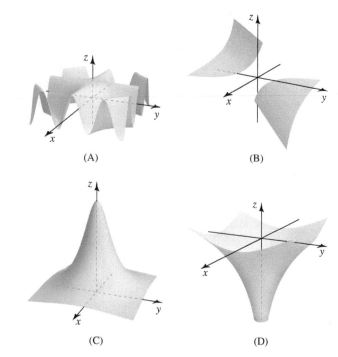

(A)   (B)

(C)   (D)

30–37. Level curves *Graph several level curves of the following functions using the given window. Label at least two level curves with their z-values.*

30. $z = x^2 + y^2$; $[-4, 4] \times [-4, 4]$

31. $z = x - y^2$; $[0, 4] \times [-2, 2]$

32. $z = 2x - y$; $[-2, 2] \times [-2, 2]$

33. $z = \sqrt{x^2 + 4y^2}$; $[-8, 8] \times [-8, 8]$

34. $z = e^{-x^2 - 2y^2}$; $[-2, 2] \times [-2, 2]$

35. $z = \sqrt{25 - x^2 - y^2}$; $[-6, 6] \times [-6, 6]$

36. $z = \sqrt{y - x^2 - 1}$; $[-5, 5] \times [-5, 5]$

37. $z = 3\cos(2x + y)$; $[-2, 2] \times [-2, 2]$

38. **Matching level curves with surfaces** Match surfaces a–f in the figure with level curves A–F.

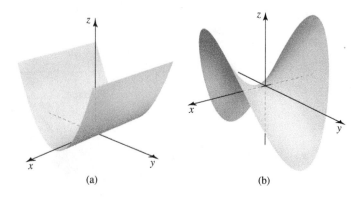

(a)   (b)

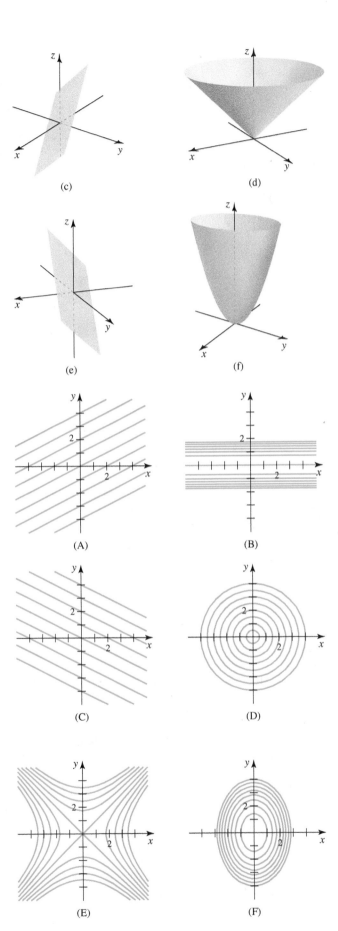

(c)

(d)

(e)

(f)

(A)

(B)

(C)

(D)

(E)

(F)

39. A volume function The volume of a right circular cone of radius r and height h is $V(r, h) = \pi r^2 h / 3$.

   a. Graph the function in the window $[0, 5] \times [0, 5] \times [0, 150]$.

   b. What is the domain of the volume function?

   c. What is the relationship between the values of r and h when $V = 100$?

40. Earned run average A baseball pitcher's earned run average (ERA) is $A(e, i) = 9e/i$, where e is the number of earned runs given up by the pitcher and i is the number of innings pitched. Good pitchers have low ERAs. Assume that $e \geq 0$ and $i > 0$ are real numbers.

   a. The single-season major league record for the lowest ERA was set by Dutch Leonard of the Detroit Tigers in 1914. During that season, Dutch pitched a total of 224 innings and gave up just 24 earned runs. What was his ERA?

   b. Determine the ERA of a relief pitcher who gives up 4 earned runs in one-third of an inning.

   c. Graph the level curve $A(e, i) = 3$, and describe the relationship between e and i in this case.

41. Electric potential function The electric potential function for two positive charges, one at $(0, 1)$ with twice the strength as the charge at $(0, -1)$, is given by

$$\varphi(x, y) = \frac{2}{\sqrt{x^2 + (y - 1)^2}} + \frac{1}{\sqrt{x^2 + (y + 1)^2}}.$$

   a. Graph the electric potential using the window $[-5, 5] \times [-5, 5] \times [0, 10]$.

   b. For what values of x and y is the potential φ defined?

   c. Is the electric potential greater at $(3, 2)$ or $(2, 3)$?

   d. Describe how the electric potential varies along the line $y = x$.

42. Cobb-Douglas production function The output Q of an economic system subject to two inputs, such as labor L and capital K, is often modeled by the Cobb-Douglas production function $Q(L, K) = cL^a K^b$, where $a, b,$ and c are positive real numbers. When $a + b = 1$, the case is called *constant returns to scale*. Suppose $a = \frac{1}{3}, b = \frac{2}{3},$ and $c = 40$.

   a. Graph the output function using the window $[0, 20] \times [0, 20] \times [0, 500]$.

   b. If L is held constant at $L = 10$, write the function that gives the dependence of Q on K.

   c. If K is held constant at $K = 15$, write the function that gives the dependence of Q on L.

43. Resistors in parallel Two resistors wired in parallel in an electrical circuit give an effective resistance of $R(x, y) = \dfrac{xy}{x + y}$, where x and y are the positive resistances of the individual resistors (typically measured in ohms).

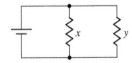

   a. Graph the resistance function using the window $[0, 10] \times [0, 10] \times [0, 5]$.

   b. Estimate the maximum value of R, for $0 < x \leq 10$ and $0 < y \leq 10$.

   c. Explain what it means to say that the resistance function is symmetric in x and y.

44. Water waves A snapshot of a water wave moving toward shore is described by the function $z = 10 \sin(2x - 3y)$, where z is the height of the water surface above (or below) the xy-plane, which is the level of undisturbed water.

   a. Graph the height function using the window $[-5, 5] \times [-5, 5] \times [-15, 15]$.

   b. For what values of x and y is z defined?

   c. What are the maximum and minimum values of the water height?

   d. Give a vector in the xy-plane that is orthogonal to the level curves of the crests and troughs of the wave (which is parallel to the direction of wave propagation).

45. Approximate mountains Suppose the elevation of Earth's surface over a 16-mi by 16-mi region is approximated by the function

$$z = 10e^{-(x^2+y^2)} + 5e^{-((x+5)^2+(y-3)^2)/10} + 4e^{-2((x-4)^2+(y+1)^2)}.$$

   a. Graph the height function using the window $[-8, 8] \times [-8, 8] \times [0, 15]$.

   b. Approximate the points (x, y) where the peaks in the landscape appear.

   c. What are the approximate elevations of the peaks?

46–52. Domains of functions of three or more variables *Find the domain of the following functions. If possible, give a description of the domains (for example, all points outside a sphere of radius 1 centered at the origin).*

46. $f(x, y, z) = 2xyz - 3xz + 4yz$

47. $g(x, y, z) = \dfrac{1}{x - z}$

48. $p(x, y, z) = \sqrt{x^2 + y^2 + z^2 - 9}$

49. $f(x, y, z) = \sqrt{y - z}$

50. $Q(x, y, z) = \dfrac{10}{1 + x^2 + y^2 + 4z^2}$

51. $F(x, y, z) = \sqrt{y - x^2}$

52. $f(w, x, y, z) = \sqrt{1 - w^2 - x^2 - y^2 - z^2}$

Further Explorations

53. Explain why or why not Determine whether the following statements are true and give an explanation or counterexample.

   a. The domain of the function $f(x, y) = 1 - |x - y|$ is $\{(x, y): x \geq y\}$.

   b. The domain of the function $Q = g(w, x, y, z)$ is a region in $\mathbb{R}^3$.

   c. All level curves of the plane $z = 2x - 3y$ are lines.

54–60. Graphing functions

   a. *Determine the domain and range of the following functions.*

   b. *Graph each function using a graphing utility. Be sure to experiment with the window and orientation to give the best perspective of the surface.*

54. $g(x, y) = e^{-xy}$

55. $f(x, y) = |xy|$

56. $p(x, y) = 1 - |x - 1| + |y + 1|$

57. $h(x, y) = (x + y)/(x - y)$

58. $G(x, y) = \ln(2 + \sin(x + y))$

59. $F(x, y) = \tan^2(x - y)$

60. $P(x, y) = \cos x \sin 2y$

61–64. Peaks and valleys *The following functions have exactly one isolated peak or one isolated depression (one local maximum or minimum). Use a graphing utility to approximate the coordinates of the peak or depression.*

61. $f(x, y) = x^2y^2 - 8x^2 - y^2 + 6$

62. $g(x, y) = (x^2 - x - 2)(y^2 + 2y)$

63. $h(x, y) = 1 - e^{-(x^2+y^2-2x)}$

64. $p(x, y) = 2 + |x - 1| + |y - 1|$

65. Level curves of planes Prove that the level curves of the plane $ax + by + cz = d$ are parallel lines in the xy-plane, provided $a^2 + b^2 \neq 0$ and $c \neq 0$.

66–69. Level surfaces *Find an equation for the family of level surfaces corresponding to f. Describe the level surfaces.*

66. $f(x, y, z) = \dfrac{1}{x^2 + y^2 + z^2}$

67. $f(x, y, z) = x^2 + y^2 - z$

68. $f(x, y, z) = x^2 - y^2 - z$

69. $f(x, y, z) = \sqrt{x^2 + 2z^2}$

Applications

70. Level curves of a savings account Suppose you make a one-time deposit of P dollars into a savings account that earns interest at an annual rate of $p\%$ compounded continuously. The balance in the account after t years is $B(P, r, t) = Pe^{rt}$, where $r = p/100$ (for example, if the annual interest rate is 4%, then $r = 0.04$). Let the interest rate be fixed at $r = 0.04$.

   a. With a target balance of $2000, find the set of all points (P, t) that satisfy $B = 2000$. This curve gives all deposits P and times t that result in a balance of $2000.

   b. Repeat part (a) with $B = \$500, \$1000, \$1500$, and $2500, and draw the resulting level curves of the balance function.

   c. In general, on one level curve, if t increases, does P increase or decrease?

71. Level curves of a savings plan Suppose you make monthly deposits of P dollars into an account that earns interest at a *monthly* rate of $p\%$. The balance in the account after t years is

$$B(P, r, t) = P\left[\frac{(1 + r)^{12t} - 1}{r}\right], \text{ where } r = p/100 \text{ (for}$$

example, if the annual interest rate is 9%, then $p = \frac{9}{12} = 0.75$ and $r = 0.0075$). Let the time of investment be fixed at $t = 20$ years.

   a. With a target balance of $20,000, find the set of all points (P, r) that satisfy $B = 20,000$. This curve gives all deposits P and monthly interest rates r that result in a balance of $20,000 after 20 years.

   b. Repeat part (a) with $B = \$5000, \$10,000, \$15,000$, and $25,000, and draw the resulting level curves of the balance function.

72. Quarterback ratings One measurement of the quality of a quarterback in the National Football League is known as the *quarterback rating*. The rating formula is

$$R(c, t, i, y) = \frac{50 + 20c + 80t - 100i + 100y}{24},$$ where c is the

percentage of passes completed, t is the percentage of passes thrown for touchdowns, i is the percentage of intercepted passes, and y is the yards gained per attempted pass.

a. In his career, Hall of Fame quarterback Johnny Unitas completed 54.57% of his passes, 5.59% of his passes were thrown for touchdowns, 4.88% of his passes were intercepted, and he gained an average of 7.76 yards per attempted pass. What was his quarterback rating?

b. If c, t, and y remained fixed, what happens to the quarterback rating as i increases? Explain your answer with and without mathematics.
(*Source: The College Mathematics Journal* (November 1993).)

73. Ideal Gas Law Many gases can be modeled by the Ideal Gas Law, $PV = nRT$, which relates the temperature (T, measured in Kelvin (K)), pressure (P, measured in Pascals (Pa)), and volume (V, measured in m³) of a gas. Assume that the quantity of gas in question is $n = 1$ mole (mol). The gas constant has a value of $R = 8.3$ m³ · Pa/mol · K.

a. Consider T to be the dependent variable and plot several level curves (called *isotherms*) of the temperature surface in the region $0 \le P \le 100{,}000$ and $0 \le V \le 0.5$.

b. Consider P to be the dependent variable and plot several level curves (called *isobars*) of the pressure surface in the region $0 \le T \le 900$ and $0 < V \le 0.5$.

c. Consider V to be the dependent variable and plot several level curves of the volume surface in the region $0 \le T \le 900$ and $0 < P \le 100{,}000$.

Additional Exercises

74–77. Challenge domains *Find the domains of the following functions. Specify the domain mathematically and then describe it in words or with a sketch.*

74. $g(x, y, z) = \dfrac{10}{x^2 - (y + z)x + yz}$

75. $f(x, y) = \sin^{-1}(x - y)^2$

76. $f(x, y, z) = \ln(z - x^2 - y^2 + 2x + 3)$

77. $h(x, y, z) = \sqrt[4]{z^2 - xz + yz - xy}$

78. Other balls The closed unit ball in $\mathbb{R}^3$ centered at the origin is the set $\{(x, y, z): x^2 + y^2 + z^2 \le 1\}$. Describe the following alternative unit balls.

a. $\{(x, y, z): |x| + |y| + |z| \le 1\}$
b. $\{(x, y, z): \max\{|x|, |y|, |z|\} \le 1\}$, where $\max\{a, b, c\}$ is the maximum value of a, b, and c.

QUICK CHECK ANSWERS

1. $\mathbb{R}^2$; $\{(x, y): y \ge 0\}$ **2.** No; no
3. $z = -\sqrt{1 + x^2 + y^2}$ **4.** No, otherwise the function would have two values at a single point.   **5.** Concentric circles   **6.** No; $z = 0$ is not in the range of the function.
7. 0.97   **8.** 8   **9.** $\{(x, y, z): x \ne 0$ and $y \ne 0$ and $z \ne 0\}$ (which is $\mathbb{R}^3$, excluding the coordinate planes)

13.3 Limits and Continuity

You have now seen examples of functions of several variables, but calculus has not yet entered the picture. In this section we revisit topics encountered in single-variable calculus and see how they apply to functions of several variables. We begin with the fundamental concepts of limits and continuity.

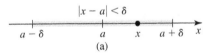

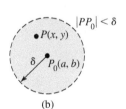

FIGURE 13.37

Limit of a Function of Two Variables

A function f of two variables has a limit L as $P(x, y)$ approaches a fixed point $P_0(a, b)$ if $|f(x, y) - L|$ can be made arbitrarily small for all P in the domain that are sufficiently close to P_0. If such a limit exists, we write

$$\lim_{(x,y)\to(a,b)} f(x, y) = \lim_{P\to P_0} f(x, y) = L.$$

To make this definition more precise, *close to* must be defined carefully.

A point x on the number line is close to another point a provided the distance $|x - a|$ is small (Figure 13.37a). In $\mathbb{R}^2$, a point $P(x, y)$ is close to another point $P_0(a, b)$ if the distance between them $|PP_0| = \sqrt{(x - a)^2 + (y - b)^2}$ is small (Figure 13.37b). When we say *for all P close to P_0*, it means that $|PP_0|$ is small for points P on all sides of P_0.

> The formal definition extends naturally to any number of variables. With n variables, the limit point is $P_0(a_1, \ldots, a_n)$, the variable point is $P(x_1, \ldots, x_n)$, and $|PP_0| = \sqrt{(x_1 - a_1)^2 + \cdots + (x_n - a_n)^2}$.

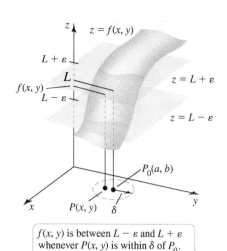

$f(x, y)$ is between $L - \varepsilon$ and $L + \varepsilon$ whenever $P(x, y)$ is within δ of P_0.

FIGURE 13.38

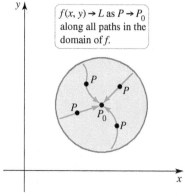

$f(x, y) \to L$ as $P \to P_0$ along all paths in the domain of f.

FIGURE 13.39

With this understanding of closeness, we can give a formal definition of a limit with two independent variables. This definition parallels the formal definition of a limit given in Section 2.7 (Figure 13.38).

DEFINITION Limit of a Function of Two Variables

The function f has the **limit** L as $P(x, y)$ approaches $P_0(a, b)$, written

$$\lim_{(x,y) \to (a,b)} f(x, y) = \lim_{P \to P_0} f(x, y) = L,$$

if, given any $\varepsilon > 0$, there exists a $\delta > 0$ such that

$$|f(x, y) - L| < \varepsilon$$

whenever (x, y) is in the domain of f and

$$0 < |PP_0| = \sqrt{(x - a)^2 + (y - b)^2} < \delta.$$

The condition $|PP_0| < \delta$ means that the distance between $P(x, y)$ and $P_0(a, b)$ is less than δ as P approaches P_0 from all possible directions (Figure 13.39). Therefore, the limit exists only if $f(x, y)$ approaches L as P approaches P_0 *along all possible paths* in the domain of f. As shown in upcoming examples, this interpretation is critical in determining whether or not a limit exists.

As with functions of one variable, we first establish limits of the simplest functions.

THEOREM 13.1   Limits of Constant and Linear Functions

Let a, b, and c be real numbers.

1. Constant function $f(x, y) = c$: $\displaystyle\lim_{(x,y) \to (a,b)} c = c$

2. Linear function $f(x, y) = x$: $\displaystyle\lim_{(x,y) \to (a,b)} x = a$

3. Linear function $f(x, y) = y$: $\displaystyle\lim_{(x,y) \to (a,b)} y = b$

Proof:

1. Consider the constant function $f(x, y) = c$ and assume $\varepsilon > 0$ is given. To prove that the value of the limit is $L = c$, we must produce a $\delta > 0$ such that $|f(x, y) - L| < \varepsilon$ whenever $0 < \sqrt{(x - a)^2 + (y - b)^2} < \delta$. For constant functions, we may use *any* $\delta > 0$. Then, for every (x, y) in the domain of f,

$$|f(x, y) - L| = |f(x, y) - c| = |c - c| = 0 < \varepsilon$$

whenever $0 < \sqrt{(x - a)^2 + (y - b)^2} < \delta$.

2. Assume $\varepsilon > 0$ is given and take $\delta = \varepsilon$. The condition $0 < \sqrt{(x - a)^2 + (y - b)^2} < \delta$ implies that

$$0 < \sqrt{(x - a)^2 + (y - b)^2} < \varepsilon \quad \delta = \varepsilon$$
$$\sqrt{(x - a)^2} < \varepsilon \quad (x - a)^2 \leq (x - a)^2 + (y - b)^2$$
$$|x - a| < \varepsilon. \quad \sqrt{x^2} = |x| \text{ for real numbers } x$$

Because $f(x, y) = x$ and $a = L$, we have shown that $|f(x, y) - L| < \varepsilon$ whenever $0 < \sqrt{(x - a)^2 + (y - b)^2} < \delta$. Therefore, $\displaystyle\lim_{(x,y) \to (a,b)} f(x, y) = L$, or $\displaystyle\lim_{(x,y) \to (a,b)} x = a$.

The proof that $\displaystyle\lim_{(x,y) \to (a,b)} y = b$ is similar (Exercise 82).   ◀

Using the three basic limits in Theorem 13.1, we can compute limits of more complicated functions. The only tools needed are limit laws analogous to those given in Theorem 2.3. The proofs of these laws are examined in Exercises 84–85.

THEOREM 13.2 Limit Laws for Functions of Two Variables

Let L and M be real numbers and suppose that $\lim\limits_{(x,y)\to(a,b)} f(x,y) = L$ and $\lim\limits_{(x,y)\to(a,b)} g(x,y) = M$. Assume c is a constant, and m and n are integers.

1. **Sum** $\lim\limits_{(x,y)\to(a,b)} (f(x,y) + g(x,y)) = L + M$

2. **Difference** $\lim\limits_{(x,y)\to(a,b)} (f(x,y) - g(x,y)) = L - M$

3. **Constant multiple** $\lim\limits_{(x,y)\to(a,b)} cf(x,y) = cL$

4. **Product** $\lim\limits_{(x,y)\to(a,b)} f(x,y)g(x,y) = LM$

5. **Quotient** $\lim\limits_{(x,y)\to(a,b)} \left[\dfrac{f(x,y)}{g(x,y)}\right] = \dfrac{L}{M}$, provided $M \neq 0$

6. **Power** $\lim\limits_{(x,y)\to(a,b)} (f(x,y))^n = L^n$

7. **m/n power** If m and n have no common factors and $n \neq 0$, then
$\lim\limits_{(x,y)\to(a,b)} [f(x,y)]^{m/n} = L^{m/n}$, where we assume $L > 0$ if n is even.

> Recall that a polynomial in two variables consists of sums and products of polynomials in x and polynomials in y. A rational function is the quotient of two polynomials.

Combining Theorems 13.1 and 13.2 allows us to find limits of polynomial, rational, and algebraic functions in two variables.

EXAMPLE 1 Limits of two-variable functions Evaluate $\lim\limits_{(x,y)\to(2,8)} (3x^2y + \sqrt{xy})$.

SOLUTION All the operations in this function appear in Theorem 13.2. Therefore, we can apply the limit laws directly.

$$\lim\limits_{(x,y)\to(2,8)} (3x^2y + \sqrt{xy}) = \lim\limits_{(x,y)\to(2,8)} 3x^2y + \lim\limits_{(x,y)\to(2,8)} \sqrt{xy} \quad \text{Law 1}$$

$$= 3\left[\lim\limits_{(x,y)\to(2,8)} x\right]^2 \left[\lim\limits_{(x,y)\to(2,8)} y\right]$$

$$+ \sqrt{\left[\lim\limits_{(x,y)\to(2,8)} x\right]\left[\lim\limits_{(x,y)\to(2,8)} y\right]} \quad \text{Laws 3, 4, 6, 7}$$

$$= 3\cdot 2^2\cdot 8 + \sqrt{2\cdot 8} = 100 \quad \text{Theorem 13.1}$$

Related Exercises 11–18 ◄

In Example 1, the value of the limit equals the value of the function at (a,b); in other words $\lim\limits_{(x,y)\to(a,b)} f(x,y) = f(a,b)$, and the limit can be evaluated by substitution. This is a property of *continuous* functions, discussed later in this section.

QUICK CHECK 1 Which of the following limits exist?

a. $\lim\limits_{(x,y)\to(1,1)} 3x^{12}y^2$ **b.** $\lim\limits_{(x,y)\to(0,0)} 3x^{-2}y^2$ **c.** $\lim\limits_{(x,y)\to(1,2)} \sqrt{x - y^2}$ ◄

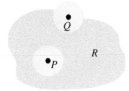

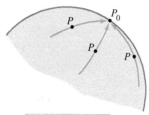

P is an interior point: There is a disk centered at P that lies entirely in R.

FIGURE 13.40

➤ The definitions of interior point and boundary point apply to regions in $\mathbb{R}^3$ if we replace *disk* by *ball*.

➤ Many sets, such as the annulus $\{(x, y): 2 \le x^2 + y^2 < 5\}$ are neither open nor closed.

P must approach P_0 along all paths in the domain of f.

FIGURE 13.41

➤ Recall that this same method was used with functions of one variable. For example, after canceling the common factor $x - 2$, the function

$$g(x) = \frac{x^2 - 4}{x - 2}$$

becomes $g(x) = x + 2$, provided $x \ne 2$. In this case, 2 plays the role of a boundary point.

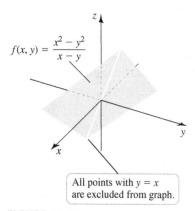

$f(x, y) = \dfrac{x^2 - y^2}{x - y}$

All points with $y = x$ are excluded from graph.

FIGURE 13.42

Limits at Boundary Points

This is an appropriate place to make some definitions that will be used in the remainder of the book.

DEFINITION Interior and Boundary Points

Let R be a region in $\mathbb{R}^2$. An **interior point** P of R lies entirely within R, which means it is possible to find a disk centered at P that contains only points of R (Figure 13.40).

A **boundary point** Q of R lies on the edge of R in the sense that *every* disk centered at Q contains at least one point in R and at least one point not in R.

For example, let R be the points in $\mathbb{R}^2$ satisfying $x^2 + y^2 < 9$. The boundary points of R lie on the circle $x^2 + y^2 = 9$. The interior points lie inside that circle and satisfy $x^2 + y^2 < 9$. Notice that the boundary points of a set need not lie in the set.

DEFINITION Open and Closed Sets

A region is **open** if it consists entirely of interior points. A region is **closed** if it contains all its boundary points.

An example of an open region in $\mathbb{R}^2$ is the open disk $\{(x, y): x^2 + y^2 < 9\}$. An example of a closed region in $\mathbb{R}^2$ is the square $\{(x, y): |x| \le 1, |y| \le 1\}$. Later in the book, we encounter interior and boundary points of three-dimensional sets such as balls, boxes, and cubes.

QUICK CHECK 2 Give an example of a set that contains none of its boundary points. ◄

Suppose $P_0(a, b)$ is a boundary point of the domain of f. The limit $\displaystyle\lim_{(x,y)\to(a,b)} f(x, y)$ exists, even if P_0 is not in the domain of f, provided $f(x, y)$ approaches the same value as (x, y) approaches (a, b) *along all paths that lie in the domain* (Figure 13.41).

Consider the function $f(x, y) = \dfrac{x^2 - y^2}{x - y}$ whose domain is $\{(x, y): x \ne y\}$. Provided $x \ne y$, we may cancel the factor $(x - y)$ from the numerator and denominator and write

$$f(x, y) = \frac{x^2 - y^2}{x - y} = \frac{(x - y)(x + y)}{x - y} = x + y.$$

The graph of f (Figure 13.42) is the plane $z = x + y$, with points corresponding to the line $x = y$ removed.

Now we examine $\displaystyle\lim_{(x,y)\to(4,4)} \frac{x^2 - y^2}{x - y}$, where $(4, 4)$ is a boundary point of the domain of f but does not lie in the domain. For this limit to exist, $f(x, y)$ must approach the same value along all paths to $(4, 4)$ that lie in the domain of f—that is, all paths approaching $(4, 4)$ that do not intersect $x = y$. To evaluate the limit, we proceed as follows:

$$\lim_{(x,y)\to(4,4)} \frac{x^2 - y^2}{x - y} = \lim_{(x,y)\to(4,4)} (x + y) \quad \text{Assume } x \ne y, \text{ cancel } x - y.$$

$$= 4 + 4 = 8. \quad \text{Same limit along all paths in the domain}$$

To emphasize, we let $(x, y) \to (4, 4)$ along all paths that do not intersect $x = y$, which lies outside the domain of f. Along all admissible paths, the function approaches 8.

QUICK CHECK 3 Can the limit $\displaystyle\lim_{(x,y)\to(0,0)} \frac{x^2 - xy}{x}$ be evaluated by direct substitution?

EXAMPLE 2   **Limits at boundary points** Evaluate $\displaystyle\lim_{(x,y)\to(4,1)} \frac{xy - 4y^2}{\sqrt{x} - 2\sqrt{y}}$.

SOLUTION Points in the domain of this function satisfy $x \geq 0$ and $y \geq 0$ (because of the square roots) and $x \neq 4y$ (to ensure the denominator is nonzero). We see that the point $(4, 1)$ lies on the boundary of the domain. Multiplying the numerator and denominator by the algebraic conjugate of the denominator, the limit is computed as follows:

$$\lim_{(x,y)\to(4,1)} \frac{xy - 4y^2}{\sqrt{x} - 2\sqrt{y}} = \lim_{(x,y)\to(4,1)} \frac{(xy - 4y^2)(\sqrt{x} + 2\sqrt{y})}{(\sqrt{x} - 2\sqrt{y})(\sqrt{x} + 2\sqrt{y})} \quad \text{Multiply by conjugate.}$$

$$= \lim_{(x,y)\to(4,1)} \frac{y(x - 4y)(\sqrt{x} + 2\sqrt{y})}{x - 4y} \quad \text{Simplify.}$$

$$= \lim_{(x,y)\to(4,1)} y(\sqrt{x} + 2\sqrt{y}). \quad \begin{array}{l}\text{Cancel } x - 4y, \\ \text{assumed to be nonzero.}\end{array}$$

$$= 4. \quad \text{Evaluate limit.}$$

Because points on the line $x = 4y$ are outside the domain of the function, we assume that $x - 4y \neq 0$. Along all other paths to $(4, 1)$, the function values approach 4 (Figure 13.43).

Related Exercises 19–26 ◀

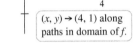

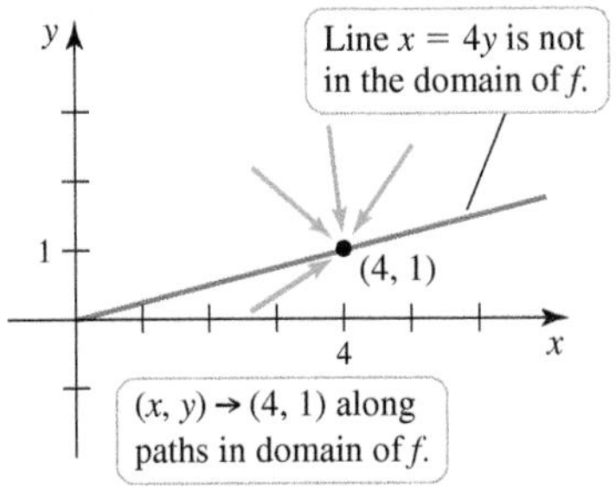

Line $x = 4y$ is not in the domain of f.

$(4, 1)$

$(x, y) \to (4, 1)$ along paths in domain of f.

FIGURE 13.43

> Notice that if we choose any path of the form $y = mx$, then $y \to 0$ as $x \to 0$. Therefore, $\displaystyle\lim_{(x,y)\to(0,0)}$ can be replaced by $\displaystyle\lim_{x\to 0}$ along this path. A similar argument applies to paths of the form $y = mx^p$, for $p > 0$.

EXAMPLE 3   **Nonexistence of a limit** Investigate the limit $\displaystyle\lim_{(x,y)\to(0,0)} \frac{(x + y)^2}{x^2 + y^2}$.

SOLUTION The domain of the function is $\{(x, y): (x, y) \neq (0, 0)\}$; therefore, the limit is at a boundary point outside the domain. Suppose we let (x, y) approach $(0, 0)$ along the line $y = mx$ for a fixed constant m. Substituting $y = mx$ and noting that $y \to 0$ as $x \to 0$, we have

$$\lim_{(x,y)\to(0,0)} \frac{(x + y)^2}{(x^2 + y^2)} = \lim_{x\to 0} \frac{(x + mx)^2}{(x^2 + m^2 x^2)} = \lim_{x\to 0} \frac{x^2(1 + m)^2}{x^2(1 + m^2)} = \frac{(1 + m)^2}{1 + m^2}.$$

The constant m determines the direction of approach to $(0, 0)$. Therefore, depending on m, the function may approach any value in the interval $[0, 2]$ (which is the range of $(1 + m)^2/(1 + m^2)$) as (x, y) approaches $(0, 0)$ (Figure 13.44). For example, if $m = 0$, the corresponding limit is 1 and if $m = -1$, the limit is 0. Because the function approaches different values along different paths, we conclude that the *limit does not exist*. The reason for this behavior is revealed if we plot the surface and look at two level curves. The lines $y = x$ and $y = -x$ (excluding the origin) are level curves of the function for $z = 2$ and $z = 0$, respectively. (Figure 13.45).

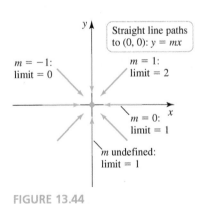

Straight line paths to $(0, 0)$: $y = mx$

$m = -1$: limit = 0

$m = 1$: limit = 2

$m = 0$: limit = 1

m undefined: limit = 1

FIGURE 13.44

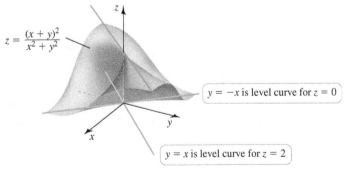

$z = \dfrac{(x + y)^2}{x^2 + y^2}$

$y = -x$ is level curve for $z = 0$

$y = x$ is level curve for $z = 2$

FIGURE 13.45

Related Exercises 27–32 ◀

The strategy used in Example 3 is one of the most effective ways to prove the nonexistence of a limit.

PROCEDURE   Two-Path Test for Nonexistence of Limits

If $f(x, y)$ approaches two different values as (x, y) approaches (a, b) along two different paths in the domain of f, then $\lim_{(x,y)\to(a,b)} f(x, y)$ does not exist.

QUICK CHECK 4 What is the analog of the Two-Path Test for functions of a single variable? ◄

Continuity of Functions of Two Variables

The following definition of continuity for functions of two variables is analogous to the continuity definition for functions of one variable.

DEFINITION   Continuity

The function f is continuous at the point (a, b) provided

1. f is defined at (a, b).

2. $\lim_{(x,y)\to(a,b)} f(x, y)$ exists.

3. $\lim_{(x,y)\to(a,b)} f(x, y) = f(a, b)$

A function of two (or more) variables is continuous at a point, provided its limit equals its value at that point (which implies the limit and the value both exist). The definition of continuity applies at boundary points of the domain of f provided the limits in the definition are taken along paths that lie in the domain.

Because limits of polynomials and rational functions can be evaluated by substitution at points of their domains (that is, $\lim_{(x,y)\to(a,b)} f(x, y) = f(a, b)$), it follows that polynomials and rational functions are continuous at all points of their domains. Similarly, trigonometric, logarithmic, and exponential functions are continuous on their domains.

EXAMPLE 4   Checking continuity Determine the points at which the following function is continuous.

$$f(x, y) = \begin{cases} \dfrac{3xy^2}{x^2 + y^4} & \text{if } (x, y) \neq (0, 0) \\ 0 & \text{if } (x, y) = (0, 0) \end{cases}$$

SOLUTION The function $\dfrac{3xy^2}{x^2 + y^4}$ is a rational function, so it is continuous at all points of its domain, which consists of all points of $\mathbb{R}^2$ except $(0, 0)$. In order for f to be continuous at $(0, 0)$, we must show that

$$\lim_{(x,y)\to(0,0)} \frac{3xy^2}{x^2 + y^4} = f(0, 0) = 0.$$

You can verify that as (x, y) approaches $(0, 0)$ along paths of the form $y = mx$, where m is any constant, the function values approach $f(0, 0) = 0$. Now consider parabolic paths

▷ The choice of $x = my^2$ for paths to $(0, 0)$ is not obvious. Notice that if x is replaced by my^2 in f, the result involves the same power of y (in this case, y^4) in the numerator and denominator, which may be canceled.

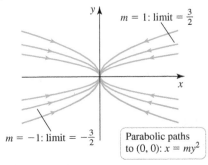

$m = 1$: limit $= \frac{3}{2}$

$m = -1$: limit $= -\frac{3}{2}$

Parabolic paths to $(0, 0)$: $x = my^2$

FIGURE 13.46

of the form $x = my^2$, where m is a nonzero constant (Figure 13.46). This time we substitute $x = my^2$ and note that $x \to 0$ as $y \to 0$:

$$\lim_{(x,y)\to(0,0)} \frac{3xy^2}{x^2 + y^4} = \lim_{y\to 0} \frac{3(my^2)y^2}{(my^2)^2 + y^4} \quad \text{Substitute } x = my^2.$$

$$= \lim_{y\to 0} \frac{3my^4}{m^2 y^4 + y^4} \quad \text{Simplify.}$$

$$= \lim_{y\to 0} \frac{3m}{m^2 + 1} \quad \text{Cancel } y^4.$$

$$= \frac{3m}{m^2 + 1}.$$

We see that along parabolic paths, the limit depends on the approach path. For example, with $m = 1$, along the path $x = y^2$, the function values approach $\frac{3}{2}$; with $m = -1$, along the path $x = -y^2$, the function values approach $-\frac{3}{2}$ (Figure 13.47). Because function values approach two different numbers along two different paths, the limit at $(0, 0)$ does not exist, and f is not continuous at $(0, 0)$.

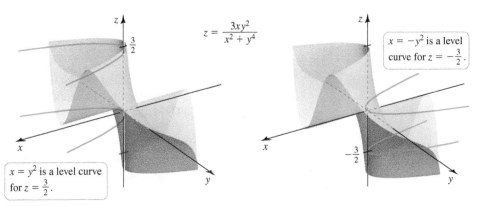

$z = \frac{3xy^2}{x^2 + y^4}$

$x = y^2$ is a level curve for $z = \frac{3}{2}$.

$x = -y^2$ is a level curve for $z = -\frac{3}{2}$.

FIGURE 13.47

Related Exercises 33–40◀

QUICK CHECK 5 Which of the following functions are continuous at $(0, 0)$?
a. $f(x, y) = 2x^2 y^5$
b. $f(x, y) = \dfrac{2x^2 y^5}{x - 1}$
c. $f(x, y) = 2x^{-2} y^5$ ◀

Composite Functions   Recall that for functions of a single variable, compositions of continuous functions are also continuous. The following theorem gives the analogous result for functions of two variables; it is proved in Appendix B.

> **THEOREM 13.3   Continuity of Composite Functions**
> If $u = g(x, y)$ is continuous at (a, b) and $z = f(u)$ is continuous at $g(a, b)$, then the composite function $z = f(g(x, y))$ is continuous at (a, b).

EXAMPLE 5   Continuity of composite functions. Determine the points at which the following functions are continuous.

a. $h(x, y) = \ln(x^2 + y^2 + 4)$ **b.** $h(x, y) = e^{x/y}$

SOLUTION

a. This function is the composition $f(g(x, y))$, where

$$f(u) = \ln u \quad \text{and} \quad u = g(x, y) = x^2 + y^2 + 4.$$

As a polynomial, g is continuous for all (x, y) in $\mathbb{R}^2$. The function f is continuous for $u > 0$. Because $u = x^2 + y^2 + 4 > 0$, for all (x, y), it follows that h is continuous at all points of $\mathbb{R}^2$.

b. Letting $f(u) = e^u$ and $u = g(x, y) = x/y$, we have $h(x, y) = f(g(x, y))$. Note that f is continuous at all points of $\mathbb{R}$ and g is continuous at all points of $\mathbb{R}^2$ provided $y \neq 0$. Therefore, h is continuous on the set $\{(x, y): y \neq 0\}$.

Related Exercises 41–52 ◀

Functions of Three Variables

The work we have done with limits and continuity of functions of two variables extends to functions of three or more variables. Specifically, the limit laws of Theorem 13.2 apply to functions of the form $w = f(x, y, z)$. Polynomials and rational functions are continuous at all points of their domains, and limits of these functions may be evaluated by direct substitution at all points of their domains. Compositions of continuous functions of the form $f(g(x, y, z))$ are also continuous.

EXAMPLE 6   Functions of three variables

a. Evaluate $\displaystyle\lim_{(x,y,z)\to(2,\pi/2,0)} \frac{x^2 \sin y}{z^2 + 4}$.

b. Find the points at which $h(x, y, z) = \sqrt{x^2 + y^2 + z^2 - 1}$ is continuous.

SOLUTION

a. This function consists of products and quotients of functions that are continuous at $(2, \pi/2, 0)$. Therefore, the limit is evaluated by direct substitution:

$$\lim_{(x,y,z)\to(2,\pi/2,0)} \frac{x^2 \sin y}{z^2 + 4} = \frac{2^2 \sin(\pi/2)}{0^2 + 4} = 1.$$

b. This function is a composition in which the outer function $f(u) = \sqrt{u}$ is continuous for $u \geq 0$. The inner function

$$g(x, y, z) = x^2 + y^2 + z^2 - 1$$

is nonnegative provided $x^2 + y^2 + z^2 \geq 1$. Therefore, the function is continuous at all points on or outside the unit sphere in $\mathbb{R}^3$.

Related Exercises 53–58 ◀

SECTION 13.3 EXERCISES

Review Questions

1. Explain what $\displaystyle\lim_{(x,y)\to(a,b)} f(x, y) = L$ means.

2. Explain why $f(x, y)$ must approach L as (x, y) approaches (a, b) along *all* paths in the domain in order for $\displaystyle\lim_{(x,y)\to(a,b)} f(x, y)$ to exist.

3. What does it mean to say that limits of polynomials may be evaluated by direct substitution?

4. Suppose (a, b) is on the boundary of the domain of f. Explain how you would determine whether $\displaystyle\lim_{(x,y)\to(a,b)} f(x, y)$ exists.

5. Explain how examining limits along multiple paths may prove the nonexistence of a limit.

6. Explain why evaluating a limit along a finite number of paths does not prove the existence of a limit of a function of several variables.

7. What three conditions must be met for a function f to be continuous at the point (a, b)?

8. Let R be the unit disk $\{(x, y): x^2 + y^2 \leq 1\}$ with $(0, 0)$ removed. Is $(0, 0)$ a boundary point of R? Is R open or closed?

9. At what points of $\mathbb{R}^2$ is a rational function of two variables continuous?

10. Evaluate $\displaystyle\lim_{(x,y,z)\to(1,1,-1)} xy^2 z^3$.

Basic Skills

11–18. Limits of functions *Evaluate the following limits.*

11. $\displaystyle\lim_{(x,y)\to(2,9)} 101$

12. $\displaystyle\lim_{(x,y)\to(1,-3)} (3x + 4y - 2)$

13. $\displaystyle\lim_{(x,y)\to(-3,3)} (4x^2 - y^2)$

14. $\displaystyle\lim_{(x,y)\to(2,-1)} (xy^8 - 3x^2 y^3)$

15. $\displaystyle\lim_{(x,y)\to(0,\pi)}\frac{\cos xy + \sin xy}{2y}$

16. $\displaystyle\lim_{(x,y)\to(e^2,4)}\ln\sqrt{xy}$

17. $\displaystyle\lim_{(x,y)\to(2,0)}\frac{x^2 - 3xy^2}{x + y}$

18. $\displaystyle\lim_{(x,y)\to(1,-1)}\frac{10xy - 2y^2}{x^2 + y^2}$

19–26. Limits at boundary points *Evaluate the following limits.*

19. $\displaystyle\lim_{(x,y)\to(6,2)}\frac{x^2 - 3xy}{x - 3y}$

20. $\displaystyle\lim_{(x,y)\to(1,-2)}\frac{y^2 + 2xy}{y + 2x}$

21. $\displaystyle\lim_{(x,y)\to(3,1)}\frac{x^2 - 7xy + 12y^2}{x - 3y}$

22. $\displaystyle\lim_{(x,y)\to(-1,1)}\frac{2x^2 - xy - 3y^2}{x + y}$

23. $\displaystyle\lim_{(x,y)\to(2,2)}\frac{y^2 - 4}{xy - 2x}$

24. $\displaystyle\lim_{(x,y)\to(4,5)}\frac{\sqrt{x + y} - 3}{x + y - 9}$

25. $\displaystyle\lim_{(x,y)\to(1,2)}\frac{\sqrt{y} - \sqrt{x + 1}}{y - x - 1}$

26. $\displaystyle\lim_{(x,y)\to(8,8)}\frac{x^{1/3} - y^{1/3}}{x^{2/3} - y^{2/3}}$

27–32. Nonexistence of limits *Use the Two-Path Test to prove that the following limits do not exist.*

27. $\displaystyle\lim_{(x,y)\to(0,0)}\frac{x + 2y}{x - 2y}$

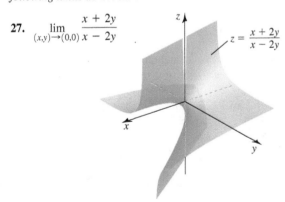

$z = \dfrac{x + 2y}{x - 2y}$

28. $\displaystyle\lim_{(x,y)\to(0,0)}\frac{4xy}{3x^2 + y^2}$

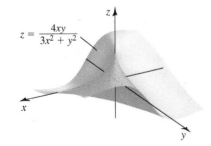

$z = \dfrac{4xy}{3x^2 + y^2}$

29. $\displaystyle\lim_{(x,y)\to(0,0)}\frac{y^4 - 2x^2}{y^4 + x^2}$

30. $\displaystyle\lim_{(x,y)\to(0,0)}\frac{x^3 - y^2}{x^3 + y^2}$

31. $\displaystyle\lim_{(x,y)\to(0,0)}\frac{y^3 + x^3}{xy^2}$

32. $\displaystyle\lim_{(x,y)\to(0,0)}\frac{y}{\sqrt{x^2 - y^2}}$

33–40. Continuity *At what points of $\mathbb{R}^2$ are the following functions continuous?*

33. $f(x, y) = x^2 + 2xy - y^3$

34. $f(x, y) = \dfrac{xy}{x^2 y^2 + 1}$

35. $p(x, y) = \dfrac{4x^2 y^2}{x^4 + y^2}$

36. $S(x, y) = \dfrac{4x^2 y^2}{x^2 + y^2}$

37. $f(x, y) = \dfrac{2}{x(y^2 + 1)}$

38. $f(x, y) = \dfrac{x^2 + y^2}{x(y^2 - 1)}$

39. $f(x, y) = \begin{cases} \dfrac{xy}{x^2 + y^2} & \text{if } (x, y) \neq (0, 0) \\ 0 & \text{if } (x, y) = (0, 0) \end{cases}$

40. $f(x, y) = \begin{cases} \dfrac{y^4 - 2x^2}{y^4 + x^2} & \text{if } (x, y) \neq (0, 0) \\ 0 & \text{if } (x, y) = (0, 0) \end{cases}$

41–52. Continuity of composite functions *At what points of $\mathbb{R}^2$ are the following functions continuous?*

41. $f(x, y) = \sqrt{x^2 + y^2}$

42. $f(x, y) = e^{x^2 + y^2}$

43. $f(x, y) = \sin xy$

44. $g(x, y) = \ln(x - y)$

45. $h(x, y) = \cos(x + y)$

46. $p(x, y) = e^{x - y}$

47. $f(x, y) = \ln(x^2 + y^2)$

48. $f(x, y) = \sqrt{4 - x^2 - y^2}$

49. $g(x, y) = \sqrt[3]{x^2 + y^2 - 9}$

50. $h(x, y) = \dfrac{\sqrt{x - y}}{4}$

51. $f(x, y) = \begin{cases} \dfrac{\sin(x^2 + y^2)}{x^2 + y^2} & \text{if } (x, y) \neq (0, 0) \\ 1 & \text{if } (x, y) = (0, 0) \end{cases}$

52. $f(x, y) = \begin{cases} \dfrac{1 - \cos(x^2 + y^2)}{x^2 + y^2} & \text{if } (x, y) \neq (0, 0) \\ 0 & \text{if } (x, y) = (0, 0) \end{cases}$

53–58. Limits of functions of three variables *Evaluate the following limits.*

53. $\displaystyle\lim_{(x,y,z)\to(1,\ln 2,3)} z e^{xy}$

54. $\displaystyle\lim_{(x,y,z)\to(0,1,0)}\ln e^{xz}(1 + y)$

55. $\displaystyle\lim_{(x,y,z)\to(1,1,1)}\frac{yz - xy - xz - x^2}{yz + xy + xz - y^2}$

56. $\displaystyle\lim_{(x,y,z)\to(1,1,1)}\frac{x - \sqrt{xz} - \sqrt{xy} + \sqrt{yz}}{x - \sqrt{xz} + \sqrt{xy} - \sqrt{yz}}$

57. $\displaystyle\lim_{(x,y,z)\to(1,1,1)}\frac{x^2 + xy - xz - yz}{x - z}$

58. $\displaystyle\lim_{(x,y,z)\to(1,-1,1)} \frac{xz + 5x + yz + 5y}{x + y}$

Further Explorations

59. Explain why or why not Determine whether the following statements are true and give an explanation or counterexample.

a. If the limits $\displaystyle\lim_{(x,0)\to(0,0)} f(x, 0)$ and $\displaystyle\lim_{(0,y)\to(0,0)} f(0, y)$ exist and equal L, then $\displaystyle\lim_{(x,y)\to(0,0)} f(x, y) = L$.

b. If $\displaystyle\lim_{(x,y)\to(a,b)} f(x, y) = L$, then f is continuous at (a, b).

c. If f is continuous at (a, b), then $\displaystyle\lim_{(x,y)\to(a,b)} f(x, y)$ exists.

d. If P is a boundary point of the domain of f, then P is in the domain of f.

60–67. Miscellaneous limits *Use the method of your choice to evaluate the following limits.*

60. $\displaystyle\lim_{(x,y)\to(0,0)} \frac{y^2}{x^8 + y^2}$

61. $\displaystyle\lim_{(x,y)\to(0,1)} \frac{y \sin x}{x(y + 1)}$

62. $\displaystyle\lim_{(x,y)\to(1,1)} \frac{x^2 + xy - 2y^2}{2x^2 - xy - y^2}$

63. $\displaystyle\lim_{(x,y)\to(1,0)} \frac{y \ln y}{x}$

64. $\displaystyle\lim_{(x,y)\to(0,0)} \frac{|xy|}{xy}$

65. $\displaystyle\lim_{(x,y)\to(0,0)} \frac{|x - y|}{|x + y|}$

66. $\displaystyle\lim_{(x,y)\to(-1,0)} \frac{xye^{-y}}{x^2 + y^2}$

67. $\displaystyle\lim_{(x,y)\to(2,0)} \frac{1 - \cos y}{xy^2}$

68–71. Limits using polar coordinates *Limits at $(0, 0)$ may be easier to evaluate by converting to polar coordinates. Remember that the same limit must be obtained as $r \to 0$ along all paths to $(0, 0)$. Evaluate the following limits or state that they do not exist.*

68. $\displaystyle\lim_{(x,y)\to(0,0)} \frac{x - y}{\sqrt{x^2 + y^2}}$

69. $\displaystyle\lim_{(x,y)\to(0,0)} \frac{x^2}{x^2 + y^2}$

70. $\displaystyle\lim_{(x,y)\to(0,0)} \frac{(x - y)^2}{x^2 + xy + y^2}$

71. $\displaystyle\lim_{(x,y)\to(0,0)} \frac{(x - y)^2}{(x^2 + y^2)^{3/2}}$

Additional Exercises

72. Sine limits Evaluate the following limits.

a. $\displaystyle\lim_{(x,y)\to(0,0)} \frac{\sin(x + y)}{x + y}$

b. $\displaystyle\lim_{(x,y)\to(0,0)} \frac{\sin x + \sin y}{x + y}$

73. Piecewise function Let

$$f(x, y) = \begin{cases} \dfrac{\sin(x^2 + y^2 - 1)}{x^2 + y^2 - 1} & \text{if } x^2 + y^2 \neq 1 \\ b & \text{if } x^2 + y^2 = 1. \end{cases}$$

Find the value of b for which f is continuous at all points in $\mathbb{R}^2$.

74. Piecewise function Let

$$f(x, y) = \begin{cases} \dfrac{1 + 2xy - \cos(xy)}{xy} & \text{if } xy \neq 0 \\ a & \text{if } xy = 0. \end{cases}$$

Find the value of a for which f is continuous at all points in $\mathbb{R}^2$.

75. Nonexistence of limits Show that $\displaystyle\lim_{(x,y)\to(0,0)} \frac{ax^m y^n}{bx^{m+n} + cy^{m+n}}$ does not exist when a, b, and c are nonzero real numbers and m and n are positive integers.

76. Nonexistence of limits Show that $\displaystyle\lim_{(x,y)\to(0,0)} \frac{ax^{2(p-n)} y^n}{bx^{2p} + cy^p}$ does not exist when a, b, and c are nonzero real numbers and n and p are positive integers with $p \geq n$.

77–80. Limits of composite functions *Evaluate the following limits.*

77. $\displaystyle\lim_{(x,y)\to(1,0)} \frac{\sin xy}{xy}$

78. $\displaystyle\lim_{(x,y)\to(4,0)} x^2 y \ln xy$

79. $\displaystyle\lim_{(x,y)\to(0,2)} (2xy)^{xy}$

80. $\displaystyle\lim_{(x,y)\to(0,\pi/2)} \frac{1 - \cos xy}{4x^2 y^3}$

81. Filling in a function value The domain of $f(x, y) = e^{-1/(x^2+y^2)}$ excludes $(0, 0)$. How should f be defined at $(0, 0)$ to make it continuous there?

82. Limit proof Use the formal definition of a limit to prove that $\displaystyle\lim_{(x,y)\to(a,b)} y = b$. (*Hint:* Take $\delta = \varepsilon$.)

83. Limit proof Use the formal definition of a limit to prove that $\displaystyle\lim_{(x,y)\to(a,b)} (x + y) = a + b$. (*Hint:* Take $\delta = \varepsilon/2$.)

84. Proof of Limit Law 1 Use the formal definition of a limit to prove that $\displaystyle\lim_{(x,y)\to(a,b)} (f(x, y) + g(x, y)) = \lim_{(x,y)\to(a,b)} f(x, y) + \lim_{(x,y)\to(a,b)} g(x, y)$.

85. Proof of Limit Law 3 Use the formal definition of a limit to prove that $\displaystyle\lim_{(x,y)\to(a,b)} cf(x, y) = c \lim_{(x,y)\to(a,b)} f(x, y)$.

QUICK CHECK ANSWERS

1. The limit exists only for (a). **2.** $\{(x, y): x^2 + y^2 < 2\}$
3. If a factor of x is first canceled, then the limit may be evaluated by substitution. **4.** If the left and right limits at a point are not equal, then the two-sided limit does not exist.
5. (a) and (b) are continuous at $(0, 0)$. ◄

13.4 Partial Derivatives

The derivative of a function of one variable, $y = f(x)$, measures the rate of change of y with respect to x, and it gives slopes of tangent lines. The analogous idea for functions of several variables presents a new twist: Derivatives may be defined with respect to any of the independent variables. For example, we can compute the derivative of $f(x, y)$ with respect to x or y. The resulting derivatives are called *partial derivatives*; they still represent rates of change and they are associated with slopes of tangents. So, much of what you have learned about derivatives applies to functions of several variables. However, much is also different.

Derivatives with Two Variables

Consider a function f defined on a domain D in the xy-plane. Suppose that f represents the elevation of the land (above sea level) over D. Imagine that you are on the surface $z = f(x, y)$ at the point $(a, b, f(a, b))$ and you are asked to determine the slope of the surface where you are standing. Your answer should be, *it depends*!

Figure 13.48a shows a function that resembles the landscape in Figure 13.48b. Suppose you are standing at the point $P(0, 0, f(0, 0))$, which lies on the pass or the saddle. The surface behaves differently, depending on the direction in which you walk. If you walk east (positive x-direction), the elevation increases and your path takes you upward on the surface. If you walk north (positive y-direction), the elevation decreases and your path takes you downward on the surface. In fact, in every direction you walk from the point P, the function values change at different rates. So how should the slope or the rate of change at a given point be defined?

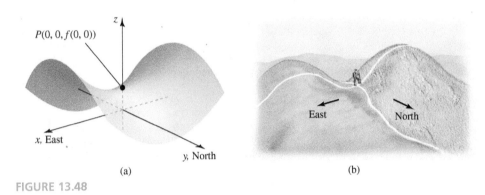

(a)   (b)

FIGURE 13.48

The answer to this question involves *partial derivatives*, which arise when we hold all but one independent variable fixed and then compute an ordinary derivative with respect to the remaining variable. Suppose we move along the surface $z = f(x, y)$, starting at the point $(a, b, f(a, b))$ in such a way that $y = b$ is fixed and only x varies. The resulting path is a curve (a trace) on the surface that varies in the x-direction (Figure 13.49). This curve is the intersection of the surface with the vertical plane $y = b$; it is described by $z = f(x, b)$, which is a function of the single variable x. We know how to compute the slope of this curve: It is the ordinary derivative of $f(x, b)$ with respect to x. This derivative is called the *partial derivative of f with respect to x*, denoted $\partial f / \partial x$ or f_x. When evaluated at (a, b) its value is defined by the limit

$$f_x(a, b) = \lim_{h \to 0} \frac{f(a + h, b) - f(a, b)}{h},$$

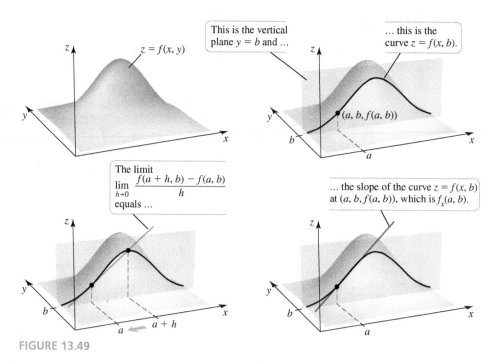

FIGURE 13.49

provided this limit exists. Notice that the y-coordinate is fixed at $y = b$ in this limit. If we replace (a, b) by the variable point (x, y), then f_x becomes a function of x and y.

In a similar way, we can move along the surface $z = f(x, y)$ from the point $(a, b, f(a, b))$ in such a way that $x = a$ is fixed and only y varies. Now, the result is a trace described by $z = f(a, y)$, which is the intersection of the surface and the plane $x = a$ (Figure 13.50). The slope of this curve at (a, b) is given by the ordinary derivative of $f(a, y)$ with respect to y. This derivative is called the *partial derivative of f with respect to y*, denoted $\partial f/\partial y$ or f_y. When evaluated at (a, b), it is defined by the limit

$$f_y(a, b) = \lim_{h \to 0} \frac{f(a, b + h) - f(a, b)}{h},$$

provided this limit exists. If we replace (a, b) by the variable point (x, y), then f_y becomes a function of x and y.

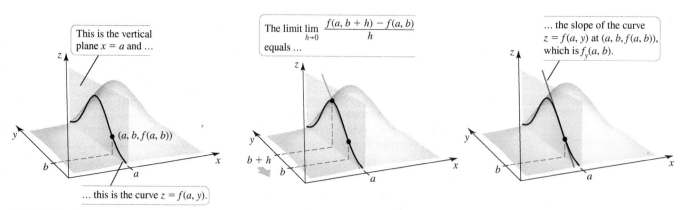

FIGURE 13.50

> DEFINITION **Partial Derivatives**
>
> The **partial derivative of f with respect to x at the point (a, b)** is
> $$f_x(a, b) = \lim_{h \to 0} \frac{f(a + h, b) - f(a, b)}{h}.$$
>
> The **partial derivative of f with respect to y at the point (a, b)** is
> $$f_y(a, b) = \lim_{h \to 0} \frac{f(a, b + h) - f(a, b)}{h},$$
>
> provided these limits exist.

> ➤ Recall that f' is a function, while $f'(a)$ is the value of the derivative at $x = a$. In the same way, f_x and f_y are functions of x and y, while $f_x(a, b)$ and $f_y(a, b)$ are their values at (a, b).

Notation The partial derivatives evaluated at a point (a, b) are denoted in any of the following ways:

$$\frac{\partial f}{\partial x}(a, b) = \left.\frac{\partial f}{\partial x}\right|_{(a,b)} = f_x(a, b) \quad \text{and} \quad \frac{\partial f}{\partial y}(a, b) = \left.\frac{\partial f}{\partial y}\right|_{(a,b)} = f_y(a, b).$$

Notice that the d in the ordinary derivative df/dx has been replaced by ∂ in the partial derivatives $\partial f/\partial x$ and $\partial f/\partial y$. The notation $\partial/\partial x$ is an instruction or operator: It says, "take the partial derivative with respect to x of the function that follows."

Calculating Partial Derivatives All the rules and results for ordinary derivatives can be used to compute partial derivatives. Specifically, to compute $f_x(x, y)$, we treat y as a constant and take an ordinary derivative with respect to x. Similarly, to compute $f_y(x, y)$, we treat x as a constant and differentiate with respect to y. Some examples illustrate the process.

EXAMPLE 1 **Partial derivatives** Let $f(x, y) = x^2 - y^2 + 4$.

a. Compute $\dfrac{\partial f}{\partial x}$ and $\dfrac{\partial f}{\partial y}$.

b. Evaluate each derivative at $(2, -4)$.

SOLUTION

a. We compute the partial derivative with respect to x assuming that y is a constant; the Power Rule gives

$$\frac{\partial f}{\partial x} = \frac{\partial}{\partial x}\underbrace{(x^2}_{\text{variable}} - \underbrace{y^2 + 4)}_{\substack{\text{constant with} \\ \text{respect to } x}} = 2x + 0 = 2x.$$

The partial derivative with respect to y is computed by treating x as a constant; using the Power Rule gives

$$\frac{\partial f}{\partial y} = \frac{\partial}{\partial y}(\underbrace{x^2}_{\substack{\text{constant} \\ \text{with respect} \\ \text{to } y}} - \underbrace{y^2}_{\text{variable}} + \underbrace{4}_{\text{constant}}) = -2y.$$

QUICK CHECK 1 Compute f_x and f_y for $f(x, y) = 2xy$. ◄

b. It follows that $f_x(2, -4) = (2x)|_{(2,-4)} = 4$ and $f_y(2, -4) = (-2y)|_{(2,-4)} = 8$.

Related Exercises 7–24 ◄

EXAMPLE 2   **Partial derivatives** Compute the partial derivatives of the following functions.

a. $f(x, y) = \sin xy$ **b.** $g(x, y) = x^2 e^{xy}$

SOLUTION

a. Treating y as a constant and differentiating with respect to x, we have

$$\frac{\partial f}{\partial x} = \frac{\partial}{\partial x}(\sin xy) = y \cos xy.$$

> Recall that
>
> $$\frac{d}{dx}(\sin 2x) = 2 \cos 2x.$$
>
> Replacing 2 by the constant y, we have
>
> $$\frac{\partial}{\partial x}(\sin xy) = y \cos (xy).$$

Holding x fixed and differentiating with respect to y, we have

$$\frac{\partial f}{\partial y} = \frac{\partial}{\partial y}(\sin xy) = x \cos xy.$$

b. To compute the partial derivative with respect to x, we call on the Product Rule. Holding y fixed, we have

$$\frac{\partial g}{\partial x} = \frac{\partial}{\partial x}(x^2 e^{xy})$$

$$= \frac{\partial}{\partial x}(x^2)e^{xy} + x^2 \frac{\partial}{\partial x}(e^{xy}) \quad \text{Product Rule}$$

$$= 2x \cdot e^{xy} + x^2 \cdot y e^{xy} \quad \text{Evaluate partial derivatives.}$$

$$= xe^{xy}(2 + xy). \quad \text{Simplify.}$$

> Because x and y are *independent* variables,
>
> $$\frac{\partial}{\partial x}(y) = 0 \quad \text{and} \quad \frac{\partial}{\partial y}(x) = 0.$$

Treating x as a constant, the partial derivative with respect to y is

$$\frac{\partial g}{\partial y} = \frac{\partial}{\partial y}(x^2 e^{xy}) = x^2 \underbrace{\frac{\partial}{\partial y}(e^{xy})}_{xe^{xy}} = x^3 e^{xy}.$$

Related Exercises 7–24 ◄

Higher-Order Partial Derivatives

Just as we have higher-order derivatives of functions of one variable, we also have higher-order partial derivatives. For example, given a function f and its partial derivative f_x, we can take the derivative of f_x with respect to x or with respect to y, which accounts for two of the four possible *second-order partial derivatives*. Table 13.4 summarizes the notation for second partial derivatives.

Table 13.4

Notation 1	Notation 2	What we say . . .
$\dfrac{\partial}{\partial x}\left(\dfrac{\partial f}{\partial x}\right) = \dfrac{\partial^2 f}{\partial x^2}$	$(f_x)_x = f_{xx}$	*d squared f dx squared* or *f-x-x*
$\dfrac{\partial}{\partial y}\left(\dfrac{\partial f}{\partial y}\right) = \dfrac{\partial^2 f}{\partial y^2}$	$(f_y)_y = f_{yy}$	*d squared f dy squared* or *f-y-y*
$\dfrac{\partial}{\partial x}\left(\dfrac{\partial f}{\partial y}\right) = \dfrac{\partial^2 f}{\partial x \partial y}$	$(f_y)_x = f_{yx}$	*f-y-x*
$\dfrac{\partial}{\partial y}\left(\dfrac{\partial f}{\partial x}\right) = \dfrac{\partial^2 f}{\partial y \partial x}$	$(f_x)_y = f_{xy}$	*f-x-y*

The order of differentiation can make a difference in the **mixed partial derivatives** f_{xy} and f_{yx}. So, it is important to use the correct notation to reflect the order in which derivatives are taken. For example, the notations $\dfrac{\partial^2 f}{\partial x \partial y}$ and f_{yx} both mean $\dfrac{\partial}{\partial x}\left(\dfrac{\partial f}{\partial y}\right)$; that is, differentiate first with respect to y, then with respect to x.

QUICK CHECK 2 Which of the following expressions are equivalent to each other: (a) f_{xy}; (b) f_{yx}; or (c) $\dfrac{\partial^2 f}{\partial y \partial x}$? Write $\dfrac{\partial^2 f}{\partial p \partial q}$ in subscript notation. ◄

EXAMPLE 3   **Second partial derivatives** Find the four second partial derivatives of $f(x, y) = 3x^4 y - 2xy + 5xy^3$.

SOLUTION First, we compute

$$\frac{\partial f}{\partial x} = \frac{\partial}{\partial x}(3x^4 y - 2xy + 5xy^3) = 12x^3 y - 2y + 5y^3$$

and

$$\frac{\partial f}{\partial y} = \frac{\partial}{\partial y}(3x^4 y - 2xy + 5xy^3) = 3x^4 - 2x + 15xy^2.$$

For the second partial derivatives, we have

$$\frac{\partial^2 f}{\partial x^2} = \frac{\partial}{\partial x}\left(\frac{\partial f}{\partial x}\right) = \frac{\partial}{\partial x}(12x^3 y - 2y + 5y^3) = 36x^2 y$$

$$\frac{\partial^2 f}{\partial y^2} = \frac{\partial}{\partial y}\left(\frac{\partial f}{\partial y}\right) = \frac{\partial}{\partial y}(3x^4 - 2x + 15xy^2) = 30xy$$

$$\frac{\partial^2 f}{\partial x \partial y} = \frac{\partial}{\partial x}\left(\frac{\partial f}{\partial y}\right) = \frac{\partial}{\partial x}(3x^4 - 2x + 15xy^2) = 12x^3 - 2 + 15y^2$$

$$\frac{\partial^2 f}{\partial y \partial x} = \frac{\partial}{\partial y}\left(\frac{\partial f}{\partial x}\right) = \frac{\partial}{\partial y}(12x^3 y - 2y + 5y^3) = 12x^3 - 2 + 15y^2.$$

QUICK CHECK 3 Compute f_{xxx} and f_{xxy} for $f(x, y) = x^3 y$. ◄

Related Exercises 25–40 ◄

Equality of Mixed Partial Derivatives   Notice that the two mixed partial derivatives in Example 3 are equal; that is, $f_{xy} = f_{yx}$. It turns out that most of the functions we encounter in this book have this property. Sufficient conditions for equality of mixed partial derivatives are given in a theorem attributed to the French mathematician Alexis Clairaut (1713–1765). The proof is found in advanced texts.

> **THEOREM 13.4 (Clairaut)**   **Equality of Mixed Partial Derivatives**
> Assume that f is defined on an open set D of $\mathbb{R}^2$, and f_{xy} and f_{yx} are continuous throughout D. Then $f_{xy} = f_{yx}$ at all points of D.

Assuming sufficient continuity, Theorem 13.4 can be extended to higher derivatives of f. For example, $f_{xyx} = f_{xxy} = f_{yxx}$.

Functions of Three Variables

Everything we learned about partial derivatives of functions with two variables carries over to functions of three or more variables, as illustrated in Example 4.

EXAMPLE 4 **Partial derivatives with more than two variables** Find $f_x, f_y,$ and f_z when $f(x, y, z) = e^{-xy}\cos z$.

SOLUTION To find f_x, we treat y and z as constants and differentiate with respect to x:

$$\frac{\partial f}{\partial x} = \frac{\partial}{\partial x}\left(\underbrace{e^{-xy}}_{\substack{y \text{ is} \\ \text{constant}}} \underbrace{\cos z}_{\text{constant}}\right) = -ye^{-xy}\cos z.$$

Holding x and z constant and differentiating with respect to y, we have

$$\frac{\partial f}{\partial y} = \frac{\partial}{\partial y}\left(\underbrace{e^{-xy}}_{\substack{x \text{ is} \\ \text{constant}}} \underbrace{\cos z}_{\text{constant}}\right) = -xe^{-xy}\cos z.$$

To find f_z, we hold x and y constant and differentiate with respect to z:

$$\frac{\partial f}{\partial z} = \frac{\partial}{\partial z}\left(\underbrace{e^{-xy}}_{\text{constant}}\cos z\right) = -e^{-xy}\sin z.$$

> **QUICK CHECK 4** Compute f_{xz} and f_{zz} for $f(x, y, z) = xyz - x^2z + yz^2$. ◄

Related Exercises 41–50 ◄

Applications of Partial Derivatives When functions are used in realistic applications (for example, to describe velocity, pressure, investment fund balance, or population), they often involve more than one independent variable. For this reason, partial derivatives appear frequently in mathematical modeling.

EXAMPLE 5 **Ideal Gas Law** The pressure P, volume V, and temperature T of an ideal gas are related by the equation $PV = kT$, where $k > 0$ is a constant depending on the amount of gas.

a. Determine the rate of change of the pressure with respect to the volume at constant temperature. Interpret the result.

b. Determine the rate of change of the pressure with respect to the temperature at constant volume. Interpret the result.

c. Explain these results using level curves.

> Implicit differentiation can also be used with partial derivatives. Instead of solving for P, we could differentiate both sides of $PV = kT$ with respect to V holding T fixed. Using the Product Rule, $P + VP_V = 0$, which implies that $P_V = -P/V$. Substituting $P = kT/V$, we have $P_V = -kT/V^2$.

> In the Ideal Gas Law, temperature is a positive variable because it is measured in degrees Kelvin.

SOLUTION Expressing the pressure as a function of volume and temperature, we have $P = k\dfrac{T}{V}$.

a. We find the partial derivative $\partial P/\partial V$ by holding T constant and differentiating P with respect to V:

$$\frac{\partial P}{\partial V} = \frac{\partial}{\partial V}\left(k\frac{T}{V}\right) = kT\frac{\partial}{\partial V}(V^{-1}) = -\frac{kT}{V^2}.$$

Recognizing that P, V, and T are always positive, we see that $\dfrac{\partial P}{\partial V} < 0$, which means that the pressure is a decreasing function of volume at a constant temperature.

b. The partial derivative $\partial P/\partial T$ is found by holding V constant and differentiating P with respect to T:

$$\frac{\partial P}{\partial T} = \frac{\partial}{\partial T}\left(k\frac{T}{V}\right) = \frac{k}{V}.$$

In this case $\partial P/\partial T > 0$, which says that the pressure is an increasing function of temperature at constant volume.

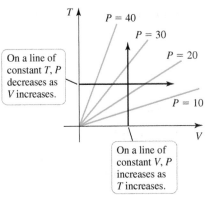

On a line of constant T, P decreases as V increases.

On a line of constant V, P increases as T increases.

FIGURE 13.51

c. The level curves (Section 13.2) of the pressure function are curves in the VT-plane that satisfy $k\dfrac{T}{V} = P_0$, where P_0 is a constant. Solving for T, the level curves are given by $T = \dfrac{1}{k}P_0 V$. Because $\dfrac{P_0}{k}$ is a positive constant, the level curves are lines in the first quadrant (Figure 13.51) with slope P_0/k. The fact that $\dfrac{\partial P}{\partial V} < 0$ (from part (a)) means that if we hold $T > 0$ fixed and move in the direction of increasing V on a *horizontal* line, we cross level curves corresponding to decreasing pressures. Similarly, $\dfrac{\partial P}{\partial T} > 0$ (from part (b)) means that if we hold $V > 0$ fixed and move in the direction of increasing T on a *vertical* line, we cross level curves corresponding to increasing pressures.

Related Exercises 51–52 ◄

QUICK CHECK 5 Explain why, in Figure 13.51, the slopes of the level curves increase as the pressures increase. ◄

Differentiability

We close this section with a technical matter that bears on the remainder of the chapter. Although we know how to compute partial derivatives of a function of several variables, we have not said what it means for such a function to be *differentiable* at a point. It is tempting to conclude that if the partial derivatives f_x and f_y exist at a point, then f is differentiable there. However, it is not so simple.

Recall that a function f of one variable is differentiable at $x = a$ provided the limit

$$f'(a) = \lim_{\Delta x \to 0} \frac{f(a + \Delta x) - f(a)}{\Delta x}$$

exists. If f is differentiable at a, it means that the curve is smooth at the point $(a, f(a))$ (no jumps, corners, or cusps); furthermore, the curve has a unique tangent line at that point with slope $f'(a)$. Differentiability for a function of several variables should carry the same properties: The surface should be smooth at the point in question and something analogous to a unique tangent line should exist at the point.

Staying analogy with the one-variable case, we define the quantity

$$\varepsilon = \underbrace{\frac{f(a + \Delta x) - f(a)}{\Delta x}}_{\text{slope of secant line}} - \underbrace{f'(a),}_{\substack{\text{slope of} \\ \text{tangent line}}}$$

where ε is viewed as a function of Δx. Notice that ε is the difference between the slopes of secant lines and the slope of the tangent line at the point $(a, f(a))$. If f is differentiable at a, then this difference approaches zero as $\Delta x \to 0$; therefore, $\lim\limits_{\Delta x \to 0} \varepsilon = 0$. Multiplying both sides of this expression by Δx gives

$$\varepsilon \Delta x = f(a + \Delta x) - f(a) - f'(a)\Delta x.$$

Rearranging, we have the change in the function $y = f(x)$:

$$\Delta y = f(a + \Delta x) - f(a) = f'(a)\Delta x + \underbrace{\varepsilon \, \Delta x.}_{\to 0 \text{ as } \Delta x \to 0}$$

> Notice that $f'(a)\Delta x$ is the approximate change in the function given by a linear approximation.

This expression says that, in the one-variable case, if f is differentiable at a, then the change in f between a and a nearby point $a + \Delta x$ is represented by $f'(a)\Delta x$ plus a quantity $\varepsilon \, \Delta x$, where $\lim\limits_{\Delta x \to 0} \varepsilon = 0$.

The analogous requirement with several variables is the definition of differentiability for functions or two (or more) variables.

DEFINITION   Differentiability

The function $z = f(x, y)$ is **differentiable at** (a, b) provided $f_x(a, b)$ and $f_y(a, b)$ exist and the change $\Delta z = f(a + \Delta x, b + \Delta y) - f(a, b)$ equals

$$\Delta z = f_x(a, b)\,\Delta x + f_y(a, b)\,\Delta y + \varepsilon_1 \Delta x + \varepsilon_2 \Delta y,$$

where for fixed a and b, ε_1 and ε_2 are functions that depend only on Δx and Δy, with $(\varepsilon_1, \varepsilon_2) \to (0, 0)$ as $(\Delta x, \Delta y) \to (0, 0)$. A function is **differentiable** on an open set R if it is differentiable at every point of R.

Several observations are needed here. First, the definition extends to functions of more than two variables. Second, we show how differentiability is related to linear approximation and the existence of a *tangent plane* in Section 13.7. Finally, the conditions of the definition are generally difficult to verify. The following theorem may be useful in checking differentiability.

THEOREM 13.5   Conditions for Differentiability

Suppose the function f has partial derivatives f_x and f_y defined on an open set containing (a, b), with f_x and f_y continuous at (a, b). Then f is differentiable at (a, b).

This theorem states that existence of f_x and f_y at (a, b) is not enough to ensure differentiability of f at (a, b); we also need their continuity. Polynomials and rational functions are differentiable at all points of their domains, as are compositions of exponential, logarithmic, and trigonometric functions with other differentiable functions. The proof of this theorem is given in Appendix B.

We close with the analog of Theorem 3.1, which states that differentiability implies continuity.

THEOREM 13.6   Differentiability Implies Continuity

If a function f is differentiable at (a, b), then it is continuous at (a, b).

Proof: By the definition of differentiability,

$$\Delta z = f_x(a, b)\,\Delta x + f_y(a, b)\,\Delta y + \varepsilon_1 \Delta x + \varepsilon_2 \Delta y,$$

where $(\varepsilon_1, \varepsilon_2) \to (0, 0)$ as $(\Delta x, \Delta y) \to (0, 0)$. Because f is assumed to be differentiable, as Δx and Δy approach 0, we see that

$$\lim_{(\Delta x, \Delta y) \to (0,0)} \Delta z = 0.$$

> Recall that continuity requires that
> $$\lim_{(x,y) \to (a,b)} f(x, y) = f(a, b),$$
> which is equivalent to
> $$\lim_{(\Delta x, \Delta y) \to (0,0)} f(a + \Delta x, b + \Delta y) = f(a, b).$$

Also, because $\Delta z = f(a + \Delta x, b + \Delta y) - f(a, b)$, it follows that

$$\lim_{(\Delta x, \Delta y) \to (0,0)} f(a + \Delta x, b + \Delta y) = f(a, b),$$

which implies continuity of f at (a, b).   ◄

EXAMPLE 6   **A nondifferentiable function** Discuss the differentiability and continuity of the function

$$f(x, y) = \begin{cases} \dfrac{3xy}{x^2 + y^2} & \text{if } (x, y) \neq (0, 0) \\ 0 & \text{if } (x, y) = (0, 0). \end{cases}$$

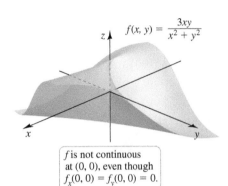

$$f(x, y) = \frac{3xy}{x^2 + y^2}$$

f is not continuous at (0, 0), even though $f_x(0, 0) = f_y(0, 0) = 0.$

FIGURE 13.52

SOLUTION As a rational function, f is continuous and differentiable at all points $(x, y) \neq (0, 0)$. The interesting behavior occurs at the origin. Using calculations similar to those in Example 4 in Section 13.3, it can be shown that if the origin is approached along the line $y = mx$, then

$$\lim_{(x,y)\to(0,0)} \frac{3xy}{x^2 + y^2} = \frac{3m}{m^2 + 1}.$$

Therefore, the value of the limit depends on the direction of approach, which implies that the limit does not exist, and f is not continuous at $(0, 0)$. By Theorem 13.6, it follows that f is not differentiable at $(0, 0)$. Figure 13.52 shows the discontinuity of f at the origin.

Let's look at the first partial derivatives of f at $(0, 0)$. A short calculation shows that

$$f_x(0, 0) = \lim_{h\to 0} \frac{f(0 + h, 0) - f(0, 0)}{h} = \lim_{h\to 0} \frac{0 - 0}{h} = 0,$$

$$f_y(0, 0) = \lim_{h\to 0} \frac{f(0, 0 + h) - f(0, 0)}{h} = \lim_{h\to 0} \frac{0 - 0}{h} = 0.$$

Despite the fact that f is not differentiable at $(0, 0)$, its first partial derivatives exist at $(0, 0)$. Existence of first partial derivatives at a point is not enough to ensure differentiability at that point. As expressed in Theorem 13.5, continuity of first partial derivatives is required for differentiability. It can be shown in this case that f_x and f_y are not continuous at $(0, 0)$.

Related Exercises 53–54 ◄

SECTION 13.4 EXERCISES

Review Questions

1. Suppose you are standing on the surface $z = f(x, y)$ at the point $(a, b, f(a, b))$. Interpret the meaning of $f_x(a, b)$ and $f_y(a, b)$ in terms of slopes or rates of change.

2. Find f_x and f_y when $f(x, y) = 3x^2y + xy^3$.

3. Find f_x and f_y when $f(x, y) = x \cos(xy)$.

4. Find the four second partial derivatives of $f(x, y) = 3x^2y + xy^3$.

5. Explain how you would evaluate f_z for the differentiable function $w = f(x, y, z)$.

6. The volume of a right circular cylinder with radius r and height h is $V = \pi r^2 h$. Is the volume an increasing or decreasing function of the radius at a fixed height (assume $r > 0$ and $h > 0$)?

Basic Skills

7–24. Partial derivatives *Find the first partial derivatives of the following functions.*

7. $f(x, y) = 3x^2 + 4y^3$

8. $f(x, y) = x^2y$

9. $f(x, y) = 3x^2y + 2$

10. $f(x, y) = y^8 + 2x^6 + 2xy$

11. $f(x, y) = xe^y$

12. $f(x, y) = \ln(x/y)$

13. $g(x, y) = \cos 2xy$

14. $h(x, y) = (y^2 + 1)e^x$

15. $f(x, y) = e^{x^2y}$

16. $f(s, t) = \dfrac{s - t}{s + t}$

17. $f(w, z) = \dfrac{w}{w^2 + z^2}$

18. $g(x, z) = x \ln(z^2 + x^2)$

19. $s(y, z) = z^2 \tan yz$

20. $F(p, q) = \sqrt{p^2 + pq + q^2}$

21. $G(s, t) = \dfrac{\sqrt{st}}{s + t}$

22. $h(u, v) = \sqrt{\dfrac{uv}{u - v}}$

23. $f(x, y) = x^{2y}$

24. $f(x, y) = \sqrt{x^2y^3}$

25–34. Second partial derivatives *Find the four second partial derivatives of the following functions.*

25. $h(x, y) = x^3 + xy^2 + 1$

26. $f(x, y) = 2x^5y^2 + x^2y$

27. $f(x, y) = x^2y^3$

28. $f(x, y) = (x + 3y)^2$

29. $f(x, y) = y^3 \sin 4x$

30. $f(x, y) = \cos xy$

31. $p(u, v) = \ln(u^2 + v^2 + 4)$ **32.** $Q(r, s) = r/s$

33. $F(r, s) = r\,e^s$ **34.** $H(x, y) = \sqrt{4 + x^2 + y^2}$

35–40. Equality of mixed partial derivatives *Verify that* $f_{xy} = f_{yx}$ *for the following functions.*

35. $f(x, y) = 2x^3 + 3y^2 + 1$ **36.** $f(x, y) = xe^y$

37. $f(x, y) = \cos xy$ **38.** $f(x, y) = 3x^2y^{-1} - 2x^{-1}y^2$

39. $f(x, y) = e^{x+y}$ **40.** $f(x, y) = \sqrt{xy}$

41–50. Partial derivatives with more than two variables *Find the first partial derivatives of the following functions.*

41. $f(x, y, z) = xy + xz + yz$

42. $g(x, y, z) = 2x^2y - 3xz^4 + 10y^2z^2$

43. $h(x, y, z) = \cos(x + y + z)$

44. $Q(x, y, z) = \tan xyz$

45. $F(u, v, w) = \dfrac{u}{v + w}$

46. $G(r, s, t) = \sqrt{rs + rt + st}$

47. $f(w, x, y, z) = w^2xy^2 + xy^3z^2$

48. $g(w, x, y, z) = \cos(w + x)\sin(y - z)$

49. $h(w, x, y, z) = \dfrac{wz}{xy}$

50. $F(w, x, y, z) = w\sqrt{x + 2y + 3z}$

51. Gas law calculations Consider the Ideal Gas Law $PV = kT$, where $k > 0$ is a constant. Solve this equation for V in terms of P and T.

  a. Determine the rate of change of the volume with respect to the pressure at constant temperature. Interpret the result.

  b. Determine the rate of change of the volume with respect to the temperature at constant pressure. Interpret the result.

  c. Assuming $k = 1$, draw several level curves of the volume function and interpret the results as in Example 5.

52. Volume of a box A box with a square base of length x and height h has a volume $V = x^2h$.

  a. Compute the partial derivatives V_x and V_h.

  b. For a box with $h = 1.5$ m, use linear approximation to estimate the change in volume if x increases from $x = 0.5$ m to $x = 0.51$ m.

  c. For a box with $x = 0.5$ m, use linear approximation to estimate the change in volume if h decreases from $h = 1.5$ m to $h = 1.49$ m.

  d. For a fixed height, does a 10% change in x always produce (approximately) a 10% change in V? Explain.

  e. For a fixed base length, does a 10% change in h always produce (approximately) a 10% change in V? Explain.

53–54. Nondifferentiability? *Consider the following functions f.*

a. Is f continuous at $(0, 0)$?

b. Is f differentiable at $(0, 0)$?

c. If possible, evaluate $f_x(0, 0)$ *and* $f_y(0, 0)$.

d. Determine whether f_x *and* f_y *are continuous at* $(0, 0)$.

e. Explain why Theorems 13.5 and 13.6 are consistent with the results in parts (a)–(d).

53. $f(x, y) = \begin{cases} -\dfrac{xy}{x^2 + y^2} & \text{if } (x, y) \neq (0, 0) \\ 0 & \text{if } (x, y) = (0, 0) \end{cases}$

54. $f(x, y) = \begin{cases} \dfrac{2xy^2}{x^2 + y^4} & \text{if } (x, y) \neq (0, 0) \\ 0 & \text{if } (x, y) = (0, 0) \end{cases}$

Further Explorations

55. Explain why or why not Determine whether the following statements are true and give an explanation or counterexample.

  a. $\dfrac{\partial}{\partial x}(y^{10}) = 10y^9$ **b.** $\dfrac{\partial^2}{\partial x \partial y}(\sqrt{xy}) = \dfrac{1}{\sqrt{xy}}$

  c. If f has continuous partial derivatives of all orders, then $f_{xxy} = f_{yxx}$.

56–59. Estimating partial derivatives *The following table shows values of a function* $f(x, y)$ *for select values of x from 2 to 2.5 and select values of y from 3 to 3.5. Use this table to estimate the values of the following partial derivates.*

y \ x	2	2.1	2.2	2.3	2.4	2.5
3	4.243	4.347	4.450	4.550	4.648	4.743
3.1	4.384	4.492	4.598	4.701	4.802	4.902
3.2	4.525	4.637	4.746	4.853	4.957	5.060
3.3	4.667	4.782	4.895	5.005	5.112	5.218
3.4	4.808	4.930	5.043	5.156	5.267	5.376
3.5	4.950	5.072	5.191	5.308	5.422	5.534

56. $f_x(2, 3)$ **57.** $f_y(2, 3)$

58. $f_x(2.2, 3.4)$ **59.** $f_y(2.4, 3.3)$

60–64. Miscellaneous partial derivatives *Compute the first partial derivatives of the following functions.*

60. $f(x, y) = \ln(1 + e^{-xy})$

61. $f(x, y) = 1 - \tan^{-1}(x^2 + y^2)$

62. $f(x, y) = 1 - \cos(2(x + y)) + \cos^2(x + y)$

63. $h(x, y, z) = (1 + x + 2y)^z$

64. $g(x, y, z) = \dfrac{4x - 2y - 2z}{3y - 6x - 3z}$

65. Partial derivatives and level curves Consider the function $z = x/y^2$.

  a. Compute z_x and z_y.

  b. Sketch the level curves for $z = 1, 2, 3,$ and 4.

  c. Move along the horizontal line $y = 1$ in the xy-plane and describe how the corresponding z-values change. Explain how this observation is consistent with z_x as computed in part (a).

  d. Move along the vertical line $x = 1$ in the xy-plane and describe how the corresponding z-values change. Explain how this observation is consistent with z_y as computed in part (a).

66. Spherical caps The volume of the cap of a sphere of radius r and thickness h is $V = \dfrac{\pi}{3} h^2(3r - h)$, for $0 \le h \le r$.

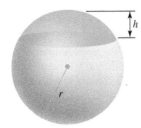

$$V = \tfrac{\pi}{3} h^2(3r - h)$$

a. Compute the partial derivatives V_h and V_r.
b. For a sphere of any radius, is the rate of change of volume with respect to r greater when $h = 0.2r$ or when $h = 0.8r$?
c. For a sphere of any radius, for what value of h is the rate of change of volume with respect to r equal to 1?
d. For a fixed radius r, for what value of h ($0 \le h \le r$) is the rate of change of volume with respect to h the greatest?

67. Law of Cosines All triangles satisfy the Law of Cosines $c^2 = a^2 + b^2 - 2ab \cos \theta$ (see figure). Notice that when $\theta = \pi/2$, the Law of Cosines becomes the Pythagorean Theorem. Consider all triangles with a fixed angle $\theta = \pi/3$, in which case, c is a function of a and b, where $a > 0$ and $b > 0$.

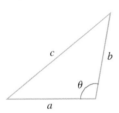

a. Compute $\dfrac{\partial c}{\partial a}$ and $\dfrac{\partial c}{\partial b}$ by solving for c and differentiating.
b. Compute $\dfrac{\partial c}{\partial a}$ and $\dfrac{\partial c}{\partial b}$ by implicit differentiation. Check for agreement with part (a).
c. What relationship between a and b makes c an increasing function of a (for constant b)?

Applications

68. Body mass index The body mass index (BMI) for an adult human is given by the function $B = w/h^2$, where w is the weight measured in kilograms and h is the height measured in meters. (The BMI for units of pounds and inches is $B = 703\, w/h^2$.)

a. Find the rate of change of the BMI with respect to weight at a constant height.
b. For fixed h, is the BMI an increasing or decreasing function of w? Explain.
c. Find the rate of change of the BMI with respect to height at a constant weight.
d. For fixed w, is the BMI an increasing or decreasing function of h? Explain.

69. Electric potential function The electric potential in the xy-plane associated with two positive charges, one at $(0, 1)$ with twice the magnitude as the charge at $(0, -1)$, is

$$\varphi(x, y) = \frac{2}{\sqrt{x^2 + (y - 1)^2}} + \frac{1}{\sqrt{x^2 + (y + 1)^2}}.$$

a. Compute φ_x and φ_y.
b. Describe how φ_x and φ_y behave as $x, y \to \pm \infty$.
c. Evaluate $\varphi_x(0, y)$, for all $y \ne \pm 1$. Interpret this result.
d. Evaluate $\varphi_y(x, 0)$, for all x. Interpret this result.

70. Cobb-Douglas production function The output Q of an economic system subject to two inputs, such as labor L and capital K, is often modeled by the Cobb-Douglas production function $Q(L, K) = cL^a K^b$. Suppose $a = \frac{1}{3}, b = \frac{2}{3}$, and $c = 1$.

a. Evaluate the partial derivatives Q_L and Q_K.
b. Suppose $L = 10$ is fixed and K increases from $K = 20$ to $K = 20.5$. Use linear approximation to estimate the change in Q.
c. Suppose $K = 20$ is fixed and L decreases from $L = 10$ to $L = 9.5$. Use linear approximation to estimate the change in Q.
d. Graph the level curves of the production function in the first quadrant of the LK-plane for $Q = 1, 2$, and 3.
e. Use the graph of part (d). If you move along the vertical line $L = 2$ in the positive K-direction, how does Q change? Is this consistent with Q_K computed in part (a)?
f. Use the graph of part (d). If you move along the horizontal line $K = 2$ in the positive L-direction, how does Q change? Is this consistent with Q_L computed in part (a)?

71. Resistors in parallel Two resistors in an electrical circuit with resistance R_1 and R_2 wired in parallel with a constant voltage give an effective resistance of R, where $\dfrac{1}{R} = \dfrac{1}{R_1} + \dfrac{1}{R_2}$.

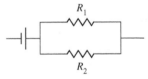

a. Find $\dfrac{\partial R}{\partial R_1}$ and $\dfrac{\partial R}{\partial R_2}$ by solving for R and differentiating.
b. Find $\dfrac{\partial R}{\partial R_1}$ and $\dfrac{\partial R}{\partial R_2}$ by differentiating implicitly.
c. Describe how an increase in R_1 with R_2 constant affects R.
d. Describe how a decrease in R_2 with R_1 constant affects R.

72. Wave on a string Imagine a string that is fixed at both ends (for example, a guitar string). When plucked, the string forms a standing wave. The displacement u of the string varies with position x and with time t. Suppose it is given by $u = f(x, t) = 2 \sin(\pi x) \sin(\pi t/2)$, for $0 \le x \le 1$ and $t \ge 0$ (see figure). At a fixed point in time, the string forms a wave on $[0, 1]$. Alternatively, if you focus on a point on the string (fix a value of x), that point oscillates up and down in time.

a. What is the period of the motion in time?
b. Find the rate of change of the displacement with respect to time at a constant position (which is the vertical velocity of a point on the string).

c. At a fixed time, what point on the string is moving fastest?

d. At a fixed position on the string, when is the string moving fastest?

e. Find the rate of change of the displacement with respect to position at a constant time (which is the slope of the string).

f. At a fixed time, where is the slope of the string greatest?

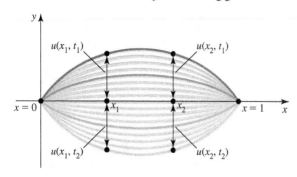

73–75. Wave equation *Traveling waves (for example, water waves or electromagnetic waves) exhibit periodic motion in both time and position. In one dimension (for example, a wave on a string) wave motion is governed by the one-dimensional wave equation*

$$\frac{\partial^2 u}{\partial t^2} = c^2 \frac{\partial^2 u}{\partial x^2},$$

where $u(x, t)$ is the height or displacement of the wave surface at position x and time t, and c is the constant speed of the wave. Show that the following functions are solutions of the wave equation.

73. $u(x, t) = \cos(2(x + ct))$

74. $u(x, t) = 5 \cos(2(x + ct)) + 3 \sin(x - ct)$

75. $u(x, t) = A f(x + ct) + B g(x - ct)$, where A and B are constants and f and g are twice differentiable functions of one variable

76–79. Laplace's equation *A classical equation of mathematics is Laplace's equation, which arises in both theory and applications. It governs ideal fluid flow, electrostatic potentials, and the steady-state distribution of heat in a conducting medium. In two dimensions, Laplace's equation is*

$$\frac{\partial^2 u}{\partial x^2} + \frac{\partial^2 u}{\partial y^2} = 0.$$

Show that the following functions are harmonic; that is, they satisfy Laplace's equation.

76. $u(x, y) = e^{-x} \sin y$

77. $u(x, y) = x(x^2 - 3y^2)$

78. $u(x, y) = e^{ax} \cos ay$, for any real number a

79. $u(x, y) = \tan^{-1}\left(\dfrac{y}{x - 1}\right) - \tan^{-1}\left(\dfrac{y}{x + 1}\right)$

80–83. Heat equation *The flow of heat along a thin conducting bar is governed by the one-dimensional heat equation (with analogs for thin plates in two dimensions and for solids in three dimensions)*

$$\frac{\partial u}{\partial t} = k \frac{\partial^2 u}{\partial x^2},$$

where u is a measure of the temperature at a location x on the bar at time t and the positive constant k is related to the conductivity of the material. Show that the following functions satisfy the heat equation with $k = 1$.

80. $u(x, t) = 10e^{-t} \sin x$

81. $u(x, t) = 4e^{-4t} \cos 2x$

82. $u(x, t) = e^{-t}(2 \sin x + 3 \cos x)$

83. $u(x, t) = Ae^{-a^2 t} \cos ax$, for any real numbers a and A

Additional Exercises

84–85. Differentiability *Use the definition of differentiability to prove that the following functions are differentiable at $(0, 0)$. You must produce functions ε_1 and ε_2 with the required properties.*

84. $f(x, y) = x + y$ **85.** $f(x, y) = xy$

86–87. Nondifferentiability? *Consider the following functions f.*

a. *Is f continuous at $(0, 0)$?*

b. *Is f differentiable at $(0, 0)$?*

c. *If possible, evaluate $f_x(0, 0)$ and $f_y(0, 0)$.*

d. *Determine whether f_x and f_y are continuous at $(0, 0)$.*

e. *Explain why Theorems 13.5 and 13.6 are consistent with the results in parts (a)–(d).*

86. $f(x, y) = 1 - |xy|$

87. $f(x, y) = \sqrt{|xy|}$

88. Mixed partial derivatives

a. Consider the function $w = f(x, y, z)$. List all possible second partial derivatives that could be computed.

b. Let $f(x, y, z) = x^2 y + 2xz^2 - 3y^2 z$ and determine which second partial derivatives are equal.

c. How many second partial derivatives does $p = g(w, x, y, z)$ have?

89. Derivatives of an integral Let h be continuous for all real numbers.

a. Find f_x and f_y when $f(x, y) = \displaystyle\int_x^y h(s)\, ds$.

b. Find f_x and f_y when $f(x, y) = \displaystyle\int_1^{xy} h(s)\, ds$.

90. An identity Show that if $f(x, y) = \dfrac{ax + by}{cx + dy}$, where a, b, c, and d are real numbers with $ad - bc = 0$, then $f_x = f_y = 0$, for all x and y in the domain of f. Give an explanation.

91. Cauchy-Riemann equations In the advanced subject of complex variables, a function typically has the form $f(x, y) = u(x, y) + i\,v(x, y)$, where u and v are real-valued functions and $i = \sqrt{-1}$ is the imaginary unit. A function $f = u + iv$ is said to be *analytic* (analogous to differentiable) if it satisfies the Cauchy-Riemann equations: $u_x = v_y$ and $u_y = -v_x$.

a. Show that $f(x, y) = (x^2 - y^2) + i(2xy)$ is analytic.
b. Show that $f(x, y) = x(x^2 - 3y^2) + iy(3x^2 - y^2)$ is analytic.
c. Show that if $f = u + iv$ is analytic, then $u_{xx} + u_{yy} = 0$ and $v_{xx} + v_{yy} = 0$.

QUICK CHECK ANSWERS

1. $f_x = 2y; f_y = 2x$ **2.** (a) and (c) are the same; f_{qp}
3. $f_{xxx} = 6y; f_{xxy} = 6x$ **4.** $f_{xz} = y - 2x; f_{zz} = 2y$

5. The equations of the level curves are $T = \dfrac{1}{k}P_0 V$. As the pressure P_0 increases, the slopes of these lines increase. ◄

13.5 The Chain Rule

In this section, we combine ideas based on the Chain Rule (Section 3.6) with what we know about partial derivatives (Section 13.4) to develop new methods for finding derivatives of functions of several variables. To illustrate the importance of these methods, consider the following situation.

Economists modeling the output of a manufacturing system often work with *production functions* that relate the productivity of the system (output) to all the variables on which it depends (input). A simplified production function might take the form $P = F(L, K, R)$, where L, K, and R represent the availability of labor, capital, and natural resources, respectively. However, the variables L, K, and R may be intermediate variables that depend on other variables. For example, it might be that L is a function of the unemployment rate u, K is a function of the prime interest rate i, and R is a function of time t (seasonal availability of resources). Even in this simplified model we see that productivity, which is the dependent variable, is ultimately related to many other variables (Figure 13.53). Of critical interest to an economist is how changes in one variable determine changes in other variables. For instance, if the unemployment rate increases by 0.1% and the interest rate decreases by 0.2%, what is the effect on productivity? In this section we develop the tools needed to answer such questions.

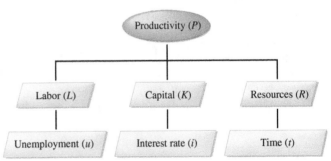

FIGURE 13.53

The Chain Rule with One Independent Variable

Recall the basic Chain Rule: If y is a function of u and u is a function of t, then $\dfrac{dy}{dt} = \dfrac{dy}{du}\dfrac{du}{dt}$.

We first extend the Chain Rule to composite functions of the form $z = f(x, y)$, where x and y are functions of t. What is $\dfrac{dz}{dt}$?

We illustrate the relationships among the variables t, x, y, and z using a *tree diagram* (Figure 13.54). To find dz/dt, first notice that z depends on x, which in turn depends on t. The change in z with respect to x is the partial derivative $\partial z/\partial x$, while the change in x with

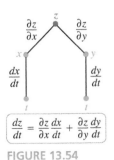

$$\frac{dz}{dt} = \frac{\partial z}{\partial x}\frac{dx}{dt} + \frac{\partial z}{\partial y}\frac{dy}{dt}$$

FIGURE 13.54

respect to t is the ordinary derivative dx/dt. These derivatives appear on the corresponding branches of the tree diagram. Using the Chain Rule idea, the product of these derivatives gives the change in z with respect to t through x.

Similarly, z also depends on y. The change in z with respect to y is $\partial z/\partial y$, while the change in y with respect to t is dy/dt. The product of these derivatives, which appear on the corresponding branches of the tree, gives the change in z with respect to t through y. Summing the contributions to dz/dt along each branch of the tree leads to the following theorem, whose proof is found in Appendix B.

> A subtle observation about notation should be made. If $z = f(x, y)$, where x and y are functions of another variable t, it is common to write $z = f(t)$ to show that z ultimately depends on t. However, the two functions denoted f are actually different. To be careful, we should write (or at least remember) that in fact $z = F(t)$, where F is a function other than f. This distinction is often overlooked for the sake of convenience.

THEOREM 13.7   Chain Rule (One Independent Variable)
Let z be a differentiable function of x and y on its domain, where x and y are differentiable functions of t on an interval I. Then

$$\frac{dz}{dt} = \frac{\partial z}{\partial x}\frac{dx}{dt} + \frac{\partial z}{\partial y}\frac{dy}{dt}.$$

QUICK CHECK 1 Explain why Theorem 13.7 reduces to the Chain Rule for a function of one variable in the case that $z = f(x)$ and $x = g(t)$. ◄

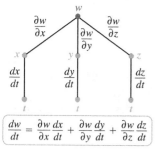

$$\frac{dw}{dt} = \frac{\partial w}{\partial x}\frac{dx}{dt} + \frac{\partial w}{\partial y}\frac{dy}{dt} + \frac{\partial w}{\partial z}\frac{dz}{dt}$$

FIGURE 13.55

> If f, x, and y are simple, as in Example 1, it is possible to substitute $x(t)$ and $y(t)$ into f, producing a function of t only, and then differentiate with respect to t. But this approach quickly becomes impractical with more complicated functions and the Chain Rule offers a great advantage.

Before presenting examples, several comments are in order.

- With $z = f(x(t), y(t))$, the dependent variable is z and the sole independent variable is t. The variables x and y are **intermediate variables**.

- The choice of notation for partial and ordinary derivatives in the Chain Rule is important. We write ordinary derivatives dx/dt and dy/dt because x and y depend only on t. We write partial derivatives $\partial z/\partial x$ and $\partial z/\partial y$ because z is a function of both x and y. Finally, we write dz/dt as an ordinary derivative because z ultimately depends only on t.

- Theorem 13.7 generalizes directly to functions of more than two intermediate variables (Figure 13.55). For example, if $w = f(x, y, z)$, where x, y, and z are functions of the single independent variable t, then

$$\frac{dw}{dt} = \frac{\partial w}{\partial x}\frac{dx}{dt} + \frac{\partial w}{\partial y}\frac{dy}{dt} + \frac{\partial w}{\partial z}\frac{dz}{dt}.$$

EXAMPLE 1   Chain Rule with one independent variable Let $z = x^2 - 3y^2 + 20$, where $x = 2\cos t$ and $y = 2\sin t$.

a. Find $\dfrac{dz}{dt}$ and evaluate it at $t = \pi/4$.

b. Interpret the result geometrically.

SOLUTION

a. Computing the intermediate derivatives and applying the Chain Rule (Theorem 13.7), we find that

$$\frac{dz}{dt} = \frac{\partial z}{\partial x}\frac{dx}{dt} + \frac{\partial z}{\partial y}\frac{dy}{dt}$$

$$= \underbrace{(2x)}_{\frac{\partial z}{\partial x}}\underbrace{(-2\sin t)}_{\frac{dx}{dt}} + \underbrace{(-6y)}_{\frac{\partial z}{\partial y}}\underbrace{(2\cos t)}_{\frac{dy}{dt}} \qquad \text{Evaluate derivatives.}$$

$$= -4x\sin t - 12y\cos t \qquad\qquad \text{Simplify.}$$

$$= -8\cos t\sin t - 24\sin t\cos t \qquad \text{Substitute } x = 2\cos t, y = 2\sin t.$$

$$= -16\sin 2t. \qquad\qquad \text{Simplify; } \sin 2t = 2\sin t\cos t.$$

Substituting $t = \pi/4$ gives $\dfrac{dz}{dt}\bigg|_{t=\pi/4} = -16.$

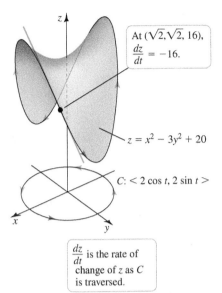

At $(\sqrt{2}, \sqrt{2}, 16)$, $\dfrac{dz}{dt} = -16$.

$z = x^2 - 3y^2 + 20$

$C: < 2\cos t, 2\sin t >$

$\dfrac{dz}{dt}$ is the rate of change of z as C is traversed.

FIGURE 13.56

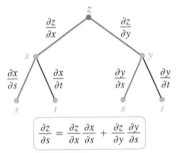

$$\frac{\partial z}{\partial s} = \frac{\partial z}{\partial x}\frac{\partial x}{\partial s} + \frac{\partial z}{\partial y}\frac{\partial y}{\partial s}$$

FIGURE 13.57

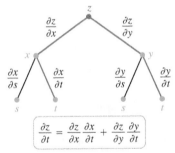

$$\frac{\partial z}{\partial t} = \frac{\partial z}{\partial x}\frac{\partial x}{\partial t} + \frac{\partial z}{\partial y}\frac{\partial y}{\partial t}$$

FIGURE 13.58

b. The parametric equations $x = 2\cos t$, $y = 2\sin t$, for $0 \le t \le 2\pi$, describe a circle C of radius 2 in the xy-plane. Imagine walking on the surface $z = x^2 - 3y^2 + 20$ while staying directly above the circle C in the xy-plane. Your path rises and falls as you walk (Figure 13.56); the rate of change of your elevation z with respect to t is given by dz/dt. For example, when $t = \pi/4$, the corresponding point on the surface is $(\sqrt{2}, \sqrt{2}, 16)$, and z changes with respect to t at a rate of -16 (by part (a)).

Related Exercises 7–18◄

The Chain Rule with Several Independent Variables

The ideas behind the Chain Rule of Theorem 13.7 can be modified to cover a variety of situations in which functions of several variables are composed with one another. For example, suppose z depends on two intermediate variables x and y, each of which depends on the independent variables s and t. Once again, a tree diagram (Figure 13.57) helps us organize the relationships among variables. The dependent variable z now ultimately depends on the two independent variables s and t, so it makes sense to ask about the rates of change of z with respect to either s or t, which are $\partial z/\partial s$ and $\partial z/\partial t$, respectively.

To compute $\partial z/\partial s$, we note that there are two paths in the tree (in red in Figure 13.57) that connect z to s and contribute to $\partial z/\partial s$. Along one path, z changes with respect to x (with rate of change $\partial z/\partial x$) and x changes with respect to s (with rate of change $\partial x/\partial s$). Along the other path, z changes with respect to y (with rate of change $\partial z/\partial y$) and y changes with respect to s (with rate of change $\partial y/\partial s$). We use a Chain Rule calculation along each path and combine the results. A similar argument leads to $\partial z/\partial t$ (Figure 13.58).

> **THEOREM 13.8 Chain Rule (Two Independent Variables)**
>
> Let z be a differentiable function of x and y, where x and y are differentiable functions of s and t. Then
>
> $$\frac{\partial z}{\partial s} = \frac{\partial z}{\partial x}\frac{\partial x}{\partial s} + \frac{\partial z}{\partial y}\frac{\partial y}{\partial s} \quad \text{and} \quad \frac{\partial z}{\partial t} = \frac{\partial z}{\partial x}\frac{\partial x}{\partial t} + \frac{\partial z}{\partial y}\frac{\partial y}{\partial t}.$$

QUICK CHECK 2 Suppose that $w = f(x, y, z)$, where $x = g(s, t)$, $y = h(s, t)$, and $z = p(s, t)$. Extend Theorem 13.8 to write a formula for $\partial w/\partial t$. ◄

EXAMPLE 2   Chain Rule with two independent variables Let $z = \sin 2x \cos 3y$, where $x = s + t$ and $y = s - t$. Evaluate $\partial z/\partial s$ and $\partial z/\partial t$.

SOLUTION The tree diagram in Figure 13.57 gives the Chain Rule formula for $\partial z/\partial s$: We form products of the derivatives along the red branches connecting z to s and add the results. The partial derivative is

$$\frac{\partial z}{\partial s} = \frac{\partial z}{\partial x}\frac{\partial x}{\partial s} + \frac{\partial z}{\partial y}\frac{\partial y}{\partial s}$$

$$= \underbrace{2\cos 2x \cos 3y}_{\frac{\partial z}{\partial x}} \cdot \underbrace{1}_{\frac{\partial x}{\partial s}} + \underbrace{(-3\sin 2x \sin 3y)}_{\frac{\partial z}{\partial y}} \cdot \underbrace{1}_{\frac{\partial y}{\partial s}}$$

$$= 2\cos\big(2\underbrace{(s + t)}_{x}\big)\cos\big(3\underbrace{(s - t)}_{y}\big) - 3\sin\big(2\underbrace{(s + t)}_{x}\big)\sin\big(3\underbrace{(s - t)}_{y}\big).$$

Following the branches of Figure 13.58 connecting z to t, we have

$$\frac{\partial z}{\partial t} = \frac{\partial z}{\partial x}\frac{\partial x}{\partial t} + \frac{\partial z}{\partial y}\frac{\partial y}{\partial t}$$

$$= \underbrace{2\cos 2x \cos 3y}_{\frac{\partial z}{\partial x}} \cdot \underbrace{1}_{\frac{\partial x}{\partial t}} + \underbrace{(-3\sin 2x \sin 3y)}_{\frac{\partial z}{\partial y}} \cdot \underbrace{-1}_{\frac{\partial y}{\partial t}}$$

$$= 2\cos\underbrace{(2(s+t))}_{x}\cos\underbrace{(3(s-t))}_{y} + 3\sin\underbrace{(2(s+t))}_{x}\sin\underbrace{(3(s-t))}_{y}.$$

Related Exercises 19–26 ◄

EXAMPLE 3   More variables Let w be a function of x, y, and z, each of which is a function of s and t.

a. Draw a labeled tree diagram showing the relationships among the variables.

b. Write the Chain Rule formula for $\dfrac{\partial w}{\partial s}$.

SOLUTION

a. Because w is a function of x, y, and z, the upper branches of the tree (Figure 13.59) are labeled with the partial derivatives w_x, w_y, and w_z. Each of x, y, and z is a function of two variables, so the lower branches of the tree also require partial derivative labels.

b. Extending Theorem 13.8, we take the three paths through the tree that connect w to s (red branches in Figure 13.59). Multiplying the derivatives that appear on each path and adding gives the result

$$\frac{\partial w}{\partial s} = \frac{\partial w}{\partial x}\frac{\partial x}{\partial s} + \frac{\partial w}{\partial y}\frac{\partial y}{\partial s} + \frac{\partial w}{\partial z}\frac{\partial z}{\partial s}.$$

Related Exercises 19–26 ◄

It is probably clear by now that we can create a Chain Rule for any set of relationships among variables. The key is to draw an accurate tree diagram and label the branches of the tree with the appropriate derivatives.

EXAMPLE 4   A different kind of tree Let w be a function of z, where z is a function of x and y, and each of x and y is a function of t. Draw a labeled tree diagram and write the Chain Rule formula for dw/dt.

SOLUTION The dependent variable w is related to the independent variable t through two paths in the tree: $w \to z \to x \to t$ and $w \to z \to y \to t$ (Figure 13.60). At the top of the tree, w is a function of the single variable z, so the rate of change is the ordinary derivative dw/dz. The tree below z looks like Figure 13.54. Multiplying the derivatives on each of the two branches connecting w to t, and adding the results, we have

$$\frac{dw}{dt} = \frac{dw}{dz}\frac{\partial z}{\partial x}\frac{dx}{dt} + \frac{dw}{dz}\frac{\partial z}{\partial y}\frac{dy}{dt} = \frac{dw}{dz}\left(\frac{\partial z}{\partial x}\frac{dx}{dt} + \frac{\partial z}{\partial y}\frac{dy}{dt}\right).$$

Related Exercises 27–30 ◄

Implicit Differentiation

Using the Chain Rule for partial derivatives, the technique of implicit differentiation can be put in a larger perspective. Recall that if x and y are related through an implicit relationship, such as $\sin xy + \pi y^2 = x$, then dy/dx is computed using implicit differentiation (Section 3.7). Another way to compute dy/dx is to define the function $F(x, y) = \sin xy + \pi y^2 - x$. Notice that the original relationship $\sin xy + \pi y^2 = x$ is $F(x, y) = 0$.

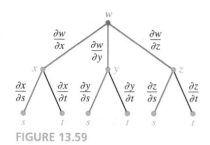

FIGURE 13.59

QUICK CHECK 3 If Q is a function of w, x, y, and z, each of which is a function of r, s, and t, how many dependent variables, intermediate variables, and independent variables are there? ◄

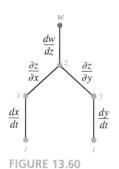

FIGURE 13.60

To find dy/dx, we treat x as the independent variable and differentiate both sides of $F(x, y(x)) = 0$ with respect to x. The derivative of the right side is 0. On the left side, we use the Chain Rule of Theorem 13.7:

$$\frac{\partial F}{\partial x}\underbrace{\frac{dx}{dx}}_{1} + \frac{\partial F}{\partial y}\frac{dy}{dx} = 0.$$

Noting that $dx/dx = 1$ and solving for dy/dx, we obtain the following theorem.

> The question of whether a relationship of the form $F(x, y) = 0$ or $F(x, y, z) = 0$ determines a function is addressed by a theorem of advanced calculus called the Implicit Function Theorem.

THEOREM 13.9 Implicit Differentiation

Let F be differentiable on its domain and suppose that $F(x, y) = 0$ defines y as a differentiable function of x. Provided $F_y \neq 0$,

$$\frac{dy}{dx} = -\frac{F_x}{F_y}.$$

EXAMPLE 5 Implicit differentiation Find dy/dx when $F(x, y) = \sin xy + \pi y^2 - x = 0$.

SOLUTION Computing the partial derivatives of F with respect to x and y, we find that

$$F_x = y \cos xy - 1 \quad \text{and} \quad F_y = x \cos xy + 2\pi y.$$

> The preceding method generalizes to computing $\dfrac{\partial z}{\partial x}$ and $\dfrac{\partial z}{\partial y}$ with functions of the form $F(x, y, z) = 0$ (Exercise 48).

Therefore,

$$\frac{dy}{dx} = -\frac{F_x}{F_y} = -\frac{y \cos xy - 1}{x \cos xy + 2\pi y}.$$

As with many implicit differentiation calculations, the result is left in terms of both x and y. The same result is obtained using the methods of Section 3.7.

Related Exercises 31–36 ◄

EXAMPLE 6 Fluid flow A basin of circulating water is represented by the square region $\{(x, y): 0 \leq x \leq 1, 0 \leq y \leq 1\}$, where x is positive in the eastward direction and y is positive in the northward direction. The velocity components of the water,

East-west velocity: $u(x, y) = 2 \sin \pi x \cos \pi y$

North-south velocity: $v(x, y) = -2 \cos \pi x \sin \pi y$,

produce the flow pattern shown in Figure 13.61. The *streamlines* shown in the figure are the paths followed by small parcels of water. The speed of the water at a point (x, y) is given by the function $s(x, y) = \sqrt{u(x, y)^2 + v(x, y)^2}$. Find $\partial s/\partial x$ and $\partial s/\partial y$, the rates of change of the water speed in the x- and y-directions, respectively.

SOLUTION The dependent variable s depends on the independent variables x and y through the intermediate variables u and v (Figure 13.62). Theorem 13.8 applies here in the form

$$\frac{\partial s}{\partial x} = \frac{\partial s}{\partial u}\frac{\partial u}{\partial x} + \frac{\partial s}{\partial v}\frac{\partial v}{\partial x} \quad \text{and} \quad \frac{\partial s}{\partial y} = \frac{\partial s}{\partial u}\frac{\partial u}{\partial y} + \frac{\partial s}{\partial v}\frac{\partial v}{\partial y}.$$

The derivatives $\partial s/\partial u$ and $\partial s/\partial v$ are easier to find if we square the speed function to obtain $s^2 = u^2 + v^2$ and then use implicit differentiation. To compute $\partial s/\partial u$, we differentiate both sides of $s^2 = u^2 + v^2$ with respect to u:

$$2s\frac{\partial s}{\partial u} = 2u, \quad \text{which implies that} \quad \frac{\partial s}{\partial u} = \frac{u}{s}.$$

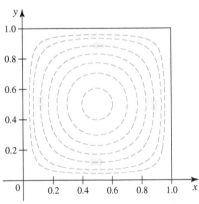

FIGURE 13.61

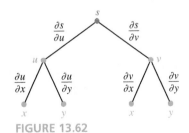

FIGURE 13.62

Similarly, differentiating $s^2 = u^2 + v^2$ with respect to v gives

$$2s\frac{\partial s}{\partial v} = 2v, \quad \text{which implies that} \quad \frac{\partial s}{\partial v} = \frac{v}{s}.$$

Now the Chain Rule leads to $\frac{\partial s}{\partial x}$:

$$\frac{\partial s}{\partial x} = \frac{\partial s}{\partial u}\frac{\partial u}{\partial x} + \frac{\partial s}{\partial v}\frac{\partial v}{\partial x}$$

$$= \underbrace{\frac{u}{s}}_{\frac{\partial s}{\partial u}}\underbrace{(2\pi \cos \pi x \cos \pi y)}_{\frac{\partial u}{\partial x}} + \underbrace{\frac{v}{s}}_{\frac{\partial s}{\partial v}}\underbrace{(2\pi \sin \pi x \sin \pi y)}_{\frac{\partial v}{\partial x}}$$

$$= \frac{2\pi}{s}(u \cos \pi x \cos \pi y + v \sin \pi x \sin \pi y).$$

A similar calculation shows that

$$\frac{\partial s}{\partial y} = -\frac{2\pi}{s}(u \sin \pi x \sin \pi y + v \cos \pi x \cos \pi y).$$

As a final step, you could replace s, u, and v by their definitions in terms of x and y.

Related Exercises 37–38 ◄

SECTION 13.5 EXERCISES

Review Questions

1. Suppose $z = f(x, y)$, where x and y are functions of t. How many dependent, intermediate, and independent variables are there?

2. Let z be a function of x and y, while x and y are functions of t. Explain how to find $\frac{dz}{dt}$.

3. Suppose w is a function of x, y, and z, which are each functions of t. Explain how to find $\frac{dw}{dt}$.

4. Let $z = f(x, y)$, $x = g(s, t)$, and $y = h(s, t)$. Explain how to find $\partial z/\partial t$.

5. Given that $w = F(x, y, z)$, and x, y, and z are functions of r and s, sketch a Chain Rule tree diagram with branches labeled with the appropriate derivatives.

6. Suppose $F(x, y) = 0$ and y is a differentiable function of x. Explain how to find dy/dx.

Basic Skills

7–16. Chain Rule with one independent variable *Use Theorem 13.7 to find the following derivatives. When feasible, express your answer in terms of the independent variable.*

7. dz/dt, where $z = x^2 + y^3$, $x = t^2$, and $y = t$

8. dz/dt, where $z = xy^2$, $x = t^2$, and $y = t$

9. dz/dt, where $z = x \sin y$, $x = t^2$, and $y = 4t^3$

10. dz/dt, where $z = x^2y - xy^3$, $x = t^2$, and $y = t^{-2}$

11. dw/dt, where $w = \cos 2x \sin 3y$, $x = t/2$, and $y = t^4$

12. dz/dt, where $z = \sqrt{r^2 + s^2}$, $r = \cos 2t$, and $s = \sin 2t$

13. dw/dt, where $w = xy \sin z$, $x = t^2$, $y = 4t^3$, and $z = t + 1$

14. dQ/dt, where $Q = \sqrt{x^2 + y^2 + z^2}$, $x = \sin t$, $y = \cos t$, and $z = \cos t$

15. dU/dt, where $U = \ln(x + y + z)$, $x = t$, $y = t^2$, and $z = t^3$

16. dV/dt, where $V = \frac{x - y}{y + z}$, $x = t$, $y = 2t$, and $z = 3t$

17. **Changing cylinder** The volume of a right circular cylinder with radius r and height h is $V = \pi r^2 h$.

   a. Assume that r and h are functions of t. Find $V'(t)$.
   b. Suppose that $r = e^t$ and $h = e^{-2t}$, for $t \geq 0$. Use part (a) to find $V'(t)$.
   c. Does the volume of the cylinder in part (b) increase or decrease as t increases?

18. **Changing pyramid** The volume of a pyramid with a square base x units on a side and a height of h is $V = \frac{1}{3}x^2h$.

   a. Assume that x and h are functions of t. Find $V'(t)$.
   b. Suppose that $x = t/(t + 1)$ and $h = 1/(t + 1)$, for $t \geq 0$. Use part (a) to find $V'(t)$.
   c. Does the volume of the pyramid in part (b) increase or decrease as t increases?

19–26. Chain Rule with several independent variables *Find the following derivatives.*

19. z_s and z_t, where $z = x^2 \sin y$, $x = s - t$, and $y = t^2$

20. z_s and z_t, where $z = \sin(2x + y)$, $x = s^2 - t^2$, and $y = s^2 + t^2$

21. z_s and z_t, where $z = xy - x^2y$, $x = s + t$, and $y = s - t$

22. z_s and z_t, where $z = \sin x \cos 2y$, $x = s + t$, and $y = s - t$

23. z_s and z_t, where $z = e^{x+y}$, $x = st$, and $y = s + t$

24. z_s and z_t, where $z = xy - 2x + 3y$, $x = \cos s$, and $y = \sin t$

25. w_s and w_t, where $w = \dfrac{x - z}{y + z}$, $x = s + t$, $y = st$, and $z = s - t$

26. w_r, w_s, and w_t, where $w = \sqrt{x^2 + y^2 + z^2}$, $x = st$, $y = rs$, and $z = rt$

27–30. Making trees *Use a tree diagram to write the required Chain Rule formula.*

27. w is a function of z, where z is a function of x and y, each of which is a function of t. Find dw/dt.

28. $w = f(x, y, z)$, where $x = g(t)$, $y = h(s, t)$, and $z = p(r, s, t)$. Find $\partial w/\partial t$.

29. $u = f(v)$, where $v = g(w, x, y)$, $w = h(z)$, $x = p(t, z)$, and $y = q(t, z)$. Find $\partial u/\partial z$.

30. $u = f(v, w, x)$, where $v = g(r, s, t)$, $w = h(r, s, t)$, $x = p(r, s, t)$, and $r = F(z)$. Find $\partial u/\partial z$.

31–36. Implicit differentiation *Given the following equations, evaluate dy/dx. Assume that each equation implicitly defines y as a differentiable function of x.*

31. $x^2 - 2y^2 - 1 = 0$

32. $x^3 + 3xy^2 - y^5 = 0$

33. $2 \sin xy = 1$

34. $ye^{xy} - 2 = 0$

35. $\sqrt{x^2 + 2xy + y^4} = 3$

36. $y \ln(x^2 + y^2 + 4) = 3$

37–38. Fluid flow *The x- and y-components of a fluid moving in two dimensions are given by the following functions u and v. The speed of the fluid at (x, y) is $s(x, y) = \sqrt{u(x, y)^2 + v(x, y)^2}$. Use the Chain Rule to find $\partial s/\partial x$ and $\partial s/\partial y$.*

37. $u(x, y) = 2y$ and $v(x, y) = -2x$; $x \geq 0$ and $y \geq 0$

38. $u(x, y) = x(1 - x)(1 - 2y)$ and $v(x, y) = y(y - 1)(1 - 2x)$; $0 \leq x \leq 1$, $0 \leq y \leq 1$

Further Explorations

39. Explain why or why not Determine whether the following statements are true and give an explanation or counterexample. Assume all partial derivatives exist.

a. If $z = (x + y) \sin xy$, where x and y are functions of s, then
$$\frac{\partial z}{\partial s} = \frac{dz}{dx} \frac{dx}{ds}.$$

b. Given that $w = f(x(s, t), y(s, t), z(s, t))$, the rate of change of w with respect to t is dw/dt.

40–41. Derivative practice two ways *Find the indicated derivative in two ways:*

a. *Replace x and y to write z as a function of t and differentiate.*

b. *Use the Chain Rule.*

40. $z'(t)$, where $z = \ln(x + y)$, $x = te^t$, and $y = e^t$

41. $z'(t)$, where $z = \dfrac{1}{x} + \dfrac{1}{y}$, $x = t^2 + 2t$, and $y = t^3 - 2$

42–46. Derivative practice *Find the indicated derivative for the following functions.*

42. $\partial z/\partial p$, where $z = x/y$, $x = p + q$, and $y = p - q$

43. dw/dt, where $w = xyz$, $x = 2t^4$, $y = 3t^{-1}$, and $z = 4t^{-3}$

44. $\partial w/\partial x$, where $w = \cos z - \cos x \cos y + \sin x \sin y$, and $z = x + y$

45. $\dfrac{\partial z}{\partial x}$, where $\dfrac{1}{x} + \dfrac{1}{y} + \dfrac{1}{z} = 1$

46. $\partial z/\partial x$, where $xy - z = 1$.

47. Change on a line Suppose $w = f(x, y, z)$ and ℓ is the line $\mathbf{r}(t) = \langle at, bt, ct \rangle$, for $-\infty < t < \infty$.

a. Find $w'(t)$ on ℓ (in terms of a, b, c, w_x, w_y, and w_z).

b. Apply part (a) to find $w'(t)$ when $f(x, y, z) = xyz$.

c. Apply part (a) to find $w'(t)$ when $f(x, y, z) = \sqrt{x^2 + y^2 + z^2}$.

d. For a general function $w = f(x, y, z)$, find $w''(t)$.

48. Implicit differentiation rule with three variables Assume that $F(x, y, z(x, y)) = 0$ implicitly defines z as a differentiable function of x and y. Extend Theorem 13.9 to show that
$$\frac{\partial z}{\partial x} = -\frac{F_x}{F_z} \quad \text{and} \quad \frac{\partial z}{\partial y} = -\frac{F_y}{F_z}.$$

49–51. Implicit differentiation with three variables *Use the result of Exercise 48 to evaluate $\dfrac{\partial z}{\partial x}$ and $\dfrac{\partial z}{\partial y}$ for the following relations.*

49. $xy + xz + yz = 3$

50. $x^2 + 2y^2 - 3z^2 = 1$

51. $xyz + x + y - z = 0$

52. More than one way Let $e^{xyz} = 2$. Find z_x and z_y in three ways (and check for agreement).

a. Use the result of Exercise 48.

b. Take logarithms of both sides and differentiate $xyz = \ln 2$.

c. Solve for z and differentiate $z = \ln 2/(xy)$.

53–56. Walking on a surface *Consider the following surfaces specified in the form $z = f(x, y)$ and the curve C in the xy-plane given parametrically in the form $x = g(t), y = h(t)$.*

a. In each case, find $z'(t)$.

b. Imagine that you are walking on the surface directly above the curve C in the direction of increasing t. Find the values of t for which you are walking uphill (that is, z is increasing).

53. $z = x^2 + 4y^2 + 1, C: x = \cos t, y = \sin t; \ 0 \le t \le 2\pi$

54. $z = 4x^2 - y^2 + 1, C: x = \cos t, y = \sin t; \ 0 \le t \le 2\pi$

55. $z = \sqrt{1 - x^2 - y^2}, C: x = e^{-t}, y = e^{-t}; \ t \ge \frac{1}{2}\ln 2$

56. $z = 2x^2 + y^2 + 1, C: x = 1 + \cos t, y = \sin t; 0 \le t \le 2\pi$

Applications

57. Conservation of energy A projectile with mass m is launched into the air on a parabolic trajectory. For $t \ge 0$, its horizontal and vertical coordinates are $x(t) = u_0 t$ and $y(t) = -\frac{1}{2}gt^2 + v_0 t$, respectively, where u_0 is the initial horizontal velocity, v_0 is the initial vertical velocity, and g is the acceleration due to gravity. Recalling that $u(t) = x'(t)$ and $v(t) = y'(t)$ are the components of the velocity, the energy of the projectile (kinetic plus potential) is

$$E(t) = \frac{1}{2}m(u^2 + v^2) + mgy.$$

Use the Chain Rule to compute $E'(t)$ and show that $E'(t) = 0$, for all $t \ge 0$. Interpret the result.

58. Utility functions in economics Economists use *utility functions* to describe consumers' relative preference for two or more commodities (for example, vanilla vs. chocolate ice cream or leisure time vs. material goods). The Cobb-Douglas family of utility functions has the form $U(x, y) = x^a y^{1-a}$, where x and y are the amounts of two commodities and $0 < a < 1$ is a parameter. Level curves on which the utility function is constant are called *indifference curves*; the utility is the same for all combinations of x and y along an indifference curve (see figure).

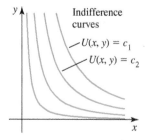

a. The marginal utilities of the commodities x and y are defined to be $\partial U/\partial x$ and $\partial U/\partial y$, respectively. Compute the marginal utilities for the utility function $U(x, y) = x^a y^{1-a}$.

b. The marginal rate of substitution (MRS) is the slope of the indifference curve at the point (x, y). Use the Chain Rule to show that for $U(x, y) = x^a y^{1-a}$, the MRS is

$$-\frac{a}{1 - a}\frac{y}{x}.$$

c. Find the MRS for the utility function $U(x, y) = x^{0.4}y^{0.6}$ at $(x, y) = (8, 12)$.

59. Constant volume tori The volume of a solid torus (a bagel or doughnut) is given by $V = (\pi^2/4)(R + r)(R - r)^2$, where r and R are the inner and outer radii and $R > r$ (see figure).

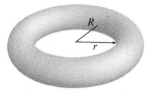

a. If R and r increase at the same rate, does the volume of the torus increase, decrease, or remain constant?

b. If R and r decrease at the same rate, does the volume of the torus increase, decrease, or remain constant?

60. Body surface area One of several empirical formulas that relates the surface area S of a human body to the height h and weight w of the body is the Mosteller formula $S(h, w) = \frac{1}{60}\sqrt{hw}$, where h is measured in centimeters, w is measured in kilograms, and S is measured in square meters. Suppose that h and w are functions of t.

a. Find $S'(t)$.

b. Show that the condition that the surface area remains constant as h and w change is $wh'(t) + hw'(t) = 0$.

c. Show that part (b) implies that for constant surface area, h and w must be inversely related; that is, $h = C/w$, where C is a constant.

61. The Ideal Gas Law The pressure, temperature, and volume of an ideal gas are related by $PV = kT$, where $k > 0$ is a constant. Any two of the variables may be considered independent, which determines the third variable.

a. Use implicit differentiation to compute the partial derivatives $\dfrac{\partial P}{\partial V}, \dfrac{\partial T}{\partial P},$ and $\dfrac{\partial V}{\partial T}.$

b. Show that $\dfrac{\partial P}{\partial V}\dfrac{\partial T}{\partial P}\dfrac{\partial V}{\partial T} = -1$. (See Exercise 67 for a generalization.)

62. Variable density The density of a thin circular plate of radius 2 is given by $\rho(x, y) = 4 + xy$. The edge of the plate is described by the parametric equations $x = 2\cos t, y = 2\sin t$, for $0 \le t \le 2\pi$.

a. Find the rate of change of the density with respect to t on the edge of the plate.

b. At what point(s) on the edge of the plate is the density a maximum?

63. Spiral through a domain Suppose you follow the spiral path $C: x = \cos t, y = \sin t, z = t$, for $t \geq 0$, through the domain of the function $w = f(x, y, z) = (xyz)/(z^2 + 1)$.

  a. Find $w'(t)$ along C.

  b. Estimate the point (x, y, z) on C at which w has its maximum value.

Additional Exercises

64. Change of coordinates Recall that Cartesian and polar coordinates are related through the transformation equations

$$\begin{cases} x = r \cos \theta \\ y = r \sin \theta \end{cases} \quad \text{or} \quad \begin{cases} r^2 = x^2 + y^2 \\ \tan \theta = y/x. \end{cases}$$

  a. Evaluate the partial derivatives $x_r, y_r, x_\theta,$ and y_θ.

  b. Evaluate the partial derivatives $r_x, r_y, \theta_x,$ and θ_y.

  c. For a function $z = f(x, y)$, find z_r and z_θ, where x and y are expressed in terms of r and θ.

  d. For a function $z = g(r, \theta)$, find z_x and z_y, where r and θ are expressed in terms of x and y.

  e. Show that $\left(\dfrac{\partial z}{\partial x}\right)^2 + \left(\dfrac{\partial z}{\partial y}\right)^2 = \left(\dfrac{\partial z}{\partial r}\right)^2 + \dfrac{1}{r^2}\left(\dfrac{\partial z}{\partial \theta}\right)^2$.

65. Change of coordinates continued An important derivative operation in many applications is called the Laplacian; in Cartesian coordinates, for $z = f(x, y)$, the Laplacian is $z_{xx} + z_{yy}$. Determine the Laplacian in polar coordinates using the following steps.

  a. Begin with $z = g(r, \theta)$ and write z_x and z_y in terms of polar coordinates (see Exercise 64).

  b. Use the Chain Rule to find $z_{xx} = \dfrac{\partial}{\partial x}(z_x)$. There should be two major terms, which, when expanded and simplified, result in five terms.

  c. Use the Chain Rule to find $z_{yy} = \dfrac{\partial}{\partial y}(z_y)$. There should be two major terms, which, when expanded and simplified, result in five terms.

  d. Combine parts (b) and (c) to show that

$$z_{xx} + z_{yy} = z_{rr} + \frac{1}{r} z_r + \frac{1}{r^2} z_{\theta\theta}.$$

66. Geometry of implicit differentiation Suppose x and y are related by the equation $F(x, y) = 0$. Interpret the solution of this equation as the set of points (x, y) that lie on the intersection of the surface $z = F(x, y)$ with the xy-plane $(z = 0)$.

  a. Make a sketch of a surface and its intersection with the xy-plane. Give a geometric interpretation of the result that $\dfrac{dy}{dx} = -\dfrac{F_x}{F_y}$.

  b. Explain geometrically what happens at points where $F_y = 0$.

67. General three-variable relationship In the implicit relationship $F(x, y, z) = 0$, any two of the variables may be considered independent, which then determines the third variable. To avoid confusion, we use a subscript to indicate which variable is held fixed in a derivative calculation; for example $\left(\dfrac{\partial z}{\partial x}\right)_y$ means that y is held fixed in taking the partial derivative of z with respect to x. (In this context, the subscript does *not* mean a derivative.)

  a. Differentiate $F(x, y, z) = 0$ with respect to x holding y fixed to show that $\left(\dfrac{\partial z}{\partial x}\right)_y = -\dfrac{F_x}{F_z}$.

  b. As in part (a), find $\left(\dfrac{\partial y}{\partial z}\right)_x$ and $\left(\dfrac{\partial x}{\partial y}\right)_z$.

  c. Show that $\left(\dfrac{\partial z}{\partial x}\right)_y \left(\dfrac{\partial y}{\partial z}\right)_x \left(\dfrac{\partial x}{\partial y}\right)_z = -1$.

  d. Find the relationship analogous to part (c) for the case $F(w, x, y, z) = 0$.

68. Second derivative Let $f(x, y) = 0$ define y as a twice differentiable function of x.

  a. Show that $y''(x) = -\dfrac{f_{xx}f_y{}^2 - 2f_x f_y f_{xy} + f_{yy}f_x{}^2}{f_y{}^3}$.

  b. Verify part (a) using the function $f(x, y) = xy - 1$.

69. Subtleties of the Chain Rule Let $w = f(x, y, z) = 2x + 3y + 4z$, which is defined for all (x, y, z) in $\mathbb{R}^3$. Suppose that we are interested in the partial derivative w_x on a subset of $\mathbb{R}^3$, such as the plane P given by $z = 4x - 2y$. The point to be made is that the result is not unique unless we specify which variables are considered independent.

  a. We could proceed as follows. On the plane P, consider x and y as the independent variables, which means z depends on x and y, so we write $w = f(x, y, z(x, y))$. Differentiate with respect to x holding y fixed to show that $\left(\dfrac{\partial w}{\partial x}\right)_y = 18$, where the subscript y indicates that y is held fixed.

  b. Alternatively, on the plane P, we could consider x and z as the independent variables, which means y depends on x and z, so we write $w = f(x, y(x, z), z)$ and differentiate with respect to x holding z fixed. Show that $\left(\dfrac{\partial w}{\partial x}\right)_z = 8$, where the subscript z indicates that z is held fixed.

  c. Make a sketch of the plane $z = 4x - 2y$ and interpret the results of parts (a) and (b) geometrically.

  d. Repeat the arguments of parts (a) and (b) to find $\left(\dfrac{\partial w}{\partial y}\right)_x$, $\left(\dfrac{\partial w}{\partial y}\right)_z$, $\left(\dfrac{\partial w}{\partial z}\right)_x$, and $\left(\dfrac{\partial w}{\partial z}\right)_y$.

QUICK CHECK ANSWERS

1. If $z = f(x(t))$, then $\dfrac{\partial z}{\partial y} = 0$, and the original Chain Rule results. **2.** $\dfrac{\partial w}{\partial t} = \dfrac{\partial w}{\partial x}\dfrac{\partial x}{\partial t} + \dfrac{\partial w}{\partial y}\dfrac{\partial y}{\partial t} + \dfrac{\partial w}{\partial z}\dfrac{\partial z}{\partial t}$

3. One dependent variable, four intermediate variables, and three independent variables

13.6 Directional Derivatives and the Gradient

Partial derivatives tell us a lot about the rate of change of a function on its domain. However, they do not *directly* answer some important questions. For example, suppose you are standing at a point $(a, b, f(a, b))$ on the surface $z = f(x, y)$. The partial derivatives f_x and f_y tell you the rate of change (or slope) of the surface at that point in the directions parallel to the x-axis and y-axis, respectively. But you could walk in an infinite number of directions from that point and find a different rate of change in every direction. With this observation in mind, we pose several questions.

• Suppose you are standing on a surface and you walk in a direction *other* than a coordinate direction—say, northwest or south-southeast. What is the rate of change of the function in such a direction?

• Suppose you are standing on a surface and you release a ball at your feet and let it roll. In which direction will it roll?

• If you are hiking up a mountain, in what direction should you walk after each step if you want to follow the steepest path?

These questions will be answered in this section as we introduce the *directional derivative*, followed by one of the central concepts of calculus—the *gradient*.

Directional Derivatives

Let $(a, b, f(a, b))$ be a point on the surface $z = f(x, y)$ and let $\mathbf{u}$ be a unit vector in the xy-plane (Figure 13.63). Our aim is to find the rate of change of f in the direction $\mathbf{u}$ at $P_0(a, b)$. In general, this rate of change is neither $f_x(a, b)$ nor $f_y(a, b)$ (unless $\mathbf{u} = \langle 1, 0 \rangle$ or $\mathbf{u} = \langle 0, 1 \rangle$), but it turns out to be a combination of $f_x(a, b)$ and $f_y(a, b)$.

Figure 13.64a shows the unit vector $\mathbf{u}$ at an angle θ to the positive x-axis; its components are $\mathbf{u} = \langle u_1, u_2 \rangle = \langle \cos \theta, \sin \theta \rangle$. The derivative we seek must be computed along the line ℓ in the xy-plane through P_0 in the direction of $\mathbf{u}$. A neighboring point P, which is h units from P_0 along ℓ, has coordinates $P(a + h \cos \theta, b + h \sin \theta)$ (Figure 13.64b).

Now imagine the plane Q perpendicular to the xy-plane, containing ℓ. This plane cuts the surface $z = f(x, y)$ in a curve C. Consider two points on C corresponding to P_0 and P; they have z-coordinates $f(a, b)$ and $f(a + h \cos \theta, b + h \sin \theta)$ (Figure 13.65). The slope of the secant line between these points is

$$\frac{f(a + h \cos \theta, b + h \sin \theta) - f(a, b)}{h}.$$

The derivative of f in the direction of $\mathbf{u}$ is obtained by letting $h \to 0$; when the limit exists, it is called the *directional derivative of f at (a, b) in the direction of $\mathbf{u}$*. It gives the slope of the line tangent to the curve C in the plane Q.

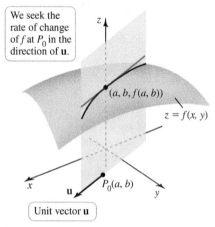

We seek the rate of change of f at P_0 in the direction of $\mathbf{u}$.

Unit vector $\mathbf{u}$

FIGURE 13.63

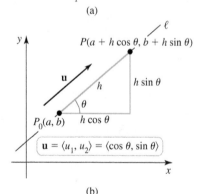

(a)

(b)

FIGURE 13.64

DEFINITION Directional Derivative

Let f be differentiable at (a, b) and let $\mathbf{u} = \langle \cos \theta, \sin \theta \rangle$ be a unit vector in the xy-plane. The **directional derivative of f at (a, b) in the direction of $\mathbf{u}$** is

$$D_{\mathbf{u}} f(a, b) = \lim_{h \to 0} \frac{f(a + h \cos \theta, b + h \sin \theta) - f(a, b)}{h},$$

provided the limit exists.

QUICK CHECK 1 Explain why, when $\theta = 0$ in the definition of the directional derivative, the result is $f_x(a, b)$ and when $\theta = \pi/2$, the result is $f_y(a, b)$. ◄

▶ The definition of the directional derivative looks like the definition of the ordinary derivative if we write it as

$$\lim_{P \to P_0} \frac{f(P) - f(P_0)}{|P - P_0|},$$

where P approaches P_0 along the line determined by the angle θ.

Slope of tangent line
$= \lim_{h \to 0} \dfrac{f(a + h \cos \theta, b + h \sin \theta) - f(a, b)}{h}$

Slope of secant line $= \dfrac{f(a + h \cos \theta, b + h \sin \theta) - f(a, b)}{h}$

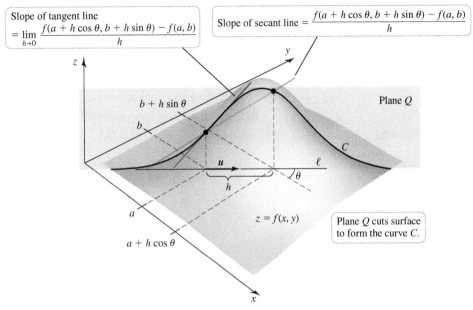

Plane Q

$z = f(x, y)$

Plane Q cuts surface to form the curve C.

FIGURE 13.65

As with ordinary derivatives, we would prefer to evaluate directional derivatives without taking limits. Fortunately, there is an easy way to express the directional derivative in terms of partial derivatives.

The key is to define a function that is equal to f along the line ℓ through (a, b) in the direction of the unit vector $\mathbf{u} = \langle u_1, u_2 \rangle$. The points on ℓ satisfy the parametric equations

$$x = a + su_1 \quad \text{and} \quad y = b + su_2,$$

▶ To see that s is an arc length parameter, note that the line ℓ may be written in the form

$$\mathbf{r}(s) = \langle a + su_1, b + su_2 \rangle.$$

Therefore, $\mathbf{r}'(s) = \langle u_1, u_2 \rangle$ and $|\mathbf{r}'(s)| = 1$. It follows by the discussion in Section 12.8 that s is an arc length parameter. Because the directional derivative is a derivative with respect to length along ℓ, it is essential that s be an arc length parameter, which occurs only if $\mathbf{u}$ is a unit vector.

where $-\infty < s < \infty$. Because $\mathbf{u}$ is a unit vector, the parameter s corresponds to arc length. As s increases, the points (x, y) move along ℓ in the direction of $\mathbf{u}$ with $s = 0$ corresponding to (a, b). Now we define the function

$$g(s) = f(\underbrace{a + su_1}_{x}, \underbrace{b + su_2}_{y}),$$

which gives the values of f along ℓ. The derivative of f along ℓ is $g'(s)$, and when evaluated at $s = 0$, it is the directional derivative of f at (a, b); that is, $g'(0) = D_{\mathbf{u}}f(a, b)$.

Noting that $\dfrac{dx}{ds} = u_1$ and $\dfrac{dy}{ds} = u_2$, we apply the Chain Rule to find that

$$D_{\mathbf{u}}f(a, b) = g'(0) = \left[\frac{\partial f}{\partial x} \underbrace{\frac{dx}{ds}}_{u_1} + \frac{\partial f}{\partial y} \underbrace{\frac{dy}{ds}}_{u_2} \right]\Bigg|_{s=0} \qquad \text{Chain Rule}$$

$$= f_x(a, b)u_1 + f_y(a, b)u_2. \qquad s = 0 \text{ corresponds to } (a, b).$$

We see that the directional derivative is a weighted average of the partial derivatives $f_x(a, b)$ and $f_y(a, b)$, with the components of $\mathbf{u}$ serving as the weights. In other words, knowing the slope of the surface in the x- and y-directions allows us to find the slope in any direction. Notice that the directional derivative can be written as a dot product, which provides a practical formula for computing directional derivatives.

QUICK CHECK 2 In the parametric description $x = a + su_1$ and $y = b + su_2$, where $\mathbf{u} = \langle u_1, u_2 \rangle$ is a unit vector, show that any positive change Δs in s produces a line segment of length Δs. ◄

THEOREM 13.10   Directional Derivative

Let f be differentiable at (a, b) and let $\mathbf{u} = \langle u_1, u_2 \rangle$ be a unit vector in the xy-plane. The **directional derivative of f at (a, b) in the direction of u** is

$$D_{\mathbf{u}}f(a, b) = \langle f_x(a, b), f_y(a, b) \rangle \cdot \langle u_1, u_2 \rangle$$

EXAMPLE 1   **Computing directional derivatives** Consider the paraboloid $z = f(x, y) = \frac{1}{4}(x^2 + 2y^2) + 2$. Let P_0 be the point $(3, 2)$ and consider the unit vectors

$$\mathbf{u} = \left\langle \frac{1}{\sqrt{2}}, \frac{1}{\sqrt{2}} \right\rangle \quad \text{and} \quad \mathbf{v} = \left\langle \frac{1}{2}, -\frac{\sqrt{3}}{2} \right\rangle.$$

a. Find the directional derivative of f at P_0 in the directions of $\mathbf{u}$ and $\mathbf{v}$.

b. Graph the surface and interpret the directional derivatives.

SOLUTION

a. We see that $f_x = x/2$ and $f_y = y$; evaluated at $(3, 2)$, we have $f_x(3, 2) = 3/2$ and $f_y(3, 2) = 2$. The directional derivatives in the directions $\mathbf{u}$ and $\mathbf{v}$ are

$$D_{\mathbf{u}}f(3, 2) = \langle f_x(3, 2), f_y(3, 2) \rangle \cdot \langle u_1, u_2 \rangle$$

$$= \frac{3}{2} \cdot \frac{1}{\sqrt{2}} + 2 \cdot \frac{1}{\sqrt{2}} = \frac{7}{2\sqrt{2}} \approx 2.47 \text{ and}$$

$$D_{\mathbf{v}}f(3, 2) = \langle f_x(3, 2), f_y(3, 2) \rangle \cdot \langle v_1, v_2 \rangle$$

$$= \frac{3}{2} \cdot \frac{1}{2} + 2\left(-\frac{\sqrt{3}}{2}\right) = \frac{3}{4} - \sqrt{3} \approx -0.98.$$

> It is understood that the line tangent to the curve C in the direction of $\mathbf{u}$ lies in the plane Q containing $\mathbf{u}$ perpendicular to the xy-plane.

b. In the direction of $\mathbf{u}$, the directional derivative is approximately 2.47. Because it is positive, the function is increasing at $(3, 2)$ in this direction. Equivalently, the slope of the line tangent to the curve C in the direction of $\mathbf{u}$ is approximately 2.47 (Figure 13.66a). In the direction of $\mathbf{v}$, the directional derivative is approximately -0.98. Because it is negative, the function is decreasing in this direction. In this case, the slope of the line tangent to the curve C in the direction of $\mathbf{v}$ is approximately -0.98 (Figure 13.66b).

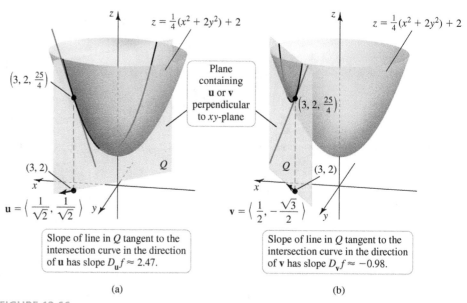

$z = \frac{1}{4}(x^2 + 2y^2) + 2$

$\left(3, 2, \frac{25}{4}\right)$

$(3, 2)$

x

Q

$\mathbf{u} = \left\langle \frac{1}{\sqrt{2}}, \frac{1}{\sqrt{2}} \right\rangle$ y

Plane containing $\mathbf{u}$ or $\mathbf{v}$ perpendicular to xy-plane

Slope of line in Q tangent to the intersection curve in the direction of $\mathbf{u}$ has slope $D_{\mathbf{u}}f \approx 2.47$.

(a)

$z = \frac{1}{4}(x^2 + 2y^2) + 2$

$\left(3, 2, \frac{25}{4}\right)$

$(3, 2)$

x

Q

$\mathbf{v} = \left\langle \frac{1}{2}, -\frac{\sqrt{3}}{2} \right\rangle$ y

Slope of line in Q tangent to the intersection curve in the direction of $\mathbf{v}$ has slope $D_{\mathbf{v}}f \approx -0.98$.

(b)

FIGURE 13.66

Related Exercises 7–8 ◄

QUICK CHECK 3 In Example 1, evaluate $D_{-\mathbf{u}}f(a, b)$ and $D_{-\mathbf{v}}f(a, b)$. ◄

The Gradient Vector

We have seen that the directional derivative can be written as a dot product: $D_\mathbf{u} f(a, b) = \langle f_x(a, b), f_y(a, b) \rangle \cdot \langle u_1, u_2 \rangle$. The vector $\langle f_x(a, b), f_y(a, b) \rangle$ that appears in the dot product is important in its own right and is called the *gradient* of f.

> Recall that the unit coordinate vectors in $\mathbb{R}^2$ are $\mathbf{i} = \langle 1, 0 \rangle$ and $\mathbf{j} = \langle 0, 1 \rangle$. The gradient of f is also written grad f, read *grad f*.

DEFINITION Gradient (Two Dimensions)

Let f be differentiable at the point (x, y). The **gradient** of f at (x, y) is the vector-valued function

$$\nabla f(x, y) = \langle f_x(x, y), f_y(x, y) \rangle = f_x(x, y)\,\mathbf{i} + f_y(x, y)\,\mathbf{j}.$$

With the definition of the gradient, the directional derivative of f at (a, b) in the direction of the unit vector $\mathbf{u}$ can be written

$$D_\mathbf{u} f(a, b) = \nabla f(a, b) \cdot \mathbf{u}.$$

The gradient satisfies sum, product, and quotient rules analogous to those for ordinary derivatives (Exercise 81).

EXAMPLE 2   Computing gradients Find ∇f and $\nabla f(3, 2)$ for $f(x, y) = x^2 + 2xy - y^3$.

SOLUTION Computing $f_x = 2x + 2y$ and $f_y = 2x - 3y^2$, we have

$$\nabla f(x, y) = \langle 2(x + y), 2x - 3y^2 \rangle = 2(x + y)\,\mathbf{i} + (2x - 3y^2)\,\mathbf{j}.$$

Substituting $x = 3$ and $y = 2$ gives

$$\nabla f(3, 2) = \langle 10, -6 \rangle = 10\,\mathbf{i} - 6\,\mathbf{j}.$$

Related Exercises 9–16 ◄

EXAMPLE 3   Computing directional derivatives with gradients Let

$$f(x, y) = 3 - \frac{x^2}{10} + \frac{xy^2}{10}.$$

a. Compute $\nabla f(3, -1)$.

b. Compute $D_\mathbf{u} f(3, -1)$, where $\mathbf{u} = \left\langle \dfrac{1}{\sqrt{2}}, -\dfrac{1}{\sqrt{2}} \right\rangle$.

c. Compute the directional derivative of f at $(3, -1)$ in the direction of the vector $\langle 3, 4 \rangle$.

SOLUTION

a. Note that $f_x = -x/5 + y^2/10$ and $f_y = xy/5$. Therefore,

$$\nabla f(3, -1) = \left\langle -\frac{x}{5} + \frac{y^2}{10}, \frac{xy}{5} \right\rangle \bigg|_{(3, -1)} = \left\langle -\frac{1}{2}, -\frac{3}{5} \right\rangle.$$

b. Before computing the directional derivative, it is important to verify that $\mathbf{u}$ is a unit vector (in this case, it is). The required directional derivative is

$$D_\mathbf{u} f(3, -1) = \nabla f(3, -1) \cdot \mathbf{u} = \left\langle -\frac{1}{2}, -\frac{3}{5} \right\rangle \cdot \left\langle \frac{1}{\sqrt{2}}, -\frac{1}{\sqrt{2}} \right\rangle = \frac{1}{10\sqrt{2}}.$$

Figure 13.67 shows the line tangent to the intersection curve in the plane corresponding to $\mathbf{u}$ whose slope is $D_\mathbf{u} f(3, -1)$.

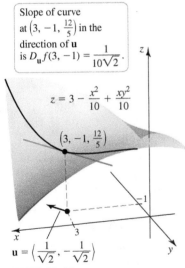

Slope of curve at $\left(3, -1, \frac{12}{5}\right)$ in the direction of $\mathbf{u}$ is $D_\mathbf{u} f(3, -1) = \dfrac{1}{10\sqrt{2}}$.

$z = 3 - \dfrac{x^2}{10} + \dfrac{xy^2}{10}$

$\left(3, -1, \frac{12}{5}\right)$

$\mathbf{u} = \left\langle \dfrac{1}{\sqrt{2}}, -\dfrac{1}{\sqrt{2}} \right\rangle$

FIGURE 13.67

c. In this case, the direction is given in terms of a nonunit vector. The vector $\langle 3, 4 \rangle$ has length 5, so the unit vector in the direction of $\langle 3, 4 \rangle$ is $\mathbf{u} = \langle \frac{3}{5}, \frac{4}{5} \rangle$. The directional derivative at $(3, -1)$ in the direction of $\mathbf{u}$ is

$$D_{\mathbf{u}}f(3, -1) = \nabla f(3, -1) \cdot \mathbf{u} = \left\langle -\frac{1}{2}, -\frac{3}{5} \right\rangle \cdot \left\langle \frac{3}{5}, \frac{4}{5} \right\rangle = -\frac{39}{50},$$

which gives the slope of the surface in the direction of $\mathbf{u}$ at $(3, -1)$.

Related Exercises 17–26 ◄

Interpretations of the Gradient

The gradient is important not only in calculating directional derivatives; it plays many other roles in multivariable calculus. Our present goal is to develop some intuition about the meaning of the gradient.

> Recall that $\mathbf{u} \cdot \mathbf{v} = |\mathbf{u}||\mathbf{v}| \cos \theta$, where θ is the angle between $\mathbf{u}$ and $\mathbf{v}$.

We have seen that the directional derivative of f at (a, b) in the direction of the unit vector $\mathbf{u}$ is $D_{\mathbf{u}}f(a, b) = \nabla f(a, b) \cdot \mathbf{u}$. Using properties of the dot product, we have

$$
\begin{aligned}
D_{\mathbf{u}}f(a, b) &= \nabla f(a, b) \cdot \mathbf{u} \\
&= |\nabla f(a, b)||\mathbf{u}| \cos \theta \\
&= |\nabla f(a, b)| \cos \theta, \qquad |\mathbf{u}| = 1
\end{aligned}
$$

where θ is the angle between $\nabla f(a, b)$ and $\mathbf{u}$. It follows that $D_{\mathbf{u}}f(a, b)$ has its maximum value when $\cos \theta = 1$, which corresponds to $\theta = 0$. Therefore, $D_{\mathbf{u}}f(a, b)$ has its maximum value and f has its greatest rate of *increase* when $\nabla f(a, b)$ and $\mathbf{u}$ point in the same direction. Notice that when $\cos \theta = 1$, the actual rate of increase is $D_{\mathbf{u}}f(a, b) = |\nabla f(a, b)|$ (Figure 13.68).

> It is important to remember and easy to forget that $\nabla f(a, b)$ lies in the same plane as the domain of f.

Similarly, when $\theta = \pi$, we have $\cos \theta = -1$, and f has its greatest rate of *decrease* when $\nabla f(a, b)$ and $\mathbf{u}$ point in opposite directions. The actual rate of decrease is $D_{\mathbf{u}}f(a, b) = -|\nabla f(a, b)|$. These observations are summarized as follows: The gradient $\nabla f(a, b)$ points in the *direction of steepest ascent* at (a, b), while $-\nabla f(a, b)$ points in the *direction of steepest descent*.

Notice that $D_{\mathbf{u}}f(a, b) = 0$ when the angle between $\nabla f(a, b)$ and $\mathbf{u}$ is $\pi/2$, which means $\nabla f(a, b)$ and $\mathbf{u}$ are orthogonal (Figure 13.68). These observations justify the following theorem.

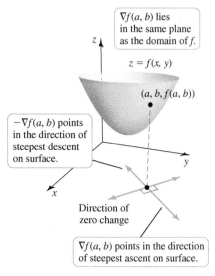

$\nabla f(a, b)$ lies in the same plane as the domain of f.

$z = f(x, y)$

$(a, b, f(a, b))$

$-\nabla f(a, b)$ points in the direction of steepest descent on surface.

Direction of zero change

$\nabla f(a, b)$ points in the direction of steepest ascent on surface.

FIGURE 13.68

THEOREM 13.11   Directions of Change

Let f be differentiable at (a, b) with $\nabla f(a, b) \neq \mathbf{0}$.

1. f has its maximum rate of increase at (a, b) in the direction of the gradient $\nabla f(a, b)$. The rate of increase in this direction is $|\nabla f(a, b)|$.

2. f has its maximum rate of decrease at (a, b) in the direction of $-\nabla f(a, b)$. The rate of decrease in this direction is $-|\nabla f(a, b)|$.

3. The directional derivative is zero in any direction orthogonal to $\nabla f(a, b)$.

EXAMPLE 4   Steepest ascent and descent Consider the bowl-shaped paraboloid $z = f(x, y) = 4 + x^2 + 3y^2$.

a. If you are located on the paraboloid at the point $\left(2, -\frac{1}{2}, \frac{35}{4} \right)$, in which direction should you move in order to *ascend* on the surface at the maximum rate? What is the rate of change?

b. If you are located at the point $\left(2, -\frac{1}{2}, \frac{35}{4} \right)$, in which direction should you walk in order to *descend* on the surface at the maximum rate? What is the rate of change?

c. At the point $(3, 1, 16)$, in what direction(s) is there no change in the function values?

SOLUTION

a. At the point $\left(2, -\frac{1}{2}\right)$, the value of the gradient is

$$\nabla f\left(2, -\frac{1}{2}\right) = \langle 2x, 6y \rangle|_{(2, -1/2)} = \langle 4, -3 \rangle.$$

Therefore, the direction of steepest ascent in the xy-plane is in the direction of the gradient vector $\langle 4, -3 \rangle$ (or $\mathbf{u} = \frac{1}{5}\langle 4, -3 \rangle$, as a unit vector). The rate of change is $\left|\nabla f\left(2, -\frac{1}{2}\right)\right| = \left|\langle 4, -3 \rangle\right| = 5$ (Figure 13.69a).

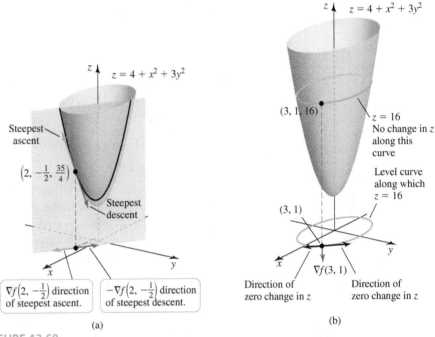

$\nabla f\left(2, -\frac{1}{2}\right)$ direction of steepest ascent. $-\nabla f\left(2, -\frac{1}{2}\right)$ direction of steepest descent.

(a)

FIGURE 13.69

b. The direction of steepest *descent* is the direction of $-\nabla f\left(2, -\frac{1}{2}\right) = \langle -4, 3 \rangle$ (or $\mathbf{u} = \frac{1}{5}\langle -4, 3 \rangle$, as a unit vector). The rate of change is $-\left|\nabla f\left(2, -\frac{1}{2}\right)\right| = -5$.

> Note that $\langle 6, 6 \rangle$ and $\langle 6, -6 \rangle$ are orthogonal because $\langle 6, 6 \rangle \cdot \langle 6, -6 \rangle = 0$.

c. At the point $(3, 1)$, the value of the gradient is $\nabla f(3, 1) = \langle 6, 6 \rangle$. The function has zero change if we move in either of the two directions orthogonal to $\langle 6, 6 \rangle$; these two directions are parallel to $\langle 6, -6 \rangle$. In terms of unit vectors, the directions of no change are $\mathbf{u} = \frac{1}{\sqrt{2}}\langle -1, 1 \rangle$ and $\mathbf{u} = \frac{1}{\sqrt{2}}\langle 1, -1 \rangle$ (Figure 13.69b).

Related Exercises 27–32 ◄

EXAMPLE 5   Interpreting directional derivatives Consider the function $f(x, y) = 3x^2 - 2y^2$.

a. Compute $\nabla f(x, y)$ and $\nabla f(2, 3)$.

b. Let $\mathbf{u} = \langle \cos\theta, \sin\theta \rangle$ be a unit vector. For what values of θ (measured relative to the positive x-axis), with $0 \le \theta < 2\pi$, does the directional derivative have its maximum and minimum values and what are those values?

SOLUTION

a. The gradient is $\nabla f(x, y) = \langle f_x, f_y \rangle = \langle 6x, -4y \rangle$, and at $(2, 3)$, we have $\nabla f(2, 3) = \langle 12, -12 \rangle$.

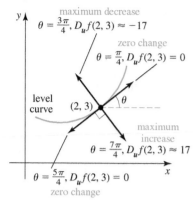

maximum decrease
$\theta = \frac{3\pi}{4}, D_u f(2, 3) \approx -17$

zero change
$\theta = \frac{\pi}{4}, D_u f(2, 3) = 0$

level curve   (2, 3)

maximum increase
$\theta = \frac{7\pi}{4}, D_u f(2, 3) \approx 17$

$\theta = \frac{5\pi}{4}, D_u f(2, 3) = 0$
zero change

FIGURE 13.70

b. The gradient $\nabla f(2, 3) = \langle 12, -12 \rangle$ makes an angle of $7\pi/4$ with the positive x-axis. So, the maximum rate of change of f occurs in this direction, and that rate of change is $|\nabla f(2, 3)| = |\langle 12, -12 \rangle| = 12\sqrt{2} \approx 17$. The direction of maximum decrease is opposite to the direction of the gradient, which corresponds to $\theta = 3\pi/4$. The maximum rate of decrease is the negative of the maximum rate of increase, or $-12\sqrt{2} \approx -17$. The function has zero change in the directions orthogonal to the gradient, which correspond to $\theta = \pi/4$ and $\theta = 5\pi/4$.

Figure 13.70 summarizes these conclusions. Notice that the gradient at $(2, 3)$ appears to be orthogonal to the level curve of f passing through $(2, 3)$. We next see that this is always the case.

Related Exercises 33–42 ◄

The Gradient and Level Curves

Theorem 13.11 states that in any direction orthogonal to the gradient $\nabla f(a, b)$, the function f does not change at (a, b). Recall from Section 13.2 that the curve $f(x, y) = z_0$, where z_0 is a constant, is a *level curve*, on which function values are constant. Combining these two observations, we conclude that the gradient $\nabla f(a, b)$ is orthogonal to the line tangent to the level curve through (a, b).

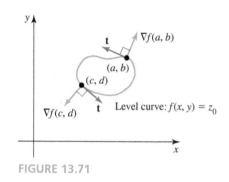

FIGURE 13.71

> We have used the fact that the vector $\langle a, b \rangle$ has slope b/a.

THEOREM 13.12   The Gradient and Level Curves
Given a function f differentiable at (a, b), the line tangent to the level curve of f at (a, b) is orthogonal to the gradient $\nabla f(a, b)$, provided $\nabla f(a, b) \neq \mathbf{0}$.

Proof: A level curve of the function $z = f(x, y)$ is a curve in the xy-plane of the form $f(x, y) = z_0$, where z_0 is a constant. By Theorem 13.9, the slope of the line tangent to the level curve is $y'(x) = -f_x/f_y$.

It follows that any vector that points in the direction of the tangent line at the point (a, b) is a scalar multiple of the vector $\mathbf{t} = \langle -f_y(a, b), f_x(a, b) \rangle$ (Figure 13.71). At that same point, the gradient points in the direction $\nabla f(a, b) = \langle f_x(a, b), f_y(a, b) \rangle$. The dot product of $\mathbf{t}$ and $\nabla f(a, b)$ is

$$\mathbf{t} \cdot \nabla f(a, b) = \langle -f_y, f_x \rangle_{(a,b)} \cdot \langle f_x, f_y \rangle_{(a,b)} = (-f_x f_y + f_x f_y)_{(a,b)} = 0,$$

which implies that $\mathbf{t}$ and $\nabla f(a, b)$ are orthogonal. ◄

An immediate consequence of Theorem 13.12 is an alternative equation of the tangent line. The curve described by $f(x, y) = z_0$ can be viewed as a level curve in the xy-plane for a surface. By Theorem 13.12, the line tangent to the curve at (a, b) is orthogonal to $\nabla f(a, b)$. Therefore, if (x, y) is a point on the tangent line, then $\nabla f(a, b) \cdot \langle x - a, y - b \rangle = 0$, which, when simplified, gives an equation of the line tangent to the curve $f(x, y) = z_0$:

$$f_x(a, b)(x - a) + f_y(a, b)(y - b) = 0.$$

QUICK CHECK 4 Draw a circle in the xy-plane centered at the origin and regard it is as a level curve of the surface $z = x^2 + y^2$. At the point (a, a) of the level curve in the xy-plane, the slope of the tangent line is -1. Show that the gradient at (a, a) is orthogonal to the tangent line. ◄

EXAMPLE 6   Gradients and level curves Consider the upper sheet $z = f(x, y) = \sqrt{1 + 2x^2 + y^2}$ of a hyperboloid of two sheets.

a. Verify that the gradient at $(1, 1)$ is orthogonal to the corresponding level curve at that point.

b. Find an equation of the line tangent to the level curve at $(1, 1)$.

SOLUTION

a. You can verify that $(1, 1, 2)$ is on the surface; therefore, $(1, 1)$ is on the level curve corresponding to $z = 2$. Setting $z = 2$ in the equation of the surface and squaring both sides, the equation of the level curve is $4 = 1 + 2x^2 + y^2$, or $2x^2 + y^2 = 3$, which is the equation of an ellipse (Figure 13.72). Differentiating $2x^2 + y^2 = 3$ with respect to x gives $4x + 2yy'(x) = 0$, which implies that the slope of the level curve is $y'(x) = -\dfrac{2x}{y}$. Therefore, at the point $(1, 1)$, the slope of the tangent line is -2. Any vector proportional to $\mathbf{t} = \langle 1, -2 \rangle$ has slope -2 and points in the direction of the tangent line.

We now compute the gradient:

$$\nabla f(x, y) = \langle f_x, f_y \rangle = \left\langle \frac{2x}{\sqrt{1 + 2x^2 + y^2}}, \frac{y}{\sqrt{1 + 2x^2 + y^2}} \right\rangle.$$

It follows that $\nabla f(1, 1) = \langle 1, \frac{1}{2} \rangle$ (Figure 13.72). The tangent vector $\mathbf{t}$ and the gradient are orthogonal because

$$\mathbf{t} \cdot \nabla f(1, 1) = \langle 1, -2 \rangle \cdot \langle 1, \tfrac{1}{2} \rangle = 0.$$

b. An equation of the line tangent to the level curve at $(1, 1)$ is

$$\underbrace{f_x(1, 1)}_{1}(x - 1) + \underbrace{f_y(1, 1)}_{\frac{1}{2}}(y - 1) = 0,$$

or $y = -2x + 3$.

Related Exercises 43–50 ◄

EXAMPLE 7 **Path of steepest descent** Consider the paraboloid $z = f(x, y) = 4 + x^2 + 3y^2$ (Figure 13.73). Beginning at the point $(3, 4, 61)$ on the surface, find the path in the xy-plane that points in the direction of steepest descent on the surface.

SOLUTION Imagine releasing a ball at $(3, 4, 61)$ and assume that it rolls in the direction of steepest descent at all points. The projection of this path in the xy-plane points in the direction of $-\nabla f(x, y) = \langle -2x, -6y \rangle$, which means that at the point (x, y) the line tangent to the path has slope $y'(x) = (-6y)/(-2x) = 3y/x$. Therefore, the path in the xy-plane satisfies $y'(x) = 3y/x$ and passes through the initial point $(3, 4)$. You can verify that the solution to this differential equation is $y = 4x^3/27$ and the projection of the path of steepest descent in the xy-plane is the curve $y = 4x^3/27$. The descent ends at $(0, 0)$, which corresponds to the vertex of the paraboloid (Figure 13.73). At all points of the descent, the curve in the xy-plane is orthogonal to the level curves of the surface.

Related Exercises 51–54 ◄

QUICK CHECK 5 Verify that $y = 4x^3/27$ satisfies the equation $y'(x) = 3y/x$, with $y(3) = 4$. ◄

The Gradient in Three Dimensions

The directional derivative, the gradient, and the idea of a level curve extend immediately to functions of three variables of the form $w = f(x, y, z)$. The main differences are that the gradient is a vector in $\mathbb{R}^3$ and level curves become *level surfaces* (Section 13.2). Here is how the gradient looks when we step up one dimension.

The easiest way to visualize the surface $w = f(x, y, z)$ is to picture its level surfaces—the surfaces in $\mathbb{R}^3$ on which f has a constant value. The level surfaces are given by the equation $f(x, y, z) = C$, where C is a constant (Figure 13.74). The level surfaces *can* be graphed, and they may be viewed as layers of the full four-dimensional surface (like layers of an onion). With this image in mind, we now extend the concept of a gradient.

> The fact that $y' = -2x/y$ may also be obtained using Theorem 13.9: If $F(x, y) = 0$, then $y'(x) = -F_x/F_y$.

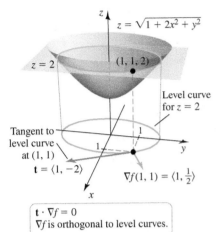

$z = \sqrt{1 + 2x^2 + y^2}$

$z = 2$ $(1, 1, 2)$

Level curve for $z = 2$

Tangent to level curve at $(1, 1)$

$\mathbf{t} = \langle 1, -2 \rangle$ $\nabla f(1, 1) = \langle 1, \frac{1}{2} \rangle$

$\mathbf{t} \cdot \nabla f = 0$
∇f is orthogonal to level curves.

FIGURE 13.72

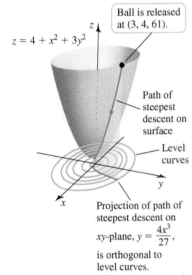

$z = 4 + x^2 + 3y^2$

Ball is released at $(3, 4, 61)$.

Path of steepest descent on surface

Level curves

Projection of path of steepest descent on xy-plane, $y = \dfrac{4x^3}{27}$, is orthogonal to level curves.

FIGURE 13.73

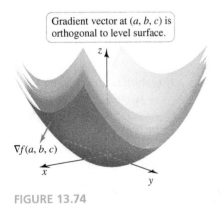

Gradient vector at (a, b, c) is orthogonal to level surface.

$\nabla f(a, b, c)$

FIGURE 13.74

Given the function $w = f(x, y, z)$, we argue just as we did in the two-variable case and define the directional derivative. Given a unit vector $\mathbf{u} = \langle u_1, u_2, u_3 \rangle$, the directional derivative of f in the direction of $\mathbf{u}$ at the point (a, b, c) is

$$D_\mathbf{u} f(a, b, c) = f_x(a, b, c) u_1 + f_y(a, b, c) u_2 + f_z(a, b, c) u_3.$$

As before, we recognize this expression as a dot product of the vector $\mathbf{u}$ and the vector $\nabla f(x, y, z) = \left\langle \dfrac{\partial f}{\partial x}, \dfrac{\partial f}{\partial y}, \dfrac{\partial f}{\partial z} \right\rangle$, which is the *gradient* in three dimensions. Therefore, the directional derivative in the direction of $\mathbf{u}$ at the point (a, b, c) is

$$D_\mathbf{u} f(a, b, c) = \nabla f(a, b, c) \cdot \mathbf{u}.$$

Following the line of reasoning in the two-variable case, f has its maximum rate of *increase* in the direction of $\nabla f(a, b, c)$. The actual rate of increase is $|\nabla f(a, b, c)|$. Similarly, f has its maximum rate of *decrease* in the direction of $-\nabla f(a, b, c)$. Also, in all directions orthogonal to $\nabla f(a, b, c)$, the directional derivative at (a, b, c) is zero.

▷ When we introduce the tangent plane in Section 13.7, we can also claim that $\nabla f(a, b, c)$ is orthogonal to the level surface that passes through (a, b, c).

QUICK CHECK 6 Compute $\nabla f(-1, 2, 1)$ when $f(x, y, z) = xy/z$. ◁

DEFINITION   Gradient and Directional Derivative in Three Dimensions

Let f be differentiable at the point (x, y, z). The **gradient** of f at (x, y, z) is the vector-valued function

$$\nabla f(x, y, z) = \langle f_x(x, y, z), f_y(x, y, z), f_z(x, y, z) \rangle$$
$$= f_x(x, y, z)\, \mathbf{i} + f_y(x, y, z)\, \mathbf{j} + f_z(x, y, z)\, \mathbf{k}.$$

The **directional derivative** of f in the direction of the unit vector $\mathbf{u} = \langle u_1, u_2, u_3 \rangle$ at the point (a, b, c) is $D_\mathbf{u} f(a, b, c) = \nabla f(a, b, c) \cdot \mathbf{u}$.

EXAMPLE 8   Gradients in three dimensions Consider the function $f(x, y, z) = x^2 + 2y^2 + 4z^2 - 1$ and its level surface $f(x, y, z) = 3$.

a. Find and interpret the gradient at the points $P(2, 0, 0)$, $Q(0, \sqrt{2}, 0)$, $R(0, 0, 1)$, and $S(1, 1, \frac{1}{2})$ on the level surface.

b. What are the actual rates of change of f in the directions of the gradients in part (a)?

SOLUTION

a. The gradient is

$$\nabla f = \langle f_x, f_y, f_z \rangle = \langle 2x, 4y, 8z \rangle.$$

Evaluating the gradient at the four points we find that

$$\nabla f(2, 0, 0) = \langle 4, 0, 0 \rangle, \qquad \nabla f(0, \sqrt{2}, 0) = \langle 0, 4\sqrt{2}, 0 \rangle,$$
$$\nabla f(0, 0, 1) = \langle 0, 0, 8 \rangle, \qquad \nabla f(1, 1, \tfrac{1}{2}) = \langle 2, 4, 4 \rangle.$$

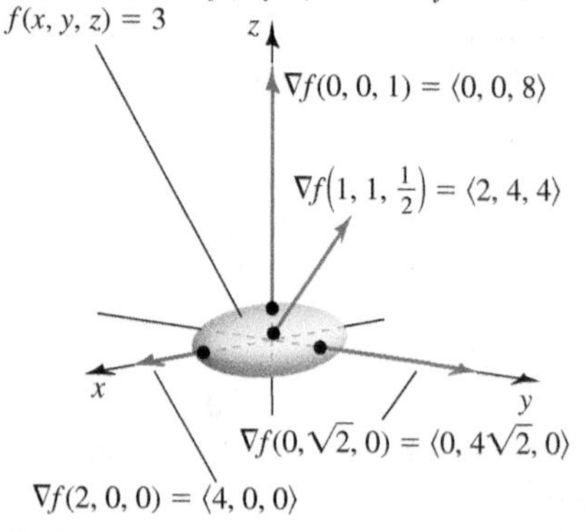

The level surface $f(x, y, z) = 3$ is an ellipsoid (Figure 13.75), which is one layer of a four-dimensional surface. The four points P, Q, R, and S are shown on the level surface with the respective gradient vectors. In each case, the gradient points in the direction that f has its maximum rate of increase. Of particular importance is the fact—to be made clear in the next section—that at each point the gradient is orthogonal to the level surface.

b. The actual rate of increase of f at (a, b, c) in the direction of the gradient is $|\nabla f(a, b, c)|$. At P, the rate of increase of f in the direction of the gradient is $|\langle 4, 0, 0 \rangle| = 4$; at Q, the rate of increase is $|\langle 0, 4\sqrt{2}, 0 \rangle| = 4\sqrt{2}$; at R the rate of increase is $|\langle 0, 0, 8 \rangle| = 8$; and at S, the rate of increase is $|\langle 2, 4, 4 \rangle| = 6$.

Related Exercises 55–62 ◀

Level surface of $f(x, y, z) = x^2 + 2y^2 + 4z^2 - 1$
$f(x, y, z) = 3$

$\nabla f(0, 0, 1) = \langle 0, 0, 8 \rangle$

$\nabla f\left(1, 1, \frac{1}{2}\right) = \langle 2, 4, 4 \rangle$

$\nabla f(0, \sqrt{2}, 0) = \langle 0, 4\sqrt{2}, 0 \rangle$

$\nabla f(2, 0, 0) = \langle 4, 0, 0 \rangle$

FIGURE 13.75

SECTION 13.6 EXERCISES

Review Questions

1. Explain how a directional derivative is formed from the two partial derivatives f_x and f_y.

2. How do you compute the gradient of the functions $f(x, y)$ and $f(x, y, z)$?

3. Interpret the direction of the gradient vector at a point.

4. Interpret the magnitude of the gradient vector at a point.

5. Given a function f, explain the relationship between the gradient and the level curves of f.

6. The level curves of the surface $z = x^2 + y^2$ are circles in the xy-plane centered at the origin. Without computing the gradient, what is the direction of the gradient at $(1, 1)$ and $(-1, -1)$ (determined up to a scalar multiple)?

Basic Skills

7. **Directional derivatives** Consider the function $f(x, y) = 8 - x^2/2 - y^2$, whose graph is a paraboloid (see figure).

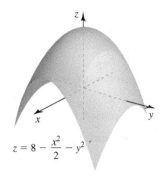

$$z = 8 - \frac{x^2}{2} - y^2$$

a. Fill in the table with the values of the directional derivative at the points (a, b) in the directions $\langle \cos \theta, \sin \theta \rangle$.

	$(a, b) = (2, 0)$	$(a, b) = (0, 2)$	$(a, b) = (1, 1)$
$\theta = \pi/4$			
$\theta = 3\pi/4$			
$\theta = 5\pi/4$			

b. Sketch the xy-plane and indicate the points and the direction of the directional derivative for each of the table entries in part (a).

8. **Directional derivatives** Consider the function $f(x, y) = 2x^2 + y^2$, whose graph is a paraboloid (see figure).

a. Fill in the table with the values of the directional derivative at the points (a, b) in the directions $\langle \cos \theta, \sin \theta \rangle$.

	$(a, b) = (1, 0)$	$(a, b) = (1, 1)$	$(a, b) = (1, 2)$
$\theta = 0$			
$\theta = \pi/4$			
$\theta = \pi/2$			

b. Sketch the xy-plane and indicate the points and the direction of the directional derivative for each of the table entries in part (a).

9–16. Computing gradients *Compute the gradient of the following functions and evaluate it at the given point P.*

9. $f(x, y) = 2 + 3x^2 - 5y^2;\ P(2, -1)$

10. $f(x, y) = 4x^2 - 2xy + y^2;\ P(-1, -5)$

11. $g(x, y) = x^2 - 4x^2y - 8xy^2;\ P(-1, 2)$

12. $p(x, y) = \sqrt{12 - 4x^2 - y^2};\ P(-1, -1)$

13. $f(x, y) = xe^{2xy};\ P(1, 0)$

14. $f(x, y) = \sin(3x + 2y);\ P(\pi, 3\pi/2)$

15. $F(x, y) = e^{-x^2-2y^2};\ P(-1, 2)$

16. $h(x, y) = \ln(1 + x^2 + 2y^2);\ P(2, -3)$

17–26. Computing directional derivatives with the gradient *Compute the directional derivative of the following functions at the given point P in the direction of the given vector. Be sure to use a unit vector for the direction vector.*

17. $f(x, y) = x^2 - y^2;\ P(-1, -3);\ \left\langle \frac{3}{5}, -\frac{4}{5} \right\rangle$

18. $f(x, y) = 3x^2 + y^3;\ P(3, 2);\ \left\langle \frac{5}{13}, \frac{12}{13} \right\rangle$

19. $f(x, y) = 10 - 3x^2 + \dfrac{y^4}{4}$; $P(2, -3)$; $\left\langle \dfrac{\sqrt{3}}{2}, -\dfrac{1}{2} \right\rangle$

20. $g(x, y) = \sin \pi(2x - y)$; $P(-1, -1)$; $\left\langle \dfrac{5}{13}, -\dfrac{12}{13} \right\rangle$

21. $f(x, y) = \sqrt{4 - x^2 - 2y}$; $P(2, -2)$; $\left\langle \dfrac{1}{\sqrt{5}}, \dfrac{2}{\sqrt{5}} \right\rangle$

22. $f(x, y) = 13e^{xy}$; $P(1, 0)$; $\langle 5, 12 \rangle$

23. $f(x, y) = 3x^2 + 2y + 5$; $P(1, 2)$; $\langle -3, 4 \rangle$

24. $h(x, y) = e^{-x-y}$; $P(\ln 2, \ln 3)$; $\langle 1, 1 \rangle$

25. $P(x, y) = \ln(4 + x^2 + y^2)$; $P(-1, 2)$; $\langle 2, 1 \rangle$

26. $f(x, y) = x/(x - y)$; $P(4, 1)$; $\langle -1, 2 \rangle$

27–32. Direction of steepest ascent and descent *Consider the following functions and points P.*

a. *Find the unit vectors that give the direction of steepest ascent and steepest descent at P.*

b. *Find a vector that points in a direction of no change in the function at P.*

27. $f(x, y) = x^2 - 4y^2 - 9$; $P(1, -2)$

28. $f(x, y) = x^2 + 4xy - y^2$; $P(2, 1)$

29. $f(x, y) = x^4 - x^2y + y^2 + 6$; $P(-1, 1)$

30. $p(x, y) = \sqrt{20 + x^2 + 2xy - y^2}$; $P(1, 2)$

31. $F(x, y) = e^{-x^2/2 - y^2/2}$; $P(-1, 1)$

32. $f(x, y) = 2 \sin(2x - 3y)$; $P(0, \pi)$

33–38. Interpreting directional derivatives *A function f and a point P are given. Let θ correspond to the direction of the directional derivative.*

a. *Find the gradient and evaluate it at P.*

b. *Find the angles θ (with respect to the positive x-axis) associated with the directions of maximum increase, maximum decrease, and zero change.*

c. *Write the directional derivative at P as a function of θ; call this function g(θ).*

d. *Find the value of θ that maximizes g(θ) and find the maximum value.*

e. *Verify that the value of θ that maximizes g corresponds to the direction of the gradient. Verify that the maximum value of g equals the magnitude of the gradient.*

33. $f(x, y) = 10 - 2x^2 - 3y^2$; $P(3, 2)$

34. $f(x, y) = 8 + x^2 + 3y^2$; $P(-3, -1)$

35. $f(x, y) = \sqrt{2 + x^2 + y^2}$; $P(\sqrt{3}, 1)$

36. $f(x, y) = \sqrt{12 - x^2 - y^2}$; $P(-1, -1/\sqrt{3})$

37. $f(x, y) = e^{-x^2 - 2y^2}$; $P(-1, 0)$

38. $f(x, y) = \ln(1 + 2x^2 + 3y^2)$; $P\left(\frac{3}{4}, -\sqrt{3}\right)$

39–42. Directions of change *Consider the following functions f and points P. Sketch the xy-plane showing P and the level curve through P. Indicate (as in Figure 13.70) the directions of maximum increase, maximum decrease, and no change for f.*

39. $f(x, y) = 8 + 4x^2 + 2y^2$; $P(2, -4)$

40. $f(x, y) = -4 + 6x^2 + 3y^2$; $P(-1, -2)$

41. $f(x, y) = x^2 + xy + y^2 + 7$; $P(-3, 3)$

42. $f(x, y) = \tan(2x + 2y)$; $P(\pi/16, \pi/16)$

43–46. Level curves *Consider the paraboloid $f(x, y) = 16 - x^2/4 - y^2/16$ and the point P on the given level curve of f. Compute the slope of the line tangent to the level curve at P and verify that the tangent line is orthogonal to the gradient at that point.*

43. $f(x, y) = 0$; $P(0, 16)$

44. $f(x, y) = 0$; $P(8, 0)$

45. $f(x, y) = 12$; $P(4, 0)$

46. $f(x, y) = 12$; $P(2\sqrt{3}, 4)$

47–50. Level curves *Consider the upper half of the ellipsoid $f(x, y) = \sqrt{1 - \dfrac{x^2}{4} - \dfrac{y^2}{16}}$ and the point P on the given level curve of f. Compute the slope of the line tangent to the level curve at P and verify that the tangent line is orthogonal to the gradient at that point.*

47. $f(x, y) = \sqrt{3}/2$; $P(1/2, \sqrt{3})$

48. $f(x, y) = 1/\sqrt{2}$; $P(0, \sqrt{8})$

49. $f(x, y) = 1/\sqrt{2}$; $P(\sqrt{2}, 0)$

50. $f(x, y) = 1/\sqrt{2}$; $P(1, 2)$

51–54. Path of steepest descent *Consider each of the following surfaces and the point P on the surface.*

a. *Find the gradient of f.*

b. *Let C′ be the path of steepest descent on the surface beginning at P and let C be the projection of C′ on the xy-plane. Find an equation of C in the xy-plane.*

51. $f(x, y) = 4 + x$ (a plane); $P(4, 4, 8)$

52. $f(x, y) = y + x$ (a plane); $P(2, 2, 4)$

53. $f(x, y) = 4 - x^2 - 2y^2$; $P(1, 1, 1)$

54. $f(x, y) = y + x^{-1}$; $P(1, 2, 3)$

55–62. Gradients in three dimensions *Consider the following functions f, points P, and unit vectors* **u.**

a. *Compute the gradient of f and evaluate it at P.*

b. *Find the unit vector in the direction of maximum increase of f at P.*

c. *Find the rate of change of the function in the direction of maximum increase at P.*

d. *Find the directional derivative at P in the direction of the given vector.*

55. $f(x, y, z) = x^2 + 2y^2 + 4z^2 + 10$; $P(1, 0, 4)$; $\left\langle \dfrac{1}{\sqrt{2}}, 0, \dfrac{1}{\sqrt{2}} \right\rangle$

56. $f(x, y, z) = 4 - x^2 + 3y^2 + \dfrac{z^2}{2}$; $P(0, 2, -1)$; $\left\langle 0, \dfrac{1}{\sqrt{2}}, -\dfrac{1}{\sqrt{2}} \right\rangle$

57. $f(x, y, z) = 1 + 4xyz$; $P(1, -1, -1)$; $\left\langle \dfrac{1}{\sqrt{3}}, \dfrac{1}{\sqrt{3}}, -\dfrac{1}{\sqrt{3}} \right\rangle$

58. $f(x, y, z) = xy + yz + xz + 4$; $P(2, -2, 1)$; $\left\langle 0, -\dfrac{1}{\sqrt{2}}, -\dfrac{1}{\sqrt{2}} \right\rangle$

59. $f(x, y, z) = 1 + \sin(x + 2y - z)$; $P\left(\dfrac{\pi}{6}, \dfrac{\pi}{6}, -\dfrac{\pi}{6}\right)$; $\left\langle \dfrac{1}{3}, \dfrac{2}{3}, \dfrac{2}{3} \right\rangle$

60. $f(x, y, z) = e^{xyz-1};\ P(0, 1, -1);\ \left\langle -\dfrac{2}{3}, \dfrac{2}{3}, -\dfrac{1}{3} \right\rangle$

61. $f(x, y, z) = \ln(1 + x^2 + y^2 + z^2);\ P(1, 1, -1);\ \left\langle \dfrac{2}{3}, \dfrac{2}{3}, -\dfrac{1}{3} \right\rangle$

62. $f(x, y, z) = \dfrac{x - z}{y - z};\ P(3, 2, -1);\ \left\langle \dfrac{1}{3}, \dfrac{2}{3}, -\dfrac{1}{3} \right\rangle$

Further Explorations

63. Explain why or why not Determine whether the following statements are true and give an explanation or counterexample.

   a. If $f(x, y) = x^2 + y^2 - 10$, then $\nabla f(x, y) = 2x + 2y$.

   b. Because the gradient gives the direction of maximum increase of a function, the gradient is always positive.

   c. The gradient of $f(x, y, z) = 1 + xyz$ has four components.

   d. If $f(x, y, z) = 4$, then $\nabla f = \mathbf{0}$.

64. Gradient of a composite function Consider the function $F(x, y, z) = e^{xyz}$.

   a. Write F as a composite function $f \circ g$, where f is a function of one variable and g is a function of three variables.

   b. Relate ∇F to ∇g.

65–68. Directions of zero change *Find the directions in the xy-plane in which the following functions have zero change at the given point. Express the directions in terms of unit vectors.*

65. $f(x, y) = 12 - 4x^2 - y^2;\ P(1, 2, 4)$

66. $f(x, y) = x^2 - 4y^2 - 8;\ P(4, 1, 4)$

67. $f(x, y) = \sqrt{3 + 2x^2 + y^2};\ P(1, -2, 3)$

68. $f(x, y) = e^{1-xy};\ P(1, 0, e)$

69. Steepest ascent on a plane Suppose a long sloping hillside is described by the plane $z = ax + by + c$, where a, b, and c are constants. Find the path in the xy-plane, beginning at (x_0, y_0), that corresponds to the path of steepest ascent on the hillside.

70. Gradient of a distance function Let (a, b) be a fixed point in $\mathbb{R}^2$ and let $d = f(x, y)$ be the distance between (a, b) and an arbitrary point (x, y).

   a. Show that the graph of f is a cone.

   b. Show that the gradient of f at any point other than (a, b) is a unit vector.

   c. Interpret the direction and magnitude of ∇f.

71–74. Looking ahead—tangent planes *Consider the following surfaces $f(x, y, z) = 0$, which may be regarded as a level surface of the function $w = f(x, y, z)$. A point $P(a, b, c)$ on the surface is also given.*

   a. *Find the (three-dimensional) gradient of f and evaluate it at P.*

   b. *The heads of all vectors orthogonal to the gradient with their tails at P form a plane. Find an equation of that plane (soon to be called the* tangent plane*).*

71. $f(x, y, z) = x^2 + y^2 + z^2 - 3 = 0;\ P(1, 1, 1)$

72. $f(x, y, z) = 8 - xyz = 0;\ P(2, 2, 2)$

73. $f(x, y, z) = e^{x+y-z} - 1 = 0;\ P(1, 1, 2)$

74. $f(x, y, z) = xy + xz - yz - 1;\ P(1, 1, 1)$

Applications

75. A traveling wave A snapshot (frozen in time) of a water wave is described by the function $z = 1 + \sin(x - y)$, where z gives the height of the wave relative to a reference point and (x, y) are coordinates in a horizontal plane.

   a. Use a graphing utility to graph $z = 1 + \sin(x - y)$.

   b. The crests and the troughs of the waves are aligned in the direction in which the height function has zero change. Find the direction in which the crests and troughs are aligned.

   c. If you were surfing on this wave and wanted the steepest descent from a crest to a trough, in which direction would you point your surfboard (given in terms of a unit vector in the xy-plane)?

   d. Check that your answers to parts (b) and (c) are consistent with the graph of part (a).

76. Traveling waves in general Generalize Exercise 75 by considering a wave described by the function $z = A + \sin(ax - by)$, where a, b, and A are real numbers.

   a. Find the direction in which the crests and troughs of the wave are aligned. Express your answer as a unit vector in terms of a and b.

   b. Find the surfer's direction—that is, the direction of steepest descent from a crest to a trough. Express your answer as a unit vector in terms of a and b.

77–79. Potential functions *Potential functions arise frequently in physics and engineering. A potential function has the property that a field of interest (for example, an electric field, a gravitational field, or a velocity field) is the gradient of the potential (or sometimes the negative of the gradient of the potential). (Potential functions are considered in depth in Chapter 15.)*

77. Electric potential due to a point charge The electric field due to a point charge of strength Q at the origin has a potential function $V = kQ/r$, where $r^2 = x^2 + y^2 + z^2$ is the square of the distance between a variable point $P(x, y, z)$ and the charge, and $k > 0$ is a physical constant. The electric field is given by $\mathbf{E} = -\nabla V$, where ∇V is the gradient in three dimensions.

   a. Show that the three-dimensional electric field due to a point charge is given by

$$\mathbf{E}(x, y, z) = kQ \left\langle \frac{x}{r^3}, \frac{y}{r^3}, \frac{z}{r^3} \right\rangle.$$

   b. Show that the electric field at a point has a magnitude $|\mathbf{E}| = kQ/r^2$. Explain why this relationship is called an inverse square law.

78. Gravitational potential The gravitational potential associated with two objects of mass M and m is $V = -GMm/r$, where G is the gravitational constant. If one of the objects is at the origin and the other object is at $P(x, y, z)$, then $r^2 = x^2 + y^2 + z^2$ is the square of the distance between the objects. The gravitational field at P is given by $\mathbf{F} = -\nabla V$, where ∇V is the gradient in three dimensions. Show that the force has a magnitude $|\mathbf{F}| = GMm/r^2$. Explain why this relationship is called an inverse square law.

79. Velocity potential In two dimensions, the motion of an ideal fluid (an incompressible and irrotational fluid) is governed by a velocity potential φ. The velocity components of the fluid, u in the x-direction and v in the y-direction, are given by $\langle u, v \rangle = \nabla \varphi$.

Find the velocity components associated with the velocity potential $\varphi(x, y) = \sin \pi x \sin 2\pi y$.

Additional Exercises

80. Gradients for planes Prove that for the plane described by $f(x, y) = Ax + By$, where A and B are nonzero constants, the gradient is constant (independent of (x, y)). Interpret this result.

81. Rules for gradients Use the definition of the gradient (in two or three dimensions), assume that f and g are differentiable functions on $\mathbb{R}^2$ or $\mathbb{R}^3$, and let c be a constant. Prove the following gradient rules.

  a. Constants Rule: $\nabla(cf) = c\nabla f$
  b. Sum Rule: $\nabla(f + g) = \nabla f + \nabla g$
  c. Product Rule: $\nabla(fg) = (\nabla f)\,g + f\nabla g$
  d. Quotient Rule: $\nabla\left(\dfrac{f}{g}\right) = \dfrac{g\nabla f - f\nabla g}{g^2}$
  e. Chain Rule: $\nabla(f \circ g) = f'(g)\nabla g$, where f is a function of one variable

82–87. Using gradient rules *Use the gradient rules of Exercise 81 to find the gradient of the following functions.*

82. $f(x, y) = xy \cos(xy)$

83. $f(x, y) = \dfrac{x + y}{x^2 + y^2}$

84. $f(x, y) = \ln(1 + x^2 + y^2)$

85. $f(x, y, z) = \sqrt{25 - x^2 - y^2 - z^2}$

86. $f(x, y, z) = (x + y + z)\,e^{xyz}$

87. $f(x, y, z) = \dfrac{x + yz}{y + xz}$

QUICK CHECK ANSWERS

1. If $\theta = 0$ then

$$D_{\mathbf{u}} f(a, b) = \lim_{h \to 0} \frac{f(a + h\cos\theta, b + h\sin\theta) - f(a, b)}{h}$$

$$= \lim_{h \to 0} \frac{f(a + h, b) - f(a, b)}{h} = f_x(a, b).$$

Similarly, when $\theta = \pi/2$, $\mathbf{u} = \langle 0, 1 \rangle$ is parallel to the y-axis, and the partial derivative $f_y(a, b)$ results. **2.** The vector from (a, b) to $(a + \Delta s u_1, b + \Delta s u_2)$ is $\langle \Delta s u_1, \Delta s u_2 \rangle = \Delta s \langle u_1, u_2 \rangle = \Delta s \mathbf{u}$. Its length is $|\Delta s \mathbf{u}| = \Delta s |\mathbf{u}| = \Delta s$. Therefore, s measures arc length. **3.** Reversing (negating) the direction vector negates the directional derivative. So, the respective values are approximately -2.47 and 0.98. **4.** The gradient is $\langle 2x, 2y \rangle$, which, evaluated at (a, a), is $\langle 2a, 2a \rangle$. Taking the dot product of the gradient and the vector $\langle -1, 1 \rangle$ (a vector parallel to a line of slope -1), we see that $\langle 2a, 2a \rangle \cdot \langle -1, 1 \rangle = 0$. **6.** $\langle 2, -1, 2 \rangle$

13.7 Tangent Planes and Linear Approximation

In Section 4.5, we saw that if we zoom in on a point on a smooth curve (one described by a differentiable function), the curve looks more and more like the tangent line at that point. Once we have the tangent line at a point, it can be used to approximate function values and to estimate changes in the dependent variable. In this section, an analogous story is developed, elevated by one dimension. Now we see that differentiability at a point (as discussed in Section 13.4) implies the existence of a tangent *plane* at that point (Figure 13.76).

Consider a smooth surface described by a differentiable function f and focus on a single point on the surface. As we zoom in on that point (Figure 13.77), the surface appears more and more like a plane. The first step is to define this plane carefully; it is called the *tangent plane*. Once we have the tangent plane, we can use it to approximate function values and to estimate changes in the dependent variable.

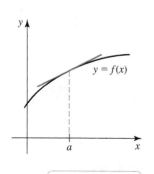

f differentiable at $a \Longrightarrow$ tangent line at $(a, f(a))$

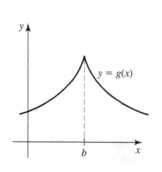

g not differentiable at $b \Longrightarrow$ no tangent line at $(b, f(b))$

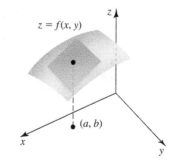

f differentiable at $(a, b) \Longrightarrow$ tangent plane at $(a, b, f(a, b))$

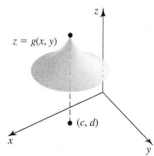

g not differentiable at $(c, d) \Longrightarrow$ no tangent plane at $(c, d, g(c, d))$

FIGURE 13.76

Tangent Planes

Recall that a surface in $\mathbb{R}^3$ may be defined in at least two different ways:

- **Explicitly** in the form $z = f(x, y)$ or
- **Implicitly** in the form $F(x, y, z) = 0$.

It is easiest to begin by considering a surface defined implicitly by $F(x, y, z) = 0$, where F is differentiable at a particular point. Such a surface may be viewed as a level surface of a function $w = F(x, y, z)$; it is the level surface for $w = 0$.

QUICK CHECK 1 Write the function $z = xy + x - y$ in the form $F(x, y, z) = 0$. ◄

Tangent Planes for $F(x, y, z) = 0$ To find an equation of the tangent plane, consider a smooth curve $C: \mathbf{r} = \langle x(t), y(t), z(t) \rangle$ that lies on the surface $F(x, y, z) = 0$ (Figure 13.78a). Because the points of C lie on the surface, we have $F(x(t), y(t), z(t)) = 0$. Differentiating both sides of this equation with respect to t, a useful relationship emerges. The derivative of the right side is 0. The Chain Rule applied to the left side yields

$$\frac{d}{dt}\left[F(x(t), y(t), z(t))\right] = \frac{\partial F}{\partial x}\frac{dx}{dt} + \frac{\partial F}{\partial y}\frac{dy}{dt} + \frac{\partial F}{\partial z}\frac{dz}{dt}$$

$$= \underbrace{\left\langle \frac{\partial F}{\partial x}, \frac{\partial F}{\partial y}, \frac{\partial F}{\partial z} \right\rangle}_{\nabla F(x, y, z)} \cdot \underbrace{\left\langle \frac{dx}{dt}, \frac{dy}{dt}, \frac{dz}{dt} \right\rangle}_{\mathbf{r}'(t)}$$

$$= \nabla F(x, y, z) \cdot \mathbf{r}'(t).$$

Therefore, $\nabla F(x, y, z) \cdot \mathbf{r}'(t) = 0$ and at any point on the curve, the tangent vector $\mathbf{r}'(t)$ is orthogonal to the gradient.

Now fix a point $P_0(a, b, c)$ on the surface, assume that $\nabla F(a, b, c) \neq \mathbf{0}$, and let C be any smooth curve on the surface passing through P_0. We have shown that the vector tangent to C is orthogonal to $\nabla F(a, b, c)$ at P_0. Because this argument applies to *all* smooth curves on the surface passing through P_0, the tangent vectors for all these curves (with their tails at P_0) are orthogonal to $\nabla F(a, b, c)$, and thus they all lie in the same plane (Figure 13.78b). This plane is called the *tangent plane* at P_0. We can easily find an equation of the tangent plane because we know both a point on the plane $P_0(a, b, c)$ and a normal vector $\nabla F(a, b, c)$; an equation is simply

$$\nabla F(a, b, c) \cdot \langle x - a, y - b, z - c \rangle = 0.$$

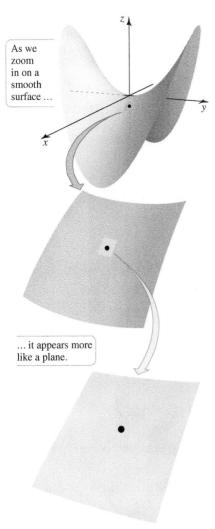

As we zoom in on a smooth surface ...

... it appears more like a plane.

FIGURE 13.77

▷ Recall that an equation of the plane passing though (a, b, c) with a normal vector $\mathbf{n} = \langle n_1, n_2, n_3 \rangle$ is $n_1(x - a) + n_2(y - b) + n_3(z - c) = 0$.

▷ If $\mathbf{r}$ is a position vector corresponding to an arbitrary point on the tangent plane and $\mathbf{r}_0$ is a position vector corresponding to a fixed point (a, b, c) on the plane, then an equation of the tangent plane may be written concisely as

$$\nabla F(a, b, c) \cdot (\mathbf{r} - \mathbf{r}_0) = 0.$$

Notice the analogy with tangent lines and level curves (Section 13.6). An equation of the line tangent to $f(x, y) = 0$ at (a, b) is

$$\nabla f(a, b) \cdot \langle x - a, y - b \rangle = 0.$$

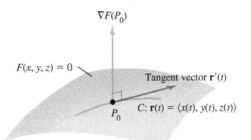

$\nabla F(P_0)$

$F(x, y, z) = 0$

Tangent vector $\mathbf{r}'(t)$

$C: \mathbf{r}(t) = \langle x(t), y(t), z(t) \rangle$

P_0

Vector tangent to C at P_0 is orthogonal to $\nabla F(P_0)$.

(a)

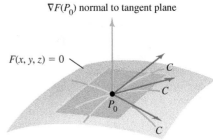

$\nabla F(P_0)$ normal to tangent plane

$F(x, y, z) = 0$

C

C

P_0

C

Tangent plane formed by tangent vectors for all curves C on the surface passing through P_0

(b)

FIGURE 13.78

> **DEFINITION** **Equation of the Tangent Plane for $F(x, y, z) = 0$**
>
> Let F be differentiable at the point $P_0(a, b, c)$ with $\nabla F(a, b, c) \neq \mathbf{0}$. The plane tangent to the surface $F(x, y, z) = 0$ at P_0, called the **tangent plane**, is the plane passing through P_0 orthogonal to $\nabla F(a, b, c)$. An equation of the tangent plane is
>
> $$F_x(a, b, c)(x - a) + F_y(a, b, c)(y - b) + F_z(a, b, c)(z - c) = 0.$$

EXAMPLE 1 **Equation of a tangent plane** Consider the ellipsoid

$$F(x, y, z) = \frac{x^2}{9} + \frac{y^2}{25} + z^2 - 1 = 0.$$

a. Find the equation of the plane tangent to the ellipsoid at $\left(0, 4, \frac{3}{5}\right)$.

b. At what points on the ellipsoid is the tangent plane horizontal?

SOLUTION

a. Notice that we have written the equation of the ellipsoid in the implicit form $F(x, y, z) = 0$. The gradient of F is $\nabla F(x, y, z) = \left\langle \frac{2x}{9}, \frac{2y}{25}, 2z \right\rangle$. Evaluated at $\left(0, 4, \frac{3}{5}\right)$, we have

$$\nabla F\left(0, 4, \frac{3}{5}\right) = \left\langle 0, \frac{8}{25}, \frac{6}{5} \right\rangle.$$

An equation of the tangent plane at this point is

$$0 \cdot (x - 0) + \frac{8}{25}(y - 4) + \frac{6}{5}\left(z - \frac{3}{5}\right) = 0,$$

or $4y + 15z = 25$. The equation does not involve x, so the tangent plane is parallel to the x-axis (Figure 13.79).

b. A horizontal plane has a normal vector of the form $\langle 0, 0, c \rangle$, where $c \neq 0$. A plane tangent to the ellipsoid has a normal vector $\nabla F(x, y, z) = \left\langle \frac{2x}{9}, \frac{2y}{25}, 2z \right\rangle$. Therefore, the ellipsoid has a horizontal tangent plane when $F_x = \frac{2x}{9} = 0$ and $F_y = \frac{2y}{25} = 0$, or when $x = 0$ and $y = 0$. Substituting these values into the original equation for the ellipsoid, we find that horizontal planes occur at $(0, 0, 1)$ and $(0, 0, -1)$.

Related Exercises 9–16 ◀

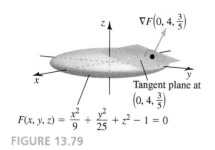

$$\nabla F\left(0, 4, \tfrac{3}{5}\right)$$

Tangent plane at $\left(0, 4, \frac{3}{5}\right)$

$$F(x, y, z) = \frac{x^2}{9} + \frac{y^2}{25} + z^2 - 1 = 0$$

FIGURE 13.79

> This result extends Theorem 13.12, which states that for functions $f(x, y) = 0$, the gradient at a point is orthogonal to the level curve that passes through that point.

The preceding discussion allows us to confirm a claim made in Section 13.6. The surface $F(x, y, z) = 0$ is a level surface of the function $w = F(x, y, z)$ (corresponding to $w = 0$). At any point on that surface, the tangent plane has a normal vector $\nabla F(x, y, z)$. Therefore, the gradient $\nabla F(x, y, z)$ is orthogonal to the level surface $F(x, y, z) = 0$ at all points of the domain at which F is differentiable.

Tangent Planes for $z = f(x, y)$ Surfaces in $\mathbb{R}^3$ are often defined explicitly in the form $z = f(x, y)$. In this situation, the equation of the tangent plane is a special case of the general equation just derived. The equation $z = f(x, y)$ is written as $F(x, y, z) = z - f(x, y) = 0$, and the gradient of F at the point $(a, b, f(a, b))$ is

> To be clear, when $F(x, y, z) = z - f(x, y)$, we have $F_x = -f_x$, $F_y = -f_y$, and $F_z = 1$.

$$\nabla F(a, b, f(a, b)) = \langle -f_x(a, b), -f_y(a, b), 1 \rangle.$$

Proceeding as before, an equation of the plane tangent to the surface $z = f(x, y)$ at the point $(a, b, f(a, b))$ is

$$-f_x(a, b)(x - a) - f_y(a, b)(y - b) + 1(z - f(a, b)) = 0.$$

After some rearranging, we obtain an equation of the tangent plane.

Tangent Plane for $z = f(x, y)$

Let f be differentiable at the point (a, b). An equation of the plane tangent to the surface $z = f(x, y)$ at the point $(a, b, f(a, b))$ is

$$z = f_x(a, b)(x - a) + f_y(a, b)(y - b) + f(a, b).$$

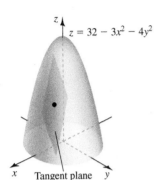

$z = 32 - 3x^2 - 4y^2$

Tangent plane
at $(2, 1, 16)$

FIGURE 13.80

EXAMPLE 2   Tangent plane for $z = f(x, y)$ Find an equation of the plane tangent to the paraboloid $z = f(x, y) = 32 - 3x^2 - 4y^2$ at $(2, 1, 16)$.

SOLUTION The partial derivatives are $f_x = -6x$ and $f_y = -8y$. Evaluating the partial derivatives at $(2, 1)$, we have $f_x(2, 1) = -12$ and $f_y(2, 1) = -8$. Therefore, an equation of the tangent plane (Figure 13.80) is

$$\begin{aligned} z &= f_x(a, b)(x - a) + f_y(a, b)(y - b) + f(a, b) \\ &= -12(x - 2) - 8(y - 1) + 16 \\ &= -12x - 8y + 48. \end{aligned}$$

Related Exercises 17–24 ◄

▶ The term *linear approximation* applies in both $\mathbb{R}^2$ and $\mathbb{R}^3$ because lines in $\mathbb{R}^2$ and planes in $\mathbb{R}^3$ are described by linear functions of the independent variables. In both cases, we call the linear approximation L.

Linear Approximation

With a function of the form $y = f(x)$, the tangent line at a point often gives good approximations to the function near that point. A straightforward extension of this idea applies to approximating functions of two variables with tangent planes. As before, the method is called *linear approximation*.

Figure 13.81 shows the details of linear approximation in the one- and two-variable cases. In the one-variable case (Section 4.5), if f is differentiable at a, the equation of the line tangent to the curve $y = f(x)$ at the point $(a, f(a))$ is

$$L(x) = f(a) + f'(a)(x - a).$$

The tangent line gives an approximation to the function. At points near a, we have $f(x) \approx L(x)$.

The two-variable case is analogous. If f is differentiable at (a, b), an equation of the plane tangent to the surface $z = f(x, y)$ at the point $(a, b, f(a, b))$ is

$$L(x, y) = f_x(a, b)(x - a) + f_y(a, b)(y - b) + f(a, b).$$

This tangent plane is the linear approximation to f at (a, b). At points near (a, b), we have $f(x, y) \approx L(x, y)$.

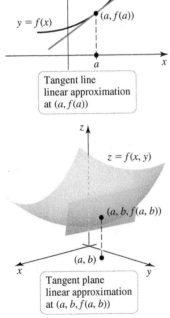

$y = f(x)$

$(a, f(a))$

Tangent line
linear approximation
at $(a, f(a))$

$z = f(x, y)$

$(a, b, f(a, b))$

(a, b)

Tangent plane
linear approximation
at $(a, b, f(a, b))$

FIGURE 13.81

DEFINITION Linear Approximation

Let f be differentiable at (a, b). The linear approximation to the surface $z = f(x, y)$ at the point $(a, b, f(a, b))$ is the tangent plane at that point, given by the equation

$$L(x, y) = f_x(a, b)(x - a) + f_y(a, b)(y - b) + f(a, b).$$

EXAMPLE 3 **Linear approximation** Let $f(x, y) = \dfrac{5}{x^2 + y^2}$.

a. Find the linear approximation to the function at the point $(-1, 2, 1)$.

b. Use the linear approximation to estimate the value of $f(-1.05, 2.1)$.

SOLUTION

a. The partial derivatives of f are

$$f_x = -\frac{10x}{(x^2 + y^2)^2} \quad \text{and} \quad f_y = -\frac{10y}{(x^2 + y^2)^2}.$$

Evaluated at $(-1, 2)$, we have $f_x(-1, 2) = \frac{2}{5} = 0.4$ and $f_y(-1, 2) = -\frac{4}{5} = -0.8$. Therefore, the linear approximation to the function at $(-1, 2, 1)$ is

$$\begin{aligned} L(x, y) &= f_x(-1, 2)(x - (-1)) + f_y(-1, 2)(y - 2) + f(-1, 2) \\ &= 0.4(x + 1) - 0.8(y - 2) + 1 \\ &= 0.4x - 0.8y + 3. \end{aligned}$$

The surface and the tangent plane are shown in Figure 13.82.

b. The value of the function at the point $(-1.05, 2.1)$ is approximated by the value of the linear approximation at that point, which is

$$L(-1.05, 2.1) = 0.4(-1.05) - 0.8(2.1) + 3 = 0.90.$$

In this case, we can easily evaluate $f(-1.05, 2.1) \approx 0.907$ and compare the linear approximation with the exact value; the approximation has a relative error of about 0.8%.

Related Exercises 25–30 ◄

> Relative error =
> $\dfrac{|\text{approximation} - \text{exact value}|}{|\text{exact value}|}$

QUICK CHECK 2 Look at the graph of the surface in Example 3 (Figure 13.82) and explain why $f_x(-1, 2) > 0$ and $f_y(-1, 2) < 0$. ◄

Differentials and Change

Recall that for a function of the form $y = f(x)$, if the independent variable changes from x to $x + dx$, the corresponding change Δy in the dependent variable is approximated by the differential $dy = f'(x)\,dx$, which is the change in the linear approximation. Therefore, $\Delta y \approx dy$, with the approximation improving as dx approaches 0.

For functions of the form $z = f(x, y)$, we start with the linear approximation to the surface

$$f(x, y) \approx L(x, y) = f_x(a, b)(x - a) + f_y(a, b)(y - b) + f(a, b).$$

The exact change in the function between the points (a, b) and (x, y) is

$$\Delta z = f(x, y) - f(a, b).$$

Replacing $f(x, y)$ by its linear approximation, the change Δz is approximated by

$$\Delta z \approx \underbrace{L(x, y) - f(a, b)}_{dz} = f_x(a, b)\underbrace{(x - a)}_{dx} + f_y(a, b)\underbrace{(y - b)}_{dy}.$$

The change in the x-coordinate is $dx = x - a$ and the change in the y-coordinate is $dy = y - b$ (Figure 13.83). As before, we let the differential dz denote the change in the linear approximation. Therefore, the approximate change in the z-coordinate is

$$\Delta z \approx dz = \underbrace{f_x(a, b)\,dx}_{\substack{\text{change in } z \text{ due} \\ \text{to change in } x}} + \underbrace{f_y(a, b)\,dy}_{\substack{\text{change in } z \text{ due} \\ \text{to change in } y}}.$$

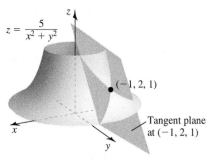

$z = \dfrac{5}{x^2 + y^2}$

$(-1, 2, 1)$

Tangent plane at $(-1, 2, 1)$

FIGURE 13.82

> Alternative notation for the differential at (a, b) is $dz|_{(a,b)}$ or $df|_{(a,b)}$.

This expression says that if we move the independent variables from (a, b) to $(a + dx, b + dy)$, the corresponding change in the dependent variable Δz has two contributions—one due to the change in x and one due to the change in y. If dx and dy are small in magnitude, then so is Δz. The approximation $\Delta z \approx dz$ improves as dx and dy approach 0. The relationships among the differentials are illustrated in Figure 13.83.

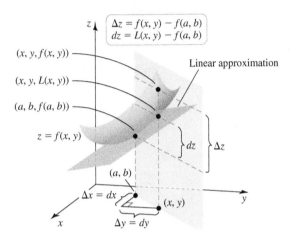

FIGURE 13.83

QUICK CHECK 3 Explain why, if $dx = 0$ or $dy = 0$ in the change formula for Δz, the result is the change formula for one variable. ◄

DEFINITION **The differential** dz

Let f be differentiable at the point (a, b). The change in $z = f(x, y)$ as the independent variables change from (a, b) to $(a + dx, b + dy)$ is denoted Δz and is approximated by the differential dz:

$$\Delta z \approx dz = f_x(a, b)\, dx + f_y(a, b)\, dy.$$

EXAMPLE 4 **Approximating function change** Let $z = f(x, y) = \dfrac{5}{x^2 + y^2}$.

Approximate the change in z when the independent variables change from $(-1, 2)$ to $(-0.93, 1.94)$.

SOLUTION If the independent variables change from $(-1, 2)$ to $(-0.93, 1.94)$, then $dx = 0.07$ (an increase) and $dy = -0.06$ (a decrease). Using the values of the partial derivatives evaluated in Example 3, the corresponding change in z is approximately

$$\begin{aligned}
dz &= f_x(-1, 2)\, dx + f_y(-1, 2)\, dy \\
&= 0.4(0.07) + (-0.8)(-0.06) \\
&= 0.076.
\end{aligned}$$

Again, we can check the accuracy of the approximation. The actual change is $f(-0.93, 1.94) - f(-1, 2) \approx 0.080$, so the approximation has a 5% error.

Related Exercises 31–34 ◄

EXAMPLE 5   **Body mass index** The body mass index (BMI) for an adult human is given by the function $B(w, h) = w/h^2$, where w is weight measured in kilograms and h is height measured in meters.

a. Use differentials to approximate the change in the BMI when weight increases from 55 to 56.5 kg and height increases from 1.65 to 1.66 m.

b. Which produces a greater *percentage* change in the BMI, a 1% change in the weight (at a constant height) or a 1% change in the height (at a constant weight)?

SOLUTION

a. The approximate change in the BMI is $dB = B_w\, dw + B_h\, dh$, where the derivatives are evaluated at $w = 55$ and $h = 1.65$, and the changes in the independent variables are $dw = 1.5$ and $dh = 0.01$. Evaluating the partial derivatives, we find that

$$B_w(w, h) = \frac{1}{h^2}, \qquad B_w(55, 1.65) \approx 0.37,$$

$$B_h(w, h) = -\frac{2w}{h^3}, \qquad B_h(55, 1.65) \approx -24.49.$$

Therefore, the approximate change in the BMI is

$$\begin{aligned} dB &= B_w(55, 1.65)\, dw + B_h(55, 1.65)\, dh \\ &\approx (0.37)(1.5) + (-24.49)(0.01) \\ &\approx 0.56 - 0.25 \\ &= 0.31. \end{aligned}$$

As expected, an increase in weight *increases* the BMI, while an increase in height *decreases* the BMI. In this case, the two contributions combine for a net increase in the BMI.

b. The changes dw, dh, and dB that appear in the differential change formula in part (a) are *absolute changes*. The corresponding *relative*, or *percentage*, changes are $\dfrac{dw}{w}, \dfrac{dh}{h}$, and $\dfrac{dB}{B}$. To introduce relative changes into the change formula, we divide both sides of $dB = B_w\, dw + B_h\, dh$ by $B = w/h^2 = wh^{-2}$. The result is

$$\begin{aligned} \frac{dB}{B} &= B_w \frac{dw}{wh^{-2}} + B_h \frac{dh}{wh^{-2}} \\[2mm] &= \frac{1}{h^2}\frac{dw}{wh^{-2}} - \frac{2w}{h^3}\frac{dh}{wh^{-2}} \qquad \text{Substitute for } B_w \text{ and } B_h. \\[2mm] &= \underbrace{\frac{dw}{w}}_{\substack{\text{relative}\\\text{change}\\\text{in } w}} - 2\underbrace{\frac{dh}{h}}_{\substack{\text{relative}\\\text{change}\\\text{in } h}}. \qquad \text{Simplify.} \end{aligned}$$

See Exercises 64–65 for general results about relative or percentage changes in functions.

This expression relates the relative changes in w, h, and B. With h constant $(dh = 0)$, a 1% change in w $(dw/w = 0.01)$ produces approximately a 1% change of the same sign in B. With w constant $(dw = 0)$, a 1% change in h $(dh/h = 0.01)$ produces approximately a 2% change in B of the opposite sign. We see that the BMI formula is more sensitive to small changes in h than in w.

Related Exercises 35–38 ◄

QUICK CHECK 4   In Example 5, interpret the facts that $B_w > 0$ and $B_h < 0$, for $w, h > 0$. ◄

The differential for functions of two variables extends naturally to more variables. For example, if f is differentiable at (a, b, c) with $w = f(x, y, z)$, then

$$dw = f_x(a, b, c) \, dx + f_y(a, b, c) \, dy + f_z(a, b, c) \, dz.$$

The differential dw (or df) gives the approximate change in f at the point (a, b, c) due to changes of dx, dy, and dz in the independent variables.

EXAMPLE 6 **Manufacturing errors** A company manufactures cylindrical aluminum tubes to rigid specifications. The tubes are designed to have an outside radius of $r = 10$ cm, a height of $h = 50$ cm, and a thickness of $t = 0.1$ cm (Figure 13.84). The manufacturing process produces tubes with a maximum error of ± 0.05 cm in the radius and height and a maximum error of ± 0.0005 cm in the thickness. The volume of the material used to construct a cylindrical tube is $V(r, h, t) = \pi h t (2r - t)$. Use differentials to estimate the maximum error in the volume of a tube.

SOLUTION The approximate change in the volume of a tube due to changes dr, dh, and dt in the radius, height, and thickness, respectively, is

$$dV = V_r \, dr + V_h \, dh + V_t \, dt.$$

The partial derivatives evaluated at $r = 10$, $h = 50$, and $t = 0.1$ are

$$
\begin{aligned}
V_r(r, h, t) &= 2\pi h t, & V_r(10, 50, 0.1) &= 10\pi, \\
V_h(r, h, t) &= \pi t(2r - t), & V_h(10, 50, 0.1) &= 1.99\pi, \\
V_t(r, h, t) &= 2\pi h(r - t), & V_t(10, 50, 0.1) &= 990\pi.
\end{aligned}
$$

We let $dr = dh = 0.05$ and $dt = 0.0005$ be the maximum errors in the radius, height, and thickness, respectively. The maximum error in the volume is approximately

$$
\begin{aligned}
dV &= V_r(10, 50, 0.1) \, dr + V_h(10, 50, 0.1) \, dh + V_t(10, 50, 0.1) \, dt \\
&= 10\pi(0.05) + 1.99\pi(0.05) + 990\pi(0.0005) \\
&\approx 1.57 + 0.31 + 1.56 \\
&= 3.44.
\end{aligned}
$$

The maximum error in the volume is approximately 3.44 cm³. Notice that the "magnification factor" for the thickness (990π) is roughly 100 and 500 times greater than the magnification factors for the radius and height, respectively. This means that for the same errors in r, h, and t, the volume is far more sensitive to errors in the thickness. The partial derivatives allow us to do a sensitivity analysis to determine which independent (input) variables are most critical in producing change in the dependent (output) variable.

Related Exercises 39–44 ◄

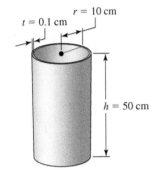

$r = 10$ cm
$t = 0.1$ cm
$h = 50$ cm

FIGURE 13.84

SECTION 13.7 EXERCISES

Review Questions

1. Suppose **n** is a vector normal to the tangent plane of the surface $F(x, y, z) = 0$ at a point. How is **n** related to the gradient of F at that point?

2. Write the explicit function $z = xy^2 + x^2y - 10$ in the implicit form $F(x, y, z) = 0$.

3. Write an equation for the plane tangent to the surface $F(x, y, z) = 0$ at the point (a, b, c).

4. Write an equation for the plane tangent to the surface $z = f(x, y)$ at the point $(a, b, f(a, b))$.

5. Explain how to approximate a function f at a point near (a, b) where the values of f, f_x, and f_y are known at (a, b).

6. Explain how to approximate the change in a function f when the independent variables change from (a, b) to $(a + \Delta x, b + \Delta y)$.

7. Write the approximate change formula for a function $z = f(x, y)$ at the point (a, b) in terms of differentials.

8. Write the differential dw for the function $w = f(x, y, z)$.

Basic Skills

9–16. Tangent planes for $F(x, y, z) = 0$ *Find an equation of the plane tangent to the following surfaces at the given points.*

9. $x^2 + y + z = 3$; $(1, 1, 1)$ and $(2, 0, -1)$

10. $x^2 + y^3 + z^4 = 2$; $(1, 0, 1)$ and $(-1, 0, 1)$

11. $xy + xz + yz - 12 = 0$; $(2, 2, 2)$ and $(2, 0, 6)$

12. $x^2 + y^2 - z^2 = 0$; $(3, 4, 5)$ and $(-4, -3, 5)$

13. $xy \sin z = 1$; $(1, 2, \pi/6)$ and $(-2, -1, 5\pi/6)$

14. $yze^{xz} - 8 = 0$; $(0, 2, 4)$ and $(0, -8, -1)$

15. $z^2 - x^2/16 - y^2/9 - 1 = 0$; $(4, 3, -\sqrt{3})$ and $(-8, 9, \sqrt{14})$

16. $2x + y^2 - z^2 = 0$; $(0, 1, 1)$ and $(4, 1, -3)$

17–24. Tangent planes for $z = f(x, y)$ *Find an equation of the plane tangent to the following surfaces at the given points.*

17. $z = 4 - 2x^2 - y^2$; $(2, 2, -8)$ and $(-1, -1, 1)$

18. $z = 2 + 2x^2 + \dfrac{y^2}{2}$; $\left(-\dfrac{1}{2}, 1, 3\right)$ and $(3, -2, 22)$

19. $z = e^{xy}$; $(1, 0, 1)$ and $(0, 1, 1)$

20. $z = \sin xy + 2$; $(1, 0, 2)$ and $(0, 5, 2)$

21. $z = x^2 e^{x-y}$; $(2, 2, 4)$ and $(-1, -1, 1)$

22. $z = \ln(1 + xy)$; $(1, 2, \ln 3)$ and $(-2, -1, \ln 3)$

23. $z = (x - y)/(x^2 + y^2)$; $\left(1, 2, -\frac{1}{5}\right)$ and $\left(2, -1, \frac{3}{5}\right)$

24. $z = 2 \cos(x - y) + 2$; $(\pi/6, -\pi/6, 3)$ and $(\pi/3, \pi/3, 4)$

25–30. Linear approximation

a. Find the linear approximation for the following functions at the given point.

b. Use part (a) to estimate the given function value.

25. $f(x, y) = xy + x - y$; $(2, 3)$; estimate $f(2.1, 2.99)$.

26. $f(x, y) = 12 - 4x^2 - 8y^2$; $(-1, 4)$; estimate $f(-1.05, 3.95)$.

27. $f(x, y) = -x^2 + 2y^2$; $(3, -1)$; estimate $f(3.1, -1.04)$.

28. $f(x, y) = \sqrt{x^2 + y^2}$; $(3, -4)$; estimate $f(3.06, -3.92)$.

29. $f(x, y) = \ln(1 + x + y)$; $(0, 0)$; estimate $f(0.1, -0.2)$.

30. $f(x, y) = (x + y)/(x - y)$; $(3, 2)$; estimate $f(2.95, 2.05)$.

31–34. Approximate function change *Use differentials to approximate the change in z for the given changes in the independent variables.*

31. $z = 2x - 3y - 2xy$ when (x, y) changes from $(1, 4)$ to $(1.1, 3.9)$

32. $z = -x^2 + 3y^2 + 2$ when (x, y) changes from $(-1, 2)$ to $(-1.05, 1.9)$

33. $z = e^{x+y}$ when (x, y) changes from $(0, 0)$ to $(0.1, -0.05)$

34. $z = \ln(1 + x + y)$ when (x, y) changes from $(0, 0)$ to $(-0.1, 0.03)$

35. Changes in torus surface area The surface area of a torus (an ideal bagel or doughnut) with an inner radius r and an outer radius $R > r$ is $S = 4\pi^2(R^2 - r^2)$.

a. If r increases and R decreases, does S increase or decrease, or is it impossible to say?

b. If r increases and R increases, does S increase or decrease, or is it impossible to say?

c. Estimate the change in the surface area of the torus when r changes from $r = 3.00$ to $r = 3.05$ and R changes from $R = 5.50$ to $R = 5.65$.

d. Estimate the change in the surface area of the torus when r changes from $r = 3.00$ to $r = 2.95$ and R changes from $R = 7.00$ to $R = 7.04$.

e. Find the relationship between the changes in r and R that leaves the surface area (approximately) unchanged.

36. Changes in cone volume The volume of a right circular cone with radius r and height h is $V = \pi r^2 h/3$.

a. Approximate the change in the volume of the cone when the radius changes from $r = 6.5$ to $r = 6.6$ and the height changes from $h = 4.20$ to $h = 4.15$.

b. Approximate the change in the volume of the cone when the radius changes from $r = 5.40$ to $r = 5.37$ and the height changes from $h = 12.0$ to $h = 11.96$.

37. Area of an ellipse The area of an ellipse with axes of length $2a$ and $2b$ is $A = \pi ab$. Approximate the percent change in the area when a increases by 2% and b increases by 1.5%.

38. Volume of a paraboloid The volume of a segment of a circular paraboloid (see figure) with radius r and height h is $V = \pi r^2 h/2$. Approximate the percent change in the volume when the radius decreases by 1.5% and the height increases by 2.2%.

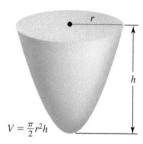

$$V = \frac{\pi}{2} r^2 h$$

39–42. Differentials with more than two variables *Write the differential dw in terms of the differentials of the independent variables.*

39. $w = f(x, y, z) = xy^2 + zx^2 + yz^2$

40. $w = f(x, y, z) = \sin(x + y - z)$

41. $w = f(u, x, y, z) = (u + x)/(y + z)$

42. $w = f(p, q, r, s) = pq/(rs)$

43. Law of Cosines The side lengths of any triangle are related by the Law of Cosines,

$$c^2 = a^2 + b^2 - 2ab \cos \theta.$$

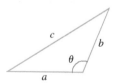

a. Estimate the change in the side length c when a changes from $a = 2$ to $a = 2.03$, b changes from $b = 4.00$ to $b = 3.96$, and θ changes from $\theta = \pi/3$ to $\theta = \pi/3 + \pi/90$.

b. If a changes from $a = 2$ to $a = 2.03$ and b changes from $b = 4.00$ to $b = 3.96$, is the resulting change in c greater in magnitude when $\theta = \pi/20$ (small angle) or when $\theta = 9\pi/20$ (close to a right angle)?

44. Travel cost The cost of a trip that is L miles long, driving a car that gets m miles per gallon, with gas costs of \$$p$/gal is $C = Lp/m$ dollars. Suppose you plan a trip of $L = 1500$ mi in a car that gets $m = 32$ mi/gal, with gas costs of $p = \$3.80$/gal.

a. Explain how the cost function is derived.

b. Compute the partial derivatives C_L, C_m, and C_p. Explain the meaning of the signs of the derivatives in the context of this problem.

c. Estimate the change in the total cost of the trip if L changes from $L = 1500$ to $L = 1520$, m changes from $m = 32$ to 31, and p changes from \$3.80 to \$3.85.

d. Is the total cost of the trip (with $L = 1500$ mi, $m = 32$ mi/gal, and $p = \$3.80$) more sensitive to a 1% change in L, m, or p (assuming the other two variables are fixed)? Explain.

Further Explorations

45. Explain why or why not Determine whether the following statements are true and give an explanation or counterexample.

a. The planes tangent to the cylinder $x^2 + z^2 = 1$ in $\mathbb{R}^3$ all have the form $ax + bz + c = 0$.

b. Suppose $w = xy/z$, for $x > 0$, $y > 0$, and $z > 0$. A decrease in z with x and y fixed results in an increase in w.

c. The gradient $\nabla F(a, b, c)$ lies in the plane tangent to the surface $F(x, y, z) = 0$ at (a, b, c).

46–49. Tangent planes *Find an equation of the plane tangent to the following surfaces at the given point.*

46. $z = \tan^{-1}(x + y)$; $(0, 0, 0)$

47. $z = \tan^{-1}(xy)$; $(1, 1, \pi/4)$

48. $(x + z)/(y - z) = 2$; $(4, 2, 0)$

49. $\sin xyz = \frac{1}{2}$; $(\pi, 1, \frac{1}{6})$

50–53. Horizontal tangent planes *Find the points at which the following surfaces have horizontal tangent planes.*

50. $z = \sin(x - y)$ in the region $-2\pi \le x \le 2\pi$, $-2\pi \le y \le 2\pi$

51. $x^2 + y^2 - z^2 - 2x + 2y + 3 = 0$

52. $x^2 + 2y^2 + z^2 - 2x - 2z - 2 = 0$

53. $z = \cos 2x \sin y$ in the region $-\pi \le x \le \pi$, $-\pi \le y \le \pi$

54. Heron's formula The area of a triangle with sides of length a, b, and c is given by a formula from antiquity called Heron's formula:

$$A = \sqrt{s(s - a)(s - b)(s - c)},$$

where $s = (a + b + c)/2$ is the *semiperimeter* of the triangle.

a. Find the partial derivatives A_a, A_b, and A_c.

b. A triangle has sides of length $a = 2$, $b = 4$, and $c = 5$. Estimate the change in the area when a increases by 0.03, b decreases by 0.08, and c increases by 0.6.

c. For an equilateral triangle with $a = b = c$, estimate the percent change in the area when all sides increase in length by $p\%$.

55. Surface area of a cone A cone with height h and radius r has a lateral surface area (the curved surface only, excluding the base) of $S = \pi r\sqrt{r^2 + h^2}$.

a. Estimate the change in the surface area when r increases from $r = 2.50$ to $r = 2.55$ and h decreases from $h = 0.60$ to $h = 0.58$.

b. When $r = 100$ and $h = 200$, is the surface area more sensitive to a small change in r or a small change in h? Explain.

56. Line tangent to an intersection curve Consider the paraboloid $z = x^2 + 3y^2$ and the plane $z = x + y + 4$, which intersects the paraboloid in a curve C at $(2, 1, 7)$ (see figure). Find the equation of the line tangent to C at the point $(2, 1, 7)$. Proceed as follows.

a. Find a vector normal to the plane at $(2, 1, 7)$.

b. Find a vector normal to the plane tangent to the paraboloid at $(2, 1, 7)$.

c. Argue that the line tangent to C at $(2, 1, 7)$ is orthogonal to both normal vectors found in parts (a) and (b). Use this fact to find a direction vector for the tangent line.

d. Knowing a point on the tangent line and the direction of the tangent line, write an equation of the tangent line in parametric form.

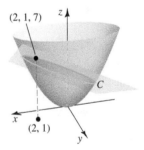

(2, 1, 7)

C

(2, 1)

Applications

57. Batting averages Batting averages in baseball are defined by $A = x/y$, where $x \ge 0$ is the total number of hits and $y > 0$ is the total number of at-bats. Treat x and y as positive real numbers and note that $0 \le A \le 1$.

a. Use differentials to estimate the change in the batting average if the number of hits increases from 60 to 62 and the number of at-bats increases from 175 to 180.

b. If a batter currently has a batting average of $A = 0.350$, does the average decrease if the batter fails to get a hit more than it increases if the batter gets a hit?

c. Does the answer to part (b) depend on the current batting average? Explain.

58. Water-level changes A conical tank with radius 0.50 m and height 2.00 m is filled with water (see figure). Water is released from the tank, and the water level drops by 0.05 m (from 2.00 m to 1.95 m). Approximate the change in the volume of water in the tank. (*Hint:* When the water level drops, both the radius and height of the cone of water change.)

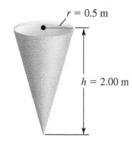

$r = 0.5$ m

$h = 2.00$ m

59. Flow in a cylinder Poiseuille's Law is a fundamental law of fluid dynamics that describes the flow velocity of a viscous incompressible fluid in a cylinder (it is used to model blood flow through veins and arteries). It says that in a cylinder of radius R and length L, the velocity of the fluid $r \leq R$ units from the centerline of the cylinder is $V = \dfrac{P}{4Lv}(R^2 - r^2)$, where P is the difference in the pressure between the ends of the cylinder and v is the viscosity of the fluid (see figure). Assuming that P and v are constant, the velocity V along the centerline of the cylinder ($r = 0$) is $V = kR^2/L$, where k is a constant that we will take to be $k = 1$.

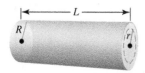

L

R

r

a. Estimate the change in the centerline velocity ($r = 0$) if the radius of the flow cylinder increases from $R = 3$ cm to $R = 3.05$ cm and the length increases from $L = 50$ cm to $L = 50.5$ cm.
b. Estimate the percent change in the centerline velocity if the radius of the flow cylinder R decreases by 1% and the length L increases by 2%.
c. Complete the following sentence: If the radius of the cylinder increases by $p\%$, then the length of the cylinder must increase by approximately _____% in order for the velocity to remain constant.

60. Floating-point operations In general, real numbers (with infinite decimal expansions) cannot be represented exactly in a computer by floating-point numbers (with finite decimal expansions). Suppose that floating-point numbers on a particular computer carry an error of at most 10^{-16}. Estimate the maximum error that is committed in doing the following arithmetic operations. Express the error in absolute and relative (percent) terms.

a. $f(x, y) = xy$ b. $f(x, y) = x/y$
c. $F(x, y, z) = xyz$ d. $F(x, y, z) = (x/y)/z$

61. Probability of at least one encounter Suppose that in a large group of people a fraction $0 \leq r \leq 1$ of the people have flu. The probability that in n random encounters, you will meet at least one person with flu is $P = f(n, r) = 1 - (1 - r)^n$. Although n is a positive integer, regard it as a positive real number.

a. Compute f_r and f_n.
b. How sensitive is the probability P to the flu rate r? Suppose you meet $n = 20$ people. Approximately how much does the probability P increase if the flu rate increases from $r = 0.1$ to $r = 0.11$ (with n fixed)?
c. Approximately how much does the probability P increase if the flu rate increases from $r = 0.9$ to $r = 0.91$ with $n = 20$?
d. Interpret the results of parts (b) and (c).

62. Two electrical resistors When two electrical resistors with resistance $R_1 > 0$ and $R_2 > 0$ are wired in parallel in a circuit (see figure), the combined resistance R, measured in ohms (Ω), is given by $\dfrac{1}{R} = \dfrac{1}{R_1} + \dfrac{1}{R_2}$.

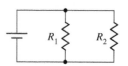

R_1 R_2

a. Estimate the change in R if R_1 increases from 2 Ω to 2.05 Ω and R_2 decreases from 3 Ω to 2.95 Ω.
b. Is it true that if $R_1 = R_2$ and R_1 increases by the same small amount as R_2 decreases, then R is approximately unchanged? Explain.
c. Is it true that if R_1 and R_2 increase, then R increases? Explain.
d. Suppose $R_1 > R_2$ and R_1 increases by the same small amount as R_2 decreases. Does R increase or decrease?

63. Three electrical resistors Extending Exercise 62, when three electrical resistors with resistance $R_1 > 0$, $R_2 > 0$, and $R_3 > 0$ are wired in parallel in a circuit (see figure), the combined resistance R, measured in ohms (Ω), is given by $\dfrac{1}{R} = \dfrac{1}{R_1} + \dfrac{1}{R_2} + \dfrac{1}{R_3}$. Estimate the change in R if R_1 increases from 2 Ω to 2.05 Ω, R_2 decreases from 3 Ω to 2.95 Ω, and R_3 increases from 1.5 Ω to 1.55 Ω.

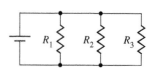

R_1 R_2 R_3

Additional Exercises

64. Power functions and percent change Suppose that $z = f(x, y) = x^a y^b$, where a and b are real numbers. Let dx/x, dy/y, and dz/z be the approximate relative (percent) changes in x, y, and z, respectively. Show that $dz/z = a(dx)/x + b(dy)/y$; that is, the relative changes are additive when weighted by the exponents a and b.

65. Logarithmic differentials Let f be a differentiable function of one or more variables that is positive on its domain.

a. Show that $d(\ln f) = \dfrac{df}{f}$.
b. Use part (a) to explain the statement that the absolute change in $\ln f$ is approximately equal to the relative change in f.
c. Let $f(x, y) = xy$, note that $\ln f = \ln x + \ln y$, and show that relative changes add; that is, $df/f = dx/x + dy/y$.

d. Let $f(x, y) = x/y$, note that $\ln f = \ln x - \ln y$, and show that relative changes subtract; that is $df/f = dx/x - dy/y$.

e. Show that in a product of n numbers, $f = x_1 x_2 \cdots x_n$, the relative change in f is approximately equal to the sum of the relative changes in the variables.

66. Distance from a plane to an ellipsoid (Adapted from 1938 Putnam Exam) Consider the ellipsoid $x^2/a^2 + y^2/b^2 + z^2/c^2 = 1$ and the plane P given by $Ax + By + Cz + 1 = 0$. Let $h = (A^2 + B^2 + C^2)^{-1/2}$ and $m = (a^2 A^2 + b^2 B^2 + c^2 C^2)^{1/2}$.

a. Find the equation of the plane tangent to the ellipsoid at the point (p, q, r).

b. Find the two points on the ellipsoid at which the tangent plane is parallel to P and find equations of the tangent planes.

c. Show that the distance between the origin and the plane P is h.

d. Show that the distance between the origin and the tangent planes is hm.

e. Find a condition that guarantees that the plane P does not intersect the ellipsoid.

1. $F(x, y, z) = z - xy - x + y = 0$ **2.** If you walk in the positive x-direction from $(-1, 2, 1)$, then you walk uphill. If you walk in the positive y-direction from $(-1, 2, 1)$, then you walk downhill.   **3.** If $\Delta x = 0$, then the change formula becomes $\Delta z \approx f_y(a, b)\, \Delta y$, which is the change formula for the single variable y. If $\Delta y = 0$, then the change formula becomes $\Delta z \approx f_x(a, b)\, \Delta x$, which is the change formula for the single variable x.   **4.** The BMI increases with weight w and decreases with height h.

13.8 Maximum/Minimum Problems

In Chapter 4 we showed how to use derivatives to find maximum and minimum values of functions of a single variable. When those techniques are extended to functions of two variables, we discover both similarities and differences. The landscape of a surface is far more complicated than the profile of a curve in the plane, so we see more interesting features when working with several variables. In addition to peaks (maximum values) and hollows (minimum values), we encounter winding ridges, long valleys, and mountain passes. Yet despite these complications, many of the ideas used for single-variable functions reappear in higher dimensions. For example, the Second Derivative Test, suitably adapted for two variables, plays a central role. As with single-variable functions, the techniques developed here are useful for solving practical optimization problems.

Local Maximum / Minimum Values

The concepts of local maximum and minimum values encountered in Chapter 4 extend readily to functions of two variables of the form $z = f(x, y)$. Figure 13.85 shows a general surface defined on a domain D, which is a subset of $\mathbb{R}^2$. The surface has peaks (local high points) and hollows (local low points) at points in the interior of D. The goal is to locate and classify these extreme points.

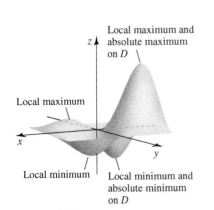

Local maximum and absolute maximum on D

Local maximum

Local minimum

Local minimum and absolute minimum on D

FIGURE 13.85

> We maintain the convention adopted in Chapter 4 that local maxima or minima occur at interior points of the domain. Recall that an open disk centered at (a, b) is the set of points within a circle centered at (a, b).

DEFINITIONS Local Maximum / Minimum Values

A function f has a **local maximum value** at (a, b) if $f(x, y) \le f(a, b)$ for all (x, y) in the domain of f in some open disk centered at (a, b). A function f has a **local minimum value** at (a, b) if $f(x, y) \ge f(a, b)$ for all (x, y) in the domain of f in some open disk centered at (a, b). Local maximum and local minimum values are also called **local extreme values** or **local extrema**.

In familiar terms, a local maximum is a point on a surface from which you cannot walk uphill. A local minimum is a point from which you cannot walk downhill. The following theorem is the analog of Theorem 4.2.

> **THEOREM 13.13   Derivatives and Local Maximum / Minimum Values**
> If f has a local maximum or minimum value at (a, b) and the partial derivatives
> f_x and f_y exist at (a, b), then $f_x(a, b) = f_y(a, b) = 0$.

Proof: Suppose f has a local maximum value at (a, b). The function of one variable $g(x) = f(x, b)$, obtained by holding $y = b$ fixed, also has a local maximum at (a, b). By Theorem 4.2, $g'(a) = 0$. However, $g'(a) = f_x(a, b)$; therefore, $f_x(a, b) = 0$. Similarly, the function $h(y) = f(a, y)$, obtained by holding $x = a$ fixed, has a local maximum at (a, b), which implies that $f_y(a, b) = h'(b) = 0$. An analogous argument is used for the local minimum case.   ◄

Suppose f is differentiable at (a, b) (ensuring the existence of a tangent plane) and f has a local extremum at (a, b). Then, $f_x(a, b) = f_y(a, b) = 0$, which, when substituted into the equation of the tangent plane, gives the equation $z = f(a, b)$ (a constant). Therefore, if the tangent plane exists at a local extremum, then it is horizontal there.

QUICK CHECK 1 The paraboloid $z = x^2 + y^2 - 4x + 2y + 5$ has a local minimum at $(2, -1)$. Verify the conclusion of Theorem 13.13 for this function. ◄

Recall that for a function of one variable the condition $f'(a) = 0$ does not guarantee a local extremum at a. A similar precaution must be taken with Theorem 13.13. The conditions $f_x(a, b) = f_y(a, b) = 0$ do not imply that f has a local extremum at (a, b), as we show momentarily. Theorem 13.13 provides *candidates* for local extrema. We call these candidates *critical points*, as we did for functions of one variable. Therefore, the procedure for locating local maximum and minimum values is to find the critical points and then determine whether these candidates correspond to genuine local maximum and minimum values.

> **DEFINITION   Critical Point**
> An interior point (a, b) in the domain of f is a **critical point** of f if either
>
> **1.** $f_x(a, b) = f_y(a, b) = 0$, or
>
> **2.** one (or both) of f_x or f_y does not exist at (a, b).

EXAMPLE 1   Finding critical points Find the critical points of $f(x, y) = xy(x - 2)(y + 3)$.

SOLUTION This function is differentiable at all points of $\mathbb{R}^2$, so the critical points occur only at points where $f_x(x, y) = f_y(x, y) = 0$. Computing and simplifying the partial derivatives, these conditions become

$$f_x(x, y) = 2y(x - 1)(y + 3) = 0$$
$$f_y(x, y) = x(x - 2)(2y + 3) = 0.$$

We must now identify all (x, y) pairs that satisfy both equations. The first equation is satisfied if and only if $y = 0$, $x = 1$, or $y = -3$. We consider each of these cases.

- Substituting $y = 0$, the second equation is $3x(x - 2) = 0$, which has solutions $x = 0$ and $x = 2$. So, $(0, 0)$ and $(2, 0)$ are critical points.

- Substituting $x = 1$, the second equation is $-(2y + 3) = 0$, which has the solution $y = -\frac{3}{2}$. So, $\left(1, -\frac{3}{2}\right)$ is a critical point.

- Substituting $y = -3$, the second equation is $-3x(x - 2) = 0$, which has roots $x = 0$ and $x = 2$. So, $(0, -3)$ and $(2, -3)$ are critical points.

We find that there are five critical points: $(0, 0)$, $(2, 0)$, $(1, -\frac{3}{2})$, $(0, -3)$, and $(2, -3)$. Some of these critical points may correspond to local maximum or minimum values. We return to this example and a complete analysis shortly.

Related Exercises 9–18 ◄

Second Derivative Test

Critical points are candidates for local extreme values. With functions of one variable, the Second Derivative Test may be used to determine whether critical points correspond to local maxima or minima (it can also be inconclusive). The analogous test for functions of two variables not only detects local maxima and minima, but also identifies another type of point known as a *saddle point*.

> The usual image of a saddle point is that of a mountain pass (or a horse saddle), where you can walk upward in some directions and downward in other directions. The definition of a saddle point we have given includes other less common situations. For example, with this definition, the cylinder $z = x^3$ has a line of saddle points along the y-axis.

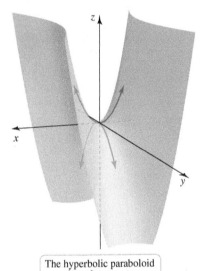

The hyperbolic paraboloid $z = x^2 - y^2$ has a saddle point at $(0, 0)$.

FIGURE 13.86

> The Second Derivative Test for functions of a single variable states that if a is a critical point with $f'(a) = 0$, then $f''(a) > 0$ implies that f has a local minimum at a, $f''(a) < 0$ implies that f has a local maximum at a, and if $f''(a) = 0$, the test is inconclusive. Theorem 13.14 is easier to remember if you notice the parallels between the two second derivative tests.

DEFINITION Saddle Point

A function f has a **saddle point** at a critical point (a, b) if, in every open disk centered at (a, b), there are points (x, y) for which $f(x, y) > f(a, b)$ and points for which $f(x, y) < f(a, b)$.

A saddle point on the surface $z = f(x, y)$ is a point $(a, b, f(a, b))$ from which it is possible to walk uphill in some directions and downhill in other directions. The function $f(x, y) = x^2 - y^2$ (a hyperbolic paraboloid) is a good example to remember. The surface *rises* from $(0, 0)$ along the x-axis and *falls* from $(0, 0)$ along the y-axis (Figure 13.86). We can easily check that $f_x(0, 0) = f_y(0, 0) = 0$, demonstrating that critical points do not necessarily correspond to local maxima or minima.

QUICK CHECK 2 Consider the plane tangent to a surface at a saddle point. In what direction does the normal to the plane point? ◄

THEOREM 13.14 Second Derivative Test

Suppose that the second partial derivatives of f are continuous throughout an open disk centered at the point (a, b), where $f_x(a, b) = f_y(a, b) = 0$. Let $D(x, y) = f_{xx}(x, y) f_{yy}(x, y) - (f_{xy}(x, y))^2$.

1. If $D(a, b) > 0$ and $f_{xx}(a, b) < 0$, then f has a local maximum value at (a, b).

2. If $D(a, b) > 0$ and $f_{xx}(a, b) > 0$, then f has a local minimum value at (a, b).

3. If $D(a, b) < 0$, then f has a saddle point at (a, b).

4. If $D(a, b) = 0$, then the test is inconclusive.

The proof of this theorem is given in Appendix B, but a few comments are in order. The test relies on the quantity $D(x, y) = f_{xx} f_{yy} - (f_{xy})^2$, which is called the **discriminant** of f. It can be remembered as the 2×2 determinant of the **Hessian** matrix $\begin{pmatrix} f_{xx} & f_{xy} \\ f_{yx} & f_{yy} \end{pmatrix}$, where $f_{xy} = f_{yx}$, provided these derivatives are continuous (Theorem 13.4). The condition $D(x, y) > 0$ means that the surface has the same general behavior in all directions near (a, b); either the surface rises in all directions, or it falls in all directions. In the case that $D(a, b) = 0$, the test is inconclusive: (a, b) could correspond to a local maximum, a local minimum, or a saddle point.

Finally, another useful characterization of a saddle point can be derived from Theorem 13.14: The tangent plane at a saddle point lies both above and below the surface.

QUICK CHECK 3 Compute the discriminant $D(x, y)$ of $f(x, y) = x^2 y^2$. ◄

$z = x^2 + 2y^2 - 4x + 4y + 6$

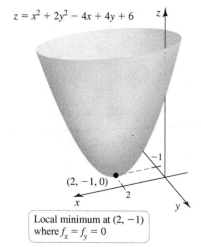

$(2, -1, 0)$

Local minimum at $(2, -1)$ where $f_x = f_y = 0$

FIGURE 13.87

EXAMPLE 2 **Analyzing critical points** Use the Second Derivative Test to classify the critical points of $f(x, y) = x^2 + 2y^2 - 4x + 4y + 6$.

SOLUTION We begin with the following derivative calculations:

$$f_x = 2x - 4 \qquad f_y = 4y + 4$$
$$f_{xx} = 2 \qquad\qquad f_{xy} = f_{yx} = 0 \qquad f_{yy} = 4.$$

Setting both f_x and f_y equal to zero yields the single critical point $(2, -1)$. The value of the discriminant at the critical point is $D(2, -1) = f_{xx}f_{yy} - (f_{xy})^2 = 8 > 0$. Furthermore, $f_{xx}(2, -1) = 2 > 0$. By the Second Derivative Test, f has a local minimum at $(2, -1)$; the value of the function at that point is $f(2, -1) = 0$ (Figure 13.87).

Related Exercises 19–34 ◄

EXAMPLE 3 **Analyzing critical points** Use the Second Derivative Test to classify the critical points of $f(x, y) = xy(x - 2)(y + 3)$.

SOLUTION In Example 1, we determined that the critical points of f are $(0, 0)$, $(2, 0)$, $\left(1, -\frac{3}{2}\right)$, $(0, -3)$, and $(2, -3)$. The derivatives needed to evaluate the discriminant are

$$f_x = 2y(x - 1)(y + 3), \qquad f_y = x(x - 2)(2y + 3),$$
$$f_{xx} = 2y(y + 3), \qquad\qquad f_{xy} = 2(2y + 3)(x - 1), \qquad f_{yy} = 2x(x - 2).$$

The values of the discriminant at the critical points and the conclusions of the Second Derivative Test are shown in Table 13.5.

Table 13.5

(x, y)	$D(x, y)$	f_{xx}	Conclusion
$(0, 0)$	-36	0	Saddle point
$(2, 0)$	-36	0	Saddle point
$\left(1, -\frac{3}{2}\right)$	9	$-\frac{9}{2}$	Local maximum
$(0, -3)$	-36	0	Saddle point
$(2, -3)$	-36	0	Saddle point

The surface described by f has one local maximum at $\left(1, -\frac{3}{2}\right)$, surrounded by four saddle points (Figure 13.88a). The structure of the surface may also be visualized by plotting the level curves of f (Figure 13.88b).

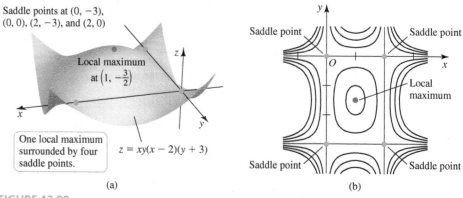

Saddle points at $(0, -3)$, $(0, 0)$, $(2, -3)$, and $(2, 0)$

Local maximum at $\left(1, -\frac{3}{2}\right)$

One local maximum surrounded by four saddle points.

$z = xy(x - 2)(y + 3)$

(a)

Saddle point

Saddle point

Local maximum

Saddle point

Saddle point

(b)

FIGURE 13.88

Related Exercises 19–34 ◄

> Example 4 is a *constrained optimization problem*, in which the goal is to maximize the volume subject to an additional condition called a *constraint*. We return to such problems in the next section and present another method of solution.

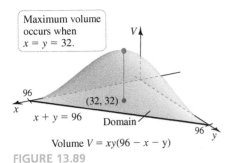

Maximum volume occurs when $x = y = 32$.

Volume $V = xy(96 - x - y)$

FIGURE 13.89

EXAMPLE 4 **Shipping regulations** A shipping company handles rectangular boxes provided the sum of the length, width, and height of the box does not exceed 96 in. Find the dimensions of the box that meets this condition and has the largest volume.

SOLUTION Let x, y, and z be the dimensions of the box; its volume is $V = xyz$. The box with the maximum volume satisfies the condition $x + y + z = 96$, which is used to eliminate any one of the variables from the volume function. Noting that $z = 96 - x - y$, the volume function becomes

$$V(x, y) = xy(96 - x - y).$$

Notice that because x, y, and $96 - x - y$ are dimensions of the box, they must be non-negative. The condition $96 - x - y \geq 0$ implies that $x + y \leq 96$. Therefore, among points in the xy-plane, the constraint is met only if (x, y) lies in the triangle bounded by the lines $x = 0$, $y = 0$, and $x + y = 96$ (Figure 13.89). This triangle is the domain of the problem, and on its boundary, $V = 0$.

The goal is to find the maximum value of V. The critical points of V satisfy

$$V_x = 96y - 2xy - y^2 = y(96 - 2x - y) = 0$$
$$V_y = 96x - 2xy - x^2 = x(96 - 2y - x) = 0.$$

You can check that these two equations have four solutions: $(0, 0)$, $(96, 0)$, $(0, 96)$, and $(32, 32)$. The first three solutions lie on the boundary of the domain, where $V = 0$. Therefore, the only critical point is $(32, 32)$. The required second derivatives are

$$V_{xx} = -2y, \qquad V_{xy} = 96 - 2x - 2y, \qquad V_{yy} = -2x.$$

The discriminant is

$$D(x, y) = V_{xx}V_{yy} - (V_{xy})^2 = 4xy - (96 - 2x - 2y)^2,$$

which, when evaluated at $(32, 32)$, has the value $D(32, 32) = 3072 > 0$. Therefore, the critical point corresponds to either a local maximum or minimum. Noting that $V_{xx}(32, 32) = -64 < 0$, we conclude that the critical point corresponds to a local maximum. The dimensions of the box with maximum volume are $x = 32$, $y = 32$, and $z = 96 - x - y = 32$ (it is a cube). Its volume is 32,768 in^3, which is the maximum volume on the domain.

Related Exercises 35–38 ◄

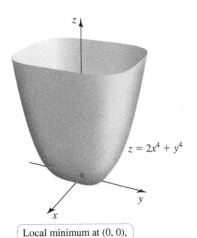

Local minimum at $(0, 0)$, but the Second Derivative Test is inconclusive.

FIGURE 13.90

> The same "flat" behavior occurs with functions of one variable, such as $f(x) = x^4$. Although f has a local minimum at $x = 0$, the Second Derivative Test is inconclusive.

EXAMPLE 5 **Inconclusive tests** Apply the Second Derivative Test to the following functions and interpret the results.

a. $f(x, y) = 2x^4 + y^4$ **b.** $f(x, y) = 2 - xy^2$

SOLUTION

a. The critical points of f satisfy the conditions

$$f_x = 8x^3 = 0 \quad \text{and} \quad f_y = 4y^3 = 0,$$

so the sole critical point is $(0, 0)$. The second partial derivatives evaluated at $(0, 0)$ are

$$f_{xx}(0, 0) = f_{xy}(0, 0) = f_{yy}(0, 0) = 0.$$

We see that $D(0, 0) = 0$, and the Second Derivative Test is inconclusive. While the bowl-shaped surface (Figure 13.90) described by f has a local minimum at $(0, 0)$, the surface also has a broad flat bottom, which makes the local minimum "invisible" to the Second Derivative Test.

b. The critical points of this function satisfy

$$f_x(x, y) = -y^2 = 0 \quad \text{and} \quad f_y(x, y) = -2xy = 0.$$

> It is not surprising that the Second Derivative Test is inconclusive in Example 5b. The function has a line of local maxima at $(a, 0)$ for $a > 0$, a line of local minima at $(a, 0)$ for $a < 0$, and a saddle point at $(0, 0)$.

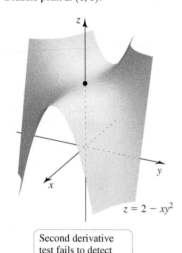

$z = 2 - xy^2$

Second derivative test fails to detect saddle point at $(0, 0)$.

FIGURE 13.91

> Recall that a *closed set* in $\mathbb{R}^2$ is a set that includes its boundary. A *bounded set* in $\mathbb{R}^2$ is a set that may be enclosed by a circle of finite radius.

The solutions of these equations have the form $(a, 0)$, where a is a real number. It is easy to check that the second partial derivatives evaluated at $(a, 0)$ are

$$f_{xx}(a, 0) = f_{xy}(a, 0) = 0 \quad \text{and} \quad f_{yy}(a, 0) = -2a.$$

Therefore, the discriminant is $D(a, 0) = 0$, and the Second Derivative Test is inconclusive. Figure 13.91 shows that f has a flat ridge above the x-axis that the Second Derivative Test is unable to classify.　　　*Related Exercises 39–42* ◄

Absolute Maximum and Minimum Values

As in the one-variable case, we are often interested in knowing where a function of two or more variables attains its extreme values over its entire domain.

DEFINITIONS　Absolute Maximum/Minimum Values

If $f(x, y) \leq f(a, b)$ for all (x, y) in the domain of f, then f has an **absolute maximum value** at (a, b). If $f(x, y) \geq f(a, b)$ for all (x, y) in the domain of f, then f has an **absolute minimum value** at (a, b).

The concepts of absolute maximum and minimum values may also be applied to a specified subset of the domain, as shown in Example 6. It should be noted that the Extreme Value Theorem of Chapter 4 has an analog in $\mathbb{R}^2$ (or in higher dimensions): A function that is continuous on a closed bounded set in $\mathbb{R}^2$ attains its absolute maximum and absolute minimum values on that set. Absolute maximum and minimum values on a closed bounded set R occur in two ways.

• They may be local maximum or minimum values at interior points of R, where they are associated with critical points.

• They may occur on the boundary of R.

Therefore, the search for absolute maximum and minimum values on a closed bounded set is accomplished in the following three steps.

PROCEDURE　Finding Absolute Maximum/Minimum Values on Closed, Bounded Sets

Let f be continuous on a closed bounded set R in $\mathbb{R}^2$. To find the absolute maximum and minimum values of f on R:

1. Determine the values of f at all critical points in R.

2. Find the maximum and minimum values of f on the boundary of R.

3. The greatest function value found in Steps 1 and 2 is the absolute maximum value of f on R, and the least function value found in Steps 1 and 2 is the absolute minimum value of f on R.

The techniques for carrying out Step 1 of this process have been presented. The challenge generally lies in locating extreme values on the boundary. For now, we restrict our attention to sets whose boundaries are described parametrically; then, finding extreme values on the boundary becomes a one-variable problem. In the next section, we discuss an alternative method for finding extreme values on boundaries.

EXAMPLE 6　Absolute maximum and minimum values Find the absolute maximum and minimum values of $f(x, y) = x^2 + y^2 - 2x + 2y + 5$ on the set $R = \{(x, y): x^2 + y^2 \leq 4\}$ (the closed disk centered at $(0, 0)$ with radius 2).

SOLUTION We begin by locating the critical points and the local maxima and minima. The critical points satisfy the equations

$$f_x(x, y) = 2x - 2 = 0 \quad \text{and} \quad f_y(x, y) = 2y + 2 = 0,$$

which have the solution $x = 1$ and $y = -1$. The value of the function at this point is $f(1, -1) = 3$.

We now determine the maximum and minimum values of f on the boundary of R, which is a circle of radius 2 described by the parametric equations

> Recall that a parametric description of a circle of radius a centered at the origin is $x = a \cos \theta$, $y = a \sin \theta$, for $0 \le \theta \le 2\pi$.

$$x = 2 \cos \theta, \quad y = 2 \sin \theta, \quad \text{for} \quad 0 \le \theta \le 2\pi.$$

Substituting x and y in terms of θ into the function f, we obtain a new function $g(\theta)$ that gives the values of f on the boundary of R:

$$\begin{aligned}
g(\theta) &= (2 \cos \theta)^2 + (2 \sin \theta)^2 - 2(2 \cos \theta) + 2(2 \sin \theta) + 5 \\
&= 4(\cos^2 \theta + \sin^2 \theta) - 4 \cos \theta + 4 \sin \theta + 5 \\
&= -4 \cos \theta + 4 \sin \theta + 9.
\end{aligned}$$

Finding the maximum and minimum boundary values is now a one-variable problem. The critical points of g satisfy

$$g'(\theta) = 4 \sin \theta + 4 \cos \theta = 0,$$

or $\tan \theta = -1$. Therefore, g has critical points $\theta = -\pi/4$ and $\theta = 3\pi/4$, which correspond to the points $(\sqrt{2}, -\sqrt{2})$ and $(-\sqrt{2}, \sqrt{2})$. The function values at these points are $f(\sqrt{2}, -\sqrt{2}) = 9 - 4\sqrt{2} \approx 3.3$ and $f(-\sqrt{2}, \sqrt{2}) = 9 + 4\sqrt{2} \approx 14.7$.

Having completed the first two steps of this procedure, we have three function values to consider:

- $f(1, -1) = 3$ (critical point),
- $f(\sqrt{2}, -\sqrt{2}) = 9 - 4\sqrt{2} \approx 3.3$ (boundary point), and
- $f(-\sqrt{2}, \sqrt{2}) = 9 + 4\sqrt{2} \approx 14.7$ (boundary point).

The greatest value, $f(-\sqrt{2}, \sqrt{2}) = 9 + 4\sqrt{2}$, is the absolute maximum value, and it occurs at a boundary point. The least value, $f(1, -1) = 3$, is the absolute minimum value, and it occurs at an interior point (Figure 13.92a). Also revealing is the plot of the level curves of the surface with the boundary of R superimposed (Figure 13.92b). As the boundary of R is traversed, the values of f vary, reaching a maximum value at $\theta = 3\pi/4$, or $(-\sqrt{2}, \sqrt{2})$, and a minimum value at $\theta = -\pi/4$, or $(\sqrt{2}, -\sqrt{2})$.

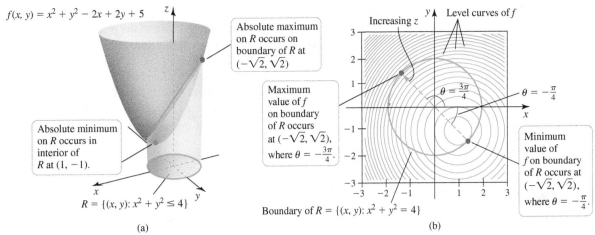

(a)

(b)

FIGURE 13.92

Related Exercises 43–50◄

Open and/or Unbounded Domains   Finding absolute maximum and minimum values of a function on an open domain (for example, $R = \{(x, y) = x^2 + y^2 < 9\}$) or an unbounded domain (for example, $R = \{(x, y): x > 0, y > 0\}$) presents additional challenges. Because there is no systematic procedure for dealing with such problems, some ingenuity is generally needed. Notice that absolute extrema may not exist on such domains.

EXAMPLE 7   Absolute extreme values on an open set   Find the absolute maximum and minimum values of $f(x, y) = 4 - x^2 - y^2$ on the open disk $R = \{(x, y): x^2 + y^2 < 1\}$ (if they exist).

SOLUTION   You should verify that f has a critical point at $(0, 0)$ and it corresponds to a local maximum (on an inverted paraboloid). Moving away from $(0, 0)$ in all directions, the function values decrease, so f also has an absolute maximum at $(0, 0)$. The boundary of R is the unit circle $\{(x, y): x^2 + y^2 = 1\}$, which is not contained in R. As (x, y) approaches any point on the unit circle along any path in R, the function values $f(x, y) = 4 - (x^2 + y^2)$ decrease and approach 3 but never reach 3. Therefore, f does not have an absolute minimum on R.

Related Exercises 51–58◄

QUICK CHECK 4   Does the linear function $f(x, y) = 2x + 3y$ have an absolute maximum or minimum value on the open unit square $\{(x, y): 0 < x < 1, 0 < y < 1\}$? ◄

EXAMPLE 8   Absolute extreme values on an open set   Find the point(s) on the plane $x + 2y + z = 2$ closest to the point $P(2, 0, 4)$.

SOLUTION   Suppose that (x, y, z) is a point on the plane, which means that $z = 2 - x - 2y$. The distance between $P(2, 0, 4)$ and (x, y, z) that we seek to minimize is

$$d(x, y, z) = \sqrt{(x - 2)^2 + y^2 + (z - 4)^2}.$$

> Notice that $\dfrac{\partial}{\partial x}(d^2) = 2d\dfrac{\partial d}{\partial x}$ and $\dfrac{\partial}{\partial y}(d^2) = 2d\dfrac{\partial d}{\partial y}$. Because $d \geq 0$, d^2 and d have the same critical points.

It is easier to minimize d^2, which has the same critical points as d. Squaring d and eliminating z using $z = 2 - x - 2y$, we have

$$f(x, y) = (d(x, y, z))^2 = (x - 2)^2 + y^2 + (-x - 2y - 2)^2$$
$$= 2x^2 + 5y^2 + 4xy + 8y + 8.$$

The critical points of f satisfy the equations

$$f_x = 4x + 4y = 0 \quad \text{and} \quad f_y = 4x + 10y + 8 = 0,$$

whose only solution is $x = \frac{4}{3}, y = -\frac{4}{3}$. The Second Derivative Test confirms that this point corresponds to a local minimum of f. We now ask: Does $\left(\frac{4}{3}, -\frac{4}{3}\right)$ correspond to the *absolute* minimum value of f over the entire domain of the problem, which is $\mathbb{R}^2$? Because the domain has no boundary, we cannot check values of f on the boundary. Instead, we argue geometrically that there is exactly one point on the plane that is closest to P. We have found a point that is closest to P among nearby points on the plane. As we move away from this point, the values of f increase without bound. Therefore, $\left(\frac{4}{3}, -\frac{4}{3}\right)$ corresponds to the absolute minimum value of f. A graph of f (Figure 13.93) confirms this reasoning, and we conclude that the point $\left(\frac{4}{3}, -\frac{4}{3}, \frac{10}{3}\right)$ is the point on the plane nearest P.

Related Exercises 51–58◄

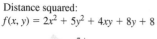

Distance squared:
$f(x, y) = 2x^2 + 5y^2 + 4xy + 8y + 8$

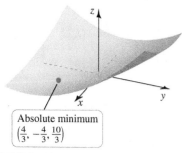

Absolute minimum
$\left(\frac{4}{3}, -\frac{4}{3}, \frac{10}{3}\right)$

FIGURE 13.93

SECTION 13.8 EXERCISES

Review Questions

1. Describe the appearance of a smooth surface with a local maximum at a point.

2. Describe the usual appearance of a smooth surface at a saddle point.

3. What are the conditions for a critical point of a function f?

4. If $f_x(a, b) = f_y(a, b) = 0$, does it follow that f has a local maximum or local minimum at (a, b)? Explain.

5. What is the discriminant and how do you compute it?

6. Explain how the Second Derivative Test is used.

7. What is an absolute minimum value of a function f on a set R in $\mathbb{R}^2$?

8. What is the procedure for locating absolute maximum and minimum values on a closed bounded domain?

Basic Skills

9–18. Critical points *Find all critical points of the following functions.*

9. $f(x, y) = 1 + x^2 + y^2$

10. $f(x, y) = x^2 - 6x + y^2 + 8y$

11. $f(x, y) = (3x - 2)^2 + (y - 4)^2$

12. $f(x, y) = 3x^2 - 4y^2$

13. $f(x, y) = x^4 + y^4 - 16xy$

14. $f(x, y) = x^3/3 - y^3/3 + 3xy$

15. $f(x, y) = x^4 - 2x^2 + y^2 - 4y + 5$

16. $f(x, y) = x^2 + xy - 2x - y + 1$

17. $f(x, y) = x^2 + 6x + y^2 + 8$

18. $f(x, y) = e^{x^2 y^2 - 2xy^2 + y^2}$

19–34. Analyzing critical points *Find the critical points of the following functions. Use the Second Derivative Test to determine (if possible) whether each critical point corresponds to a local maximum, local minimum, or saddle point. Confirm your results using a graphing utility.*

19. $f(x, y) = 4 + 2x^2 + 3y^2$

20. $f(x, y) = (4x - 1)^2 + (2y + 4)^2 + 1$

21. $f(x, y) = -4x^2 + 8y^2 - 3$

22. $f(x, y) = x^4 + y^4 - 4x - 32y + 10$

23. $f(x, y) = x^4 + 2y^2 - 4xy$

24. $f(x, y) = xye^{-x-y}$

25. $f(x, y) = \sqrt{x^2 + y^2 - 4x + 5}$

26. $f(x, y) = \tan^{-1} xy$

27. $f(x, y) = 2xye^{-x^2-y^2}$

28. $f(x, y) = x^2 + xy^2 - 2x + 1$

29. $f(x, y) = \dfrac{x}{1 + x^2 + y^2}$

30. $f(x, y) = \dfrac{x - 1}{x^2 + y^2}$

31. $f(x, y) = x^4 + 4x^2(y - 2) + 8(y - 1)^2$

32. $f(x, y) = xe^{-x-y} \sin y$, for $|x| \leq 2, 0 \leq y \leq \pi$

33. $f(x, y) = ye^x - e^y$

34. $f(x, y) = \sin(2\pi x)\cos(\pi y)$, for $|x| \leq \frac{1}{2}$ and $|y| \leq \frac{1}{2}$.

35. **Shipping regulations** A shipping company handles rectangular boxes provided the sum of the height and the girth of the box does not exceed 96 in. (The girth is the perimeter of the smallest base of the box.) Find the dimensions of the box that meets this condition and has the largest volume.

36. **Cardboard boxes** A lidless box is to be made using 2 m² of cardboard. Find the dimensions of the box with the largest possible volume.

37. **Cardboard boxes** A lidless cardboard box is to be made with a volume of 4 m³. Find the dimensions of the box that requires the least amount of cardboard.

38. **Optimal box** Find the dimensions of the largest rectangular box in the first octant of the *xyz*-coordinate system that has one vertex at the origin and the opposite vertex on the plane $x + 2y + 3z = 6$.

39–42. Inconclusive tests *Show that the Second Derivative Test is inconclusive when applied to the following functions at $(0, 0)$. Describe the behavior of the function at the critical point.*

39. $f(x, y) = 4 + x^4 + 3y^4$

40. $f(x, y) = x^2y - 3$

41. $f(x, y) = x^4y^2$

42. $f(x, y) = \sin(x^2y^2)$

43–50. Absolute maxima and minima *Find the absolute maximum and minimum values of the following functions on the given set R.*

43. $f(x, y) = x^2 + y^2 - 2y + 1$; $R = \{(x, y): x^2 + y^2 \leq 4\}$

44. $f(x, y) = 2x^2 + y^2$; $R = \{(x, y): x^2 + y^2 \leq 16\}$

45. $f(x, y) = 4 + 2x^2 + y^2$;
$R = \{(x, y): -1 \leq x \leq 1, -1 \leq y \leq 1\}$

46. $f(x, y) = 6 - x^2 - 4y^2$;
$R = \{(x, y): -2 \leq x \leq 2, -1 \leq y \leq 1\}$

47. $f(x, y) = 2x^2 - 4x + 3y^2 + 2$;
$R = \{(x, y): (x - 1)^2 + y^2 \leq 1\}$

48. $f(x, y) = x^2 + y^2 - 2x - 2y$; R is the closed set bounded by the triangle with vertices $(0, 0)$, $(2, 0)$, and $(0, 2)$.

49. $f(x, y) = -2x^2 + 4x - 3y^2 - 6y - 1$;
$R = \{(x, y): (x - 1)^2 + (y + 1)^2 \leq 1\}$

50. $f(x, y) = \sqrt{x^2 + y^2 - 2x + 2}$; R is the closed half disk $\{(x, y): x^2 + y^2 \leq 4 \text{ with } y \geq 0\}$.

51–54. Absolute extrema on open and/or unbounded sets *If possible, find the absolute maximum and minimum values of the following functions on the set R.*

51. $f(x, y) = x^2 + y^2 - 4$; $R = \{(x, y): x^2 + y^2 < 4\}$

52. $f(x, y) = x + 3y$; $R = \{(x, y): |x| < 1, |y| < 2\}$

53. $f(x, y) = 2e^{-x-y}$; $R = \{(x, y): x \geq 0, y \geq 0\}$

54. $f(x, y) = x^2 - y^2$; $R = \{(x, y); |x| < 1, |y| < 1\}$

55–58. Absolute extrema on open and/or unbounded sets

55. Find the point on the plane $x + y + z = 4$ nearest the point $P(0, 3, 6)$.

56. Find the point(s) on the cone $z^2 = x^2 + y^2$ nearest the point $P(1, 4, 0)$.

57. Find the point on the surface curve $y = x^2$ nearest the line $y = x - 1$. Identify the point on the line.

58. Rectangular boxes with a volume of 10 m³ are made of two materials. The material for the top and bottom of the box costs $10/m² and the material for the sides of the box costs $1/m². What are the dimensions of the box that minimize the cost of the box?

Further Explorations

59. Explain why or why not Determine whether the following statements are true and give an explanation or counterexample. Assume that f is differentiable at the points in question.

   a. The fact that $f_x(2, 2) = f_y(2, 2) = 0$ implies that f has a local maximum, local minimum, or saddle point at $(2, 2)$.

   b. The function f could have a local maximum at (a, b) where $f_y(a, b) \neq 0$.

   c. The function f could have both an absolute maximum and an absolute minimum at two different points that are not critical points.

   d. The tangent plane is horizontal at a point on a surface corresponding to a critical point.

60–61. Extreme points from contour plots *Based on the level curves that are visible in the following graphs, identify the approximate locations of the local maxima, local minima, and saddle points.*

60.

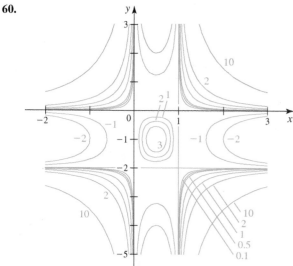

61.

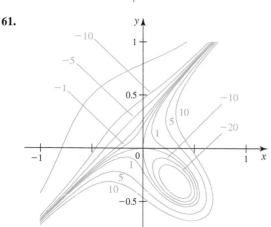

62. Optimal box Find the dimensions of the rectangular box with maximum volume in the first octant with one vertex at the origin and the opposite vertex on the ellipsoid $36x^2 + 4y^2 + 9z^2 = 36$.

63. Least distance What point on the plane $x - y + z = 2$ is closest to the point $(1, 1, 1)$?

64. Maximum/minimum of linear functions Let R be a closed bounded set in $\mathbb{R}^2$ and let $f(x, y) = ax + by + c$, where a, b, and c are real numbers, with a and b not both zero. Give a geometrical argument explaining why the absolute maximum and minimum values of f over R occur on the boundaries of R.

65. Magic triples Let x, y, and z be nonnegative numbers with $x + y + z = 200$.

   a. Find the values of x, y, and z that minimize $x^2 + y^2 + z^2$.

   b. Find the values of x, y, and z that minimize $\sqrt{x^2 + y^2 + z^2}$.

   c. Find the values of x, y, and z that maximize xyz.

   d. Find the values of x, y, and z that maximize $x^2y^2z^2$.

66. Powers and roots Assume that $x + y + z = 1$ with $x \geq 0$, $y \geq 0$, and $z \geq 0$.

   a. Find the maximum and minimum values of $(1 + x^2)(1 + y^2)(1 + z^2)$.

   b. Find the maximum and minimum values of $(1 + \sqrt{x})(1 + \sqrt{y})(1 + \sqrt{z})$.

(*Source: Math Horizons* (April 2004))

Applications

67. Optimal locations Suppose n houses are located at the distinct points $(x_1, y_1), (x_2, y_2), \ldots, (x_n, y_n)$. A power substation must be located at a point such that the *sum of the squares* of the distances between the houses and the substation is minimized.

   a. Find the optimal location of the substation in the case that $n = 3$ and the houses are located at $(0, 0), (2, 0)$, and $(1, 1)$.

   b. Find the optimal location of the substation in the case that $n = 3$ and the houses are located at distinct points (x_1, y_1), (x_2, y_2), and (x_3, y_3).

   c. Find the optimal location of the substation in the general case of n houses located at distinct points $(x_1, y_1), (x_2, y_2), \ldots,$ (x_n, y_n).

   d. You might argue that the locations found in parts (a), (b), and (c) are not optimal because they result from minimizing the sum of the *squares* of the distances, not the sum of the distances themselves. Use the locations in part (a) and write the function that gives the sum of the distances. Note that minimizing this function is much more difficult than in part (a). Then use a graphing utility to determine whether the optimal location is the same in the two cases. (Also see Exercise 75 about Steiner's problem.)

68–69. Least squares approximation *In its many guises, the least squares approximation arises in numerous areas of mathematics and statistics. Suppose you collect data for two variables (for example, height and shoe size) in the form of pairs $(x_1, y_1), (x_2, y_2), \ldots, (x_n, y_n)$. The data may be plotted as a scatterplot in the xy-plane, as shown in the figure. The technique known as* linear regression *asks the question: What is the equation of the line that "best fits" the data? The least squares* *criterion for best fit requires that the sum of the squares of the vertical distances between the line and the data points is a minimum.*

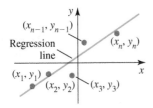

68. Let the equation of the best-fit line be $y = mx + b$, where the slope m and the y-intercept b must be determined using the least squares condition. First assume that there are three data points $(1, 2)$, $(3, 5)$, and $(4, 6)$. Show that the function of m and b that gives the sum of the squares of the vertical distances between the line and the three data points is

$$E(m, b) = ((m + b) - 2)^2 + ((3m + b) - 5)^2 + ((4m + b) - 6)^2.$$

Find the critical points of E and find the values of m and b that minimize E. Graph the three data points and the best-fit line.

69. Generalize the procedure in Exercise 68 by assuming that n data points (x_1, y_1), (x_2, y_2), . . . , (x_n, y_n) are given. Write the function $E(m, b)$ (summation notation allows for a more compact calculation). Show that the coefficients of the best-fit line are

$$m = \frac{\left(\sum x_k\right)\left(\sum y_k\right) - n\sum x_k y_k}{\left(\sum x_k\right)^2 - n\sum x_k^2} \text{ and}$$

$$b = \frac{1}{n}\left(\sum y_k - m\sum x_k\right),$$

where all sums run from $k = 1$ to $k = n$.

70–71. Least squares practice *Use the results of Exercise 69 to find the best-fit line for the following data sets. Plot the points and the best-fit line.*

70. $(0, 0)$, $(2, 3)$, $(4, 5)$

71. $(-1, 0)$, $(0, 6)$, $(3, 8)$

Additional Exercises

72. Second Derivative Test Use the Second Derivative Test to prove that if (a, b) is a critical point of f at which $f_x(a, b) = f_y(a, b) = 0$ and $f_{xx}(a, b) < 0 < f_{yy}(a, b)$ or $f_{yy}(a, b) < 0 < f_{xx}(a, b)$, then f has a saddle point at (a, b).

73. Maximum area triangle Among all triangles with a perimeter of 9 units, find the dimensions of the triangle with the maximum area. It may be easiest to use Heron's formula, which states that the area of a triangle with side length a, b, and c is $A = \sqrt{s(s - a)(s - b)(s - c)}$, where $2s$ is the perimeter of the triangle.

74. Ellipsoid inside a tetrahedron (1946 Putnam Exam) Let P be a plane tangent to the ellipsoid $x^2/a^2 + y^2/b^2 + z^2/c^2 = 1$ at a point in the first octant. Let T be the tetrahedron in the first octant bounded by P and the coordinate planes $x = 0$, $y = 0$, and $z = 0$. Find the minimum volume of T. (The volume of a tetrahedron is one-third the area of the base times the height.)

75. Steiner's problem for three points Given three distinct noncollinear points A, B, and C in the plane, find the point P in the plane such that the sum of the distances $|AP| + |BP| + |CP|$ is a

minimum. Here is how to proceed with three points, assuming that the triangle formed by the three points has no angle greater than $2\pi/3$ ($120°$).

a. Assume the coordinates of the three given points are $A(x_1, y_1)$, $B(x_2, y_2)$, and $C(x_3, y_3)$. Let $d_1(x, y)$ be the distance between $A(x_1, y_1)$ and a variable point $P(x, y)$. Compute the gradient of d_1 and show that it is a unit vector pointing along the line between the two points.

b. Define d_2 and d_3 in a similar way and show that ∇d_2 and ∇d_3 are also unit vectors in the direction of the line between the two points.

c. The goal is to minimize $f(x, y) = d_1 + d_2 + d_3$. Show that the condition $f_x = f_y = 0$ implies that $\nabla d_1 + \nabla d_2 + \nabla d_3 = 0$.

d. Explain why part (c) implies that the optimal point P has the property that the three line segments AP, BP, and CP all intersect symmetrically in angles of $2\pi/3$.

e. What is the optimal solution if one of the angles in the triangle is greater than $2\pi/3$ (just draw a picture)?

f. Estimate the Steiner point for the three points $(0, 0)$, $(0, 1)$, and $(2, 0)$.

76. Slicing plane Find an equation of the plane passing through the point $(3, 2, 1)$ that slices off the region in the first octant with the least volume.

77. Two mountains without a saddle Show that the following two functions have two local maxima but no other extreme points (thus no saddle or basin between the mountains).

a. $f(x, y) = -(x^2 - 1)^2 - (x^2 - e^y)^2$

b. $f(x, y) = 4x^2 e^y - 2x^4 - e^{4y}$

(*Source:* Proposed by Ira Rosenholtz, *Mathematics Magazine* (February, 1987))

78. Solitary critical points A function of *one* variable has the property that a local maximum (or minimum) occurring at the only critical point is also the absolute maximum (or minimum) (for example, $f(x) = x^2$). Does the same result hold for a function of *two* variables? Show that the following functions have the property that they have a single local maximum (or minimum), occurring at the only critical point, but that the local maximum (or minimum) is not an absolute maximum (or minimum) on $\mathbb{R}^2$.

a. $f(x, y) = 3xe^y - x^3 - e^{3y}$

b. $f(x, y) = (2y^2 - y^4)\left(e^x + \frac{1}{1 + x^2}\right) - \frac{1}{1 + x^2}$

This property has the following interpretation. Suppose that a surface has a single local minimum that is not the absolute minimum. Then water can be poured into the basin around the local minimum and the surface never overflows, even though there are points on the surface below the local minimum.

(*Source:* See three articles in *Mathematics Magazine* (May 1985) and *Calculus and Analytical Geometry*, 2nd ed., Philip Gillett.)

QUICK CHECK ANSWERS

1. $f_x(2, -1) = f_y(2, -1) = 0$ **2.** Vertically, in the directions $\langle 0, 0, \pm 1 \rangle$ **3.** $D(x, y) = -12x^2 y^2$ **4.** It has neither an absolute maximum nor absolute minimum value on this set. ◄

13.9 Lagrange Multipliers

One of many challenges in economics and marketing is predicting the behavior of consumers. Basic models of consumer behavior often involve a *utility function* that expresses consumers' combined preference for several different amenities. For example, a simple utility function might have the form $U = f(\ell, g)$, where ℓ represents the amount of leisure time and g represents the number of consumable goods. The model assumes that consumers try to maximize their utility function, but they do so under certain constraints on the variables of the problem. For example, increasing leisure time may increase utility, but leisure time produces no income for consumable goods. Similarly, consumable goods may also increase utility, but they require income, which reduces leisure time. We first develop a general method for solving such constrained optimization problems and then return to economics problems later in the section.

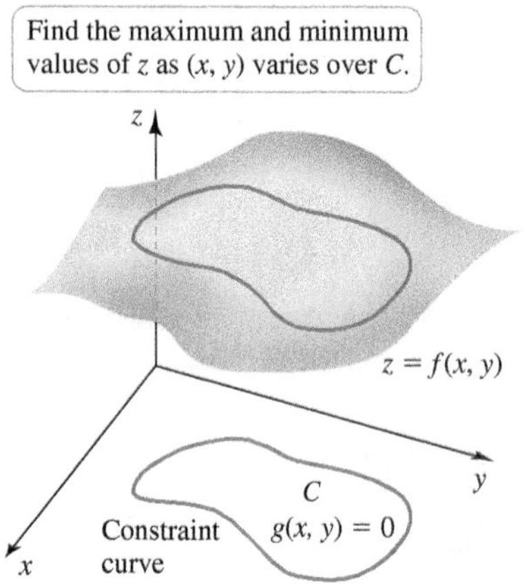

Find the maximum and minimum values of z as (x, y) varies over C.

$z = f(x, y)$

C
Constraint curve $g(x, y) = 0$

FIGURE 13.94

The Basic Idea

We start with a typical constrained optimization problem with two independent variables and give its method of solution; a generalization to more variables then follows. We seek maximum and/or minimum values of a differentiable function f (the **objective function**) with the restriction that x and y must lie on a **constraint** curve C in the xy-plane given by $g(x, y) = 0$ (Figure 13.94).

The problem and a method of solution are easy to visualize if we return to Example 6 of Section 13.8. Part of that problem was to find the maximum value of $f(x, y) = x^2 + y^2 - 2x + 2y + 5$ on the circle $C: \{(x, y): x^2 + y^2 = 4\}$ (Figure 13.95a). In Figure 13.95b we see the level curves of f and the point $P(-\sqrt{2}, \sqrt{2})$ on C at which f has a maximum value. Imagine moving along C toward P; as we approach P, the values of f increase and reach a maximum value at P. Moving past P, the values of f decrease.

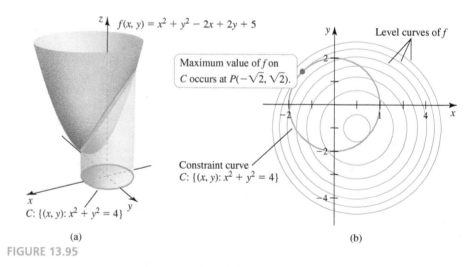

z $f(x, y) = x^2 + y^2 - 2x + 2y + 5$

$C: \{(x, y): x^2 + y^2 = 4\}$

(a)

Level curves of f

Maximum value of f on C occurs at $P(-\sqrt{2}, \sqrt{2})$.

Constraint curve
$C: \{(x, y): x^2 + y^2 = 4\}$

(b)

FIGURE 13.95

$\nabla f(a, b)$ y Level curves of f
$\nabla g(a, b)$

$P(a, b)$

Constraint x
curve
$C: g(x, y) = 0$

Tangent
to C
at (a, b) $\nabla f(a, b)$ is parallel to $\nabla g(a, b)$ at $P(a, b)$.

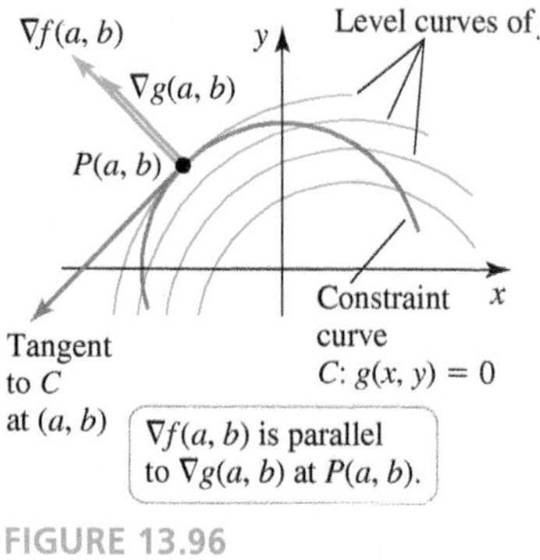

FIGURE 13.96

Figure 13.96 shows what is special about the point P. We already know that at any point $P(a, b)$, the line tangent to the level curve of f at P is orthogonal to the gradient $\nabla f(a, b)$ (Theorem 13.12). We also see that the line tangent to the level curve at P is tangent to the constraint curve C at P. We prove this fact shortly.

Furthermore, if we think of the constraint curve C as just one level curve of the function $z = g(x, y)$, then it follows that the gradient $\nabla g(a, b)$ is also orthogonal to C at (a, b), where we assume that $\nabla g(a, b) \neq \mathbf{0}$ (Theorem 13.12). Therefore, the gradients $\nabla f(a, b)$ and $\nabla g(a, b)$ are parallel. These properties characterize the point P at which f has an extreme value on the constraint curve. They are the basis for the method of Lagrange multipliers that we now formalize.

Lagrange Multipliers with Two Independent Variables

The major step in establishing the method of Lagrange multipliers is to prove that Figure 13.96 is drawn correctly; that is, at the point on the constraint curve C where f has an extreme value, the line tangent to C is orthogonal to $\nabla f(a, b)$ and $\nabla g(a, b)$.

> **THEOREM 13.15   Parallel Gradients (Ball Park Theorem)**
> Let f be a differentiable function in a region of $\mathbb{R}^2$ that contains the smooth curve C given by $g(x, y) = 0$. Assume that f has a local extreme value (relative to values of f on C) at a point $P(a, b)$ on C. Then $\nabla f(a, b)$ is orthogonal to the line tangent to C at P. Assuming $\nabla g(a, b) \neq \mathbf{0}$, it follows that there is a real number λ (called a **Lagrange multiplier**) such that $\nabla f(a, b) = \lambda \nabla g(a, b)$.

> The Greek lowercase ℓ is λ; it is read *lambda*.

Proof: Because C is smooth it can be expressed parametrically in the form $C : \mathbf{r}(t) = \langle x(t), y(t) \rangle$, where x and y are differentiable functions on an interval in t that contains t_0 with $P(a, b) = (x(t_0), y(t_0))$. As we vary t and follow C, the rate of change of f is given by the Chain Rule:

$$\frac{df}{dt} = \frac{\partial f}{\partial x}\frac{dx}{dt} + \frac{\partial f}{\partial y}\frac{dy}{dt} = \nabla f \cdot \mathbf{r}'(t).$$

At the point $(x(t_0), y(t_0)) = (a, b)$ at which f has a local maximum or minimum value, we have $\left.\dfrac{df}{dt}\right|_{t=t_0} = 0$, which implies that $\nabla f(a, b) \cdot \mathbf{r}'(t_0) = 0$. Because $\mathbf{r}'(t)$ is tangent to C, the gradient $\nabla f(a, b)$ is orthogonal to the line tangent to C at P.

To prove the second assertion, note that the constraint curve C given by $g(x, y) = 0$ is also a level curve of the surface $z = g(x, y)$. Recall that gradients are orthogonal to level curves. Therefore, at the point $P(a, b)$, $\nabla g(a, b)$ is orthogonal to C at (a, b). Because both $\nabla f(a, b)$ and $\nabla g(a, b)$ are orthogonal to C, the two gradients are parallel, so there is a real number λ such that $\nabla f(a, b) = \lambda \nabla g(a, b)$.   ◄

Theorem 13.15 has a nice geometric interpretation that makes it easy to remember. Suppose you walk along the outfield fence at a ballpark, which represents the constraint curve C, and record the distance $d(x, y)$ between you and home plate (which is the objective function). At some instant you reach a point P that maximizes the distance; it is the point on the fence farthest from home plate. The point P has the property that the line ℓ from P to home plate is orthogonal to the (line tangent to the) fence at P (Figure 13.97).

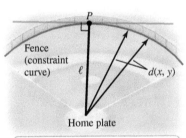

Distance is maximized at P.
ℓ is orthogonal to tangent to the fence.

FIGURE 13.97

QUICK CHECK 1 Explain in terms of functions and gradients why the ballpark analogy for Theorem 13.15 is true. ◄

> **PROCEDURE   Method of Lagrange Multipliers in Two Variables**
> Let the objective function f and the constraint function g be differentiable on a region of $\mathbb{R}^2$ with $\nabla g(x, y) \neq \mathbf{0}$ on the curve $g(x, y) = 0$. To locate the maximum and minimum values of f subject to the constraint $g(x, y) = 0$, carry out the following steps.
>
> 1. Find the values of x, y, and λ (if they exist) that satisfy the equations
>
> $$\nabla f(x, y) = \lambda \nabla g(x, y) \quad \text{and} \quad g(x, y) = 0.$$
>
> 2. Among the values (x, y) found in Step 1, select the largest and smallest corresponding function values, which are the maximum and minimum values of f subject to the constraint.

> *In principle*, it is possible to solve a constrained optimization problem by solving the constraint equation for one of the variables and eliminating that variable in the objective function. In practice, this method is often prohibitive, particularly with three or more variables or two or more constraints.

Notice that $\nabla f = \lambda \nabla g$ is a vector equation: $\langle f_x, f_y \rangle = \lambda \langle g_x, g_y \rangle$. It is satisfied provided $f_x = \lambda g_x$ and $f_y = \lambda g_y$. Therefore, the crux of the method is solving the three equations

$$f_x = \lambda g_x, \qquad f_y = \lambda g_y, \qquad \text{and} \qquad g(x, y) = 0$$

for the three variables x, y, and λ.

EXAMPLE 1 Lagrange multipliers with two variables Find the maximum and minimum values of the objective function $f(x, y) = 2x^2 + y^2 + 2$, where x and y lie on the ellipse C given by $g(x, y) = x^2 + 4y^2 - 4 = 0$.

SOLUTION Figure 13.98a shows the elliptic paraboloid $z = f(x, y)$ above the ellipse C in the xy-plane. As the ellipse is traversed, the corresponding function values on the surface vary. The goal is to find the minimum and maximum of these function values. An alternative view is given in Figure 13.98b, where we see the level curves of f and the constraint curve C. As the ellipse is traversed, the values of f vary, reaching maximum and minimum values along the way.

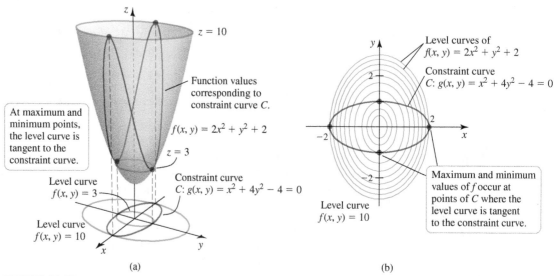

FIGURE 13.98

Noting that $\nabla f(x, y) = \langle 4x, 2y \rangle$ and $\nabla g(x, y) = \langle 2x, 8y \rangle$, the equations that result from $\nabla f = \lambda \nabla g$ and the constraint are

$$\underbrace{4x = \lambda(2x)}_{f_x = \lambda g_x} \qquad \underbrace{2y = \lambda(8y)}_{f_y = \lambda g_y} \qquad \underbrace{x^2 + 4y^2 - 4 = 0}_{g(x, y) = 0}$$

$$x(2 - \lambda) = 0 \; (1) \qquad y(1 - 4\lambda) = 0 \; (2) \qquad x^2 + 4y^2 - 4 = 0. \; (3)$$

The solutions of equation (1) are $x = 0$ or $\lambda = 2$. If $x = 0$, then equation (3) implies that $y = \pm 1$ and (2) implies that $\lambda = \frac{1}{4}$. On the other hand, if $\lambda = 2$, then equation (2) implies that $y = 0$; from (3), we get $x = \pm 2$. Therefore, the candidates for locations of extreme values are $(0, \pm 1)$, with $f(0, \pm 1) = 3$, and $(\pm 2, 0)$, with $f(\pm 2, 0) = 10$. We see that the maximum value of f on C is 10, which occurs at $(2, 0)$ and $(-2, 0)$; the minimum value of f on C is 3, which occurs at $(0, 1)$ and $(0, -1)$.

Related Exercises 5–14 ◄

QUICK CHECK 2 Choose any point on the constraint curve in Figure 13.98b other than a solution point. Draw ∇f and ∇g at that point and show that they are not parallel. ◄

Lagrange Multipliers with Three Independent Variables

The technique just outlined extends to three or more independent variables. With three variables, suppose an objective function $w = f(x, y, z)$ is given; its level surfaces are surfaces in $\mathbb{R}^3$ (Figure 13.99a). The constraint equation takes the form $g(x, y, z) = 0$, which is another surface S in $\mathbb{R}^3$ (Figure 13.99b). To find the maximum and minimum values of f on S (assuming they exist), we must find the points (a, b, c) on S at which $\nabla f(a, b, c)$ is parallel to $\nabla g(a, b, c)$, assuming $\nabla g(a, b, c) \neq \mathbf{0}$ (Figure 13.99c, d). The procedure for finding the maximum and minimum values of $f(x, y, z)$, where the point (x, y, z) is constrained to lie on S, is similar to the procedure for two variables.

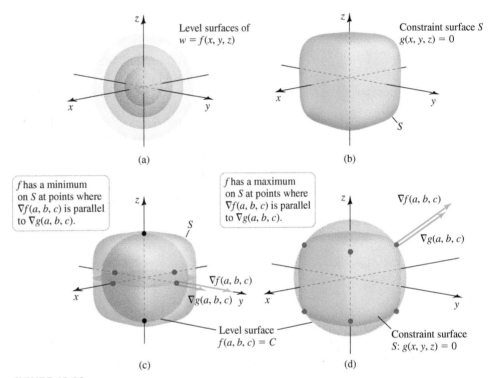

FIGURE 13.99

PROCEDURE   Method of Lagrange Multipliers in Three Variables

Let f and g be differentiable on a region of $\mathbb{R}^3$ with $\nabla g(x, y, z) \neq \mathbf{0}$ on the surface $g(x, y, z) = 0$. To locate the maximum and minimum values of f subject to the constraint $g(x, y, z) = 0$, carry out the following steps.

1. Find the values of x, y, z, and λ that satisfy the equations

$$\nabla f(x, y, z) = \lambda \nabla g(x, y, z) \quad \text{and} \quad g(x, y, z) = 0.$$

2. Among the points (x, y, z) found in Step 1, select the largest and smallest corresponding values of the objective function. These values are the maximum and minimum values of f subject to the constraint.

> Some books formulate the Lagrange multiplier method by defining $L = f - \lambda g$. The conditions of the method then become $\nabla L = \mathbf{0}$, where $\nabla L = \langle L_x, L_y, L_z, L_\lambda \rangle$.

Now, there are four equations to be solved for x, y, z, and λ:

$$f_x(x, y, z) = \lambda g_x(x, y, z), \qquad f_y(x, y, z) = \lambda g_y(x, y, z),$$
$$f_z(x, y, z) = \lambda g_z(x, y, z), \qquad g(x, y, z) = 0.$$

> Problems similar to Example 2 were solved in Section 13.8 using ordinary optimization techniques. These methods may or may not be easier to apply than Lagrange multipliers.

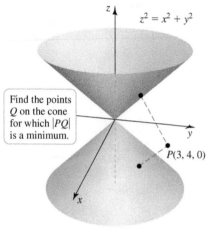

Find the points Q on the cone for which $|PQ|$ is a minimum.

FIGURE 13.100

> With three independent variables, it is possible to impose two constraints. These problems are explored in Exercises 61–65.

QUICK CHECK 3 In Example 2, is there a point that *maximizes* the distance between $(3, 4, 0)$ and the cone? If the point $(3, 4, 0)$ were replaced by $(3, 4, 1)$, how many minimizing solutions would there be? ◄

EXAMPLE 2   A geometry problem Find the least distance between the point $P(3, 4, 0)$ and the surface of the cone $z^2 = x^2 + y^2$.

SOLUTION Figure 13.100 shows both sheets of the cone and the point $P(3, 4, 0)$. Because P is in the xy-plane, we anticipate two solutions, one for each sheet of the cone. The distance between P and any point $Q(x, y, z)$ on the cone is

$$d(x, y, z) = \sqrt{(x - 3)^2 + (y - 4)^2 + z^2}.$$

In many distance problems it is easier to work with the *square* of the distance to avoid dealing with square roots. This maneuver is allowable because if a point minimizes $(d(x, y, z))^2$, it also minimizes $d(x, y, z)$. Therefore, we define

$$f(x, y, z) = (d(x, y, z))^2 = (x - 3)^2 + (y - 4)^2 + z^2.$$

The constraint is the condition that the point (x, y, z) must lie on the cone, which implies $z^2 = x^2 + y^2$, or $g(x, y, z) = z^2 - x^2 - y^2 = 0$.

Now we proceed with Lagrange multipliers; the conditions are

$$f_x(x, y, z) = \lambda g_x(x, y, z), \text{ or } 2(x - 3) = \lambda(-2x), \text{ or } x(1 + \lambda) = 3, \tag{4}$$

$$f_y(x, y, z) = \lambda g_y(x, y, z), \text{ or } 2(y - 4) = \lambda(-2y), \text{ or } y(1 + \lambda) = 4, \tag{5}$$

$$f_z(x, y, z) = \lambda g_z(x, y, z), \text{ or } 2z = \lambda(2z), \text{ or } z = \lambda z, \text{ and} \tag{6}$$

$$g(x, y, z) = z^2 - x^2 - y^2 = 0. \tag{7}$$

The solutions of equation (6) (the simplest of the four equations) are either $z = 0$, or $\lambda = 1$ and $z \neq 0$. In the first case, if $z = 0$, then by equation (7), $x = y = 0$; however, $x = 0$ and $y = 0$ do not satisfy (4) and (5). So no solution results from this case.

On the other hand if $\lambda = 1$, then by (4) and (5), we find that $x = \frac{3}{2}$ and $y = 2$. Using (7), the corresponding values of z are $\pm\frac{5}{2}$. Therefore, the two solutions and the values of f are

$$x = \tfrac{3}{2}, \qquad y = 2, \qquad z = \tfrac{5}{2} \qquad \text{with } f\left(\tfrac{3}{2}, 2, \tfrac{5}{2}\right) = \tfrac{25}{2}, \text{ and}$$

$$x = \tfrac{3}{2}, \qquad y = 2, \qquad z = -\tfrac{5}{2} \qquad \text{with } f\left(\tfrac{3}{2}, 2, -\tfrac{5}{2}\right) = \tfrac{25}{2}.$$

You can check that moving away from $\left(\frac{3}{2}, 2, \pm\frac{5}{2}\right)$ in any direction on the cone has the effect of increasing the values of f. Therefore, the points correspond to *local* minima of f. Do these points also correspond to *absolute* minima? The domain of this problem is unbounded; however, one can argue geometrically that f increases without bound moving away from $\left(\frac{3}{2}, 2, \pm\frac{5}{2}\right)$ with $|x| \to \infty$ and $|y| \to \infty$. Therefore, these points correspond to absolute minimum values and the points on the cone nearest to $(3, 4, 0)$ are $\left(\frac{3}{2}, 2, \pm\frac{5}{2}\right)$, at a distance of $\sqrt{\dfrac{25}{2}} = \dfrac{5}{\sqrt{2}}$. (Recall that $f = d^2$.)

Related Exercises 15–34 ◄

Economic Models   In the opening of this section, we briefly described how utility functions are used to model consumer behavior. We now look in more detail at some specific—admittedly simple—utility functions and the constraints that are imposed upon them.

As described earlier, a prototype model for consumer behavior uses two independent variables: leisure time ℓ and consumable goods g. A utility function $U = f(\ell, g)$ measures consumer preferences for various combinations of leisure time and consumable goods. The following assumptions about utility functions are commonly made.

1. Utility increases if any variable increases (essentially, *more is better*).

2. Various combinations of leisure time and consumable goods have the same utility; that is, giving up some leisure time for additional consumable goods results in the same utility.

The level curves of a typical utility function are shown in Figure 13.101. Assumption 1 is reflected by the fact that the utility values on the level curves increase as either ℓ or g

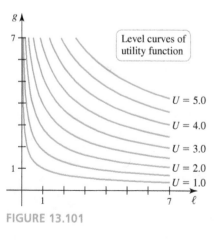

FIGURE 13.101

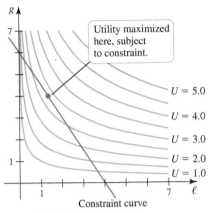

FIGURE 13.102

increases. Consistent with Assumption 2, a single level curve shows the combinations of ℓ and g that have the same utility; for this reason, economists call the level curves *indifference curves*. Notice that if ℓ increases, then g must decrease on a level curve to maintain the same utility, and vice versa.

Economic models assert that consumers maximize utility subject to constraints on leisure time and consumable goods. One assumption that leads to a reasonable constraint is that an increase in leisure time implies a linear decrease in consumable goods. Therefore, the constraint curve is a line with negative slope (Figure 13.102). When such a constraint is superimposed on the level curves of the utility function, the optimization problem becomes evident. Among all points on the constraint line, which one maximizes utility? A solution is marked in the figure; at this point the utility has a maximum value (between 2.5 and 3.0).

EXAMPLE 3   Constrained optimization of utility Find the maximum value of the utility function $U = f(\ell, g) = \ell^{1/3}g^{2/3}$, subject to the constraint $G(\ell, g) = 3\ell + 2g - 12 = 0$, where $\ell \geq 0$ and $g \geq 0$.

SOLUTION The level curves of the utility function and the linear constraint are shown in Figure 13.102. The solution follows the Lagrange multiplier method with two variables. The gradient of the utility function is

$$\nabla f(\ell, g) = \left\langle \frac{\ell^{-2/3}g^{2/3}}{3}, \frac{2\ell^{1/3}g^{-1/3}}{3} \right\rangle = \frac{1}{3}\left\langle \left(\frac{g}{\ell}\right)^{2/3}, 2\left(\frac{\ell}{g}\right)^{1/3} \right\rangle.$$

The gradient of the constraint function is $\nabla G(\ell, g) = \langle 3, 2 \rangle$. Therefore, the equations that must be solved are

$$\frac{1}{3}\left(\frac{g}{\ell}\right)^{2/3} = 3\lambda, \quad \frac{2}{3}\left(\frac{\ell}{g}\right)^{1/3} = 2\lambda, \quad \text{and} \quad G(\ell, g) = 3\ell + 2g - 12 = 0.$$

QUICK CHECK 4 In Figure 13.102, explain why, if you move away from the optimal point along the constraint line, the utility decreases. ◄

Eliminating λ from the first two equations leads to the condition $g = 3\ell$, which, when substituted into the constraint equation, gives the solution $\ell = \frac{4}{3}$ and $g = 4$. The actual value of the utility function at this point is $U = f\left(\frac{4}{3}, 4\right) = 4/\sqrt[3]{3} \approx 2.8$. This solution is consistent with Figure 13.102.

Related Exercises 35–38 ◄

SECTION 13.9 EXERCISES

Review Questions

1. Explain why, at a point that maximizes or minimizes f subject to a constraint $g(x, y) = 0$, the gradient of f is parallel to the gradient of g. Use a diagram.

2. If $f(x, y) = x^2 + y^2$ and $g(x, y) = 2x + 3y - 4 = 0$, write the Lagrange multiplier conditions that must be satisfied by a point that maximizes or minimizes f subject to $g(x, y) = 0$.

3. If $f(x, y, z) = x^2 + y^2 + z^2$ and $g(x, y, z) = 2x + 3y - 5z + 4 = 0$, write the Lagrange multiplier conditions that must be satisfied by a point that maximizes or minimizes f subject to $g(x, y, z) = 0$.

4. Sketch several level curves of $f(x, y) = x^2 + y^2$ and sketch the constraint line $g(x, y) = 2x + 3y - 4 = 0$. Describe the extrema (if any) that f attains on the constraint line.

Basic Skills

5–14. Lagrange multipliers in two variables *Use Lagrange multipliers to find the maximum and minimum values of f (when they exist) subject to the given constraint.*

5. $f(x, y) = x + 2y$ subject to $x^2 + y^2 = 4$

6. $f(x, y) = xy^2$ subject to $x^2 + y^2 = 1$

7. $f(x, y) = x + y$ subject to $x^2 - xy + y^2 = 1$

8. $f(x, y) = x^2 + y^2$ subject to $2x^2 + 3xy + 2y^2 = 7$

9. $f(x, y) = xy$ subject to $x^2 + y^2 - xy = 9$

10. $f(x, y) = x - y$ subject to $x^2 + y^2 - 3xy = 20$

11. $f(x, y) = e^{2xy}$ subject to $x^2 + y^2 = 16$

12. $f(x, y) = x^2 + y^2$ subject to $x^6 + y^6 = 1$

13. $f(x, y) = y^2 - 4x^2$ subject to $x^2 + 2y^2 = 4$

14. $f(x, y) = xy + x + y$ subject to $x^2y^2 = 4$

15–24. Lagrange multipliers in three variables *Use Lagrange multipliers to find the maximum and minimum values of f (when they exist) subject to the given constraint.*

15. $f(x, y, z) = x + 3y - z$ subject to $x^2 + y^2 + z^2 = 4$

16. $f(x, y, z) = xyz$ subject to $x^2 + 2y^2 + 4z^2 = 9$

17. $f(x, y, z) = x$ subject to $x^2 + y^2 + z^2 - z = 1$

18. $f(x, y, z) = x - z$ subject to $x^2 + y^2 + z^2 - y = 2$

19. $f(x, y, z) = x^2 + y^2 + z^2$ subject to $x^2 + y^2 + z^2 - 4xy = 1$

20. $f(x, y, z) = x + y + z$ subject to $x^2 + y^2 + z^2 - 2x - 2y = 1$

21. $f(x, y, z) = 2x + z^2$ subject to $x^2 + y^2 + 2z^2 = 25$

22. $f(x, y, z) = x^2 + y^2 - z$ subject to $z = 2x^2y^2 + 1$

23. $f(x, y, z) = x^2 + y^2 + z^2$ subject to $xyz = 4$

24. $f(x, y, z) = (xyz)^{1/2}$ subject to $x + y + z = 1$ with $x \geq 0$, $y \geq 0, z \geq 0$

25–34. Applications of Lagrange multipliers *Use Lagrange multipliers in the following problems. When the domain of the objective function is unbounded or open, explain why you have found an absolute maximum or minimum value.*

25. Shipping regulations A shipping company requires that the sum of length plus girth of rectangular boxes must not exceed 108 in. Find the dimensions of the box with maximum volume that meets this condition. (The girth is the perimeter of the smallest base of the box.)

26. Box with minimum surface area Find the rectangular box with a volume of 16 ft^3 that has minimum surface area.

27. Extreme distances to an ellipse Find the minimum and maximum distances between the ellipse $x^2 + xy + 2y^2 = 1$ and the origin.

28. Maximum area rectangle in an ellipse Find the dimensions of the rectangle of maximum area with sides parallel to the coordinate axes that can be inscribed in the ellipse $4x^2 + 16y^2 = 16$.

29. Maximum perimeter rectangle in an ellipse Find the dimensions of the rectangle of maximum perimeter with sides parallel to the coordinate axes that can be inscribed in the ellipse $2x^2 + 4y^2 = 3$.

30. Minimum distance to a plane Find the point on the plane $2x + 3y + 6z - 10 = 0$ closest to the point $(-2, 5, 1)$.

31. Minimum distance to a surface Find the point on the surface $4x + y - 1 = 0$ closest to the point $(1, 2, -3)$.

32. Minimum distance to a cone Find the points on the cone $z^2 = x^2 + y^2$ closest to the point $(1, 2, 0)$.

33. Extreme distances to a sphere Find the minimum and maximum distances between the sphere $x^2 + y^2 + z^2 = 9$ and the point $(2, 3, 4)$.

34. Maximum volume cylinder in a sphere Find the dimensions of a right circular cylinder of maximum volume that can be inscribed in a sphere of radius 16.

35–38. Maximizing utility functions *Find the values of ℓ and g with $\ell \geq 0$ and $g \geq 0$ that maximize the following utility functions subject to the given constraints. Give the value of the utility function at the optimal point.*

35. $U = f(\ell, g) = 10\ell^{1/2}g^{1/2}$ subject to $3\ell + 6g = 18$

36. $U = f(\ell, g) = 32\ell^{2/3}g^{1/3}$ subject to $4\ell + 2g = 12$

37. $U = f(\ell, g) = 8\ell^{4/5}g^{1/5}$ subject to $10\ell + 8g = 40$

38. $U = f(\ell, g) = \ell^{1/6}g^{5/6}$ subject to $4\ell + 5g = 20$

Further Explorations

39. Explain why or why not Determine whether the following statements are true and give an explanation or counterexample.

    a. Suppose you are standing at the center of a sphere looking at a point P on the surface of the sphere. Your line of sight to P is orthogonal to the plane tangent to the sphere at P.

    b. At a point that maximizes f on the curve $g(x, y) = 0$, the dot product $\nabla f \cdot \nabla g$ is zero.

40–45. *Solve the following problems from Section 13.8 using Lagrange multipliers.*

40. Exercise 35   **41.** Exercise 36   **42.** Exercise 37

43. Exercise 38   **44.** Exercise 62   **45.** Exercise 63

46–49. Absolute maximum and minimum values *Find the absolute maximum and minimum values of the following functions over the given regions R. Use Lagrange multipliers to check for extreme points on the boundary.*

46. $f(x, y) = x^2 + 4y^2 + 1$; $R = \{(x, y) : x^2 + 4y^2 \leq 1\}$

47. $f(x, y) = x^2 - 4y^2 + xy$; $R = \{(x, y) : 4x^2 + 9y^2 \leq 36\}$

48. $f(x, y) = 2x^2 + y^2 + 2x - 3y$; $R = \{(x, y) : x^2 + y^2 \leq 1\}$

49. $f(x, y) = (x - 1)^2 + (y + 1)^2$; $R = \{(x, y) : x^2 + y^2 \leq 4\}$

50–51. Graphical Lagrange multipliers *The following figures show the level curves of f and the constraint curve $g(x, y) = 0$. Estimate the maximum and minimum values of f subject to the constraint. At each point where an extreme value occurs, indicate the direction of ∇f and a possible direction of ∇g.*

50.

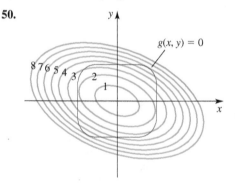

51.

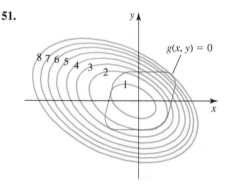

52. Extreme points on flattened spheres The equation $x^{2n} + y^{2n} + z^{2n} = 1$, where n is a positive integer, describes a flattened sphere. Define the extreme points to be the points on the flattened sphere with a maximum distance from the origin.

a. Find all the extreme points on the flattened sphere with $n = 2$. What is the distance between the extreme points and the origin?

b. Find all the extreme points on the flattened sphere for integers $n > 2$. What is the distance between the extreme points and the origin?

c. Give the location of the extreme points in the limit as $n \to \infty$. What is the limiting distance between the extreme points and the origin as $n \to \infty$?

Applications

53–55. Production functions *Economists model the output of manufacturing systems using production functions that have many of the same properties as utility functions. The family of Cobb-Douglas production functions has the form $P = f(K, L) = CK^a L^{1-a}$, where K represents capital, L represents labor, and C and a are positive real numbers with $0 < a < 1$. If the cost of capital is p dollars per unit, the cost of labor is q dollars per unit, and the total available budget is B, then the constraint takes the form $pK + qL = B$. Find the values of K and L that maximize the following production functions subject to the given constraint, assuming $K \geq 0$ and $L \geq 0$.*

53. $P = f(K, L) = K^{1/2} L^{1/2}$ for $20K + 30L = 300$

54. $P = f(K, L) = 10K^{1/3} L^{2/3}$ for $30K + 60L = 360$

55. Given the production function $P = f(K, L) = K^a L^{1-a}$ and the budget constraint $pK + qL = B$, where a, p, q, and B are given, show that P is maximized when $K = aB/p$ and $L = (1 - a)B/q$.

56. Temperature of an elliptical plate The temperature of points on an elliptical plate $x^2 + y^2 + xy \leq 1$ is given by $T(x, y) = 25(x^2 + y^2)$. Find the hottest and coldest temperatures on the edge of the elliptical plate.

Additional Exercises
57–59. Maximizing a sum

57. Find the maximum value of $x_1 + x_2 + x_3 + x_4$ subject to the condition that $x_1{}^2 + x_2{}^2 + x_3{}^2 + x_4{}^2 = 16$.

58. Generalize Exercise 57 and find the maximum value of $x_1 + x_2 + \cdots + x_n$ subject to the condition that $x_1{}^2 + x_2{}^2 + \cdots + x_n{}^2 = c^2$, for a real number c and a positive integer n.

59. Generalize Exercise 57 and find the maximum value of $a_1 x_1 + a_2 x_2 + \cdots + a_n x_n$ subject to the condition that $x_1{}^2 + x_2{}^2 + \cdots + x_n{}^2 = 1$, for given positive real numbers $a_1, \ldots, a_n$ and a positive integer n.

60. Geometric and arithmetic means Prove that the geometric mean of a set of positive numbers $(x_1 x_2 \cdots x_n)^{1/n}$ is no greater than the arithmetic mean $(x_1 + \cdots + x_n)/n$ in the following cases.

a. Find the maximum value of xyz, subject to $x + y + z = k$, where k is a real number and $x > 0$, $y > 0$, and $z > 0$. Use the result to prove that

$$(xyz)^{1/3} \leq \frac{x + y + z}{3}.$$

b. Generalize part (a) and show that

$$(x_1 x_2 \cdots x_n)^{1/n} \leq \frac{x_1 + \cdots + x_n}{n}.$$

61. Problems with two constraints Given a differentiable function $w = f(x, y, z)$, the goal is to find its maximum and minimum values subject to the constraints $g(x, y, z) = 0$ and $h(x, y, z) = 0$, where g and h are also differentiable.

a. Imagine a level surface of the function f and the constraint surfaces $g(x, y, z) = 0$ and $h(x, y, z) = 0$. Note that g and h intersect (in general) in a curve C on which maximum and minimum values of f must be found. Explain why ∇g and ∇h are orthogonal to their respective surfaces.

b. Explain why ∇f lies in the plane formed by ∇g and ∇h at a point of C where f has a maximum or minimum value.

c. Explain why part (b) implies that $\nabla f = \lambda \nabla g + \mu \nabla h$ at a point of C where f has a maximum or minimum value, where λ and μ (the Lagrange multipliers) are real numbers.

d. Conclude from part (c) that the equations that must be solved for maximum or minimum values of f subject to two constraints are $\nabla f = \lambda \nabla g + \mu \nabla h$, $g(x, y, z) = 0$, and $h(x, y, z) = 0$.

62–65. Two-constraint problems *Use the result of Exercise 61 to solve the following problems.*

62. The planes $x + 2z = 12$ and $x + y = 6$ intersect in a line L. Find the point on L nearest the origin.

63. Find the maximum and minimum values of $f(x, y, z) = xyz$ subject to the conditions that $x^2 + y^2 = 4$ and $x + y + z = 1$.

64. The paraboloid $z = x^2 + 2y^2 + 1$ and the plane $x - y + 2z = 4$ intersect in a curve C. Find the points on C that have maximum and minimum distance from the origin.

65. Find the maximum and minimum values of $f(x, y, z) = x^2 + y^2 + z^2$ on the curve on which the cone $z^2 = 4x^2 + 4y^2$ and the plane $2x + 4z = 5$ intersect.

QUICK CHECK ANSWERS

1. Let $d(x, y)$ be the distance between any point $P(x, y)$ on the fence and home plate O. The key fact is that ∇d always points along the line OP. As P moves along the fence (the constraint curve), $d(x, y)$ increases until a point is reached at which ∇d is orthogonal to the fence. At such a point, d has a maximum value. **3.** The distance between $(3, 4, 0)$ and the cone can be arbitrarily large, so there is no maximizing solution. If the point of interest is not in the xy-plane, there is one minimizing solution. **4.** If you move along the constraint line away from the optimal solution in either direction, you cross level curves of the utility function with decreasing values.

CHAPTER 13 REVIEW EXERCISES

1. **Explain why or why not** Determine whether the following statements are true and give an explanation or counterexample.

   a. The equation $4x - 3y = 12$ describes a line in $\mathbb{R}^3$.
   b. The equation $z^2 = 2x^2 - 6y^2$ determines z as a single function of x and y.
   c. If f has continuous partial derivatives of all orders, then $f_{xxy} = f_{yyx}$.
   d. Given the surface $z = f(x, y)$, the gradient $\nabla f(a, b)$ lies in the plane tangent to the surface at $(a, b, f(a, b))$.
   e. There is always a plane orthogonal to both of two distinct intersecting planes.

2. **Equations of planes** Consider the plane that passes through the point $(6, 0, 1)$ with a normal vector $\mathbf{n} = \langle 3, 4, -6 \rangle$.

   a. Find an equation of the plane.
   b. Find the intercepts of the plane with the three coordinate axes.
   c. Make a sketch of the plane.

3. **Equations of planes** Consider the plane passing through the points $(0, 0, 3)$, $(1, 0, -6)$, and $(1, 2, 3)$.

   a. Find an equation of the plane.
   b. Find the intercepts of the plane with the three coordinate axes.
   c. Make a sketch of the plane.

4–5. Intersecting planes *Find an equation of the line that forms the intersection of the following planes Q and R.*

4. $Q: 2x + y - z = 0$, $R: -x + y + z = 1$

5. $Q: -3x + y + 2z = 0$, $R: 3x + 3y + 4z - 12 = 0$

6–7. Equations of planes *Find an equation of the following planes.*

6. The plane passing through $(2, -3, 1)$ normal to the line $\langle x, y, z \rangle = \langle 2 + t, 3t, 2 - 3t \rangle$

7. The plane passing through $(-2, 3, 1)$, $(1, 1, 0)$, and $(-1, 0, 1)$

8–22. Identifying surfaces *Consider the surfaces defined by the following equations.*

a. *Identify and briefly describe the surface.*
b. *Find the xy-, xz-, and yz-traces, if they exist.*
c. *Find the intercepts with the three coordinate axes, if they exist.*
d. *Make a sketch of the surface.*

8. $z - \sqrt{x} = 0$

9. $3z = \dfrac{x^2}{12} - \dfrac{y^2}{48}$

10. $\dfrac{x^2}{100} + 4y^2 + \dfrac{z^2}{16} = 1$

11. $y^2 = 4x^2 + z^2/25$

12. $\dfrac{4x^2}{9} + \dfrac{9z^2}{4} = y^2$

13. $4z = \dfrac{x^2}{4} + \dfrac{y^2}{9}$

14. $\dfrac{x^2}{16} + \dfrac{z^2}{36} - \dfrac{y^2}{100} = 1$

15. $y^2 + 4z^2 - 2x^2 = 1$

16. $-\dfrac{x^2}{16} + \dfrac{z^2}{36} - \dfrac{y^2}{25} = 4$

17. $\dfrac{x^2}{4} + \dfrac{y^2}{16} - z^2 = 4$

18. $x = \dfrac{y^2}{64} - \dfrac{z^2}{9}$

19. $\dfrac{x^2}{4} + \dfrac{y^2}{16} + z^2 = 4$

20. $y - e^{-x} = 0$

21. $\dfrac{y^2}{49} + \dfrac{x^2}{9} = \dfrac{z^2}{64}$

22. $y = 4x^2 + \dfrac{z^2}{9}$

23–26. Domains *Find the domain of the following functions. Make a sketch of the domain in the xy-plane.*

23. $f(x, y) = \dfrac{1}{x^2 + y^2}$

24. $f(x, y) = \ln xy$

25. $f(x, y) = \sqrt{x - y^2}$

26. $f(x, y) = \tan(x + y)$

27. **Matching surfaces** Match functions a–d with surfaces A–D.

   a. $z = \sqrt{2x^2 + 3y^2 + 1} - 1$
   b. $z = -3y^2$
   c. $z = 2x^2 - 3y^2 + 1$
   d. $z = \sqrt{2x^2 + 3y^2} - 1$

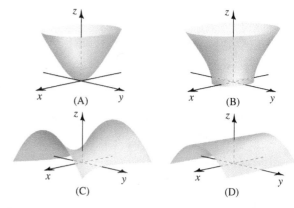

28–29. Level curves *Make a sketch of several level curves of the following functions. Label at least two level curves with their z-values.*

28. $f(x, y) = x^2 - y$

29. $f(x, y) = 2x^2 + 4y^2$

30. **Matching level curves with surfaces** Match level curve plots a–d with surfaces A–D.

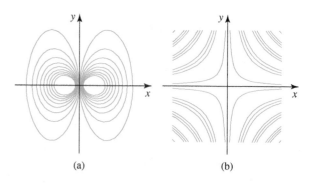

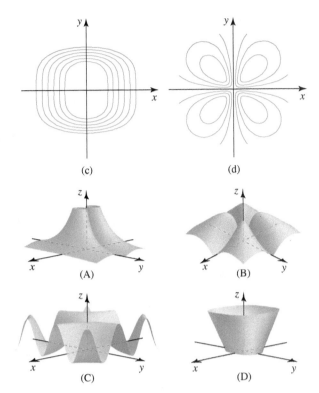

(c)   (d)

(A)   (B)

(C)   (D)

31–38. Limits *Evaluate the following limits or determine that they do not exist.*

31. $\lim\limits_{(x,y)\to(4,-2)} (10x - 5y + 6xy)$ **32.** $\lim\limits_{(x,y)\to(1,1)} \dfrac{xy}{x+y}$

33. $\lim\limits_{(x,y)\to(0,0)} \dfrac{x+y}{xy}$ **34.** $\lim\limits_{(x,y)\to(0,0)} \dfrac{\sin xy}{x^2 + y^2}$

35. $\lim\limits_{(x,y)\to(-1,1)} \dfrac{x^2 - y^2}{x^2 - xy - 2y^2}$.

36. $\lim\limits_{(x,y)\to(1,2)} \dfrac{x^2 y}{x^4 + 2y^2}$

37. $\lim\limits_{(x,y,z)\to\left(\frac{\pi}{2},0,\frac{\pi}{2}\right)} 4\cos y \sin\sqrt{xz}$

38. $\lim\limits_{(x,y,z)\to(5,2,-3)} \tan^{-1}\left(\dfrac{x+y^2}{z^2}\right)$

39–46. Partial derivatives *Find the first partial derivatives of the following functions.*

39. $f(x,y) = 3x^2 y^5$ **40.** $g(x,y,z) = 4xyz^2 - \dfrac{3x}{y}$

41. $f(x,y) = \dfrac{x^2}{x^2 + y^2}$ **42.** $g(x,y,z) = \dfrac{xyz}{x+y}$

43. $f(x,y) = xye^{xy}$ **44.** $g(u,v) = u\cos v - v\sin u$

45. $f(x,y,z) = e^{x+2y+3z}$ **46.** $H(p,q,r) = p^2\sqrt{q+r}$

47–48. Laplace's equation *Verify that the following functions satisfy Laplace's equation* $\dfrac{\partial^2 u}{\partial x^2} + \dfrac{\partial^2 u}{\partial y^2} = 0.$

47. $u(x,y) = y(3x^2 - y^2)$ **48.** $u(x,y) = \ln(x^2 + y^2)$

49. Region between spheres Two spheres have the same center and radii r and R, where $0 < r < R$. The volume of the region between the spheres is $V(r, R) = \dfrac{4\pi}{3}(R^3 - r^3)$.

  a. First, use your intuition. If r is held fixed, how does V change as R increases? What is the sign of V_R? If R is held fixed, how does V change as r increases (up to the value of R)? What is the sign of V_r?
  b. Compute V_r and V_R. Are the results consistent with part (a)?
  c. Consider spheres with $R = 3$ and $r = 1$. Does the volume change more if R is increased by $\Delta R = 0.1$ (with r fixed) or if r is decreased by $\Delta r = 0.1$ (with R fixed)?

50–53. Chain Rule *Use the Chain Rule to evaluate the following derivatives.*

50. $w'(t)$, where $w = xy\sin z$, $x = t^2$, $y = 4t^3$, and $z = t + 1$

51. $w'(t)$, where $w = \sqrt{x^2 + y^2 + z^2}$, $x = \sin t$, $y = \cos t$, and $z = \cos t$

52. w_s and w_t, where $w = xyz$, $x = 2st$, $y = st^2$, and $z = s^2 t$

53. w_r, w_s, and w_t, where $w = \ln(xy^2)$, $x = rst$, and $y = r + s$

54–55. Implicit differentiation *Find dy/dx for the following implicit relations.*

54. $2x^2 + 3xy - 3y^4 = 2$ **55.** $y\ln(x^2 + y^2) = 4$

56–57. Walking on a surface *Consider the following surfaces and parameterized curves C in the xy-plane.*

  a. *In each case find $z'(t)$ on C.*
  b. *Imagine that you are walking on the surface directly above C. Find the values of t for which you are walking uphill.*

56. $z = 4x^2 + y^2 - 2$; $C: x = \cos t$, $y = \sin t$, for $0 \le t \le 2\pi$

57. $z = x^2 - 2y^2 + 4$; $C: x = 2\cos t$, $y = 2\sin t$, for $0 \le t \le 2\pi$

58. Constant volume cones Suppose the radius of a right circular cone increases as $r(t) = t^a$ and the height decreases as $h(t) = t^{-b}$, for $t \ge 1$, where a and b are positive constants. What is the relationship between a and b such that the volume of the cone remains constant (that is, $V'(t) = 0$, where $V = (\pi/3)r^2 h$)?

59. Directional derivatives Consider the function $f(x,y) = 2x^2 - 4y^2 + 10$, whose graph is shown in the figure.

  a. Fill in the table showing the value of the directional derivative at points (a, b) in the direction θ.

	$(a,b) = (0,0)$	$(a,b) = (2,0)$	$(a,b) = (1,1)$
$\theta = \pi/4$			
$\theta = 3\pi/4$			
$\theta = 5\pi/4$			

  b. Indicate in a sketch of the xy-plane the point and direction for each of the table entries in part (a).

60–65. Computing gradients *Compute the gradient of the following functions, evaluate it at the given point, and evaluate the directional derivative at that point in the given direction.*

60. $f(x, y) = x^2$; $(1, 2)$; $\mathbf{u} = \left\langle \dfrac{1}{\sqrt{2}}, -\dfrac{1}{\sqrt{2}} \right\rangle$

61. $g(x, y) = x^2 y^3$; $(-1, 1)$; $\mathbf{u} = \left\langle \dfrac{5}{13}, \dfrac{12}{13} \right\rangle$

62. $f(x, y) = \dfrac{x}{y^2}$; $(0, 3)$; $\mathbf{u} = \left\langle \dfrac{\sqrt{3}}{2}, \dfrac{1}{2} \right\rangle$

63. $h(x, y) = \sqrt{2 + x^2 + 2y^2}$; $(2, 1)$; $\mathbf{u} = \left\langle \dfrac{3}{5}, \dfrac{4}{5} \right\rangle$

64. $f(x, y, z) = xy + yz + xz + 4$; $(2, -2, 1)$; $\mathbf{u} = \left\langle 0, -\dfrac{1}{\sqrt{2}}, -\dfrac{1}{\sqrt{2}} \right\rangle$

65. $f(x, y, z) = 1 + \sin(x + 2y - z)$; $\left(\dfrac{\pi}{6}, \dfrac{\pi}{6}, -\dfrac{\pi}{6} \right)$; $\mathbf{u} = \left\langle \dfrac{1}{3}, \dfrac{2}{3}, \dfrac{2}{3} \right\rangle$

66–67. Direction of steepest ascent and descent

a. *Find the unit vectors that give the direction of steepest ascent and steepest descent at P.*
b. *Find a unit vector that points in a direction of no change.*

66. $f(x, y) = \ln(1 + xy)$; $P(2, 3)$
67. $f(x, y) = \sqrt{4 - x^2 - y^2}$; $P(-1, 1)$

68–69. Level curves *Let $f(x, y) = 8 - 2x^2 - y^2$. For the following level curves $f(x, y) = C$ and points (a, b), compute the slope of the line tangent to the level curve at (a, b) and verify that the tangent line is orthogonal to the gradient at that point.*

68. $f(x, y) = 5$; $(a, b) = (1, 1)$ **69.** $f(x, y) = 0$; $(a, b) = (2, 0)$

70. Directions of zero change Find the directions in which the function $f(x, y) = 4x^2 - y^2$ has zero change at the point $(1, 1, 3)$. Express the directions in terms of unit vectors.

71. Electric potential due to a charged cylinder. An infinitely long charged cylinder of radius R with its axis along the z-axis has an electric potential $V = k \ln(R/r)$, where r is the distance between a variable point $P(x, y)$ and the axis of the cylinder ($r^2 = x^2 + y^2$) and k is a physical constant. The electric field at a point (x, y) in the xy-plane is given by $\mathbf{E} = -\nabla V$, where ∇V is the two-dimensional gradient. Compute the electric field at a point (x, y) with $r > R$.

72–77. Tangent planes *Find an equation of the plane tangent to the following surfaces at the given points.*

72. $z = 2x^2 + y^2$; $(1, 1, 3)$ and $(0, 2, 4)$

73. $x^2 + \dfrac{y^2}{4} - \dfrac{z^2}{9} = 1$; $(0, 2, 0)$ and $\left(1, 1, \dfrac{3}{2} \right)$

74. $xy \sin z - 1 = 0$; $\left(1, 2, \dfrac{\pi}{6} \right)$ and $\left(-2, -1, \dfrac{5\pi}{6} \right)$

75. $yze^{xz} - 8 = 0$; $(0, 2, 4)$ and $(0, -8, -1)$

76. $z = x^2 e^{x-y}$; $(2, 2, 4)$ and $(-1, -1, 1)$

77. $z = \ln(1 + xy)$; $(1, 2, \ln 3)$ and $(-2, -1, \ln 3)$

78–79. Linear approximation

a. *Find the linear approximation (the equation of the tangent plane) at the point (a, b).*
b. *Use part (a) to estimate the given function value.*

78. $f(x, y) = 4 \cos(2x - y)$; $(a, b) = \left(\dfrac{\pi}{4}, \dfrac{\pi}{4} \right)$; estimate $f(0.8, 0.8)$.

79. $f(x, y) = (x + y)e^{xy}$; $(a, b) = (2, 0)$; estimate $f(1.95, 0.05)$.

80. Changes in a function Estimate the change in the function $f(x, y) = -2y^2 + 3x^2 + xy$ when (x, y) changes from $(1, -2)$ to $(1.05, -1.9)$.

81. Volume of a cylinder The volume of a cylinder with radius r and height h is $V = \pi r^2 h$. Find the approximate percent change in the volume when the radius decreases by 3% and the height increases by 2%.

82. Volume of an ellipsoid The volume of an ellipsoid with axes of length $2a$, $2b$, and $2c$ is $V = \pi abc$. Find the percent change in the volume when a increases by 2%, b increases by 1.5%, and c decreases by 2.5%.

83. Water-level changes A hemispherical tank with a radius of 1.50 m is filled with water to a depth of 1.00 m. Water is released from the tank and the water level drops by 0.05 m (from 1.00 m to 0.95 m).

a. Approximate the change in the volume of water in the tank. The volume of a spherical cap is $V = \pi h^2(3r - h)/3$, where r is the radius of the sphere and h is the thickness of the cap (in this case, the depth of the water).
b. Approximate the change in the surface area of the water in the tank.

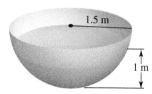

84–87. Analyzing critical points *Identify the critical points of the following functions. Then determine whether each critical point corresponds to a local maximum, local minimum, or saddle point. State when your analysis is inconclusive. Confirm your results using a graphing utility.*

84. $f(x, y) = x^4 + y^4 - 16xy$

85. $f(x, y) = x^3/3 - y^3/3 + 2xy$

86. $f(x, y) = xy(2 + x)(y - 3)$

87. $f(x, y) = 10 - x^3 - y^3 - 3x^2 + 3y^2$

88–91. Absolute maxima and minima *Find the absolute maximum and minimum values of the following functions on the specified set.*

88. $f(x, y) = x^3/3 - y^3/3 + 2xy$ on the rectangle $\{(x, y): 0 \leq x \leq 3, -1 \leq y \leq 1\}$

89. $f(x, y) = x^4 + y^4 - 4xy + 1$ on the square $\{(x, y): -2 \leq x \leq 2, -2 \leq y \leq 2\}$

90. $f(x, y) = x^2 y - y^3$ on the triangle $\{(x, y): 0 \leq x \leq 2, 0 \leq y \leq 2 - x\}$

91. $f(x, y) = xy$ on the semicircular disk
$\{(x, y): -1 \le x \le 1, 0 \le y \le \sqrt{1 - x^2}\}$

92. Least distance What point on the plane $x + y + 4z = 8$ is closest to the origin? Give an argument showing you have found an absolute minimum of the distance function.

93–96. Lagrange multipliers *Use Lagrange multipliers to find the maximum and minimum values of f (if they exist) subject to the given constraint.*

93. $f(x, y) = 2x + y + 10$ subject to $2(x - 1)^2 + 4(y - 1)^2 = 1$

94. $f(x, y) = x^2 y^2$ subject to $2x^2 + y^2 = 1$

95. $f(x, y, z) = x + 2y - z$ subject to $x^2 + y^2 + z^2 = 1$

96. $f(x, y, z) = x^2 y^2 z$ subject to $2x^2 + y^2 + z^2 = 25$

97. Maximum perimeter rectangle Use Lagrange multipliers to find the dimensions of the rectangle with the maximum perimeter that can be inscribed with sides parallel to the coordinate axes in the ellipse $x^2/a^2 + y^2/b^2 = 1$.

98. Minimum surface area cylinder Use Lagrange multipliers to find the dimensions of the right circular cylinder of minimum surface area (including the circular ends) with a volume of 32π in^3.

99. Minimum distance to a cone Find the point(s) on the cone $z^2 - x^2 - y^2 = 0$ that are closest to the point $(1, 3, 1)$. Give an argument showing you have found an absolute minimum of the distance function.

100. Gradient of a distance function Let $P_0(a, b, c)$ be a fixed point in $\mathbb{R}^3$ and let $d(x, y, z)$ be the distance between P_0 and a variable point $P(x, y, z)$.

  a. Compute $\nabla d(x, y, z)$.
  b. Show that $\nabla d(x, y, z)$ points in the direction from P_0 to P and has magnitude 1 for all (x, y, z).
  c. Describe the level surfaces of d and give the direction of $\nabla d(x, y, z)$ relative to the level surfaces of d.
  d. Discuss $\lim_{P \to P_0} \nabla d(x, y, z)$.

Chapter 13 Guided Projects

Applications of the material in this chapter and related topics can be found in the following Guided Projects. For additional information, see the Preface.

- Traveling waves
- Ecological diversity

- Economic production functions

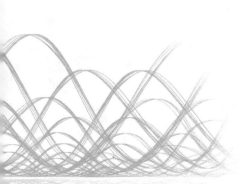

14

Multiple Integration

Chapter Preview We have now generalized limits and derivatives to functions of several variables. The next step is to carry out a similar process with respect to integration. As you know, single (one-variable) integrals are developed from Riemann sums and are used to compute areas of regions in $\mathbb{R}^2$. In an analogous way, we use Riemann sums to develop double (two-variable) and triple (three-variable) integrals, which are used to compute volumes of solid regions in $\mathbb{R}^3$. These multiple integrals have many applications in statistics, science, and engineering, including calculating the mass, the center of mass, and moments of inertia of solids with a variable density. Another significant development in this chapter is the appearance of cylindrical and spherical coordinates. These alternative coordinate systems often simplify the evaluation of integrals in three-dimensional space. The chapter closes with the two- and three-dimensional versions of the substitution (change of variables) rule. The overall lesson of the chapter is that we can integrate functions over most geometrical objects, from intervals on the x-axis to regions in the plane bounded by curves to complicated three-dimensional solids.

14.1 Double Integrals over Rectangular Regions

In Chapter 13 the concept of differentiation was extended to functions of several variables. In this chapter we extend integration to multivariable functions. By the close of the chapter, we will have completed Table 14.1, which is a basic road map for calculus.

Table 14.1

	Derivatives	Integrals
Single variable: $f(x)$	$f'(x)$	$\displaystyle\int_a^b f(x)\, dx$
Several variables: $f(x, y)$ and $f(x, y, z)$	$\dfrac{\partial f}{\partial x}, \dfrac{\partial f}{\partial y}, \dfrac{\partial f}{\partial z}$	$\displaystyle\iint_R f(x, y)\, dA, \iiint_D f(x, y, z)\, dV$

Volumes of Solids

The problem of finding the net area of a region bounded by a curve led to the definite integral in Chapter 5. Recall that we began that discussion by approximating the region with a collection of rectangles and then formed a Riemann sum of the areas of the rectangles. Under appropriate conditions, as the number of rectangles increases, the sum approaches the value of the definite integral, which is the net area of the region.

We now carry out an analogous procedure with surfaces defined by functions of the form $z = f(x, y)$, where, for the moment, we assume that $f(x, y) \geq 0$ on a region R in the xy-plane (Figure 14.1a). The goal is to determine the volume of the solid bounded by the surface and R. In general terms, the solid is first approximated by *boxes* (Figure 14.1b). The sum of the volumes of these boxes, which is a Riemann sum, approximates the volume of the solid. Under appropriate conditions, as the number of boxes increases, the approximations converge to the value of a *double integral*, which is the volume of the solid.

A three-dimensional solid bounded by $z = f(x, y)$ and a region R in the xy-plane is approximated by a collection of boxes.

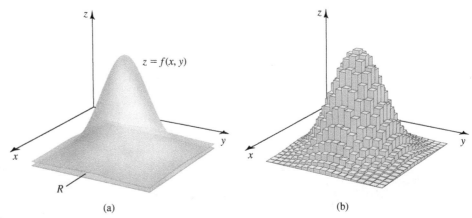

(a)   (b)

FIGURE 14.1

> We adopt the convention that Δx_k and Δy_k are the side lengths of the kth rectangle, for $k = 1, \ldots, n$, even though there are generally fewer than n different values of Δx_k and Δy_k. This convention is used throughout the chapter.

We assume that $z = f(x, y)$ is a nonnegative function defined on a *rectangular* region $R = \{(x, y): a \leq x \leq b, c \leq y \leq d\}$. A **partition** of R is formed by dividing R into n rectangular subregions using lines parallel to the x- and y-axes (not necessarily uniformly spaced). The subregions may be numbered in any systematic way; for example, left to right, and then bottom to top. The side lengths of the kth rectangle are denoted Δx_k and Δy_k, so the area of the kth subregion is $\Delta A_k = \Delta x_k \Delta y_k$. We also let (x_k^*, y_k^*) be any point in the kth subregion, for $1 \leq k \leq n$ (Figure 14.2).

To approximate the volume of the solid bounded by the surface $z = f(x, y)$ and the region R, we construct boxes on each of the n subregions; each box has a height of $f(x_k^*, y_k^*)$ and a base with area ΔA_k, for $1 \leq k \leq n$ (Figure 14.3). Therefore, the volume of the kth box is

$$f(x_k^*, y_k^*)\Delta A_k = f(x_k^*, y_k^*)\Delta x_k \Delta y_k.$$

The sum of the volumes of the n boxes gives an approximation to the volume of the solid:

$$V \approx \sum_{k=1}^{n} f(x_k^*, y_k^*) \Delta A_k.$$

QUICK CHECK 1 Explain why the preceding sum for the volume is an approximation. How can the approximation be improved?

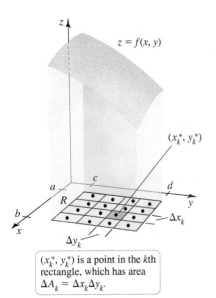

(x_k^*, y_k^*) is a point in the kth rectangle, which has area $\Delta A_k = \Delta x_k \Delta y_k$.

FIGURE 14.2

We now let Δ be the maximum length of the diagonals of the rectangular subregions in the partition. As $\Delta \to 0$, the areas of *all* the subregions approach zero ($\Delta A_k \to 0$) and the number of subregions increases ($n \to \infty$). If the approximations given by these Riemann sums have a limit as $\Delta \to 0$, then we define the volume of the solid to be that limit (Figure 14.4).

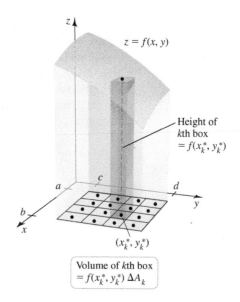

Height of
kth box
$= f(x_k^*, y_k^*)$

$z = f(x, y)$

(x_k^*, y_k^*)

Volume of kth box
$= f(x_k^*, y_k^*) \Delta A_k$

FIGURE 14.3

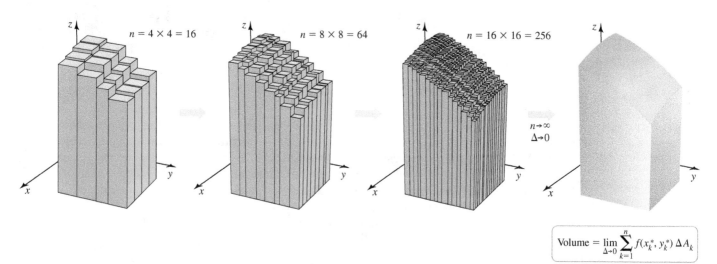

$n = 4 \times 4 = 16$

$n = 8 \times 8 = 64$

$n = 16 \times 16 = 256$

$n \to \infty$
$\Delta \to 0$

Volume $= \lim_{\Delta \to 0} \sum_{k=1}^{n} f(x_k^*, y_k^*) \, \Delta A_k$

FIGURE 14.4

> If f is negative on parts of R, the value of the double integral may be zero or negative, and the result is interpreted as a *net volume* (in analogy with *net area* for single variable integrals). See Example 5 of this section.

DEFINITION Volumes and Double Integrals

A function f defined on a rectangular region R in the xy-plane is **integrable** on R if $\lim_{\Delta \to 0} \sum_{k=1}^{n} f(x_k^*, y_k^*) \Delta A_k$ exists for all partitions of R and for all choices of (x_k^*, y_k^*) within those partitions. The limit is the **double integral of f over R**, which we write

$$\iint\limits_{R} f(x, y) \, dA = \lim_{\Delta \to 0} \sum_{k=1}^{n} f(x_k^*, y_k^*) \Delta A_k.$$

If f is nonnegative on R, then the double integral equals the volume of the solid bounded by $z = f(x, y)$ and the xy-plane over R.

The functions that we encounter in this book are integrable. Advanced methods are needed to prove that continuous functions and many functions with finite discontinuities are also integrable.

Iterated Integrals

Evaluating double integrals using limits of Riemann sums is tedious and rarely done. Fortunately, there is a practical method that reduces a double integral to two single (one-variable) integrals. An example illustrates the technique.

Suppose we wish to compute the volume of the solid region bounded by the plane $z = f(x, y) = 6 - 2x - y$ over the rectangular region $R = \{(x, y): 0 \le x \le 1, 0 \le y \le 2\}$ (Figure 14.5). By definition, the volume is given by the double integral

$$V = \iint\limits_{R} f(x, y) \, dA = \iint\limits_{R} (6 - 2x - y) \, dA.$$

> Recall the General Slicing Method. If a solid is sliced parallel to the y-axis and perpendicular to the xy-plane, and the cross-sectional area of the slice at the point x is $A(x)$, then the volume of the solid region is
>
> $$V = \int_{a}^{b} A(x) \, dx.$$

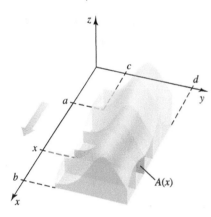

According to the General Slicing Method (Section 6.3), we can compute this volume by taking slices through the solid parallel to the y-axis and perpendicular to the xy-plane (Figure 14.5). The slice at the point x has a cross-sectional area denoted $A(x)$. In general, as x varies, the area $A(x)$ also changes, so we integrate these cross-sectional areas from $x = 0$ to $x = 1$ to obtain the volume

$$V = \int_{0}^{1} A(x) \, dx.$$

The important observation is that for a fixed value of x, $A(x)$ is the area of the plane region under the curve $z = 6 - 2x - y$. This area is computed by integrating f with respect to y from $y = 0$ to $y = 2$, holding x fixed; that is,

$$A(x) = \int_{0}^{2} (6 - 2x - y) \, dy,$$

where $0 \le x \le 1$, and x is treated as a constant in the integration. Substituting for $A(x)$, we have

$$V = \int_{0}^{1} A(x) \, dx = \int_{0}^{1} \left[\int_{0}^{2} (6 - 2x - y) \, dy \right] dx.$$

$$\underbrace{\qquad\qquad\qquad}_{A(x)}$$

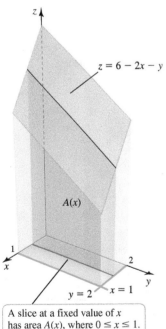

A slice at a fixed value of x has area $A(x)$, where $0 \le x \le 1$.

FIGURE 14.5

The expression that appears on the right side of this equation is called an **iterated integral** (meaning repeated integral). We first evaluate the inner integral with respect to y holding x fixed; the result is a function of x. Then the outer integral is evaluated with respect to x; the result is a real number, which is the volume of the solid in Figure 14.5. Both these integrals are ordinary one-variable integrals.

EXAMPLE 1 **Evaluating an iterated integral** Evaluate $V = \int_{0}^{1} A(x) \, dx$, where $A(x) = \int_{0}^{2} (6 - 2x - y) \, dy$.

SOLUTION Using the Fundamental Theorem of Calculus, holding x constant, we have

$$A(x) = \int_{0}^{2} (6 - 2x - y) \, dy$$

$$= \left(6y - 2xy - \frac{y^2}{2} \right) \Big|_{0}^{2} \quad \text{Fundamental Theorem of Calculus}$$

$$= (12 - 4x - 2) - 0 \quad \text{Simplify; limits are in } y.$$

$$= 10 - 4x. \quad \text{Simplify.}$$

Substituting $A(x) = 10 - 4x$ into the volume integral, we have

$$V = \int_0^1 A(x)\,dx$$

$$= \int_0^1 (10 - 4x)\,dx \quad \text{Substitute for } A(x).$$

$$= (10x - 2x^2)\Big|_0^1 \quad \text{Fundamental Theorem}$$

$$= 8. \quad \text{Simplify.}$$

Related Exercises 5–25◀

EXAMPLE 2   Same double integral, different order Example 1 used slices through the solid parallel to the y-axis. Compute the volume of the same solid using slices through the solid parallel to the x-axis and perpendicular to the xy-plane, for $0 \le y \le 2$ (Figure 14.6).

SOLUTION In this case, $A(y)$ is the area of a slice through the solid for a fixed value of y in the interval $0 \le y \le 2$. This area is computed by integrating $z = 6 - 2x - y$ from $x = 0$ to $x = 1$, holding y fixed; that is,

$$A(y) = \int_0^1 (6 - 2x - y)\,dx,$$

where $0 \le y \le 2$.

Using the General Slicing Method again, the volume is

$$V = \int_0^2 A(y)\,dy \quad \text{General Slicing Method}$$

$$= \int_0^2 \underbrace{\left[\int_0^1 (6 - 2x - y)\,dx \right]}_{A(y)} dy \quad \text{Substitute for } A(y).$$

$$= \int_0^2 \left[(6x - x^2 - yx)\Big|_0^1 \right] dy \quad \begin{array}{l}\text{Fundamental Theorem of Calculus;}\\ y \text{ is constant.}\end{array}$$

$$= \int_0^2 (5 - y)\,dy \quad \text{Simplify; limits are in } x.$$

$$= \left(5y - \frac{y^2}{2} \right)\Big|_0^2 \quad \text{Evaluate outer integral.}$$

$$= 8. \quad \text{Simplify.}$$

Related Exercises 5–25◀

Several important comments are in order. First, the two iterated integrals give the same value for the double integral. Second, the notation of the iterated integral must be used carefully. When we write $\int_c^d \int_a^b f(x, y)\,dx\,dy$, it means $\int_c^d \left[\int_a^b f(x, y)\,dx \right] dy$. The *inner* integral with respect to x is evaluated first, holding y fixed, and the variable runs from $x = a$ to $x = b$. The result of that integration is a constant or a function of y, which is then integrated in the *outer* integral, with the variable running from $y = c$ to $y = d$. The order of integration is signified by the order of dx and dy.

Similarly, $\int_a^b \int_c^d f(x, y)\,dy\,dx$ means $\int_a^b \left[\int_c^d f(x, y)\,dy \right] dx$. The inner integral with respect to y is evaluated first, holding x fixed. The result is then integrated with respect to x.

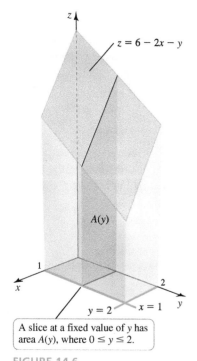

A slice at a fixed value of y has area $A(y)$, where $0 \le y \le 2$.

FIGURE 14.6

QUICK CHECK 2 Consider the integral $\int_3^4 \int_1^2 f(x, y)\,dx\,dy$. Give the limits of integration and the variable of integration for the first (inner) integral and the second (outer) integral. Sketch the region of integration. ◀

Examples 1 and 2 illustrate one version of *Fubini's theorem*, a deep result that relates double integrals to iterated integrals. The first version of the theorem applies to double integrals over rectangular regions.

> The area of the kth rectangular subregion in the partition is $\Delta A_k = \Delta x_k \Delta y_k$, where Δx_k and Δy_k are the lengths of the sides of that rectangle. Accordingly, the *element of area* in the double integral dA becomes $dx\,dy$ or $dy\,dx$ in the iterated integral.

THEOREM 14.1 (Fubini)   Double Integrals on Rectangular Regions

Let f be continuous on the rectangular region $R = \{(x, y): a \le x \le b, c \le y \le d\}$. The double integral of f over R may be evaluated by either of two iterated integrals:

$$\iint\limits_{R} f(x, y)\, dA = \int_{c}^{d} \int_{a}^{b} f(x, y)\, dx\, dy = \int_{a}^{b} \int_{c}^{d} f(x, y)\, dy\, dx.$$

The importance of Fubini's Theorem is twofold: It says that double integrals may be evaluated by iterated integrals. It *also* says that the order of integration in the iterated integrals does not matter (although in practice, one order of integration is often easier to use than the other).

EXAMPLE 3   A double integral Find the volume of the solid bounded by the surface $z = 4 + 9x^2y^2$ over the region $R = \{(x, y): -1 \le x \le 1, 0 \le y \le 2\}$. Use both possible orders of integration.

SOLUTION The volume of the region is given by the double integral $\iint_{R} (4 + 9x^2y^2)\, dA$. By Fubini's Theorem, the double integral is evaluated as an iterated integral. If we first integrate with respect to x, the area of a cross section of the solid for a fixed value of y is given by $A(y)$ (Figure 14.7a). The volume of the region is

$$\iint\limits_{R} (4 + 9x^2y^2)\, dA = \int_{0}^{2} \underbrace{\int_{-1}^{1} (4 + 9x^2y^2)\, dx}_{A(y)}\, dy \qquad \text{Convert to an iterated integral.}$$

$$= \int_{0}^{2} (4x + 3x^3y^2)\Big|_{-1}^{1}\, dy \qquad \begin{array}{l}\text{Evaluate the inner integral} \\ \text{with respect to } x.\end{array}$$

$$= \int_{0}^{2} (8 + 6y^2)\, dy \qquad \text{Simplify.}$$

$$= (8y + 2y^3)\Big|_{0}^{2} \qquad \begin{array}{l}\text{Evaluate the outer integral} \\ \text{with respect to } y.\end{array}$$

$$= 32. \qquad \text{Simplify.}$$

Alternatively, if we integrate first with respect to y, the area of a cross section of the solid for a fixed value of x is given by $A(x)$ (Figure 14.7b). The volume of the region is

$$\iint\limits_{R} (4 + 9x^2y^2)\, dA = \int_{-1}^{1} \underbrace{\int_{0}^{2} (4 + 9x^2y^2)\, dy}_{A(x)}\, dx \qquad \text{Convert to an iterated integral.}$$

$$= \int_{-1}^{1} (4y + 3x^2y^3)\Big|_{0}^{2}\, dx \qquad \begin{array}{l}\text{Evaluate the inner integral} \\ \text{with respect to } y.\end{array}$$

$$= \int_{-1}^{1} (8 + 24x^2)\, dx \qquad \text{Simplify.}$$

$$= (8x + 8x^3)\Big|_{-1}^{1} = 32. \qquad \begin{array}{l}\text{Evaluate the outer integral} \\ \text{with respect to } x.\end{array}$$

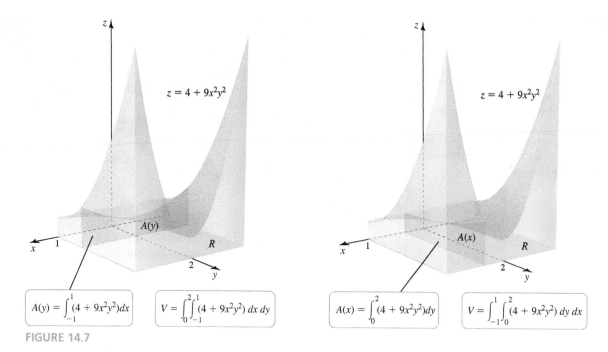

FIGURE 14.7

As guaranteed by Fubini's Theorem, the iterated integrals agree, both giving the value of the double integral and the volume of the solid.

Related Exercises 5–25 ◄

QUICK CHECK 3 Write the iterated integral $\int_{-10}^{10} \int_{0}^{20} (x^2 y + 2xy^3)\, dy\, dx$ with the order of integration reversed. ◄

The following example shows that sometimes the order of integration must be chosen carefully either to save work or to make the integration possible.

EXAMPLE 4 Choosing a convenient order of integration Evaluate $\iint_R ye^{xy}\, dA$, where $R = \{(x, y): 0 \le x \le 1, 0 \le y \le \ln 2\}$.

SOLUTION The iterated integral $\int_{0}^{1} \int_{0}^{\ln 2} ye^{xy}\, dy\, dx$ requires first integrating ye^{xy} with respect to y, which entails integration by parts. An easier approach is to integrate first with respect to x:

$$\int_{0}^{\ln 2} \int_{0}^{1} ye^{xy}\, dx\, dy = \int_{0}^{\ln 2} (e^{xy})\Big|_{0}^{1} dy \qquad \text{Evaluate the inner integral with respect to } x.$$

$$= \int_{0}^{\ln 2} (e^{y} - 1)\, dy \qquad \text{Simplify.}$$

$$= (e^{y} - y)\Big|_{0}^{\ln 2} \qquad \text{Evaluate the outer integral with respect to } y.$$

$$= 1 - \ln 2. \qquad \text{Simplify.}$$

Related Exercises 26–31 ◄

Average Value

The concept of the average value of a function (Section 5.4) extends naturally to functions of two variables. Recall that the average value of the integrable function f over the interval $[a, b]$ is

$$\bar{f} = \frac{1}{b - a} \int_a^b f(x)\, dx.$$

To find the average value of an integrable function f over a region R, we integrate f over R and divide the result by the "size" of R, which is the area of R in the two-variable case.

> The same definition of average value applies to more general regions in the plane.

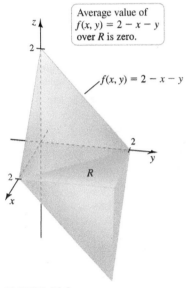

Average value of $f(x, y) = 2 - x - y$ over R is zero.

$f(x, y) = 2 - x - y$

FIGURE 14.8

> An average value of 0 means that over the region R, the volume of the solid above the xy-plane and below the surface equals the volume of the solid below the xy-plane and above the surface.

DEFINITION Average Value of a Function over a Plane Region

The **average value** of an integrable function f over a region R is

$$\bar{f} = \frac{1}{\text{area of } R} \iint_R f(x, y)\, dA.$$

EXAMPLE 5 Average value Find the average value of the quantity $2 - x - y$ over the square $R = \{(x, y): 0 \le x \le 2, 0 \le y \le 2\}$ (Figure 14.8).

SOLUTION The area of the region R is 4. Letting $f(x, y) = 2 - x - y$, the average value of f is

$$
\begin{aligned}
\frac{1}{\text{area of } R} \iint_R f(x, y)\, dA &= \frac{1}{4} \iint_R (2 - x - y)\, dA \\
&= \frac{1}{4} \int_0^2 \int_0^2 (2 - x - y)\, dx\, dy \quad \text{Convert to an iterated integral.} \\
&= \frac{1}{4} \int_0^2 \left(2x - \frac{x^2}{2} - xy \right) \Big|_0^2 dy \quad \text{Evaluate the inner integral.} \\
&= \frac{1}{4} \int_0^2 (2 - 2y)\, dy \quad \text{Simplify.} \\
&= 0. \quad \text{Evaluate the outer integral.}
\end{aligned}
$$

Related Exercises 32–36 ◄

SECTION 14.1 EXERCISES

1. Write an iterated integral that gives the volume of the solid bounded by the surface $f(x, y) = xy$ over the square $R = \{(x, y): 0 \le x \le 2, 1 \le y \le 3\}$.

2. Write an iterated integral that gives the volume of a box with height 10 and base $\{(x, y): 0 \le x \le 5, -2 \le y \le 4\}$.

3. Write two iterated integrals that equal $\iint_R f(x, y)\, dA$, where $R = \{(x, y): -2 \le x \le 4, 1 \le y \le 5\}$.

4. Consider the integral $\int_1^3 \int_{-1}^1 (2y^2 + xy)\, dy\, dx$. Give the variable of integration in the first (inner) integral and the limits of integration. Give the variable of integration in the second (outer) integral and the limits of integration.

Basic Skills

5–16. Iterated integrals *Evaluate the following iterated integrals.*

5. $\int_0^2 \int_0^1 4xy\, dx\, dy$

6. $\int_1^2 \int_0^1 (3x^2 + 4y^3)\, dy\, dx$

7. $\int_1^3 \int_0^2 x^2 y\, dx\, dy$

8. $\int_0^3 \int_{-2}^1 (2x + 3y)\, dx\, dy$

9. $\int_1^3 \int_0^{\pi/2} x \sin y\, dy\, dx$

10. $\int_1^3 \int_1^2 (y^2 + y)\, dx\, dy$

11. $\int_1^4 \int_0^4 \sqrt{uv}\, du\, dv$

12. $\int_0^{\pi/2} \int_0^1 x \cos xy\, dy\, dx$

13. $\int_0^{\ln 2} \int_0^1 6xe^{3y}\, dx\, dy$

14. $\int_0^1 \int_0^1 \frac{y}{1+x^2}\, dx\, dy$

15. $\int_1^{\ln 5} \int_0^{\ln 3} e^{x+y}\, dx\, dy$

16. $\int_0^{\pi/4} \int_0^3 r \sec\theta\, dr\, d\theta$

17–25. Iterated integrals *Evaluate the following double integrals over the region R.*

17. $\iint_R (x + 2y)\, dA;\ R = \{(x, y): 0 \le x \le 3, 1 \le y \le 4\}$

18. $\iint_R (x^2 + xy)\, dA;\ R = \{(x, y): 1 \le x \le 2, -1 \le y \le 1\}$

19. $\iint_R 4x^3 \cos y\, dA;\ R = \{(x, y): 1 \le x \le 2, 0 \le y \le \pi/2\}$

20. $\iint_R \frac{y}{\sqrt{1-x^2}}\, dA;\ R = \{(x, y): \frac{1}{2} \le x \le \frac{\sqrt{3}}{2}, 1 \le y \le 2\}$

21. $\iint_R \sqrt{\frac{x}{y}}\, dA;\ R = \{(x, y): 0 \le x \le 1, 1 \le y \le 4\}$

22. $\iint_R xy \sin x^2\, dA;\ R = \{(x, y): 0 \le x \le \sqrt{\pi/2}, 0 \le y \le 1\}$

23. $\iint_R e^{x+2y}\, dA;\ R = \{(x, y): 0 \le x \le \ln 2, 1 \le y \le \ln 3\}$

24. $\iint_R (x^2 - y^2)^2\, dA;\ R = \{(x, y): -1 \le x \le 2, 0 \le y \le 1\}$

25. $\iint_R (x^5 - y^5)^2\, dA;\ R = \{(x, y): 0 \le x \le 1, -1 \le y \le 1\}$

26–31. Choose a convenient order *When converted to an iterated integral, the following double integrals are easier to evaluate in one order than the other. Find the best order and evaluate the integral.*

26. $\iint_R y \cos xy\, dA;\ R = \{(x, y): 0 \le x \le 1, 0 \le y \le \pi/3\}$

27. $\iint_R (y + 1)e^{x(y+1)}\, dA;\ R = \{(x, y): 0 \le x \le 1, -1 \le y \le 1\}$

28. $\iint_R x \sec^2 xy\, dA;\ R = \{(x, y): 0 \le x \le \pi/3, 0 \le y \le 1\}$

29. $\iint_R 6x^5 e^{x^3 y}\, dA;\ R = \{(x, y): 0 \le x \le 2, 0 \le y \le 2\}$

30. $\iint_R y^3 \sin xy^2\, dA;\ R = \{(x, y): 0 \le x \le 2, 0 \le y \le \sqrt{\pi/2}\}$

31. $\iint_R \frac{x}{(1+xy)^2}\, dA;\ R = \{(x, y): 0 \le x \le 4, 1 \le y \le 2\}$

32–34. Average value *Compute the average value of the following functions over the region R.*

32. $f(x, y) = 4 - x - y;\ R = \{(x, y): 0 \le x \le 2, 0 \le y \le 2\}$

33. $f(x, y) = e^{-y};\ R = \{(x, y): 0 \le x \le 6, 0 \le y \le \ln 2\}$

34. $f(x, y) = \sin x \sin y;\ R = \{(x, y): 0 \le x \le \pi, 0 \le y \le \pi\}$

35–36. Average value

35. Find the average squared distance between the points of $R = \{(x, y): -2 \le x \le 2, 0 \le y \le 2\}$ and the origin.

36. Find the average squared distance between the points of $R = \{(x, y): 0 \le x \le 3, 0 \le y \le 3\}$ and the point $(3, 3)$.

Further Explorations

37. Explain why or why not Determine whether the following statements are true and give an explanation or counterexample.

   a. The region of integration for $\int_4^6 \int_1^3 4\, dx\, dy$ is a square.

   b. If f is continuous on $\mathbb{R}^2$, then
$$\int_4^6 \int_1^3 f(x, y)\, dx\, dy = \int_4^6 \int_1^3 f(x, y)\, dy\, dx.$$

   c. If f is continuous on $\mathbb{R}^2$, then
$$\int_4^6 \int_1^3 f(x, y)\, dx\, dy = \int_1^3 \int_4^6 f(x, y)\, dy\, dx.$$

38. Symmetry Evaluate the following integrals using symmetry arguments. Let $R = \{(x, y): -a \le x \le a, -b \le y \le b\}$, where a and b are positive real numbers.

   a. $\iint_R xye^{-(x^2+y^2)}\, dA$

   b. $\iint_R \frac{\sin(x-y)}{x^2+y^2+1}\, dA$

39. Computing populations The population densities in nine districts of a rectangular county are shown in the figure.

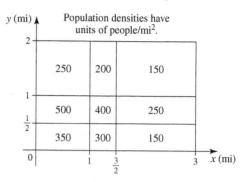

   a. Use the fact that population = (population density) × (area) to estimate the population of the county.

   b. Explain how the calculation of part (a) is related to Riemann sums and double integrals.

40. Approximating water volume The varying depth of an 18 m × 25 m swimming pool is measured in 15 different rectangles of equal area (see figure). Approximate the volume of water in the pool.

0.75	1.25	1.75	2.25	2.75
1	1.5	2.0	2.5	3.0
1	1.5	2.0	2.5	3.0

y (m) — 18; Depth readings have units of m. 0, 25, *x* (m)

41–42. Pictures of solids *Draw the solid region whose volume is given by the following double integrals. Then find the volume of the solid.*

41. $\int_0^6 \int_1^2 10 \, dy \, dx$

42. $\int_0^1 \int_{-1}^1 (4 - x^2 - y^2) \, dx \, dy$

43–46. More integration practice *Evaluate the following iterated integrals.*

43. $\int_1^2 \int_1^2 \frac{x}{x+y} \, dy \, dx$

44. $\int_0^2 \int_0^1 x^5 y^2 e^{x^3 y^3} \, dy \, dx$

45. $\int_0^1 \int_1^4 \frac{3y}{\sqrt{x+y^2}} \, dx \, dy$

46. $\int_1^4 \int_0^2 e^{y\sqrt{x}} \, dy \, dx$

47–51. Volumes of solids *Find the volume of the following solids.*

47. The solid between the cylinder $f(x, y) = e^{-x}$ and the region $R = \{(x, y): 0 \le x \le \ln 4, -2 \le y \le 2\}$

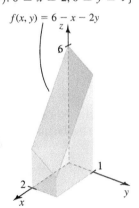

$f(x, y) = e^{-x}$

48. The solid beneath the plane $f(x, y) = 6 - x - 2y$ and above the region $R = \{(x, y): 0 \le x \le 2, 0 \le y \le 1\}$

$f(x, y) = 6 - x - 2y$

49. The solid beneath the plane $f(x, y) = 24 - 3x - 4y$ and above the region $R = \{(x, y): -1 \le x \le 3, 0 \le y \le 2\}$

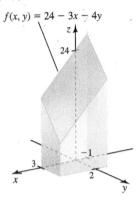

$f(x, y) = 24 - 3x - 4y$

50. The solid beneath the paraboloid $f(x, y) = 12 - x^2 - 2y^2$ and above the region $R = \{(x, y): 1 \le x \le 2, 0 \le y \le 1\}$

$f(x, y) = 12 - x^2 - 2y^2$

51. Net volume Let $R = \{(x, y): 0 \le x \le \pi, 0 \le y \le a\}$. For what values of a, with $0 \le a \le \pi$, is $\iint_R \sin(x + y) \, dA$ equal to 1?

52–53. Zero average value *Let $R = \{(x, y): 0 \le x \le a, 0 \le y \le a\}$. Find the value of $a > 0$ such that the average value of the following functions over R is zero.*

52. $f(x, y) = x + y - 8$

53. $f(x, y) = 4 - x^2 - y^2$

54. Maximum integral Consider the plane $x + 3y + z = 6$ over the rectangle R with vertices at $(0, 0)$, $(a, 0)$, $(0, b)$, and (a, b), where the vertex (a, b) lies on the line where the plane intersects the xy-plane (so $a + 3b = 6$). Find the point (a, b) for which the volume of the solid between the plane and R is a maximum.

Applications

55. Density and mass Suppose a thin rectangular plate, represented by a region R in the xy-plane, has a density given by the function $\rho(x, y)$; this function gives the *area density* in units such as grams per square centimeter (g/cm²). The mass of the plate is $\iint_R \rho(x, y) \, dA$. Assume that $R = \{(x, y): 0 \le x \le \pi/2, 0 \le y \le \pi\}$ and find the mass of the plates with the following density functions.

a. $\rho(x, y) = 1 + \sin x$
b. $\rho(x, y) = 1 + \sin y$
c. $\rho(x, y) = 1 + \sin x \sin y$

56. Approximating volume Propose a method based on Riemann sums to approximate the volume of the shed shown in the figure (the peak of the roof is directly above the rear corner of the shed). Carry out the method and provide an estimate of the volume.

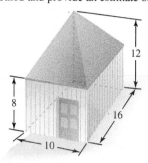

Additional Exercises

57. Cylinders Let S be the solid in $\mathbb{R}^3$ between the cylinder $z = f(x)$ and the region $R = \{(x, y): a \le x \le b, c \le y \le d\}$, where $f(x) \ge 0$ on R. Explain why $\int_c^d \int_a^b f(x)\, dx\, dy$ equals the area of the constant cross section of S multiplied by $(d - c)$, which is the volume of S.

58. Product of integrals Suppose $f(x, y) = g(x)h(y)$, where g and h are continuous functions for all real values.

   a. Show that $\int_c^d \int_a^b f(x, y)\, dx\, dy = \left(\int_a^b g(x)\, dx\right)\left(\int_c^d h(y)\, dy\right)$. Interpret this result geometrically.

   b. Write $\left(\int_a^b g(x)\, dx\right)^2$ as an iterated integral.

   c. Use the result of part (a) to evaluate $\int_0^{2\pi} \int_{10}^{30} \cos x\, e^{-4y^2}\, dy\, dx$.

59. An identity Suppose the second partial derivatives of f are continuous on $R = \{(x, y): 0 \le x \le a, 0 \le y \le b\}$. Simplify $$\iint_R \frac{\partial^2 f}{\partial x\, \partial y}\, dA.$$

60. Two integrals Let $R = \{(x, y): 0 \le x \le 1, 0 \le y \le 1\}$.

   a. Evaluate $\iint_R \cos(x\sqrt{y})\, dA$

   b. Evaluate $\iint_R x^3 y \cos(x^2 y^2)\, dA$

61. A generalization Let R be as in Exercise 60, let F be an antiderivative of f with $F(0) = 0$, and let G be an antiderivative of F. Show that if f and F are integrable, and $r \ge 1$ and $s \ge 1$ are real numbers, then $$\iint_R x^{2r-1} y^{s-1} f(x^r y^s)\, dA = \frac{G(1) - G(0)}{rs}.$$

QUICK CHECK ANSWERS

1. The sum gives the volume of a collection of rectangular boxes and these boxes do not exactly fill the solid region under the surface. The approximation is improved by using more boxes.   **2.** Inner integral: x runs from $x = 1$ to $x = 2$; outer integral: y runs from $y = 3$ to $y = 4$. The region is the rectangle $\{(x, y): 1 \le x \le 2, 3 \le y \le 4\}$.
3. $\int_0^{20} \int_{-10}^{10} (x^2 y + 2xy^3)\, dx\, dy$ ◄

14.2   Double Integrals over General Regions

Evaluating double integrals over rectangular regions is a useful place to begin our study of multiple integrals. Problems of practical interest, however, usually involve nonrectangular regions of integration. The goal of this section is to extend the methods presented in Section 14.1 so that they apply to more general regions of integration.

General Regions of Integration

Consider a function f defined over a closed bounded *nonrectangular* region R in the xy-plane. As with rectangular regions, we use a partition consisting of rectangles, but now, such a partition does not cover R exactly. In this case, only the n rectangles that lie entirely within R are considered to be in the partition (Figure 14.9). When f is nonnegative on R, the volume of the solid bounded by the surface $z = f(x, y)$ and the xy-plane over R is approximated by the Riemann sum

$$V \approx \sum_{k=1}^{n} f(x_k^*, y_k^*)\Delta A_k,$$

where $\Delta A_k = \Delta x_k \Delta y_k$ is the area of the kth rectangle and (x_k^*, y_k^*) is any point in the kth rectangle, for $1 \le k \le n$. As before, we define Δ to be the maximum length of the diagonals of the rectangles in the partition.

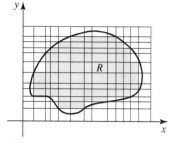

FIGURE 14.9

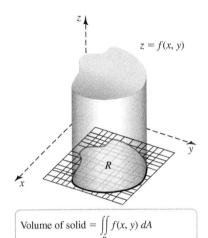

$$\text{Volume of solid} = \iint\limits_R f(x, y) \, dA$$

$$= \lim_{\Delta \to 0} \sum_{k=1}^{n} f(x_k^*, y_k^*) \, \Delta A_k$$

FIGURE 14.10

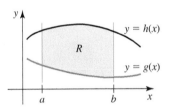

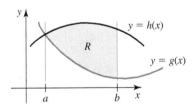

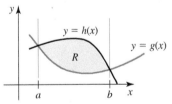

FIGURE 14.11

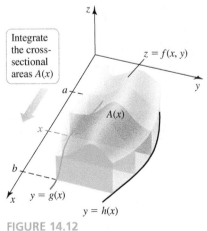

Integrate the cross-sectional areas $A(x)$

FIGURE 14.12

Under the assumptions that f is continuous on R and that the boundary of R consists of a finite number of smooth curves, two things occur as $\Delta \to 0$ and the number of subregions increases $(n \to \infty)$.

- The rectangles in the partition fill R more and more completely; that is, the union of the rectangles approaches R.

- Over all partitions and all choices of (x_k^*, y_k^*) within a partition, the Riemann sums approach a (unique) limit.

The limit approached by the Riemann sums is the **double integral of f over R**; that is,

$$\iint\limits_R f(x, y) \, dA = \lim_{\Delta \to 0} \sum_{k=1}^{n} f(x_k^*, y_k^*) \Delta A_k.$$

When this limit exists, f is **integrable** over R. If f is nonnegative on R, then the double integral equals the volume of the solid bounded by the surface $z = f(x, y)$ and the xy-plane over R (Figure 14.10).

The double integral $\iint_R f(x, y) \, dA$ has another common interpretation. Suppose R represents a thin plate whose density at the point (x, y) is $f(x, y)$. The units of density are mass per unit area, so the product $f(x_k^*, y_k^*) \Delta A_k$ approximates the mass of the kth rectangle in R. Summing the masses of the rectangles gives an approximation to the total mass of R. In the limit as $n \to \infty$ and $\Delta \to 0$, the double integral equals the mass of the plate.

Iterated Integrals

Double integrals over nonrectangular regions are also evaluated using iterated integrals. However, in this more general setting the order of integration is critical. Most of the double integrals we encounter fall into one of two categories determined by the shape of the region R.

The first type of region has the property that its lower and upper boundaries are the graphs of continuous functions $y = g(x)$ and $y = h(x)$, respectively, for $a \le x \le b$. Such regions have any of the forms shown in Figure 14.11.

Once again, we appeal to the general slicing method. Assume for the moment that f is nonnegative on R and consider the solid bounded by the surface $z = f(x, y)$ and R (Figure 14.12). Imagine taking vertical slices through the solid parallel to the y-axis. The cross section through the solid at a fixed value of x extends from the lower curve $y = g(x)$ to the upper curve $y = h(x)$. The area of that cross section is

$$A(x) = \int_{g(x)}^{h(x)} f(x, y) \, dy, \qquad \text{for } a \le x \le b.$$

The volume of the region is given by a double integral; it is evaluated by integrating the cross-sectional areas $A(x)$ from $x = a$ to $x = b$:

$$\iint\limits_R f(x, y) \, dA = \int_a^b \underbrace{\int_{g(x)}^{h(x)} f(x, y) \, dy}_{A(x)} \, dx.$$

EXAMPLE 1 **Evaluating a double integral** Express the integral $\iint_R 2x^2 y \, dA$ as an iterated integral, where R is the region bounded by the parabolas $y = 3x^2$ and $y = 16 - x^2$. Then evaluate the integral.

SOLUTION The region R is bounded below and above by the graphs of $g(x) = 3x^2$ and $h(x) = 16 - x^2$, respectively. Solving $3x^2 = 16 - x^2$, we find that these curves intersect at $x = -2$ and $x = 2$, which are the limits of integration in the x-direction (Figure 14.13).

The bounding curves determine the limits of integration in y.

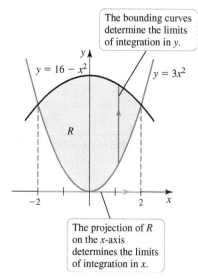

R

$y = 16 - x^2$

$y = 3x^2$

-2 2   x

The projection of R on the x-axis determines the limits of integration in x.

FIGURE 14.13

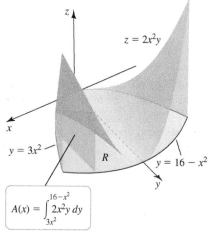

$z = 2x^2y$

$y = 3x^2$

R

$y = 16 - x^2$

$A(x) = \int_{3x^2}^{16-x^2} 2x^2y \, dy$

FIGURE 14.14

Figure 14.14 shows the solid bounded by the surface $z = 2x^2y$ and the region R. A typical vertical cross section through the solid parallel to the y-axis at a fixed value of x has area

$$A(x) = \int_{3x^2}^{16-x^2} 2x^2y \, dy.$$

Integrating these cross-sectional areas between $x = -2$ and $x = 2$, the iterated integral becomes

$$\iint_R 2x^2y \, dA = \int_{-2}^{2} \underbrace{\int_{3x^2}^{16-x^2} 2x^2y \, dy}_{A(x)} \, dx \qquad \text{Convert to an iterated integral.}$$

$$= \int_{-2}^{2} (x^2y^2)\Big|_{3x^2}^{16-x^2} dx \qquad \text{Evaluate the inner integral with respect to } y.$$

$$= \int_{-2}^{2} x^2((16 - x^2)^2 - (3x^2)^2) \, dx \qquad \text{Simplify.}$$

$$= \int_{-2}^{2} (-8x^6 - 32x^4 + 256x^2) \, dx \qquad \text{Simplify.}$$

$$\approx 663.2. \qquad \text{Evaluate the outer integral with respect to } x.$$

Related Exercises 7–30 ◄

QUICK CHECK 1 A region R is bounded by the x- and y-axes and the line $x + y = 2$. Suppose you integrate first with respect to y. Give the limits of the iterated integral over R. ◄

Change of Perspective Suppose that the region of integration R is bounded on the left and right by the graphs of continuous functions $x = g(y)$ and $x = h(y)$, respectively, on the interval $c \le y \le d$. Such regions may take any of the forms shown in Figure 14.15.

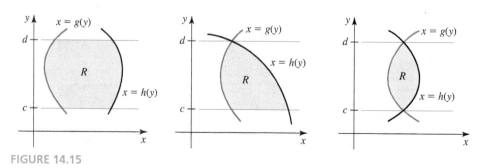

FIGURE 14.15

To find the volume of the solid bounded by the surface $z = f(x, y)$ and R, we now take slices parallel to the x-axis and perpendicular to the xy-plane. In so doing, the double integral $\iint_R f(x, y) \, dA$ is converted to an iterated integral in which the inner integration is with respect to x over the interval $g(y) \le x \le h(y)$ and the outer integration is with respect to y over the interval $c \le y \le d$. The evaluation of double integrals in these two cases is summarized in the following theorem.

Theorem 14.2 is another version of Fubini's Theorem. With integrals over nonrectangular regions, the order of integration cannot be simply switched; that is,

$$\int_a^b \int_{g(x)}^{h(x)} f(x, y)\, dy\, dx$$

$$\neq \int_{g(x)}^{h(x)} \int_a^b f(x, y)\, dx\, dy.$$

The term dA, called an *element of area*, corresponds to the area of a small rectangle in the partition. Comparing the double integral to the iterated integral, we see that the element of area is $dA = dy\, dx$ or $dA = dx\, dy$, which is consistent with the area formula for rectangles.

> The bounding curves determine the limits of integration in x.

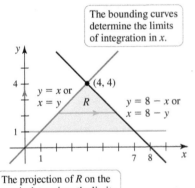

> The projection of R on the y-axis determines the limits of integration in y.

FIGURE 14.16

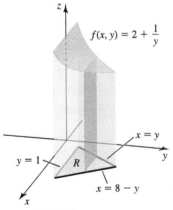

FIGURE 14.17

THEOREM 14.2   Double Integrals over Nonrectangular Regions

Let R be a region bounded below and above by the graphs of the continuous functions $y = g(x)$ and $y = h(x)$, respectively, and by the lines $x = a$ and $x = b$ (Figure 14.11). If f is continuous on R, then

$$\iint\limits_R f(x, y)\, dA = \int_a^b \int_{g(x)}^{h(x)} f(x, y)\, dy\, dx.$$

Let R be a region bounded on the left and right by the graphs of the continuous functions $x = g(y)$ and $x = h(y)$, respectively, and the lines $y = c$ and $y = d$ (Figure 14.15). If f is continuous on R, then

$$\iint\limits_R f(x, y)\, dA = \int_c^d \int_{g(y)}^{h(y)} f(x, y)\, dx\, dy.$$

EXAMPLE 2   Computing a volume Find the volume of the solid below the surface $f(x, y) = 2 + \dfrac{1}{y}$ and above the region R in the xy-plane bounded by the lines $y = x$, $y = 8 - x$, and $y = 1$. Notice that $f(x, y) > 0$ on R.

SOLUTION The region R is bounded on the left by $x = y$ and bounded on the right by $y = 8 - x$, or $x = 8 - y$ (Figure 14.16). These lines intersect at the point $(4, 4)$. We take vertical slices through the solid parallel to the x-axis from $y = 1$ to $y = 4$. (To visualize these slices, it helps to draw lines through R parallel to the x-axis.)

Integrating the cross-sectional areas of slices from $y = 1$ to $y = 4$, the volume of the solid beneath the graph of f and above R (Figure 14.17) is given by

$$\iint\limits_R \left(2 + \frac{1}{y}\right) dA = \int_1^4 \int_y^{8-y} \left(2 + \frac{1}{y}\right) dx\, dy \quad \text{Convert to an iterated integral.}$$

$$= \int_1^4 \left(2 + \frac{1}{y}\right) x \Big|_y^{8-y} dy \quad \begin{array}{l}\text{Evaluate the inner integral;}\\ 2 + \frac{1}{y} \text{ is constant.}\end{array}$$

$$= \int_1^4 \left(2 + \frac{1}{y}\right)(8 - 2y)\, dy \quad \text{Simplify.}$$

$$= \int_1^4 \left(14 - 4y + \frac{8}{y}\right) dy \quad \text{Simplify.}$$

$$= \left(14y - 2y^2 + 8 \ln |y|\right) \Big|_1^4 \quad \text{Evaluate the outer integral.}$$

$$= 12 + 8 \ln 4 \approx 23.09. \quad \text{Simplify.}$$

Related Exercises 31–52 ◀

QUICK CHECK 2 Could the integral in Example 2 be evaluated by integrating first (inner integral) with respect to y? ◀

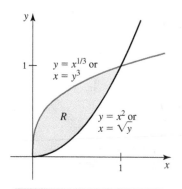

$y = x^{1/3}$ or
$x = y^3$

R

$y = x^2$ or
$x = \sqrt{y}$

R is bounded above and below,
and on the right and left by curves.

FIGURE 14.18

➤ In this case, it is just as easy to view R as
being bounded on the left and the right
by the lines $x = 0$ and $x = c/a - by/a$,
respectively, and integrating first with
respect to x.

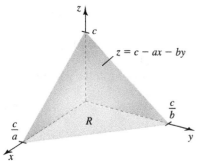

c

$z = c - ax - by$

$\dfrac{c}{b}$

$\dfrac{c}{a}$ R

x y

FIGURE 14.19

➤ The volume of *any* tetrahedron is
$\frac{1}{3}$(area of base)(height), where any
of the faces may be chosen as the base
(Exercise 98).

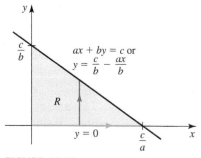

$\dfrac{c}{b}$

$ax + by = c$ or
$y = \dfrac{c}{b} - \dfrac{ax}{b}$

R

$y = 0$ $\dfrac{c}{a}$ x

FIGURE 14.20

Choosing and Changing the Order of Integration

Occasionally a region of integration is bounded above and below, *and* on the right and the left, by curves (Figure 14.18). In these cases, we can choose either of two orders of integration; however, one order of integration may be preferable. The following examples illustrate the valuable techniques of choosing and changing the order of integration.

EXAMPLE 3   Volume of a tetrahedron Find the volume of the tetrahedron (pyramid with four triangular faces) in the first octant bounded by the plane $z = c - ax - by$ and the coordinate planes ($x = 0, y = 0, z = 0$). Assume a, b, and c are positive real numbers (Figure 14.19).

SOLUTION Let R be the triangular base of the tetrahedron in the xy-plane; it is formed by the x- and y-axes and the line $ax + by = c$ (found by setting $z = 0$ in the equation of the plane; Figure 14.20). We can view R as being bounded below and above by the lines $y = 0$ and $y = c/b - ax/b$, respectively. The boundaries on the left and right are then $x = 0$ and $x = c/a$, respectively. Therefore, the volume of the solid region between the plane and R is

$$\iint\limits_{R} (c - ax - by)\, dA = \int_0^{c/a} \int_0^{c/b - ax/b} (c - ax - by)\, dy\, dx \qquad \text{Convert to an iterated integral.}$$

$$= \int_0^{c/a} \left(cy - axy - \frac{by^2}{2} \right) \Bigg|_0^{c/b - ax/b} dx \qquad \text{Evaluate the inner integral.}$$

$$= \int_0^{c/a} \frac{(ax - c)^2}{2b}\, dx \qquad \text{Simplify and factor.}$$

$$= \frac{c^3}{6ab}. \qquad \text{Evaluate the outer integral.}$$

This result illustrates the volume formula for a tetrahedron. The lengths of the legs of the triangular base are c/a and c/b, which means the area of the base is $c^2/(2ab)$. The height of the tetrahedron is c. The general volume formula is

$$V = \frac{c^3}{6ab} = \frac{1}{3} \underbrace{\frac{c^2}{2ab}}_{\substack{\text{area of}\\ \text{base}}} \cdot \underbrace{c}_{\text{height}} = \frac{1}{3}(\text{area of base})(\text{height}).$$

Related Exercises 53–56 ◄

EXAMPLE 4   Changing the order of integration Sketch the region of integration and evaluate $\int_0^{\sqrt{\pi}} \int_y^{\sqrt{\pi}} \sin x^2\, dx\, dy$.

SOLUTION The region of integration is $R = \{ (x, y): y \le x \le \sqrt{\pi}, 0 \le y \le \sqrt{\pi} \}$, which is a triangle (Figure 14.21a). Evaluating the iterated integral as given (integrating first with respect to x) requires integrating $\sin x^2$, a function whose antiderivative is not expressible in terms of elementary functions. Therefore, this order of integration is not feasible.

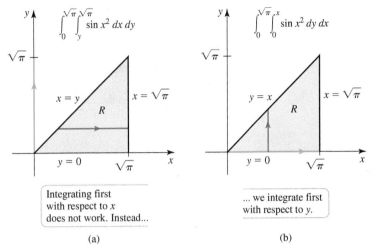

FIGURE 14.21

Instead, we change our perspective (Figure 14.21b) and integrate first with respect to y. With this order of integration, y runs from $y = 0$ to $y = x$ in the inner integral and x runs from $x = 0$ to $x = \sqrt{\pi}$ in the outer integral:

$$\iint_R \sin x^2 \, dA = \int_0^{\sqrt{\pi}} \int_0^x \sin x^2 \, dy \, dx$$

$$= \int_0^{\sqrt{\pi}} (y \sin x^2) \Big|_0^x \, dx \qquad \text{Evaluate the inner integral;} \\ \qquad \qquad \qquad \qquad \qquad \qquad \sin x^2 \text{ is constant.}$$

$$= \int_0^{\sqrt{\pi}} x \sin x^2 \, dx \qquad \text{Simplify.}$$

$$= \left(-\frac{1}{2} \cos x^2 \right) \Big|_0^{\sqrt{\pi}} \qquad \text{Evaluate the outer integral.}$$

$$= 1. \qquad \text{Simplify.}$$

This example shows that the order of integration can make a practical difference.

Related Exercises 57–68 ◄

QUICK CHECK 3 Change the order of integration of the integral $\int_0^1 \int_0^y f(x, y) \, dx \, dy$. ◄

Regions Between Two Surfaces

An extension of the preceding ideas allows us to solve more general volume problems. Let $z = g(x, y)$ and $z = f(x, y)$ be continuous functions with $g(x, y) \geq f(x, y)$ on a region R in the xy-plane. Suppose we wish to compute the volume of the solid between the two surfaces over the region R (Figure 14.22). Forming a Riemann sum for the volume, the height of a typical box within the solid is the vertical distance $g(x, y) - f(x, y)$ between the upper and lower surfaces. Therefore, the volume of the solid between the surfaces is

$$V = \iint_R (g(x, y) - f(x, y)) \, dA.$$

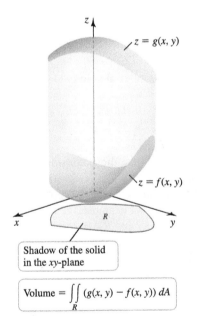

Shadow of the solid in the xy-plane

Volume $= \iint_R (g(x, y) - f(x, y)) \, dA$

FIGURE 14.22

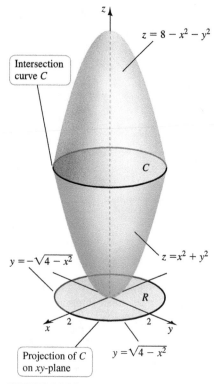

Intersection curve C

$z = 8 - x^2 - y^2$

C

$y = -\sqrt{4 - x^2}$

$z = x^2 + y^2$

R

2   2

$y = \sqrt{4 - x^2}$

Projection of C on xy-plane

FIGURE 14.23

> To use symmetry to simplify a double integral, you must check that both the region of integration and the integrand have the same symmetry.

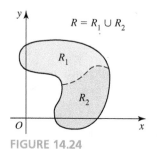

$R = R_1 \cup R_2$

R_1

R_2

FIGURE 14.24

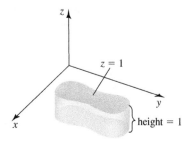

$z = 1$

height = 1

Volume of solid = (Area of R) × (height)

= Area of R = $\iint\limits_{R} 1 \, dA$

FIGURE 14.25

EXAMPLE 5 **Region bounded by two surfaces** Find the volume of the solid region bounded by the paraboloids $z = x^2 + y^2$ and $z = 8 - x^2 - y^2$ (Figure 14.23).

SOLUTION The upper surface bounding the solid is $z = 8 - x^2 - y^2$ and the lower surface is $z = x^2 + y^2$. The two surfaces intersect along a curve C. Solving $8 - x^2 - y^2 = x^2 + y^2$, we find that $x^2 + y^2 = 4$. This circle of radius 2 is the projection of C onto the xy-plane (Figure 14.23); it is also the boundary of the region of integration

$$R = \{(x, y): -\sqrt{4 - x^2} \le y \le \sqrt{4 - x^2}, -2 \le x \le 2\}.$$

Notice that R and the solid are symmetric about the x- and y-axes. Therefore, the volume of the entire solid is four times the volume over that part of R in the first quadrant. The volume of the solid is

$$4 \int_0^2 \int_0^{\sqrt{4-x^2}} (\underbrace{(8 - x^2 - y^2)}_{g(x, y)} - \underbrace{(x^2 + y^2)}_{f(x, y)}) \, dy \, dx$$

$$= 8 \int_0^2 \int_0^{\sqrt{4-x^2}} (4 - x^2 - y^2) \, dy \, dx \quad \text{Simplify the integrand.}$$

$$= 8 \int_0^2 \left((4 - x^2)y - \frac{y^3}{3}\right)\Big|_0^{\sqrt{4-x^2}} dx \quad \text{Fundamental Theorem of Calculus}$$

$$= \frac{16}{3} \int_0^2 (4 - x^2)^{3/2} \, dx \quad \text{Simplify.}$$

$$= \frac{256}{3} \int_0^{\pi/2} \cos^4 \theta \, d\theta \quad \text{Trigonometric substitution: } x = 2 \sin \theta$$

$$= 16\pi. \quad \text{Evaluate the outer integral.}$$

We return to this calculation in Section 14.3 and show how it is simplified in polar coordinates.

Related Exercises 69–74 ◄

Decomposition of Regions

We occasionally encounter regions that are more complicated than those considered so far. A technique called *decomposition* allows us to subdivide a region of integration into two (or more) subregions. If the integrals over the subregions can be evaluated separately, the results are added to obtain the value of the original integral. For example, the region R in Figure 14.24 is divided into two nonoverlapping subregions R_1 and R_2. By partitioning these regions and using Riemann sums, it can be shown that

$$\iint\limits_{R} f(x, y) \, dA = \iint\limits_{R_1} f(x, y) \, dA + \iint\limits_{R_2} f(x, y) \, dA.$$

This method is illustrated in Example 6. The analogue of decomposition with single variable integrals is the property $\int_a^b f(x) \, dx = \int_a^c f(x) \, dx + \int_c^b f(x) \, dx$.

Finding Area by Double Integrals

An interesting application of double integrals arises when the integrand is $f(x, y) = 1$. The integral $\iint\limits_{R} 1 \, dA$ gives the volume of the solid between the horizontal plane $z = 1$ and the region R. Because the height of this solid is 1, its volume equals (numerically) the area of R (Figure 14.25). Therefore, we have a way to compute areas of regions in the xy-plane using double integrals.

> We are solving a familiar area problem first encountered in Section 6.2. Suppose R is bounded above by $y = h(x)$ and below by $y = g(x)$, for $a \le x \le b$. Using a double integral, the area of R is

$$\iint_R dA = \int_a^b \int_{g(x)}^{h(x)} dy\, dx$$

$$= \int_a^b (h(x) - g(x))\, dx,$$

which is a result obtained in Section 6.2.

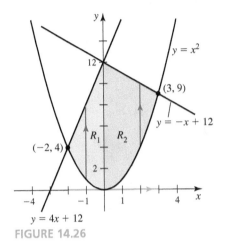

FIGURE 14.26

Areas of Regions by Double Integrals

Let R be a region in the xy-plane. Then

$$\text{area of } R = \iint_R dA.$$

EXAMPLE 6 Area of a plane region Find the area of the region R bounded by $y = x^2$, $y = -x + 12$, and $y = 4x + 12$ (Figure 14.26).

SOLUTION The region R in its entirety is bounded neither above and below by two curves, nor on the left and right by two curves. However, when decomposed along the y-axis, R may be viewed as two regions R_1 and R_2 each of which is bounded above and below by a pair of curves. Notice that the parabola $y = x^2$ and the line $y = -x + 12$ intersect in the first quadrant at the point $(3, 9)$, while the parabola and the line $y = 4x + 12$ intersect in the second quadrant at the point $(-2, 4)$.

To find the area of R, we integrate the function $f(x, y) = 1$ over R_1 and R_2; the area is

$$\iint_{R_1} 1\, dA + \iint_{R_2} 1\, dA \qquad \text{Decompose region.}$$

$$= \int_{-2}^0 \int_{x^2}^{4x+12} 1\, dy\, dx + \int_0^3 \int_{x^2}^{-x+12} 1\, dy\, dx \qquad \text{Convert to iterated integrals.}$$

$$= \int_{-2}^0 (4x + 12 - x^2)\, dx + \int_0^3 (-x + 12 - x^2)\, dx \qquad \text{Evaluate the inner integrals.}$$

$$= \left(2x^2 + 12x - \frac{x^3}{3}\right)\Big|_{-2}^0 + \left(-\frac{x^2}{2} + 12x - \frac{x^3}{3}\right)\Big|_0^3 \qquad \text{Evaluate the outer integrals.}$$

$$= \frac{40}{3} + \frac{45}{2} = \frac{215}{6}. \qquad \text{Simplify.}$$

Related Exercises 75–80 ◄

QUICK CHECK 4 Consider the triangle R with vertices $(-1, 0)$, $(1, 0)$, and $(0, 1)$ as a region of integration. If we integrate first with respect to x, does R need to be subdivided? If we integrate first with respect to y, does R need to be subdivided? ◄

SECTION 14.2 EXERCISES

Review Questions

1. Describe and sketch a region that is bounded above and below by two curves.

2. Describe and a sketch a region that is bounded on the left and on the right by two curves.

3. Which order of integration is preferable to integrate $f(x, y) = xy$ over $R = \{(x, y): y - 1 \le x \le 1 - y, 0 \le y \le 1\}$?

4. Which order of integration would you use to find the area of the region bounded by the x-axis and the lines $y = 2x + 3$ and $y = 3x - 4$ using a double integral?

5. Change the order of integration in the integral $\int_0^1 \int_{y^2}^{\sqrt{y}} f(x, y)\, dx\, dy$.

6. Sketch the region of integration for $\int_{-2}^2 \int_{x^2}^4 e^{xy}\, dy\, dx$.

7–8. Regions of integration *Consider the regions R shown in the figures and write an iterated integral of a continuous function f over R.*

7.

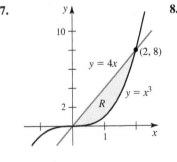

8.

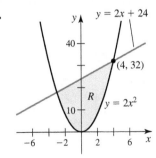

9–16. Regions of integration *Sketch the following regions and write an iterated integral of a continuous function f over the region. Use the order dy dx.*

9. $R = \{(x, y): 0 \le x \le \pi/4, \sin x \le y \le \cos x\}$

10. $R = \{(x, y): 0 \le x \le 2, 3x^2 \le y \le -6x + 24\}$

11. $R = \{(x, y): 1 \le x \le 2, x + 1 \le y \le 2x + 4\}$

12. $R = \{(x, y): 0 \le x \le 4, x^2 \le y \le 8\sqrt{x}\}$

13. R is the triangular region with vertices $(0, 0)$, $(0, 2)$, and $(1, 0)$.

14. R is the triangular region with vertices $(0, 0)$, $(0, 2)$, and $(1, 1)$.

15. R is the region in the first quadrant bounded by a circle of radius 1 centered at the origin.

16. R is the region in the first quadrant bounded by the y-axis and the parabolas $y = x^2$ and $y = 1 - x^2$.

17–26. Evaluating integrals *Evaluate the following integrals as they are written.*

17. $\displaystyle\int_0^1 \int_x^1 6y \, dy \, dx$

18. $\displaystyle\int_0^1 \int_0^{2x} 15xy^2 \, dy \, dx$

19. $\displaystyle\int_0^2 \int_{x^2}^{2x} xy \, dy \, dx$

20. $\displaystyle\int_0^3 \int_{x^2}^{x+6} (x - 1) \, dy \, dx$

21. $\displaystyle\int_{-\pi/4}^{\pi/4} \int_{\sin x}^{\cos x} dy \, dx$

22. $\displaystyle\int_0^1 \int_{-\sqrt{1-x^2}}^{\sqrt{1-x^2}} 2x^2 y \, dy \, dx$

23. $\displaystyle\int_{-2}^2 \int_{x^2}^{8-x^2} x \, dy \, dx$

24. $\displaystyle\int_0^{\ln 2} \int_{e^x}^2 dy \, dx$

25. $\displaystyle\int_0^1 \int_0^x 2e^{x^2} dy \, dx$

26. $\displaystyle\int_0^{\sqrt[3]{\pi/2}} \int_0^x y \cos x^3 \, dy \, dx$

27–30. Evaluating integrals *Evaluate the following integrals.*

27. $\iint_R xy \, dA$; R is bounded by $x = 0$, $y = 2x + 1$, and $y = -2x + 5$.

28. $\iint_R (x + y) \, dA$; R is the region in the first quadrant bounded by $x = 0$, $y = x^2$, and $y = 8 - x^2$.

29. $\iint_R y^2 \, dA$; R is bounded by $x = 1$, $y = 2x + 2$, and $y = -x - 1$.

30. $\iint_R x^2 y \, dA$; R is the region in quadrants 1 and 4 bounded by the semicircle of radius 4 centered at $(0, 0)$.

31–32. Regions of integration *Write an iterated integral of a continuous function f over the region R shown in the figure.*

31.
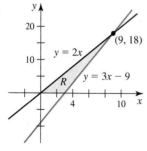

32.
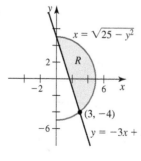

33–38. Regions of integration *Write an iterated integral of a continuous function f over the following regions.*

33. The region bounded by $y = 2x + 3$, $y = 3x - 7$, and $y = 0$

34. $R = \{(x, y): 0 \le x \le y(1 - y)\}$

35. The region bounded by $y = 4 - x$, $y = 1$, and $x = 0$

36. The region in quadrants 2 and 3 bounded by the semicircle with radius 3 centered at $(0, 0)$

37. The region bounded by the triangle with vertices $(0, 0)$, $(2, 0)$, and $(1, 1)$

38. The region in the first quadrant bounded by the x-axis, the line $x = 6 - y$, and the curve $y = \sqrt{x}$

39–46. Evaluating integrals *Sketch the region of integration and evaluate the following integrals as they are written.*

39. $\displaystyle\int_{-1}^2 \int_y^{4-y} dx \, dy$

40. $\displaystyle\int_0^2 \int_0^{4-y^2} y \, dx \, dy$

41. $\displaystyle\int_0^4 \int_{-\sqrt{16-y^2}}^{\sqrt{16-y^2}} 2xy \, dx \, dy$

42. $\displaystyle\int_0^1 \int_{-2\sqrt{1-y^2}}^{2\sqrt{1-y^2}} 2x \, dx \, dy$

43. $\displaystyle\int_0^{\ln 2} \int_{e^y}^2 \frac{y}{x} \, dx \, dy$

44. $\displaystyle\int_0^4 \int_y^{2y} xy \, dx \, dy$

45. $\displaystyle\int_0^{\pi/2} \int_y^{\pi/2} 6 \sin (2x - 3y) \, dx \, dy$

46. $\displaystyle\int_0^{\pi/2} \int_0^{\cos y} e^{\sin y} \, dx \, dy$

47–52. Evaluating integrals *Sketch the regions of integration and evaluate the following integrals.*

47. $\iint_R 12y \, dA$; R is bounded by $y = 2 - x$, $y = \sqrt{x}$, and $y = 0$.

48. $\iint_R y^2 \, dA$; R is bounded by $y = 1$, $y = 1 - x$, and $y = x - 1$.

49. $\iint_R 3xy \, dA$; R is bounded by $y = 2 - x$, $y = 0$, and $x = 4 - y^2$ in the first quadrant.

50. $\iint_R (x + y) \, dA$; R is bounded by $y = |x|$ and $y = 4$.

51. $\iint_R 3x^2 \, dA$; R is bounded by $y = 0$, $y = 2x + 4$, and $y = x^3$.

52. $\iint_R x^2 y \, dA$; R is bounded by $y = 0$, $y = \sqrt{x}$, and $y = x - 2$.

53–56. Volumes *Use double integrals to calculate the volume of the following regions.*

53. The tetrahedron bounded by the coordinate planes $(x = 0, y = 0, z = 0)$ and the plane $z = 8 - 2x - 4y$

54. The solid in the first octant bounded by the coordinate planes and the surface $z = 1 - y - x^2$

55. The segment of the cylinder $x^2 + y^2 = 1$ bounded above by the plane $z = 12 + x + y$ and below by $z = 0$

56. The solid beneath the cylinder $z = y^2$ and above the region $R = \{(x, y): 0 \le y \le 1, y \le x \le 1\}$

57–62. Changing order of integration *Reverse the order of integration in the following integrals.*

57. $\int_0^2 \int_{x^2}^{2x} f(x, y)\, dy\, dx$

58. $\int_0^3 \int_0^{6-2x} f(x, y)\, dy\, dx$

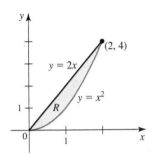

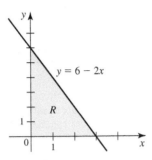

59. $\int_{1/2}^1 \int_0^{-\ln y} f(x, y)\, dx\, dy$

60. $\int_0^1 \int_1^{e^y} f(x, y)\, dx\, dy$

61. $\int_0^1 \int_0^{\cos^{-1} y} f(x, y)\, dx\, dy$

62. $\int_1^e \int_0^{\ln x} f(x, y)\, dy\, dx$

63–68. Changing order of integration *The following integrals can be evaluated only by reversing the order of integration. Sketch the region of integration, reverse the order of integration, and evaluate the integral.*

63. $\int_0^1 \int_y^1 e^{x^2}\, dx\, dy$

64. $\int_0^\pi \int_x^\pi \sin y^2\, dy\, dx$

65. $\int_0^{1/2} \int_{y^2}^{1/4} y \cos(16\pi x^2)\, dx\, dy$

66. $\int_0^4 \int_{\sqrt{x}}^2 \frac{x}{y^5 + 1}\, dy\, dx$

67. $\int_0^{\sqrt{\pi}} \int_y^{\sqrt{\pi}} x^4 \cos(x^2 y)\, dx\, dy$

68. $\int_0^2 \int_0^{4-x^2} \frac{xe^{2y}}{4 - y}\, dy\, dx$

69–74. Regions between surfaces *Find the volume of the following solid regions.*

69. The solid above the region
$R = \{(x, y): 0 \le x \le 1,$
$0 \le y \le 1 - x\}$
bounded by the parabo-
loids $z = x^2 + y^2$ and
$z = 2 - x^2 - y^2$ and the
coordinate planes in the
first octant

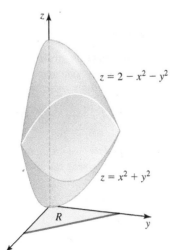

70. The solid above the
parabolic region
$R = \{(x, y): 0 \le x \le 1,$
$0 \le y \le 1 - x^2\}$ and
between the planes $z = 1$
and $z = 2 - y$

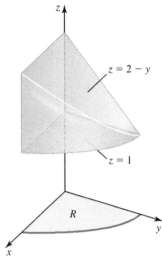

71. The solid bounded by the paraboloid $z = x^2 + y^2$ and the plane
$z = 9$

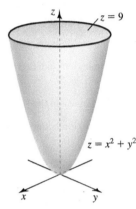

72. The solid bounded by the paraboloids $z = x^2 + y^2$ and
$z = 50 - x^2 - y^2$

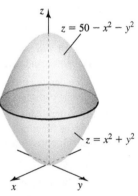

73. The solid above the region
$R = \{(x, y): 0 \le x \le 1,$
$0 \le y \le 2 - x\}$ and between
the planes $-4x - 4y + z = 0$
and $-2x - y + z = 8$

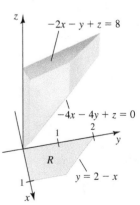

74. The solid S between the surfaces $z = e^{x-y}$ and $z = -e^{x-y}$, where S intersects the xy-plane in the region $R = \{(x, y): 0 \le x \le y, 0 \le y \le 1\}$

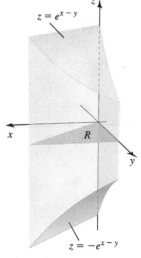

75–80. Area of plane regions *Use a double integral to compute the area of the following regions. Make a sketch of the region.*

75. The region bounded by the parabola $y = x^2$ and the line $y = 4$

76. The region bounded by the parabola $y = x^2$ and the line $y = x + 2$

77. The region in the first quadrant bounded by $y = e^x$ and $x = \ln 2$

78. The region bounded by $y = 1 + \sin x$ and $y = 1 - \sin x$ on the interval $[0, \pi]$

79. The region in the first quadrant bounded by $y = x^2$, $y = 5x + 6$, and $y = 6 - x$

80. The region bounded by the lines $x = 0$, $x = 4$, $y = x$, and $y = 2x + 1$

Further Explorations

81. Explain why or why not Determine whether the following statements are true and give an explanation or counterexample.

    a. In the iterated integral $\int_c^d \int_a^b f(x, y) \, dx \, dy$, the limits a and b must be constants or functions of x.

    b. In the iterated integral $\int_c^d \int_a^b f(x, y) \, dx \, dy$, the limits c and d must be functions of y.

    c. Changing the order of integration gives $\int_0^2 \int_1^y f(x, y) \, dx \, dy = \int_1^y \int_0^2 f(x, y) \, dy \, dx$.

82–85. Miscellaneous integrals *Evaluate the following integrals.*

82. $\displaystyle\iint\limits_R y \, dA; \quad R = \{(x, y): 0 \le y \le \sec x, 0 \le x \le \pi/3\}$

83. $\displaystyle\iint\limits_R (x + y) \, dA; \quad R$ is the region bounded by $y = 1/x$ and $y = 5/2 - x$.

84. $\displaystyle\iint\limits_R \frac{xy}{1 + x^2 + y^2} \, dA; \quad R = \{(x, y): 0 \le y \le x, 0 \le x \le 2\}$

85. $\displaystyle\iint\limits_R x \sec^2 y \, dA; \quad R = \{(x, y): 0 \le y \le x^2, 0 \le x \le \sqrt{\pi}/2\}$

86. Paraboloid sliced by plane Find the volume of the solid between the paraboloid $z = x^2 + y^2$ and the plane $z = 1 - 2y$.

87. Two integrals to one Draw the regions of integration and write the following integrals as a single iterated integral:

$$\int_0^1 \int_{e^y}^e f(x, y) \, dx \, dy + \int_{-1}^0 \int_{e^{-y}}^e f(x, y) \, dx \, dy.$$

88. Diamond region Consider the region $R = \{(x, y): |x| + |y| \le 1\}$ shown in the figure.

    a. Use a double integral to show that the area of R is 2.

    b. Find the volume of the square column whose base is R and whose upper surface is $z = 12 - 3x - 4y$.

    c. Find the volume of the solid above R and beneath the cylinder $x^2 + z^2 = 1$.

    d. Find the volume of the pyramid whose base is R and whose vertex is on the z-axis at $(0, 0, 6)$.

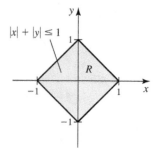

89–90. Average value *Use the definition for the average value of a function over a region R (Section 14.1),* $\overline{f} = \dfrac{1}{\text{area of } R} \displaystyle\iint\limits_R f(x, y) \, dA.$

89. Find the average value of $a - x - y$ over the region $R = \{(x, y): x + y \le a, x \ge 0, y \ge 0\}$, where $a > 0$.

90. Find the average value of $z = a^2 - x^2 - y^2$ over the region $R = \{(x, y): x^2 + y^2 \le a^2\}$, where $a > 0$.

91–92. Area integrals *Consider the following regions R.*
a. Sketch the region R.
b. Evaluate $\iint_R dA$ to determine the area of the region.
c. Evaluate $\iint_R xy \, dA$.

91. R is the region between both branches of $y = 1/x$ and the lines $y = x + 3/2$ and $y = x - 3/2$.

92. R is the region bounded by the ellipse $x^2/18 + y^2/36 = 1$ with $y \le 4x/3$.

93–96. Improper integrals *Many improper double integrals may be handled using the techniques for improper integrals in one variable (Section 7.8). For example, under suitable conditions on f,*

$$\int_a^\infty \int_{g(x)}^{h(x)} f(x, y) \, dy \, dx = \lim_{b \to \infty} \int_a^b \int_{g(x)}^{h(x)} f(x, y) \, dy \, dx.$$

Use or extend the one-variable methods for improper integrals to evaluate the following integrals.

93. $\displaystyle\int_1^\infty \int_0^{e^{-x}} xy \, dy \, dx$

94. $\displaystyle\int_1^\infty \int_0^{1/x^2} \frac{2y}{x} \, dy \, dx$

95. $\displaystyle\int_0^\infty \int_0^\infty e^{-x-y}\, dy\, dx$

96. $\displaystyle\int_{-\infty}^\infty \int_{-\infty}^\infty \frac{1}{(x^2+1)(y^2+1)}\, dy\, dx$

97–101. Volumes *Compute the volume of the following solids.*

97. Sliced block The solid bounded by the planes $x = 0$, $x = 5$, $z = y - 1$, $z = -2y - 1$, $z = 0$, and $z = 2$

98. Tetrahedron A tetrahedron with vertices $(0, 0, 0)$, $(a, 0, 0)$, $(b, c, 0)$, and $(0, 0, d)$, where a, b, c, and d are positive real numbers

99. Square column The column with a square base $R = \{(x, y): |x| \le 1, |y| \le 1\}$ cut by the plane $z = 4 - x - y$

100. Wedge The wedge sliced from the cylinder $x^2 + y^2 = 1$ by the planes $z = 1 - x$ and $z = x - 1$

101. Wedge The wedge sliced from the cylinder $x^2 + y^2 = 1$ by the planes $z = a(2 - x)$ and $z = a(x - 2)$, where $a > 0$

Additional Exercises

102. Existence of improper double integral For what values of m and n does the integral $\displaystyle\int_1^\infty \int_0^{1/x} \frac{y^m}{x^n}\, dy\, dx$ have a finite value?

103. Existence of improper double integral Let
$R_1 = \{(x, y): x \ge 1, 1 \le y \le 2\}$ and
$R_2 = \{(x, y): 1 \le x \le 2, y \ge 1\}$. For $n > 1$, which integral(s) have finite values: $\iint_{R_1} x^{-n}\, dA$ or $\iint_{R_2} x^{-n}\, dA$?

QUICK CHECK ANSWERS

1. Inner integral: $0 \le y \le 2 - x$; outer integral: $0 \le x \le 2$
2. Yes; however, two separate iterated integrals would be required.   **3.** $\int_0^1 \int_x^1 f(x, y)\, dy\, dx$ **4.** No; yes

14.3 Double Integrals in Polar Coordinates

> Recall the conversions from Cartesian to polar coordinates (Section 11.2):
>
> $x = r \cos\theta$, $y = r \sin\theta$, or
> $r^2 = x^2 + y^2$, $\tan\theta = y/x$.

In Chapter 11 we explored polar coordinates and saw that in certain situations they simplify problems considerably. The same is true when it comes to integration over plane regions. In this section, we learn how to formulate double integrals in polar coordinates and how to change double integrals from Cartesian coordinates to polar coordinates.

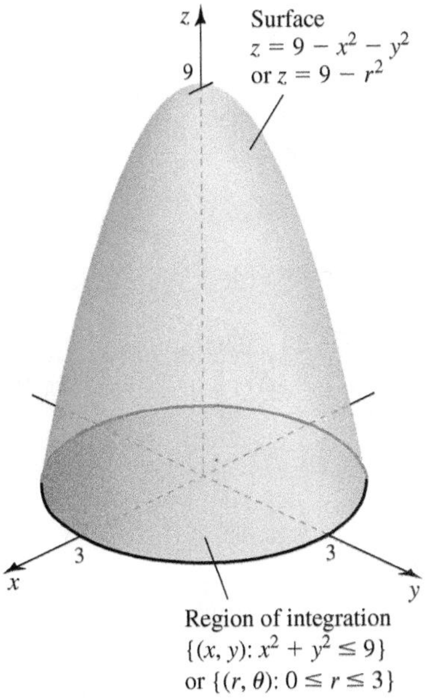

Polar Rectangular Regions

Suppose we want to find the volume of the solid bounded by the paraboloid $z = 9 - x^2 - y^2$ and the xy-plane (Figure 14.27). The intersection of the paraboloid and the xy-plane ($z = 0$) is the curve $9 - x^2 - y^2 = 0$, or $x^2 + y^2 = 9$. Therefore, the region of integration is the disk of radius 3 centered at the origin in the xy-plane. If we use the relationship $r^2 = x^2 + y^2$ for converting Cartesian to polar coordinates, the region of integration is simply $\{(r, \theta): 0 \le r \le 3\}$. Furthermore, the paraboloid is expressed in polar coordinates as $z = 9 - r^2$. This problem (which is solved in Example 1) illustrates how both the integrand and the region of integration in a double integral can be simplified by working in polar coordinates.

The region of integration in this problem is an example of a **polar rectangle**. It has the form $R = \{(r, \theta): 0 \le a \le r \le b, \alpha \le \theta \le \beta\}$, where $\beta - \alpha \le 2\pi$ and a, b, α, and β are constants (Figure 14.28). Polar rectangles are the analogs of rectangles in Cartesian coordinates. For this reason, the methods used in Section 14.1 for evaluating double integrals over rectangles can be extended to polar rectangles. The goal is to evaluate integrals of the form $\iint_R f(r, \theta)\, dA$, where f is a continuous function of r and θ, and R is a polar rectangle. If f is nonnegative on R, this integral equals the volume of the solid bounded by the surface $z = f(r, \theta)$ and the region R in the xy-plane.

Surface
$z = 9 - x^2 - y^2$
or $z = 9 - r^2$

Region of integration
$\{(x, y): x^2 + y^2 \le 9\}$
or $\{(r, \theta): 0 \le r \le 3\}$

FIGURE 14.27

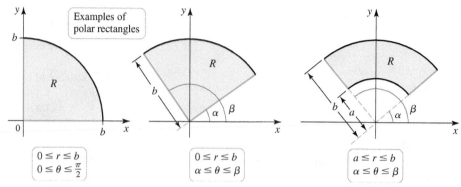

FIGURE 14.28

$$R = \{(r, \theta): a \le r \le b, \alpha \le \theta \le \beta\}$$

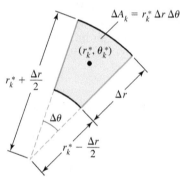

FIGURE 14.29

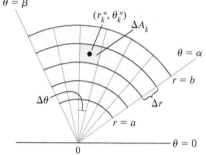

FIGURE 14.30

▶ Recall that the area of a sector of a circle of radius r subtended by an angle θ is $\frac{1}{2}r^2\theta$.

Our approach is to divide $[a, b]$ into M subintervals of equal length $\Delta r = (b - a)/M$. We similarly divide $[\alpha, \beta]$ into m subintervals of equal length $\Delta\theta = (\beta - \alpha)/m$. Now look at the arcs of the circles centered at the origin with radii

$$r = a, r = a + \Delta r, r = a + 2\Delta r, \ldots, r = b$$

and the rays

$$\theta = \alpha, \theta = \alpha + \Delta\theta, \theta = \alpha + 2\Delta\theta, \ldots, \theta = \beta$$

emanating from the origin (Figure 14.29). These arcs and rays divide the region R into $n = Mm$ polar rectangles that we number in a convenient way from $k = 1$ to $k = n$. The area of the kth rectangle is denoted ΔA_k, and we let (r_k^*, θ_k^*) be an arbitrary point in that rectangle.

Consider the "box" whose base is the kth polar rectangle and whose height is $f(r_k^*, \theta_k^*)$; its volume is $f(r_k^*, \theta_k^*)\,\Delta A_k$, for $k = 1, \ldots, n$. Therefore, the volume of the solid region beneath the surface $z = f(r, \theta)$ with a base R is approximately

$$V \approx \sum_{k=1}^{n} f(r_k^*, \theta_k^*)\Delta A_k.$$

This approximation to the volume is another Riemann sum. We let Δ be the maximum value of Δr and $\Delta\theta$. If f is continuous on R, then as $\Delta \to 0$, the sum approaches a double integral; that is,

$$\iint\limits_{R} f(r, \theta)\, dA = \lim_{\Delta \to 0} \sum_{k=1}^{n} f(r_k^*, \theta_k^*)\Delta A_k.$$

The next step is to write the double integral as an iterated integral. In order to do so, we must express ΔA_k in terms of Δr and $\Delta\theta$.

Figure 14.30 shows the kth polar rectangle, with an area ΔA_k. The point (r_k^*, θ_k^*) is chosen so that the outer arc of the polar rectangle has radius $r_k^* + \Delta r/2$ and the inner arc has radius $r_k^* - \Delta r/2$. The area of the polar rectangle is

$$\Delta A_k = (\text{area of outer sector}) - (\text{area of inner sector})$$

$$= \frac{1}{2}\left(r_k^* + \frac{\Delta r}{2}\right)^2 \Delta\theta - \frac{1}{2}\left(r_k^* - \frac{\Delta r}{2}\right)^2 \Delta\theta \qquad \text{Area of sector} = \frac{r^2}{2}\Delta\theta$$

$$= r_k^* \Delta r \Delta\theta. \qquad \text{Expand and simplify.}$$

Substituting this expression for ΔA_k into the Riemann sum, we have

$$\sum_{k=1}^{n} f(r_k^*, \theta_k^*)\Delta A_k = \sum_{k=1}^{n} f(r_k^*, \theta_k^*)\, r_k^* \Delta r \Delta\theta.$$

This observation leads to another version of Fubini's Theorem, which is needed to write the double integral as an iterated integral; the proof is found in advanced texts.

▷ The most common error in evaluating integrals in polar coordinates is to omit the factor of r that appears in the integrand. In Cartesian coordinates the element of area is $dx\,dy$; in polar coordinates, the element of area is $r\,dr\,d\theta$, and without the factor of r, area is not measured correctly.

> **THEOREM 14.3   Double Integrals over Polar Rectangular Regions**
> Let f be continuous on the region in the xy-plane $R = \{(r, \theta): 0 \leq a \leq r \leq b, \alpha \leq \theta \leq \beta\}$, where $\beta - \alpha \leq 2\pi$. Then
> $$\iint_R f(r, \theta)\, dA = \int_\alpha^\beta \int_a^b f(r, \theta)\, r\, dr\, d\theta.$$

QUICK CHECK 1 Describe in polar coordinates the region in the first quadrant between the circles of radius 1 and 2. ◁

Frequently, an integral $\iint_R f(x, y)\, dA$ is given in Cartesian coordinates, but the region of integration is easier to handle in polar coordinates. By using the relations $x = r\cos\theta$, $y = r\sin\theta$, and $x^2 + y^2 = r^2$, the function $f(x, y)$ can be expressed in polar form as $f(r\cos\theta, r\sin\theta)$. This procedure is a change of variables in two variables.

EXAMPLE 1   Volume of a paraboloid cap Find the volume of the solid bounded by the paraboloid $z = 9 - x^2 - y^2$ and the xy-plane.

SOLUTION Using $x^2 + y^2 = r^2$, the surface is described in polar coordinates by $z = 9 - r^2$. The paraboloid intersects the xy-plane ($z = 0$) when $z = 9 - r^2 = 0$, or $r = 3$. Therefore, the intersection curve is the circle of radius 3 centered at the origin. The resulting region of integration is the disk $R = \{(r, \theta): 0 \leq r \leq 3, 0 \leq \theta \leq 2\pi\}$ (Figure 14.31). Integrating over R in polar coordinates, the volume is

$$V = \int_0^{2\pi} \int_0^3 \underbrace{(9 - r^2)}_{z}\, r\, dr\, d\theta \qquad \text{Iterated integral for volume}$$

$$= \int_0^{2\pi} \left(\frac{9r^2}{2} - \frac{r^4}{4}\right)\bigg|_0^3 d\theta \qquad \text{Evaluate the inner integral.}$$

$$= \int_0^{2\pi} \left(\frac{81}{4}\right) d\theta = \frac{81\pi}{2}. \qquad \text{Evaluate the outer integral.}$$

Related Exercises 7–18 ◀

QUICK CHECK 2 Express the functions $f(x, y) = (x^2 + y^2)^{5/2}$ and $h(x, y) = x^2 - y^2$ in polar coordinates. ◁

EXAMPLE 2   Region bounded by two surfaces Find the volume of the region bounded by the paraboloids $z = x^2 + y^2$ and $z = 8 - x^2 - y^2$. This problem was solved in rectangular coordinates in Example 5 of Section 14.2.

SOLUTION As shown in Figure 14.32, the two surfaces intersect in a curve C whose projection onto the xy-plane is the circle $x^2 + y^2 = 4$. This circle is the boundary of the region of integration R, which is written in polar coordinates as

$$R = \{(r, \theta): 0 \leq r \leq 2, 0 \leq \theta \leq 2\pi\}.$$

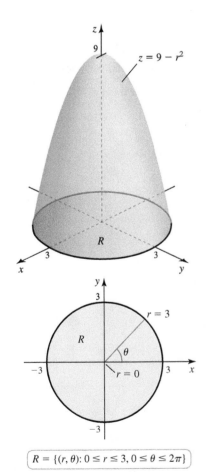

$z = 9 - r^2$

$r = 3$

R

$r = 0$

θ

$R = \{(r, \theta): 0 \leq r \leq 3, 0 \leq \theta \leq 2\pi\}$

FIGURE 14.31

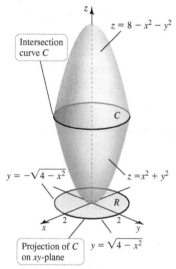

FIGURE 14.32

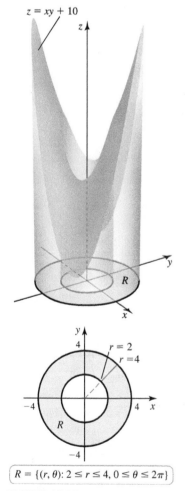

$R = \{(r, \theta): 2 \le r \le 4, 0 \le \theta \le 2\pi\}$

FIGURE 14.33

In polar coordinates, the upper bounding surface of the solid is $z = 8 - r^2$, and the lower bounding surface is $z = r^2$. The volume of the solid is

$$V = \int_0^{2\pi} \int_0^2 \left(\underbrace{(8 - r^2)}_{\text{upper}} - \underbrace{r^2}_{\text{lower}} \right) r\, dr\, d\theta$$

$$= \int_0^{2\pi} \int_0^2 (8r - 2r^3)\, dr\, d\theta \qquad \text{Simplify integrand.}$$

$$= \int_0^{2\pi} \left(4r^2 - \frac{r^4}{2} \right) \Big|_0^2 d\theta \qquad \text{Evaluate inner integral.}$$

$$= \int_0^{2\pi} 8\, d\theta \qquad \text{Simplify.}$$

$$= 16\,\pi. \qquad \text{Evaluate outer integral.}$$

Related Exercises 19–22◀

EXAMPLE 3   Annular region Find the volume of the region beneath the surface $z = xy + 10$ and above the annular region $R = \{(r, \theta): 2 \le r \le 4, 0 \le \theta \le 2\pi\}$. (An *annulus* is the region between two concentric circles.)

SOLUTION The region of integration suggests working in polar coordinates (Figure 14.33). Substituting $x = r\cos\theta$ and $y = r\sin\theta$, the integrand becomes

$$xy + 10 = (r\cos\theta)(r\sin\theta) + 10 \qquad \text{Substitute for } x \text{ and } y.$$

$$= r^2 \sin\theta\cos\theta + 10 \qquad \text{Simplify.}$$

$$= \tfrac{1}{2} r^2 \sin 2\theta + 10. \qquad \sin 2\theta = 2\sin\theta\cos\theta$$

Substituting the integrand into the volume integral, we have

$$V = \int_0^{2\pi} \int_2^4 \left(\tfrac{1}{2} r^2 \sin 2\theta + 10 \right) r\, dr\, d\theta \qquad \text{Iterated integral for volume}$$

$$= \int_0^{2\pi} \int_2^4 \left(\tfrac{1}{2} r^3 \sin 2\theta + 10r \right) dr\, d\theta \qquad \text{Simplify.}$$

$$= \int_0^{2\pi} \left(\frac{r^4}{8} \sin 2\theta + 5r^2 \right) \Big|_2^4 d\theta \qquad \text{Evaluate the inner integral.}$$

$$= \int_0^{2\pi} (30 \sin 2\theta + 60)\, d\theta \qquad \text{Simplify.}$$

$$= (15(-\cos 2\theta) + 60\theta) \Big|_0^{2\pi} = 120\pi. \qquad \text{Evaluate the outer integral.}$$

Related Exercises 23–32◀

More General Polar Regions

In Section 14.2 we generalized double integrals over rectangular regions to double integrals over nonrectangular regions. In an analogous way, the method for integrating over a polar rectangle may be extended to more general regions. Consider a region bounded by two rays $\theta = \alpha$ and $\theta = \beta$, where $\beta - \alpha \le 2\pi$, and two curves $r = g(\theta)$ and $r = h(\theta)$ (Figure 14.34):

$$R = \{(r, \theta): 0 \le g(\theta) \le r \le h(\theta), \alpha \le \theta \le \beta\}.$$

The double integral $\iint_R f(r, \theta)\, dA$ is expressed as an iterated integral in which the inner integral has limits $r = g(\theta)$ and $r = h(\theta)$, and the outer integral runs from $\theta = \alpha$ to $\theta = \beta$.

If f is nonnegative on R, the double integral gives the volume of the solid bounded by the surface $z = f(r, \theta)$ and R.

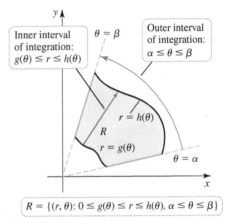

$R = \{(r, \theta): 0 \le g(\theta) \le r \le h(\theta), \alpha \le \theta \le \beta\}$

FIGURE 14.34

> For the type of region described in Theorem 14.4, with the boundaries in the radial direction expressed as functions of θ, the inner integral is always with respect to r.

THEOREM 14.4 Double Integrals over More General Polar Regions
Let f be continuous on the region in the xy-plane

$$R = \{(r, \theta): 0 \le g(\theta) \le r \le h(\theta), \alpha \le \theta \le \beta\},$$

where $0 < \beta - \alpha \le 2\pi$. Then

$$\iint_R f(r, \theta)\, dA = \int_\alpha^\beta \int_{g(\theta)}^{h(\theta)} f(r, \theta)\, r\, dr\, d\theta.$$

> Recall from Section 11.2 that the polar equation $r = 2a \sin \theta$ describes a circle of radius a with center $(0, a)$. The polar equation $r = 2a \cos \theta$ describes a circle of radius a with center $(a, 0)$.

EXAMPLE 4 Specifying regions Write an iterated integral for $\iint_R f(r, \theta)\, dA$ for the following regions R in the xy-plane.

a. The region outside the circle $r = 2$ (with radius 2 centered at $(0, 0)$) and inside the circle $r = 4 \cos \theta$ (with radius 2 centered at $(2, 0)$)

b. The region inside both circles of part (a)

SOLUTION

a. Equating the two expressions for r, we have $4 \cos \theta = 2$ or $\cos \theta = \frac{1}{2}$, so the circles intersect when $\theta = \pm \pi/3$ (Figure 14.35). The inner boundary of R is the circle $r = 2$, and the outer boundary is the circle $r = 4 \cos \theta$. Therefore, the region of integration is $R = \{(r, \theta): 2 \le r \le 4 \cos \theta, -\pi/3 \le \theta \le \pi/3\}$ and the iterated integral is

$$\iint_R f(r, \theta)\, dA = \int_{-\pi/3}^{\pi/3} \int_2^{4\cos\theta} f(r, \theta)\, r\, dr\, d\theta.$$

b. From part (a) we know that the circles intersect when $\theta = \pm \pi/3$. The region R consists of three subregions R_1, R_2, and R_3 (Figure 14.36).

- For $-\pi/2 \le \theta \le -\pi/3$, R_1 is bounded by $r = 0$ (inner curve) and $r = 4 \cos \theta$ (outer curve).
- For $-\pi/3 \le \theta \le \pi/3$, R_2 is bounded by $r = 0$ (inner curve) and $r = 2$ (outer curve).
- For $\pi/3 \le \theta \le \pi/2$, R_3 is bounded by $r = 0$ (inner curve) and $r = 4 \cos \theta$ (outer curve).

Radial lines enter the region R at $r = 2$ and exit the region at $r = 4 \cos \theta$.

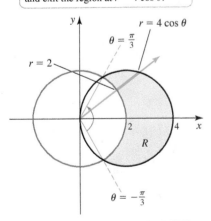

The inner and outer boundaries of R are traversed, for $-\frac{\pi}{3} \le \theta \le \frac{\pi}{3}$.

FIGURE 14.35

Therefore, the double integral is expressed in three parts:

$$\iint\limits_{R} f(r, \theta)\, dA = \int_{-\pi/2}^{-\pi/3} \int_{0}^{4\cos\theta} f(r, \theta)\, r\, dr\, d\theta + \int_{-\pi/3}^{\pi/3} \int_{0}^{2} f(r, \theta)\, r\, dr\, d\theta$$

$$+ \int_{\pi/3}^{\pi/2} \int_{0}^{4\cos\theta} f(r, \theta)\, r\, dr\, d\theta.$$

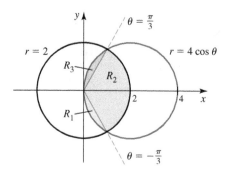

| In R_1 radial lines begin at the origin and exit at $r = 4\cos\theta$. | In R_2 radial lines begin at the origin and exit at $r = 2$. | In R_3 radial lines begin at the origin and exit at $r = 4\cos\theta$. |

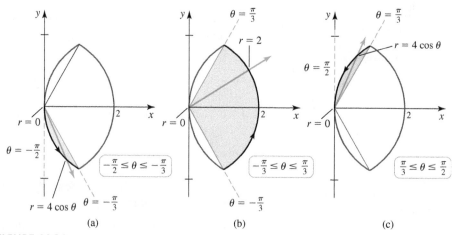

(a)   (b)   (c)

FIGURE 14.36

Related Exercises 33–38 ◄

Areas of Regions

In Cartesian coordinates, the area of a region R in the xy-plane is computed by integrating the function $f(x, y) = 1$ over R; that is, $A = \iint_R dA$. This fact extends to polar coordinates.

> Do not forget the factor of r in the area integral!

Area of Polar Regions

The area of the region $R = \{(r, \theta): 0 \le g(\theta) \le r \le h(\theta), \alpha \le \theta \le \beta\}$, where $0 < \beta - \alpha \le 2\pi$, is

$$A = \iint\limits_{R} dA = \int_{\alpha}^{\beta} \int_{g(\theta)}^{h(\theta)} r\, dr\, d\theta.$$

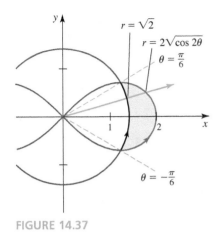

FIGURE 14.37

QUICK CHECK 3 Express the area of the disk $R = \{(r, \theta): 0 \le r \le a, 0 \le \theta \le 2\pi\}$ in terms of a double integral in polar coordinates. ◄

EXAMPLE 5 Area within a lemniscate Compute the area of the region in the first and fourth quadrants outside the circle $r = \sqrt{2}$ and inside the lemniscate $r^2 = 4 \cos 2\theta$ (Figure 14.37).

SOLUTION The equation of the circle can be written as $r^2 = 2$. Equating the two expressions for r^2, the circle and the lemniscate intersect when $2 = 4 \cos 2\theta$, or $\cos 2\theta = \frac{1}{2}$. The angles in the first and fourth quadrants that satisfy this equation are $\theta = \pm\pi/6$ (Figure 14.37). The region between the two curves is bounded by the inner curve $r = g(\theta) = \sqrt{2}$ and the outer curve $r = h(\theta) = 2\sqrt{\cos 2\theta}$. Therefore, the area of the region is

$$
\begin{aligned}
A &= \int_{-\pi/6}^{\pi/6} \int_{\sqrt{2}}^{2\sqrt{\cos 2\theta}} r\, dr\, d\theta \\[2mm]
&= \int_{-\pi/6}^{\pi/6} \left(\frac{r^2}{2}\right)\Bigg|_{\sqrt{2}}^{2\sqrt{\cos 2\theta}} d\theta \qquad \text{\small Evaluate the inner integral.} \\[2mm]
&= \int_{-\pi/6}^{\pi/6} (2 \cos 2\theta - 1)\, d\theta \qquad \text{\small Simplify.} \\[2mm]
&= (\sin 2\theta - \theta)\Big|_{-\pi/6}^{\pi/6} \qquad \text{\small Evaluate the outer integral.} \\[2mm]
&= \sqrt{3} - \frac{\pi}{3}. \qquad \text{\small Simplify.}
\end{aligned}
$$

Related Exercises 39–44 ◄

Average Value over a Planar Polar Region

We have encountered the average value of a function in several different settings. To find the average value of a function over a region in polar coordinates, we again integrate the function over the region and divide by the area of the region.

EXAMPLE 6 Average y-coordinate Find the average value of the y-coordinates of the points in the semicircular disk of radius a given by $R = \{(r, \theta): 0 \le r \le a, 0 \le \theta \le \pi\}$.

SOLUTION Because the y-coordinates of points in the disk are given by $y = r \sin \theta$, the function whose average value we seek is $f(r, \theta) = r \sin \theta$. We use the fact that the area of R is $\pi a^2/2$. Evaluating the average value integral we find that

$$
\begin{aligned}
\bar{y} &= \frac{2}{\pi a^2} \int_0^\pi \int_0^a r \sin \theta\, r\, dr\, d\theta \\[2mm]
&= \frac{2}{\pi a^2} \int_0^\pi \sin \theta \left(\frac{r^3}{3}\right)\Bigg|_0^a d\theta \qquad \text{\small Evaluate the inner integral.} \\[2mm]
&= \frac{2}{\pi a^2}\frac{a^3}{3} \int_0^\pi \sin \theta\, d\theta \qquad \text{\small Simplify.} \\[2mm]
&= \frac{2a}{3\pi} (-\cos \theta)\Big|_0^\pi \qquad \text{\small Evaluate the outer integral.} \\[2mm]
&= \frac{4a}{3\pi}. \qquad \text{\small Simplify.}
\end{aligned}
$$

Note that $4/(3\pi) \approx 0.42$, so the average value of the y-coordinates is less than half the radius of the disk.

Related Exercises 45–48 ◄

SECTION 14.3 EXERCISES

Review Questions

1. Draw the region $\{(r, \theta): 1 \leq r \leq 2, 0 \leq \theta \leq \pi/2\}$. Why is it called a polar rectangle?

2. Write the double integral $\iint_R f(x, y)\, dA$ as an iterated integral in polar coordinates when $R = \{(r, \theta): a \leq r \leq b, \alpha \leq \theta \leq \beta\}$.

3. Sketch the region of integration for the integral
$\int_{-\pi/6}^{\pi/6} \int_{1/2}^{\cos 2\theta} f(r, \theta)\, r\, dr\, d\theta$.

4. Explain why the element of area in Cartesian coordinates $dx\, dy$ becomes $r\, dr\, d\theta$ in polar coordinates.

5. How do you find the area of a region
$R = \{(r, \theta): g(\theta) \leq r \leq h(\theta), \alpha \leq \theta \leq \beta\}$?

6. How do you find the average value of a function over a region that is expressed in polar coordinates?

Basic Skills

7–10. Polar rectangles *Sketch the following polar rectangles.*

7. $R = \{(r, \theta): 0 \leq r \leq 5, 0 \leq \theta \leq \pi/2\}$

8. $R = \{(r, \theta): 2 \leq r \leq 3, \pi/4 \leq \theta \leq 5\pi/4\}$

9. $R = \{(r, \theta): 1 \leq r \leq 4, -\pi/4 \leq \theta \leq 2\pi/3\}$

10. $R = \{(r, \theta): 4 \leq r \leq 5, -\pi/3 \leq \theta \leq \pi/2\}$

11–14. Solids bounded by paraboloids *Find the volume of the solid below the paraboloid $z = 4 - x^2 - y^2$ and above the following regions.*

11. $R = \{(r, \theta): 0 \leq r \leq 1, 0 \leq \theta \leq 2\pi\}$

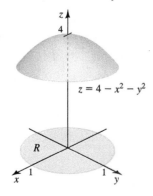

12. $R = \{(r, \theta): 0 \leq r \leq 2, 0 \leq \theta \leq 2\pi\}$

13. $R = \{(r, \theta): 1 \leq r \leq 2, 0 \leq \theta \leq 2\pi\}$

14. $R = \{(r, \theta): 1 \leq r \leq 2, -\pi/2 \leq \theta \leq \pi/2\}$

15–18. Solids bounded by hyperboloids *Find the volume of the solid below the hyperboloid $z = 5 - \sqrt{1 + x^2 + y^2}$ and above the following regions.*

15. $R = \{(r, \theta): 0 \leq r \leq 2, 0 \leq \theta \leq 2\pi\}$

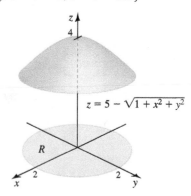

16. $R = \{(r, \theta): 0 \leq r \leq 1, 0 \leq \theta \leq \pi\}$

17. $R = \{(r, \theta): \sqrt{3} \leq r \leq 2\sqrt{2}, 0 \leq \theta \leq 2\pi\}$

18. $R = \{(r, \theta): \sqrt{3} \leq r \leq \sqrt{15}, -\pi/2 \leq \theta \leq \pi\}$

19–22. Volume between surfaces *Find the volume of the following solids.*

19. The solid bounded between the paraboloids $z = x^2 + y^2$ and $z = 2 - x^2 - y^2$

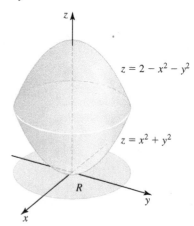

20. The solid bounded between the paraboloids $z = 2x^2 + y^2$ and $z = 27 - x^2 - 2y^2$

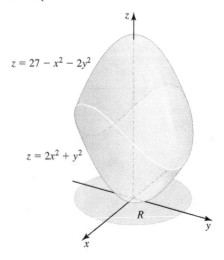

21. The solid bounded by the paraboloid $z = 2 - x^2 - y^2$ and the plane $z = 1$

22. The solid bounded by the paraboloid $z = 8 - x^2 - 3y^2$ and the hyperbolic paraboloid $z = x^2 - y^2$

23–28. Cartesian to polar coordinates *Sketch the given region of integration R and evaluate the integral over R using polar coordinates.*

23. $\iint_R (x^2 + y^2) \, dA; \ R = \{(r, \theta): 0 \le r \le 4, 0 \le \theta \le 2\pi\}$

24. $\iint_R 2xy \, dA; \ R = \{(r, \theta): 1 \le r \le 3, 0 \le \theta \le \pi/2\}$

25. $\iint_R 2xy \, dA; \ R = \{(x, y): x^2 + y^2 \le 9, y \ge 0\}$

26. $\iint_R \dfrac{1}{1 + x^2 + y^2} \, dA; \ R = \{(r, \theta): 1 \le r \le 2, 0 \le \theta \le \pi\}$

27. $\iint_R \dfrac{1}{\sqrt{16 - x^2 - y^2}} \, dA;$
$R = \{(x, y): x^2 + y^2 \le 4, x \ge 0, y \ge 0\}$

28. $\iint_R e^{-x^2 - y^2} \, dA; \ R = \{(x, y): x^2 + y^2 \le 9\}$

29–32. Island problems *The surface of an island is defined by the following functions over the region on which the function is nonnegative. Find the volume of the island.*

29. $z = e^{-(x^2+y^2)/8} - e^{-2}$

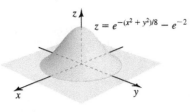

$z = e^{-(x^2 + y^2)/8} - e^{-2}$

30. $z = 100 - 4(x^2 + y^2)$

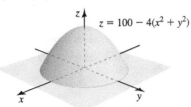

$z = 100 - 4(x^2 + y^2)$

31. $z = 25 - \sqrt{x^2 + y^2}$

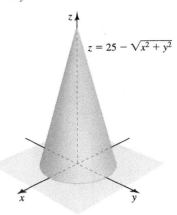

$z = 25 - \sqrt{x^2 + y^2}$

32. $z = \dfrac{20}{1 + x^2 + y^2} - 2$

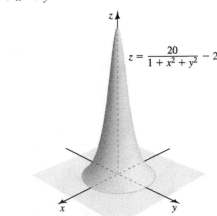

$z = \dfrac{20}{1 + x^2 + y^2} - 2$

33–38. Describing general regions *Sketch the following regions R. Then express $\iint_R f(r, \theta) \, dA$ as an iterated integral over R.*

33. The region inside the limaçon $r = 1 + \frac{1}{2}\cos\theta$

34. The region inside the leaf of the rose $r = 2\sin 2\theta$ in the first quadrant

35. The region inside the lobe of the lemniscate $r^2 = 2\sin 2\theta$ in the first quadrant

36. The region outside the circle $r = 2$ and inside the circle $r = 4\sin\theta$

37. The region outside the circle $r = 1$ and inside the rose $r = 2\sin 3\theta$ in the first quadrant

38. The region outside the circle $r = \frac{1}{2}$ and inside the cardioid $r = 1 + \cos\theta$

39–44. Computing areas *Sketch each region and use integration to find its area.*

39. The annular region $\{(r, \theta): 1 \leq r \leq 2, 0 \leq \theta \leq \pi\}$

40. The region bounded by the cardioid $r = 2(1 - \sin \theta)$

41. The region bounded by all leaves of the rose $r = 2 \cos 3\theta$

42. The region inside both the cardioid $r = 1 - \cos \theta$ and the circle $r = 1$

43. The region inside both the cardioid $r = 1 + \sin \theta$ and the cardioid $r = 1 + \cos \theta$

44. The region bounded by the spiral $r = 2\theta$, for $0 \leq \theta \leq \pi$, and the x-axis

45–48. Average values *Find the following average values.*

45. The average distance between points of the disk $\{(r, \theta): 0 \leq r \leq a\}$ and the origin

46. The average distance between points within the cardioid $r = 1 + \cos \theta$ and the origin

47. The average distance squared between points on the unit disk $\{(r, \theta): 0 \leq r \leq 1\}$ and the point $(1, 1)$

48. The average value of $1/r^2$ over the annulus $\{(r, \theta): 2 \leq r \leq 4\}$

Further Explorations

49. Explain why or why not Determine whether the following statements are true and give an explanation or counterexample.

   a. Let R be the unit disk centered at $(0, 0)$. Then $\iint_R (x^2 + y^2)\, dA = \int_0^{2\pi} \int_0^1 r^2\, dr\, d\theta$.

   b. The average distance between the points of the hemisphere $z = \sqrt{4 - x^2 - y^2}$ and the origin is 2 (no integral needed).

   c. The integral $\int_0^1 \int_0^{\sqrt{1-y^2}} e^{x^2+y^2}\, dx\, dy$ is easier to evaluate in polar coordinates than in Cartesian coordinates.

50–57. Miscellaneous integrals *Sketch the region of integration and evaluate the following integrals, using the method of your choice.*

50. $\displaystyle \int_0^3 \int_0^{\sqrt{9-x^2}} \sqrt{x^2 + y^2}\, dy\, dx$

51. $\displaystyle \int_{-1}^{1} \int_{-\sqrt{1-x^2}}^{\sqrt{1-x^2}} (x^2 + y^2)^{3/2}\, dy\, dx$

52. $\displaystyle \int_{-4}^{4} \int_0^{\sqrt{16-y^2}} (16 - x^2 - y^2)\, dx\, dy$

53. $\displaystyle \int_0^{\pi/4} \int_0^{\sec \theta} r^3\, dr\, d\theta$

54. $\displaystyle \iint_R \sqrt{x^2 + y^2}\, dA; \ R = \{(x, y): 0 \leq y \leq x \leq 1\}$

55. $\displaystyle \iint_R \sqrt{x^2 + y^2}\, dA; \ R = \{(x, y): 1 \leq x^2 + y^2 \leq 4\}$

56. $\displaystyle \iint_R \frac{x - y}{x^2 + y^2 + 1}\, dA; \ R$ is the region bounded by the unit circle centered at the origin.

57. $\displaystyle \iint_R \frac{1}{4 + \sqrt{x^2 + y^2}}\, dA; \ R = \{(r, \theta): 0 \leq r \leq 2, \ \pi/2 \leq \theta \leq 3\pi/2\}$

58. Areas of circles Use integration to show that the circles $r = 2a \cos \theta$ and $r = 2a \sin \theta$ have the same area, which is πa^2.

59. Filling bowls with water Which bowl holds more water if it is filled to a depth of four units?
- The paraboloid $z = x^2 + y^2$, for $0 \leq z \leq 4$
- The cone $z = \sqrt{x^2 + y^2}$, for $0 \leq z \leq 4$
- The hyperboloid $z = \sqrt{1 + x^2 + y^2}$, for $1 \leq z \leq 5$

60. Equal volumes To what height (above the bottom of the bowl) must the cone and paraboloid bowls of Exercise 59 be filled to hold the same volume of water as the hyperboloid bowl filled to a depth of 4 units ($1 \leq z \leq 5$)?

61. Volume of a hyperbolic paraboloid Consider the surface $z = x^2 - y^2$.

   a. Find the region in the xy-plane in polar coordinates for which $z \geq 0$.

   b. Let $R = \{(r, \theta): 0 \leq r \leq a, -\pi/4 \leq \theta \leq \pi/4\}$, which is a sector of a circle of radius a. Find the volume of the region below the hyperbolic paraboloid and above the region R.

62. Slicing a hemispherical cake A cake is shaped like a hemisphere of radius 4 with its base on the xy-plane. A wedge of the cake is removed by making two slices from the center of the cake outward, perpendicular to the xy-plane and separated by an angle of φ.

   a. Use a double integral to find the volume of the slice for $\varphi = \pi/4$. Use geometry to check your answer.

   b. Now suppose the cake is sliced by a plane perpendicular to the xy-plane at $x = a > 0$. Let D be the smaller of the two pieces produced. For what value of a is the volume of D equal to the volume in part (a)?

63–66. Improper integrals *Improper integrals arise in polar coordinates when the radial coordinate r becomes arbitrarily large. Under certain conditions, these integrals are treated in the usual way:*

$$\int_\alpha^\beta \int_a^\infty g(r, \theta)\, r\, dr\, d\theta = \lim_{b \to \infty} \int_\alpha^\beta \int_a^b g(r, \theta)\, r\, dr\, d\theta.$$

Use this technique to evaluate the following integrals.

63. $\displaystyle \int_0^{\pi/2} \int_1^\infty \frac{\cos \theta}{r^3}\, r\, dr\, d\theta$

64. $\displaystyle \iint_R \frac{dA}{(x^2 + y^2)^{5/2}}; \ R = \{(r, \theta): 1 \leq r < \infty, 0 \leq \theta \leq 2\pi\}$

65. $\displaystyle \iint_R e^{-x^2-y^2}\, dA; \ R = \{(r, \theta): 0 \leq r < \infty, 0 \leq \theta \leq \pi/2\}$

66. $\displaystyle \iint_R \frac{1}{(1 + x^2 + y^2)^2}\, dA; \ R$ is the first quadrant.

67. Limaçon loops The limaçon $r = b + a \cos \theta$ has an inner loop if $b < a$ and no inner loop if $b > a$.

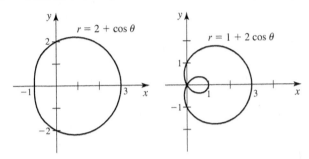

a. Find the area of the region bounded by the limaçon $r = 2 + \cos \theta$.

b. Find the area of the region outside the inner loop and inside the outer loop of the limaçon $r = 1 + 2 \cos \theta$.

c. Find the area of the region inside the inner loop of the limaçon $r = 1 + 2 \cos \theta$.

Applications

68. Mass from density data The following table gives the density (in units of g/cm² at selected points of a thin semicircular plate of radius 3. Estimate the mass of the plate and explain your method.

	$\theta = 0$	$\theta = \pi/4$	$\theta = \pi/2$	$\theta = 3\pi/4$	$\theta = \pi$
$r = 1$	2.0	2.1	2.2	2.3	2.4
$r = 2$	2.5	2.7	2.9	3.1	3.3
$r = 3$	3.2	3.4	3.5	3.6	3.7

69. A mass calculation Suppose the density of a thin plate represented by the region R is $\rho(r, \theta)$ (in units of mass per area). The mass of the plate is $\iint_R \rho(r, \theta) \, dA$. Find the mass of the thin half annulus $R = \{(r, \theta): 1 \le r \le 4, 0 \le \theta \le \pi\}$ with a density $\rho(r, \theta) = 4 + r \sin \theta$.

Additional Exercises

70. Area formula In Section 11.3 it was shown that the area of a region enclosed by the polar curve $r = g(\theta)$ and the rays $\theta = \alpha$ and $\theta = \beta$, where $\beta - \alpha \le 2\pi$, is $A = \frac{1}{2}\int_\alpha^\beta r^2 \, d\theta$. Prove this result using the area formula with double integrals.

71. Normal distribution An important integral in statistics associated with the normal distribution is $I = \int_{-\infty}^{\infty} e^{-x^2} \, dx$. It is evaluated in the following steps.

a. Assume that $I^2 = \left(\int_{-\infty}^{\infty} e^{-x^2} \, dx\right)\left(\int_{-\infty}^{\infty} e^{-y^2} \, dy\right) = \int_{-\infty}^{\infty} \int_{-\infty}^{\infty} e^{-x^2 - y^2} \, dx \, dy$, where we have chosen the variables of integration to be x and y and then written the product as an iterated integral. Evaluate this integral in polar coordinates and show that $I = \sqrt{\pi}$.

b. Evaluate $\int_0^{\infty} e^{-x^2} \, dx$, $\int_0^{\infty} xe^{-x^2} \, dx$, and $\int_0^{\infty} x^2 e^{-x^2} \, dx$ (using part (a) if needed).

72. Existence of integrals For what values of p does the integral

$$\iint_R \frac{k}{(x^2 + y^2)^p} \, dA$$

exist in the following cases?

a. $R = \{(r, \theta): 1 \le r < \infty, 0 \le \theta \le 2\pi\}$

b. $R = \{(r, \theta): 0 \le r \le 1, 0 \le \theta \le 2\pi\}$

73. Integrals in strips Consider the integral

$$I = \iint_R \frac{1}{(1 + x^2 + y^2)^2} \, dA,$$

where $R = \{(x, y): 0 \le x \le 1, 0 \le y \le a\}$.

a. Evaluate I for $a = 1$. (*Hint:* Use polar coordinates.)

b. Evaluate I for arbitrary $a > 0$.

c. Let $a \to \infty$ in part (b) to find I over the infinite strip $R = \{(x, y): 0 \le x \le 1, 0 \le y < \infty\}$.

74. Area of an ellipse In polar coordinates an equation of an ellipse with eccentricity $0 < e < 1$ and semimajor axis a is

$$r = \frac{a(1 - e^2)}{1 + e \cos \theta}.$$

a. Write the integral that gives the area of the ellipse.

b. Show that the area of an ellipse is πab, where $b^2 = a^2(1 - e^2)$.

QUICK CHECK ANSWERS

1. $R = \{(r, \theta): 1 \le r \le 2, 0 \le \theta \le \pi/2\}$
2. $r^5, r^2(\cos^2 \theta - \sin^2 \theta) = r^2 \cos 2\theta$
3. $\int_0^{2\pi} \int_0^a r \, dr \, d\theta = \pi a^2$

14.4 Triple Integrals

At this point, you may be able to see the pattern that is developing with respect to integration. In Chapter 5 we introduced integrals of single-variable functions. In the first three sections of this chapter, we moved up one dimension to double integrals of two-variable functions. In this section we take one more step and investigate triple integrals of three-variable functions. There is no end to the progression of multiple integrals. It is possible to define integrals with respect to any number of variables. For example, problems in statistics and statistical mechanics involve integration over regions of many dimensions.

Triple Integrals in Rectangular Coordinates

Consider a function $w = f(x, y, z)$ that is defined on a closed and bounded region D of $\mathbb{R}^3$. The graph of f is the set of points $(x, y, z, f(x, y, z))$, where (x, y, z) is in D, for which there is no complete three-dimensional representation. Despite the difficulties in representing f in $\mathbb{R}^3$, we may still define the integral of f over D. We first create a partition of D by slicing the region with three sets of planes that run parallel to the xz-, yz-, and xy-planes (Figure 14.38). This partition subdivides D into small boxes that are ordered in a convenient way from $k = 1$ to $k = n$. The partition includes all boxes that are wholly contained in D. The kth box has side lengths Δx_k, Δy_k, and Δz_k, and volume $\Delta V_k = \Delta x_k \Delta y_k \Delta z_k$. We let (x_k^*, y_k^*, z_k^*) be an arbitrary point in the kth box, for $k = 1, \ldots, n$.

A Riemann sum is now formed, in which the kth term is the function value $f(x_k^*, y_k^*, z_k^*)$ multiplied by the volume of the kth box:

$$\sum_{k=1}^{n} f(x_k^*, y_k^*, z_k^*) \Delta V_k.$$

We let Δ denote the maximum length of the diagonals of the boxes. As the number of boxes n increases, while Δ approaches zero, two things happen.

• For commonly encountered regions, the region formed by the collection of boxes approaches the region D.

• If f is continuous, the Riemann sum approaches a limit.

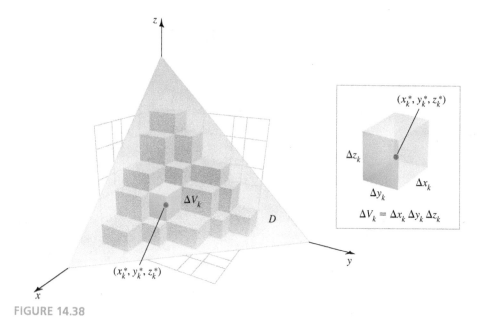

FIGURE 14.38

The limit of the Riemann sum is the **triple integral of f over D**, and we write

$$\iiint_D f(x, y, z)\, dV = \lim_{\Delta \to 0} \sum_{k=1}^{n} f(x_k^*, y_k^*, z_k^*) \Delta V_k.$$

We have two immediate interpretations of a triple integral. First, if $f(x, y, z) = 1$, then the Riemann sum simply adds up the volumes of the boxes in the partition. In the limit as $\Delta \to 0$, the triple integral $\iiint_D dV$ gives the volume of the region D.

Second, suppose that D is a solid three-dimensional object and its density varies from point to point according to the function $f(x, y, z)$. The units of density are mass per unit volume, so the product $f(x_k^*, y_k^*, z_k^*) \Delta V_k$ approximates the mass of the kth box in D. Summing the masses of the boxes gives an approximation to the total mass of D. In the limit as $\Delta \to 0$, the triple integral gives the mass of the object.

> Notice the analogy between double and triple integrals:
>
> $$\text{area }(R) = \iint_R dA \quad \text{and}$$
>
> $$\text{volume }(D) = \iiint_D dV.$$
>
> The use of triple integrals to compute the mass of an object is discussed in detail in Section 14.6.

As with double integrals, a version of Fubini's Theorem expresses a triple integral in terms of an iterated integral in x, y, and z. The situation becomes interesting because with three variables, there are *six* possible orders of integration.

The kth box in the partition has volume $\Delta V_k = \Delta x_k \Delta y_k \Delta z_k$, where Δx_k, Δy_k, and Δz_k are the side lengths of the box. Accordingly, the element of volume in the triple integral, which we denote dV, becomes $dx\, dy\, dz$ (or some rearrangement of dx, dy, and dz) in an iterated integral.

QUICK CHECK 1 List the six orders in which the three differentials dx, dy, and dz may be written. ◀

Finding Limits of Integration   We discuss one of the six orders of integration in detail; the others are examined in the examples. Suppose a region D in $\mathbb{R}^3$ is bounded above by a surface $z = H(x, y)$ and below by a surface $z = G(x, y)$ (Figure 14.39). These two surfaces determine the limits of integration in the z-direction.

Once we know the upper and lower boundaries of D, the next step is to project the region D onto the xy-plane to form a region that we call R (Figure 14.40). You can think of R as the shadow of D in the xy-plane. Assume R is bounded above and below by the curves $y = h(x)$ and $y = g(x)$, respectively, and bounded on the right and left by the lines $x = a$ and $x = b$, respectively (Figure 14.40). The remaining integration over R is carried out as a double integral (Section 14.2).

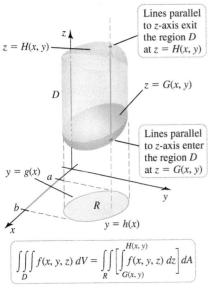

$$\iiint_D f(x, y, z)\, dV = \iint_R \left[\int_{G(x,y)}^{H(x,y)} f(x, y, z)\, dz \right] dA$$

FIGURE 14.39

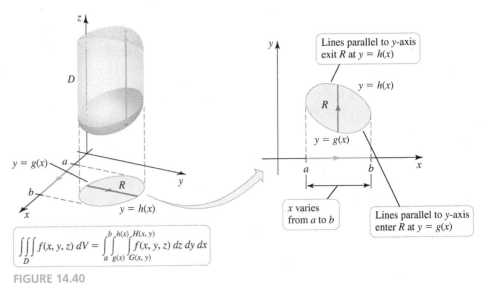

$$\iiint_D f(x, y, z)\, dV = \int_a^b \int_{g(x)}^{h(x)} \int_{G(x,y)}^{H(x,y)} f(x, y, z)\, dz\, dy\, dx$$

FIGURE 14.40

Table 14.2

The intervals that describe D are summarized in Table 14.2, which can then be used to formulate the limits of integration. To integrate over all points of D we

Integral	Variable	Interval
Inner	z	$G(x, y) \le z \le H(x, y)$
Middle	y	$g(x) \le y \le h(x)$
Outer	x	$a \le x \le b$

- first integrate with respect to z from $z = G(x, y)$ to $z = H(x, y)$,
- then integrate with respect to y from $y = g(x)$ to $y = h(x)$, and
- finally integrate with respect to x from $x = a$ to $x = b$.

▷ Theorem 14.5 is a version of Fubini's Theorem. Five other versions could be written for the other orders of integration.

THEOREM 14.5   Triple Integrals

Let f be continuous over the region

$$D = \{(x, y, z): a \le x \le b, g(x) \le y \le h(x), G(x, y) \le z \le H(x, y)\},$$

where g, h, G, and H are continuous functions. Then f is integrable over D and the triple integral is evaluated as the iterated integral

$$\iiint_D f(x, y, z)\, dV = \int_a^b \int_{g(x)}^{h(x)} \int_{G(x,y)}^{H(x,y)} f(x, y, z)\, dz\, dy\, dx.$$

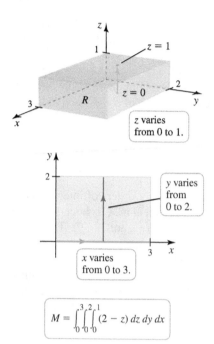

z varies
from 0 to 1.

y varies
from
0 to 2.

x varies
from 0 to 3.

$$M = \int_0^3 \int_0^2 \int_0^1 (2 - z)\, dz\, dy\, dx$$

FIGURE 14.41

Table 14.3

Integral	Variable	Interval
Inner	z	$0 \le z \le 1$
Middle	y	$0 \le y \le 2$
Outer	x	$0 \le x \le 3$

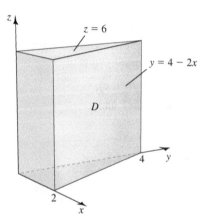

FIGURE 14.42

Notice that the first (inner) integral is with respect to z, and the result is a function of x and y; the second (middle) integral is with respect to y, and the result is a function of x; and the last (outer) integral is with respect to x, and the result is a real number.

EXAMPLE 1   Mass of a box   A solid box D is bounded by the planes $x = 0$, $x = 3$, $y = 0$, $y = 2$, $z = 0$, and $z = 1$. The density of the box decreases linearly in the z-direction and is given by $f(x, y, z) = 2 - z$. Find the mass of the box.

SOLUTION   The mass of the box is found by integrating the density $f(x, y, z) = 2 - z$ over the box. Because the limits of integration for all three variables are constant, the iterated integral may be written in any order (Figure 14.41). Using the order of integration $dz\, dy\, dx$, the limits of integration are shown in Table 14.3.

The mass of the box is

$$M = \iiint_D (2 - z)\, dV$$

$$= \int_0^3 \int_0^2 \int_0^1 (2 - z)\, dz\, dy\, dx \qquad \text{Convert to an iterated integral.}$$

$$= \int_0^3 \int_0^2 \left(2z - \frac{z^2}{2}\right)\Big|_0^1 dy\, dx \qquad \text{Evaluate the inner integral with respect to } z.$$

$$= \int_0^3 \int_0^2 \left(\frac{3}{2}\right) dy\, dx \qquad \text{Simplify.}$$

$$= \int_0^3 \left(\frac{3y}{2}\right)\Big|_0^2 dx \qquad \text{Evaluate the middle integral with respect to } y.$$

$$= \int_0^3 3\, dx = 9. \qquad \text{Evaluate the outer integral and simplify.}$$

The result makes sense: The density of the box varies linearly from 1 to 2; if the box had a constant density of 1, its mass would be (volume) · (density) $= 6$; if the box had a constant density of 2, its mass would be 12. The actual mass is the average of 6 and 12, as you might expect.

Any other order of integration produces the same result. For example with the order $dy\, dx\, dz$, the iterated integral is

$$M = \iiint_D (2 - z)\, dV = \int_0^1 \int_0^3 \int_0^2 (2 - z)\, dy\, dx\, dz = 9.$$

Related Exercises 7–14 ◀

QUICK CHECK 2   Write the integral in Example 1 in the orders $dx\, dy\, dz$ and $dx\, dz\, dy$. ◀

EXAMPLE 2   Volume of a prism   Find the volume of the prism D in the first octant bounded by the planes $y = 4 - 2x$ and $z = 6$ (Figure 14.42).

SOLUTION   The prism may be viewed in several different ways. If the base of the prism is in the xz-plane, then the upper surface of the prism is the plane $y = 4 - 2x$, and the lower surface is $y = 0$. The projection of the prism onto the xz-plane is the rectangle $R = \{(x, z): 0 \le x \le 2, 0 \le z \le 6\}$. One possible order of integration in this case is $dy\, dx\, dz$.

Inner integral with respect to y: A line through the prism parallel to the y-axis enters the prism through the rectangle R at $y = 0$ and exits the prism at the plane $y = 4 - 2x$. Therefore, we first integrate with respect to y over the interval $0 \leq y \leq 4 - 2x$ (Figure 14.43a).

Middle integral with respect to x: The limits of integration for the middle and outer integrals must cover the region R in the xz-plane. A line parallel to the x-axis enters R at $x = 0$ and exits R at $x = 2$. So we integrate with respect to x over the interval $0 \leq x \leq 2$ (Figure 14.43b).

Outer integral with respect to z: To cover all of R, the line segments from $x = 0$ to $x = 2$ must run from $z = 0$ to $z = 6$. So we integrate with respect to z over the interval $0 \leq z \leq 6$ (Figure 14.43b).

Integrating $f(x, y, z) = 1$, the volume of the prism is

> The volume of the prism could also be found using geometry: The area of the triangular base in the xy-plane is 4 and the height of the prism is 6. Therefore, the volume is $6 \cdot 4 = 24$.

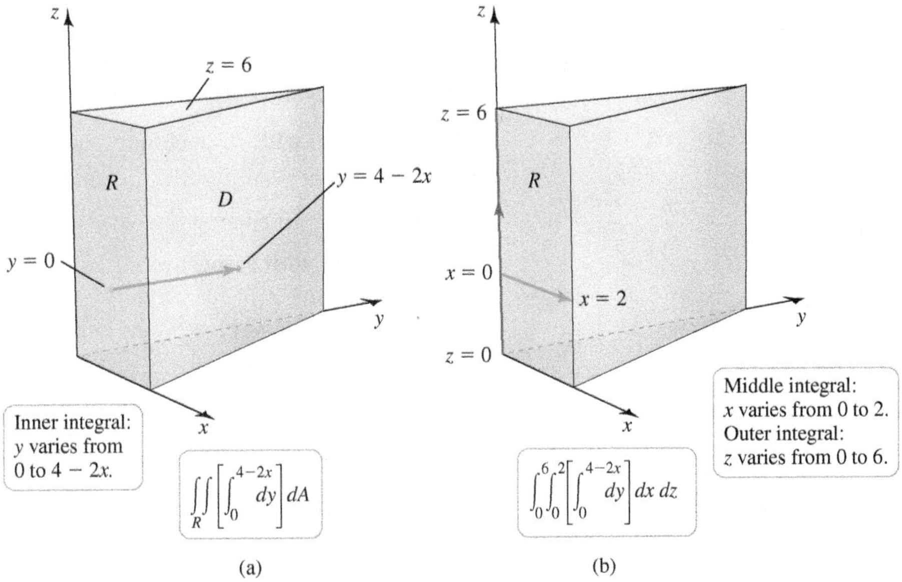

$$V = \iiint_D dV = \int_0^6 \int_0^2 \int_0^{4-2x} dy\, dx\, dz$$

$$= \int_0^6 \int_0^2 (4 - 2x)\, dx\, dz \qquad \text{Evaluate the inner integral with respect to } y.$$

$$= \int_0^6 (4x - x^2)\Big|_0^2\, dz \qquad \text{Evaluate the middle integral with respect to } x.$$

$$= \int_0^6 4\, dz \qquad \text{Simplify.}$$

$$= 24. \qquad \text{Evaluate the outer integral with respect to } z.$$

Inner integral:
y varies from
0 to $4 - 2x$.

$$\iint_R \left[\int_0^{4-2x} dy \right] dA$$

(a)

Middle integral:
x varies from 0 to 2.
Outer integral:
z varies from 0 to 6.

$$\int_0^6 \int_0^2 \left[\int_0^{4-2x} dy \right] dx\, dz$$

(b)

FIGURE 14.43

Related Exercises 15–24 ◄

QUICK CHECK 3 Write the integral in Example 2 in the orders $dz\, dy\, dx$ and $dx\, dy\, dz$. ◄

EXAMPLE 3   A volume integral Find the volume of the region D bounded by the paraboloids $y = x^2 + z^2$ and $y = 16 - 3x^2 - z^2$ (Figure 14.44).

SOLUTION We identify the right boundary of D as the surface $y = 16 - 3x^2 - z^2$; the left boundary is $y = x^2 + z^2$. These surfaces are functions of x and z, so they determine the limits of integration for the inner integral in the y-direction.

A key step in the calculation is finding the curve of intersection between the two surfaces and projecting it onto the xz-plane to form the boundary of the region R. Equating the y-coordinates of the two surfaces, we have $x^2 + z^2 = 16 - 3x^2 - z^2$, which becomes the equation of an ellipse:

$$4x^2 + 2z^2 = 16, \quad \text{or} \quad z = \pm\sqrt{8 - 2x^2}.$$

The projection of the solid region D onto the xz-plane is the region R bounded by this ellipse (centered at the origin with axes of length 4 and $4\sqrt{2}$). Here are the observations that lead to the limits of integration with the ordering $dy\,dz\,dx$.

> Note that the problem is symmetric about the x- and z-axes. Therefore, the integral over R could be evaluated over one-quarter of R,
>
> $$\{(x, z): 0 \le z \le \sqrt{8 - 2x^2},$$
> $$0 \le x \le 2\},$$
>
> in which case the final result must be multiplied by 4.

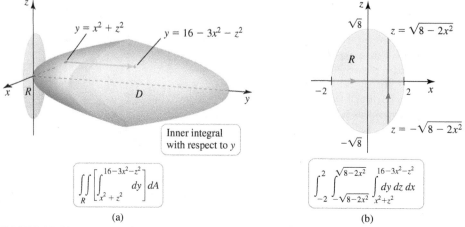

FIGURE 14.44

Inner integral with respect to y: A line through the solid parallel to the y-axis enters the solid at $y = x^2 + z^2$ and exits at $y = 16 - 3x^2 - z^2$. Therefore, for fixed values of x and z, we integrate over the interval $x^2 + z^2 \le y \le 16 - 3x^2 - z^2$ (Figure 14.44a).

Middle integral with respect to z: Now we must cover the region R. A line parallel to the z-axis enters R at $z = -\sqrt{8 - 2x^2}$ and exits R at $z = \sqrt{8 - 2x^2}$. Therefore, for a fixed value of x, we integrate over the interval $-\sqrt{8 - 2x^2} \le z \le \sqrt{8 - 2x^2}$ (Figure 14.44b).

Outer integral with respect to x: To cover all of R, x must run from $x = -2$ to $x = 2$ (Figure 14.44b).

Integrating $f(x, y, z) = 1$, the iterated integral for the volume is

$$V = \int_{-2}^{2}\int_{-\sqrt{8 - 2x^2}}^{\sqrt{8 - 2x^2}}\int_{x^2 + z^2}^{16 - 3x^2 - z^2} dy\,dz\,dx$$

$$= \int_{-2}^{2}\int_{-\sqrt{8 - 2x^2}}^{\sqrt{8 - 2x^2}} (16 - 4x^2 - 2z^2)\,dz\,dx \qquad \text{Evaluate the inner integral and simplify.}$$

$$= \int_{-2}^{2}\left(16z - 4x^2z - \frac{2z^3}{3}\right)\Bigg|_{-\sqrt{8 - 2x^2}}^{\sqrt{8 - 2x^2}} dx \qquad \text{Evaluate the middle integral.}$$

$$= \frac{16\sqrt{2}}{3}\int_{-2}^{2}(4 - x^2)^{3/2}\,dx = 32\pi\sqrt{2}. \qquad \text{Evaluate the outer integral.}$$

The last (outer) integral in this calculation requires the trigonometric substitution $x = 2\sin\theta$.

Related Exercises 25–34 ◄

Changing the Order of Integration

As with double integrals, choosing an appropriate order of integration may simplify the evaluation of a triple integral. Therefore, it is important to become proficient at changing the order of integration.

EXAMPLE 4   **Changing the order of integration**   Consider the integral

$$\int_0^{\sqrt[4]{\pi}} \int_0^z \int_y^z 12y^2 z^3 \sin x^4 \, dx \, dy \, dz.$$

a. Sketch the region of integration D.

b. Evaluate the integral by changing the order of integration.

SOLUTION

a. We begin by finding the projection of the region of integration D on the appropriate coordinate plane; call the projection R. Because the inner integration is with respect to x, R lies in the yz-plane, and it is determined by the limits on the middle and outer integrals. We see that

$$R = \{(y, z): 0 \le y \le z, 0 \le z \le \sqrt[4]{\pi}\},$$

which is a triangular region in the yz-plane bounded by the z-axis and the lines $y = z$ and $z = \sqrt[4]{\pi}$. Using the limits on the inner integral, for each point in R we let x vary from the plane $x = y$ to the plane $x = z$. In so doing, the points fill an inverted tetrahedron in the first octant with its vertex at the origin, which is D (Figure 14.45).

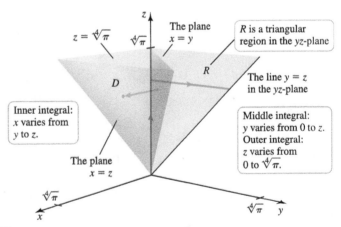

FIGURE 14.45

How do we know to switch the order of integration so the inner integral is with respect to y? Often we do not know in advance whether a new order of integration will work, and some trial and error is needed. In this case, either y^2 or z^3 is easier to integrate than $\sin x^4$, so either y or z is a likely variable for the inner integral. However, we are given that z varies between two constants, so z is the best choice for the variable in the outer integral.

b. It is difficult to evaluate the integral in the given order ($dx \, dy \, dz$) because the antiderivative of $\sin x^4$ is not expressible in terms of elementary functions. If we integrate first with respect to y, we introduce a factor in the integrand that enables us to use a substitution to integrate $\sin x^4$. With the order of integration $dy \, dx \, dz$, the bounds of integration for the inner integral extend from the plane $y = 0$ to the plane $y = x$ (Figure 14.46a). Furthermore, the projection of D onto the xz-plane is the region R, which must be covered by the middle and outer integrals (Figure 14.46b). In this case, we draw a line segment parallel to the x-axis to see that the limits of the middle integral run from $x = 0$ to $x = z$. Then we include all these segments from $z = 0$ to

$z = \sqrt[4]{\pi}$ to obtain the outer limits of integration in z. The integration proceeds as follows:

$$\int_0^{\sqrt[4]{\pi}} \int_0^z \int_0^x 12y^2z^3 \sin x^4 \, dy \, dx \, dz = \int_0^{\sqrt[4]{\pi}} \int_0^z (4y^3z^3 \sin x^4)\Big|_0^x \, dx \, dz \qquad \text{Evaluate the inner integral.}$$

$$= \int_0^{\sqrt[4]{\pi}} \int_0^z 4x^3z^3 \sin x^4 \, dx \, dz \qquad \text{Simplify.}$$

$$= \int_0^{\sqrt[4]{\pi}} z^3(-\cos x^4)\Big|_0^z \, dz \qquad \begin{array}{l}\text{Evaluate the} \\ \text{middle integral;} \\ u = x^4.\end{array}$$

$$= \int_0^{\sqrt[4]{\pi}} z^3(1 - \cos z^4) \, dz \qquad \text{Simplify.}$$

$$= \left(\frac{z^4}{4} - \frac{\sin z^4}{4}\right)\Big|_0^{\sqrt[4]{\pi}} \qquad \begin{array}{l}\text{Evaluate the} \\ \text{outer integral;} \\ u = z^4.\end{array}$$

$$= \frac{\pi}{4}. \qquad \text{Simplify.}$$

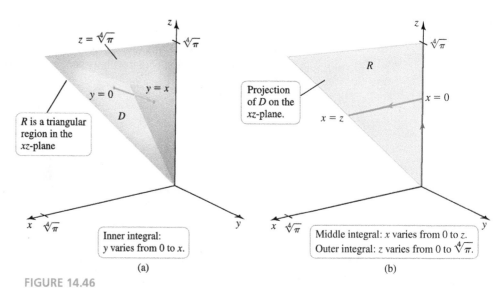

FIGURE 14.46

Related Exercises 35–38◄

Average Value of a Function of Three Variables

The idea of the average value of a function extends naturally from the one- and two-variable cases. The average value of a function of three variables is found by integrating the function over the region of interest and dividing by the volume of the region.

DEFINITION Average Value of a Function of Three Variables

If f is continuous on a region D of $\mathbb{R}^3$, then the average value of f over D is

$$\bar{f} = \frac{1}{\text{volume }(D)} \iiint_D f(x, y, z) \, dV.$$

EXAMPLE 5   Average temperature Consider a block of a conducting material occupying the region

$$D = \{(x, y, z): 0 \le x \le 2, 0 \le y \le 2, 0 \le z \le 1\}.$$

Due to heat sources on its boundaries, the temperature in the block is given by $T(x, y, z) = 250xy \sin \pi z$. Find the average temperature over the block.

SOLUTION We must integrate the temperature function over the block and divide by the volume of the block, which is 4. One way to evaluate the temperature integral is as follows:

$$\iiint_D 250xy \sin \pi z \, dV = 250 \int_0^2 \int_0^2 \int_0^1 xy \sin \pi z \, dz \, dy \, dx \qquad \text{Convert to an iterated integral.}$$

$$= 250 \int_0^2 \int_0^2 xy \frac{1}{\pi}(-\cos \pi z)\Big|_0^1 dy \, dx \qquad \text{Evaluate the inner integral.}$$

$$= \frac{500}{\pi} \int_0^2 \int_0^2 xy \, dy \, dx \qquad \text{Simplify.}$$

$$= \frac{500}{\pi} \int_0^2 x \left(\frac{y^2}{2}\right)\Big|_0^2 dx \qquad \text{Evaluate the middle integral.}$$

$$= \frac{1000}{\pi} \int_0^2 x \, dx \qquad \text{Simplify.}$$

$$= \frac{1000}{\pi} \left(\frac{x^2}{2}\right)\Big|_0^2 = \frac{2000}{\pi}. \qquad \text{Evaluate the outer integral.}$$

Dividing by the volume of the region, the average temperature is $(2000/\pi)/4 = 500/\pi \approx 159.2$.

Related Exercises 39–44◄

QUICK CHECK 4 Without integrating, what is the average value of $f(x, y, z) = \sin x \sin y \sin z$ on the cube

$$\{(x, y, z): -1 \le x \le 1, -1 \le y \le 1, -1 \le z \le 1\}?$$

Use symmetry arguments. ◄

SECTION 14.4 EXERCISES

Review Questions

1. Sketch the region $D = \{(x, y, z): x^2 + y^2 \le 4, 0 \le z \le 4\}$.

2. Write an iterated integral for $\iiint_D f(x, y, z) \, dV$, where D is the box $\{(x, y, z): 0 \le x \le 3, 0 \le y \le 6, 0 \le z \le 4\}$.

3. Write an iterated integral for $\iiint_D f(x, y, z) \, dV$, where D is a sphere of radius 9 centered at $(0, 0, 0)$. Use the order $dz \, dy \, dx$.

4. Sketch the region of integration for the integral
$\int_0^1 \int_0^{\sqrt{1-z^2}} \int_0^{\sqrt{1-y^2-z^2}} f(x, y, z) \, dx \, dy \, dz$.

5. Write the integral in Exercise 4 in the order $dy \, dx \, dz$.

6. Write an integral for the average value of $f(x, y, z) = xyz$ over the region bounded by the paraboloid $z = 9 - x^2 - y^2$ and the xy-plane (assuming the volume of the region is known).

Basic Skills

7–14. Integrals over boxes *Evaluate the following integrals. A sketch of the region of integration may be useful.*

7. $\int_{-2}^2 \int_3^6 \int_0^2 dx \, dy \, dz$

8. $\int_{-1}^1 \int_{-1}^2 \int_0^1 6xyz \, dy \, dx \, dz$

9. $\int_{-2}^2 \int_1^2 \int_1^e \frac{xy^2}{z} dz \, dx \, dy$

10. $\int_0^{\ln 4} \int_0^{\ln 3} \int_0^{\ln 2} e^{-x+y+z} dx \, dy \, dz$

11. $\displaystyle\int_{0}^{\pi/2}\int_{0}^{1}\int_{0}^{\pi/2} \sin \pi x \cos y \sin 2z \, dy \, dx \, dz$

12. $\displaystyle\int_{0}^{2}\int_{1}^{2}\int_{0}^{1} yze^{x} \, dx \, dz \, dy$

13. $\displaystyle\iiint_{D} (xy + xz + yz) \, dV; \quad D = \{(x, y, z): -1 \le x \le 1,$
$-2 \le y \le 2, -3 \le z \le 3\}$

14. $\displaystyle\iiint_{D} xyze^{-x^{2}-y^{2}} \, dV; \quad D = \{(x, y, z): 0 \le x \le \sqrt{\ln 2},$
$0 \le y \le \sqrt{\ln 4}, 0 \le z \le 1\}$

15–24. Volumes of solids *Find the volume of the following solids using triple integrals.*

15. The region in the first octant bounded by the plane $2x + 3y + 6z = 12$ and the coordinate planes

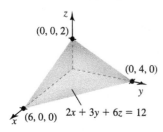

16. The region in the first octant formed when the cylinder $z = \sin y$, for $0 \le y \le \pi$, is sliced by the planes $y = x$ and $x = 0$

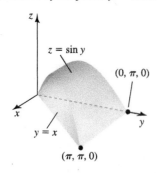

17. The region bounded below by the cone $z = \sqrt{x^2 + y^2}$ and bounded above by the sphere $x^2 + y^2 + z^2 = 8$

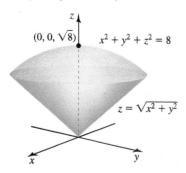

18. The prism in the first octant bounded by $z = 2 - 4x$ and $y = 8$

19. The wedge above the xy-plane formed when the cylinder $x^2 + y^2 = 4$ is cut by the planes $z = 0$ and $y = -z$

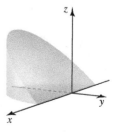

20. The region bounded by the parabolic cylinder $y = x^2$ and the planes $z = 3 - y$ and $z = 0$

21. The region between the sphere $x^2 + y^2 + z^2 = 19$ and the hyperboloid $z^2 - x^2 - y^2 = 1$, for $z > 0$

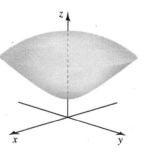

22. The region bounded by the surfaces $z = e^y$ and $z = 1$ over the rectangle $\{(x, y): 0 \le x \le 1, 0 \le y \le \ln 2\}$

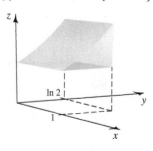

23. The wedge of the cylinder $x^2 + 4y^2 = 4$ created by the planes $z = 3 - x$ and $z = x - 3$

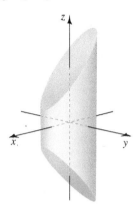

24. The region in the first octant bounded by the cone $z = 1 - \sqrt{x^2 + y^2}$ and the plane $x + y + z = 1$

25–34. Triple integrals *Evaluate the following integrals.*

25. $\int_0^1 \int_0^{\sqrt{1-x^2}} \int_0^{\sqrt{1-x^2}} dz\, dy\, dx$

26. $\int_0^1 \int_0^{\sqrt{1-x^2}} \int_0^{\sqrt{1-x^2-y^2}} 2xz\, dz\, dy\, dx$

27. $\int_0^4 \int_{-2\sqrt{16-y^2}}^{2\sqrt{16-y^2}} \int_0^{16-(x^2/4)-y^2} dz\, dx\, dy$

28. $\int_1^6 \int_0^{4-2y/3} \int_0^{12-2y-3z} \frac{1}{y}\, dx\, dz\, dy$

29. $\int_0^3 \int_0^{\sqrt{9-z^2}} \int_0^{\sqrt{1+x^2+z^2}} dy\, dx\, dz$

30. $\int_0^\pi \int_0^\pi \int_0^{\sin x} \sin y\, dz\, dx\, dy$

31. $\int_1^{\ln 8} \int_1^{\sqrt{z}} \int_{\ln y}^{\ln 2y} e^{x+y^2-z}\, dx\, dy\, dz$

32. $\int_0^1 \int_0^{\sqrt{1-x^2}} \int_0^{2-x} 4yz\, dz\, dy\, dx$

33. $\int_0^2 \int_0^4 \int_{y^2}^4 \sqrt{x}\, dz\, dx\, dy$ **34.** $\int_0^1 \int_y^{2-y} \int_0^{2-x-y} xy\, dz\, dx\, dy$

35–38. Changing the order of integration *Rewrite the following integrals using the indicated order of integration and then evaluate the resulting integral.*

35. $\int_0^5 \int_{-1}^0 \int_0^{4x+4} dy\, dx\, dz$ in the order $dz\, dx\, dy$

36. $\int_0^1 \int_{-2}^2 \int_0^{\sqrt{4-y^2}} dz\, dy\, dx$ in the order $dy\, dz\, dx$

37. $\int_0^1 \int_0^{\sqrt{1-x^2}} \int_0^{\sqrt{1-x^2}} dy\, dz\, dx$ in the order $dz\, dy\, dx$

38. $\int_0^4 \int_0^{\sqrt{16-x^2}} \int_0^{\sqrt{16-x^2-z^2}} dy\, dz\, dx$ in the order $dx\, dy\, dz$

39–44. Average value *Find the following average values.*

39. The average temperature in the box $D = \{(x, y, z): 0 \le x \le \ln 2, 0 \le y \le \ln 4, 0 \le z \le \ln 8\}$ with a temperature distribution of $T(x, y, z) = 128\, e^{-x-y-z}$

40. The average value of $f(x, y, z) = 6xyz$ over the points inside the hemisphere of radius 4 centered at the origin with its base in the xy-plane

41. The average of the *squared* distance between the origin and points in the solid cylinder $D = \{(x, y, z): x^2 + y^2 \le 4, 0 \le z \le 2\}$

42. The average of the *squared* distance between the origin and points in the solid paraboloid $D = \{(x, y, z): 0 \le z \le 4 - x^2 - y^2\}$

43. The average z-coordinate of points in a hemisphere of radius 4 centered at the origin with its base in the xy-plane

44. The average of the *squared* distance between the z-axis and points in the conical region $D = \{(x, y, z): 2\sqrt{x^2 + y^2} \le z \le 8\}$

Further Explorations

45. Explain why or why not Determine whether the following statements are true and give an explanation or counterexample.

   a. An iterated integral of a function over the box $D = \{(x, y, z): 0 \le x \le a, 0 \le y \le b, 0 \le z \le c\}$ can be expressed in eight different ways.

   b. One possible iterated integral of f over the prism $D = \{(x, y, z): 0 \le x \le 1, 0 \le y \le 3x - 3, 0 \le z \le 5\}$ is $\int_0^{3x-3} \int_0^1 \int_0^5 f(x, y, z)\, dz\, dx\, dy$.

   c. The region $D = \{(x, y, z): 0 \le x \le 1, 0 \le y \le \sqrt{1 - x^2}, 0 \le z \le \sqrt{1 - x^2}\}$ is a sphere.

46. Changing the order of integration Use another order of integration to evaluate $\int_1^4 \int_z^{4z} \int_0^{\pi^2} \frac{\sin \sqrt{yz}}{x^{3/2}}\, dy\, dx\, dz$.

47–51. Miscellaneous volumes *Use a triple integral to compute the volume of the following regions.*

47. The parallelepiped (slanted box) with vertices $(0, 0, 0)$, $(1, 0, 0)$, $(0, 1, 0)$, $(1, 1, 0)$, $(0, 1, 1)$, $(1, 1, 1)$, $(0, 2, 1)$, and $(1, 2, 1)$. (Use integration and find the best order of integration.)

48. The larger of two solids formed when the parallelepiped (slanted box) with vertices $(0, 0, 0)$, $(2, 0, 0)$, $(0, 2, 0)$, $(2, 2, 0)$, $(0, 1, 1)$, $(2, 1, 1)$, $(0, 3, 1)$, and $(2, 3, 1)$ is sliced by the plane $y = 2$.

49. The pyramid with vertices $(0, 0, 0)$, $(2, 0, 0)$, $(2, 2, 0)$, $(0, 2, 0)$, and $(0, 0, 4)$

50. The solid common to the cylinders $z = \sin x$ and $z = \sin y$ over the square $R = \{(x, y): 0 \le x \le \pi, 0 \le y \le \pi\}$ (The figure shows the cylinders, but not the common region.)

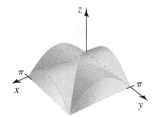

51. The wedge of the square column $|x| + |y| = 1$ created by the planes $z = 0$ and $x + y + z = 1$

52. Partitioning a cube Consider the region $D_1 = \{(x, y, z): 0 \le x \le y \le z \le 1\}$.

  a. Find the volume of D_1.
  b. Let $D_2, \ldots, D_6$ be the "cousins" of D_1 formed by rearranging x, y, and z in the inequality $0 \le x \le y \le z \le 1$. Show that the volumes of $D_1, \ldots, D_6$ are equal.
  c. Show that the union of $D_1, \ldots, D_6$ is a unit cube.

Applications

53. Comparing two masses Two different tetrahedrons fill the region in the first octant bounded by the coordinate planes and the plane $x + y + z = 4$. Both solids have densities that vary in the z-direction between $\rho = 4$ and $\rho = 8$, according to the functions $\rho_1 = 8 - z$ and $\rho_2 = 4 + z$. Find the mass of each solid.

54. Dividing the cheese Suppose a wedge of cheese fills the region in the first octant bounded by the planes $y = z$, $y = 4$, and $x = 4$. You could divide the wedge into two equal pieces (by volume) if you sliced the wedge with the plane $x = 2$. Instead find a with $0 < a < 4$ such that slicing the wedge with the plane $y = a$ divides the wedge into two equal pieces.

55–59. General volume formulas *Find equations for the bounding surfaces, set up a volume integral, and evaluate the integral to obtain a volume formula for each region. Assume that a, b, c, r, R, and h are positive constants.*

55. Cone Find the volume of a right circular cone with height h and base radius r.

56. Tetrahedron Find the volume of a tetrahedron whose vertices are located at $(0, 0, 0)$, $(a, 0, 0)$, $(0, b, 0)$, and $(0, 0, c)$.

57. Spherical cap Find the volume of the cap of a sphere of radius R with height h.

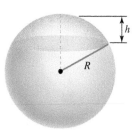

58. Frustum of a cone Find the volume of a truncated cone of height h whose ends have radii r and R.

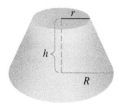

59. Ellipsoid Find the volume of an ellipsoid with axes of length $2a$, $2b$, and $2c$.

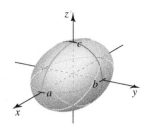

60. Exponential distribution The occurrence of random events (such as phone calls or e-mail messages) is often idealized using an exponential distribution. If λ is the average rate of occurrence of such an event, assumed to be constant over time, then the average time between occurrences is λ^{-1} (for example, if phone calls arrive at a rate of $\lambda = 2/\text{min}$, then the mean time between phone calls is $\lambda^{-1} = \frac{1}{2}$ min). The exponential distribution is given by $f(t) = \lambda e^{-\lambda t}$, for $0 \le t < \infty$.

  a. Suppose you work at a customer service desk and phone calls arrive at an average rate of $\lambda_1 = 0.8/\text{min}$ (meaning the average time between phone calls is $1/0.8 = 1.25$ min). The probability that a phone call arrives during the interval $[0, T]$ is $p(T) = \int_0^T \lambda_1 e^{-\lambda_1 t}\, dt$. Find the probability that a phone call arrives during the first 45 s (0.75 min) that you work at the desk.
  b. Now suppose that walk-in customers also arrive at your desk at an average rate of $\lambda_2 = 0.1/\text{min}$. The probability that a phone call *and* a customer arrive during the interval $[0, T]$ is $p(T) = \int_0^T \int_0^T \lambda_1 e^{-\lambda_1 t} \lambda_2 e^{-\lambda_2 s}\, dt\, ds$. Find the probability that a phone call and a customer arrive during the first 45 s that you work at the desk.
  c. E-mail messages also arrive at your desk at an average rate of $\lambda_3 = 0.05/\text{min}$. The probability that a phone call *and* a customer *and* an e-mail message arrive during the interval $[0, T]$ is $p(T) = \int_0^T \int_0^T \int_0^T \lambda_1 e^{-\lambda_1 t} \lambda_2 e^{-\lambda_2 s} \lambda_3 e^{-\lambda_3 u}\, dt\, ds\, du$. Find the probability that a phone call and a customer and an e-mail message arrive during the first 45 s that you work at the desk.

Additional Exercises

61. Hypervolume Find the volume of the four-dimensional pyramid bounded by $w + x + y + z + 1 = 0$ and the coordinate planes $w = 0, x = 0, y = 0$, and $z = 0$.

62. An identity (Putnam Exam 1941) Let f be a continuous function on $[0, 1]$. Prove that

$$\int_0^1 \int_x^1 \int_x^y f(x)f(y)f(z) \, dz \, dy \, dx = \frac{1}{6}\left(\int_0^1 f(x) \, dx\right)^3.$$

QUICK CHECK ANSWERS

1. $dx \, dy \, dz, \, dx \, dz \, dy, \, dy \, dx \, dz, \, dy \, dz \, dx, \, dz \, dx \, dy, \, dz \, dy \, dx$

2. $\displaystyle\int_0^1 \int_0^2 \int_0^3 (2 - z) \, dx \, dy \, dz, \; \int_0^2 \int_0^1 \int_0^3 (2 - z) \, dx \, dz \, dy$

3. $\displaystyle\int_0^2 \int_0^{4-2x} \int_0^6 dz \, dy \, dx, \; \int_0^6 \int_0^4 \int_0^{2-y/2} dx \, dy \, dz$

4. 0 ($\sin x, \sin y$, and $\sin z$ are odd functions.)

14.5 Triple Integrals in Cylindrical and Spherical Coordinates

When evaluating triple integrals, you may have noticed that some regions (such as spheres, cones, and cylinders) have awkward descriptions in Cartesian coordinates. In this section we examine two other coordinate systems in $\mathbb{R}^3$ that are easier to use when working with certain types of regions. These coordinate systems are helpful not only for integration, but also for general problem solving.

Cylindrical Coordinates

When we extend polar coordinates from $\mathbb{R}^2$ to $\mathbb{R}^3$, the result is *cylindrical coordinates*. In this coordinate system, a point P in $\mathbb{R}^3$ has coordinates (r, θ, z), where r is the distance between P and the z-axis and θ is the usual polar angle measured counterclockwise from the positive x-axis. As in Cartesian coordinates, the z-coordinate is the signed vertical distance between P and the xy-plane (Figure 14.47). Any point in $\mathbb{R}^3$ can be represented by cylindrical coordinates using the intervals $0 \le r < \infty, 0 \le \theta \le 2\pi$, and $-\infty < z < \infty$.

▷ In cylindrical coordinates, r and θ are the usual polar coordinates, with the additional restriction that $r \ge 0$.

Many sets of points have simple representations in cylindrical coordinates. For example, the set $\{(r, \theta, z): r = a\}$ is the set of points whose distance from the z-axis is a, which is a right circular cylinder of radius a. The set $\{(r, \theta, z): \theta = \theta_0\}$ is the set of points with a constant θ coordinate; it is a vertical half plane emanating from the z-axis in the direction $\theta = \theta_0$. Table 14.4 summarizes these and other sets that are ideal for integration in cylindrical coordinates.

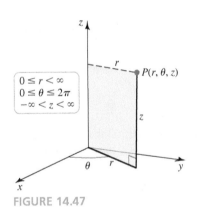

$0 \le r < \infty$
$0 \le \theta \le 2\pi$
$-\infty < z < \infty$

FIGURE 14.47

Table 14.4

Name	Description	Example
Cylinder	$\{(r, \theta, z): r = a\}, a > 0$	
Cylindrical shell	$\{(r, \theta, z): 0 < a \le r \le b\}$	

(Continued)

Table 14.4 **(Continued)**

Name	Description	Example
Vertical half plane	$\{(r,\theta,z): \theta = \theta_0\}$	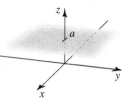
Horizontal plane	$\{(r,\theta,z): z = a\}$	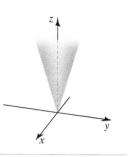
Cone	$\{(r,\theta,z): z = ar\}, a \neq 0$	

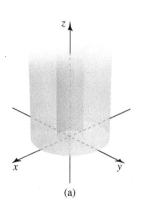

(a)

(b)

FIGURE 14.48

EXAMPLE 1   Sets in cylindrical coordinates Identify and sketch the following sets in cylindrical coordinates.

a. $Q = \{(r,\theta,z): 1 \leq r \leq 3, z \geq 0\}$

b. $S = \{(r,\theta,z): z = 1 - r, 0 \leq r \leq 1\}$

SOLUTION

a. The set Q is a cylindrical shell with inner radius 1 and outer radius 3 that extends indefinitely along the positive z-axis (Figure 14.48a). Because θ is unspecified, it takes on all values.

b. To identify this solid, it helps to work in steps. The set $S_1 = \{(r,\theta,z): z = r\}$ is a cone that opens *upward* with its vertex at the origin. Similarly, the set $S_2 = \{(r,\theta,z): z = -r\}$ is a cone that opens *downward* with its vertex at the origin. Therefore, S is S_2 shifted vertically upward by one unit; it is a cone that opens downward with its vertex at $(0, 0, 1)$. Because $0 \leq r \leq 1$, the base of the cone is on the xy-plane (Figure 14.48b).

Related Exercises 11–14 ◄

Equations for transforming Cartesian coordinates to cylindrical coordinates, and vice versa, are often needed for integration. We simply use the rules for polar coordinates (Section 11.2) with no change in the z-coordinate (Figure 14.49).

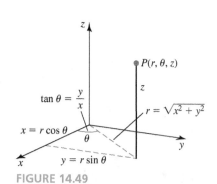

FIGURE 14.49

Transformations Between Cylindrical and Rectangular Coordinates	
Rectangular $\longrightarrow$ Cylindrical	**Cylindrical $\longrightarrow$ Rectangular**
$r^2 = x^2 + y^2$	$x = r \cos \theta$
$\tan \theta = y/x$	$y = r \sin \theta$
$z = z$	$z = z$

QUICK CHECK 1 Find the cylindrical coordinates of the point with rectangular coordinates $(1, -1, 5)$. Find the rectangular coordinates of the point with cylindrical coordinates $(2, \pi/3, 5)$.

Integration in Cylindrical Coordinates

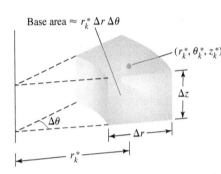

Base area $\approx r_k^* \, \Delta r \, \Delta \theta$

$(r_k^*, \theta_k^*, z_k^*)$

Approximate volume $\Delta V_k \approx r_k^* \, \Delta r \, \Delta \theta \, \Delta z$

FIGURE 14.50

Among the uses of cylindrical coordinates is the evaluation of triple integrals. We begin with a region D in $\mathbb{R}^3$ and partition it into cylindrical wedges formed by changes of Δr, $\Delta \theta$, and Δz in the coordinate directions (Figure 14.50). Those wedges that lie entirely within D are labeled from $k = 1$ to $k = n$ in some convenient order. We let $(r_k^*, \theta_k^*, z_k^*)$ be an arbitrary point in the kth wedge.

As shown in Figure 14.50, the base of the kth wedge is a polar rectangle with an approximate area of $r_k^* \Delta r \Delta \theta$ (Section 14.3). The height of the wedge is Δz. Multiplying these dimensions together, the approximate volume of the wedge is $\Delta V_k = r_k^* \Delta r \Delta \theta \Delta z$, for $k = 1, \ldots, n$.

We now assume that f is continuous on D and form a Riemann sum over the region by adding function values multiplied by the corresponding approximate volumes:

$$\sum_{k=1}^{n} f(r_k^*, \theta_k^*, z_k^*) \Delta V_k = \sum_{k=1}^{n} f(r_k^*, \theta_k^*, z_k^*) \, r_k^* \Delta r \, \Delta \theta \, \Delta z.$$

Let Δ be the maximum value of Δr, $\Delta \theta$, and Δz, for $k = 1, 2, \ldots, n$. As $n \to \infty$ and $\Delta \to 0$, the Riemann sums approach a limit called the **triple integral of f over D in cylindrical coordinates**:

$$\iiint_D f(r, \theta, z) \, dV = \lim_{\Delta \to 0} \sum_{k=1}^{n} f(r_k^*, \theta_k^*, z_k^*) \, r_k^* \Delta r \, \Delta \theta \, \Delta z.$$

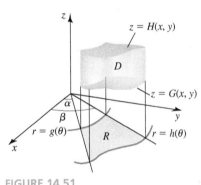

FIGURE 14.51

Finding Limits of Integration We show how to find the limits of integration in one common situation involving cylindrical coordinates. Suppose D is a region in $\mathbb{R}^3$ consisting of points between the surfaces $z = G(x, y)$ and $z = H(x, y)$, where x and y belong to a region R in the xy-plane and $G(x, y) \leq H(x, y)$ on R (Figure 14.51). Assuming f is continuous on D, the triple integral of f over D may be expressed as the iterated integral

$$\iiint_D f(x, y, z) \, dV = \iint_R \left[\int_{G(x, y)}^{H(x, y)} f(x, y, z) \, dz \right] dA.$$

The inner integral with respect to z runs from the lower surface $z = G(x, y)$ to the upper surface $z = H(x, y)$, leaving an outer double integral over R.

If the region R is described in polar coordinates by

$$\{ (r, \theta) : g(\theta) \leq r \leq h(\theta), \alpha \leq \theta \leq \beta \},$$

then it makes sense to evaluate the double integral over R in polar coordinates (Section 14.3). The effect is a change of variables from rectangular to cylindrical coordinates. Letting $x = r \cos \theta$ and $y = r \sin \theta$, we have the following result, which is another version of Fubini's Theorem.

> The order of the differentials specifies the order in which the integrals are evaluated, so we write the volume element as $dz\, r\, dr\, d\theta$. Do not lose sight of the factor of r in the integrand! It plays the same role as it does in the area element $dA = r\, dr\, d\theta$ in polar coordinates.

THEOREM 14.6   **Triple Integrals in Cylindrical Coordinates**

Let f be continuous over the region

$$D = \{(r, \theta, z): g(\theta) \leq r \leq h(\theta), \alpha \leq \theta \leq \beta, G(x, y) \leq z \leq H(x, y)\}.$$

Then f is integrable over D and the triple integral of f over D in cylindrical coordinates is

$$\iiint\limits_{D} f(r, \theta, z)\, dV = \int_{\alpha}^{\beta} \int_{g(\theta)}^{h(\theta)} \int_{G(r\cos\theta,\, r\sin\theta)}^{H(r\cos\theta,\, r\sin\theta)} f(r, \theta, z)\, dz\, r\, dr\, d\theta.$$

Notice that the integrand and the limits of integration are converted from Cartesian to cylindrical coordinates. As with triple integrals in Cartesian coordinates, there are two immediate interpretations of this integral. If $f = 1$, then the triple integral $\iiint_{D} dV$ equals the volume of the region D. Also, if f describes the density of an object occupying the region D, the triple integral equals the mass of the object.

EXAMPLE 2   **Switching coordinate systems**   Evaluate the integral

$$I = \int_{0}^{2\sqrt{2}} \int_{-\sqrt{8-x^2}}^{\sqrt{8-x^2}} \int_{-1}^{2} \sqrt{1 + x^2 + y^2}\, dz\, dy\, dx.$$

SOLUTION   Evaluating this integral as it is given in Cartesian coordinates requires a tricky trigonometric substitution in the middle integral, followed by an even more difficult integral. Notice that z varies between the planes $z = -1$ and $z = 2$, while x and y vary over half of a disk in the xy-plane. Therefore, D is half of a solid cylinder (Figure 14.52a), which suggests a change to cylindrical coordinates.

The limits of integration in cylindrical coordinates are determined as follows:

Inner integral with respect to z   A line through the half cylinder parallel to the z-axis enters at $z = -1$ and leaves at $z = 2$, so we integrate over the interval $-1 \leq z \leq 2$ (Figure 14.52b).

Middle integral with respect to r   The projection of the half cylinder onto the xy-plane is the half disk R of radius $2\sqrt{2}$ centered at the origin, so r varies over the interval $0 \leq r \leq 2\sqrt{2}$.

Outer integral with respect to θ   The half disk R is swept out by letting θ vary over the interval $-\pi/2 \leq \theta \leq \pi/2$ (Figure 14.52c).

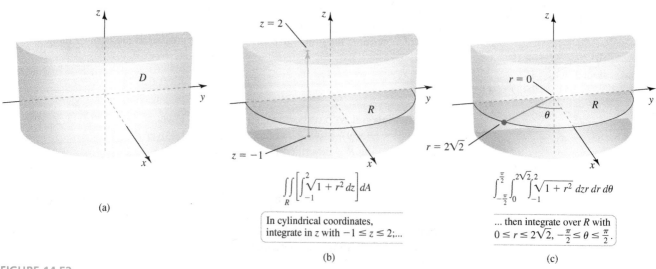

FIGURE 14.52

We also convert the integrand to cylindrical coordinates:

$$f(x, y, z) = \sqrt{1 + \underbrace{x^2 + y^2}_{r^2}} = \sqrt{1 + r^2}.$$

The evaluation of the integral in cylindrical coordinates now follows:

$$I = \int_{-\pi/2}^{\pi/2}\int_{0}^{2\sqrt{2}}\int_{-1}^{2}\sqrt{1 + r^2}\, dz\, r\, dr\, d\theta \qquad \text{Convert to cylindrical coordinates.}$$

$$= 3\int_{-\pi/2}^{\pi/2}\int_{0}^{2\sqrt{2}}\sqrt{1 + r^2}\, r\, dr\, d\theta \qquad \text{Evaluate the inner integral.}$$

$$= \int_{-\pi/2}^{\pi/2}(1 + r^2)^{3/2}\Big|_{0}^{2\sqrt{2}}\, d\theta \qquad \text{Evaluate the middle integral.}$$

$$= \int_{-\pi/2}^{\pi/2} 26\, d\theta = 26\pi. \qquad \text{Evaluate the outer integral.}$$

QUICK CHECK 2 Find the limits of integration for a triple integral in cylindrical coordinates that gives the volume of a cylinder with height 20 and a circular base centered at the origin in the xy-plane of radius 10. ◄

Related Exercises 15–22 ◄

As illustrated in Example 2, triple integrals given in rectangular coordinates may be more easily evaluated after converting to cylindrical coordinates. The following questions may help you choose the best coordinate system for a particular integral.

- In which coordinate system is the region of integration most easily described?
- In which coordinate system is the integrand most easily expressed?
- In which coordinate system is the triple integral most easily evaluated?

In general, if an integral in one coordinate system looks difficult, consider using a different coordinate system.

EXAMPLE 3   Mass of a solid paraboloid Find the mass of the solid D bounded by the paraboloid $z = 4 - r^2$ and the plane $z = 0$ (Figure 14.53a) when the density of the region is $f(r, \theta, z) = 5 - z$ (heavy near the base and light near the vertex).

SOLUTION The z-coordinate runs from the base ($z = 0$) to the surface $z = 4 - r^2$ (Figure 14.53b). The projection R of the region D onto the xy-plane is found by setting

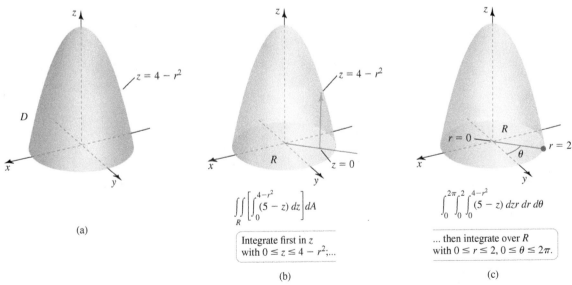

(a)

$$\iint_{R}\left[\int_{0}^{4-r^2}(5 - z)\, dz\right]dA$$

Integrate first in z
with $0 \le z \le 4 - r^2;\ldots$

(b)

$$\int_{0}^{2\pi}\int_{0}^{2}\int_{0}^{4-r^2}(5 - z)\, dz r\, dr\, d\theta$$

... then integrate over R
with $0 \le r \le 2, 0 \le \theta \le 2\pi.$

(c)

FIGURE 14.53

$z = 0$ in the equation of the surface, $z = 4 - r^2$. Solving $4 - r^2 = 0$ (and discarding the negative root), we have $r = 2$, so $R = \{(r, \theta): 0 \leq r \leq 2, 0 \leq \theta \leq 2\pi\}$ is a disk of radius 2 (Figure 14.53c).

The mass is computed by integrating the density function over D:

> In Example 3, the integrand is independent of θ, so the integral with respect to θ could have been done first, producing a factor of 2π.

$$\iiint_D f(r, \theta, z)\, dV = \int_0^{2\pi} \int_0^2 \int_0^{4-r^2} (5 - z)\, dz\, r\, dr\, d\theta \quad \text{Integrate density.}$$

$$= \int_0^{2\pi} \int_0^2 \left(5z - \frac{z^2}{2}\right)\Big|_0^{4-r^2} r\, dr\, d\theta \quad \text{Evaluate the inner integral.}$$

$$= \frac{1}{2}\int_0^{2\pi} \int_0^2 (24r - 2r^3 - r^5)\, dr\, d\theta \quad \text{Simplify.}$$

$$= \int_0^{2\pi} \frac{44}{3}\, d\theta \quad \text{Evaluate the middle integral.}$$

$$= \frac{88\pi}{3}. \quad \text{Evaluate the outer integral.}$$

Related Exercises 23–28 ◀

> Recall that to find the volume of a region D using a triple integral, we set $f = 1$ and evaluate
> $$V = \iiint_D dV.$$

EXAMPLE 4 Volume between two surfaces Find the volume of the solid D between the cone $z = \sqrt{x^2 + y^2}$ and the inverted paraboloid $z = 12 - x^2 - y^2$ (Figure 14.54a).

SOLUTION Because $x^2 + y^2 = r^2$, the equation of the cone becomes $z = r$, and the equation of the paraboloid becomes $z = 12 - r^2$. The inner integral in z runs from the cone $z = r$ (the lower surface) to the paraboloid $z = 12 - r^2$ (the upper surface) (Figure 14.54b). We project D onto the xy-plane to produce the region R, whose boundary is determined by the intersection of the two surfaces. Equating the z-coordinates in the equations of the two surfaces, we have $12 - r^2 = r$, or $(r - 3)(r + 4) = 0$. Because $r \geq 0$, the relevant root is $r = 3$. Therefore, the projection of D on the xy-plane is $R = \{(r, \theta): 0 \leq r \leq 3, 0 \leq \theta \leq 2\pi\}$, which is a disk of radius 3 centered at $(0, 0)$ (Figure 14.54c).

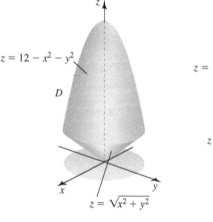

$z = 12 - x^2 - y^2$

D

$z = \sqrt{x^2 + y^2}$

(a)

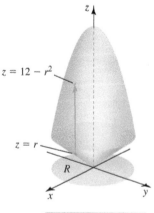

$z = 12 - r^2$

$z = r$

R

Integrate first in z
with $r \leq z \leq 12 - r^2$; ...

(b)

R

$r = 0$

θ

$r = 3$

... then integrate over R
with $0 \leq r \leq 3, 0 \leq \theta \leq 2\pi$.

(c)

FIGURE 14.54

The volume of the region is

$$\iiint_D dV = \int_0^{2\pi} \int_0^3 \int_r^{12-r^2} dz\, r\, dr\, d\theta$$

$$= \int_0^{2\pi} \int_0^3 (12 - r^2 - r)\, r\, dr\, d\theta \qquad \text{Evaluate the inner integral.}$$

$$= \int_0^{2\pi} \frac{99}{4}\, d\theta \qquad\qquad \text{Evaluate the middle integral.}$$

$$= \frac{99\pi}{2}. \qquad\qquad\qquad \text{Evaluate the outer integral.}$$

Related Exercises 29–34 ◄

Spherical Coordinates

In spherical coordinates, a point P in $\mathbb{R}^3$ is represented by three coordinates (ρ, φ, θ) (Figure 14.55).

- ρ is the distance from the origin to P.
- φ is the angle between the positive z-axis and the line OP.
- θ is the same angle as in cylindrical coordinates; it measures rotation about the z-axis relative to the positive x-axis.

All points in $\mathbb{R}^3$ can be represented by spherical coordinates using the intervals $0 \le \rho < \infty, 0 \le \varphi \le \pi$, and $0 \le \theta \le 2\pi$.

Figure 14.56 allows us to find the relationships among rectangular and spherical coordinates. Given the spherical coordinates (ρ, φ, θ) of a point P, the distance from P to the z-axis is $r = \rho \sin \varphi$. We also see from Figure 14.56 that $x = r \cos \theta = \rho \sin \varphi \cos \theta$, $y = r \sin \theta = \rho \sin \varphi \sin \theta$, and $z = \rho \cos \varphi$.

> The coordinate ρ (pronounced "rho") in spherical coordinates should not be confused with r in cylindrical coordinates, which is the distance from P to the z-axis.

> The coordinate φ is called the *colatitude* because it is $\pi/2$ minus the latitude of points in the northern hemisphere. Physicists may reverse the roles of θ and φ; that is, θ is the colatitude and φ is the polar angle. Use caution!

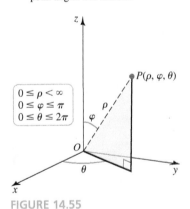

$0 \le \rho < \infty$
$0 \le \varphi \le \pi$
$0 \le \theta \le 2\pi$

FIGURE 14.55

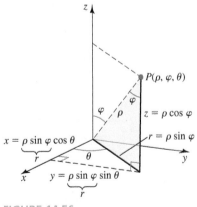

$z = \rho \cos \varphi$
$r = \rho \sin \varphi$
$x = \rho \sin \varphi \cos \theta$
$y = \rho \sin \varphi \sin \theta$

FIGURE 14.56

Transformations Between Spherical and Rectangular Coordinates	
Rectangular $\to$ Spherical	**Spherical $\to$ Rectangular**
$\rho^2 = x^2 + y^2 + z^2$	$x = \rho \sin \varphi \cos \theta$
Use trigonometry to find	$y = \rho \sin \varphi \sin \theta$
φ and θ	$z = \rho \cos \varphi$

QUICK CHECK 3 Find the spherical coordinates of the point with rectangular coordinates $(1, \sqrt{3}, 2)$. Find the rectangular coordinates of the point with spherical coordinates $(2, \pi/4, \pi/4)$. ◄

In spherical coordinates, some sets of points have simple representations. For instance, the set $\{(\rho, \varphi, \theta): \rho = a\}$ is the set of points whose ρ coordinate is constant, which is a sphere of radius a centered at the origin. The set $\{(\rho, \varphi, \theta): \varphi = \varphi_0\}$ is the set of points with a constant φ-coordinate; it is a cone with its vertex at the origin and whose sides make an angle φ_0 with the positive z-axis.

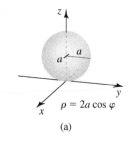

$\rho = 2a \cos \varphi$

(a)

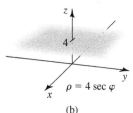

$\rho = 4 \sec \varphi$

(b)

FIGURE 14.57

EXAMPLE 5   Sets in spherical coordinates Express the following sets in rectangular coordinates and identify the set. Assume that a is a positive real number.

a. $\{(\rho, \varphi, \theta): \rho = 2a \cos \varphi, 0 \leq \varphi \leq \pi/2, 0 \leq \theta \leq 2\pi\}$

b. $\{(\rho, \varphi, \theta): \rho = 4 \sec \varphi, 0 \leq \varphi < \pi/2, 0 \leq \theta \leq 2\pi\}$

SOLUTION

a. To avoid working with square roots, we multiply both sides of $\rho = 2a \cos \varphi$ by ρ to obtain $\rho^2 = 2a \rho \cos \varphi$. Substituting rectangular coordinates we have $x^2 + y^2 + z^2 = 2az$. Completing the square results in the equation

$$x^2 + y^2 + (z - a)^2 = a^2.$$

This is the equation of a sphere centered at $(0, 0, a)$ with radius a (Figure 14.57a). With the limits $0 \leq \varphi \leq \pi/2$ and $0 \leq \theta \leq 2\pi$, the set describes a full sphere.

b. The equation $\rho = 4 \sec \varphi$ is first written $\rho \cos \varphi = 4$. Noting that $z = \rho \cos \varphi$, the set consists of all points with $z = 4$, which is a horizontal plane (Figure 14.57b).

Related Exercises 35–38 ◄

Table 14.5 summarizes some sets that have simple descriptions in spherical coordinates.

Table 14.5

Name	Description	Example
Sphere, radius a, center $(0, 0, 0)$	$\{(\rho, \varphi, \theta): \rho = a\}, a > 0$	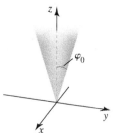
Cone	$\{(\rho, \varphi, \theta): \varphi = \varphi_0\}, \varphi_0 \neq 0, \pi/2, \pi$	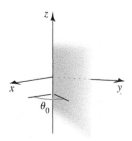
Vertical half plane	$\{(\rho, \varphi, \theta): \theta = \theta_0\}$	

> Notice that the set (ρ, φ, θ) with $\varphi = \pi/2$ is the xy-plane, and if $\pi/2 < \varphi_0 < \pi$, the set $\varphi = \varphi_0$ is a cone that opens downward.

(Continued)

Table 14.5 **(Continued)**

Name	Description	Example
Horizontal plane, $z = a$	$\{(\rho, \varphi, \theta): \rho = a \sec \varphi, 0 \leq \varphi < \pi/2\}$	
Cylinder, radius $a > 0$	$\{(\rho, \varphi, \theta): \rho = a \csc \varphi, 0 < \varphi < \pi\}$	
Sphere, radius $a > 0$, center $(0, 0, a)$	$\{(\rho, \varphi, \theta): \rho = 2a \cos \varphi, 0 \leq \varphi \leq \pi/2\}$	

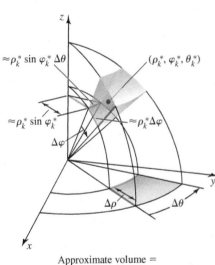

Approximate volume =
$$\Delta V_k \approx \rho_k^{*2} \sin \varphi_k^* \, \Delta\rho \, \Delta\varphi \, \Delta\theta$$

FIGURE 14.58

> Recall that the length s of a circular arc of radius r subtended by an angle θ is $s = r\theta$.

Integration in Spherical Coordinates

We now investigate triple integrals in spherical coordinates over a region D in $\mathbb{R}^3$. The region D is partitioned into "spherical boxes" that are formed by changes of $\Delta\rho$, $\Delta\varphi$, and $\Delta\theta$ in the coordinate directions (Figure 14.58). Those boxes that lie entirely within D are labeled from $k = 1$ to $k = n$. We let $(\rho_k^*, \varphi_k^*, \theta_k^*)$ be an arbitrary point in the kth box.

To approximate the volume of a typical box, note that the length of the box in the ρ-direction is $\Delta\rho$ (Figure 14.58). The approximate length of the kth box in the θ-direction is the length of an arc of a circle of radius $\rho_k^* \sin \varphi_k^*$ subtended by an angle $\Delta\theta$; this length is $\rho_k^* \sin \varphi_k^* \Delta\theta$. The approximate length of the box in the φ-direction is the length of an arc of radius ρ_k^* subtended by an angle $\Delta\varphi$; this length is $\rho_k^* \Delta\varphi$. Multiplying these dimensions together, the approximate volume of the kth spherical box is $\Delta V_k = \rho_k^{*2} \sin \varphi_k^* \Delta\rho \, \Delta\varphi \, \Delta\theta$, for $k = 1, \ldots, n$.

We now assume that f is continuous on D and form a Riemann sum over the region by adding function values multiplied by the corresponding approximate volumes:

$$\sum_{k=1}^{n} f(\rho_k^*, \varphi_k^*, \theta_k^*)\Delta V_k = \sum_{k=1}^{n} f(\rho_k^*, \varphi_k^*, \theta_k^*)\, \rho_k^{*2} \sin \varphi_k^* \Delta\rho \, \Delta\varphi \, \Delta\theta.$$

We let Δ denote the maximum value of $\Delta\rho$, $\Delta\varphi$, and $\Delta\theta$. As $n \to \infty$ and $\Delta \to 0$, the Riemann sums approach a limit called the **triple integral of f over D in spherical coordinates**:

$$\iiint\limits_{D} f(\rho, \varphi, \theta)\, dV = \lim_{\Delta \to 0} \sum_{k=1}^{n} f(\rho_k^*, \varphi_k^*, \theta_k^*)\, \rho_k^{*2} \sin \varphi_k^* \Delta\rho \, \Delta\varphi \, \Delta\theta.$$

Finding Limits of Integration   We consider a common situation in which the region of integration has the form

$$D = \{(\rho, \varphi, \theta): g(\varphi, \theta) \leq \rho \leq h(\varphi, \theta), a \leq \varphi \leq b, \alpha \leq \theta \leq \beta\}.$$

In other words, D is bounded in the ρ-direction by two surfaces given by g and h. In the angular directions, the region lies between two cones ($a \leq \varphi \leq b$) and two half planes ($\alpha \leq \theta \leq \beta$) (Figure 14.59).

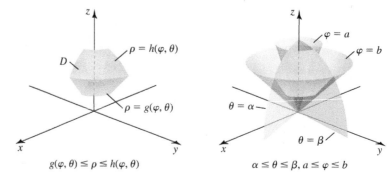

$$g(\varphi, \theta) \leq \rho \leq h(\varphi, \theta) \qquad\qquad \alpha \leq \theta \leq \beta, a \leq \varphi \leq b$$

FIGURE 14.59

For this type of region, the inner integral is with respect to ρ, which varies from $\rho = g(\varphi, \theta)$ to $\rho = h(\varphi, \theta)$. As ρ varies between these limits, imagine letting θ and φ vary over the intervals $a \leq \varphi \leq b$ and $\alpha \leq \theta \leq \beta$. The effect is to sweep out all points of D. Notice that the middle and outer integrals, with respect to θ and φ, may be done in either order (Figure 14.60).

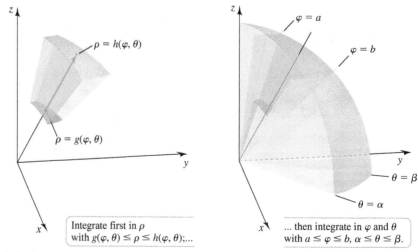

Integrate first in ρ
with $g(\varphi, \theta) \leq \rho \leq h(\varphi, \theta);\ldots$

... then integrate in φ and θ
with $a \leq \varphi \leq b, \alpha \leq \theta \leq \beta$.

FIGURE 14.60

In summary, to integrate over D we

• first integrate with respect to ρ from $\rho = g(\varphi, \theta)$ to $\rho = h(\varphi, \theta)$,

• then integrate with respect to φ from $\varphi = a$ to $\varphi = b$, and

• finally integrate with respect to θ from $\theta = \alpha$ to $\theta = \beta$.

Another version of Fubini's Theorem expresses the triple integral as an iterated integral.

> The element of volume in spherical coordinates is $dV = \rho^2 \sin\varphi \, d\rho \, d\varphi \, d\theta$.

THEOREM 14.7   Triple Integrals in Spherical Coordinates

Let f be continuous over the region

$$D = \{(\rho, \varphi, \theta): g(\varphi, \theta) \le \rho \le h(\varphi, \theta), a \le \varphi \le b, \alpha \le \theta \le \beta\}.$$

Then f is integrable over D, and the triple integral of f over D in spherical coordinates is

$$\iiint_D f(\rho, \varphi, \theta)\, dV = \int_\alpha^\beta \int_a^b \int_{g(\varphi,\theta)}^{h(\varphi,\theta)} f(\rho, \varphi, \theta)\, \rho^2 \sin\varphi \, d\rho \, d\varphi \, d\theta.$$

If the integrand is given in terms of Cartesian coordinates x, y, and z, it must be expressed in spherical coordinates before integrating. As with other triple integrals, if $f = 1$, then the triple integral equals the volume of D. If f is a density function for an object occupying the region D, then the triple integral equals the mass of the object.

EXAMPLE 6   A triple integral Evaluate $\iiint_D (x^2 + y^2 + z^2)^{-3/2}\, dV$, where D is the region in the first octant between two spheres of radius 1 and 2 centered at the origin.

SOLUTION Both the integrand f and region D are greatly simplified when expressed in spherical coordinates. The integrand becomes

$$(x^2 + y^2 + z^2)^{-3/2} = (\rho^2)^{-3/2} = \rho^{-3},$$

while the region of integration is (Figure 14.61)

$$D = \{(\rho, \varphi, \theta): 1 \le \rho \le 2, 0 \le \varphi \le \pi/2, 0 \le \theta \le \pi/2\}.$$

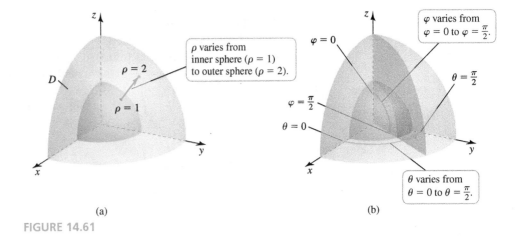

(a)   (b)

FIGURE 14.61

The integral is evaluated as follows:

$$\iiint_D f(x, y, z)\, dV = \int_0^{\pi/2} \int_0^{\pi/2} \int_1^2 \rho^{-3} \rho^2 \sin\varphi \, d\rho \, d\varphi \, d\theta \qquad \text{Convert to spherical coordinates.}$$

$$= \int_0^{\pi/2} \int_0^{\pi/2} \int_1^2 \rho^{-1} \sin\varphi \, d\rho \, d\varphi \, d\theta \qquad \text{Simplify.}$$

$$= \int_0^{\pi/2} \int_0^{\pi/2} \ln|\rho|\, \Big|_1^2 \sin\varphi \, d\varphi \, d\theta \qquad \text{Evaluate the inner integral.}$$

$$= \ln 2 \int_0^{\pi/2} \int_0^{\pi/2} \sin \varphi \, d\varphi \, d\theta \qquad \text{Simplify.}$$

$$= \ln 2 \int_0^{\pi/2} (-\cos \varphi) \Big|_0^{\pi/2} d\theta \qquad \text{Evaluate the middle integral.}$$

$$= \ln 2 \int_0^{\pi/2} d\theta = \frac{\pi \ln 2}{2}. \qquad \text{Evaluate the outer integral.}$$

Related Exercises 39–45 ◄

EXAMPLE 7   Ice cream cone Find the volume of the solid region D that lies inside the cone $\varphi = \pi/6$ and inside the sphere $\rho = 4$ (Figure 14.62a).

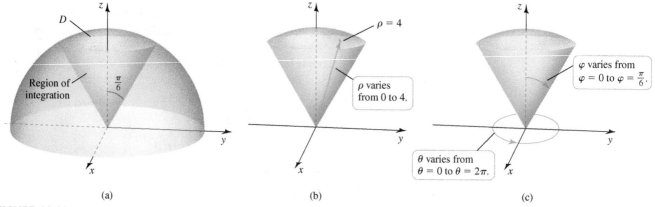

(a)   (b)   (c)

FIGURE 14.62

SOLUTION To find the volume, we evaluate a triple integral with $f(\rho, \varphi, \theta) = 1$. In the radial direction, the region extends from the origin $\rho = 0$ to the sphere $\rho = 4$. To sweep out all points of D, φ varies from 0 to $\pi/6$ and θ varies from 0 to 2π (Figure 14.62b, c). Integrating the function $f = 1$, the volume of the region is

$$\iiint_D dV = \int_0^{2\pi} \int_0^{\pi/6} \int_0^4 \rho^2 \sin \varphi \, d\rho \, d\varphi \, d\theta \qquad \text{Convert to an iterated integral.}$$

$$= \int_0^{2\pi} \int_0^{\pi/6} \frac{\rho^3}{3} \Big|_0^4 \sin \varphi \, d\varphi \, d\theta \qquad \text{Evaluate the inner integral.}$$

$$= \frac{64}{3} \int_0^{2\pi} \int_0^{\pi/6} \sin \varphi \, d\varphi \, d\theta \qquad \text{Simplify.}$$

$$= \frac{64}{3} \int_0^{2\pi} \underbrace{(-\cos \varphi) \Big|_0^{\pi/6}}_{1 \, - \, \sqrt{3}/2} d\theta \qquad \text{Evaluate the middle integral.}$$

$$= \frac{32}{3} (2 - \sqrt{3}) \int_0^{2\pi} d\theta \qquad \text{Simplify.}$$

$$= \frac{64\pi}{3} (2 - \sqrt{3}). \qquad \text{Evaluate the outer integral.}$$

Related Exercises 46–52 ◄

SECTION 14.5 EXERCISES

Review Questions

1. Explain how cylindrical coordinates are used to describe a point in $\mathbb{R}^3$.

2. Explain how spherical coordinates are used to describe a point in $\mathbb{R}^3$.

3. Describe the set $\{(r, \theta, z): r = 4z\}$ in cylindrical coordinates.

4. Describe the set $\{(\rho, \varphi, \theta): \varphi = \pi/4\}$ in spherical coordinates.

5. Explain why $dz\, r\, dr\, d\theta$ is the volume of a small "box" in cylindrical coordinates.

6. Explain why $\rho^2 \sin \varphi\, d\rho\, d\varphi\, d\theta$ is the volume of a small "box" in spherical coordinates.

7. Write the integral $\iiint_D f(r, \theta, z)\, dV$ as an iterated integral where $D = \{(r, \theta, z): G(r, \theta) \le z \le H(r, \theta), g(\theta) \le r \le h(\theta), \alpha \le \theta \le \beta\}$.

8. Write the integral $\iiint_D f(\rho, \varphi, \theta)\, dV$ as an iterated integral, where $D = \{(\rho, \varphi, \theta): g(\varphi, \theta) \le \rho \le h(\varphi, \theta), a \le \varphi \le b, \alpha \le \theta \le \beta\}$.

9. What coordinate system is *suggested* if the integrand of a triple integral involves $x^2 + y^2$?

10. What coordinate system is *suggested* if the integrand of a triple integral involves $x^2 + y^2 + z^2$?

Basic Skills

11–14. Sets in cylindrical coordinates *Identify and sketch the following sets in cylindrical coordinates.*

11. $\{(r, \theta, z): 0 \le r \le 3, 0 \le \theta \le \pi/3, 1 \le z \le 4\}$

12. $\{(r, \theta, z): 0 \le \theta \le \pi/2, z = 1\}$

13. $\{(r, \theta, z): 2r \le z \le 4\}$

14. $\{(r, \theta, z): 0 \le z \le 8 - 2r\}$

15–18. Integrals in cylindrical coordinates *Evaluate the following integrals in cylindrical coordinates.*

15. $\displaystyle\int_0^{2\pi}\int_0^1\int_{-1}^1 dz\, r\, dr\, d\theta$

16. $\displaystyle\int_0^3\int_{-\sqrt{9-y^2}}^{\sqrt{9-y^2}}\int_0^{9-3\sqrt{x^2+y^2}} dz\, dx\, dy$

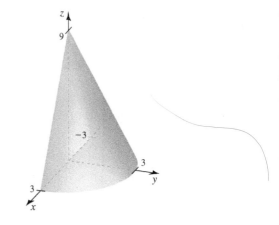

17. $\displaystyle\int_{-1}^1\int_{-\sqrt{1-y^2}}^{\sqrt{1-y^2}}\int_{-1}^1 (x^2 + y^2)^{3/2}\, dz\, dx\, dy$

18. $\displaystyle\int_{-3}^3\int_0^{\sqrt{9-x^2}}\int_0^2 \frac{1}{1 + x^2 + y^2}\, dz\, dy\, dx$

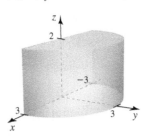

19–22. Integrals in cylindrical coordinates *Evaluate the following integrals in cylindrical coordinates.*

19. $\displaystyle\int_0^4\int_0^{\sqrt{2}/2}\int_x^{\sqrt{1-x^2}} e^{-x^2-y^2}\, dy\, dx\, dz$

20. $\displaystyle\int_{-4}^4\int_{-\sqrt{16-x^2}}^{\sqrt{16-x^2}}\int_{\sqrt{x^2+y^2}}^4 dz\, dy\, dx$

21. $\displaystyle\int_0^3\int_0^{\sqrt{9-x^2}}\int_0^{\sqrt{x^2+y^2}} (x^2 + y^2)^{-1/2}\, dz\, dy\, dx$

22. $\int_{-1}^{1} \int_{0}^{1/2} \int_{\sqrt{3}y}^{\sqrt{1-y^2}} (x^2 + y^2)^{1/2} \, dx \, dy \, dz$

23–26. Mass from density *Find the mass of the following objects with the given density functions.*

23. The solid cylinder $D = \{(r, \theta, z): 0 \le r \le 4, 0 \le z \le 10\}$ with density $\rho(r, \theta, z) = 1 + z/2$

24. The solid cylinder $D = \{(r, \theta, z): 0 \le r \le 3, 0 \le z \le 2\}$ with density $\rho(r, \theta, z) = 5e^{-r^2}$

25. The solid cone $D = \{(r, \theta, z): 0 \le z \le 6 - r, 0 \le r \le 6\}$ with density $\rho(r, \theta, z) = 7 - z$

26. The solid paraboloid $D = \{(r, \theta, z): 0 \le z \le 9 - r^2,\\ 0 \le r \le 3\}$ with density $\rho(r, \theta, z) = 1 + z/9$

27. Which weighs more? For $0 \le r \le 1$, the solid bounded by the cone $z = 4 - 4r$ and the solid bounded by the paraboloid $z = 4 - 4r^2$ have the same base in the xy-plane and the same height. Which object has the greater mass if the density of both objects is $\rho(r, \theta, z) = 10 - 2z$?

28. Which weighs more? Which of the objects in Exercise 27 weighs more if the density of both objects is $\rho(r, \theta, z) = \dfrac{8}{\pi} e^{-z}$?

29–34. Volumes in cylindrical coordinates *Use cylindrical coordinates to find the volume of the following solid regions.*

29. The region bounded by the plane $z = 0$ and the hyperboloid $z = \sqrt{17} - \sqrt{1 + x^2 + y^2}$

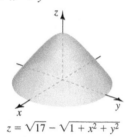

$z = \sqrt{17} - \sqrt{1 + x^2 + y^2}$

30. The region bounded by the plane $z = 25$ and the paraboloid $z = x^2 + y^2$

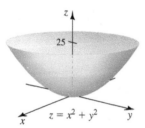

$z = x^2 + y^2$

31. The region bounded by the plane $z = \sqrt{29}$ and the hyperboloid $z = \sqrt{4 + x^2 + y^2}$

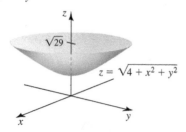

$z = \sqrt{4 + x^2 + y^2}$

32. The solid cylinder whose height is 4 and whose base is the disk $\{(r, \theta): 0 \le r \le 2 \cos \theta\}$

33. The region in the first octant bounded by the cylinder $r = 1$, and the planes $z = x$ and $z = 0$.

34. The region bounded by the cylinders $r = 1$ and $r = 2$, and the planes $z = 4 - x - y$ and $z = 0$

35–38. Sets in spherical coordinates *Identify and sketch the following sets in spherical coordinates.*

35. $\{(\rho, \varphi, \theta): 1 \le \rho \le 3\}$

36. $\{(\rho, \varphi, \theta): \rho = 2 \csc \varphi, 0 < \varphi < \pi\}$

37. $\{(\rho, \varphi, \theta): \rho = 4 \cos \varphi, 0 \le \varphi \le \pi/2\}$

38. $\{(\rho, \varphi, \theta): \rho = 2 \sec \varphi, 0 \le \varphi < \pi/2\}$

39–45. Integrals in spherical coordinates *Evaluate the following integrals in spherical coordinates.*

39. $\displaystyle\iiint_D (x^2 + y^2 + z^2)^{5/2} \, dV$; D is the unit ball.

40. $\displaystyle\iiint_D e^{-(x^2+y^2+z^2)^{3/2}} \, dV$; D is the unit ball.

41. $\displaystyle\iiint_D \frac{1}{(x^2 + y^2 + z^2)^{3/2}} \, dV$; D is the region between the spheres

of radius 1 and 2 centered at the origin.

42. $\displaystyle\int_0^{2\pi} \int_0^{\pi/3} \int_0^{4 \sec \varphi} \rho^2 \sin \varphi \, d\rho \, d\varphi \, d\theta$

43. $\displaystyle\int_0^{\pi} \int_0^{\pi/6} \int_{2 \sec \varphi}^{4} \rho^2 \sin \varphi \, d\rho \, d\varphi \, d\theta$

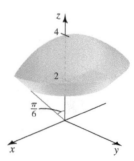

44. $\int_0^{2\pi} \int_0^{\pi/4} \int_1^{2\sec\varphi} (\rho^{-3})\, \rho^2 \sin\varphi\, d\rho\, d\varphi\, d\theta$

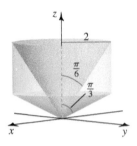

45. $\int_0^{2\pi} \int_{\pi/6}^{\pi/3} \int_0^{2\csc\varphi} \rho^2 \sin\varphi\, d\rho\, d\varphi\, d\theta$

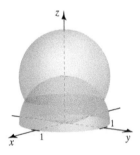

46–52. Volumes in spherical coordinates *Use spherical coordinates to find the volume of the following regions.*

46. A ball of radius $a > 0$

47. The region bounded by the sphere $\rho = 2\cos\varphi$ and the hemisphere $\rho = 1, z \geq 0$

48. The cardioid of revolution
$D = \{(\rho, \varphi, \theta): 0 \leq \rho \leq 1 + \cos\varphi, 0 \leq \varphi \leq \pi, 0 \leq \theta \leq 2\pi\}$

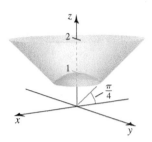

49. The region outside the cone $\varphi = \pi/4$ and inside the sphere $\rho = 4\cos\varphi$

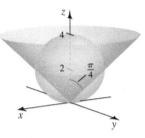

50. The region bounded by the cylinders $r = 1$ and $r = 2$, and the cones $\varphi = \pi/6$ and $\varphi = \pi/3$

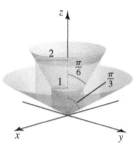

51. That part of the ball $\rho \leq 4$ that lies between the planes $z = 2$ and $z = 2\sqrt{3}$

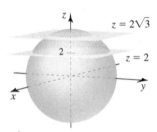

52. The region inside the cone $z = (x^2 + y^2)^{1/2}$ that lies between the planes $z = 1$ and $z = 2$

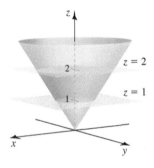

Further Explorations

53. Explain why or why not Determine whether the following statements are true and give an explanation or counterexample.

  a. Any point on the z-axis has more than one representation in both cylindrical and spherical coordinates.

  b. The sets $\{(r, \theta, z): r = z\}$ and $\{(\rho, \varphi, \theta): \varphi = \pi/4\}$ are the same.

54. Spherical to rectangular Convert the equation $\rho^2 = \sec 2\varphi$, where $0 \le \varphi < \pi/4$, to rectangular coordinates and identify the surface.

55. Spherical to rectangular Convert the equation $\rho^2 = -\sec 2\varphi$, where $\pi/4 < \varphi \le \pi/2$, to rectangular coordinates and identify the surface.

56–59. Mass from density *Find the mass of the following objects with the given density functions.*

56. The ball of radius 4 centered at the origin with a density $f(\rho, \varphi, \theta) = 1 + \rho$

57. The ball of radius 8 centered at the origin with a density $f(\rho, \varphi, \theta) = 2e^{-\rho^3}$

58. The solid cone $\{(\rho, \varphi, \theta): \varphi \le \pi/3, 0 \le z \le 4\}$ with a density $f(\rho, \varphi, \theta) = 5 - z$

59. The solid cylinder $\{(r, \theta, z): 0 \le r \le 2, 0 \le \theta \le 2\pi, -1 \le z \le 1\}$ with a density of $\rho(r, z) = (2 - |z|)(4 - r)$

60–61. Changing order of integration *If possible, write iterated integrals in cylindrical coordinates for the following regions in the specified orders. Sketch the region of integration.*

60. The region outside the cylinder $r = 1$ and inside the sphere $\rho = 5$, for $z \ge 0$, in the orders $dz\, dr\, d\theta$, $dr\, dz\, d\theta$, and $d\theta\, dz\, dr$

61. The region above the cone $z = r$ and below the sphere $\rho = 2$, for $z \ge 0$, in the orders $dz\, dr\, d\theta$, $dr\, dz\, d\theta$, and $d\theta\, dz\, dr$

62–63. Changing order of integration *If possible, write iterated integrals in spherical coordinates for the following regions in the specified orders. Sketch the region of integration. Assume that f is continuous on the region.*

62. $\displaystyle\int_0^{2\pi} \int_0^{\pi/4} \int_0^{4\sec\varphi} f(\rho, \varphi, \theta)\, \rho^2 \sin\varphi\, d\rho\, d\varphi\, d\theta$ in the orders $d\rho\, d\theta\, d\varphi$ and $d\theta\, d\rho\, d\varphi$

63. $\displaystyle\int_0^{2\pi} \int_{\pi/6}^{\pi/2} \int_{\csc\varphi}^{2} f(\rho, \varphi, \theta)\, \rho^2 \sin\varphi\, d\rho\, d\varphi\, d\theta$ in the orders $d\rho\, d\theta\, d\varphi$ and $d\theta\, d\rho\, d\varphi$

64–72. Miscellaneous volumes *Choose the best coordinate system and find the volume of the following solid regions. Surfaces are specified using the coordinates that give the simplest description, but the simplest integration may be with respect to different variables.*

64. The region inside the sphere $\rho = 1$ and below the cone $\varphi = \pi/4$, for $z \ge 0$

65. That part of the solid cylinder $r \le 2$ that lies between the cones $\varphi = \pi/3$ and $\varphi = 2\pi/3$

66. That part of the ball $\rho \le 2$ that lies between the cones $\varphi = \pi/3$ and $\varphi = 2\pi/3$

67. The region bounded by the cylinder $r = 1$, for $0 \le z \le x + y$

68. The region inside the cylinder $r = 2\cos\theta$, for $0 \le z \le 4 - x$

69. The wedge cut from the cardioid cylinder $r = 1 + \cos\theta$ by the planes $z = 2 - x$ and $z = x - 2$

70. Volume of a drilled hemisphere Find the volume of material remaining in a hemisphere of radius 2 after a cylindrical hole of radius 1 is drilled through the center of the hemisphere perpendicular to its base.

71. Two cylinders The x- and y-axes form the axes of two right circular cylinders with radius 1 (see figure). Find the volume of the solid that is common to the two cylinders.

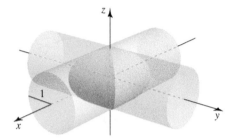

72. Three cylinders The coordinate axes form the axes of three right circular cylinders with radius 1 (see figure). Find the volume of the solid that is common to the three cylinders.

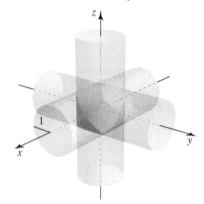

Applications

73. Density distribution A right circular cylinder with height 8 cm and radius 2 cm is filled with water. A heated filament running along its axis produces a variable density in the water given by $\rho(r) = 1 - 0.05e^{-0.01r^2}$ g/cm³ (ρ stands for density here, not the radial spherical coordinate). Find the mass of the water in the cylinder. Neglect the volume of the filament.

74. Charge distribution A spherical cloud of electric charge has a known charge density $Q(\rho)$, where ρ is the spherical coordinate. Find the total charge in the interior of the cloud in the following cases.

a. $Q(\rho) = \dfrac{2 \times 10^{-4}}{\rho^4}, 1 \le \rho < \infty$

b. $Q(\rho) = (2 \times 10^{-4})e^{-0.01\rho^3}, 0 \le \rho < \infty$

75. Gravitational field due to spherical shell A point mass m is a distance d from the center of a thin spherical shell of mass M and radius R. The magnitude of the gravitational force on the point mass is given by the integral

$$F(d) = \frac{GMm}{4\pi} \int_0^{2\pi} \int_0^{\pi} \frac{(d - R\cos\varphi)\sin\varphi}{(R^2 + d^2 - 2Rd\cos\varphi)^{3/2}}\, d\varphi\, d\theta,$$

where G is the gravitational constant.

a. Use the change of variable $x = \cos \varphi$ to evaluate the integral and show that if $d > R$, then $F(d) = \dfrac{GMm}{d^2}$, which means the force is the same as if the mass of the shell were concentrated at its center.

b. Show that if $d < R$ (the point mass is inside the shell), then $F = 0$.

76. Water in a gas tank Before a gasoline-powered engine is started, water must be drained from the bottom of the fuel tank. Suppose the tank is a right circular cylinder on its side with a length of 2 ft and a radius of 1 ft. If the water level is 6 in above the lowest part of the tank, determine how much water must be drained from the tank.

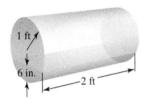

Additional Exercises

77–80. General volume formulas *Use integration to find the volume of the following solids. In each case, choose a convenient coordinate system, find equations for the bounding surfaces, set up a triple integral, and evaluate the integral. Assume that a, b, c, r, R, and h are positive constants.*

77. Cone Find the volume of a solid right circular cone with height h and base radius r.

78. Spherical cap Find the volume of the cap of a sphere of radius R with thickness h.

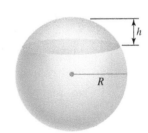

79. Frustum of a cone Find the volume of a truncated solid cone of height h whose ends have radii r and R.

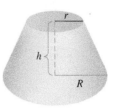

80. Ellipsoid Find the volume of a solid ellipsoid with axes of length $2a$, $2b$, and $2c$.

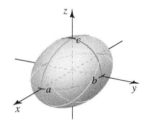

81. Intersecting spheres One sphere is centered at the origin and has a radius of R. Another sphere is centered at $(0, 0, r)$ and has a radius of r, where $r > R/2$. What is the volume of the region common to the two spheres?

> **QUICK CHECK ANSWERS**
>
> **1.** $\left(\sqrt{2}, 7\pi/4, 5 \right), \left(1, \sqrt{3}, 5 \right)$
> **2.** $0 \le r \le 10, 0 \le \theta \le 2\pi, 0 \le z \le 20$
> **3.** $\left(2\sqrt{2}, \pi/4, \pi/3 \right), \left(1, 1, \sqrt{2} \right)$ ◄

14.6 Integrals for Mass Calculations

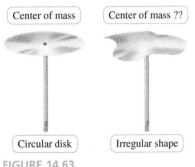

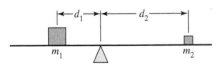

FIGURE 14.63

FIGURE 14.64

Intuition says that a thin circular disk (like a DVD without a hole) should balance on a pencil placed at the center of the disk (Figure 14.63). If, however, you were given a thin plate with an irregular shape, then at what point does it balance? This question asks about the *center of mass* of a thin object (thin enough that it can be treated as a two-dimensional region). Similarly, given a solid object with an irregular shape and variable density, where is the point at which all of the mass of the object would be located if it were treated as a point mass? In this section we use integration to compute the center of mass of one-, two-, and three-dimensional objects.

Sets of Individual Objects

Methods for finding the center of mass of an object are ultimately based on a well-known playground principle: If two people with masses m_1 and m_2 sit at distances d_1 and d_2 from the pivot point of a seesaw (with no mass), then the seesaw balances provided $m_1 d_1 = m_2 d_2$ (Figure 14.64).

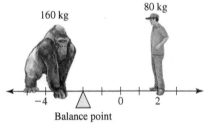

$$\bar{x} = \frac{m_1 x_1 + m_2 x_2}{m_1 + m_2}$$

FIGURE 14.65

> The center of mass may be viewed as the weighted average of the x-coordinates with the masses serving as the weights. Notice how the units work out: If x_1 and x_2 have units of meters and m_1 and m_2 have units of kilograms, then $\bar{x}$ has units of meters.

QUICK CHECK 1 A 90-kg person sits 2 m from the balance point of a seesaw. How far from that point must a 60-kg person sit to balance the seesaw? Assume the seesaw has no mass. ◄

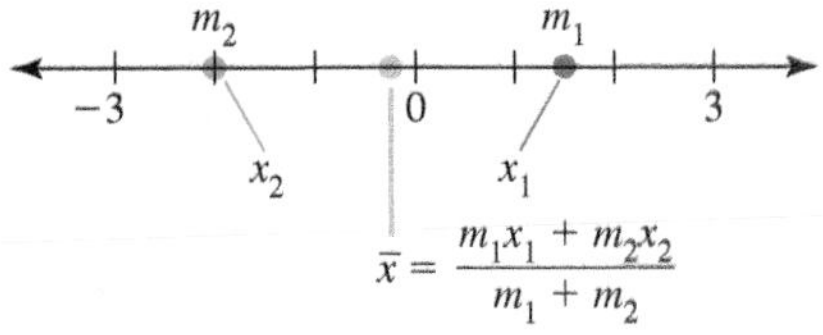

To generalize the problem we introduce a coordinate system with the origin at $x = 0$ (Figure 14.65). Suppose the location of the balance point $\bar{x}$ is unknown. The coordinates of the two masses m_1 and m_2 are denoted x_1 and x_2, respectively, with $x_1 > x_2$. The mass m_1 is a distance $x_1 - \bar{x}$ from the balance point (because distance is positive and $x_1 > \bar{x}$). The mass m_2 is a distance $\bar{x} - x_2$ from the balance point (because $\bar{x} > x_2$). The playground principle becomes

$$m_1(x_1 - \bar{x}) = m_2(\bar{x} - x_2),$$

$$\underbrace{\phantom{m_1(x_1 - \bar{x})}}_{\substack{\text{distance from} \\ \text{balance point} \\ \text{to } m_1}} \quad \underbrace{\phantom{m_2(\bar{x} - x_2)}}_{\substack{\text{distance from} \\ \text{balance point} \\ \text{to } m_2}}$$

or $m_1(x_1 - \bar{x}) + m_2(x_2 - \bar{x}) = 0$.

Solving this equation for $\bar{x}$, the balance point or *center of mass* of the two-mass system is located at

$$\bar{x} = \frac{m_1 x_1 + m_2 x_2}{m_1 + m_2}.$$

The quantities $m_1 x_1$ and $m_2 x_2$ are called *moments about the origin* (or just *moments*). The location of the center of mass is the sum of the moments divided by the sum of the masses.

QUICK CHECK 2 Solve the equation $m_1(x_1 - \bar{x}) + m_2(x_2 - \bar{x}) = 0$ for $\bar{x}$ to verify the preceding expression for the center of mass. ◄

For example, an 80-kg man sitting 2 m to the right of the origin will balance a 160-kg gorilla sitting 4 m to the left of the origin provided the pivot on their seesaw is placed at

$$\bar{x} = \frac{80 \cdot 2 + 160(-4)}{80 + 160} = -2,$$

or 2 m to the left of the origin (Figure 14.66).

160 kg   80 kg

−4   0   2

Balance point

FIGURE 14.66

Several Objects on a Line   Generalizing the preceding argument to n objects having masses $m_1, m_2, \ldots, m_n$ with coordinates $x_1, x_2, \ldots, x_n$, respectively, the balance condition becomes

$$m_1(x_1 - \bar{x}) + m_2(x_2 - \bar{x}) + \cdots + m_n(x_n - \bar{x}) = \sum_{k=1}^{n} m_k(x_k - \bar{x}) = 0.$$

Solving this equation for the location of the center of mass, we find that

$$\bar{x} = \frac{m_1 x_1 + m_2 x_2 + \cdots + m_n x_n}{m_1 + m_2 + \cdots + m_n} = \frac{\displaystyle\sum_{k=1}^{n} m_k x_k}{\displaystyle\sum_{k=1}^{n} m_k}.$$

Again, the location of the center of mass is the sum of the moments $m_1 x_1, m_2 x_2, \ldots, m_n x_n$ divided by the sum of the masses.

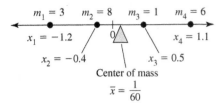

FIGURE 14.67

EXAMPLE 1 **Center of mass for four objects** Find the point at which the system shown in Figure 14.67 balances.

SOLUTION The center of mass is

$$\bar{x} = \frac{m_1 x_1 + m_2 x_2 + m_3 x_3 + m_4 x_4}{m_1 + m_2 + m_3 + m_4}$$

$$= \frac{3(-1.2) + 8(-0.4) + 1(0.5) + 6(1.1)}{3 + 8 + 1 + 6}$$

$$= \frac{1}{60} \approx 0.017.$$

The balancing point is slightly to the right of the origin.

Related Exercises 7–8 ◄

Continuous Objects in One Dimension

Now consider a thin rod or wire with density ρ that varies along the length of the rod (Figure 14.68). The density in this case has units of mass per length (for example, g/cm). As before, we want to determine the location $\bar{x}$ at which the rod balances on a pivot.

> Density is usually measured in units of *mass per volume*. However, for thin, narrow objects such as rods or wires, linear density with units of *mass per length* is used. For thin, flat objects, such as plates and sheets, area density with units of *mass per area* is used.

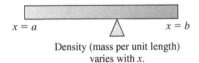

Density (mass per unit length) varies with x.

FIGURE 14.68

QUICK CHECK 3 In Figure 14.68, suppose $a = 0$, $b = 3$, and the density of the rod in g/cm is $\rho(x) = 4 - x$. Where is the rod lightest? Heaviest? ◄

Using the slice-and-sum strategy, we divide the rod, which corresponds to the interval $a \leq x \leq b$, into n subintervals, each with a width of $\Delta x = \dfrac{b - a}{n}$ (Figure 14.69). The corresponding grid points are

$$x_0 = a, x_1 = a + \Delta x, \ldots, x_k = a + k\,\Delta x, \ldots, x_n = b.$$

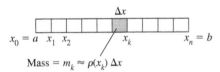

Mass $= m_k \approx \rho(x_k)\,\Delta x$

FIGURE 14.69

The mass of the kth segment of the rod is approximately the density at x_k multiplied by the length of the interval, or $m_k \approx \rho(x_k)\,\Delta x$.

We now use the center-of-mass formula for several distinct objects to write the approximate center of mass of the rod as

$$\bar{x} = \frac{\sum\limits_{k=1}^{n} m_k x_k}{\sum\limits_{k=1}^{n} m_k} \approx \frac{\sum\limits_{k=1}^{n} (\rho(x_k)\,\Delta x)\,x_k}{\sum\limits_{k=1}^{n} \rho(x_k)\,\Delta x}.$$

> An object consisting of two different materials that meet at an interface has a discontinuous density function. Physical density functions are either continuous or have a finite number of discontinuities.

> We assume that the rod has nonzero mass and the limits in the numerator and denominator exist, so the limit of the quotient is the quotient of the limits.

To model a rod with a continuous density, we let $\Delta x \to 0$ and $n \to \infty$; the center of mass of the rod is

$$\bar{x} = \lim_{\Delta x \to 0} \frac{\sum\limits_{k=1}^{n} (\rho(x_k)\,\Delta x)\,x_k}{\sum\limits_{k=1}^{n} \rho(x_k)\,\Delta x} = \frac{\lim\limits_{\Delta x \to 0} \sum\limits_{k=1}^{n} x_k \rho(x_k)\,\Delta x}{\lim\limits_{\Delta x \to 0} \sum\limits_{k=1}^{n} \rho(x_k)\,\Delta x} = \frac{\displaystyle\int_a^b x\rho(x)\,dx}{\displaystyle\int_a^b \rho(x)\,dx}.$$

As discussed in Section 6.6, we identify the denominator of the last fraction, $\int_a^b \rho(x)\,dx$, as the mass of the rod. The numerator is the "sum" of the moments of each piece of the rod, which is called the *total moment*.

> The units of a moment are mass × length. The center of mass is a moment divided by a mass, which has units of length. Notice that if the density is constant, then ρ effectively does not enter the calculation of $\bar{x}$.

DEFINITION   Center of Mass in One Dimension

Let ρ be an integrable density function on the interval $[a, b]$ (which represents a thin rod or wire). The **center of mass** is located at the point $\bar{x} = \dfrac{M}{m}$, where the **total moment** M and mass m are

$$M = \int_a^b x\rho(x)\,dx \quad \text{and} \quad m = \int_a^b \rho(x)\,dx.$$

Observe the parallels between the discrete and continuous cases:

$$n \text{ individual masses:} \quad \bar{x} = \frac{\displaystyle\sum_{k=1}^{n} x_k m_k}{\displaystyle\sum_{k=1}^{n} m_k}; \qquad \text{continuous mass:} \quad \bar{x} = \frac{\displaystyle\int_a^b x\rho(x)\,dx}{\displaystyle\int_a^b \rho(x)\,dx}.$$

EXAMPLE 2   Center of mass of a one-dimensional object Suppose a thin 2-m bar is made of an alloy whose density in kg/m is $\rho(x) = 1 + x^2$, where $0 \le x \le 2$. Find the center of mass of the bar.

SOLUTION The total mass of the bar in kilograms is

$$m = \int_a^b \rho(x)\,dx = \int_0^2 (1 + x^2)\,dx = \left(x + \frac{x^3}{3} \right)\Big|_0^2 = \frac{14}{3}.$$

The total moment of the bar, with units kg · m, is

> Notice that the density of the bar increases with x. As a consistency check, our calculation must result in a center of mass to the right of the midpoint of the bar.

$$M = \int_a^b x\rho(x)\,dx = \int_0^2 x(1 + x^2)\,dx = \left(\frac{x^2}{2} + \frac{x^4}{4} \right)\Big|_0^2 = 6.$$

Therefore, the center of mass is located at $\bar{x} = \dfrac{M}{m} = \dfrac{9}{7} \approx 1.29$ m.

Related Exercises 9–14◀

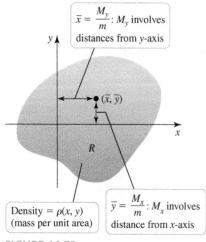

Density = $\rho(x, y)$
(mass per unit area)

FIGURE 14.70

$\bar{x} = \dfrac{M_y}{m}$: M_y involves distances from y-axis

$\bar{y} = \dfrac{M_x}{m}$: M_x involves distance from x-axis

Two-Dimensional Objects

In two dimensions, we start with an integrable density function $\rho(x, y)$ defined over a closed bounded region R in the xy-plane. The density is now an *area density* with units of mass per area (for example, kg/m^2). The region represents a thin plate (or *lamina*). The center of mass is the point at which a pivot must be located to balance the plate. If the density is constant, the location of the center of mass depends only on the shape of the plate, in which case the center of mass is called the *centroid*.

For a two- or three-dimensional object, the coordinates for the center of mass are computed independently by applying the one-dimensional argument in each coordinate direction (Figure 14.70). The mass of the plate is the integral of the density function over R:

$$m = \iint_R \rho(x, y)\,dA.$$

In analogy with the moment calculation in the one-dimensional case, we now define two moments.

The moment with respect to the y-axis M_y is a weighted average of distances from the y-axis, so it has x in the integrand (the distance between a point and the y-axis). Similarly, the moment with respect to the x-axis M_x is a weighted average of distances from the x-axis, so it has y in the integrand.

> **DEFINITION   Center of Mass in Two Dimensions**
>
> Let ρ be an integrable area density function defined over a closed bounded region R in $\mathbb{R}^2$. The coordinates of the center of mass of the object represented by R are
>
> $$\bar{x} = \frac{M_y}{m} = \frac{1}{m} \iint\limits_{R} x\rho(x, y)\, dA \quad \text{and} \quad \bar{y} = \frac{M_x}{m} = \frac{1}{m} \iint\limits_{R} y\rho(x, y)\, dA,$$
>
> where $m = \iint_R \rho(x, y)\, dA$ is the mass, and M_y and M_x are the moments with respect to the y-axis and x-axis, respectively. If ρ is constant, the center of mass is called the **centroid** and is independent of the density.

As before, the center of mass coordinates are weighted averages of the distances from the coordinate axes. For two- and three-dimensional objects, the center of mass need not lie within the object (Exercises 51, 61, and 62).

QUICK CHECK 4 Explain why the integral for M_y has x in the integrand. Explain why the density drops out of the center of mass calculation if it is constant. ◄

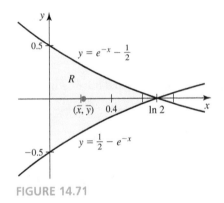

FIGURE 14.71

> The density does not enter the center of mass calculation when the density is constant. So, it is easiest to set $\rho = 1$.

> If possible, try to arrange the coordinate system so that at least one of the integrations in the center of mass calculation can be avoided by using symmetry. Often the mass (or area) can be found using geometry if the density is constant.

EXAMPLE 3   Centroid calculation Find the centroid (center of mass) of the unit density, dart-shaped region bounded by the y-axis and the curves $y = e^{-x} - \frac{1}{2}$ and $y = \frac{1}{2} - e^{-x}$ (Figure 14.71).

SOLUTION Because the region is symmetric about the x-axis and the density is constant, the y-coordinate of the center of mass is $\bar{y} = 0$. This leaves the integrals for m and M_y to evaluate.

The first task is to find the point at which the curves intersect. Solving $e^{-x} - \frac{1}{2} = \frac{1}{2} - e^{-x}$, we find that $x = \ln 2$, from which it follows that $y = 0$. Therefore, the intersection point is $(\ln 2, 0)$. The moment M_y (with $p = 1$) is given by

$$M_y = \int_0^{\ln 2} \int_{1/2 - e^{-x}}^{e^{-x} - 1/2} x\, dy\, dx$$

$$= \int_0^{\ln 2} x \left[\left(e^{-x} - \frac{1}{2} \right) - \left(\frac{1}{2} - e^{-x} \right) \right] dx$$

$$= \int_0^{\ln 2} x(2e^{-x} - 1)\, dx.$$

Using integration by parts for this integral, we find that

$$M_y = \int_0^{\ln 2} \underbrace{x}_{u}\, \underbrace{(2e^{-x} - 1)\, dx}_{dv}$$

$$= -x(2e^{-x} + x) \Big|_0^{\ln 2} + \int_0^{\ln 2} (2e^{-x} + x)\, dx \qquad \text{Integration by parts}$$

$$= 1 - \ln 2 - \frac{1}{2}\ln^2 2 \approx 0.067. \qquad \text{Evaluate and simplify.}$$

With $p = 1$, the mass of the region is given by

$$m = \int_0^{\ln 2} \int_{1/2 - e^{-x}}^{e^{-x} - 1/2} dy \, dx$$

$$= \int_0^{\ln 2} (2e^{-x} - 1) \, dx$$

$$= (-2e^{-x} - x)\Big|_0^{\ln 2} \qquad \text{Fundamental Theorem}$$

$$= 1 - \ln 2 \approx 0.307. \qquad \text{Evaluate and simplify.}$$

Therefore, the x-coordinate of the center of mass is $\bar{x} = \dfrac{M_y}{m} \approx 0.217$. The center of mass is located approximately at $(0.217, 0)$.

Related Exercises 15–20◄

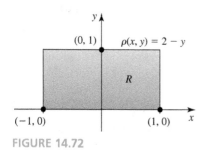

$(0, 1)$ $\rho(x, y) = 2 - y$

R

$(-1, 0)$ $(1, 0)$ x

FIGURE 14.72

➤ To verify that $\bar{x} = 0$, notice that to find M_y, we integrate an odd function in x over $-1 \le x \le 1$; the result is zero.

EXAMPLE 4   Variable-density plate   Find the center of mass of the rectangular plate $R = \{(x, y): -1 \le x \le 1, 0 \le y \le 1\}$ with a density of $\rho(x, y) = 2 - y$ (heavy at the lower edge and light at the top edge; Figure 14.72).

SOLUTION   Because the plate is symmetric with respect to the y-axis and because the density is independent of x, we have $\bar{x} = 0$. We must still compute m and M_x.

$$m = \iint_R \rho(x, y) \, dA = \int_{-1}^1 \int_0^1 (2 - y) \, dy \, dx = \frac{3}{2} \int_{-1}^1 dx = 3$$

$$M_x = \iint_R y\rho(x, y) \, dA = \int_{-1}^1 \int_0^1 y(2 - y) \, dy \, dx = \frac{2}{3} \int_{-1}^1 dx = \frac{4}{3}$$

Therefore, the center of mass coordinates are

$$\bar{x} = \frac{M_y}{m} = 0 \quad \text{and} \quad \bar{y} = \frac{M_x}{m} = \frac{4/3}{3} = \frac{4}{9}.$$

Related Exercises 21–26◄

Three-Dimensional Objects

We now extend the preceding arguments to compute the center of mass of three-dimensional solids. Assume that D is a closed bounded region in $\mathbb{R}^3$, on which an integrable density function ρ is defined. The units of the density are now mass per volume (for example, g/cm³). The coordinates of the center of mass depend on the mass of the region, which by Section 14.4 is the integral of the density function over D. Three moments now enter the picture: M_{yz} involves distances from the yz-plane; therefore, it has an x in the integrand. Similarly, M_{xz} involves distances from the xz-plane, so it has a y in the integrand, and M_{xy} involves distances from the xy-plane, so it has a z in the integrand. As before, the coordinates of the center of mass are the total moments divided by the total mass (Figure 14.73).

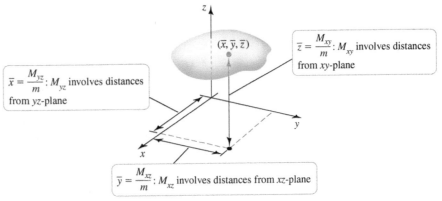

FIGURE 14.73

QUICK CHECK 5 Explain why the integral for the moment M_{xy} has z in the integrand.

DEFINITION Center of Mass in Three Dimensions

Let ρ be an integrable density function on a closed bounded region D in $\mathbb{R}^3$. The coordinates of the center of mass of the region are

$$\bar{x} = \frac{M_{yz}}{m} = \frac{1}{m} \iiint_D x\rho(x, y, z)\, dV, \quad \bar{y} = \frac{M_{xz}}{m} = \frac{1}{m} \iiint_D y\rho(x, y, z)\, dV, \text{ and}$$

$$\bar{z} = \frac{M_{xy}}{m} = \frac{1}{m} \iiint_D z\rho(x, y, z)\, dV,$$

where $m = \iiint_D \rho(x, y, z)\, dV$ is the mass, and M_{yz}, M_{xz}, and M_{xy} are the moments with respect to the coordinate planes.

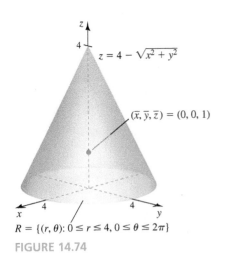

$R = \{(r, \theta): 0 \le r \le 4, 0 \le \theta \le 2\pi\}$

FIGURE 14.74

EXAMPLE 5   Center of mass with constant density Find the center of mass of the constant-density solid cone D bounded by the surface $z = 4 - \sqrt{x^2 + y^2}$ and $z = 0$ (Figure 14.74).

SOLUTION Because the cone is symmetric about the z-axis and has uniform density, the center of mass lies on the z-axis; that is, $\bar{x} = 0$ and $\bar{y} = 0$. Setting $z = 0$, the base of the cone in the xy-plane is the disk of radius 4 centered at the origin. Therefore, the cone has height 4 and radius 4; by the volume formula, its volume is $\pi r^2 h / 3 = 64\pi/3$. The cone has a constant density, so we assume that $\rho = 1$ and its mass is $m = 64\pi/3$.

To obtain the value of $\bar{z}$, only M_{xy} needs to be calculated, which is most easily done in cylindrical coordinates. The cone is described by the equation $z = 4 - \sqrt{x^2 + y^2} = 4 - r$. The projection of the cone on the xy-plane, which is the region of integration in the xy-plane, is $R = \{(r, \theta): 0 \le r \le 4, 0 \le \theta \le 2\pi\}$. The integration for M_{xy} now follows:

$$M_{xy} = \iiint_D z\, dV \qquad \text{Definition of } M_{xy} \text{ with } \rho = 1$$

$$= \int_0^{2\pi} \int_0^4 \int_0^{4-r} z\, dz\, r\, dr\, d\theta \qquad \text{Convert to an iterated integral.}$$

$$= \int_0^{2\pi} \int_0^4 \frac{z^2}{2} \Big|_0^{4-r} r \, dr \, d\theta \qquad \text{Evaluate the inner integral.}$$

$$= \frac{1}{2} \int_0^{2\pi} \int_0^4 r(4-r)^2 \, dr \, d\theta \qquad \text{Simplify.}$$

$$= \frac{1}{2} \int_0^{2\pi} \frac{64}{3} \, d\theta \qquad \text{Evaluate the middle integral.}$$

$$= \frac{64\pi}{3}. \qquad \text{Evaluate the outer integral.}$$

The z-coordinate of the center of mass is $\bar{z} = \dfrac{M_{xy}}{m} = \dfrac{64\pi/3}{64\pi/3} = 1$, and the center of mass is located at $(0, 0, 1)$. It can be shown (Exercise 55) that the center of mass of a constant-density cone height of h is located $h/4$ units from the base on the axis of the cone, independent of the radius.

Related Exercises 27–32 ◄

EXAMPLE 6   Center of mass with variable density Find the center of mass of the interior of the hemisphere D of radius a with its base on the xy-plane. The density of the object is $f(\rho, \varphi, \theta) = 2 - \rho/a$ (heavy near the center and light near the outer surface; Figure 14.75).

SOLUTION The center of mass lies on the z-axis because of the symmetry of the solid and the density function; therefore, $\bar{x} = \bar{y} = 0$. Only the integrals for m and M_{xy} need to be evaluated, and they should be done in spherical coordinates.

The integral for the mass is

$$m = \iiint\limits_D f(\rho, \varphi, \theta) \, dV \qquad \text{Definition of } m$$

$$= \int_0^{2\pi} \int_0^{\pi/2} \int_0^a \left(2 - \frac{\rho}{a}\right) \rho^2 \sin\varphi \, d\rho \, d\varphi \, d\theta \qquad \text{Convert to an iterated integral.}$$

$$= \int_0^{2\pi} \int_0^{\pi/2} \left(\frac{2\rho^3}{3} - \frac{\rho^4}{4a}\right)\Big|_0^a \sin\varphi \, d\varphi \, d\theta \qquad \text{Evaluate the inner integral.}$$

$$= \int_0^{2\pi} \int_0^{\pi/2} \frac{5a^3}{12} \sin\varphi \, d\varphi \, d\theta \qquad \text{Simplify.}$$

$$= \frac{5a^3}{12} \int_0^{2\pi} \underbrace{(-\cos\varphi)\Big|_0^{\pi/2}}_{1} \, d\theta \qquad \text{Evaluate the middle integral.}$$

$$= \frac{5a^3}{12} \int_0^{2\pi} d\theta \qquad \text{Simplify.}$$

$$= \frac{5\pi a^3}{6}. \qquad \text{Evaluate the outer integral.}$$

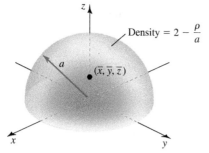

Density $= 2 - \dfrac{\rho}{a}$

a

$(\bar{x}, \bar{y}, \bar{z})$

FIGURE 14.75

In spherical coordinates, $z = \rho \cos \varphi$, so the integral for the moment M_{xy} is

$$M_{xy} = \iiint_D z\, f(\rho, \varphi, \theta)\, dV \qquad \text{Definition of } M_{xy}$$

$$= \int_0^{2\pi} \int_0^{\pi/2} \int_0^a \underbrace{\rho \cos \varphi}_{z}\left(2 - \frac{\rho}{a}\right)\rho^2 \sin \varphi\, d\rho\, d\varphi\, d\theta \qquad \text{Convert to an iterated integral.}$$

$$= \int_0^{2\pi} \int_0^{\pi/2} \left(\frac{\rho^4}{2} - \frac{\rho^5}{5a}\right)\Bigg|_0^a \sin \varphi \cos \varphi\, d\varphi\, d\theta \qquad \text{Evaluate the inner integral.}$$

$$= \int_0^{2\pi} \int_0^{\pi/2} \frac{3a^4}{10} \underbrace{\sin \varphi \cos \varphi}_{(\sin 2\varphi)/2}\, d\varphi\, d\theta \qquad \text{Simplify.}$$

$$= \frac{3a^4}{10} \int_0^{2\pi} \underbrace{\left(-\frac{\cos 2\varphi}{4}\right)\Bigg|_0^{\pi/2}}_{1/2}\, d\theta \qquad \text{Evaluate the middle integral.}$$

$$= \frac{3a^4}{20} \int_0^{2\pi} d\theta \qquad \text{Simplify.}$$

$$= \frac{3\pi a^4}{10}. \qquad \text{Evaluate the outer integral.}$$

The z-coordinate of the center of mass is $\bar{z} = \dfrac{M_{xy}}{m} = \dfrac{3\pi a^4/10}{5\pi a^3/6} = \dfrac{9a}{25} = 0.36a$. It can be shown (Exercise 56) that the center of mass of a uniform-density hemispherical solid of radius a is $3a/8 = 0.375a$ units above the base. In this particular case, the variable density shifts the center of mass.

Related Exercises 33–38◄

SECTION 14.6 EXERCISES

Review Questions

1. Explain how to find the balance point for two people on opposite ends of a (massless) plank that rests on a pivot.

2. If a thin 1-m cylindrical rod has a density of $\rho = 1$ g/cm for its left half and a density of $\rho = 2$ g/cm for its right half, what is its mass and where is its center of mass?

3. Explain how to find the center of mass of a thin plate with a variable density.

4. In the integral for the moment M_x of a thin plate, why does y appear in the integrand?

5. Explain how to find the center of mass of a three-dimensional object with a variable density.

6. In the integral for the moment M_{xz} with respect to the xz-plane of a solid, why does y appear in the integrand?

Basic Skills

7–8. Individual masses on a line *Sketch the following systems on a number line and find the location of the center of mass.*

7. $m_1 = 10$ kg located at $x = 3$ m; $m_2 = 3$ kg located at $x = -1$ m

8. $m_1 = 8$ kg located at $x = 2$ m; $m_2 = 4$ kg located at $x = -4$ m; $m_3 = 1$ kg located at $x = 0$ m

9–14. One-dimensional objects *Find the mass and center of mass of the thin rods with the following density functions.*

9. $\rho(x) = 1 + \sin x$, for $0 \le x \le \pi$

10. $\rho(x) = 1 + x^3$, for $0 \le x \le 1$

11. $\rho(x) = 2 - x^2/16$, for $0 \le x \le 4$

12. $\rho(x) = 2 + \cos x$, for $0 \le x \le \pi$

13. $\rho(x) = \begin{cases} 1 & \text{if } 0 \le x \le 2 \\ 1 + x & \text{if } 2 < x \le 4 \end{cases}$

14. $\rho(x) = \begin{cases} x^2 & \text{if } 0 \le x \le 1 \\ x(2 - x) & \text{if } 1 < x \le 2 \end{cases}$

15–20. Centroid calculations *Find the mass and centroid (center of mass) of the following thin plates, assuming constant density. Sketch the region corresponding to the plate and indicate the location of the center of mass. Use symmetry when possible to simplify your work.*

15. The region bounded by $y = \sin x$ and $y = 1 - \sin x$ between $x = \pi/4$ and $x = 3\pi/4$

16. The region in the first quadrant bounded by $x^2 + y^2 = 16$

17. The region bounded by $y = 1 - |x|$ and the x-axis

18. The region bounded by $y = e^x, y = e^{-x}, x = 0$, and $x = \ln 2$

19. The region bounded by $y = \ln x$, the x-axis, and $x = e$

20. The region bounded by $x^2 + y^2 = 1$ and $x^2 + y^2 = 9$, for $y \geq 0$

21–26. Variable-density plates *Find the coordinates of the center of mass of the following plane regions with variable density. Describe the distribution of mass in the region.*

21. $R = \{(x, y): 0 \leq x \leq 4, 0 \leq y \leq 2\}$; $\rho(x, y) = 1 + x/2$

22. $R = \{(x, y): 0 \leq x \leq 1, 0 \leq y \leq 5\}$; $\rho(x, y) = 2e^{-y/2}$

23. The triangular plate in the first quadrant bounded by $x + y = 4$ with $\rho(x, y) = 1 + x + y$

24. The upper half $(y \geq 0)$ of the disk bounded by the circle $x^2 + y^2 = 4$ with $\rho(x, y) = 1 + y/2$

25. The upper half $(y \geq 0)$ of the plate bounded by the ellipse $x^2 + 9y^2 = 9$ with $\rho(x, y) = 1 + y$

26. The quarter disk in the first quadrant bounded by $x^2 + y^2 = 4$ with $\rho(x, y) = 1 + x^2 + y^2$

27–32. Center of mass of constant-density solids *Find the center of mass of the following solids, assuming a constant density of 1. Sketch the region and indicate the location of the centroid. Use symmetry when possible and choose a convenient coordinate system.*

27. The upper half of the ball $x^2 + y^2 + z^2 \leq 16$ (for $z \geq 0$)

28. The region bounded by the paraboloid $z = x^2 + y^2$ and the plane $z = 25$

29. The tetrahedron in the first octant bounded by $z = 1 - x - y$ and the coordinate planes

30. The region bounded by the cone $z = 16 - r$ and the plane $z = 0$

31. The sliced solid cylinder bounded by $x^2 + y^2 = 1, z = 0$, and $y + z = 1$

32. The region bounded by the upper half $(z \geq 0)$ of the ellipsoid $4x^2 + 4y^2 + z^2 = 16$

33–38. Variable-density solids *Find the coordinates of the center of mass of the following solids with variable density.*

33. $R = \{(x, y, z): 0 \leq x \leq 4, 0 \leq y \leq 1, 0 \leq z \leq 1\}$; $\rho(x, y, z) = 1 + x/2$

34. The region bounded by the paraboloid $z = 4 - x^2 - y^2$ and $z = 0$ with $\rho(x, y, z) = 5 - z$

35. The region bounded by the upper half of the sphere $\rho = 6$ and $z = 0$ with density $f(\rho, \varphi, \theta) = 1 + \rho/4$

36. The interior of the cube in the first octant formed by the planes $x = 1, y = 1$, and $z = 1$ with $\rho(x, y, z) = 2 + x + y + z$

37. The interior of the prism formed by $z = x, x = 1, y = 4$, and the coordinate planes with $\rho(x, y, z) = 2 + y$

38. The region bounded by the cone by $z = 9 - r$ and $z = 0$ with $\rho(r, \theta, z) = 1 + z$

Further Explorations

39. Explain why or why not Determine whether the following statements are true and give an explanation or counterexample.

  a. A thin plate of constant density that is symmetric about the x-axis has a center of mass with an x-coordinate of zero.

  b. A thin plate of constant density that is symmetric about both the x-axis and the y-axis has its center of mass at the origin.

  c. The center of mass of a thin plate must lie on the plate.

  d. The center of mass of a connected solid region (all in one piece) must lie within the region.

40. Limiting center of mass A thin rod of length L has a linear density given by $\rho(x) = 2e^{-x/3}$ on the interval $0 \leq x \leq L$. Find the mass and center of mass of the rod. How does the center of mass change as $L \to \infty$?

41. Limiting center of mass A thin rod of length L has a linear density given by $\rho(x) = \dfrac{10}{1 + x^2}$ on the interval $0 \leq x \leq L$. Find the mass and center of mass of the rod. How does the center of mass change as $L \to \infty$?

42. Limiting center of mass A thin plate is bounded by the graphs of $y = e^{-x}, y = -e^{-x}, x = 0$, and $x = L$. Find its center of mass. How does the center of mass change as $L \to \infty$?

43–44. Two-dimensional plates *Find the mass and center of mass of the thin constant-density plates shown in the figure.*

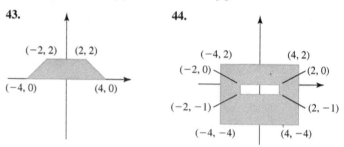

43.

$(-2, 2)$ $(2, 2)$

$(-4, 0)$ $(4, 0)$

44.

$(-4, 2)$ $(4, 2)$

$(-2, 0)$ $(2, 0)$

$(-2, -1)$ $(2, -1)$

$(-4, -4)$ $(4, -4)$

45–50. Centroids *Use polar coordinates to find the centroid of the following constant-density plane regions.*

45. The semicircular disk $R = \{(r, \theta): 0 \leq r \leq 2, 0 \leq \theta \leq \pi\}$

46. The quarter-circular disk $R = \{(r, \theta): 0 \leq r \leq 2, 0 \leq \theta \leq \pi/2\}$

47. The region bounded by the cardioid $r = 1 + \cos \theta$

48. The region bounded by the cardioid $r = 3 - 3 \cos \theta$

49. The region bounded by one leaf of the rose $r = \sin 2\theta$, for $0 \leq \theta \leq \pi/2$

50. The region bounded by the limaçon $r = 2 + \cos \theta$

51. Semicircular wire A thin (one-dimensional) wire of constant density is bent into the shape of a semicircle of radius a. Find the location of its center of mass.

52. Parabolic region A thin plate of unit density occupies the region between the parabola $y = ax^2$ and the horizontal line $y = b$, where $a > 0$ and $b > 0$. Show that the center of mass is $\left(0, \dfrac{3b}{5}\right)$, independent of a.

53. Circular crescent Find the center of mass of the region in the first quadrant bounded by the circle $x^2 + y^2 = a^2$ and the lines $x = a$ and $y = a$, where $a > 0$.

54–59. Centers of mass for general objects *Consider the following two- and three-dimensional regions. Specify the surfaces and curves that bound the region, choose a convenient coordinate system, and compute the center of mass assuming constant density. All parameters are positive real numbers.*

54. A solid rectangular box has sides of length a, b, and c. Where is the center of mass relative to the faces of the box?

55. A solid cone has a base with a radius of a and a height of h. How far from the base is the center of mass?

56. A solid is enclosed by a hemisphere of radius a. How far from the base is the center of mass?

57. A region is enclosed by an isosceles triangle with two sides of length s and a base of length b. How far from the base is the center of mass?

58. A tetrahedron is bounded by the coordinate planes and the plane $x/a + y/a + z/a = 1$. What are the coordinates of the center of mass?

59. A solid is enclosed by the upper half of an ellipsoid with a circular base of radius r and a height of a. How far from the base is the center of mass?

Applications

60. Geographic vs. population center Geographers measure the *geographical center* of a country (which is the centroid) and the *population center* of a country (which is the center of mass computed with the population density). A hypothetical country is shown in the figure with the location and population of five towns. Assuming no one lives outside the towns, find the geographical center of the country and the population center of the country.

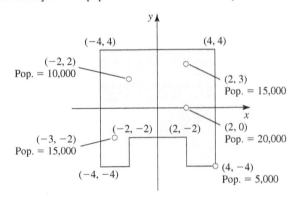

61. Center of mass on the edge Consider the thin constant-density plate $\{(r, \theta): 0 < a \le r \le 1, 0 \le \theta \le \pi\}$ bounded by two semicircles and the x-axis.

    a. Find and graph the y-coordinate of the center of mass of the plate as a function of a.

    b. For what value of a is the center of mass on the edge of the plate?

62. Center of mass on the edge Consider the constant-density solid $\{(\rho, \varphi, \theta): 0 < a \le \rho \le 1, 0 \le \varphi \le \pi/2, 0 \le \theta \le 2\pi\}$ bounded by two hemispheres and the xy-plane.

    a. Find and graph the z-coordinate of the center of mass of the plate as a function of a.

    b. For what value of a is the center of mass on the edge of the solid?

63. Draining a soda can A cylindrical soda can has a radius of 4 cm and a height of 12 cm. When the can is full of soda, the center of mass of the contents of the can is 6 cm above the base on the axis of the can (halfway along the axis of the can). As the can is drained, the center of mass descends for a while. However, when the can is empty (filled only with air), the center of mass is once again 6 cm above the base on the axis of the can. Find the depth of soda in the can for which the center of mass is at its lowest point. Neglect the mass of the can, and assume the density of the soda is 1 g/cm³ and the density of air is 0.001 g/cm³.

Additional Exercises

64. Triangle medians A triangular region has a base that connects the vertices $(0, 0)$ and $(b, 0)$, and a third vertex at (a, h), where $a > 0, b > 0$, and $h > 0$.

    a. Show that the centroid of the triangle is $\left(\dfrac{a + b}{3}, \dfrac{h}{3}\right)$.

    b. Recall that the three medians of a triangle extend from each vertex to the midpoint of the opposite side. Knowing that the medians of a triangle intersect in a point M and that each median bisects the triangle, conclude that the centroid of the triangle is M.

65. The golden earring A disk of radius r is removed from a larger disk of radius R to form an earring (see figure). Assume the earring is a thin plate of uniform density.

    a. Find the center of mass of the earring in terms of r and R. (*Hint:* Place the origin of a coordinate system either at the center of the large disk or at Q; either way, the earring is symmetric about the x-axis.)

    b. Show that the ratio R/r such that the center of mass lies at the point P (on the edge of the inner disk) is the golden mean $(1 + \sqrt{5})/2 \approx 1.618$.

    (*Source:* P. Glaister, "Golden Earrings," *Mathematical Gazette* 80 (1996): 224–225)

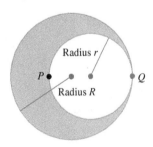

QUICK CHECK ANSWERS

1. 3 m   **3.** It is heaviest at $x = 0$ and lightest at $x = 3$.   **4.** The distance from the point (x, y) to the y-axis is x. The constant density appears in the integral for the moment, and it appears in the integral for the mass. Therefore, the density cancels when we divide the two integrals.   **5.** The distance from the xy-plane to a point (x, y, z) is z. ◄

14.7   Change of Variables in Multiple Integrals

Converting double integrals from rectangular coordinates to polar coordinates (Section 14.3) and converting triple integrals from rectangular coordinates to cylindrical or spherical coordinates (Section 14.5) are examples of a general procedure known as a *change of variables*. The idea is not new: The Substitution Rule introduced in Chapter 5 with single-variable integrals is also an example of a change of variables. The aim of this section is to show how to change variables in double and triple integrals.

Recap of Change of Variables

Recall how a change of variables is used to simplify a single-variable integral. For example, to simplify the integral $\int_0^1 2\sqrt{2x+1}\, dx$, we choose a new variable $u = 2x + 1$, which means that $du = 2\, dx$. Therefore,

$$\int_0^1 2\sqrt{2x+1}\, dx = \int_1^3 \sqrt{u}\, du.$$

This equality means that the area under the curve $y = 2\sqrt{2x+1}$ from $x = 0$ to $x = 1$ equals the area under the curve $y = \sqrt{u}$ from $u = 1$ to $u = 3$ (Figure 14.76). The relation $du = 2\, dx$ relates the length of a small interval on the u-axis to the length of the corresponding interval on the x-axis.

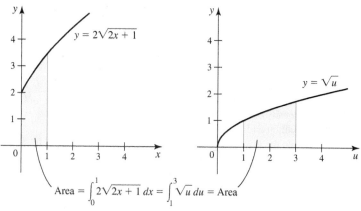

$$\text{Area} = \int_0^1 2\sqrt{2x+1}\, dx = \int_1^3 \sqrt{u}\, du = \text{Area}$$

FIGURE 14.76

Similarly, some double and triple integrals can be simplified through a change of variables. For example, the region of integration for

$$\int_0^1 \int_0^{\sqrt{1-x^2}} e^{1-x^2-y^2}\, dy\, dx$$

is the quarter disk $R = \{(x, y): x \ge 0, y \ge 0, x^2 + y^2 \le 1\}$. Changing variables to polar coordinates with $x = r\cos\theta$, $y = r\sin\theta$, and $dy\, dx = r\, dr\, d\theta$, we have

$$\int_0^1 \int_0^{\sqrt{1-x^2}} e^{1-x^2-y^2}\, dy\, dx \overset{\substack{x = r\cos\theta \\ y = r\sin\theta}}{=} \int_0^{\pi/2} \int_0^1 e^{1-r^2} r\, dr\, d\theta.$$

In this case, the original region of integration R is transformed into a new region $S = \{(r, \theta): 0 \le r \le 1, 0 \le \theta \le \pi/2\}$, which is a rectangle in the $r\theta$-plane.

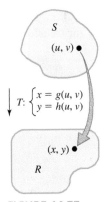

FIGURE 14.77

▷ In Example 1, we have replaced the coordinates u and v by the familiar polar coordinates r and θ.

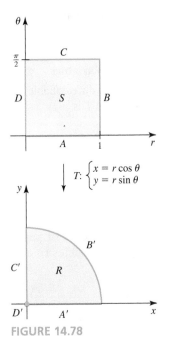

FIGURE 14.78

Transformations in the Plane

A change of variables in a double integral is a *transformation* that relates two sets of variables, (u, v) and (x, y). It is written compactly as $(x, y) = T(u, v)$. Because it relates pairs of variables, T has two components,

$$T: x = g(u, v) \quad \text{and} \quad y = h(u, v).$$

Geometrically, T takes a region S in the uv-plane and "maps" it point by point to a region R in the xy-plane (Figure 14.77). We write the outcome of this process as $R = T(S)$ and call R the **image** of S under T.

EXAMPLE 1 **Image of a transformation** Consider the transformation from polar to rectangular coordinates given by

$$T: \quad x = g(r, \theta) = r \cos \theta \quad \text{and} \quad y = h(r, \theta) = r \sin \theta.$$

Find the image under this transformation of the rectangle

$$S = \left\{ (r, \theta) : 0 \le r \le 1, 0 \le \theta \le \pi/2 \right\}.$$

SOLUTION If we apply T to every point of S (Figure 14.78), what is the resulting set R in the xy-plane? One way to answer this question is to walk around the boundary of S, let's say counterclockwise, and determine the corresponding path in the xy-plane. In the $r\theta$-plane, we let the horizontal axis be the r-axis and the vertical axis be the θ-axis. Starting at the origin, we denote the edges of the rectangle S as follows.

$$A = \left\{ (r, \theta) : 0 \le r \le 1, \theta = 0 \right\} \quad \text{Lower boundary}$$

$$B = \left\{ (r, \theta) : r = 1, 0 \le \theta \le \frac{\pi}{2} \right\} \quad \text{Right boundary}$$

$$C = \left\{ (r, \theta) : 0 \le r \le 1, \theta = \frac{\pi}{2} \right\} \quad \text{Upper boundary}$$

$$D = \left\{ (r, \theta) : r = 0, 0 \le \theta \le \frac{\pi}{2} \right\} \quad \text{Left boundary}$$

Table 14.6 shows the effect of the transformation on the four boundaries of S; the corresponding boundaries of R in the xy-plane are denoted A', B', C', and D' (Figure 14.78).

Table 14.6

Boundary of S in $r\theta$-plane	Transformation equations	Boundary of R in xy-plane
A: $0 \le r \le 1, \theta = 0$	$x = r \cos \theta = r,$ $y = r \sin \theta = 0$	A': $0 \le x \le 1, y = 0$
B: $r = 1, 0 \le \theta \le \pi/2$	$x = r \cos \theta = \cos \theta,$ $y = r \sin \theta = \sin \theta$	B': quarter unit circle
C: $0 \le r \le 1, \theta = \pi/2$	$x = r \cos \theta = 0,$ $y = r \sin \theta = r$	C': $x = 0, 0 \le y \le 1$
D: $r = 0, 0 \le \theta \le \pi/2$	$x = r \cos \theta = 0,$ $y = r \sin \theta = 0$	D': single point $(0, 0)$

QUICK CHECK 1 How would the image of S change in Example 1 if $S = \left\{ (r, \theta) : 0 \le r \le 1, 0 \le \theta \le \pi \right\}$?

The image of the rectangular boundary of S is the boundary of R. Furthermore, it can be shown that every point in the interior of R is the image of one point in the interior of S. Therefore, the image of S is the quarter disk R in the xy-plane.

Related Exercises 5–16 ◄

Recall that a function f is *one-to-one* on an interval I if $f(x_1) = f(x_2)$ only when $x_1 = x_2$, where x_1 and x_2 are points of I. We need an analogous property for transformations when changing variables.

> **DEFINITION One-to-One Transformation**
>
> A transformation T from a region S to a region R is one-to-one on S if $T(P) = T(Q)$ only when $P = Q$, where P and Q are points in S.

Notice that the polar coordinate transformation in Example 1 is *not* one-to-one on the rectangle $S = \{(r, \theta): 0 \le r \le 1, 0 \le \theta \le \pi/2\}$ (because all points with $r = 0$ map to the point $(0, 0)$). However, this transformation *is* one-to-one on the interior of S.

We can now anticipate how a transformation (change of variables) is used to simplify a double integral. Suppose we have the integral $\iint_R f(x, y)\, dA$. The goal is to find a transformation to a new set of coordinates (u, v) such that the new equivalent integral $\iint_S f(x(u, v), y(u, v))\, dA$ involves a simple region S (such as a rectangle), a simple integrand, or both. The next theorem allows us to do exactly that, but it first requires a new concept.

> The Jacobian is named after the German mathematician Carl Gustav Jacob Jacobi (1804–1851). In some books, the Jacobian is the matrix of partial derivatives. In others, as here, the Jacobian is the determinant of the matrix of partial derivatives. Both $J(u, v)$ and $\dfrac{\partial(x, y)}{\partial(u, v)}$ are used to refer to the Jacobian.

> **DEFINITION Jacobian Determinant of a Transformation of Two Variables**
>
> Given a transformation $T: x = g(u, v), y = h(u, v)$, where g and h are differentiable on a region of the uv-plane, the **Jacobian determinant** (or **Jacobian**) of T is
>
> $$J(u, v) = \frac{\partial(x, y)}{\partial(u, v)} = \begin{vmatrix} \dfrac{\partial x}{\partial u} & \dfrac{\partial x}{\partial v} \\ \dfrac{\partial y}{\partial u} & \dfrac{\partial y}{\partial v} \end{vmatrix} = \frac{\partial x}{\partial u} \frac{\partial y}{\partial v} - \frac{\partial x}{\partial v} \frac{\partial y}{\partial u}.$$

The Jacobian is easiest to remember as the determinant of a 2×2 matrix of partial derivatives. With the Jacobian in hand, we can state the change-of-variables rule for double integrals.

> **QUICK CHECK 2** Find $J(u, v)$ if $x = u + v, y = 2v$. ◄

> The condition that g and h have continuous first partial derivatives ensures that the new integrand is integrable.

> **THEOREM 14.8 Change of Variables for Double Integrals**
>
> Let $T: x = g(u, v), y = h(u, v)$ be a transformation that maps a closed bounded region S in the uv-plane onto a region R in the xy-plane. Assume that T is one-to-one on the interior of S and that g and h have continuous first partial derivatives there. If f is continuous on R, then
>
> $$\iint\limits_R f(x, y)\, dA = \iint\limits_S f(g(u, v), h(u, v)) |J(u, v)|\, dA.$$

> In the integral over R, dA corresponds to $dx\, dy$. In the integral over S, dA corresponds to $du\, dv$. The relation $dx\, dy = |J|\, du\, dv$ is the analog of $du = g'(x)\, dx$ in a change of variables with one variable.

The proof of this result is technical and is found in advanced texts. The factor $|J(u, v)|$ that appears in the second integral is the absolute value of the Jacobian. Matching the area elements in the two integrals of Theorem 14.8, we see that $dx\, dy = |J(u, v)|\, du\, dv$. This expression shows that the Jacobian is a magnification (or reduction) factor: It relates the area of a small region $dx\, dy$ in the xy-plane to the area of the corresponding region $du\, dv$ in the uv-plane. If the transformation equations are linear, then this relationship is exact in the sense that $\text{area}(T(S)) = |J(u, v)|\, \text{area}(S)$ (see Exercise 60). The way in which the Jacobian arises is explored in Exercise 61.

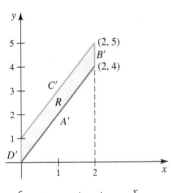

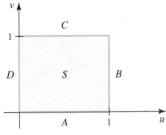

FIGURE 14.79

> The relations that "go the other direction" comprise the inverse transformation, usually denoted T^{-1}.

Table 14.7

(x, y)	(u, v)
$(0, 0)$	$(0, 0)$
$(0, 1)$	$(0, 1)$
$(2, 5)$	$(1, 1)$
$(2, 4)$	$(1, 0)$

EXAMPLE 2 Jacobian of the polar-to-rectangular transformation Compute the Jacobian of the transformation

$$T: \quad x = g(r, \theta) = r \cos \theta, \quad y = h(r, \theta) = r \sin \theta.$$

SOLUTION The necessary partial derivatives are

$$\frac{\partial x}{\partial r} = \cos \theta, \quad \frac{\partial x}{\partial \theta} = -r \sin \theta, \quad \frac{\partial y}{\partial r} = \sin \theta, \quad \frac{\partial y}{\partial \theta} = r \cos \theta.$$

Therefore,

$$J(r, \theta) = \frac{\partial(x, y)}{\partial(r, \theta)} = \begin{vmatrix} \frac{\partial x}{\partial r} & \frac{\partial x}{\partial \theta} \\ \frac{\partial y}{\partial r} & \frac{\partial y}{\partial \theta} \end{vmatrix} = \begin{vmatrix} \cos \theta & -r \sin \theta \\ \sin \theta & r \cos \theta \end{vmatrix} = r(\cos^2 \theta + \sin^2 \theta) = r.$$

This determinant calculation confirms the change-of-variables formula for polar coordinates: $dx\, dy$ becomes $r\, dr\, d\theta$.

Related Exercises 17–26 ◄

We are now ready for a change of variables. To transform the integral $\iint_R f(x, y)\, dA$ into $\iint_S f(x(u, v), y(u, v)) |J(u, v)|\, dA$, we must find the transformation $x = g(u, v)$ and $y = h(u, v)$, and then use it to find the new region of integration S. The next example illustrates how the region S is found, assuming the transformation is given.

EXAMPLE 3 Double integral with a change of variables given Evaluate the integral $\iint_R \sqrt{2x(y - 2x)}\, dA$, where R is the parallelogram in the xy-plane with vertices $(0, 0)$, $(0, 1)$, $(2, 4)$, and $(2, 5)$ (Figure 14.79). Use the transformation

$$T: x = 2u, y = 4u + v.$$

SOLUTION To what region S in the uv-plane is R mapped? Because T takes points in the uv-plane and assigns them to points in the xy-plane, we must reverse the process by solving $x = 2u, y = 4u + v$ for u and v.

$$\text{First equation: } x = 2u \implies u = \frac{x}{2}$$

$$\text{Second equation: } y = 4u + v \implies v = y - 4u = y - 2x$$

Rather than walk around the boundary of R in the xy-plane to determine the resulting region S in the uv-plane, it suffices to find the images of the vertices of R. You should confirm that the vertices map as shown in Table 14.7.

Connecting the points in the uv-plane in order, we see that S is the unit square $\{(u, v): 0 \le u \le 1, 0 \le v \le 1\}$ (Figure 14.79). These inequalities determine the limits of integration in the uv-plane.

Replacing $2x$ by $4u$ and $y - 2x$ by v, the original integrand becomes $\sqrt{2x(y - 2x)} = \sqrt{4uv}$. The Jacobian is

$$J(u, v) = \begin{vmatrix} \frac{\partial x}{\partial u} & \frac{\partial x}{\partial v} \\ \frac{\partial y}{\partial u} & \frac{\partial y}{\partial v} \end{vmatrix} = \begin{vmatrix} 2 & 0 \\ 4 & 1 \end{vmatrix} = 2.$$

> ▷ T is an example of a *shearing transformation*. The greater the u-coordinate of a point, the more that point is displaced in the v-direction. It also involves a uniform stretch in the u-direction.

The integration now follows:

$$\iint\limits_R \sqrt{2x(y-2x)}\, dA = \iint\limits_S \sqrt{4uv}\, \underbrace{|J(u,v)|}_{2}\, dA \qquad \text{Change variables.}$$

$$= \int_0^1 \int_0^1 \sqrt{4uv}\, 2\, du\, dv \qquad \text{Convert to an iterated integral.}$$

$$= 4 \int_0^1 \frac{2}{3} \sqrt{v}\, \left(u^{3/2}\right)\Big|_0^1\, dv \qquad \text{Evaluate the inner integral.}$$

$$= \frac{8}{3} \cdot \frac{2}{3} \left(v^{3/2}\right)\Big|_0^1 = \frac{16}{9}. \qquad \text{Evaluate the outer integral.}$$

The effect of the change of variables is illustrated in Figure 14.80, where we see the surface $z = \sqrt{2x(y-2x)}$ over the region R and the surface $w = 2\sqrt{4uv}$ over the region S. The volumes of the solids beneath the two surfaces are equal, but the integral over S is easier to evaluate.

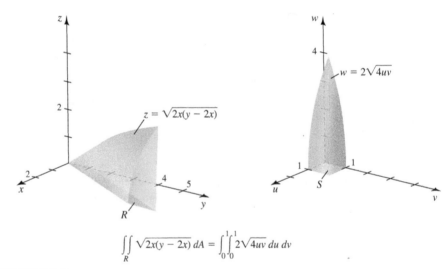

$$\iint\limits_R \sqrt{2x(y-2x)}\, dA = \int_0^1 \int_0^1 2\sqrt{4uv}\, du\, dv$$

FIGURE 14.80

Related Exercises 27–30 ◀

QUICK CHECK 3 Solve the equations $u = x + y$, $v = -x + 2y$ for x and y. ◀

In Example 3, the required transformation was given. More practically, we must deduce an appropriate transformation from the form of either the integrand or the region of integration.

EXAMPLE 4   Change of variables determined by the integrand Evaluate $\iint\limits_R \sqrt{\dfrac{x-y}{x+y+1}}\, dA$, where R is the square with vertices $(0,0)$, $(1,-1)$, $(2,0)$, and $(1,1)$ (Figure 14.81).

SOLUTION Evaluating the integral as it stands requires splitting the region R into two subregions; furthermore, the integrand presents difficulties. The terms $x + y$ and $x - y$ in the integrand suggest the new variables

$$u = x - y \quad \text{and} \quad v = x + y.$$

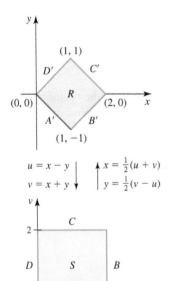

FIGURE 14.81

To determine the region S in the uv-plane that corresponds to R under this transformation, we find the images of the vertices of R in the uv-plane and connect them in order. The result is the square $S = \{(u, v): 0 \le u \le 2, 0 \le v \le 2\}$. Before computing the Jacobian, we express x and y in terms of u and v. Adding the two equations and solving for x, we have $x = (u + v)/2$. Subtracting the two equations and solving for y gives $y = (v - u)/2$. The Jacobian now follows:

$$J(u, v) = \begin{vmatrix} \dfrac{\partial x}{\partial u} & \dfrac{\partial x}{\partial v} \\ \dfrac{\partial y}{\partial u} & \dfrac{\partial y}{\partial v} \end{vmatrix} = \begin{vmatrix} \dfrac{1}{2} & \dfrac{1}{2} \\ -\dfrac{1}{2} & \dfrac{1}{2} \end{vmatrix} = \frac{1}{2}.$$

> The transformation in Example 4 is a *rotation*. It rotates the points of R about the origin $45°$ in the counterclockwise direction (it also increases lengths by a factor of $\sqrt{2}$). In this example, the change of variables $u = x + y$ and $v = x - y$ would work just as well.

With the choice of new variables, the original integrand $\sqrt{\dfrac{x - y}{x + y + 1}}$ becomes $\sqrt{\dfrac{u}{v + 1}}$. The integration in the uv-plane may now be done:

$$\iint_R \sqrt{\frac{x - y}{x + y + 1}}\, dA = \iint_S \sqrt{\frac{u}{v + 1}}\, |J(u, v)|\, dA \qquad \text{Change of variables}$$

$$= \int_0^2 \int_0^2 \sqrt{\frac{u}{v + 1}}\, \frac{1}{2}\, du\, dv \qquad \text{Convert to an iterated integral.}$$

$$= \frac{1}{2} \int_0^2 (v + 1)^{-1/2}\, \frac{2}{3}\, (u^{3/2}) \Big|_0^2 \, dv \qquad \text{Evaluate the inner integral.}$$

$$= \frac{2^{3/2}}{3}\, 2(v + 1)^{1/2} \Big|_0^2 \qquad \text{Evaluate the outer integral.}$$

$$= \frac{4\sqrt{2}}{3}\, (\sqrt{3} - 1). \qquad \text{Simplify.}$$

Related Exercises 31–36 ◀

> An appropriate change of variables for a double integral is not always obvious. Some trial and error is often needed to come up with a transformation that simplifies the integrand and/or the region of integration. Strategies are discussed at the end of this section.

QUICK CHECK 4 In Example 4, what is the ratio of the area of S to the area of R? How is this ratio related to J? ◀

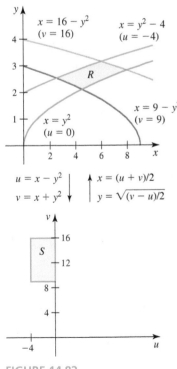

FIGURE 14.82

EXAMPLE 5   Change of variables determined by the region Let R be the region in the first quadrant bounded by the parabolas $x = y^2$, $x = y^2 - 4$, $x = 9 - y^2$, and $x = 16 - y^2$ (Figure 14.82). Evaluate $\iint_R y^2\, dA$.

SOLUTION Notice that the bounding curves may be written as $x - y^2 = 0$, $x - y^2 = -4$, $x + y^2 = 9$, and $x + y^2 = 16$. The first two parabolas have the form $x - y^2 = C$, where C is a constant, which suggests the new variable $u = x - y^2$. The last two parabolas have the form $x + y^2 = C$, which suggests the new variable $v = x + y^2$. Therefore, the new variables are

$$u = x - y^2, \quad v = x + y^2.$$

The boundary curves of S are $u = -4$, $u = 0$, $v = 9$, and $v = 16$. Therefore, the new region is $S = \{(u, v): -4 \le u \le 0, 9 \le v \le 16\}$ (Figure 14.82). To compute the Jacobian, we must find the transformation T by writing x and y in terms of u and v. Solving for x and y, and observing that $y \ge 0$ for all points in R, we find that

$$T: \quad x = \frac{u + v}{2}, \quad y = \sqrt{\frac{v - u}{2}}.$$

The points of S satisfy $v > u$, so $\sqrt{v - u}$ is defined. Now the Jacobian may be computed:

$$J(u, v) = \begin{vmatrix} \dfrac{\partial x}{\partial u} & \dfrac{\partial x}{\partial v} \\ \dfrac{\partial y}{\partial u} & \dfrac{\partial y}{\partial v} \end{vmatrix} = \begin{vmatrix} \dfrac{1}{2} & \dfrac{1}{2} \\ -\dfrac{1}{2\sqrt{2(v - u)}} & \dfrac{1}{2\sqrt{2(v - u)}} \end{vmatrix} = \frac{1}{2\sqrt{2(v - u)}}.$$

The change of variables proceeds as follows:

$$\iint\limits_{R} y^2 \, dA = \int_9^{16} \int_{-4}^{0} \underbrace{\frac{v-u}{2}}_{y^2} \underbrace{\frac{1}{2\sqrt{2(v-u)}}}_{|J(u,v)|} \, du \, dv \qquad \text{Convert to an iterated integral.}$$

$$= \frac{1}{4\sqrt{2}} \int_9^{16} \int_{-4}^{0} \sqrt{v-u} \, du \, dv \qquad \text{Simplify.}$$

$$= \frac{1}{4\sqrt{2}} \frac{2}{3} \int_9^{16} \left. \left(-(v-u)^{3/2}\right) \right|_{-4}^{0} \, dv \qquad \text{Evaluate the inner integral.}$$

$$= \frac{1}{6\sqrt{2}} \int_9^{16} \left((v+4)^{3/2} - v^{3/2}\right) dv \qquad \text{Simplify.}$$

$$= \frac{1}{6\sqrt{2}} \frac{2}{5} \left. \left((v+4)^{5/2} - v^{5/2}\right) \right|_9^{16} \qquad \text{Evaluate the outer integral.}$$

$$= \frac{\sqrt{2}}{30} \left(32 \cdot 5^{5/2} - 13^{5/2} - 781\right) \qquad \text{Simplify.}$$

$$\approx 18.79.$$

Related Exercises 31–36◄

Change of Variables in Triple Integrals

With triple integrals, we work with a transformation T of the form

$$T: \qquad x = g(u, v, w), \quad y = h(u, v, w), \quad z = p(u, v, w).$$

In this case, T maps a region S in uvw-space to a region D in xyz-space. As before, the goal is to transform the integral $\iiint_D f(x, y, z) \, dV$ into a new integral over the region S that is easier to evaluate. First, we need a Jacobian.

> Recall that by expanding about the first row,
>
> $$\begin{vmatrix} a_{11} & a_{12} & a_{13} \\ a_{21} & a_{22} & a_{23} \\ a_{31} & a_{32} & a_{33} \end{vmatrix}$$
>
> $$= a_{11}(a_{22}a_{33} - a_{23}a_{32})$$
> $$\quad - a_{12}(a_{21}a_{33} - a_{23}a_{31})$$
> $$\quad + a_{13}(a_{21}a_{32} - a_{22}a_{31}).$$

DEFINITION Jacobian Determinant of a Transformation of Three Variables

Given a transformation $T: x = g(u, v, w)$, $y = h(u, v, w)$, and $z = p(u, v, w)$, where g, h, and p are differentiable on a region of uvw-space, the **Jacobian determinant** (or **Jacobian**) of T is

$$J(u, v, w) = \frac{\partial(x, y, z)}{\partial(u, v, w)} = \begin{vmatrix} \dfrac{\partial x}{\partial u} & \dfrac{\partial x}{\partial v} & \dfrac{\partial x}{\partial w} \\[2mm] \dfrac{\partial y}{\partial u} & \dfrac{\partial y}{\partial v} & \dfrac{\partial y}{\partial w} \\[2mm] \dfrac{\partial z}{\partial u} & \dfrac{\partial z}{\partial v} & \dfrac{\partial z}{\partial w} \end{vmatrix}.$$

The Jacobian is evaluated as a 3×3 determinant and is a function of u, v, and w. A change of variables with respect to three variables proceeds in analogy to the two-variable case.

▷ If we match the elements of volume in both integrals, then $dx\,dy\,dz = |J(u, v, w)|\,du\,dv\,dw$. As before, the Jacobian is a magnification (or reduction) factor, now relating the volume of a small region in xyz-space to the volume of the corresponding region in uvw-space.

▷ To see that triple integrals in cylindrical and spherical coordinates as derived in Section 14.5 are consistent with this change of variable formulation, see Exercises 46 and 47.

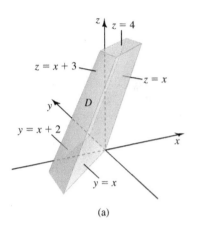

(a)

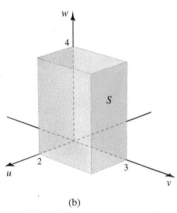

(b)

FIGURE 14.83

▷ It is easiest to expand this determinant about the third row.

THEOREM 14.9   Change of Variables for Triple Integrals

Let $T\colon x = g(u, v, w)$, $y = h(u, v, w)$, and $z = p(u, v, w)$ be a transformation that maps a closed bounded region S in uvw-space to a region $D = T(S)$ in xyz-space. Assume that T is one-to-one on the interior of S and that g, h, and p have continuous first partial derivatives there. If f is continuous on D, then

$$\iiint_D f(x, y, z)\, dV$$

$$= \iiint_S f(g(u, v, w), h(u, v, w), p(u, v, w))\, |J(u, v, w)|\, dV.$$

EXAMPLE 6   A triple integral Use a change of variables to evaluate $\iiint_D xz\, dV$, where D is a parallelepiped bounded by the planes

$$y = x, \quad y = x + 2, \quad z = x, \quad z = x + 3, \quad z = 0, \quad \text{and} \quad z = 4$$

(Figure 14.83a).

SOLUTION The key is to note that D is bounded by three pairs of parallel planes.

- $y - x = 0$ and $y - x = 2$
- $z - x = 0$ and $z - x = 3$
- $z = 0$ and $z = 4$

These combinations of variables suggest the new variables

$$u = y - x, \quad v = z - x, \quad \text{and} \quad w = z.$$

With this choice, the new region of integration (Figure 14.83b) is the rectangular box

$$S = \{(u, v, w)\colon 0 \le u \le 2, 0 \le v \le 3, 0 \le w \le 4\}.$$

To compute the Jacobian, we must express x, y, and z in terms of u, v, and w. A few steps of algebra lead to the transformation

$$T\colon \quad x = w - v, \quad y = u - v + w, \quad \text{and} \quad z = w.$$

The resulting Jacobian is

$$J(u, v, w) = \begin{vmatrix} \dfrac{\partial x}{\partial u} & \dfrac{\partial x}{\partial v} & \dfrac{\partial x}{\partial w} \\[2mm] \dfrac{\partial y}{\partial u} & \dfrac{\partial y}{\partial v} & \dfrac{\partial y}{\partial w} \\[2mm] \dfrac{\partial z}{\partial u} & \dfrac{\partial z}{\partial v} & \dfrac{\partial z}{\partial w} \end{vmatrix} = \begin{vmatrix} 0 & -1 & 1 \\ 1 & -1 & 1 \\ 0 & 0 & 1 \end{vmatrix} = 1.$$

Noting that the integrand is $xz = (w - v)w = w^2 - vw$, the integral may now be evaluated:

$$\iiint_D xz\, dV = \iiint_S (w^2 - vw)\, |J(u, v, w)|\, dV \qquad \text{Change variables.}$$

$$= \int_0^4 \int_0^3 \int_0^2 (w^2 - vw)\, \underset{|J(u, v, w)|}{1}\, du\, dv\, dw \qquad \text{Convert to an iterated integral.}$$

$$= \int_0^4 \int_0^3 2(w^2 - vw)\, dv\, dw \qquad \text{Evaluate the inner integral.}$$

$$= 2\int_0^4 \left(vw^2 - \frac{v^2 w}{2}\right)\Big|_0^3 dw \qquad \text{Evaluate the middle integral.}$$

$$= 2\int_0^4 \left(3w^2 - \frac{9w}{2}\right) dw \qquad \text{Simplify.}$$

$$= 2\left(w^3 - \frac{9w^2}{4}\right)\Big|_0^4 = 56. \qquad \text{Evaluate the outer integral.}$$

Related Exercises 37–44 ◄

QUICK CHECK 5 Interpret a Jacobian with a value of 1 (as in Example 6). ◄

Strategies for Choosing New Variables

Sometimes a change of variables simplifies the integrand but leads to an awkward region of integration. Conversely, the new region of integration may be simplified at the expense of additional complications in the integrand. Here are a few suggestions for finding new variables of integration. The observations are made with respect to double integrals, but they also apply to triple integrals. As before, R is the original region of integration in the xy-plane and S is the new region in the uv-plane.

1. **Aim for simple regions of integration in the uv-plane** The new region of integration in the uv-plane should be as simple as possible. Double integrals are easiest to evaluate over rectangular regions with sides parallel to the coordinate axes.

> Inverting the transformation means solving for x and y in terms of u and v, or vice versa.

2. **Is $(x, y) \rightarrow (u, v)$ or $(u, v) \rightarrow (x, y)$ better?** For some problems it is easiest to write (x, y) as functions of (u, v); in other cases the opposite is true. Depending on the problem, inverting the transformation (finding relations that go in the opposite direction) may be easy, difficult, or impossible.

   • If you know (x, y) in terms of (u, v) (that is, $x = g(u, v)$ and $y = h(u, v)$), then computing the Jacobian is straightforward, as is sketching the region R given the region S. However, the transformation must be inverted to determine the shape of S.

   • If you know (u, v) in terms of (x, y) (that is, $u = G(x, y)$ and $v = H(x, y)$), then sketching the region S is straightforward. However, the transformation must be inverted to compute the Jacobian.

3. **Let the integrand suggest new variables** New variables are often chosen to simplify the integrand. For example, the integrand $\sqrt{\dfrac{x - y}{x + y}}$ calls for new variables $u = x - y$ and $v = x + y$ (or $u = x + y$, $v = x - y$). There is, however, no guarantee that this change of variables will simplify the region of integration. In cases in which only one combination of variables appears, let one new variable be that combination and let the other new variable be unchanged. For example, if the integrand is $(x + 4y)^{3/2}$, try letting $u = x + 4y$ and $v = y$.

4. **Let the region suggest new variables** Example 5 illustrates an ideal situation. It occurs when the region R is bounded by two pairs of "parallel" curves in the families $g(x, y) = C_1$ and $h(x, y) = C_2$ (Figure 14.84). In this case the new region of integration is a rectangle $S = \{(u, v): a_1 \le u \le a_2, b_1 \le v \le b_2\}$, where $u = g(x, y)$ and $v = h(x, y)$.

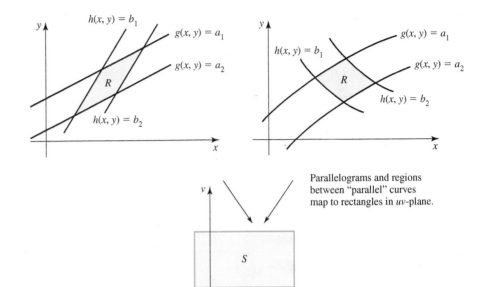

FIGURE 14.84

As another example, suppose the region is bounded by the lines $y = x$ (or $y/x = 1$) and $y = 2x$ (or $y/x = 2$) and by the hyperbolas $xy = 1$ and $xy = 3$. Then the new variables should be $u = xy$ and $v = y/x$ (or vice versa). The new region of integration is the rectangle $S = \{(u, v): 1 \le u \le 3, 1 \le v \le 2\}$.

SECTION 14.7 EXERCISES

Review Questions

1. Suppose S is the unit square in the first quadrant of the uv-plane. Describe the image of the transformation $T: x = 2u, y = 2v$.

2. Explain how to compute the Jacobian of the transformation $T: x = g(u, v), y = h(u, v)$.

3. Using the transformation $T: x = u + v, y = u - v$, the image of the unit square $S = \{(u, v): 0 \le u \le 1, 0 \le v \le 1\}$ is a region R in the xy-plane. Explain how to change variables in the integral $\iint_R f(x, y)\, dA$ to find a new integral over S.

4. Suppose S is the unit cube in the first octant of uvw-space with one vertex at the origin. Describe the image of the transformation $T: x = u/2, y = v/2, z = w/2$.

Basic Skills

5–12. Transforming a square *Let* $S = \{(u, v): 0 \le u \le 1,$ $0 \le v \le 1\}$ *be a unit square in the uv-plane. Find the image of S in the xy-plane under the following transformations.*

5. $T: x = 2u, y = v/2$

6. $T: x = -u, y = -v$

7. $T: x = (u + v)/2, y = (u - v)/2$

8. $T: x = 2u + v, y = 2u$

9. $T: x = u^2 - v^2, y = 2uv$

10. $T: x = 2uv, y = u^2 - v^2$

11. $T: x = u \cos(\pi v), y = u \sin(\pi v)$

12. $T: x = v \sin(\pi u), y = v \cos(\pi u)$

13–16. Images of regions *Find the image R in the xy-plane of the region S using the given transformation T. Sketch both R and S.*

13. $S = \{(u, v): v \le 1 - u, u \ge 0, v \ge 0\}$; $T: x = u, y = v^2$

14. $S = \{(u, v): u^2 + v^2 \le 1\}$; $T: x = 2u, y = 4v$

15. $S = \{(u, v): 1 \le u \le 3, 2 \le v \le 4\}$; $T: x = u/v, y = v$

16. $S = \{(u, v): 2 \le u \le 3, 3 \le v \le 6\}$; $T: x = u, y = v/u$

17–22. Computing Jacobians *Compute the Jacobian J(u, v) for the following transformations.*

17. $T: x = 3u, y = -3v$

18. $T: x = 4v, y = -2u$

19. $T: x = 2uv, y = u^2 - v^2$

20. $T: x = u \cos(\pi v), y = u \sin(\pi v)$

21. $T: x = (u + v)/\sqrt{2}, y = (u - v)/\sqrt{2}$

22. $T: x = u/v, y = v$

23–26. Solve and compute Jacobians *Solve the following relations for x and y, and compute the Jacobian J(u, v).*

23. $u = x + y, v = 2x - y$

24. $u = xy, v = x$

25. $u = 2x - 3y, v = y - x$

26. $u = x + 4y, v = 3x + 2y$

27–30. Double integrals—transformation given *To evaluate the following integrals carry out these steps.*

a. Sketch the original region of integration R in the xy-plane and the new region S in the uv-plane using the given change of variables.
b. Find the limits of integration for the new integral with respect to u and v.
c. Compute the Jacobian.
d. Change variables and evaluate the new integral.

27. $\iint_R xy\, dA$, where R is the square with vertices $(0, 0)$, $(1, 1)$, $(2, 0)$, and $(1, -1)$; use $x = u + v, y = u - v$.

28. $\iint_R x^2 y\, dA$, where $R = \{(x, y): 0 \le x \le 2, x \le y \le x + 4\}$; use $x = 2u, y = 4v + 2u$.

29. $\iint_R x^2\sqrt{x + 2y}\, dA$, where
$R = \{(x, y): 0 \le x \le 2, -x/2 \le y \le 1 - x\}$; use $x = 2u, y = v - u$.

30. $\iint_R xy\, dA$, where R is bounded by the ellipse $9x^2 + 4y^2 = 36$; use $x = 2u, y = 3v$.

31–36. Double integrals—your choice of transformation *Evaluate the following integrals using a change of variables of your choice. Sketch the original and new regions of integration, R and S.*

31. $\int_0^1 \int_y^{y+2} \sqrt{x - y}\, dx\, dy$

32. $\iint_R \sqrt{y^2 - x^2}\, dA$, where R is the diamond bounded by $y - x = 0, y - x = 2, y + x = 0$, and $y + x = 2$

33. $\iint_R \left(\dfrac{y - x}{y + 2x + 1}\right)^4 dA$, where R is the parallelogram bounded by $y - x = 1, y - x = 2, y + 2x = 0$, and $y + 2x = 4$

34. $\iint_R e^{xy}\, dA$, where R is the region bounded by the hyperbolas $xy = 1$ and $xy = 4$, and the lines $y/x = 1$ and $y/x = 3$

35. $\iint_R xy\, dA$, where R is the region bounded by the hyperbolas $xy = 1$ and $xy = 4$, and the lines $y = 1$ and $y = 3$

36. $\iint_R (x - y)\sqrt{x - 2y}\, dA$, where R is the triangular region bounded by $y = 0, x - 2y = 0$, and $x - y = 1$

37–40. Jacobians in three variables *Evaluate the Jacobians J(u, v, w) for the following transformations.*

37. $x = v + w, y = u + w, z = u + v$

38. $x = u + v - w, y = u - v + w, z = -u + v + w$

39. $x = vw, y = uw, z = u^2 - v^2$

40. $u = x - y, v = x - z, w = y + z$ (Solve for x, y, and z first.)

41–44. Triple integrals *Use a change of variables to evaluate the following integrals.*

41. $\iiint_D xy\, dV$; D is bounded by the planes $y - x = 0$, $y - x = 2, z - y = 0, z - y = 1, z = 0$, and $z = 3$.

42. $\iiint_D dV$; D is bounded by the planes $y - 2x = 0, y - 2x = 1$, $z - 3y = 0, z - 3y = 1, z - 4x = 0$, and $z - 4x = 3$.

43. $\iiint_D z\, dV$; D is bounded by the paraboloid $z = 16 - x^2 - 4y^2$ and the xy-plane. Use $x = 4u \cos v, y = 2u \sin v, z = w$.

44. $\iiint_D dV$; D is bounded by the upper half of the ellipsoid $x^2/9 + y^2/4 + z^2 = 1$ and the xy-plane. Use $x = 3u$, $y = 2v, z = w$.

Further Explorations

45. Explain why or why not Determine whether the following statements are true and give an explanation or counterexample.

a. If the transformation $T: x = g(u, v), y = h(u, v)$ is linear in u and v, then the Jacobian is a constant.
b. The transformation $x = au + bv, y = cu + dv$ generally maps triangular regions to triangular regions.
c. The transformation $x = 2v, y = -2u$ maps circles to circles.

46. Cylindrical coordinates Evaluate the Jacobian for the transformation from cylindrical coordinates (r, θ, Z) to rectangular coordinates $(x, y, z): x = r \cos \theta, y = r \sin \theta, z = Z$. Show that $J(r, \theta, Z) = r$.

47. Spherical coordinates Evaluate the Jacobian for the transformation from spherical to rectangular coordinates: $x = \rho \sin \varphi \cos \theta, y = \rho \sin \varphi \sin \theta, z = \rho \cos \varphi$. Show that $J(\rho, \varphi, \theta) = \rho^2 \sin \varphi$.

48–52. Ellipse problems *Let R be the region bounded by the ellipse $x^2/a^2 + y^2/b^2 = 1$, where $a > 0$ and $b > 0$ are real numbers. Let T be the transformation $x = au, y = bv$.*

48. Find the area of R.

49. Evaluate $\iint_R |xy|\, dA$.

50. Find the center of mass of the upper half of R $(y \ge 0)$ assuming it has a constant density.

51. Find the average square of the distance between points of R and the origin.

52. Find the average distance between points in the upper half of R and the x-axis.

53–56. Ellipsoid problems *Let D be the region bounded by the ellipsoid $x^2/a^2 + y^2/b^2 + z^2/c^2 = 1$, where $a > 0$, $b > 0$, and $c > 0$ are real numbers. Let T be the transformation $x = au$, $y = bv$, $z = cw$.*

53. Find the volume of D.

54. Evaluate $\displaystyle\iiint\limits_{D} |xyz|\, dA$.

55. Find the center of mass of the upper half of D ($z \geq 0$) assuming it has a constant density.

56. Find the average square of the distance between points of D and the origin.

57. Parabolic coordinates Let T be the transformation $x = u^2 - v^2$, $y = 2uv$.

   a. Show that the lines $u = a$ in the uv-plane map to parabolas in the xy-plane that open in the negative x-direction with vertices on the positive x-axis.

   b. Show that the lines $v = b$ in the uv-plane map to parabolas in the xy-plane that open in the positive x-direction with vertices on the negative x-axis.

   c. Evaluate $J(u, v)$.

   d. Use a change of variables to find the area of the region bounded by $x = 4 - y^2/16$ and $x = y^2/4 - 1$.

   e. Use a change of variables to find the area of the curved rectangle above the x-axis bounded by $x = 4 - y^2/16$, $x = 9 - y^2/36$, $x = y^2/4 - 1$, and $x = y^2/64 - 16$.

   f. Describe the effect of the transformation $x = 2uv$, $y = u^2 - v^2$ on horizontal and vertical lines in the uv-plane.

Applications

58. Shear transformations in $\mathbb{R}^2$ The transformation T in $\mathbb{R}^2$ given by $x = au + bv$, $y = cv$, where a, b, and c are positive real numbers, is a *shear transformation*. Let S be the unit square $\{(u, v): 0 \leq u \leq 1, 0 \leq v \leq 1\}$. Let $R = T(S)$ be the image of S.

   a. Explain with pictures the effect of T on S.

   b. Compute the Jacobian of T.

   c. Find the area of R and compare it to the area of S (which is 1).

   d. Assuming a constant density, find the center of mass of R (in terms of a, b, and c) and compare it to the center of mass of S (which is $\left(\frac{1}{2}, \frac{1}{2}\right)$).

   e. Find an analogous transformation that gives a shear in the y-direction.

59. Shear transformations in $\mathbb{R}^3$ The transformation T in $\mathbb{R}^3$ given by

$$x = au + bv + cw, \qquad y = dv + ew, \qquad z = w,$$

where a, b, c, d, and e are positive real numbers, is one of many possible shear transformations in $\mathbb{R}^3$. Let S be the unit cube $\{(u, v, w): 0 \leq u \leq 1, 0 \leq v \leq 1, 0 \leq w \leq 1\}$. Let $D = T(S)$ be the image of S.

   a. Explain with pictures and words the effect of T on S.

   b. Compute the Jacobian of T.

   c. Find the volume of D and compare it to the volume of S (which is 1).

   d. Assuming a constant density, find the center of mass of D and compare it to the center of mass of S (which is $\left(\frac{1}{2}, \frac{1}{2}, \frac{1}{2}\right)$).

Additional Exercises

60. Linear transformations Consider the linear transformation T in $\mathbb{R}^2$ given by $x = au + bv$, $y = cu + dv$, where a, b, c, and d are real numbers, with $ad \neq bc$.

   a. Find the Jacobian of T.

   b. Let S be the square in the uv-plane with vertices $(0, 0)$, $(1, 0)$, $(0, 1)$, and $(1, 1)$, and let $R = T(S)$. Show that area$(R) = |J(u, v)|$.

   c. Let ℓ be the line segment joining the points P and Q in the uv-plane. Show that $T(\ell)$ (the image of ℓ under T) is the line segment joining $T(P)$ and $T(Q)$ in the xy-plane. (*Hint:* Use vectors.)

   d. Show that if S is a parallelogram in the uv-plane and $R = T(S)$, then area$(R) = |J(u, v)|$ area(S). (*Hint:* Without loss of generality, assume the vertices of S are $(0, 0)$, $(A, 0)$, (B, C), and $(A + B, C)$, where A, B, and C are positive, and use vectors.)

61. Meaning of the Jacobian The Jacobian is a magnification (or reduction) factor that relates the area of a small region near the point (u, v) to the area of the image of that region near the point (x, y).

   a. Suppose S is a rectangle in the uv-plane with vertices $O(0, 0)$, $P(\Delta u, 0)$, $(\Delta u, \Delta v)$, and $Q(0, \Delta v)$ (see figure). The image of S under the transformation $x = g(u, v)$, $y = h(u, v)$ is a region R in the xy-plane. Let O', P', and Q' be the images of O, P, and Q, respectively, in the xy-plane, where O', P', and Q' do not all lie on the same line. Explain why the coordinates of O', P', and Q' are $(g(0, 0), h(0, 0))$, $(g(\Delta u, 0), h(\Delta u, 0))$, and $(g(0, \Delta v), h(0, \Delta v))$, respectively.

   b. Use a Taylor series in both variables to show that

$$g(\Delta u, 0) \approx g(0, 0) + g_u(0, 0)\Delta u$$
$$g(0, \Delta v) \approx g(0, 0) + g_v(0, 0)\Delta v$$
$$h(\Delta u, 0) \approx h(0, 0) + h_u(0, 0)\Delta u$$
$$h(0, \Delta v) \approx h(0, 0) + h_v(0, 0)\Delta v$$

where $g_u(0, 0)$ is $\dfrac{\partial x}{\partial u}$ evaluated at $(0, 0)$, with similar meanings for g_v, h_u, and h_v.

   c. Consider the vectors $\overrightarrow{O'P'}$ and $\overrightarrow{O'Q'}$ and the parallelogram, two of whose sides are $\overrightarrow{O'P'}$ and $\overrightarrow{O'Q'}$. Use the cross product to show that the area of the parallelogram is approximately $|J(u, v)|\, \Delta u\, \Delta v$.

   d. Explain why the ratio of the area of R to the area of S is approximately $|J(u, v)|$.

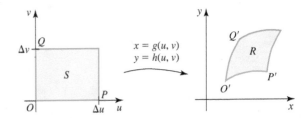

62. Open and closed boxes Consider the region R bounded by three pairs of parallel planes: $ax + by = 0$, $ax + by = 1$, $cx + dz = 0$,

$cx + dz = 1$, $ey + fz = 0$, and $ey + fz = 1$, where a, b, c, d, e, and f are real numbers. For the purposes of evaluating triple integrals, when do these six planes bound a finite region? Carry out the following steps.

a. Find three vectors $\mathbf{n}_1$, $\mathbf{n}_2$, and $\mathbf{n}_3$ each of which is normal to one of the three pairs of planes.

b. Show that the three normal vectors lie in a plane if their triple scalar product $\mathbf{n}_1 \cdot (\mathbf{n}_2 \times \mathbf{n}_3)$ is zero.

c. Show that the three normal vectors lie in a plane if $ade + bcf = 0$.

d. Assuming $\mathbf{n}_1$, $\mathbf{n}_2$, and $\mathbf{n}_3$ lie in a plane P, find a vector $\mathbf{N}$ that is normal to P. Explain why a line in the direction of $\mathbf{N}$ does not intersect any of the six planes, and thus the six planes do not form a bounded region.

e. Consider the change of variables $u = ax + by$, $v = cx + dz$, $w = ey + fz$. Show that

$$J(x, y, z) = \frac{\partial(u, v, w)}{\partial(x, y, z)} = -ade - bcf.$$

What is the value of the Jacobian if R is unbounded?

QUICK CHECK ANSWERS

1. The image is a semicircular disk of radius 1.
2. $J(u, v) = 2$ 3. $x = 2u/3 - v/3$, $y = u/3 + v/3$
4. The ratio is 2, which is $1/J(u, v)$. 5. It means that the volume of a small region in xyz-space is unchanged when it is transformed by T to a small region in uvw-space. ◀

CHAPTER 14   REVIEW EXERCISES

1. **Explain why or why not** Determine whether the following statements are true and give an explanation or counterexample.

a. Assuming g is integrable and a, b, c, and d are constants,
$$\int_c^d \int_a^b g(x, y) \, dx \, dy = \left(\int_a^b g(x, y) \, dx \right)\left(\int_c^d g(x, y) \, dy \right).$$

b. $\{(\rho, \varphi, \theta): \varphi = \pi/2\} = \{(r, \theta, z): z = 0\} = \{(x, y, z): z = 0\}$

c. The transformation $T: x = v, y = -u$ maps a square in the uv-plane into a triangle in the xy-plane.

2–4. Evaluating integrals *Evaluate the following integrals as they are written.*

'2. $\int_1^2 \int_1^4 \frac{xy}{(x^2 + y^2)^2} \, dx \, dy$

3. $\int_1^3 \int_1^{e^x} \frac{x}{y} \, dy \, dx$

4. $\int_1^2 \int_0^{\ln x} x^3 e^y \, dy \, dx$

5–7. Changing the order of integration *Assuming f is integrable, change the order of integration in the following integrals.*

5. $\int_{-1}^1 \int_{x^2}^1 f(x, y) \, dy \, dx$

6. $\int_0^2 \int_{y-1}^1 f(x, y) \, dx \, dy$

7. $\int_0^1 \int_0^{\sqrt{1-y^2}} f(x, y) \, dx \, dy$

8–10. Area of plane regions *Use double integrals to compute the area of the following regions. Make a sketch of the region.*

8. The region bounded by the lines $y = -x - 4$, $y = x$, and $y = 2x - 4$

9. The region bounded by $y = |x|$ and $y = 20 - x^2$

10. The region between the curves $y = x^2$ and $y = 1 + x - x^2$

11–16. Miscellaneous double integrals *Choose a convenient method for evaluating the following integrals.*

11. $\iint_R \frac{2y}{\sqrt{x^4 + 1}} \, dA$; R is the region bounded by $x = 1$, $x = 2$, $y = x^{3/2}$, and $y = 0$.

12. $\iint_R x^{-1/2} e^y \, dA$; R is the region bounded by $x = 1$, $x = 4$, $y = \sqrt{x}$, and $y = 0$.

13. $\iint_R (x + y) \, dA$; R is the disk bounded by the circle $r = 4 \sin \theta$.

14. $\iint_R (x^2 + y^2) \, dA$; R is the region $\{(x, y): 0 \le x \le 2, 0 \le y \le x\}$.

15. $\int_0^1 \int_{y^{1/3}}^1 x^{10} \cos(\pi x^4 y) \, dx \, dy$ 16. $\int_0^2 \int_{y^2}^4 x^8 y \sqrt{1 + x^4 y^2} \, dx \, dy$

17–18. Cartesian to polar coordinates *Evaluate the following integrals over the specified region.*

17. $\iint_R 3x^2 y \, dA$; $R = \{(r, \theta): 0 \le r \le 1, 0 \le \theta \le \pi/2\}$

18. $\iint_R \frac{1}{(1 + x^2 + y^2)^2} \, dA$; $R = \{(r, \theta): 1 \le r \le 4, 0 \le \theta \le \pi\}$

19–21. Computing areas *Sketch the following regions and use integration to find their areas.*

19. The region bounded by all leaves of the rose $r = 3 \cos 2\theta$

20. The region inside both the circles $r = 2$ and $r = 4 \cos \theta$

21. The region that lies inside both the cardioids $r = 2 - 2 \cos \theta$ and $r = 2 + 2 \cos \theta$

22–23. Average values

22. Find the average value of $z = \sqrt{16 - x^2 - y^2}$ over the disk in the xy-plane centered at the origin with radius 4.

23. Find the average distance from the points in the solid cone bounded by $z = 2\sqrt{x^2 + y^2}$ to the z-axis, for $0 \le z \le 8$.

24–26. Changing order of integration *Rewrite the following integrals using the indicated order of integration.*

24. $\displaystyle\int_0^1 \int_0^{\sqrt{1-x^2}} \int_0^{\sqrt{1-x^2}} f(x, y, z)\, dy\, dz\, dx$ in the order $dz\, dy\, dx$

25. $\displaystyle\int_0^4 \int_0^{\sqrt{16-x^2}} \int_0^{\sqrt{16-x^2-z^2}} f(x, y, z)\, dy\, dz\, dx$ in the order $dx\, dy\, dz$

26. $\displaystyle\int_0^2 \int_0^{9-x^2} \int_0^x f(x, y, z)\, dy\, dz\, dx$ in the order $dz\, dx\, dy$

27–31. Triple integrals *Evaluate the following integrals, changing the order of integration if needed.*

27. $\displaystyle\int_0^1 \int_{-z}^z \int_{-\sqrt{1-x^2}}^{\sqrt{1-x^2}} dy\, dx\, dz$ **28.** $\displaystyle\int_0^\pi \int_0^y \int_0^{\sin x} dz\, dx\, dy$

29. $\displaystyle\int_1^9 \int_0^1 \int_{2y}^2 \frac{4 \sin x^2}{\sqrt{z}}\, dx\, dy\, dz$

30. $\displaystyle\int_0^2 \int_{-\sqrt{2-x^2}/2}^{\sqrt{2-x^2}/2} \int_{x^2+3y^2}^{8-x^2-y^2} dz\, dy\, dx$

31. $\displaystyle\int_0^2 \int_0^{y^{1/3}} \int_0^{y^2} yz^5(1 + x + y^2 + z^6)^2\, dx\, dz\, dy$

32–36. Volumes of solids *Find the volume of the following solids.*

32. The prism in the first octant bounded by the planes $y = 3 - 3x$ and $z = 2$

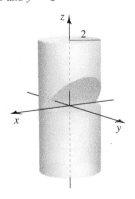

33. One of the wedges formed when the cylinder $x^2 + y^2 = 4$ is cut by the planes $z = 0$ and $y = z$

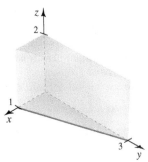

34. The region inside the parabolic cylinder $y = x^2$ between the planes $z = 3 - y$ and $z = 0$

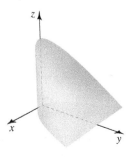

35. The solid common to the two cylinders $x^2 + y^2 = 4$ and $x^2 + z^2 = 4$

36. The tetrahedron with vertices $(0, 0, 0), (1, 0, 0), (1, 1, 0)$, and $(1, 1, 1)$

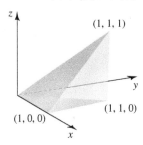

37. Single to double integral Evaluate $\int_0^{1/2}(\sin^{-1}(2x) - \sin^{-1} x)\, dx$ by converting it to a double integral.

38. Tetrahedron limits Let D be the tetrahedron with vertices at $(0, 0, 0), (1, 0, 0), (0, 2, 0)$, and $(0, 0, 3)$. Suppose the volume of D is to be found using a triple integral. Give the limits of integration for the six possible orderings of the variables.

39. A "polynomial cube" Let $D = \{(x, y, z): 0 \le x \le y^2, 0 \le y \le z^3, 0 \le z \le 2\}$.

   a. Use a triple integral to find the volume of D.
   b. In theory, how many other possible orderings of the variables (besides the one used in part (a)) can be used to find the volume of D? Verify the result of part (a) using one of these other orderings.
   c. What is the volume of the region $D = \{(x, y, z): 0 \le x \le y^p, 0 \le y \le z^q, 0 \le z \le 2\}$, where p and q are positive real numbers?

40–41. Average value

40. Find the average of the *square* of the distance between the origin and the points in the solid paraboloid $D = \{(x, y, z): 0 \le z \le 4 - x^2 - y^2\}$.

41. Find the average x-coordinate of the points in the prism $D = \{(x, y, z): 0 \le x \le 1, 0 \le y \le 3 - 3x, 0 \le z \le 2\}$.

42–43. Integrals in cylindrical coordinates *Evaluate the following integrals in cylindrical coordinates.*

42. $\displaystyle\int_0^3\int_0^{\sqrt{9-x^2}}\int_0^3 (x^2+y^2)^{3/2}\,dz\,dy\,dx$

43. $\displaystyle\int_{-2}^2\int_{-1}^1\int_0^{\sqrt{1-z^2}} \frac{1}{(1+x^2+z^2)^2}\,dx\,dz\,dy$

44–45. Volumes in cylindrical coordinates *Use integration in cylindrical coordinates to find the volume of the following regions.*

44. The region bounded by the plane $z=\sqrt{29}$ and the hyperboloid $z=\sqrt{4+x^2+y^2}$

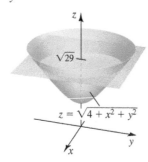

45. The solid cylinder whose height is 4 and whose base is the disk $\{(r,\theta): 0\le r\le 2\cos\theta\}$

46–47. Integrals in spherical coordinates *Evaluate the following integrals in spherical coordinates.*

46. $\displaystyle\int_0^{2\pi}\int_0^{\pi/2}\int_0^{2\cos\varphi} \rho^2\sin\varphi\,d\rho\,d\varphi\,d\theta$

47. $\displaystyle\int_0^{\pi}\int_0^{\pi/4}\int_{2\sec\varphi}^{4\sec\varphi} \rho^2\sin\varphi\,d\rho\,d\varphi\,d\theta$

48–50. Volumes in spherical coordinates *Use integration in spherical coordinates to find the volume of the following regions.*

48. The cardioid of revolution $D=\{(\rho,\varphi,\theta):$
$0\le\rho\le(1-\cos\varphi)/2, 0\le\varphi\le\pi, 0\le\theta\le 2\pi\}$

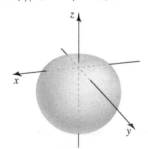

49. The rose petal of revolution $D=\{(\rho,\varphi,\theta): 0\le\rho\le 4\sin 2\varphi,$
$0\le\varphi\le\pi/2, 0\le\theta\le 2\pi\}$

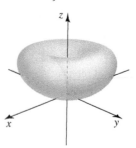

50. The region above the cone $\varphi=\pi/4$ and inside the sphere $\rho=4\cos\varphi$

51–54. Constant-density plates *Find the center of mass (centroid) of the following thin constant-density plates. Sketch the region corresponding to the plate and indicate the location of the center of mass. Use symmetry whenever possible to simplify your work.*

51. The region bounded by $y=\sin x$ and $y=0$ between $x=0$ and $x=\pi$

52. The region bounded by $y=x^3$ and $y=x^2$ between $x=0$ and $x=1$

53. The half-annulus $\{(r,\theta): 2\le r\le 4, 0\le\theta\le\pi\}$

54. The region bounded by $y=x^2$ and $y=a^2-x^2$, where $a>0$

55–56. Center of mass of constant-density solids *Find the center of mass of the following solids, assuming a constant density. Use symmetry whenever possible and choose a convenient coordinate system.*

55. The paraboloid bowl bounded by $z=x^2+y^2$ and $z=36$

56. The tetrahedron bounded by $z=4-x-2y$ and the coordinate planes

57–58. Variable-density solids *Find the coordinates of the center of mass of the following solids with the given density.*

57. The upper half of a ball $\{(\rho,\varphi,\theta): 0\le\rho\le 16, 0\le\varphi\le\dfrac{\pi}{2},$
$0\le\theta\le 2\pi\}$ with density $f(\rho,\varphi,\theta)=1+\rho/4$

58. The cube in the first octant bounded by the planes $x=2, y=2$, and $z=2$, with $\rho(x,y,z)=1+x+y+z$

59–62. Centers of mass for general objects *Consider the following two- and three-dimensional regions. Compute the center of mass assuming constant density. All parameters are positive real numbers.*

59. A region is bounded by a paraboloid with a circular base of radius R and height h. How far from the base is the center of mass?

60. Let R be the region enclosed by an equilateral triangle with sides of length s. What is the perpendicular distance between the center of mass of R and the edges of R?

61. An isosceles triangle has two sides of length s and a base of length b. How far from the base is the center of mass of the region enclosed by the triangle?

62. A tetrahedron is bounded by the coordinate planes and the plane $x + y/2 + z/3 = 1$. What are the coordinates of the center of mass?

63. Slicing a conical cake A cake is shaped like a solid cone with radius 4 and height 2, with its base on the xy-plane. A wedge of the cake is removed by making two slices from the axis of the cone outward, perpendicular to the xy-plane separated by an angle of Q radians, where $0 < Q < 2\pi$.

   a. Use a double integral to find the volume of the slice for $Q = \pi/4$. Use geometry to check your answer.

   b. Use a double integral to find the volume of the slice for any $0 < Q < 2\pi$. Use geometry to check your answer.

64. Volume and weight of a fish tank A spherical fish tank with a radius of 1 ft is filled with water to a level 6 in below the top of the tank.

   a. Determine the volume and weight of the water in the fish tank. (The weight density of water is about 62.5 lb/ft³.)

   b. How much additional water must be added to completely fill the tank?

65–68. Transforming a square Let $S = \{(u, v): 0 \le u \le 1, 0 \le v \le 1\}$ be a unit square in the uv-plane. Find the image of S in the xy-plane under the following transformations.

65. $T: x = v, y = u$

66. $T: x = -v, y = u$

67. $T: x = (u + v)/2, y = (u - v)/2$

68. $T: x = u, y = 2v + 2$

69–72. Computing Jacobians *Compute the Jacobian $J(u, v)$ of the following transformations.*

69. $T: x = 4u - v, y = -2u + 3v$

70. $T: x = u + v, y = u - v$

71. $T: x = 3u, y = 2v + 2$

72. $T: x = u^2 - v^2, y = 2uv$

73–76. Double integrals—transformation given *To evaluate the following integrals carry out the following steps.*

a. *Sketch the original region of integration R and the new region S using the given change of variables.*

b. *Find the limits of integration for the new integral with respect to u and v.*

c. *Compute the Jacobian.*

d. *Change variables and evaluate the new integral.*

73. $\iint\limits_R xy^2 \, dA; \ R = \{(x, y): y/3 \le x \le (y + 6)/3, 0 \le y \le 3\}$; use $x = u + v/3, y = v$.

74. $\iint\limits_R 3xy^2 \, dA; \ R = \{(x, y): 0 \le x \le 2, x \le y \le x + 4\}$; use $x = 2u, y = 4v + 2u$.

75. $\iint\limits_R x^2\sqrt{x + 2y} \, dA; \ R = \{(x, y): 0 \le x \le 2, -x/2 \le y \le 1 - x\}$; use $x = 2u, y = v - u$.

76. $\iint\limits_R xy^2 \, dA; \ R$ is the region between the hyperbolas $xy = 1$ and $xy = 4$ and the lines $y = 1$ and $y = 4$; use $x = u/v, y = v$.

77–78. Double integrals *Evaluate the following integrals using a change of variables of your choice. Sketch the original and new regions of integration, R and S.*

77. $\iint\limits_R y^4 \, dA; \ R$ is the region bounded by the hyperbolas $xy = 1$ and $xy = 4$ and the lines $y/x = 1$ and $y/x = 3$.

78. $\iint\limits_R (y^2 + xy - 2x^2) \, dA; \ R$ is the region bounded by the lines $y = x, y = x - 3, y = -2x + 3$, and $y = -2x - 3$.

79–80. Triple integrals *Use a change of variables to evaluate the following integrals.*

79. $\iiint\limits_D yz \, dV; \ D$ is bounded by the planes $x + 2y = 1, x + 2y = 2, x - z = 0, x - z = 2, 2y - z = 0$, and $2y - z = 3$.

80. $\iiint\limits_D x \, dV; \ D$ is bounded by the planes $y - 2x = 0, y - 2x = 1, z - 3y = 0, z - 3y = 1, z - 4x = 0$, and $z - 4x = 3$.

Chapter 14 Guided Projects

Applications of the material in this chapter and related topics can be found in the following Guided Projects. For additional information, see the Preface.

- How big are n-balls?
- Electrical field integrals
- The tilted cylinder problem

- The exponential Eiffel Tower
- Moments of inertia
- Gravitational fields

15

Vector Calculus

Chapter Preview   This culminating chapter of the book provides a beautiful, unifying conclusion to our study of calculus. Many ideas and themes that have appeared throughout the book come together in these final pages. First, we combine vector-valued functions (Chapter 12) and functions of several variables (Chapter 13) to form *vector fields*. Once vector fields have been introduced and illustrated through their many applications, we begin exploring the calculus of vector fields. Concepts such as limits and continuity carry over directly. The extension of derivatives to vector fields leads to two new operations that underlie this chapter: the *curl* and the *divergence*. When integration is extended to vector fields, we discover new versions of the Fundamental Theorem of Calculus. The chapter ends with a final look at the Fundamental Theorem of Calculus and the several related forms in which it has appeared throughout the book.

15.1 Vector Fields

> A velocity vector field models the motion of air particles in a breeze at a single moment in time. Individual vectors indicate direction of motion, and their lengths indicate speed.

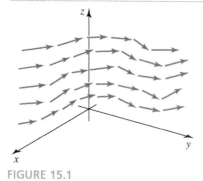

FIGURE 15.1

It is not difficult to find everyday examples of vector fields. Imagine sitting on a beach in a breeze: Focus on a point in space and consider the motion of the air at that point at a single instant of time. The motion is described by a velocity vector with three components (east-west, north-south, up-down). At another point in space at the same time, the air is moving with a different direction and speed, and a different velocity vector is associated with that point. In general, at one instant in time, every point in space has a velocity vector associated with it (Figure 15.1). This collection of velocity vectors is a vector field.

Other examples of vector fields include the wind patterns in a hurricane (Figure 15.2a), the flow of air around an airplane wing, and the circulation of water in a heat exchanger (Figure 15.2b). Gravitational, magnetic, and electric force fields are represented by vector fields (Figure 15.2c), as are the stresses and strains in buildings and bridges. Beyond physics and engineering, the transport of a chemical pollutant in a lake or human migration patterns can be modeled by vector fields.

Vector Fields in Two Dimensions

To solidify the idea of a vector field, we begin by exploring vector fields in $\mathbb{R}^2$. From there, it is a short step to vector fields in $\mathbb{R}^3$.

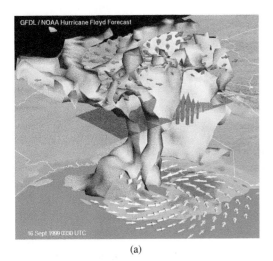

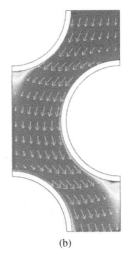

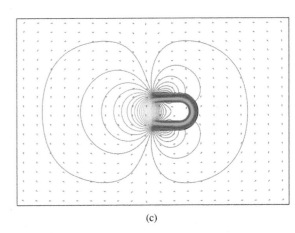

(a)   (b)   (c)

FIGURE 15.2

> **DEFINITION Vector Fields in Two Dimensions**
>
> Let f and g be defined on a region R of $\mathbb{R}^2$. A **vector field** in $\mathbb{R}^2$ is a function $\mathbf{F}$ that assigns to each point in R a vector $\langle f(x, y), g(x, y) \rangle$. The vector field is written as
>
> $$\mathbf{F}(x, y) = \langle f(x, y), g(x, y) \rangle \quad \text{or}$$
> $$\mathbf{F}(x, y) = f(x, y)\,\mathbf{i} + g(x, y)\,\mathbf{j}.$$
>
> A vector field $\mathbf{F} = \langle f, g \rangle$ is continuous or differentiable on a region R of $\mathbb{R}^2$ if f and g are continuous or differentiable on R, respectively.

A vector field cannot be represented by a single curve or surface. Instead, we plot a representative sample of vectors that illustrate the general appearance of the vector field. Consider the vector field defined by

$$\mathbf{F}(x, y) = \langle 2x, 2y \rangle = 2x\,\mathbf{i} + 2y\,\mathbf{j}.$$

At selected points $P(x, y)$, we plot a vector with its tail at P equal to the value of $\mathbf{F}(x, y)$. For example, $\mathbf{F}(1, 1) = \langle 2, 2 \rangle$, so we draw a vector equal to $\langle 2, 2 \rangle$ with its tail at the point $(1, 1)$. Similarly, $\mathbf{F}(-2, -3) = \langle -4, -6 \rangle$, so at the point $(-2, -3)$, we draw a vector equal to $\langle -4, -6 \rangle$. We can make the following general observations about the vector field $\mathbf{F}(x, y) = \langle 2x, 2y \rangle$.

- For every (x, y) except $(0, 0)$, the vector $\mathbf{F}(x, y)$ points in the direction of $\langle 2x, 2y \rangle$, which is directly outward from the origin.
- The length of $\mathbf{F}(x, y)$ is $|\mathbf{F}| = |\langle 2x, 2y \rangle| = 2\sqrt{x^2 + y^2}$, which increases with distance from the origin.

The vector field $\mathbf{F} = \langle 2x, 2y \rangle$ is an example of a *radial vector field* (because its vectors point radially away from the origin; Figure 15.3). If $\mathbf{F}$ represents the velocity of a fluid moving in two dimensions, the graph of the vector field gives a vivid image of how a small object, such as a cork, moves through the fluid. In this case, at every point of the field, a particle moves in the direction of the arrow at that point with a speed equal to the length of the arrow. For this reason, vector fields are sometimes called *flows*. When sketching vector fields, it is often useful to draw continuous curves that are aligned with the vector field. Such curves are called **streamlines** or **flow curves**.

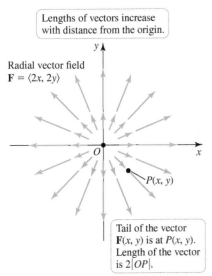

FIGURE 15.3

Shear vector field
$\mathbf{F} = \langle 0, x \rangle$

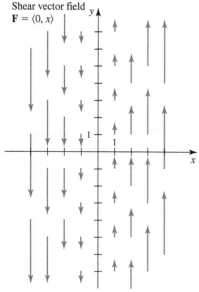

FIGURE 15.4

Drawing vectors with their actual length often leads to cluttered pictures of vector fields. For this reason, most of the vector fields in this chapter are illustrated with proportional scaling: All vectors are multiplied by a scalar chosen to make the vector field as understandable as possible.

A useful observation for two-dimensional vector fields $\mathbf{F} = \langle f, g \rangle$ is that the slope of the vector at (x, y) is $g(x, y)/f(x, y)$. In Example 1a, the slopes are everywhere undefined; in part (b), the slopes are everywhere 0, and in part (c), the slopes are $-x/y$.

EXAMPLE 1   **Vector fields** Sketch representative vectors of the following vector fields.

a. $\mathbf{F}(x, y) = \langle 0, x \rangle = x\mathbf{j}$ (a shear field)

b. $\mathbf{F}(x, y) = \langle 1 - y^2, 0 \rangle = (1 - y^2)\mathbf{i}$, for $|y| \le 1$ (channel flow)

c. $\mathbf{F}(x, y) = \langle -y, x \rangle = -y\mathbf{i} + x\mathbf{j}$ (a rotation field)

SOLUTION

a. This vector field is independent of y. Furthermore, because the x-component of $\mathbf{F}$ is zero, all vectors in the field (for $x \ne 0$) point in the y-direction: upward for $x > 0$ and downward for $x < 0$. The magnitudes of the vectors in the field increase with distance from the y-axis (Figure 15.4). The flow curves for this field are vertical lines. If $\mathbf{F}$ represents a velocity field, a particle right of the y-axis moves upward, a particle left of the y-axis moves downward, and a particle on the y-axis is stationary.

b. In this case, the vector field is independent of x and the y-component of $\mathbf{F}$ is zero. Because $1 - y^2 > 0$ for $|y| < 1$, vectors in this region point in the positive x-direction. The x-component of the vector field is zero at the boundaries $y = \pm 1$ and increases to 1 along the center of the strip, $y = 0$. The vector field might model the flow of water in a straight shallow channel (Figure 15.5); its flow curves are horizontal lines, indicating motion in the direction of the positive x-axis.

c. It often helps to determine the vector field along the coordinate axes.

• When $y = 0$ (along the x-axis), we have $\mathbf{F}(x, 0) = \langle 0, x \rangle$. With $x > 0$, this vector field consists of vectors pointing upward, increasing in length as x increases. With $x < 0$, the vectors point downward, increasing in length as $|x|$ increases.

• When $x = 0$ (along the y-axis), we have $\mathbf{F}(0, y) = \langle -y, 0 \rangle$. If $y > 0$, the vectors point in the negative x-direction, increasing in length as y increases. If $y < 0$, the vectors point in the positive x-direction, increasing in length as $|y|$ increases.

A few more representative vectors show that the vector field has a counterclockwise rotation about the origin; the magnitudes of the vectors increase with distance from the origin (Figure 15.6).

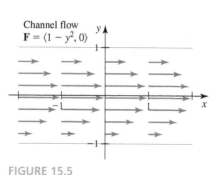

Channel flow
$\mathbf{F} = \langle 1 - y^2, 0 \rangle$

FIGURE 15.5

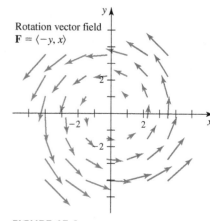

Rotation vector field
$\mathbf{F} = \langle -y, x \rangle$

FIGURE 15.6

Related Exercises 6–16 ◀

QUICK CHECK 1 If the vector field in Example 1c describes the velocity of a fluid and you place a small cork in the plane at $(2, 0)$, what path will it follow? ◀

Radial Vector Fields in $\mathbb{R}^2$ Radial vector fields in $\mathbb{R}^2$ have the property that their vectors point directly toward or away from the origin at all points (except the origin), parallel to the position vectors $\mathbf{r} = \langle x, y \rangle$. We will work with radial vector fields of the form

$$\mathbf{F}(x, y) = \frac{\mathbf{r}}{|\mathbf{r}|^p} = \frac{\langle x, y \rangle}{|\mathbf{r}|^p} = \underbrace{\frac{\mathbf{r}}{|\mathbf{r}|}}_{\substack{\text{unit} \\ \text{vector}}} \underbrace{\frac{1}{|\mathbf{r}|^{p-1}}}_{\text{magnitude}},$$

where p is a real number. Figure 15.7 illustrates radial fields with $p = 1$ and $p = 3$. These vector fields (and their three-dimensional counterparts) play an important role in many applications. For example, central forces, such as gravitational or electrostatic forces between point masses or charges, are described by radial vector fields with $p = 3$. These forces obey an inverse square law in which the magnitude of the force is proportional to $1/|\mathbf{r}|^2$.

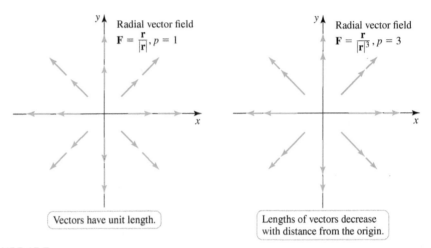

Radial vector field
$\mathbf{F} = \dfrac{\mathbf{r}}{|\mathbf{r}|}, p = 1$

Vectors have unit length.

Radial vector field
$\mathbf{F} = \dfrac{\mathbf{r}}{|\mathbf{r}|^3}, p = 3$

Lengths of vectors decrease with distance from the origin.

FIGURE 15.7

DEFINITION Radial Vector Fields in $\mathbb{R}^2$

Let $\mathbf{r} = \langle x, y \rangle$. A vector field of the form $\mathbf{F} = f(x, y)\,\mathbf{r}$, where f is a scalar-valued function, is a **radial vector field**. Of specific interest are the radial vector fields

$$\mathbf{F}(x, y) = \frac{\mathbf{r}}{|\mathbf{r}|^p} = \frac{\langle x, y \rangle}{|\mathbf{r}|^p},$$

where p is a real number. At every point (except the origin), the vectors of this field are directed outward from the origin with a magnitude of $|\mathbf{F}| = \dfrac{1}{|\mathbf{r}|^{p-1}}$.

EXAMPLE 2   Normal and tangent vectors Let C be the circle $x^2 + y^2 = a^2$, where $a > 0$.

a. Show that at each point of C, the radial vector field $\mathbf{F}(x, y) = \dfrac{\mathbf{r}}{|\mathbf{r}|} = \dfrac{\langle x, y \rangle}{\sqrt{x^2 + y^2}}$ is orthogonal to the line tangent to C at that point.

b. Show that at each point of C, the rotation vector field $\mathbf{G}(x, y) = \dfrac{\langle -y, x \rangle}{\sqrt{x^2 + y^2}}$ is parallel to the line tangent to C at that point.

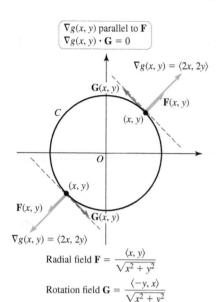

Radial field $\mathbf{F} = \dfrac{\langle x, y \rangle}{\sqrt{x^2 + y^2}}$

Rotation field $\mathbf{G} = \dfrac{\langle -y, x \rangle}{\sqrt{x^2 + y^2}}$

FIGURE 15.8

SOLUTION The circle C described by the equation $g(x, y) = x^2 + y^2 = a^2$ may be viewed as a level curve of a surface. As shown in Theorem 13.12 (Section 13.6), the gradient $\nabla g(x, y) = \langle 2x, 2y \rangle$ is orthogonal to the line tangent to C at (x, y) (Figure 15.8).

a. Notice that $\nabla g(x, y)$ is parallel to $\mathbf{F} = \langle x, y \rangle / |\mathbf{r}|$ at the point (x, y). It follows that $\mathbf{F}$ is also orthogonal to the line tangent to C at (x, y).

b. Notice that

$$\nabla g(x, y) \cdot \mathbf{G}(x, y) = \langle 2x, 2y \rangle \cdot \frac{\langle -y, x \rangle}{\mathbf{r}} = 0.$$

Therefore, $\nabla g(x, y)$ is orthogonal to the vector field $\mathbf{G}$ at (x, y), which implies that $\mathbf{G}$ is parallel to the tangent line at (x, y).

Related Exercises 17–20 ◄

QUICK CHECK 2 In Example 2 verify that $\nabla g(x, y) \cdot \mathbf{G}(x, y) = 0$. In parts (a) and (b) of Example 2, verify that $|\mathbf{F}| = 1$ and $|\mathbf{G}| = 1$ at all points excluding the origin. ◄

Vector Fields in Three Dimensions

Vector fields in three dimensions are conceptually the same as vector fields in two dimensions. The vector $\mathbf{F}$ now has three components, each of which depends on three variables.

DEFINITION Vector Fields and Radial Vector Fields in $\mathbb{R}^3$

Let f, g, and h be defined on a region D of $\mathbb{R}^3$. A **vector field** in $\mathbb{R}^3$ is a function $\mathbf{F}$ that assigns to each point in D a vector $\langle f(x, y, z), g(x, y, z), h(x, y, z) \rangle$. The vector field is written as

$$\mathbf{F}(x, y, z) = \langle f(x, y, z), g(x, y, z), h(x, y, z) \rangle \quad \text{or}$$
$$\mathbf{F}(x, y, z) = f(x, y, z)\,\mathbf{i} + g(x, y, z)\,\mathbf{j} + h(x, y, z)\,\mathbf{k}.$$

A vector field $\mathbf{F} = \langle f, g, h \rangle$ is continuous or differentiable on a region D of $\mathbb{R}^3$ if f, g, and h are continuous or differentiable on D, respectively. Of particular importance are the **radial vector fields**

$$\mathbf{F}(x, y, z) = \frac{\mathbf{r}}{|\mathbf{r}|^p} = \frac{\langle x, y, z \rangle}{|\mathbf{r}|^p},$$

where p is a real number.

EXAMPLE 3   Vector fields in $\mathbb{R}^3$ Sketch and discuss the following vector fields.

a. $\mathbf{F}(x, y, z) = \langle x, y, e^{-z} \rangle$, for $z \geq 0$

b. $\mathbf{F}(x, y, z) = \langle 0, 0, 1 - x^2 - y^2 \rangle$, for $x^2 + y^2 \leq 1$

SOLUTION

a. First consider the x- and y-components of $\mathbf{F}$ in the xy-plane ($z = 0$), where $\mathbf{F} = \langle x, y, 1 \rangle$. This vector field looks like a radial field in the first two components, increasing in magnitude with distance from the z-axis. However, each vector also has a constant vertical component of 1. In horizontal planes $z = z_0 > 0$, the radial pattern remains the same, but the vertical component decreases as z increases. As $z \to \infty$, $e^{-z} \to 0$ and the vector field becomes a horizontal radial field (Figure 15.9).

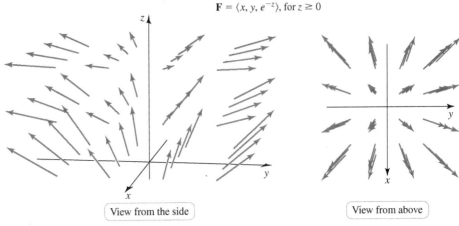

$$\mathbf{F} = \langle x, y, e^{-z}\rangle, \text{ for } z \geq 0$$

View from the side   View from above

FIGURE 15.9

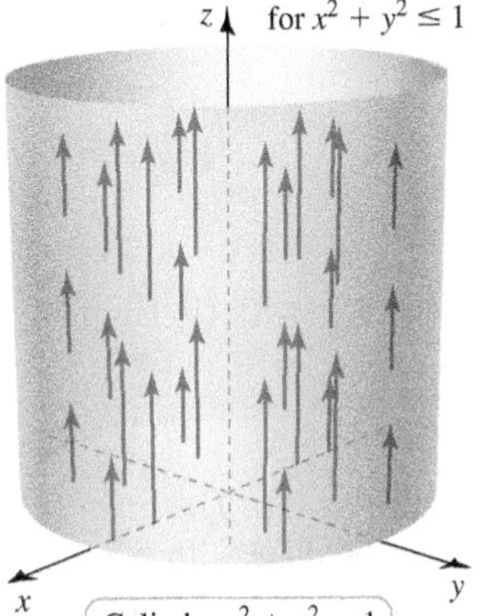

b. Regarding $\mathbf{F}$ as a velocity field, for points in and on the cylinder $x^2 + y^2 = 1$, there is no motion in the x- or y-directions. The z-component of the vector field may be written $1 - r^2$, where $r^2 = x^2 + y^2$ is the square of the distance from the z-axis. We see that the z-component increases from 0 on the boundary of the cylinder ($r = 1$) to a maximum value of 1 along the centerline of the cylinder ($r = 0$) (Figure 15.10). This vector field models the flow of a fluid inside a tube (such as a blood vessel).

Related Exercises 21–24 ◄

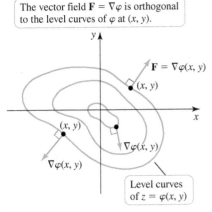

$$\mathbf{F} = \langle 0, 0, 1 - x^2 - y^2\rangle,$$
$$\text{for } x^2 + y^2 \leq 1$$

Cylinder $x^2 + y^2 = 1$

FIGURE 15.10

> Physicists often use the convention that a gradient field and its potential are related by $\mathbf{F} = -\nabla \varphi$.

Gradient Fields and Potential Functions   One way to generate a vector field is to start with a differentiable scalar-valued function φ, take its gradient, and let $\mathbf{F} = \nabla \varphi$. A vector field defined as the gradient of a scalar-valued function φ is called a *gradient field* and the function φ is called a *potential function*.

Suppose φ is a differentiable function on a region R of $\mathbb{R}^2$ and consider the surface $z = \varphi(x, y)$. Recall from Chapter 13 that this function may also be represented by level curves in the xy-plane. At each point (a, b) on a level curve, the gradient $\nabla \varphi(a, b) = \langle \varphi_x(a, b), \varphi_y(a, b)\rangle$ is orthogonal to the level curve at (a, b) (Figure 15.11). Therefore, the vectors of $\mathbf{F} = \nabla \varphi$ point in a direction orthogonal to the level curves of φ.

The idea extends to gradients of functions of three variables. If φ is differentiable on a region D of $\mathbb{R}^3$, then $\mathbf{F} = \nabla \varphi = \langle \varphi_x, \varphi_y, \varphi_z\rangle$ is a vector field that points in a direction orthogonal to the level *surfaces* of φ.

Gradient fields are useful because of the physical meaning of the gradient. For example, if φ represents the temperature in a conducting material, then the gradient $\nabla \varphi$ at a point indicates the direction in which the temperature increases most rapidly. According to a basic physical law, heat diffuses in the direction of the vector field $-\nabla \varphi$, the direction in which the temperature *decreases* most rapidly; that is, heat flows "down the gradient" from relatively hot regions to cooler regions. Similarly, water on a smooth surface tends to flow down the elevation gradient.

The vector field $\mathbf{F} = \nabla \varphi$ is orthogonal to the level curves of φ at (x, y).

$\mathbf{F} = \nabla \varphi(x, y)$

(x, y)

(x, y)

$\nabla \varphi(x, y)$

$\nabla \varphi(x, y)$

Level curves of $z = \varphi(x, y)$

FIGURE 15.11

QUICK CHECK 3 Find the gradient field associated with the function $\varphi(x, y, z) = xyz$. ◄

A potential function plays the role of an antiderivative of a vector field: Derivatives of the potential function produce the vector field. If φ is a potential function for a gradient field, then $\varphi + C$ is also a potential function for that gradient field, for any constant C.

> **DEFINITION Gradient Fields and Potential Functions**
>
> Let $z = \varphi(x, y)$ and $w = \varphi(x, y, z)$ be differentiable functions on regions of $\mathbb{R}^2$ and $\mathbb{R}^3$, respectively. The vector field $\mathbf{F} = \nabla\varphi$ is a **gradient field**, and the function φ is a **potential function** for $\mathbf{F}$.

EXAMPLE 4 Gradient fields

a. Sketch and interpret the gradient field associated with the temperature function $T = 200 - x^2 - y^2$ on the circular plate $R = \{(x, y): x^2 + y^2 \leq 25\}$.

b. Sketch and interpret the gradient field associated with the velocity potential $\varphi = \tan^{-1}(y/x)$.

SOLUTION

a. The gradient field associated with T is

$$\mathbf{F} = \nabla T = \langle -2x, -2y \rangle = -2\langle x, y \rangle.$$

This vector field points inward toward the origin at all points of R except $(0, 0)$. The magnitudes of the vectors,

$$|\mathbf{F}| = \sqrt{(-2x)^2 + (-2y)^2} = 2\sqrt{x^2 + y^2},$$

are greatest on the edge of the disk, where $x^2 + y^2 = 25$ and $|\mathbf{F}| = 10$. The magnitudes of the vectors in the field decrease toward the center of the plate with $|\mathbf{F}(0, 0)| = 0$. Figure 15.12 shows the level curves of the temperature function with several gradient vectors, all orthogonal to the level curves. Note that the plate is hottest at the center and coolest on the edge, so heat diffuses *outward*, in the direction opposite to that of the gradient.

b. The gradient of a velocity potential gives the velocity components of a two-dimensional flow; that is, $\mathbf{F} = \langle u, v \rangle = \nabla\varphi$, where u and v are the velocities in the x- and y-directions, respectively. Computing the gradient, we find that

$$\mathbf{F} = \langle \varphi_x, \varphi_y \rangle = \left\langle \frac{1}{1 + (y/x)^2} \cdot -\frac{y}{x^2}, \frac{1}{1 + (y/x)^2} \cdot \frac{1}{x} \right\rangle = \left\langle -\frac{y}{x^2 + y^2}, \frac{x}{x^2 + y^2} \right\rangle.$$

Notice that the level curves of φ are the lines $\dfrac{y}{x} = C$ or $y = Cx$. At all points off the y-axis, the vector field is orthogonal to the level curves, which gives a rotation field (Figure 15.13).

Related Exercises 25–36 ◀

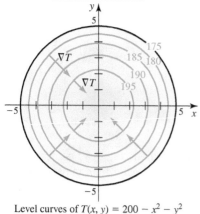

Gradient vectors ∇T (not drawn to scale) are orthogonal to the level curves.

Level curves of $T(x, y) = 200 - x^2 - y^2$

FIGURE 15.12

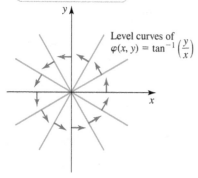

$\mathbf{F} = \nabla\varphi$ is orthogonal to level curves and gives a rotation field.

Level curves of $\varphi(x, y) = \tan^{-1}\left(\dfrac{y}{x}\right)$

FIGURE 15.13

Equipotential Curves and Surfaces   The preceding example illustrates a beautiful geometric connection between a gradient field and its associated potential function. Let φ be a potential function for the vector field $\mathbf{F}$ in $\mathbb{R}^2$; that is, $\mathbf{F} = \nabla\varphi$. The level curves of a potential function are called **equipotential curves** (curves on which the potential function is constant).

Because the equipotential curves are level curves of φ, the vector field $\mathbf{F} = \nabla\varphi$ is everywhere orthogonal to the equipotential curves (Figure 15.14). Therefore, the vector field is visualized by drawing continuous *flow curves* or *streamlines* that are everywhere orthogonal to the equipotential curves. These ideas also apply to vector fields in $\mathbb{R}^3$ in which case the vector field is orthogonal to the **equipotential surfaces**.

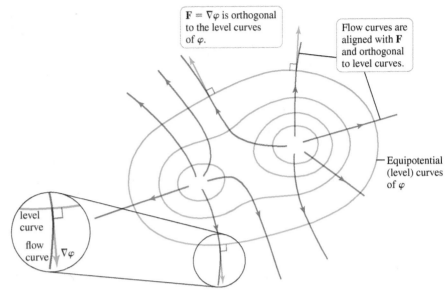

FIGURE 15.14

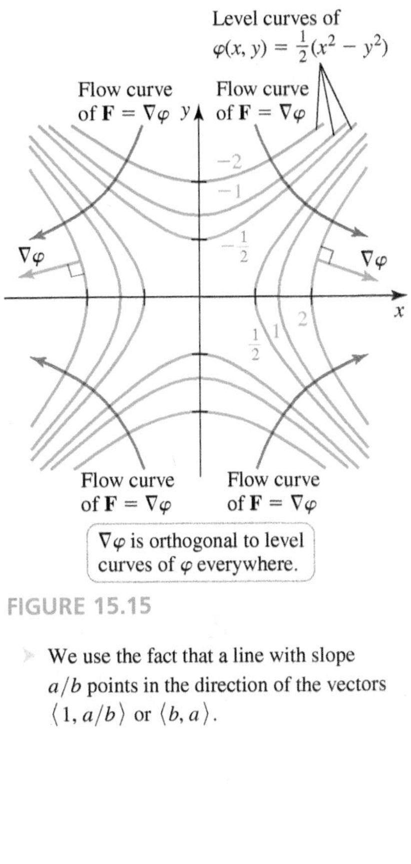

Level curves of
$\varphi(x, y) = \frac{1}{2}(x^2 - y^2)$

Flow curve of $\mathbf{F} = \nabla\varphi$ Flow curve of $\mathbf{F} = \nabla\varphi$

Flow curve of $\mathbf{F} = \nabla\varphi$ Flow curve of $\mathbf{F} = \nabla\varphi$

$\nabla\varphi$ is orthogonal to level curves of φ everywhere.

FIGURE 15.15

> We use the fact that a line with slope a/b points in the direction of the vectors $\langle 1, a/b \rangle$ or $\langle b, a \rangle$.

EXAMPLE 5 **Equipotential curves** The equipotential curves for the potential function $\varphi(x, y) = (x^2 - y^2)/2$ are shown in Figure 15.15.

a. Find the gradient field associated with φ and verify that the gradient field is orthogonal to the equipotential curve at $(2, 1)$.

b. Verify that the vector field $\mathbf{F} = \nabla\varphi$ is orthogonal to the equipotential curves at all points (x, y).

SOLUTION

a. The level (or equipotential) curves are the hyperbolas $(x^2 - y^2)/2 = C$, where C is a constant. The slope at any point on a level curve $\varphi(x, y) = C$ (Section 13.5) is

$$\frac{dy}{dx} = -\frac{\varphi_x}{\varphi_y} = \frac{x}{y}.$$

At the point $(2, 1)$, the slope of the level curve is $dy/dx = 2$, so the vector tangent to the curve points in the direction $\langle 1, 2 \rangle$. The gradient field is given by $\mathbf{F} = \nabla\varphi = \langle x, -y \rangle$, so $\mathbf{F}(2, 1) = \nabla\varphi(2, 1) = \langle 2, -1 \rangle$. The dot product of the tangent vector $\langle 1, 2 \rangle$ and the gradient is $\langle 1, 2 \rangle \cdot \langle 2, -1 \rangle = 0$; therefore, the two vectors are orthogonal.

b. In general, the line tangent to the equipotential curve at (x, y) is parallel to the vector $\langle y, x \rangle$, while the vector field at that point is $\mathbf{F} = \langle x, -y \rangle$. The vector field and the tangent vectors are orthogonal because $\langle y, x \rangle \cdot \langle x, -y \rangle = 0$.

Related Exercises 37–40 ◀

SECTION 15.1 EXERCISES

Review Questions

1. Explain how a vector field $\mathbf{F} = \langle f, g, h \rangle$ is used to describe the motion of the air in a room at one instant in time.

2. Sketch the vector field $\mathbf{F} = \langle x, y \rangle$.

3. How do you graph the vector field $\mathbf{F} = \langle f(x, y), g(x, y) \rangle$?

4. Given a function φ, how does the gradient of φ produce a vector field?

5. Interpret the gradient field of the temperature function $T = f(x, y)$.

Basic Skills

6–15. Two-dimensional vector fields *Sketch the following vector fields.*

6. $\mathbf{F} = \langle 1, y \rangle$ 7. $\mathbf{F} = \langle x, 0 \rangle$ 8. $\mathbf{F} = \langle -x, -y \rangle$

9. $\mathbf{F} = \langle x, -y \rangle$ 10. $\mathbf{F} = \langle 2x, 3y \rangle$ 11. $\mathbf{F} = \langle y, -x \rangle$

12. $\mathbf{F} = \langle x + y, y \rangle$ 13. $\mathbf{F} = \langle x, y - x \rangle$

14. $\mathbf{F} = \left\langle \dfrac{x}{\sqrt{x^2 + y^2}}, \dfrac{y}{\sqrt{x^2 + y^2}} \right\rangle$ 15. $\mathbf{F} = \langle e^{-x}, 0 \rangle$

16. **Matching vector fields with graphs** Match vector fields a–d with graphs A–D.

    a. $\mathbf{F} = \langle 0, x^2 \rangle$ b. $\mathbf{F} = \langle x - y, x \rangle$
    c. $\mathbf{F} = \langle 2x, -y \rangle$ d. $\mathbf{F} = \langle y, x \rangle$

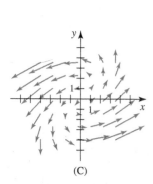
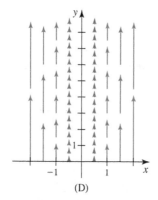

(A)   (B)

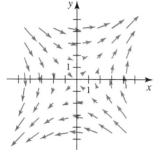
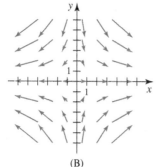

(C)   (D)

17–20. Normal and tangential components *Determine the points (if any) on the curve C at which the vector field* $\mathbf{F}$ *is tangent to C and normal to C. Sketch C and a few representative vectors of* $\mathbf{F}$.

17. $\mathbf{F} = \langle x, y \rangle$, where $C = \{(x, y): x^2 + y^2 = 4\}$

18. $\mathbf{F} = \langle y, -x \rangle$, where $C = \{(x, y): x^2 + y^2 = 1\}$

19. $\mathbf{F} = \langle x, y \rangle$, where $C = \{(x, y): x = 1\}$

20. $\mathbf{F} = \langle y, x \rangle$, where $C = \{(x, y): x^2 + y^2 = 1\}$

21–24. Three-dimensional vector fields *Sketch a few representative vectors of the following vector fields.*

21. $\mathbf{F} = \langle 1, 0, z \rangle$ 22. $\mathbf{F} = \langle x, y, z \rangle$

23. $\mathbf{F} = \langle y, -x, 0 \rangle$ 24. $\mathbf{F} = \dfrac{\langle x, y, z \rangle}{\sqrt{x^2 + y^2 + z^2}}$

25–28. Gradient fields *Find the gradient field* $\mathbf{F} = \nabla \varphi$ *for the potential function* φ. *Sketch a few level curves of* φ *and a few vectors of* $\mathbf{F}$.

25. $\varphi(x, y) = x^2 + y^2$, for $x^2 + y^2 \le 16$

26. $\varphi(x, y) = \sqrt{x^2 + y^2}$, for $x^2 + y^2 \le 9$, $(x, y) \ne (0, 0)$

27. $\varphi(x, y) = x + y$, for $|x| \le 2$, $|y| \le 2$

28. $\varphi(x, y) = 2xy$, for $|x| \le 2$, $|y| \le 2$

29–36. Gradient fields *Find the gradient field* $\mathbf{F} = \nabla \varphi$ *for the following potential functions* φ.

29. $\varphi(x, y) = x^2 y - y^2 x$

30. $\varphi(x, y) = \sqrt{xy}$

31. $\varphi(x, y) = x/y$

32. $\varphi(x, y) = \tan^{-1}(y/x)$

33. $\varphi(x, y, z) = (x^2 + y^2 + z^2)/2$

34. $\varphi(x, y, z) = \ln(1 + x^2 + y^2 + z^2)$

35. $\varphi(x, y, z) = (x^2 + y^2 + z^2)^{-1/2}$

36. $\varphi(x, y, z) = e^{-z} \sin(x + y)$

37–40. Equipotential curves *Consider the following potential functions and graphs of their equipotential curves.*

a. *Find the associated gradient field* $\mathbf{F} = \nabla \varphi$.
b. *Show that the vector field is orthogonal to the equipotential curve at the point* $(1, 1)$. *Illustrate this result on the figure.*
c. *Show that the vector field is orthogonal to the equipotential curve at all points* (x, y).
d. *Sketch two flow curves representing* $\mathbf{F}$ *that are everywhere orthogonal to the equipotential curves.*

37. $\varphi(x, y) = 2x + 3y$ 38. $\varphi(x, y) = x + y^2$

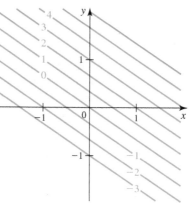
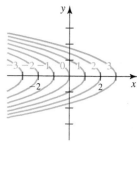

39. $\varphi(x, y) = e^{x-y}$ 40. $\varphi(x, y) = x^2 + 2y^2$

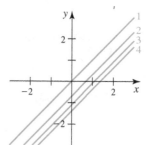
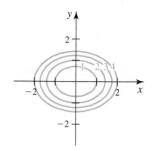

Further Explorations

41. Explain why or why not Determine whether the following statements are true and give an explanation or counterexample.

a. The vector field $\mathbf{F} = \langle 3x^2, 1 \rangle$ is a gradient field for both $\varphi_1(x, y) = x^3 + y$ and $\varphi_2(x, y) = y + x^3 + 100$.

b. The vector field $\mathbf{F} = \dfrac{\langle y, x \rangle}{\sqrt{x^2 + y^2}}$ is constant in direction and magnitude on the unit circle.

c. The vector field $\mathbf{F} = \dfrac{\langle y, x \rangle}{\sqrt{x^2 + y^2}}$ is neither a radial field nor a rotation field.

42–43. Vector fields on regions *Let* $S = \{(x, y): |x| \le 1, |y| \le 1\}$ *(a square centered at the origin)*, $D = \{(x, y): |x| + |y| \le 1\}$ *(a diamond centered at the origin)*, *and* $C = \{(x, y): x^2 + y^2 \le 1\}$ *(a disk centered at the origin). For each vector field* $\mathbf{F}$*, draw pictures and analyze the vector field to answer the following questions.*

a. *At what points of S, D, and C does the vector field have its maximum magnitude?*

b. *At what points on the boundary of each region is the vector field directed out of the region?*

42. $\mathbf{F} = \langle x, y \rangle$ **43.** $\mathbf{F} = \langle -y, x \rangle$

44–47. Design your own vector field *Specify the component functions of a vector field* $\mathbf{F}$ *in* $\mathbb{R}^2$ *with the following properties. Solutions are not unique.*

44. $\mathbf{F}$ is everywhere normal to the line $x = 2$.

45. $\mathbf{F}$ is everywhere normal to the line $x = y$.

46. The flow of $\mathbf{F}$ is counterclockwise around the origin, increasing in magnitude with distance from the origin.

47. At all points except $(0, 0)$, $\mathbf{F}$ has unit magnitude and points away from the origin along radial lines.

Applications

48. Electric field due to a point charge The electric field in the xy-plane due to a point charge at $(0, 0)$ is a gradient field with a potential function $V(x, y) = \dfrac{k}{\sqrt{x^2 + y^2}}$, where $k > 0$ is a physical constant.

a. Find the components of the electric field in the x- and y-directions, where $\mathbf{E}(x, y) = -\nabla V(x, y)$.

b. Show that the vectors of the electric field point in the radial direction (outward from the origin) and the radial component of $\mathbf{E}$ can be expressed as $E_r = k/r^2$, where $r = \sqrt{x^2 + y^2}$.

c. Show that the vector field is orthogonal to the equipotential curves at all points in the domain of V.

49. Electric field due to a line of charge The electric field in the xy-plane due to an infinite line of charge along the z-axis is a gradient field with a potential function $V(x, y) = c \ln \left(\dfrac{r_0}{\sqrt{x^2 + y^2}} \right)$,

where $c > 0$ is a constant and r_0 is a reference distance at which the potential is assumed to be 0 (see figure).

a. Find the components of the electric field in the x- and y-directions, where $\mathbf{E}(x, y) = -\nabla V(x, y)$.

b. Show that the electric field at a point in the xy-plane is directed outward from the origin and has magnitude $|\mathbf{E}| = c/r$, where $r = \sqrt{x^2 + y^2}$.

c. Show that the vector field is orthogonal to the equipotential curves at all points in the domain of V.

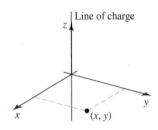

50. Gravitational force due to a mass The gravitational force on a point mass m due to a point mass M at the origin is a gradient field with potential $U(r) = \dfrac{GMm}{r}$, where G is the gravitational constant and $r = \sqrt{x^2 + y^2 + z^2}$ is the distance between the masses.

a. Find the components of the gravitational force in the x-, y-, and z-directions, where $\mathbf{F}(x, y, z) = -\nabla U(x, y, z)$.

b. Show that the gravitational force points in the radial direction (outward from point mass M) and the radial component is $F(r) = \dfrac{GMm}{r^2}$.

c. Show that the vector field is orthogonal to the equipotential surfaces at all points in the domain of U.

Additional Exercises

51–55. Streamlines in the plane *Let* $\mathbf{F}(x, y) = \langle f(x, y), g(x, y) \rangle$ *be defined on* $\mathbb{R}^2$.

51. Explain why the flow curves or streamlines of $\mathbf{F}$ satisfy $y' = g(x, y)/f(x, y)$ and are everywhere tangent to the vector field.

52. Find and graph the streamlines for the vector field $\mathbf{F} = \langle 1, x \rangle$.

53. Find and graph the streamlines for the vector field $\mathbf{F} = \langle x, x \rangle$.

54. Find and graph the streamlines for the vector field $\mathbf{F} = \langle y, x \rangle$. Note that $d/dx(y^2) = 2yy'(x)$.

55. Find and graph the streamlines for the vector field $\mathbf{F} = \langle -y, x \rangle$.

56–57. Unit vectors in polar coordinates

56. Vectors in $\mathbb{R}^2$ may also be expressed in terms of polar coordinates. The standard coordinate unit vectors in polar coordinates are denoted $\mathbf{u}_r$ and $\mathbf{u}_\theta$ (see figure). Unlike the coordinate unit vectors in Cartesian coordinates, $\mathbf{u}_r$ and $\mathbf{u}_\theta$ change their direction depending on the point (r, θ). Use the figure to show that for $r > 0$, the following relationships between the unit vectors in Cartesian and polar coordinates hold:

$$\mathbf{u}_r = \cos\theta\,\mathbf{i} + \sin\theta\,\mathbf{j} \qquad \mathbf{i} = \mathbf{u}_r \cos\theta - \mathbf{u}_\theta \sin\theta$$

$$\mathbf{u}_\theta = -\sin\theta\,\mathbf{i} + \cos\theta\,\mathbf{j} \qquad \mathbf{j} = \mathbf{u}_r \sin\theta + \mathbf{u}_\theta \cos\theta.$$

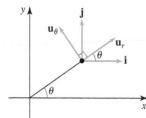

57. Verify that the relationships in Exercise 56 are consistent when $\theta = 0, \pi/2, \pi,$ and $3\pi/2$.

58–60. Vector fields in polar coordinates *A vector field in polar coordinates has the form* $\mathbf{F}(r, \theta) = f(r, \theta)\,\mathbf{u}_r + g(r, \theta)\,\mathbf{u}_\theta$, *where the unit vectors are defined in Exercise 56. Sketch the following vector fields and express them in Cartesian coordinates.*

58. $\mathbf{F} = \mathbf{u}_r$ **59.** $\mathbf{F} = \mathbf{u}_\theta$ **60.** $\mathbf{F} = r\mathbf{u}_\theta$

61. Cartesian-to-polar vector field Write the vector field $\mathbf{F} = \langle -y, x \rangle$ in polar coordinates and sketch the field.

QUICK CHECK ANSWERS

1. The particle follows a circular path around the origin.
3. $\nabla\varphi = \langle yz, xz, xy \rangle$ ◄

15.2 Line Integrals

With integrals of a single variable, we integrate over intervals in $\mathbb{R}^1$ (the real line). With double and triple integrals, we integrate over regions in $\mathbb{R}^2$ or $\mathbb{R}^3$. *Line integrals* (which really should be called *curve integrals*) are another class of integrals that play an important role in vector calculus. They are used to integrate either scalar-valued functions or vector fields along curves.

Suppose a thin, circular plate has a known temperature distribution and you must compute the average temperature along the edge of the plate. The required calculation involves integrating the temperature function over the *curved* boundary of the plate. Similarly, to calculate the amount of work needed to put a satellite into orbit, we integrate the gravitational force (a vector field) along the curved path of the satellite. Both these calculations require line integrals. As you will see, line integrals take several different forms. It is the goal of this section to distinguish these various forms and show how and when each form should be used.

Scalar Line Integrals in the Plane

We first consider line integrals of scalar-valued functions over curves in the plane. Figure 15.16 shows a surface $z = f(x, y)$ and a parameterized curve C in the xy-plane; for the moment we assume that $f(x, y) \geq 0$, for (x, y) on C. Now visualize the curtain-like surface formed by the vertical line segments joining the surface $z = f(x, y)$ and C. The goal is to find the area of one side of this curtain in terms of a line integral. As with other integrals we have studied, we begin with Riemann sums.

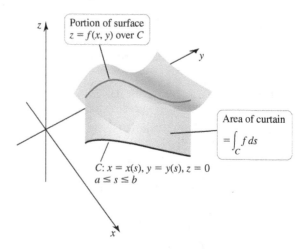

FIGURE 15.16

Assume that C is a smooth curve of finite length, parameterized in terms of arc length as $\mathbf{r}(s) = \langle x(s), y(s) \rangle$, for $a \leq s \leq b$, and let f be defined on C. We subdivide C into n small arcs by forming a partition of $[a, b]$:

$$a = s_0 < s_1 < \cdots < s_{n-1} < s_n = b.$$

Let s_k^* be a point in the kth subinterval $[s_{k-1}, s_k]$, which corresponds to a point $(x(s_k^*), y(s_k^*))$ on the kth arc of C, for $k = 1, 2, \ldots, n$. The length of the kth arc is denoted Δs_k. This partition also divides the curtain into n panels. The kth panel has an approximate height of $f(x(s_k^*), y(s_k^*))$ and a base of length Δs_k; therefore, the approximate area of the kth panel is $f(x(s_k^*), y(s_k^*))\Delta s_k$ (Figure 15.17). Summing the areas of the panels, the approximate area of the curtain is given by the Riemann sum

$$\text{area} \approx \sum_{k=1}^{n} f(x(s_k^*), y(s_k^*))\Delta s_k.$$

> The parameter s resides on the s-axis. As s varies from a to b on the s-axis, the curve C in the xy-plane is generated from the point $(x(a), y(a))$ to the point $(x(b), y(b))$.

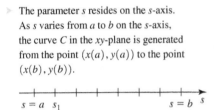

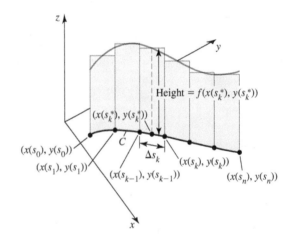

FIGURE 15.17

We now let Δ be the maximum value of $\Delta s_1, \ldots, \Delta s_n$. If the limit of the Riemann sums as $n \to \infty$ and $\Delta \to 0$ exists over all partitions, the limit is called a *line integral*, and it gives the area of the curtain.

DEFINITION Scalar Line Integral in the Plane, Arc Length Parameter

Suppose the scalar-valued function f is defined on the smooth curve $C: \mathbf{r}(s) = \langle x(s), y(s) \rangle$, parameterized by the arc length s. The **line integral of f over C** is

$$\int_C f(x(s), y(s))\, ds = \lim_{\Delta \to 0} \sum_{k=1}^{n} f(x(s_k^*), y(s_k^*))\Delta s_k,$$

provided this limit exists over all partitions of C. When the limit exists, f is said to be **integrable** on C.

The more compact notation $\int_C f(\mathbf{r}(s))\, ds$, $\int_C f(x, y)\, ds$, or $\int_C f\, ds$ is often used for the line integral of f over C. It can be shown that if f is continuous on a region containing C, then the line integral of f over C exists. If $f(x, y) = 1$, the line integral $\int_C ds$ gives the length of the curve, just as the ordinary integral $\int_a^b dx$ gives the length of the interval $[a, b]$, which is $b - a$.

> When we compute the average value by an ordinary integral, we divide by the length of the interval of integration. Analogously, when we compute the average value by a line integral, we divide by the length of the curve L:
>
> $$\bar{f} = \frac{1}{L} \int_C f \, ds.$$

EXAMPLE 1   Average temperature on a circle The temperature of the circular plate $R = \{(x, y): x^2 + y^2 \leq 1\}$ is $T(x, y) = 100(x^2 + 2y^2)$. Find the average temperature along the edge of the plate.

SOLUTION Calculating the average value requires integrating the temperature function over the boundary circle $C = \{(x, y): x^2 + y^2 = 1\}$ and dividing by the length (circumference) of C. The first step is to find a parametric description for C. Recall from Section 12.8 that a parametric description of a unit circle using arc length as the parameter is $\mathbf{r} = \langle x, y \rangle = \langle \cos s, \sin s \rangle$, for $0 \leq s \leq 2\pi$. We substitute $x = \cos s$ and $y = \sin s$ into the temperature function and express the line integral as an ordinary integral:

$$\int_C T(x, y) \, ds = \int_0^{2\pi} \underbrace{100[x(s)^2 + 2y(s)^2]}_{T(s)} ds \qquad \text{Write the line integral with respect to } s.$$

$$= 100 \int_0^{2\pi} (\cos^2 s + 2\sin^2 s) \, ds \qquad \text{Substitute for } x \text{ and } y.$$

$$= 100 \underbrace{\int_0^{2\pi} (1 + \sin^2 s) \, ds}_{3\pi} \qquad \cos^2 s + \sin^2 s = 1$$

$$= 300\pi. \qquad \text{Use } \sin^2 s = \frac{1 - \cos 2s}{2} \text{ and integrate.}$$

> The line integral in Example 1 also gives the area of the vertical cylindrical curtain that hangs between the surface and C in Figure 15.18.

The geometry of this line integral is shown in Figure 15.18. The temperature function on the boundary of C is a function of s. The line integral is an ordinary integral with respect to s over the interval $[0, 2\pi]$. To find the average value we divide the line integral of the temperature by the length of the curve, which is 2π. Therefore, the average temperature on the boundary of the plate is $300\pi/(2\pi) = 150$.

Related Exercises 11–14◄

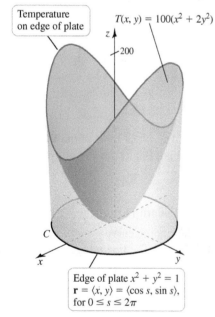

Temperature on edge of plate

$T(x, y) = 100(x^2 + 2y^2)$

Edge of plate $x^2 + y^2 = 1$
$\mathbf{r} = \langle x, y \rangle = \langle \cos s, \sin s \rangle$,
for $0 \leq s \leq 2\pi$

FIGURE 15.18

Parameters Other Than Arc Length

The line integral in Example 1 is straightforward because a circle is easily parameterized in terms of the arc length. Suppose we have a parameterized curve with a parameter t that is *not* the arc length. The key is a change of variables. Assume the curve C is described by $\mathbf{r}(t) = \langle x(t), y(t) \rangle$, for $a \leq t \leq b$. Recall from Section 12.8 that the length of C over the interval $[a, t]$ is

$$s(t) = \int_a^t |\mathbf{r}'(u)| \, du.$$

Differentiating both sides of this equation and using the Fundamental Theorem of Calculus yields $s'(t) = |\mathbf{r}'(t)|$. We now make a standard change of variables using the relationship

$$ds = s'(t) \, dt = |\mathbf{r}'(t)| \, dt.$$

The original line integral with respect to s is now converted into an ordinary integral with respect to t:

$$\int_C f \, ds = \int_a^b f(x(t), y(t)) \underbrace{|\mathbf{r}'(t)| \, dt}_{ds}.$$

> If t represents time, then the relationship $ds = |\mathbf{r}'(t)| \, dt$ is a generalization of the familiar formula
>
> $$distance = speed \cdot time.$$

QUICK CHECK 1 Explain mathematically why differentiating the arc length integral leads to $s'(t) = |\mathbf{r}'(t)|$. ◄

The value of a line integral of a scalar-valued function is independent of the parameterization of C and independent of the direction in which C is traversed (Exercises 54–55).

THEOREM 15.1 Evaluating Scalar Line Integrals in $\mathbb{R}^2$

Let f be continuous on a region containing a smooth curve $C: \mathbf{r}(t) = \langle x(t), y(t) \rangle$, for $a \le t \le b$. Then

$$\int_C f\, ds = \int_a^b f(x(t), y(t)) |\mathbf{r}'(t)|\, dt$$

$$= \int_a^b f(x(t), y(t)) \sqrt{x'(t)^2 + y'(t)^2}\, dt.$$

If t represents time and C is the path of a moving object, then $|\mathbf{r}'(t)|$ is the speed of the object. The *speed factor* $|\mathbf{r}'(t)|$ that appears in the integral relates distance traveled along the curve as measured by s to the elapsed time as measured by the parameter t.

Notice that if t is the arc length s, then $|\mathbf{r}'(t)| = 1$ and we recover the line integral with respect to the arc length s:

$$\int_C f\, ds = \int_a^b f(x(s), y(s))\, ds.$$

If $f(x, y) = 1$, then the line integral is $\int_a^b \sqrt{x'(t)^2 + y'(t)^2}\, dt$, which is the arc length formula for C. Theorem 15.1 leads to the following procedure for evaluating line integrals.

PROCEDURE Evaluating the Line Integral $\int_C f\, ds$

1. Find a parametric description of C in the form $\mathbf{r}(t) = \langle x(t), y(t) \rangle$, for $a \le t \le b$.

2. Compute $|\mathbf{r}'(t)| = \sqrt{x'(t)^2 + y'(t)^2}$.

3. Make substitutions for x and y in the integrand and evaluate an ordinary integral:

$$\int_C f\, ds = \int_a^b f(x(t), y(t)) |\mathbf{r}'(t)|\, dt.$$

EXAMPLE 2 Average temperature on a circle The temperature of the circular plate $R = \{(x, y): x^2 + y^2 \le 1\}$ is $T(x, y) = 100(x^2 + 2y^2)$ as in Example 1. Confirm the average temperature computed in Example 1 when the circle has the parametric description

$$C = \{(x, y): x = \cos t^2, y = \sin t^2, 0 \le t \le \sqrt{2\pi}\}.$$

SOLUTION The speed factor on C (using $\sin^2 t^2 + \cos^2 t^2 = 1$) is

$$|\mathbf{r}'(t)| = \sqrt{x'(t)^2 + y'(t)^2} = \sqrt{(-2t \sin t^2)^2 + (2t \cos t^2)^2} = 2t.$$

Making the appropriate substitutions, the value of the line integral is

$$\int_C T \, ds = \int_0^{\sqrt{2\pi}} 100(x(t)^2 + 2y(t)^2) \, |\mathbf{r}'(t)| \, dt \quad \text{Write the line integral with respect to } t.$$

$$= \int_0^{\sqrt{2\pi}} 100(\cos^2 t^2 + 2 \sin^2 t^2) \underbrace{2t \, dt}_{|\mathbf{r}'(t)|} \quad \text{Substitute for } x \text{ and } y.$$

$$= 100 \underbrace{\int_0^{2\pi} (\cos^2 u + 2 \sin^2 u) \, du}_{\pi + 2\pi} \quad \text{Simplify and let } u = t^2, \, du = 2t \, dt.$$

$$= 300\pi. \quad \text{Evaluate the integral.}$$

Dividing by the length of C, the average temperature on the boundary of the plate is $300\pi/(2\pi) = 150$, as found in Example 1.

Related Exercises 15–24◄

Line Integrals in $\mathbb{R}^3$

The argument that leads to line integrals on plane curves extends immediately to three or more dimensions. Here is the corresponding evaluation theorem for line integrals in $\mathbb{R}^3$.

THEOREM 15.2   Evaluating Scalar Line Integrals in $\mathbb{R}^3$

Let f be continuous on a region containing a smooth curve
$C: \mathbf{r}(t) = \langle x(t), y(t), z(t) \rangle$, for $a \le t \le b$. Then

$$\int_C f \, ds = \int_a^b f(x(t), y(t), z(t)) \, |\mathbf{r}'(t)| \, dt$$

$$= \int_a^b f(x(t), y(t), z(t)) \sqrt{x'(t)^2 + y'(t)^2 + z'(t)^2} \, dt.$$

As before, if t is the arc length s, then $|\mathbf{r}'(t)| = 1$ and

$$\int_C f \, ds = \int_a^b f(x(s), y(s), z(s)) \, ds.$$

If $f(x, y, z) = 1$, then the line integral gives the length of C.

> Recall that a parametric equation of a line is
>
> $$\mathbf{r}(t) = \langle x_0, y_0, z_0 \rangle + t \langle a, b, c \rangle,$$
>
> where $\langle x_0, y_0, z_0 \rangle$ is a position vector associated with a fixed point on the line and $\langle a, b, c \rangle$ is a vector parallel to the line.

EXAMPLE 3   Line integrals in $\mathbb{R}^3$ Evaluate $\int_C (xy + 2z) \, ds$ on the following line segments.

a. The line segment from $P(1, 0, 0)$ to $Q(0, 1, 1)$
b. The line segment from $Q(0, 1, 1)$ to $P(1, 0, 0)$

SOLUTION

a. A parametric description of the line segment from $P(1, 0, 0)$ to $Q(0, 1, 1)$ is

$$\mathbf{r}(t) = \langle 1, 0, 0 \rangle + t \langle -1, 1, 1 \rangle = \langle 1 - t, t, t \rangle, \quad \text{for } 0 \le t \le 1.$$

The speed factor is

$$|r'(t)| = \sqrt{x'(t)^2 + y'(t)^2 + z'(t)^2} = \sqrt{(-1)^2 + 1^2 + 1^2} = \sqrt{3}.$$

Substituting $x = 1 - t, y = t,$ and $z = t,$ the value of the line integral is

$$\int_C (xy + 2z)\, ds = \int_0^1 (\underbrace{(1 - t)}_{x}\, \underbrace{(t)}_{y} + 2\underbrace{(t)}_{z})\sqrt{3}\, dt \quad \text{Substitute for } x, y, z.$$

$$= \sqrt{3} \int_0^1 (3t - t^2)\, dt \qquad \text{Simplify.}$$

$$= \sqrt{3} \left(\frac{3t^2}{2} - \frac{t^3}{3} \right)\Big|_0^1 \qquad \text{Integrate.}$$

$$= \frac{7\sqrt{3}}{6}. \qquad \text{Evaluate.}$$

b. The line segment from $Q(0, 1, 1)$ to $P(1, 0, 0)$ may be described parametrically by

$$\mathbf{r}(t) = \langle 0, 1, 1 \rangle + t\langle 1, -1, -1 \rangle = \langle t, 1 - t, 1 - t \rangle, \qquad \text{for } 0 \le t \le 1.$$

The speed factor is

$$|\mathbf{r}'(t)| = \sqrt{x'(t)^2 + y'(t)^2 + z'(t)^2} = \sqrt{1^2 + (-1)^2 + (-1)^2} = \sqrt{3}.$$

We substitute $x = t, y = 1 - t,$ and $z = 1 - t$ and do a calculation similar to that in part (a). The value of the line integral is again $\dfrac{7\sqrt{3}}{6}$, emphasizing the fact that a scalar line integral is independent of the orientation and parameterization of the curve.

Related Exercises 25–30◄

EXAMPLE 4   Flight of an eagle An eagle soars on the ascending spiral path

$$C: \mathbf{r}(t) = \langle x(t), y(t), z(t) \rangle = \left\langle 2400 \cos \frac{t}{2},\ 2400 \sin \frac{t}{2},\ 500t \right\rangle,$$

where $x, y,$ and z are measured in feet and t is measured in minutes. How far does the eagle fly over the time interval $0 \le t \le 10$?

> Because we are finding the length of a curve, the integrand in this line integral is $f(x, y, z) = 1$.

SOLUTION The distance traveled is found by integrating the element of arc length ds along C, that is, $L = \int_C ds$. We now make a change of variables to the parameter t using

$$|\mathbf{r}'(t)| = \sqrt{x'(t)^2 + y'(t)^2 + z'(t)^2}$$

$$= \sqrt{\left(-1200 \sin \frac{t}{2}\right)^2 + \left(1200 \cos \frac{t}{2}\right)^2 + 500^2} \quad \text{Substitute derivatives.}$$

$$= \sqrt{1200^2 + 500^2} = 1300. \qquad \sin^2 \frac{t}{2} + \cos^2 \frac{t}{2} = 1$$

QUICK CHECK 2 What is the speed of the eagle in Example 4? ◄

It follows that the distance traveled is

$$L = \int_C ds = \int_0^{10} |\mathbf{r}'(t)|\, dt = \int_0^{10} 1300\, dt = 13{,}000 \text{ ft.}$$

Related Exercises 31–32◄

Line Integrals of Vector Fields

Line integrals along curves in $\mathbb{R}^2$ or $\mathbb{R}^3$ may also have integrands that involve vector fields. Such line integrals are different from scalar line integrals in two respects.

• Recall that an *oriented curve* is a parameterized curve for which a direction is specified. The *positive*, or *forward*, orientation is the direction in which the curve is generated as the parameter increases. For example, the positive direction of the circle

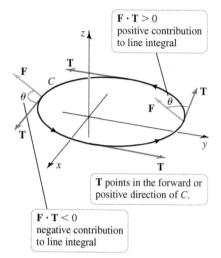

F · T > 0
positive contribution
to line integral

**T points in the forward or
positive direction of C.**

F · T < 0
negative contribution
to line integral

FIGURE 15.19

> The component of **F** in the direction of **T** is the scalar component of **F** in the direction of **T**, scal$_T$ **F**, as defined in Section 12.3. Note that $|\mathbf{T}| = 1$.

> Some books let $d\mathbf{s}$ stand for **T** ds. Then the line integral $\int_C \mathbf{F} \cdot \mathbf{T}\, ds$ is written $\int_C \mathbf{F} \cdot d\mathbf{s}$.

$\mathbf{r}(t) = \langle \cos t, \sin t \rangle$, for $0 \le t \le 2\pi$, is counterclockwise. As we will see, vector line integrals must be evaluated on oriented curves, and the value of a line integral depends on the orientation.

• The line integral of a vector field **F** along an oriented curve involves a specific component of **F** relative to the curve. We begin by defining vector line integrals for the *tangential* component of **F**, a situation that has many physical applications.

Let C: $\mathbf{r}(s) = \langle x(s), y(s), z(s) \rangle$ be a smooth oriented curve in $\mathbb{R}^3$ parameterized by arc length and let **F** be a vector field that is continuous on a region containing C. At each point of C, the unit tangent vector **T** points in the positive direction on C (Figure 15.19). The component of **F** in the direction of **T** at a point of C is $|\mathbf{F}| \cos \theta$, where θ is the angle between **F** and **T**. Because **T** is a unit vector,

$$|\mathbf{F}| \cos \theta = |\mathbf{F}||\mathbf{T}| \cos \theta = \mathbf{F} \cdot \mathbf{T}.$$

The first line integral of a vector field **F** that we introduce is the line integral of the scalar **F** · **T** along the curve C. When we integrate **F** · **T** along C, the effect is to add up the components of **F** in the direction of C at each point of C.

DEFINITION Line Integral of a Vector Field

Let **F** be a vector field that is continuous on a region containing a smooth oriented curve C parameterized by arc length. Let **T** be the unit tangent vector at each point of C consistent with the orientation. The line integral of **F** over C is $\int_C \mathbf{F} \cdot \mathbf{T}\, ds$.

We need a method for evaluating vector line integrals, particularly when the parameter is *not* the arc length. Suppose that C has a parameterization $\mathbf{r}(t) = \langle x(t), y(t), z(t) \rangle$, for $a \le t \le b$. Recall from Section 12.6 that the unit tangent vector at a point on the curve is $\mathbf{T} = \dfrac{\mathbf{r}'(t)}{|\mathbf{r}'(t)|}$. Using the fact that $ds = |\mathbf{r}'(t)|\, dt$, the line integral becomes

$$\int_C \mathbf{F} \cdot \mathbf{T}\, ds = \int_a^b \mathbf{F} \cdot \underbrace{\frac{\mathbf{r}'(t)}{|\mathbf{r}'(t)|}}_{\mathbf{T}} \underbrace{|\mathbf{r}'(t)|\, dt}_{ds} = \int_a^b \mathbf{F} \cdot \mathbf{r}'(t)\, dt.$$

This integral may be written in several different forms. If $\mathbf{F} = \langle f, g, h \rangle$, then the line integral may be evaluated in component form as

$$\int_C \mathbf{F} \cdot \mathbf{T}\, ds = \int_a^b \mathbf{F} \cdot \mathbf{r}'(t)\, dt = \int_a^b (f x'(t) + g y'(t) + h z'(t))\, dt,$$

where f stands for $f(x(t), y(t), z(t))$, with analogous expressions for g and h.

Another useful form is obtained by noting that

$$dx = x'(t)\, dt, \qquad dy = y'(t)\, dt, \qquad dz = z'(t)\, dt.$$

Making these replacements in the previous integral results in the form

$$\int_C \mathbf{F} \cdot \mathbf{T}\, ds = \int_C f\, dx + g\, dy + h\, dz.$$

Finally, if we let $d\mathbf{r} = \langle dx, dy, dz \rangle$, then $f\, dx + g\, dy + h\, dz = \mathbf{F} \cdot d\mathbf{r}$, and we have

$$\int_C \mathbf{F} \cdot \mathbf{T}\, ds = \int_C \mathbf{F} \cdot d\mathbf{r}.$$

It is helpful to become familiar with these various forms of the line integral.

Different Forms of Line Integrals of Vector Fields

The line integral $\int_C \mathbf{F} \cdot \mathbf{T} \, ds$ may be expressed in the following forms, where $\mathbf{F} = \langle f, g, h \rangle$ and C has a parameterization $\mathbf{r}(t) = \langle x(t), y(t), z(t) \rangle$, for $a \le t \le b$:

$$\int_a^b \mathbf{F} \cdot \mathbf{r}'(t) \, dt = \int_a^b (f x'(t) + g y'(t) + h z'(t)) \, dt$$

$$= \int_C f \, dx + g \, dy + h \, dz$$

$$= \int_C \mathbf{F} \cdot d\mathbf{r}.$$

For line integrals in the plane, we let $\mathbf{F} = \langle f, g \rangle$ and assume C is parameterized in the form $\mathbf{r}(t) = \langle x(t), y(t) \rangle$, for $a \le t \le b$. Then

$$\int_C \mathbf{F} \cdot \mathbf{T} \, ds = \int_a^b (f x'(t) + g y'(t)) \, dt = \int_C f \, dx + g \, dy = \int_C \mathbf{F} \cdot d\mathbf{r}.$$

> We use the convention that $-C$ is the curve C with the opposite orientation.

EXAMPLE 5 Different paths Evaluate $\int_C \mathbf{F} \cdot \mathbf{T} \, ds$ with $\mathbf{F} = \langle y - x, x \rangle$ on the following oriented paths in $\mathbb{R}^2$ (Figure 15.20).

a. The quarter circle C_1 from $P(0, 1)$ to $Q(1, 0)$
b. The quarter circle $-C_1$ from $Q(1, 0)$ to $P(0, 1)$
c. The path C_2 from P to Q via two line segments through $O(0, 0)$

SOLUTION

a. Working in $\mathbb{R}^2$, a parametric description of the curve C_1 with the required (clockwise) orientation is $\mathbf{r}(t) = \langle \sin t, \cos t \rangle$, for $0 \le t \le \pi/2$. Along C_1 the vector field is

$$\mathbf{F} = \langle y - x, x \rangle = \langle \cos t - \sin t, \sin t \rangle.$$

The velocity vector is $\mathbf{r}'(t) = \langle \cos t, -\sin t \rangle$, so the integrand of the line integral is

$$\mathbf{F} \cdot \mathbf{r}'(t) = \langle \cos t - \sin t, \sin t \rangle \cdot \langle \cos t, -\sin t \rangle = \underbrace{\cos^2 t - \sin^2 t}_{\cos 2t} - \underbrace{\sin t \cos t}_{\frac{1}{2} \sin 2t}.$$

The value of the line integral of $\mathbf{F}$ over C_1 is

$$\int_0^{\pi/2} \mathbf{F} \cdot \mathbf{r}'(t) \, dt = \int_0^{\pi/2} \left(\cos 2t - \frac{1}{2} \sin 2t \right) dt \quad \text{Substitute for } \mathbf{F} \cdot \mathbf{r}'(t).$$

$$= \left(\frac{1}{2} \sin 2t + \frac{1}{4} \cos 2t \right) \Big|_0^{\pi/2} \quad \text{Evaluate the integral.}$$

$$= -\frac{1}{2}. \quad \text{Simplify.}$$

b. A parameterization of the curve $-C_1$ from Q to P is $\mathbf{r}(t) = \langle \cos t, \sin t \rangle$, for $0 \le t \le \pi/2$. The vector field along the curve is

$$\mathbf{F} = \langle y - x, x \rangle = \langle \sin t - \cos t, \cos t \rangle,$$

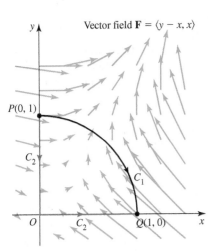

Vector field $\mathbf{F} = \langle y - x, x \rangle$

FIGURE 15.20

and the velocity vector is $\mathbf{r}'(t) = \langle -\sin t, \cos t \rangle$. A calculation very similar to that in part (a) results in

$$\int_{-C_1} \mathbf{F} \cdot \mathbf{T} \, ds = \int_0^{\pi/2} \mathbf{F} \cdot \mathbf{r}'(t) \, dt = \frac{1}{2}.$$

$$\int_{-C} \mathbf{F} \cdot \mathbf{T} \, ds = -\int_C \mathbf{F} \cdot \mathbf{T} \, ds$$

The results of parts (a) and (b) illustrate the important fact that reversing the orientation of a curve reverses the sign of the line integral of a vector field.

c. The path C_2 consists of two line segments.

- The segment from P to O is parameterized by $\mathbf{r}(t) = \langle 0, 1 - t \rangle$, for $0 \le t \le 1$. Therefore, $\mathbf{r}'(t) = \langle 0, -1 \rangle$ and $\mathbf{F} = \langle y - x, x \rangle = \langle 1 - t, 0 \rangle$.
- The line segment from O to Q is parameterized by $\mathbf{r}(t) = \langle t, 0 \rangle$, for $0 \le t \le 1$. Therefore, $\mathbf{r}'(t) = \langle 1, 0 \rangle$ and $\mathbf{F} = \langle y - x, x \rangle = \langle -t, t \rangle$.

The line integral is split into two parts and evaluated as follows:

$$\int_{C_2} \mathbf{F} \cdot \mathbf{T} \, ds = \int_{PO} \mathbf{F} \cdot \mathbf{T} \, ds + \int_{OQ} \mathbf{F} \cdot \mathbf{T} \, ds$$

$$= \int_0^1 \langle 1 - t, 0 \rangle \cdot \langle 0, -1 \rangle \, dt + \int_0^1 \langle -t, t \rangle \cdot \langle 1, 0 \rangle \, dt \qquad \text{Substitute for } x, y, \mathbf{r}'.$$

$$= \int_0^1 0 \, dt + \int_0^1 (-t) \, dt \qquad \text{Simplify.}$$

$$= -\frac{1}{2}. \qquad \text{Evaluate the integrals.}$$

The line integrals in parts (a) and (c) have the same value and run from P to Q, but along different paths. We might ask: For what vector fields are the values of a line integral independent of path? We return to this question in Section 15.3.

Related Exercises 33–38 ◀

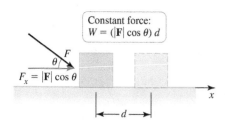

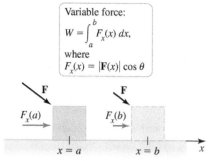

FIGURE 15.21

Work Integrals

A common application of line integrals of vector fields is computing the work done in moving an object in a force field (for example, a gravitational or electric field). First recall (Section 6.7) that if $\mathbf{F}$ is a *constant* force field, the work done in moving an object a distance d along the x-axis is $W = F_x d$, where $F_x = |\mathbf{F}| \cos \theta$ is the component of the force along the x-axis (Figure 15.21). Only the component of $\mathbf{F}$ in the direction of motion contributes to the work. More generally, if $\mathbf{F}$ is a *variable* force field, the work done in moving an object from $x = a$ to $x = b$ is $W = \int_a^b F_x(x) \, dx$, where again F_x is the component of the force in the direction of motion (parallel to the x-axis, Figure 15.21).

QUICK CHECK 3 Suppose a two-dimensional force field is everywhere directed outward from the origin and C is a circle centered at the origin. What is the angle between the field and the unit vectors tangent to C? ◀

We now take this progression one step further. Let $\mathbf{F}$ be a variable force field defined in a region D of $\mathbb{R}^3$, and suppose C is a smooth, oriented curve in D, along which an object moves. The direction of motion at each point of C is given by the unit tangent vector $\mathbf{T}$. Therefore, the component of $\mathbf{F}$ in the direction of motion is $\mathbf{F} \cdot \mathbf{T}$, which is the tangential component of $\mathbf{F}$ along C. Summing the contributions to the work at each point of C, the work done in moving an object along C in the presence of the force is the line integral of $\mathbf{F} \cdot \mathbf{T}$ (Figure 15.22).

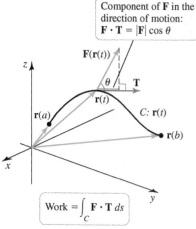

FIGURE 15.22

Just to be clear, a work integral is nothing more than a line integral of the tangential component of a force field.

> **DEFINITION Work Done in a Force Field**
>
> Let $\mathbf{F}$ be a continuous force field in a region D of $\mathbb{R}^3$ and let
> $C: \mathbf{r}(t) = \langle x(t), y(t), z(t) \rangle$, for $a \leq t \leq b$, be a smooth curve in D with a unit tangent vector $\mathbf{T}$ consistent with the orientation. The work done in moving an object along C in the positive direction is
> $$W = \int_C \mathbf{F} \cdot \mathbf{T} \, ds = \int_a^b \mathbf{F} \cdot \mathbf{r}'(t) \, dt.$$

EXAMPLE 6   An inverse square force Gravitational and electrical forces between point masses and point charges obey inverse square laws: They act along the line joining the centers and they vary as $1/r^2$, where r is the distance between the centers. The force of attraction (or repulsion) of an inverse square force field is given by the vector field $\mathbf{F} = \dfrac{k\langle x, y, z \rangle}{(x^2 + y^2 + z^2)^{3/2}}$, where k is a physical constant. Because $\mathbf{r} = \langle x, y, z \rangle$, this force may also be written $\mathbf{F} = \dfrac{k\mathbf{r}}{|\mathbf{r}|^3}$. Find the work done in moving an object along the following paths.

a. C_1 is the line segment from $(1, 1, 1)$ to (a, a, a), where $a > 1$.

b. C_2 is the extension of C_1 produced by letting $a \to \infty$.

SOLUTION

a. A parametric description of C_1 consistent with the orientation is $\mathbf{r}(t) = \langle t, t, t \rangle$, for $1 \leq t \leq a$, with $\mathbf{r}'(t) = \langle 1, 1, 1 \rangle$. In terms of the parameter t, the force field is

$$\mathbf{F} = \frac{k\langle x, y, z \rangle}{(x^2 + y^2 + z^2)^{3/2}} = \frac{k\langle t, t, t \rangle}{(3t^2)^{3/2}}.$$

The dot product that appears in the work integral is

$$\mathbf{F} \cdot \mathbf{r}'(t) = \frac{k\langle t, t, t \rangle}{(3t^2)^{3/2}} \cdot \langle 1, 1, 1 \rangle = \frac{3kt}{3\sqrt{3}\,t^3} = \frac{k}{\sqrt{3}\,t^2}.$$

Therefore, the work done is

$$W = \int_1^a \mathbf{F} \cdot \mathbf{r}'(t) \, dt = \frac{k}{\sqrt{3}} \int_1^a t^{-2} \, dt = \frac{k}{\sqrt{3}}\left(1 - \frac{1}{a}\right).$$

b. The path C_2 is obtained by letting $a \to \infty$ in part (a). The required work is

$$W = \lim_{a \to \infty} \frac{k}{\sqrt{3}}\left(1 - \frac{1}{a}\right) = \frac{k}{\sqrt{3}}.$$

If $\mathbf{F}$ is a gravitational field, this result implies that the work required to escape Earth's gravitational field is finite (which makes space flight possible).

Related Exercises 39–46 ◄

Circulation and Flux of a Vector Field

Line integrals are useful for investigating two important properties of vector fields: *circulation* and *flux*. These properties apply to any vector field, but they are particularly relevant and easy to visualize if you think of $\mathbf{F}$ as the velocity field for a moving fluid.

In the definition of circulation, a *closed curve* is a curve whose initial and terminal points are the same, as defined formally in Section 15.3.

Circulation   We assume that $\mathbf{F} = \langle f, g, h \rangle$ is a continuous vector field on a region D of $\mathbb{R}^3$, and we take C to be a *closed* smooth oriented curve in D. The *circulation* of $\mathbf{F}$ along C is a measure of how much of the vector field points in the direction of C. More simply, as you travel along C in the forward direction, how often is the vector field at your back and how often is it in your face? To determine the circulation, we simply "add up" the components of $\mathbf{F}$ in the direction of the unit tangent vector $\mathbf{T}$ at each point. Therefore, circulation integrals are another example of line integrals of vector fields.

> **DEFINITION   Circulation**
>
> Let $\mathbf{F}$ be a continuous vector field on a region D of $\mathbb{R}^3$ and let C be a closed smooth oriented curve in D. The **circulation** of $\mathbf{F}$ on C is $\int_C \mathbf{F} \cdot \mathbf{T} \, ds$, where $\mathbf{T}$ is the unit vector tangent to C consistent with the orientation.

EXAMPLE 7   Circulation of two-dimensional flows   Let C be the unit circle with counterclockwise orientation. Find the circulation on C for the following vector fields.

a. The radial flow field $\mathbf{F} = \langle x, y \rangle$

b. The rotation flow field $\mathbf{F} = \langle -y, x \rangle$

SOLUTION

a. The unit circle with the specified orientation is described parametrically by $\mathbf{r}(t) = \langle \cos t, \sin t \rangle$, for $0 \le t \le 2\pi$. Therefore, $\mathbf{r}'(t) = \langle -\sin t, \cos t \rangle$ and the circulation of the radial field $\mathbf{F} = \langle x, y \rangle$ is

$$\int_C \mathbf{F} \cdot \mathbf{T} \, ds = \int_0^{2\pi} \mathbf{F} \cdot \mathbf{r}'(t) \, dt \qquad \text{Evaluation of a line integral}$$

$$= \int_0^{2\pi} \underbrace{\langle \cos t, \sin t \rangle}_{\mathbf{F} = \langle x, y \rangle} \cdot \underbrace{\langle -\sin t, \cos t \rangle}_{\mathbf{r}'(t)} \, dt \qquad \text{Substitute for } \mathbf{F} \text{ and } \mathbf{r}'.$$

$$= \int_0^{2\pi} 0 \, dt = 0. \qquad \text{Simplify.}$$

The tangential component of the radial vector field is zero everywhere on C, so the circulation is zero (Figure 15.23a).

b. The circulation for the rotation field $\mathbf{F} = \langle -y, x \rangle$ is

$$\int_C \mathbf{F} \cdot \mathbf{T} \, ds = \int_0^{2\pi} \mathbf{F} \cdot \mathbf{r}'(t) \, dt \qquad \text{Evaluation of a line integral}$$

$$= \int_0^{2\pi} \underbrace{\langle -\sin t, \cos t \rangle}_{\mathbf{F} = \langle -y, x \rangle} \cdot \underbrace{\langle -\sin t, \cos t \rangle}_{\mathbf{r}'(t)} \, dt \qquad \text{Substitute for } \mathbf{F} \text{ and } \mathbf{r}'.$$

$$= \int_0^{2\pi} \underbrace{(\sin^2 t + \cos^2 t)}_{1} \, dt \qquad \text{Simplify.}$$

$$= 2\pi.$$

In this case, at every point of C, the vector field is in the direction of the tangent vector; the result is a positive circulation (Figure 15.23b).

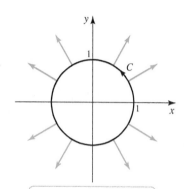

On the unit circle, $\mathbf{F} = \langle x, y \rangle$ is orthogonal to C and has zero circulation on C.

(a)

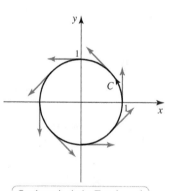

On the unit circle, $\mathbf{F} = \langle -y, x \rangle$ is tangent to C and has positive circulation on C.

(b)

FIGURE 15.23

Related Exercises 47–48 ◀

EXAMPLE 8   Circulation of a three-dimensional flow Find the circulation of the vector field $\mathbf{F} = \langle z, x, -y \rangle$ on the tilted ellipse $C: \mathbf{r}(t) = \langle \cos t, \sin t, \cos t \rangle$, for $0 \le t \le 2\pi$ (Figure 15.24a).

SOLUTION We first determine that

$$\mathbf{r}'(t) = \langle x'(t), y'(t), z'(t) \rangle = \langle -\sin t, \cos t, -\sin t \rangle.$$

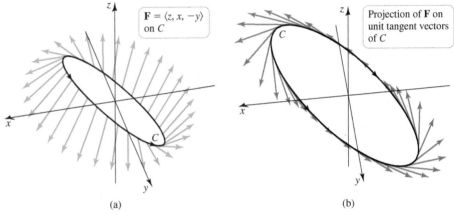

(a)   (b)

FIGURE 15.24

Substituting $x = \cos t$, $y = \sin t$, and $z = \cos t$ into $\mathbf{F} = \langle z, x, -y \rangle$, the circulation is

$$\int_C \mathbf{F} \cdot \mathbf{T} \, ds = \int_0^{2\pi} \mathbf{F} \cdot \mathbf{r}'(t) \, dt \qquad \text{Evaluation of a line integral}$$

$$= \int_0^{2\pi} \langle \cos t, \cos t, -\sin t \rangle \cdot \langle -\sin t, \cos t, -\sin t \rangle \, dt \qquad \text{Substitute for } \mathbf{F} \text{ and } \mathbf{r}'.$$

$$= \int_0^{2\pi} (-\sin t \cos t + 1) \, dt \qquad \text{Simplify; } \sin^2 t + \cos^2 t = 1.$$

$$= 2\pi. \qquad \text{Evaluate the integral.}$$

Figure 15.24b shows the projection of the vector field on the unit tangent vectors at various points on C. The circulation is the "sum" of the magnitudes of these projections, which, in this case, is positive.

Related Exercises 47–48 ◄

> In the definition of flux, the non-self-intersecting property of C means that C is a *simple* curve, as defined formally in Section 15.3.

Flux of Two-Dimensional Vector Fields   Assume that $\mathbf{F} = \langle f, g \rangle$ is a continuous vector field on a region R of $\mathbb{R}^2$. We let C be a smooth oriented curve in R that does not intersect itself; C may or may not be closed. To compute the *flux* of the vector field across C, we "add up" the components of $\mathbf{F}$ *orthogonal* or *normal* to C at each point of C. Notice that every point on C has two unit vectors normal to C. Therefore, we let $\mathbf{n}$ denote the unit vector in the xy-plane normal to C in a direction to be defined momentarily. Once the direction of $\mathbf{n}$ is defined, the component of $\mathbf{F}$ normal to C is $\mathbf{F} \cdot \mathbf{n}$, and the flux is the line integral of $\mathbf{F} \cdot \mathbf{n}$ along C, which we denote $\int_C \mathbf{F} \cdot \mathbf{n} \, ds$.

> Recall that $\mathbf{a} \times \mathbf{b}$ is orthogonal to $\mathbf{a}$ and $\mathbf{b}$.

The first step is to define the unit normal vector at a point P of C. Because C lies in the xy-plane, the unit vector $\mathbf{T}$ tangent at P also lies in the xy-plane. Therefore, its z-component is 0, and we let $\mathbf{T} = \langle T_x, T_y, 0 \rangle$. As always, $\mathbf{k} = \langle 0, 0, 1 \rangle$ is the unit vector in the z-direction. Because a unit vector $\mathbf{n}$ in the xy-plane normal to C is orthogonal to both **T** and **k**, we determine the direction of **n** by letting $\mathbf{n} = \mathbf{T} \times \mathbf{k}$. This choice has two implications (Figure 15.25a).

• If C is a closed curve oriented counterclockwise (when viewed from above), the unit normal vector points *outward* along the curve (Figure 15.25b).

• If C is not a closed curve, the unit normal vector points to the right (when viewed from above) as the curve is traversed in the forward direction.

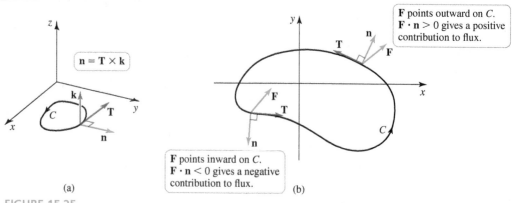

(a)

(b)

F points outward on *C*. $\mathbf{F} \cdot \mathbf{n} > 0$ gives a positive contribution to flux.

F points inward on *C*. $\mathbf{F} \cdot \mathbf{n} < 0$ gives a negative contribution to flux.

FIGURE 15.25

QUICK CHECK 4 Draw a closed curve on a sheet of paper and draw a unit tangent vector **T** on the curve pointing in the counterclockwise direction. Explain why $\mathbf{n} = \mathbf{T} \times \mathbf{k}$ is an *outward* unit normal vector. ◄

Calculating the cross product for the unit normal vector, we find that

$$\mathbf{n} = \mathbf{T} \times \mathbf{k} = \begin{vmatrix} \mathbf{i} & \mathbf{j} & \mathbf{k} \\ T_x & T_y & 0 \\ 0 & 0 & 1 \end{vmatrix} = T_y\,\mathbf{i} - T_x\,\mathbf{j}.$$

Because $\mathbf{T} = \dfrac{\mathbf{r}'(t)}{|\mathbf{r}'(t)|}$, the components of **T** are

$$\mathbf{T} = \langle T_x, T_y, 0 \rangle = \frac{\langle x'(t), y'(t), 0 \rangle}{|\mathbf{r}'(t)|}.$$

We now have an expression for the unit normal vector:

$$\mathbf{n} = T_y\,\mathbf{i} - T_x\,\mathbf{j} = \frac{y'(t)}{|\mathbf{r}'(t)|}\,\mathbf{i} - \frac{x'(t)}{|\mathbf{r}'(t)|}\,\mathbf{j} = \frac{\langle y'(t), -x'(t) \rangle}{|\mathbf{r}'(t)|}.$$

To evaluate the flux integral $\int_C \mathbf{F} \cdot \mathbf{n}\,ds$, we make a familiar change of variables by letting $ds = |\mathbf{r}'(t)|\,dt$. The flux of $\mathbf{F} = \langle f, g \rangle$ across C is then

$$\int_C \mathbf{F} \cdot \mathbf{n}\,ds = \int_a^b \mathbf{F} \cdot \underbrace{\frac{\langle y'(t), -x'(t) \rangle}{|\mathbf{r}'(t)|}}_{\mathbf{n}}\,\underbrace{|\mathbf{r}'(t)|\,dt}_{ds} = \int_a^b (f\,y'(t) - g\,x'(t))\,dt.$$

This is one useful form of the flux integral. Alternatively, we can note that $dx = x'(t)\,dt$ and $dy = y'(t)\,dt$ and write

$$\int_C \mathbf{F} \cdot \mathbf{n}\,ds = \int_C f\,dy - g\,dx.$$

> **DEFINITION Flux**
>
> Let $\mathbf{F} = \langle f, g \rangle$ be a continuous vector field on a region R of $\mathbb{R}^2$. Let
> $C: \mathbf{r}(t) = \langle x(t), y(t) \rangle$, for $a \le t \le b$, be a smooth oriented curve in R that does
> not intersect itself. The **flux** of the vector field across C is
>
> $$\int_C \mathbf{F} \cdot \mathbf{n} \, ds = \int_a^b (f y'(t) - g x'(t)) \, dt,$$
>
> where $\mathbf{n} = \mathbf{T} \times \mathbf{k}$ is the unit normal vector and $\mathbf{T}$ is the unit tangent vector consistent with the orientation. If C is a closed curve with counterclockwise orientation, $\mathbf{n}$ is the outward normal vector and the flux integral gives the **outward flux** across C.

EXAMPLE 9   Flux of two-dimensional flows Find the outward flux across the unit circle with counterclockwise orientation for the following vector fields.

a. The radial vector field $\mathbf{F} = \langle x, y \rangle$

b. The rotation flow field $\mathbf{F} = \langle -y, x \rangle$

SOLUTION

a. The unit circle with counterclockwise orientation has a description
$\mathbf{r}(t) = \langle x(t), y(t) \rangle = \langle \cos t, \sin t \rangle$, for $0 \le t \le 2\pi$. Therefore, $x'(t) = -\sin t$ and $y'(t) = \cos t$. The components of $\mathbf{F}$ are $f = x(t) = \cos t$ and $g = y(t) = \sin t$. It follows that the outward flux is

$$\int_a^b (f y'(t) - g x'(t)) \, dt = \int_0^{2\pi} (\underbrace{\cos t}_{f} \underbrace{\cos t}_{y'(t)} - \underbrace{\sin t}_{g} \underbrace{(-\sin t)}_{x'(t)}) \, dt$$

$$= \int_0^{2\pi} 1 \, dt = 2\pi. \qquad \cos^2 t + \sin^2 t = 1$$

Because the radial vector field points outward and is aligned with the unit normal vectors on C, the outward flux is positive (Figure 15.26a).

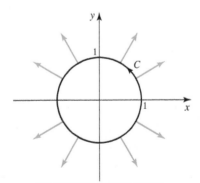

On the unit circle, $\mathbf{F} = \langle x, y \rangle$ is orthogonal to C and has positive outward flux on C.

(a)

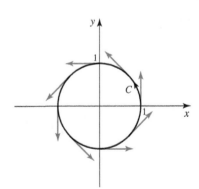

On the unit circle, $\mathbf{F} = \langle -y, x \rangle$ is tangent to C and has zero outward flux on C.

(b)

FIGURE 15.26

b. For the rotation field, $f = -y(t) = -\sin t$ and $g = x(t) = \cos t$. The outward flux is

$$\int_a^b (f\,y'(t) - g\,x'(t))\,dt = \int_0^{2\pi} (\underbrace{-\sin t}_{f}\ \underbrace{\cos t}_{y'(t)} - \underbrace{\cos t}_{g}\ \underbrace{(-\sin t)}_{x'(t)})\,dt$$

$$= \int_0^{2\pi} 0\,dt = 0.$$

Because the rotation field is orthogonal to **n** at all points of C, the outward flux across C is zero (Figure 15.26b). The results of Examples 7 and 9 are worth remembering: On a unit circle centered at the origin, the *radial* vector field $\langle x, y \rangle$ has outward flux 2π and zero circulation. The *rotation* vector field $\langle -y, x \rangle$ has zero outward flux and circulation 2π.

Related Exercises 49–50◄

SECTION 15.2 EXERCISES

Review Questions

1. Explain how a line integral differs from the single-variable integral $\int_a^b f(x)\,dx$.

2. How do you evaluate the line integral $\int_C f\,ds$, where C is parameterized by a parameter other than arc length?

3. If a curve C is given by $\mathbf{r}(t) = \langle t, t^2 \rangle$, what is $|\mathbf{r}'(t)|$?

4. Given a vector field $\mathbf{F}$ and a parameterized curve C, explain how to evaluate the line integral $\int_C \mathbf{F} \cdot \mathbf{T}\,ds$.

5. How can $\int_C \mathbf{F} \cdot \mathbf{T}\,ds$ be written in the alternate form $\int_a^b (f\,x'(t) + g\,y'(t) + h\,z'(t))\,dt$?

6. Given a vector field $\mathbf{F}$ and a closed smooth oriented curve C, what is the meaning of the circulation of $\mathbf{F}$ on C?

7. Explain how to calculate the circulation of a vector field on a closed smooth oriented curve.

8. Given a two-dimensional vector field $\mathbf{F}$ and a smooth oriented curve C, what is the meaning of the flux of $\mathbf{F}$ across C?

9. How do you calculate the flux of a two-dimensional vector field across a smooth oriented curve C?

10. Sketch the oriented quarter circle from $(1, 0)$ to $(0, 1)$ and supply a parameterization for the curve. Draw the unit normal vector (as defined in the text) at several points on the curve.

Basic Skills

11–14. Scalar line integrals with arc length as parameter *Evaluate the following line integrals.*

11. $\int_C xy\,ds$; C is the unit circle $\mathbf{r}(s) = \langle \cos s, \sin s \rangle$, for $0 \le s \le 2\pi$.

12. $\int_C (x + y)\,ds$; C is the circle of radius 1 centered at $(0, 0)$.

13. $\int_C (x^2 - 2y^2)\,ds$; C is the line $\mathbf{r}(s) = \langle s/\sqrt{2}, s/\sqrt{2} \rangle$, for $0 \le s \le 4$.

14. $\int_C x^2 y\,ds$; C is the line $\mathbf{r}(s) = \langle s/\sqrt{2}, 1 - s/\sqrt{2} \rangle$, for $0 \le s \le 4$.

15–20. Scalar line integrals in the plane

a. *Find a parametric description for C in the form $\mathbf{r}(t) = \langle x(t), y(t) \rangle$, if it is not given.*
b. *Evaluate $|\mathbf{r}'(t)|$.*
c. *Convert the line integral to an ordinary integral with respect to the parameter and evaluate it.*

15. $\int_C (x^2 + y^2)\,ds$; C is the circle of radius 4 centered at $(0, 0)$.

16. $\int_C (x^2 + y^2)\,ds$; C is the line segment from $(0, 0)$ to $(5, 5)$.

17. $\int_C \dfrac{x}{x^2 + y^2}\,ds$; C is the line segment from $(1, 1)$ to $(10, 10)$.

18. $\int_C (xy)^{1/3}\,ds$; C is the curve $y = x^2$, for $0 \le x \le 1$.

19. $\int_C xy\,ds$; C is the portion of the ellipse $\dfrac{x^2}{4} + \dfrac{y^2}{16} = 1$ in the first quadrant, oriented counterclockwise.

20. $\int_C (2x - 3y)\,ds$; C is the line segment from $(-1, 0)$ to $(0, 1)$ followed by the line segment from $(0, 1)$ to $(1, 0)$.

21–24. Average values *Find the average value of the following functions on the given curves.*

21. $f(x, y) = x + 2y$ on the line segment from $(1, 1)$ to $(2, 5)$

22. $f(x, y) = x^2 + 4y^2$ on the circle of radius 9 centered at the origin

23. $f(x, y) = \sqrt{4 + 9y^{2/3}}$ on the curve $y = x^{3/2}$, for $0 \le x \le 5$

24. $f(x, y) = xe^y$ on the unit circle centered at the origin

25–30. Scalar line integrals in $\mathbb{R}^3$ *Convert the line integral to an ordinary integral with respect to the parameter and evaluate it.*

25. $\int_C (x + y + z)\, ds$; C is the circle $\mathbf{r}(t) = \langle 2 \cos t, 0, 2 \sin t \rangle$, for $0 \leq t \leq 2\pi$.

26. $\int_C (x - y + 2z)\, ds$; C is the circle $\mathbf{r}(t) = \langle 1, 3 \cos t, 3 \sin t \rangle$, for $0 \leq t \leq 2\pi$.

27. $\int_C xyz\, ds$; C is the line segment from $(0, 0, 0)$ to $(1, 2, 3)$.

28. $\int_C \dfrac{xy}{z}\, ds$; C is the line segment from $(1, 4, 1)$ to $(3, 6, 3)$.

29. $\int_C (y - z)\, ds$; C is the helix $\mathbf{r}(t) = \langle 3 \cos t, 3 \sin t, t \rangle$, for $0 \leq t \leq 2\pi$.

30. $\int_C xe^{yz}\, ds$; C is $\mathbf{r}(t) = \langle t, 2t, -4t \rangle$, for $1 \leq t \leq 2$.

31–32. Length of curves *Use a scalar line integral to find the length of the following curves.*

31. $\mathbf{r}(t) = \langle 20 \sin t/4, 20 \cos t/4, t/2 \rangle$, for $0 \leq t \leq 2$

32. $\mathbf{r}(t) = \langle 30 \sin t, 40 \sin t, 50 \cos t \rangle$, for $0 \leq t \leq 2\pi$

33–38. Line integrals of vector fields in the plane *Given the following vector fields and oriented curves C, evaluate $\int_C \mathbf{F} \cdot \mathbf{T}\, ds$.*

33. $\mathbf{F} = \langle x, y \rangle$ on the parabola $\mathbf{r}(t) = \langle 4t, t^2 \rangle$, for $0 \leq t \leq 1$

34. $\mathbf{F} = \langle -y, x \rangle$ on the semicircle $\mathbf{r}(t) = \langle 4 \cos t, 4 \sin t \rangle$, for $0 \leq t \leq \pi$

35. $\mathbf{F} = \langle y, x \rangle$ on the line segment from $(1, 1)$ to $(5, 10)$

36. $\mathbf{F} = \dfrac{\langle x, y \rangle}{(x^2 + y^2)^{3/2}}$ on the line segment from $(2, 2)$ to $(10, 10)$

37. $\mathbf{F} = \dfrac{\langle x, y \rangle}{(x^2 + y^2)^{3/2}}$ on the curve $\mathbf{r}(t) = \langle t^2, 3t^2 \rangle$, for $1 \leq t \leq 2$

38. $\mathbf{F} = \dfrac{\langle x, y \rangle}{x^2 + y^2}$ on the line $\mathbf{r}(t) = \langle t, 4t \rangle$, for $1 \leq t \leq 10$

39–42. Work integrals *Given the force field $\mathbf{F}$, find the work required to move an object on the given oriented curve.*

39. $\mathbf{F} = \langle y, -x \rangle$ on the path consisting of the line segment from $(1, 2)$ to $(0, 0)$ followed by the line segment from $(0, 0)$ to $(0, 4)$

40. $\mathbf{F} = \langle x, y \rangle$ on the path consisting of the line segment from $(-1, 0)$ to $(0, 8)$ followed by the line segment from $(0, 8)$ to $(2, 8)$

41. $\mathbf{F} = \langle y, x \rangle$ on the parabola $y = 2x^2$ from $(0, 0)$ to $(2, 8)$

42. $\mathbf{F} = \langle y, -x \rangle$ on the line $y = 10 - 2x$ from $(1, 8)$ to $(3, 4)$

43–46. Work integrals in $\mathbb{R}^3$ *Given the force field $\mathbf{F}$, find the work required to move an object on the given oriented curve.*

43. $\mathbf{F} = \langle x, y, z \rangle$ on the tilted ellipse $\mathbf{r}(t) = \langle 4 \cos t, 4 \sin t, 4 \cos t \rangle$, for $0 \leq t \leq 2\pi$

44. $\mathbf{F} = \langle -y, x, z \rangle$ on the helix $\mathbf{r}(t) = \langle 2 \cos t, 2 \sin t, t/2\pi \rangle$, for $0 \leq t \leq 2\pi$

45. $\mathbf{F} = \dfrac{\langle x, y, z \rangle}{(x^2 + y^2 + z^2)^{3/2}}$ on the line segment from $(1, 1, 1)$ to $(10, 10, 10)$

46. $\mathbf{F} = \dfrac{\langle x, y, z \rangle}{x^2 + y^2 + z^2}$ on the line segment from $(1, 1, 1)$ to $(8, 4, 2)$

47–48. Circulation *Consider the following vector fields $\mathbf{F}$ and closed oriented curves C in the plane (see figures).*

a. *Based on the picture, make a conjecture about whether the circulation of $\mathbf{F}$ on C is positive, negative, or zero.*

b. *Compute the circulation and interpret the result.*

47. $\mathbf{F} = \langle y - x, x \rangle$; $C: \mathbf{r}(t) = \langle 2 \cos t, 2 \sin t \rangle$, for $0 \leq t \leq 2\pi$

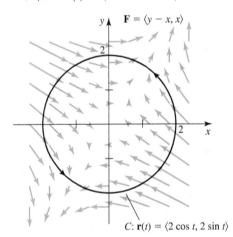

$\mathbf{F} = \langle y - x, x \rangle$

$C: \mathbf{r}(t) = \langle 2 \cos t, 2 \sin t \rangle$

48. $\mathbf{F} = \dfrac{\langle x, y \rangle}{(x^2 + y^2)^{1/2}}$; C is the boundary of the square with vertices $(\pm 2, \pm 2)$, traversed counterclockwise.

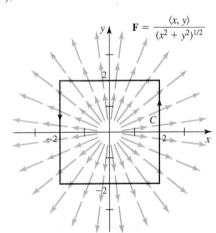

$\mathbf{F} = \dfrac{\langle x, y \rangle}{(x^2 + y^2)^{1/2}}$

49–50. Flux *Consider the vector fields and curves in Exercises 47–48.*

a. *Based on the picture, make a conjecture about whether the outward flux of* **F** *across C is positive, negative, or zero.*

b. *Compute the flux for the vector fields and curves.*

49. **F** and *C* given in Exercise 47

50. **F** and *C* given in Exercise 48

Further Explorations

51. Explain why or why not Determine whether the following statements are true and give an explanation or counterexample.

    a. If a curve has a parametric description $\mathbf{r}(t) = \langle x(t), y(t), z(t) \rangle$, where t is the arc length, then $|\mathbf{r}'(t)| = 1$.

    b. The vector field $\mathbf{F} = \langle y, x \rangle$ has both zero circulation along and zero flux across the unit circle centered at the origin.

    c. If at all points of a path, a force acts in a direction orthogonal to the path, then no work is done in moving an object along the path.

    d. The flux of a vector field across a curve in $\mathbb{R}^2$ can be computed using a line integral.

52. Flying into a headwind An airplane flies in the xz-plane, where x increases in the eastward direction and $z \geq 0$ represents vertical distance above the ground. A wind blows horizontally out of the west, producing a force $\mathbf{F} = \langle 150, 0 \rangle$. On which path between the points $(100, 50)$ and $(-100, 50)$ is the most work done overcoming the wind:

    a. The straight line $\mathbf{r}(t) = \langle x(t), z(t) \rangle = \langle -t, 50 \rangle$, for $-100 \leq t \leq 100$ or

    b. The arc of a circle $\mathbf{r}(t) = \langle 100 \cos t, 50 + 100 \sin t \rangle$, for $0 \leq t \leq \pi$?

53. Flying into a headwind

    a. How does the result of Exercise 52 change if the force due to the wind is $\mathbf{F} = \langle 141, 50 \rangle$ (approximately the same magnitude, but different direction)?

    b. How does the result of Exercise 52 change if the force due to the wind is $\mathbf{F} = \langle 141, -50 \rangle$ (approximately the same magnitude, but different direction)?

54. Changing orientation Let $f(x, y) = x + 2y$ and let C be the unit circle.

    a. Find a parameterization of C with counterclockwise orientation and evaluate $\int_C f \, ds$.

    b. Find a parameterization of C with clockwise orientation and evaluate $\int_C f \, ds$.

    c. Compare the results of (a) and (b).

55. Changing orientation Let $f(x, y) = x$ and let C be the segment of the parabola $y = x^2$ joining $O(0, 0)$ and $P(1, 1)$.

    a. Find a parameterization of C in the direction from O to P. Evaluate $\int_C f \, ds$.

    b. Find a parameterization of C in the direction from P to O. Evaluate $\int_C f \, ds$.

    c. Compare the results of (a) and (b).

56–57. Zero circulation fields

56. For what values of b and c does the vector field $\mathbf{F} = \langle by, cx \rangle$ have zero circulation on the unit circle centered at the origin and oriented counterclockwise?

57. Consider the vector field $\mathbf{F} = \langle ax + by, cx + dy \rangle$. Show that $\mathbf{F}$ has zero circulation on any oriented circle centered at the origin, for any $a, b, c,$ and d, provided $b = c$.

58–59. Zero flux fields

58. For what values of a and d does the vector field $\mathbf{F} = \langle ax, dy \rangle$ have zero flux across the unit circle centered at the origin and oriented counterclockwise?

59. Consider the vector field $\mathbf{F} = \langle ax + by, cx + dy \rangle$. Show that $\mathbf{F}$ has zero flux across any oriented circle centered at the origin, for any $a, b, c,$ and d, provided $a = -d$.

60. Work in a rotation field Consider the rotation field $\mathbf{F} = \langle -y, x \rangle$ and the three paths shown in the figure. Compute the work done on each of the three paths. Does it appear that the line integral $\int_C \mathbf{F} \cdot \mathbf{T} \, ds$ is independent of the path, where C is a path from $(1, 0)$ to $(0, 1)$?

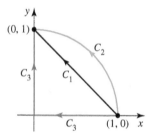

61. Work in a hyperbolic field Consider the hyperbolic force field $\mathbf{F} = \langle y, x \rangle$ (the streamlines are hyperbolas) and the three paths shown in the figure for Exercise 60. Compute the work done on each of the three paths. Does it appear that the line integral $\int_C \mathbf{F} \cdot \mathbf{T} \, ds$ is independent of the path, where C is a path from $(1, 0)$ to $(0, 1)$?

Applications

62–63. Mass and density *A thin wire represented by the smooth curve C with a density ρ (units of mass per length) has a mass $M = \int_C \rho \, ds$. Find the mass of the following wires with the given density.*

62. $C: \mathbf{r}(\theta) = \langle \cos \theta, \sin \theta \rangle$, for $0 \leq \theta \leq \pi$; $\rho(\theta) = 2\theta/\pi + 1$

63. $C: \{ (x, y): y = 2x^2, 0 \leq x \leq 3 \}$; $\rho(x, y) = 1 + xy$

64. Heat flux in a plate A square plate $R = \{ (x, y): 0 \leq x \leq 1, 0 \leq y \leq 1 \}$ has a temperature distribution $T(x, y) = 100 - 50x - 25y$.

    a. Sketch two level curves of the temperature in the plate.

    b. Find the gradient of the temperature $\nabla T(x, y)$.

    c. Assume that the flow of heat is determined by the vector field $\mathbf{F} = -\nabla T(x, y)$. Compute $\mathbf{F}$.

    d. Find the outward heat flux across the boundary $\{ (x, y): x = 1, 0 \leq y \leq 1 \}$.

    e. Find the outward heat flux across the boundary $\{ (x, y): 0 \leq x \leq 1, y = 1 \}$.

65. Inverse force fields Consider the radial field $\mathbf{F} = \dfrac{\mathbf{r}}{|\mathbf{r}|^p} = \dfrac{\langle x, y, z \rangle}{|\mathbf{r}|^p}$, where $p > 1$ (the inverse square law corresponds to $p = 3$). Let C be the line from $(1, 1, 1)$ to (a, a, a), where $a > 1$, given by $\mathbf{r}(t) = \langle t, t, t \rangle$, for $1 \leq t \leq a$.

a. Find the work done in moving an object along C with $p = 2$.

b. If $a \to \infty$ in part (a), is the work finite?

c. Find the work done in moving an object moving along C with $p = 4$.

d. If $a \to \infty$ in part (c), is the work finite?

e. Find the work done in moving an object moving along C for any $p > 1$.

f. If $a \to \infty$ in part (e), for what values of p is the work finite?

66. **Flux across curves in a flow field** Consider the flow field $\mathbf{F} = \langle y, x \rangle$ shown in the figure.

a. Compute the outward flux across the quarter circle $C: \mathbf{r}(t) = \langle 2 \cos t, 2 \sin t \rangle$, for $0 \le t \le \pi/2$.

b. Compute the outward flux across the quarter circle $C: \mathbf{r}(t) = \langle 2 \cos t, 2 \sin t \rangle$, for $\pi/2 \le t \le \pi$.

c. Explain why the flux across the quarter circle in the third quadrant equals the flux computed in part (a).

d. Explain why the flux across the quarter circle in the fourth quadrant equals the flux computed in part (b).

e. What is the outward flux across the full circle?

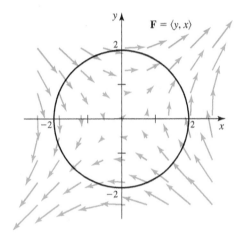

Additional Exercises

67–68. Looking ahead: Area from line integrals *The area of a region R in the plane, whose boundary is the curve C, may be computed using line integrals with the formula*

$$\text{area of } R = \int_C x \, dy = -\int_C y \, dx.$$

These ideas reappear later in the chapter.

67. Let R be the rectangle with vertices $(0, 0)$, $(a, 0)$, $(0, b)$, and (a, b) and let C be the boundary of R oriented counterclockwise. Compute the area of R using the formula $A = \int_C x \, dy$.

68. Let $R = \{ (r, \theta) : 0 \le r \le a, 0 \le \theta \le 2\pi \}$ be the disk of radius a centered at the origin and let C be the boundary of R oriented counterclockwise. Compute the area of R using the formula $A = -\int_C y \, dx$.

QUICK CHECK ANSWERS

1. The Fundamental Theorem of Calculus says that $\dfrac{d}{dt} \displaystyle\int_a^t f(u) \, du = f(t)$, which applies to differentiating the arc length integral.   2. 1300 ft/min   3. $\pi/2$ 4. **T** and **k** are unit vectors, so **n** is a unit vector. By the right-hand rule for cross products, **n** points outward from the curve.

15.3 Conservative Vector Fields

This is an action-packed section in which several fundamental ideas come together. At the heart of the matter are two questions.

• When can a vector field be expressed as the gradient of a potential function? A vector field with this property will be defined as a *conservative* vector field.

• What special properties do conservative vector fields have?

After some preliminary definitions, we present a test to determine whether a vector field in $\mathbb{R}^2$ or $\mathbb{R}^3$ is conservative. This test is followed by a procedure to find a potential function for a conservative field. We then develop several equivalent properties shared by all conservative vector fields.

Types of Curves and Regions

Many of the results in the remainder of the book rely on special properties of regions and curves. It's best to collect these definitions in one place for easy reference.

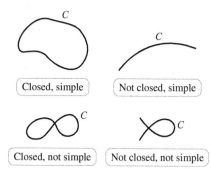

Closed, simple   Not closed, simple

Closed, not simple   Not closed, not simple

FIGURE 15.27

> ➤ Recall that all points of an open set are interior points. An open set does not contain its boundary points.

> ➤ Roughly speaking, connected means that R is all in one piece and simply connected in $\mathbb{R}^2$ means that R has no holes. $\mathbb{R}^2$ and $\mathbb{R}^3$ are themselves connected and simply connected.

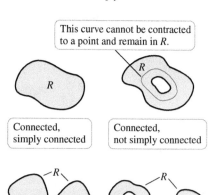

This curve cannot be contracted to a point and remain in R.

Connected, simply connected   Connected, not simply connected

Not connected, simply connected   Not connected, not simply connected

FIGURE 15.28

> ➤ The term *conservative* refers to conservation of energy. See Exercise 52 for an example of conservation of energy in a conservative force field.

> ➤ Depending on the context and the interpretation of the vector field, the potential may be defined such that $\mathbf{F} = -\nabla\varphi$ (with a negative sign).

> **DEFINITION   Simple and Closed Curves**
>
> Suppose a curve C (in $\mathbb{R}^2$ or $\mathbb{R}^3$) is described parametrically by $\mathbf{r}(t)$, where $a \leq t \leq b$. Then C is a **simple curve** if $\mathbf{r}(t_1) \neq \mathbf{r}(t_2)$ for all t_1 and t_2, with $a < t_1 < t_2 < b$; that is, C never intersects itself between its endpoints. The curve C is **closed** if $\mathbf{r}(a) = \mathbf{r}(b)$; that is, the initial and terminal points of C are the same (Figure 15.27).

In all that follows, we generally assume that R in $\mathbb{R}^2$ (or D in $\mathbb{R}^3$) is an open region. Open regions are further classified according to whether they are *connected* and whether they are *simply connected*.

> **DEFINITION   Connected and Simply Connected Regions**
>
> An open region R in $\mathbb{R}^2$ (or D in $\mathbb{R}^3$) is **connected** if it is possible to connect any two points of R by a continuous curve lying in R. An open region R is **simply connected** if every closed simple curve in R can be deformed and contracted to a point in R (Figure 15.28).

QUICK CHECK 1 Is a figure-8 curve simple? Closed? Is a torus connected? Simply connected? ◄

Test for Conservative Vector Fields

We begin with the central definition of this section.

> **DEFINITION   Conservative Vector Field**
>
> A vector field $\mathbf{F}$ is said to be **conservative** on a region (in $\mathbb{R}^2$ or $\mathbb{R}^3$) if there exists a scalar function φ such that $\mathbf{F} = \nabla\varphi$ on that region.

Suppose that the components of $\mathbf{F} = \langle f, g, h \rangle$ have continuous first partial derivatives on a region D in $\mathbb{R}^3$. Also assume that $\mathbf{F}$ is conservative, which means by definition that there is a potential function φ such that $\mathbf{F} = \nabla\varphi$. Matching the components of $\mathbf{F}$ and $\nabla\varphi$, we see that $f = \varphi_x$, $g = \varphi_y$, and $h = \varphi_z$. Recall from Theorem 13.4 that if a function has continuous second partial derivatives, the order of differentiation in the second partial derivatives does not matter. Under these conditions on φ, we conclude the following:

- $\varphi_{xy} = \varphi_{yx}$, which implies that $f_y = g_x$,
- $\varphi_{xz} = \varphi_{zx}$, which implies that $f_z = h_x$, and
- $\varphi_{yz} = \varphi_{zy}$, which implies that $g_z = h_y$.

These observations comprise half of the proof of the following theorem. The remainder of the proof is given in Section 15.4.

> **THEOREM 15.3 Test for Conservative Vector Fields**
>
> Let $\mathbf{F} = \langle f, g, h \rangle$ be a vector field defined on a connected and simply connected region D of $\mathbb{R}^3$, where f, g, and h have continuous first partial derivatives on D. Then $\mathbf{F}$ is a conservative vector field on D (there is a potential function φ such that $\mathbf{F} = \nabla\varphi$) if and only if
>
> $$\frac{\partial f}{\partial y} = \frac{\partial g}{\partial x}, \qquad \frac{\partial f}{\partial z} = \frac{\partial h}{\partial x}, \quad \text{and} \quad \frac{\partial g}{\partial z} = \frac{\partial h}{\partial y}.$$
>
> For vector fields in $\mathbb{R}^2$, we have the single condition $\dfrac{\partial f}{\partial y} = \dfrac{\partial g}{\partial x}$.

EXAMPLE 1 Testing for conservative fields Determine whether the following vector fields are conservative on $\mathbb{R}^2$ and $\mathbb{R}^3$, respectively.

a. $\mathbf{F} = \langle e^x \cos y, -e^x \sin y \rangle$

b. $\mathbf{F} = \langle 2xy - z^2, x^2 + 2z, 2y - 2xz \rangle$

SOLUTION

a. Letting $f = e^x \cos y$ and $g = -e^x \sin y$, we see that

$$\frac{\partial f}{\partial y} = -e^x \sin y = \frac{\partial g}{\partial x}.$$

The conditions of Theorem 15.3 are met and $\mathbf{F}$ is conservative.

b. Letting $f = 2xy - z^2$, $g = x^2 + 2z$, and $h = 2y - 2xz$, we have

$$\frac{\partial f}{\partial y} = 2x = \frac{\partial g}{\partial x}, \qquad \frac{\partial f}{\partial z} = -2z = \frac{\partial h}{\partial x}, \qquad \frac{\partial g}{\partial z} = 2 = \frac{\partial h}{\partial y}.$$

By Theorem 15.3, $\mathbf{F}$ is conservative.

Related Exercises 9–14 ◄

Finding Potential Functions

Like antiderivatives, potential functions, for most practical purposes, are determined up to an arbitrary additive constant. Unless an additive constant in a potential function has some physical meaning, it is usually omitted. Given a conservative vector field, there are several methods for finding a potential function. One method is shown in the following example. Another approach is illustrated in Exercise 57.

QUICK CHECK 2 Explain why a potential function for a conservative vector field is determined up to an additive constant. ◄

EXAMPLE 2 Finding potential functions Find a potential function for the conservative vector fields in Example 1.

a. $\mathbf{F} = \langle e^x \cos y, -e^x \sin y \rangle$

b. $\mathbf{F} = \langle 2xy - z^2, x^2 + 2z, 2y - 2xz \rangle$

SOLUTION

a. A potential function φ for $\mathbf{F} = \langle f, g \rangle$ has the property that $\mathbf{F} = \nabla\varphi$ and satisfies the conditions

$$\varphi_x = f(x, y) = e^x \cos y \quad \text{and} \quad \varphi_y = g(x, y) = -e^x \sin y.$$

The first equation is integrated with respect to x (holding y fixed) to obtain

$$\int \varphi_x \, dx = \int e^x \cos y \, dx,$$

which implies that

$$\varphi(x, y) = e^x \cos y + c(y).$$

> This procedure may begin with either of the two conditions, $\varphi_x = f$ or $\varphi_y = g$.

In this case, the "constant of integration" $c(y)$ is an arbitrary function of y. You can check the preceding calculation by noting that

$$\frac{\partial \varphi}{\partial x} = \frac{\partial}{\partial x} \left(e^x \cos y + c(y) \right) = e^x \cos y = f(x, y).$$

To find the arbitrary function $c(y)$, we differentiate $\varphi(x, y) = e^x \cos y + c(y)$ with respect to y and equate the result to g (recall that $\varphi_y = g$):

$$\varphi_y = -e^x \sin y + c'(y) \quad \text{and} \quad g = -e^x \sin y.$$

We conclude that $c'(y) = 0$, which implies that $c(y)$ is any real number, which we typically take to be zero. So a potential function is $\varphi(x, y) = e^x \cos y$, a result that may be checked by differentiation.

b. The method of part (a) is more elaborate with three variables. A potential function φ must now satisfy these conditions:

> This procedure may begin with any of the three conditions.

$$\varphi_x = f = 2xy - z^2 \qquad \varphi_y = g = x^2 + 2z \qquad \varphi_z = h = 2y - 2xz.$$

Integrating the first condition with respect to x (holding y and z fixed), we have

$$\varphi = \int (2xy - z^2) \, dx = x^2 y - xz^2 + c(y, z).$$

Because the integration is with respect to x, the arbitrary "constant" is a function of y and z. To find $c(y, z)$, we differentiate φ with respect to y, which results in

$$\varphi_y = x^2 + c_y(y, z).$$

Equating φ_y and $g = x^2 + 2z$, we see that $c_y(y, z) = 2z$. To obtain $c(y, z)$, we integrate $c_y(y, z) = 2z$ with respect to y (holding z fixed), which results in $c(y, z) = 2yz + d(z)$. The "constant" of integration is now a function of z, which we call $d(z)$. At this point, a potential function looks like

$$\varphi(x, y, z) = x^2 y - xz^2 + 2yz + d(z).$$

To determine $d(z)$, we differentiate φ with respect to z:

$$\varphi_z = -2xz + 2y + d'(z).$$

Equating φ_z and $h = 2y - 2xz$, we see that $d'(z) = 0$, or $d(z)$ is a real number, which we generally take to be zero. Putting it all together, a potential function is

$$\varphi = x^2 y - xz^2 + 2yz.$$

Related Exercises 15–26◄

QUICK CHECK 3 Verify by differentiation that the potential functions found in Example 2 produce the corresponding vector fields. ◄

> **PROCEDURE**   **Finding Potential Functions in** $\mathbb{R}^3$
>
> Suppose $\mathbf{F} = \langle f, g, h \rangle$ is a conservative vector field. To find φ such that $\mathbf{F} = \nabla\varphi$, take the following steps:
>
> 1. Integrate $\varphi_x = f$ with respect to x to obtain φ, which includes an arbitrary function $c(y, z)$.
> 2. Compute φ_y and equate it to g to obtain an expression for $c_y(y, z)$.
> 3. Integrate $c_y(y, z)$ with respect to y to obtain $c(y, z)$, including an arbitrary function $d(z)$.
> 4. Compute φ_z and equate it to h to get $d(z)$.
>
> Beginning the procedure with $\varphi_y = g$ or $\varphi_z = h$ may be easier in some cases.

Fundamental Theorem for Line Integrals and Path Independence

Knowing how to find potential functions, we now investigate their properties. The first property is one of several beautiful parallels to the Fundamental Theorem of Calculus.

> Compare the two versions of the Fundamental Theorem.
>
> $$\int_a^b F'(x)\,dx = F(b) - F(a)$$
>
> $$\int_C \nabla\varphi \cdot d\mathbf{r} = \varphi(B) - \varphi(A)$$

> **THEOREM 15.4   Fundamental Theorem for Line Integrals**
>
> Let $\mathbf{F}$ be a continuous vector field on an open connected region R in $\mathbb{R}^2$ (or D in $\mathbb{R}^3$). There exists a potential function φ with $\mathbf{F} = \nabla\varphi$ (which means that $\mathbf{F}$ is conservative) if and only if
>
> $$\int_C \mathbf{F} \cdot \mathbf{T}\,ds = \int_C \mathbf{F} \cdot d\mathbf{r} = \varphi(B) - \varphi(A),$$
>
> for all points A and B in R and all smooth oriented curves C from A to B.

Here is the meaning of this theorem: If $\mathbf{F}$ is a conservative vector field, then the value of a line integral of $\mathbf{F}$ depends only on the endpoints of the path. More simply, *the line integral is independent of path*, which means a parameterization of the path is not needed to evaluate line integrals of conservative fields.

If we think of φ as an antiderivative of the vector field $\mathbf{F}$, then the parallel to the Fundamental Theorem of Calculus is clear. The line integral of $\mathbf{F}$ is the difference of the values of φ evaluated at the endpoints.

Proof: We prove the theorem in one direction: If $\mathbf{F}$ is conservative, then the line integral is path-independent. The technical proof in the other direction is omitted.

Let the curve C in $\mathbb{R}^3$ be given by $\mathbf{r}(t) = \langle x(t), y(t), z(t) \rangle$, for $a \le t \le b$, where $\mathbf{r}(a)$ and $\mathbf{r}(b)$ are the position vectors for the points A and B, respectively. By the Chain Rule, the rate of change of φ with respect to t along C is

$$\frac{d\varphi}{dt} = \frac{\partial\varphi}{\partial x}\frac{dx}{dt} + \frac{\partial\varphi}{\partial y}\frac{dy}{dt} + \frac{\partial\varphi}{\partial z}\frac{dz}{dt} \qquad \text{Chain Rule}$$

$$= \left\langle \frac{\partial\varphi}{\partial x}, \frac{\partial\varphi}{\partial y}, \frac{\partial\varphi}{\partial z} \right\rangle \cdot \left\langle \frac{dx}{dt}, \frac{dy}{dt}, \frac{dz}{dt} \right\rangle \qquad \text{Identify the dot product.}$$

$$= \nabla\varphi \cdot \mathbf{r}'(t) \qquad \mathbf{r} = \langle x, y, z \rangle$$

$$= \mathbf{F} \cdot \mathbf{r}'(t). \qquad \mathbf{F} = \nabla\varphi$$

Evaluating the line integral and using the Fundamental Theorem of Calculus, it follows that

$$\int_C \mathbf{F} \cdot d\mathbf{r} = \int_a^b \mathbf{F} \cdot \mathbf{r}'(t) \, dt$$

$$= \int_a^b \frac{d\varphi}{dt} \, dt \qquad \mathbf{F} \cdot \mathbf{r}'(t) = \frac{d\varphi}{dt}$$

$$= \varphi(B) - \varphi(A). \qquad \text{Fundamental Theorem of Calculus; } t = b \text{ corresponds to } B \text{ and } t = a \text{ corresponds to } A. \qquad \blacktriangleleft$$

EXAMPLE 3 **Verifying path independence** Consider the potential function $\varphi(x, y) = (x^2 - y^2)/2$ and its gradient field $\mathbf{F} = \langle x, -y \rangle$. Let C_1 be the quarter circle $\mathbf{r}(t) = \langle \cos t, \sin t \rangle$, for $0 \le t \le \pi/2$, from $A(1, 0)$ to $B(0, 1)$. Let C_2 be the line $\mathbf{r}(t) = \langle 1 - t, t \rangle$, for $0 \le t \le 1$, also from A to B. Evaluate the line integrals of $\mathbf{F}$ on C_1 and C_2, and show that both are equal to $\varphi(B) - \varphi(A)$.

SOLUTION On C_1 we have $\mathbf{r}'(t) = \langle -\sin t, \cos t \rangle$ and $\mathbf{F} = \langle x, -y \rangle = \langle \cos t, -\sin t \rangle$. The line integral on C_1 is

$$\int_{C_1} \mathbf{F} \cdot d\mathbf{r} = \int_{C_1} \mathbf{F} \cdot \mathbf{r}'(t) \, dt$$

$$= \int_0^{\pi/2} \underbrace{\langle \cos t, -\sin t \rangle}_{\mathbf{F}} \cdot \underbrace{\langle -\sin t, \cos t \rangle}_{\mathbf{r}'(t) \, dt} dt \qquad \text{Substitute for } \mathbf{F} \text{ and } \mathbf{r}'.$$

$$= \int_0^{\pi/2} (-\sin 2t) \, dt \qquad 2 \sin t \cos t = \sin 2t$$

$$= \left(\frac{1}{2} \cos 2t \right) \Big|_0^{\pi/2} = -1. \qquad \text{Evaluate the integral.}$$

On C_2 we have $\mathbf{r}'(t) = \langle -1, 1 \rangle$ and $\mathbf{F} = \langle x, -y \rangle = \langle 1 - t, -t \rangle$; therefore,

$$\int_{C_2} \mathbf{F} \cdot d\mathbf{r} = \int_0^1 \underbrace{\langle 1 - t, -t \rangle}_{\mathbf{F}} \cdot \underbrace{\langle -1, 1 \rangle}_{d\mathbf{r}} dt \qquad \text{Substitute for } \mathbf{F} \text{ and } d\mathbf{r}.$$

$$= \int_0^1 (-1) \, dt = -1. \qquad \text{Simplify.}$$

The two line integrals have the same value, which is

$$\varphi(B) - \varphi(A) = \varphi(0, 1) - \varphi(1, 0) = -\frac{1}{2} - \frac{1}{2} = -1.$$

Related Exercises 27–32 ◄

EXAMPLE 4 **Line integral of a conservative vector field** Evaluate

$$\int_C ((2xy - z^2) \, \mathbf{i} + (x^2 + 2z) \, \mathbf{j} + (2y - 2xz) \, \mathbf{k}) \cdot d\mathbf{r},$$

where C is a simple curve from $A(-3, -2, -1)$ to $B(1, 2, 3)$.

SOLUTION This vector field is conservative and has a potential function
$\varphi = x^2y - xz^2 + 2yz$ (Example 2). By the Fundamental Theorem for line integrals,

$$\int_C ((2xy - z^2)\,\mathbf{i} + (x^2 + 2z)\,\mathbf{j} + (2y - 2xz)\,\mathbf{k}) \cdot d\mathbf{r}$$

$$= \int_C \nabla \underbrace{(x^2y - xz^2 + 2yz)}_{\varphi} \cdot d\mathbf{r}$$

$$= \varphi(1, 2, 3) - \varphi(-3, -2, -1) = 16.$$

Related Exercises 27–32◄

QUICK CHECK 4 Explain why the vector field $\nabla(xy + xz - yz)$ is a conservative field. ◄

Line Integrals on Closed Curves

It is a short step to another characterization of conservative vector fields. Suppose C is a simple *closed* smooth oriented curve in $\mathbb{R}^2$ or $\mathbb{R}^3$. To distinguish line integrals on closed curves, we adopt the notation $\oint_C \mathbf{F} \cdot d\mathbf{r}$, where the small circle on the integral sign indicates that C is a closed curve. Let A be any point on C and think of A as both the initial point and the final point of C. Assuming that $\mathbf{F}$ is a conservative vector field on an open connected region R containing C, it follows by Theorem 15.4 that

> Notice the analogy with $\int_a^a f(x)\,dx = 0$, which is true of all integrable functions.

$$\oint_C \mathbf{F} \cdot d\mathbf{r} = \varphi(A) - \varphi(A) = 0.$$

Because A is an arbitrary point on C, we see that the line integral of a conservative vector field on a closed curve is zero.

> Line integrals of vector fields satisfy properties similar to those of ordinary integrals. If C is a smooth curve from A to B and P is a point on C between A and B then

$$\int_{AB} \mathbf{F} \cdot d\mathbf{r} = -\int_{BA} \mathbf{F} \cdot d\mathbf{r}$$

and

$$\int_{AB} \mathbf{F} \cdot d\mathbf{r} = \int_{AP} \mathbf{F} \cdot d\mathbf{r}$$
$$+ \int_{PB} \mathbf{F} \cdot d\mathbf{r}$$

An argument can be made in the opposite direction as well: Suppose $\oint_C \mathbf{F} \cdot d\mathbf{r} = 0$ on all simple closed smooth oriented curves in a region R and let A and B be distinct points in R. Let C_1 denote any curve from A to B, let C_2 be any curve from B to A (distinct from and not intersecting C_1), and let C be the closed curve consisting of C_1 followed by C_2 (Figure 15.29). Then

$$\oint_C \mathbf{F} \cdot d\mathbf{r} = \int_{C_1} \mathbf{F} \cdot d\mathbf{r} + \int_{C_2} \mathbf{F} \cdot d\mathbf{r} = 0.$$

Therefore, $\int_{C_1} \mathbf{F} \cdot d\mathbf{r} = -\int_{C_2} \mathbf{F} \cdot d\mathbf{r} = \int_{-C_2} \mathbf{F} \cdot d\mathbf{r}$, where $-C_2$ is the curve C_2 traversed in the opposite direction (from A to B). We see that the line integral has the same value on two arbitrary paths between A and B. It follows that the value of the line integral is independent of path, and by Theorem 15.4, $\mathbf{F}$ is conservative. This argument is a proof of the following theorem.

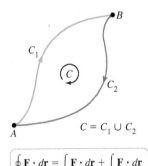

$$\oint_C \mathbf{F} \cdot d\mathbf{r} = \int_{C_1} \mathbf{F} \cdot d\mathbf{r} + \int_{C_2} \mathbf{F} \cdot d\mathbf{r}$$

FIGURE 15.29

> **THEOREM 15.5   Line Integrals on Closed Curves**
> Let R in $\mathbb{R}^2$ (or D in $\mathbb{R}^3$) be an open region. Then $\mathbf{F}$ is a conservative vector field on R if and only if $\oint_C \mathbf{F} \cdot d\mathbf{r} = 0$ on all simple closed smooth oriented curves C in R.

EXAMPLE 5   A closed curve line integral in $\mathbb{R}^3$ Evaluate $\int_C \nabla(-xy + xz + yz) \cdot d\mathbf{r}$ on the curve $C\colon \mathbf{r}(t) = \langle \sin t, \cos t, \sin t \rangle$, for $0 \le t \le 2\pi$, without using Theorems 15.4 or 15.5.

SOLUTION The components of the vector field are

$$\mathbf{F} = \nabla(-xy + xz + yz) = \langle -y + z, -x + z, x + y \rangle.$$

Note that $\mathbf{r}'(t) = \langle \cos t, -\sin t, \cos t \rangle$ and $d\mathbf{r} = \mathbf{r}'(t)\, dt$. Substituting values of x, y, and z, the value of the line integral is

$$\oint_C \mathbf{F} \cdot d\mathbf{r} = \oint_C \langle -y + z, -x + z, x + y \rangle \cdot d\mathbf{r} \quad \text{Substitute for } \mathbf{F}.$$

$$= \int_0^{2\pi} \sin 2t\, dt \quad \text{Substitute for } x, y, z, d\mathbf{r}.$$

$$= -\frac{1}{2} \cos 2t \Big|_0^{2\pi} = 0. \quad \text{Evaluate the integral.}$$

The line integral of this conservative vector field on the closed curve C is zero. In fact, by Theorem 15.5, the line integral vanishes on any simple closed curve.

Related Exercises 33–38 ◄

Summary of the Properties of Conservative Vector Fields

We have established three equivalent properties of conservative vector fields $\mathbf{F}$ defined on an open connected region R in $\mathbb{R}^2$ (or D in $\mathbb{R}^3$).

- There exists a potential function φ such that $\mathbf{F} = \nabla\varphi$ (definition).
- $\int_C \mathbf{F} \cdot d\mathbf{r} = \varphi(B) - \varphi(A)$ for all points A and B in R and all smooth oriented curves C from A to B (path independence).
- $\oint_C \mathbf{F} \cdot d\mathbf{r} = 0$ on all simple smooth closed oriented curves C in R.

The connections between these properties were established by Theorems 15.4 and 15.5 in the following way:

$$\underset{\text{Theorem 15.4}}{\text{Path-independence} \iff} \mathbf{F} \text{ is conservative } (\nabla\varphi = \mathbf{F}) \underset{\text{Theorem 15.5}}{\iff} \oint_C \mathbf{F} \cdot d\mathbf{r} = 0.$$

SECTION 15.3 EXERCISES

Review Questions

1. Explain with pictures what is meant by a simple curve and a closed curve.

2. Explain with pictures what is meant by a connected region and a simply connected region.

3. How do you determine whether a vector field in $\mathbb{R}^2$ is conservative (has a potential function φ such that $\mathbf{F} = \nabla\varphi$)?

4. How do you determine whether a vector field in $\mathbb{R}^3$ is conservative?

5. Briefly describe how to find a potential function φ for a conservative vector field $\mathbf{F} = \langle f, g \rangle$.

6. If $\mathbf{F}$ is a conservative vector field on a region R, how do you evaluate $\int_C \mathbf{F} \cdot d\mathbf{r}$, where C is a path between two points A and B in R?

7. If $\mathbf{F}$ is a conservative vector field on a region R, what is the value of $\oint_C \mathbf{F} \cdot d\mathbf{r}$, where C is a simple closed smooth oriented curve in R?

8. Give three equivalent properties of conservative vector fields.

Basic Skills

9–14. Testing for conservative vector fields *Determine whether the following vector fields are conservative on* $\mathbb{R}^2$.

9. $\mathbf{F} = \langle 1, 1 \rangle$

10. $\mathbf{F} = \langle x, y \rangle$

11. $\mathbf{F} = \langle -y, -x \rangle$

12. $\mathbf{F} = \langle -y, x + y \rangle$

13. $\mathbf{F} = \langle e^{-x} \cos y, e^{-x} \sin y \rangle$

14. $\mathbf{F} = \langle 2x^3 + xy^2, 2y^3 + x^2 y \rangle$

15–26. Finding potential functions *Determine whether the following vector fields are conservative on the specified region. If so, determine a potential function. Let R^* and D^* be open regions of $\mathbb{R}^2$ and $\mathbb{R}^3$, respectively, that do not include the origin.*

15. $\mathbf{F} = \langle x, y \rangle$ on $\mathbb{R}^2$

16. $\mathbf{F} = \langle -y, -x \rangle$ on $\mathbb{R}^2$

17. $\mathbf{F} = \left\langle x^3 - xy, \dfrac{x^2}{2} + y \right\rangle$ on $\mathbb{R}^2$

18. $\mathbf{F} = \dfrac{\langle x, y \rangle}{x^2 + y^2}$ on R^*

19. $\mathbf{F} = \dfrac{\langle x, y \rangle}{\sqrt{x^2 + y^2}}$ on R^*

20. $\mathbf{F} = \langle y, x, 1 \rangle$ on $\mathbb{R}^3$

21. $\mathbf{F} = \langle z, 1, x \rangle$ on $\mathbb{R}^3$

22. $\mathbf{F} = \langle yz, xz, xy \rangle$ on $\mathbb{R}^3$

23. $\mathbf{F} = \langle y + z, x + z, x + y \rangle$ on $\mathbb{R}^3$

24. $\mathbf{F} = \dfrac{\langle x, y, z \rangle}{x^2 + y^2 + z^2}$ on D^*

25. $\mathbf{F} = \dfrac{\langle x, y, z \rangle}{\sqrt{x^2 + y^2 + z^2}}$ on D^*

26. $\mathbf{F} = \langle x^3, 2y, -z^3 \rangle$ on $\mathbb{R}^3$

27–32. Evaluating line integrals *Evaluate the line integral* $\int_C \nabla\varphi \cdot d\mathbf{r}$ *for the following functions* φ *and oriented curves C in two ways.*

a. *Use a parametric description of C and evaluate the integral directly.*

b. *Use the Fundamental Theorem for line integrals.*

27. $\varphi(x, y) = xy$; $C: \mathbf{r}(t) = \langle \cos t, \sin t \rangle$, for $0 \le t \le \pi$

28. $\varphi(x, y) = (x^2 + y^2)/2$; $C: \mathbf{r}(t) = \langle \sin t, \cos t \rangle$, for $0 \le t \le \pi$

29. $\varphi(x, y) = x + 3y$; $C: \mathbf{r}(t) = \langle 2 - t, t \rangle$, for $0 \le t \le 2$

30. $\varphi(x, y, z) = x + y + z$; $C: \mathbf{r}(t) = \langle \sin t, \cos t, t/\pi \rangle$, for $0 \le t \le \pi$

31. $\varphi(x, y, z) = (x^2 + y^2 + z^2)/2$; $C: \mathbf{r}(t) = \langle \cos t, \sin t, t/\pi \rangle$, for $0 \le t \le 2\pi$

32. $\varphi(x, y, z) = xy + xz + yz$; $C: \mathbf{r}(t) = \langle t, 2t, 3t \rangle$, for $0 \le t \le 4$

33–38. Line integrals of vector fields on closed curves *Evaluate* $\oint_C \mathbf{F} \cdot d\mathbf{r}$ *for the following vector fields and closed oriented curves C by parameterizing C. If the integral is not zero, give an explanation.*

33. $\mathbf{F} = \langle x, y \rangle$; *C is the circle of radius 4 centered at the origin oriented counterclockwise.*

34. $\mathbf{F} = \langle y, x \rangle$; *C is the circle of radius 8 centered at the origin oriented counterclockwise.*

35. $\mathbf{F} = \langle x, y \rangle$; *C is the triangle with vertices $(0, \pm 1)$ and $(1, 0)$ oriented counterclockwise.*

36. $\mathbf{F} = \langle y, -x \rangle$; *C is the circle of radius 3 centered at the origin oriented counterclockwise.*

37. $\mathbf{F} = \langle x, y, z \rangle$; $C: \mathbf{r}(t) = \langle \cos t, \sin t, 2 \rangle$, for $0 \le t \le 2\pi$

38. $\mathbf{F} = \langle y - z, z - x, x - y \rangle$; $C: \mathbf{r}(t) = \langle \cos t, \sin t, \cos t \rangle$, for $0 \le t \le 2\pi$

Further Explorations

39. Explain why or why not Determine whether the following statements are true and give an explanation or counterexample.

a. If $\mathbf{F} = \langle -y, x \rangle$ and C is the circle of radius 4 centered at $(1, 0)$ oriented counterclockwise, then $\oint_C \mathbf{F} \cdot d\mathbf{r} = 0$.

b. If $\mathbf{F} = \langle x, -y \rangle$ and C is the circle of radius 4 centered at $(1, 0)$ oriented counterclockwise, then $\oint_C \mathbf{F} \cdot d\mathbf{r} = 0$.

c. A constant vector field is conservative on $\mathbb{R}^2$.

d. The vector field $\mathbf{F} = \langle f(x), g(y) \rangle$ is conservative on $\mathbb{R}^2$.

40–43. Line integrals *Evaluate the following line integrals using a method of your choice.*

40. $\displaystyle\int_C \nabla(1 + x^2 yz) \cdot d\mathbf{r}$, where C is the helix $\mathbf{r}(t) = \langle \cos 2t, \sin 2t, t \rangle$, for $0 \le t \le 4\pi$

41. $\displaystyle\int_C \nabla(e^{-x} \cos y) \cdot d\mathbf{r}$, where C is the line segment from $(0, 0)$ to $(\ln 2, 2\pi)$

42. $\displaystyle\oint_C e^{-x}(\cos y \, dx + \sin y \, dy)$, where C is the square with vertices $(\pm 1, \pm 1)$ oriented counterclockwise

43. $\displaystyle\oint_C \mathbf{F} \cdot d\mathbf{r}$, where $\mathbf{F} = \langle 2xy + z^2, x^2, 2xz \rangle$ and C is the circle $\mathbf{r}(t) = \langle 3 \cos t, 4 \cos t, 5 \sin t \rangle$, for $0 \le t \le 2\pi$.

44. Closed curve integrals Evaluate $\oint_C ds$, $\oint_C dx$, and $\oint_C dy$, where C is the unit circle oriented counterclockwise.

45–48. Work in force fields *Find the work required to move an object in the following force fields along a line segment between the given points. Check to see if the force is conservative.*

45. $\mathbf{F} = \langle x, 2 \rangle$ from $A(0, 0)$ to $B(2, 4)$

46. $\mathbf{F} = \langle x, y \rangle$ from $A(1, 1)$ to $B(3, -6)$

47. $\mathbf{F} = \langle x, y, z \rangle$ from $A(1, 2, 1)$ to $B(2, 4, 6)$

48. $\mathbf{F} = e^{x+y} \langle 1, 1, z \rangle$ from $A(0, 0, 0)$ to $B(-1, 2, -4)$

49–50. Work from graphs *Determine whether $\int_C \mathbf{F} \cdot d\mathbf{r}$ along the paths C_1 and C_2 shown in the following vector fields is positive or negative. Explain your reasoning.*

49.

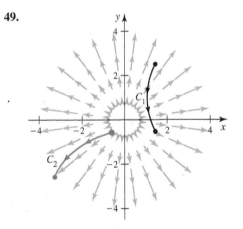

50.

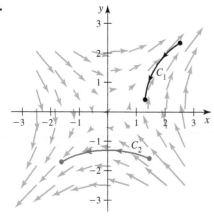

Applications

51. Work by a constant force Evaluate a line integral to show that the work done in moving an object from point A to point B in the presence of a constant force $\mathbf{F} = \langle a, b, c \rangle$ is $\mathbf{F} \cdot \overrightarrow{AB}$.

52. Conservation of energy Suppose an object with mass m moves in a region R in a conservative force field given by $\mathbf{F} = -\nabla \varphi$, where φ is a potential function in a region R. The motion of the object is governed by Newton's Second Law of Motion, $\mathbf{F} = m\mathbf{a}$, where $\mathbf{a}$ is the acceleration. Suppose the object moves from point A to point B in R.

  a. Show that the equation of motion is $m \dfrac{d\mathbf{v}}{dt} = -\nabla \varphi$.

  b. Show that $\dfrac{d\mathbf{v}}{dt} \cdot \mathbf{v} = \dfrac{1}{2} \dfrac{d}{dt} (\mathbf{v} \cdot \mathbf{v})$.

  c. Take the dot product of both sides of the equation in part (a) with $\mathbf{v}(t) = \mathbf{r}'(t)$ and integrate along a curve between A and B. Use part (b) and the fact that $\mathbf{F}$ is conservative to show that the total energy (kinetic plus potential) $\frac{1}{2} m |\mathbf{v}|^2 + \varphi$ is the same at A and B. Conclude that because A and B are arbitrary, energy is conserved in R.

53. Gravitational potential The gravitational force between two point masses M and m is

$$\mathbf{F} = GMm \frac{\mathbf{r}}{|\mathbf{r}|^3} = GMm \frac{\langle x, y, z \rangle}{(x^2 + y^2 + z^2)^{3/2}},$$

where G is the gravitational constant.

  a. Verify that this force field is conservative on any region excluding the origin.

  b. Find a potential function φ for this force field such that $\mathbf{F} = -\nabla \varphi$.

  c. Suppose the object with mass m is moved from a point A to a point B, where A is a distance r_1 from M and B is a distance r_2 from M. Show that the work done in moving the object is

$$GMm \left(\frac{1}{r_2} - \frac{1}{r_1} \right).$$

  d. Does the work depend on the path between A and B? Explain.

Additional Exercises

54. Radial fields in $\mathbb{R}^3$ are conservative Prove that the radial field $\mathbf{F} = \dfrac{\mathbf{r}}{|\mathbf{r}|^p}$, where $\mathbf{r} = \langle x, y, z \rangle$ and p is a real number, is

conservative on any region not containing the origin. For what values of p is $\mathbf{F}$ conservative on a region that contains the origin?

55. Rotation fields are usually not conservative

  a. Prove that the rotation field $\mathbf{F} = \dfrac{\langle -y, x \rangle}{|\mathbf{r}|^p}$, where $\mathbf{r} = \langle x, y \rangle$, is not conservative for $p \neq 2$.

  b. For $p = 2$, show that $\mathbf{F}$ is conservative on any region not containing the origin.

  c. Find a potential function for $\mathbf{F}$ when $p = 2$.

56. Linear and quadratic vector fields

  a. For what values of a, b, c, and d is the field $\mathbf{F} = \langle ax + by, cx + dy \rangle$ conservative?

  b. For what values of a, b, and c is the field $\mathbf{F} = \langle ax^2 - by^2, cxy \rangle$ conservative?

57. Alternative construction of potential functions in $\mathbb{R}^2$ Assume that the vector field $\mathbf{F}$ is conservative in $\mathbb{R}^2$, so that the line integral $\int_C \mathbf{F} \cdot d\mathbf{r}$ is independent of path. Use the following procedure to construct a potential function φ for the vector field $\mathbf{F} = \langle f, g \rangle = \langle 2x - y, -x + 2y \rangle$.

  a. Let A be $(0, 0)$ and let B be an arbitrary point (x, y). Define $\varphi(x, y)$ to be the work required to move an object from A to B, where $\varphi(A) = 0$. Let C_1 be the path from A to $(x, 0)$ to B and let C_2 be the path from A to $(0, y)$ to B. Draw a picture.

  b. Evaluate $\int_{C_1} \mathbf{F} \cdot d\mathbf{r} = \int_{C_1} f\, dx + g\, dy$ and conclude that $\varphi(x, y) = x^2 - xy + y^2$.

  c. Verify that the same potential function is obtained by evaluating the line integral over C_2.

58–61. Alternative construction of potential functions *Use the procedure in Exercise 57 to construct potential functions for the following fields.*

58. $\mathbf{F} = \langle -y, -x \rangle$

59. $\mathbf{F} = \langle x, y \rangle$

60. $\mathbf{F} = \mathbf{r}/|\mathbf{r}|$, where $\mathbf{r} = \langle x, y \rangle$

61. $\mathbf{F} = \langle 2x^3 + xy^2, 2y^3 + x^2 y \rangle$

QUICK CHECK ANSWERS

1. A figure-8 is closed but not simple; a torus is connected, but not simply connected.   **2.** The vector field is obtained by differentiating the potential function. So additive constants in the potential give the same vector field: $\nabla(\varphi + C) = \nabla \varphi$, when C is a constant.   **3.** Show that $\nabla(e^x \cos y) = \langle e^x \cos y, -e^x \sin y \rangle$, which is the original vector field. A similar calculation may be done for part (b).   **4.** The vector field $\nabla(xy + xz - yz)$ is the gradient of $xy + xz - yz$, so the vector field is conservative. ◄

15.4   Green's Theorem

The preceding section gave a version of the Fundamental Theorem of Calculus that applies to line integrals. In this and the remaining sections of the book, you will see additional extensions of the Fundamental Theorem that apply to regions in $\mathbb{R}^2$ and $\mathbb{R}^3$. All these fundamental theorems share a common feature.

Part 2 of the Fundamental Theorem of Calculus (Chapter 5) says

$$\int_a^b \frac{df}{dx}\,dx = f(b) - f(a),$$

which relates the integral of $\dfrac{df}{dx}$ on an interval $[a, b]$ to the values of f on the boundary of $[a, b]$. The Fundamental Theorem for line integrals says

$$\int_C \nabla\varphi \cdot d\mathbf{r} = \varphi(B) - \varphi(A),$$

which relates the integral of $\nabla\varphi$ on a smooth oriented curve C to the boundary values of φ. (The boundary consists of the two endpoints A and B.)

The subject of this section is Green's Theorem, which is another step in this progression. It relates the double integral of derivatives of a function over a region in $\mathbb{R}^2$ to function values on the boundary of that region.

Circulation Form of Green's Theorem

Throughout this section, unless otherwise stated, we assume that curves in the plane are simple closed oriented curves that have a continuous nonzero tangent vector at all points. By a result called the *Jordan Curve Theorem*, such curves have a well-defined interior such that when the curve is traversed in the counterclockwise direction (viewed from above), the interior is on the left. With this orientation, there is a unique outward unit normal vector that points to the right. We also assume that curves in the plane lie in regions that are both connected and simply connected.

Suppose the vector field $\mathbf{F}$ is defined on a region R enclosed by a closed curve C. As we have seen, the circulation $\oint_C \mathbf{F} \cdot d\mathbf{r}$ (Section 15.2) measures the net component of $\mathbf{F}$ in the direction tangent to C. It is easiest to visualize the circulation if $\mathbf{F}$ represents the velocity of a fluid moving in two dimensions. For example, let C be the unit circle with a counterclockwise orientation. The vector field $\mathbf{F} = \langle -y, x \rangle$ has a positive circulation of 2π on C (Section 15.2) because the vector field is everywhere tangent to C (Figure 15.30). A nonzero circulation on a closed curve says that the vector field must have some property *inside* the curve that produces the circulation. You can think of this property as a *net rotation*.

To visualize the rotation of a vector field, imagine a small paddle wheel, fixed at a point in the vector field, with its axis perpendicular to the xy-plane (Figure 15.30). The strength of the rotation at that point is seen in the speed at which the paddle wheel spins, while the direction of the rotation is the direction in which the paddle wheel spins. At a different point in the vector field, the paddle wheel will, in general, have a different speed and direction of rotation.

The first form of Green's Theorem relates the circulation on C to the double integral, over the region R, of a quantity that measures rotation at each point of R.

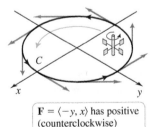

Paddle wheel at one point of vector field.

$\mathbf{F} = \langle -y, x \rangle$ has positive (counterclockwise) circulation on C.

FIGURE 15.30

> THEOREM 15.6   **Green's Theorem—Circulation Form**
>
> Let C be a simple closed smooth curve, oriented counterclockwise, that encloses a connected and simply connected region R in the plane. Assume $\mathbf{F} = \langle f, g \rangle$, where f and g have continuous first partial derivatives in R. Then
>
> $$\underbrace{\oint_C \mathbf{F} \cdot d\mathbf{r}}_{\text{circulation}} = \underbrace{\oint_C f\, dx + g\, dy}_{\text{circulation}} = \iint_R \left(\frac{\partial g}{\partial x} - \frac{\partial f}{\partial y} \right) dA.$$

> ➤ The circulation form of Green's Theorem is also called the *tangential*, or *curl*, form.

The proof of a special case of the theorem is given at the end of this section. Notice that the two line integrals on the left side of Green's Theorem give the circulation of the vector field on C. The double integral on the right side involves the factor $\dfrac{\partial g}{\partial x} - \dfrac{\partial f}{\partial y}$, which describes the rotation of the vector field *within* C that produces the circulation *on* C. This factor is called the *two-dimensional curl* of the vector field.

Figure 15.31 illustrates how the curl measures the rotation of one particular vector field at a point P. If the horizontal component of the field decreases in the y-direction at P ($f_y < 0$) and the vertical component increases in the x-direction at P ($g_x > 0$), then $\dfrac{\partial g}{\partial x} - \dfrac{\partial f}{\partial y} > 0$, and the field has a counterclockwise rotation at P. The double integral in Green's Theorem computes the net rotation of the field throughout R. The theorem says that the net rotation throughout R equals the circulation on the boundary of R.

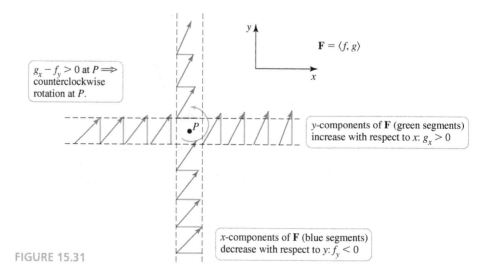

QUICK CHECK 1 Compute $\dfrac{\partial g}{\partial x} - \dfrac{\partial f}{\partial y}$ for the radial vector field $\mathbf{F} = \langle x, y \rangle$. What does this tell you about the circulation on a simple closed curve?

FIGURE 15.31

Green's Theorem has an important consequence when applied to a conservative vector field. Recall from Theorem 15.3 that if $\mathbf{F} = \langle f, g \rangle$ is conservative, then its components satisfy the condition $f_y = g_x$. If R is a region of $\mathbb{R}^2$ on which the conditions of Green's Theorem are satisfied, then for a conservative field we have

$$\oint_C \mathbf{F} \cdot d\mathbf{r} = \iint_R \underbrace{\left(\frac{\partial g}{\partial x} - \frac{\partial f}{\partial y} \right)}_{0} dA = 0.$$

> In some cases, the rotation of a vector field may not be obvious. For example, the parallel flow in a channel $\mathbf{F} = \langle 0, 1 - x^2 \rangle$, for $|x| \le 1$, has a nonzero curl for $x \ne 0$. See Exercise 66.

Green's Theorem confirms the fact (Theorem 15.5) that if $\mathbf{F}$ is a conservative vector field in a region, then the circulation $\oint_C \mathbf{F} \cdot d\mathbf{r}$ is zero on any simple closed curve in the region. A two-dimensional vector field $\mathbf{F} = \langle f, g \rangle$ for which $\dfrac{\partial g}{\partial x} - \dfrac{\partial f}{\partial y} = 0$ at all points of a region is said to be *irrotational*, because it produces zero circulation on closed curves in the region. Irrotational vector fields on simply connected regions in $\mathbb{R}^2$ are conservative.

DEFINITION Two-Dimensional Curl

The **two-dimensional curl** of the vector field $\mathbf{F} = \langle f, g \rangle$ is $\dfrac{\partial g}{\partial x} - \dfrac{\partial f}{\partial y}$. If the curl is zero throughout a region, the vector field is said to be **irrotational** on that region.

Evaluating circulation integrals of conservative vector fields on closed curves is easy. The integral is always zero. Green's Theorem provides a way to evaluate such integrals for nonconservative vector fields.

EXAMPLE 1 Circulation of a rotation field Consider the rotation vector field $\mathbf{F} = \langle -y, x \rangle$ on the unit disk $R = \{ (x, y) : x^2 + y^2 \le 1 \}$ (Figure 15.30). In Example 7 of Section 15.2, we showed that $\oint_C \mathbf{F} \cdot d\mathbf{r} = 2\pi$, where C is the boundary of R oriented counterclockwise. Confirm this result using Green's Theorem.

SOLUTION Note that $f(x, y) = -y$ and $g(x, y) = x$; therefore, the curl of $\mathbf{F}$ is $\dfrac{\partial g}{\partial x} - \dfrac{\partial f}{\partial y} = 2$. By Green's Theorem,

$$\oint_C \mathbf{F} \cdot d\mathbf{r} = \iint_R \underbrace{\left(\frac{\partial g}{\partial x} - \frac{\partial f}{\partial y} \right)}_{2} dA = \iint_R 2 \, dA = 2 \times (\text{area of } R) = 2\pi.$$

The curl $\dfrac{\partial g}{\partial x} - \dfrac{\partial f}{\partial y}$ is nonzero on R, which results in a nonzero circulation on the boundary of R.

Related Exercises 11–16 ◄

Calculating Area by Green's Theorem A useful consequence of Green's Theorem arises with the vector fields $\mathbf{F} = \langle 0, x \rangle$ and $\mathbf{F} = \langle y, 0 \rangle$. In the first case, we have $g_x = 1$ and $f_y = 0$; therefore, by Green's Theorem,

$$\oint_C \mathbf{F} \cdot d\mathbf{r} = \underbrace{\oint_C x \, dy}_{\mathbf{F} \cdot d\mathbf{r}} = \iint_R \underbrace{dA}_{\frac{\partial g}{\partial x} - \frac{\partial f}{\partial y} = 1} = \text{area of } R.$$

In the second case, $g_x = 0$ and $f_y = 1$, and Green's Theorem says

$$\oint_C \mathbf{F} \cdot d\mathbf{r} = \oint_C y \, dx = -\iint_R dA = -\text{area of } R.$$

These two results may be combined in one statement.

Area of a Plane Region by Line Integrals

Under the conditions of Green's Theorem, the area of a region R enclosed by a curve C is

$$\oint_C x \, dy = -\oint_C y \, dx = \frac{1}{2} \oint_C (x \, dy - y \, dx).$$

A remarkably simple calculation of the area of an ellipse follows from this result.

EXAMPLE 2   **Area of an ellipse**   Find the area of the ellipse $\dfrac{x^2}{a^2} + \dfrac{y^2}{b^2} = 1$.

SOLUTION   An ellipse with counterclockwise orientation is described parametrically by $\mathbf{r}(t) = \langle x, y \rangle = \langle a \cos t, b \sin t \rangle$, for $0 \le t \le 2\pi$. Noting that $dx = -a \sin t \, dt$ and $dy = b \cos t \, dt$, we have

$$\begin{aligned}
x \, dy - y \, dx &= (a \cos t)(b \cos t) \, dt - (b \sin t)(-a \sin t) \, dt \\
&= ab \, (\cos^2 t + \sin^2 t) \, dt \\
&= ab \, dt.
\end{aligned}$$

Expressing the line integral as an ordinary integral with respect to t, the area of the ellipse is

$$\frac{1}{2} \oint_C \underbrace{(x \, dy - y \, dx)}_{ab \, dt} = \frac{ab}{2} \int_0^{2\pi} dt = \pi ab.$$

Related Exercises 17–22 ◄

Flux Form of Green's Theorem

> The flux form of Green's Theorem is also called the *normal*, or *divergence*, form.

Let C be a closed curve enclosing a region R in $\mathbb{R}^2$ and let $\mathbf{F}$ be a vector field defined on R. We assume that C and R have the previously stated properties; specifically, C is oriented counterclockwise with an outward normal vector $\mathbf{n}$. Recall that the outward flux of $\mathbf{F}$ across C is $\oint_C \mathbf{F} \cdot \mathbf{n} \, ds$ (Section 15.2). The second form of Green's Theorem relates the flux across C to a property of the vector field within R that produces the flux.

THEOREM 15.7   **Green's Theorem, Flux Form**

Let C be a simple closed smooth curve, oriented counterclockwise, that encloses a connected and simply connected region R in the plane. Assume $\mathbf{F} = \langle f, g \rangle$, where f and g have continuous first partial derivatives in R. Then

$$\underbrace{\oint_C \mathbf{F} \cdot \mathbf{n} \, ds}_{\text{outward flux}} = \underbrace{\oint_C f \, dy - g \, dx}_{\text{outward flux}} = \iint_R \left(\frac{\partial f}{\partial x} + \frac{\partial g}{\partial y} \right) dA,$$

where $\mathbf{n}$ is the outward unit normal vector on the curve.

The two forms of Green's Theorem are related in the following way: Applying the circulation form of the theorem to $\mathbf{F} = \langle -g, f \rangle$ results in the flux form, and applying the flux form of the theorem to $\mathbf{F} = \langle g, -f \rangle$ results in the circulation form.

The two line integrals on the left side of Theorem 15.7 give the outward flux of the vector field across C. The double integral on the right side involves the quantity $\dfrac{\partial f}{\partial x} + \dfrac{\partial g}{\partial y}$, which is the property of the vector field that produces the flux across C. This quantity is called the *two-dimensional divergence*.

Figure 15.32 illustrates how the divergence measures the flux of one particular vector field at a point P. If $f_x > 0$ at P, it indicates an expansion of the vector field in the x-direction (if f_x is negative, it indicates a contraction). Similarly, if $g_y > 0$ at P, it indicates an expansion of the vector field in the y-direction. The combined effect of $f_x + g_y > 0$ at a point is a net outward flux across a small circle enclosing P.

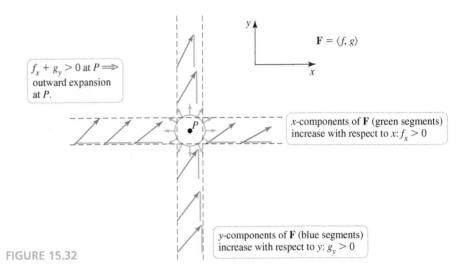

$f_x + g_y > 0$ at $P \Rightarrow$ outward expansion at P.

$\mathbf{F} = \langle f, g \rangle$

x-components of $\mathbf{F}$ (green segments) increase with respect to x: $f_x > 0$

y-components of $\mathbf{F}$ (blue segments) increase with respect to y: $g_y > 0$

FIGURE 15.32

If the divergence of $\mathbf{F}$ is zero throughout a region on which $\mathbf{F}$ satisfies the conditions of Theorem 15.7, then the outward flux across the boundary is zero. Vector fields with a zero divergence are said to be *source free*. If the divergence is positive throughout R, the outward flux across C is positive, meaning that the vector field acts as a *source* in R. If the divergence is negative throughout R, the outward flux across C is negative, meaning that the vector field acts as a *sink* in R.

> **DEFINITION Two-Dimensional Divergence**
>
> The **two-dimensional divergence** of the vector field $\mathbf{F} = \langle f, g \rangle$ is $\dfrac{\partial f}{\partial x} + \dfrac{\partial g}{\partial y}$. If the divergence is zero throughout a region, the vector field is said to be **source free** on that region.

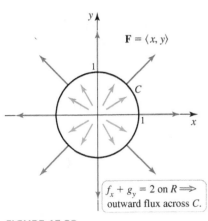

$\mathbf{F} = \langle x, y \rangle$

C

$f_x + g_y = 2$ on $R \Rightarrow$ outward flux across C.

FIGURE 15.33

QUICK CHECK 2 Compute $\dfrac{\partial f}{\partial x} + \dfrac{\partial g}{\partial y}$ for the rotation field $\mathbf{F} = \langle -y, x \rangle$. What does this tell you about the outward flux of $\mathbf{F}$ across a simple closed curve? ◄

EXAMPLE 3   Outward flux of a radial field Use Green's Theorem to compute the outward flux of the radial field $\mathbf{F} = \langle x, y \rangle$ across the unit circle $C = \{(x, y): x^2 + y^2 = 1\}$ (Figure 15.33). Interpret the result.

SOLUTION We have already calculated the outward flux of the radial field across C as a line integral and found it to be 2π (Section 15.2). Computing the outward flux using

Green's Theorem, note that $f(x, y) = x$ and $g(x, y) = y$; therefore, the divergence of $\mathbf{F}$ is $\dfrac{\partial f}{\partial x} + \dfrac{\partial g}{\partial y} = 2$. By Green's Theorem, we have

$$\oint_C \mathbf{F} \cdot \mathbf{n} \, ds = \iint_R \left(\frac{\partial f}{\partial x} + \frac{\partial g}{\partial y} \right) dA = \iint_R \underbrace{2}_{} \, dA = 2 \times (\text{area of } R) = 2\pi.$$

The positive divergence on R results in an outward flux of the vector field across the boundary of R.

Related Exercises 23–28◀

As with the circulation form, the flux form of Green's Theorem can be used in either direction: to simplify line integrals or to simplify double integrals.

EXAMPLE 4   Line integral as a double integral Evaluate $\oint_C (4x^3 + \sin y^2) \, dy - (4y^3 + \cos x^2) \, dx$, where C is the boundary of the disk $R = \{(x, y): x^2 + y^2 \le 4\}$ oriented counterclockwise.

SOLUTION Letting $f(x, y) = 4x^3 + \sin y^2$ and $g(x, y) = 4y^3 + \cos x^2$, Green's Theorem takes the form

$$\oint_C \underbrace{(4x^3 + \sin y^2)}_{f} \, dy - \underbrace{(4y^3 + \cos x^2)}_{g} \, dx$$

$$= \iint_R (\underbrace{12x^2}_{f_x} + \underbrace{12y^2}_{g_y}) \, dA \qquad \text{Green's Theorem, flux form}$$

$$= 12 \int_0^{2\pi} \int_0^2 r^2 \, r \, dr \, d\theta \qquad \text{Polar coordinates: } x^2 + y^2 = r^2$$

$$= 12 \int_0^{2\pi} \frac{r^4}{4} \Big|_0^2 \, d\theta \qquad \text{Evaluate the inner integral.}$$

$$= 48 \int_0^{2\pi} d\theta = 96\pi. \qquad \text{Evaluate the outer integral.}$$

Related Exercises 29–34◀

Circulation and Flux on More General Regions

Some ingenuity is required to extend both forms of Green's Theorem to more complicated regions. The next two examples illustrate Green's Theorem on two such regions: a half annulus and a full annulus.

EXAMPLE 5   Circulation on a half annulus Consider the vector field $\mathbf{F} = \langle y^2, x^2 \rangle$ on the half annulus $R = \{(x, y): 1 \le x^2 + y^2 \le 9, y \ge 0\}$, whose boundary is C. Find the circulation on C, assuming it has the orientation shown in Figure 15.34.

SOLUTION The circulation on C is

$$\oint_C f \, dx + g \, dy = \oint_C y^2 \, dx + x^2 \, dy.$$

With the given orientation, the curve runs counterclockwise on the outer semicircle and clockwise on the inner semicircle. Identifying $f(x, y) = y^2$ and $g(x, y) = x^2$, the

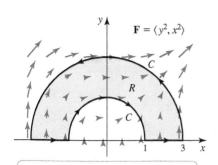

$\mathbf{F} = \langle y^2, x^2 \rangle$

Circulation on boundary of R is negative.

FIGURE 15.34

circulation form of Green's Theorem converts the line integral into a double integral. The double integral is most easily evaluated in polar coordinates using $x = r \cos \theta$ and $y = r \sin \theta$:

$$\oint_C y^2 \, dx + x^2 \, dy = \iint_R (\underbrace{2x}_{g_x} - \underbrace{2y}_{f_y}) \, dA \qquad \text{Green's Theorem}$$

$$= 2 \int_0^\pi \int_1^3 (r \cos \theta - r \sin \theta) \, r \, dr \, d\theta \qquad \text{Convert to polar coordinates.}$$

$$= 2 \int_0^\pi (\cos \theta - \sin \theta)\left(\frac{r^3}{3}\right)\Big|_1^3 \, d\theta \qquad \text{Evaluate the inner integral.}$$

$$= \frac{52}{3} \int_0^\pi (\cos \theta - \sin \theta) \, d\theta \qquad \text{Simplify.}$$

$$= -\frac{104}{3}. \qquad \text{Evaluate the outer integral.}$$

The vector field (Figure 15.34) suggests why the circulation is negative. The field is roughly *opposed* to the direction of C on the outer semicircle but roughly aligned with the direction of C on the inner semicircle. Because the outer semicircle is longer and the field has greater magnitudes on the outer curve than the inner curve, the greater contribution to the circulation is negative.

Related Exercises 35–38 ◄

EXAMPLE 6   Flux across the boundary of an annulus Find the outward flux of the vector field $\mathbf{F} = \langle xy^2, x^2y \rangle$ across the boundary of the annulus $R = \{(x, y): 1 \leq x^2 + y^2 \leq 4\} = \{(r, \theta): 1 \leq r \leq 2, 0 \leq \theta \leq 2\pi\}$ (Figure 15.35).

SOLUTION Because the annulus R is not simply connected, Green's Theorem does not apply as stated in Theorem 15.7. This difficulty is overcome by defining the curve C shown in Figure 15.35, which is simple, closed, and *piecewise* smooth. The connecting links L_1 and L_2 along the x-axis are parallel and are traversed in opposite directions. Therefore, the contributions to the line integral cancel on L_1 and L_2. Because of this cancellation, we take C to be the curve that runs counterclockwise on the outer boundary and clockwise on the inner boundary.

Using the flux form of Green's Theorem and converting to polar coordinates, we have

$$\oint_C \mathbf{F} \cdot \mathbf{n} \, ds = \oint_C f \, dy - g \, dx = \oint_C xy^2 \, dy - x^2y \, dx \qquad \text{Substitute for } f \text{ and } g.$$

$$= \iint_R (\underbrace{y^2}_{f_x} + \underbrace{x^2}_{g_y}) \, dA \qquad \text{Green's Theorem}$$

$$= \int_0^{2\pi} \int_1^2 (r^2) \, r \, dr \, d\theta \qquad \text{Polar coordinates; } x^2 + y^2 = r^2$$

$$= \int_0^{2\pi} \frac{r^4}{4}\Big|_1^2 \, d\theta \qquad \text{Evaluate the inner integral.}$$

$$= \frac{15}{4} \int_0^{2\pi} d\theta \qquad \text{Simplify.}$$

$$= \frac{15\pi}{2}. \qquad \text{Evaluate the outer integral.}$$

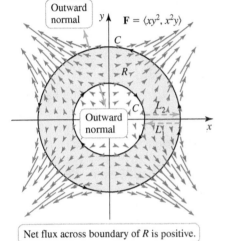

Outward normal

$\mathbf{F} = \langle xy^2, x^2y \rangle$

C

R

C L_2

Outward normal L_1

Net flux across boundary of R is positive.

FIGURE 15.35

➤ Another way to deal with the flux across the annulus is to apply Green's Theorem to the entire disk $|r| \leq 2$ and compute the flux across the outer circle. Then apply Green's Theorem to the disk $|r| \leq 1$ and compute the flux across the inner circle. Note that the flux *out* of the inner disk is a flux *into* the annulus. Therefore, the difference of the two fluxes gives the net flux for the annulus.

Notice that the divergence of the vector field in Example 6 is $x^2 + y^2$, which is positive on R, also explaining the outward flux across C.

Potential function for $\mathbf{F} = \langle f, g \rangle$:

$$\varphi_x = f \quad \text{and} \quad \varphi_y = g$$

Stream function for $\mathbf{F} = \langle f, g \rangle$:

$$\psi_x = -g \quad \text{and} \quad \psi_y = f$$

Figure 15.35 shows the vector field and explains why the flux across C is positive. Because the field increases in magnitude at greater distances from the origin, the outward flux across the outer boundary is greater than the inward flux across the inner boundary. Hence, the net outward flux across C is positive.

Related Exercises 35–38 ◀

Stream Functions

We can now see a wonderful parallel between circulation properties (and conservative vector fields) and flux properties (and source free fields). We need one more piece to complete the picture; it is the *stream function*, which plays the same role for source free fields that the potential function plays for conservative fields.

Consider a two-dimensional vector field $\mathbf{F} = \langle f, g \rangle$ that is differentiable on a region R. A **stream function** for the vector field—if it exists—is a function ψ (pronounced *psigh* or *psee*) that satisfies

$$\frac{\partial \psi}{\partial y} = f, \qquad \frac{\partial \psi}{\partial x} = -g.$$

If we compute the divergence of a vector field $\mathbf{F} = \langle f, g \rangle$ that has a stream function and use the fact that $\psi_{xy} = \psi_{yx}$, then

$$\frac{\partial f}{\partial x} + \frac{\partial g}{\partial y} = \frac{\partial}{\partial x}\left(\frac{\partial \psi}{\partial y}\right) + \frac{\partial}{\partial y}\left(-\frac{\partial \psi}{\partial x}\right) = 0.$$

$$\underbrace{\qquad\qquad\qquad\qquad}_{\psi_{yx} = \psi_{xy}}$$

We see that the existence of a stream function guarantees that the vector field has zero divergence or, equivalently, is source free. The converse is also true on simply connected regions of $\mathbb{R}^2$.

The level curves of a stream function are called **streamlines**—and for good reason. It can be shown (Exercise 64) that the vector field $\mathbf{F}$ is everywhere tangent to the streamlines, which means that a graph of the streamlines shows the flow of the vector field. Finally, just as circulation integrals of a conservative vector field are path-independent, flux integrals of a source free field are also path-independent (Exercise 63).

QUICK CHECK 3 Show that $\psi = \dfrac{1}{2}(y^2 - x^2)$ is a stream function for the vector field $\mathbf{F} = \langle y, x \rangle$. Show that $\mathbf{F}$ has zero divergence. ◀

Table 15.1 shows the parallel properties of conservative and source free vector fields in two dimensions. We assume that C is a simple smooth oriented curve and is either closed or has endpoints A and B.

Table 15.1

Conservative Fields $\mathbf{F} = \langle f, g \rangle$	**Source Free Fields $\mathbf{F} = \langle f, g \rangle$**
$\text{curl} = \dfrac{\partial g}{\partial x} - \dfrac{\partial f}{\partial y} = 0$	$\text{divergence} = \dfrac{\partial f}{\partial x} + \dfrac{\partial g}{\partial y} = 0$
Potential function φ with	Stream function ψ with
$\mathbf{F} = \nabla \varphi \quad \text{or} \quad \dfrac{\partial \varphi}{\partial x} = f, \quad \dfrac{\partial \varphi}{\partial y} = g$	$\dfrac{\partial \psi}{\partial y} = f, \quad \dfrac{\partial \psi}{\partial x} = -g$
Circulation $= \oint_C \mathbf{F} \cdot d\mathbf{r} = 0$ on all closed curves C.	Flux $= \oint_C \mathbf{F} \cdot \mathbf{n}\, ds = 0$ on all closed curves C.
Path independence	Path independence
$\displaystyle\int_C \mathbf{F} \cdot d\mathbf{r} = \varphi(B) - \varphi(A)$	$\displaystyle\int_C \mathbf{F} \cdot \mathbf{n}\, ds = \psi(B) - \psi(A)$

In fluid dynamics, velocity fields that are both conservative and source free are called *ideal flows*. They model fluids that are irrotational and incompressible.

Vector fields that are both conservative and source free are quite interesting mathematically. They have both a potential function and a stream function whose level curves form orthogonal families. Such vector fields have zero curl ($g_x - f_y = 0$) and zero divergence ($f_x + g_y = 0$). If we write the zero divergence condition in terms of the potential function φ, we find that

$$0 = f_x + g_y = \varphi_{xx} + \varphi_{yy}.$$

Writing the zero curl condition in terms of the stream function ψ, we find that

$$0 = g_x - f_y = -\psi_{xx} - \psi_{yy}.$$

Methods for finding solutions of Laplace's equation are discussed in advanced mathematics courses.

We see that the potential function and the stream function both satisfy an important equation known as **Laplace's equation**:

$$\varphi_{xx} + \varphi_{yy} = \psi_{xx} + \psi_{yy} = 0.$$

Any function satisfying Laplace's equation can be used as a potential function or stream function for a conservative, source free vector field. These vector fields are used in fluid dynamics, electrostatics, and other modeling applications.

Proof of Green's Theorem on Special Regions

The proof of Green's Theorem is straightforward when restricted to special regions. We consider regions R enclosed by a simple closed piecewise smooth curve C oriented in the counterclockwise direction. Furthermore, we require that there are functions G_1, G_2, H_1, and H_2 such that the region can be expressed in two ways (Figure 15.36):

- $R = \{(x, y): a \le x \le b, G_1(x) \le y \le G_2(x)\}$ or
- $R = \{(x, y): H_1(y) \le x \le H_2(y), c \le y \le d\}$.

This restriction on R means that lines parallel to the coordinate axes intersect the boundary of R at most twice.

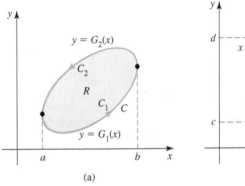
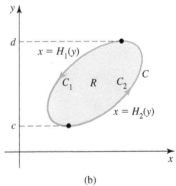

(a)   (b)

FIGURE 15.36

Under these conditions, we prove the circulation form of Green's Theorem:

$$\oint_C f\,dx + g\,dy = \iint_R \left(\frac{\partial g}{\partial x} - \frac{\partial f}{\partial y}\right) dA$$

Beginning with the term $\displaystyle\iint_R \frac{\partial f}{\partial y}\,dA$, we write this double integral as an iterated integral,

where $G_1(x) \le y \le G_2(x)$ in the inner integral and $a \le x \le b$ in the outer integral (Figure 15.36a). The upper curve is labeled C_2, and the lower curve is labeled C_1. Notice that the inner integral of $\dfrac{\partial f}{\partial y}$ with respect to y gives $f(x, y)$. Therefore, the first step of the double integration is

$$\iint\limits_{R} \frac{\partial f}{\partial y}\, dA = \int_a^b \int_{G_1(x)}^{G_2(x)} \frac{\partial f}{\partial y}\, dy\, dx \qquad \text{Convert to an iterated integral.}$$

$$= \int_a^b \big[\underbrace{f(x, G_2(x))}_{\text{on } C_2} - \underbrace{f(x, G_1(x))}_{\text{on } C_1}\big]\, dx.$$

Over the interval $a \le x \le b$, the points $(x, G_2(x))$ trace out the upper part of C (labeled C_2) in the *negative* (clockwise) direction. Similarly, over the interval $a \le x \le b$, the points $(x, G_1(x))$ trace out the lower part of C (labeled C_1) in the *positive* (counterclockwise) direction.

Therefore,

$$\iint\limits_{R} \frac{\partial f}{\partial y}\, dA = \int_a^b \big[f(x, G_2(x)) - f(x, G_1(x))\big]\, dx$$

$$= \int_{-C_2} f\, dx - \int_{C_1} f\, dx$$

$$= -\int_{C_2} f\, dx - \int_{C_1} f\, dx \qquad\qquad \int_{-C_2} = -\int_{C_2}$$

$$= -\oint_C f\, dx. \qquad\qquad\qquad\qquad \int_C = \int_{C_1} + \int_{C_2}$$

A similar argument applies to the double integral of $\dfrac{\partial g}{\partial x}$, except we use the bounding curves $x = H_1(y)$ and $x = H_2(y)$, where C_1 is the left curve and C_2 is the right curve (Figure 15.36b). We have

$$\iint\limits_{R} \frac{\partial g}{\partial x}\, dA = \int_c^d \int_{H_1(y)}^{H_2(y)} \frac{\partial g}{\partial x}\, dx\, dy \qquad \text{Convert to an iterated integral.}$$

$$= \int_c^d \big[\underbrace{g(H_2(y), y)}_{C_2} - \underbrace{g(H_1(y), y)}_{-C_1}\big]\, dy \qquad \int \frac{\partial g}{\partial x}\, dx = g$$

$$= \int_{C_2} g\, dy - \int_{-C_1} g\, dy$$

$$= \int_{C_2} g\, dy + \int_{C_1} g\, dy \qquad\qquad \int_{-C_1} = -\int_{C_1}$$

$$= \oint_C g\, dy. \qquad\qquad\qquad\qquad \int_C = \int_{C_1} + \int_{C_2}$$

Combining these two calculations results in

$$\iint_R \left(\frac{\partial g}{\partial x} - \frac{\partial f}{\partial y} \right) dA = \oint_C f\, dx + g\, dy.$$

As mentioned earlier, with a change of notation (replace g by f and f by $-g$), the flux form of Green's Theorem is obtained. This proof also completes the list of equivalent properties of conservative fields given in Section 15.3: From Green's Theorem it follows that if $\dfrac{\partial g}{\partial x} = \dfrac{\partial f}{\partial y}$ on a simply connected region R, then the vector field $\mathbf{F} = \langle f, g \rangle$ is conservative on R.

QUICK CHECK 4 Explain why Green's Theorem proves that if $g_x = f_y$, then the vector field $\mathbf{F} = \langle f, g \rangle$ is conservative. ◄

SECTION 15.4 EXERCISES

Review Questions

1. Explain why the two forms of Green's Theorem are analogs of the Fundamental Theorem of Calculus.

2. Referring to both forms of Green's Theorem, match each idea in Column 1 to an idea in Column 2:

Line integral for flux	Double integral of the curl
Line integral for circulation	Double integral of the divergence

3. Compute the two-dimensional curl of $\mathbf{F} = \langle 4x^3y, xy^2 + x^4 \rangle$.

4. Compute the two-dimensional divergence of $\mathbf{F} = \langle 4x^3y, xy^2 + x^4 \rangle$.

5. How do you use a line integral to compute the area of a plane region?

6. Why does a two-dimensional vector field with zero curl on a region have zero circulation on a closed curve that bounds the region?

7. Why does a two-dimensional vector field with zero divergence on a region have zero outward flux across a closed curve that bounds the region?

8. Sketch a two-dimensional vector field that has zero curl everywhere in the plane.

9. Sketch a two-dimensional vector field that has zero divergence everywhere in the plane.

10. Discuss one of the parallels between a conservative vector field and a source free vector field.

Basic Skills

11–16. Green's Theorem, circulation form *Consider the following regions R and vector fields* **F**.

a. *Compute the two-dimensional curl of the vector field.*
b. *Evaluate both integrals in Green's Theorem and check for consistency.*
c. *State whether the vector field is conservative.*

11. $\mathbf{F} = \langle x, y \rangle$; $R = \{(x, y): x^2 + y^2 \le 2\}$

12. $\mathbf{F} = \langle y, x \rangle$; R is the square with vertices $(0, 0)$, $(1, 0)$, $(1, 1)$, and $(0, 1)$.

13. $\mathbf{F} = \langle 2y, -2x \rangle$; R is the region bounded by $y = \sin x$ and $y = 0$, for $0 \le x \le \pi$.

14. $\mathbf{F} = \langle -3y, 3x \rangle$; R is the triangle with vertices $(0, 0)$, $(1, 0)$, and $(0, 2)$.

15. $\mathbf{F} = \langle 2xy, x^2 - y^2 \rangle$; R is the region bounded by $y = x(2 - x)$ and $y = 0$.

16. $\mathbf{F} = \langle 0, x^2 + y^2 \rangle$; $R = \{(x, y): x^2 + y^2 \le 1\}$

17–22. Area of regions *Use a line integral on the boundary to find the area of the following regions.*

17. A disk of radius 5

18. A region bounded by an ellipse with semimajor and semiminor axes of length 6 and 4, respectively.

19. $\{(x, y): x^2 + y^2 \le 16\}$

20. $\{(x, y): x^2/25 + y^2/9 \le 1\}$

21. The region bounded by the parabolas $\mathbf{r}(t) = \langle t, 2t^2 \rangle$ and $\mathbf{r}(t) = \langle t, 12 - t^2 \rangle$, for $-2 \le t \le 2$

22. The region bounded by the curve $\mathbf{r}(t) = \langle t(1 - t^2), 1 - t^2 \rangle$, for $-1 \le t \le 1$ (*Hint:* Plot the curve.)

23–28. Green's Theorem, flux form *Consider the following regions R and vector fields* **F**.

a. *Compute the two-dimensional divergence of the vector field.*
b. *Evaluate both integrals in Green's Theorem and check for consistency.*
c. *State whether the vector field is source free.*

23. $\mathbf{F} = \langle x, y \rangle$; $R = \{(x, y): x^2 + y^2 \le 4\}$

24. $\mathbf{F} = \langle y, -x \rangle$; R is the square with vertices $(0, 0)$, $(1, 0)$, $(1, 1)$, and $(0, 1)$.

25. $\mathbf{F} = \langle y, -3x \rangle$; R is the region bounded by $y = 4 - x^2$ and $y = 0$.

26. $\mathbf{F} = \langle -3y, 3x \rangle$; R is the triangle with vertices $(0, 0)$, $(3, 0)$, and $(0, 1)$.

27. $\mathbf{F} = \langle 2xy, x^2 - y^2 \rangle$; R is the region bounded by $y = x(2 - x)$ and $y = 0$.

28. $\mathbf{F} = \langle x^2 + y^2, 0 \rangle$; $R = \{(x, y): x^2 + y^2 \le 1\}$

29–34. Line integrals *Use Green's Theorem to evaluate the following line integrals. Unless stated otherwise, assume all curves are oriented counterclockwise.*

29. $\oint_C (2x + e^{y^2})\, dy - (4y^2 + e^{x^2})\, dx$, where C is the boundary of

the square with vertices $(0, 0)$, $(1, 0)$, $(1, 1)$, and $(0, 1)$

30. $\int_C (2x - 3y)\, dy - (3x + 4y)\, dx$, where C is the unit circle

31. $\int_C f\, dy - g\, dx$, where $\langle f, g \rangle = \langle 0, xy \rangle$ and C is the triangle

with vertices $(0, 0)$, $(2, 0)$, and $(0, 4)$

32. $\oint_C f\, dy - g\, dx$, where $\langle f, g \rangle = \langle x^2, 2y^2 \rangle$ and C is the upper

half of the unit circle and the line segment $-1 \le x \le 1$ oriented *clockwise*

33. The circulation line integral of $\mathbf{F} = \langle x^2 + y^2, 4x + y^3 \rangle$, where C is the boundary of $\{(x, y): 0 \le y \le \sin x, 0 \le x \le \pi\}$

34. The flux line integral of $\mathbf{F} = \langle e^{x-y}, e^{y-x} \rangle$, where C is the boundary of $\{(x, y): 0 \le y \le x, 0 \le x \le 1\}$

35–38. General regions *For the following vector fields, compute (a) the circulation on and (b) the outward flux across the boundary of the given region. Assume boundary curves are oriented counterclockwise.*

35. $\mathbf{F} = \langle x, y \rangle$; R is the half-annulus $\{(r, \theta): 1 \le r \le 2, 0 \le \theta \le \pi\}$.

36. $\mathbf{F} = \langle -y, x \rangle$; R is the annulus $\{(r, \theta): 1 \le r \le 3, 0 \le \theta \le 2\pi\}$.

37. $\mathbf{F} = \langle 2x + y, x - 4y \rangle$; R is the quarter-annulus $\{(r, \theta): 1 \le r \le 4, 0 \le \theta \le \pi/2\}$.

38. $\mathbf{F} = \langle x - y, -x + 2y \rangle$; R is the parallelogram $\{(x, y): 1 - x \le y \le 3 - x, 0 \le x \le 1\}$.

Further Explorations

39. Explain why or why not Determine whether the following statements are true and give an explanation or counterexample.

  a. The work required to move an object around a closed curve C in the presence of a vector force field is the circulation of the vector field on the curve.

  b. If a vector field has zero divergence throughout a region (on which the conditions of Green's Theorem are met), then the circulation on the boundary of that region is zero.

  c. If the two-dimensional curl of a vector field is positive throughout a region (on which the conditions of Green's Theorem are met), then the circulation on the boundary of that region is positive (assuming counterclockwise orientation).

40–43. Circulation and flux *For the following vector fields, compute (a) the circulation on and (b) the outward flux across the boundary of the given region. Assume boundary curves have counterclockwise orientation.*

40. $\mathbf{F} = \left\langle \ln(x^2 + y^2), \tan^{-1} \dfrac{y}{x} \right\rangle$, where R is the annulus $\{(r, \theta): 1 \le r \le 2, 0 \le \theta \le 2\pi\}$

41. $\mathbf{F} = \nabla\left(\sqrt{x^2 + y^2}\right)$, where R is the half annulus $\{(r, \theta): 1 \le r \le 3, 0 \le \theta \le \pi\}$

42. $\mathbf{F} = \langle y \cos x, -\sin x \rangle$, where R is the square $\{(x, y): 0 \le x \le \pi/2, 0 \le y \le \pi/2\}$

43. $\mathbf{F} = \langle x + y^2, x^2 - y \rangle$, where $R = \{(x, y): 3y^2 \le x \le 36 - y^2\}$

44–45. Special line integrals *Prove the following identities, where C is a simple closed smooth oriented curve.*

44. $\oint_C dx = \oint_C dy = 0$

45. $\oint_C f(x)\, dx + g(y)\, dy = 0$, where f and g have continuous

derivatives on the region enclosed by C

46. Double integral to line integral Use the flux form of Green's Theorem to evaluate $\iint_R (2xy + 4y^3)\, dA$, where R is the triangle with vertices $(0, 0)$, $(1, 0)$, and $(0, 1)$.

47. Area line integral Show that the value of

$$\oint_C xy^2\, dx + (x^2y + 2x)\, dy$$

depends only on the area of the region enclosed by C.

48. Area line integral In terms of the parameters a and b, how is the value of $\oint_C ay\, dx + bx\, dy$ related to the area of the region enclosed by C, assuming counterclockwise orientation of C?

49–52. Stream function *Recall that if the vector field $\mathbf{F} = \langle f, g \rangle$ is source free (zero divergence), then a stream function ψ exists such that $f = \psi_y$ and $g = -\psi_x$.*

  a. Verify that the given vector field has zero divergence.

  b. Integrate the relations $f = \psi_y$ and $g = -\psi_x$ to find a stream function for the field.

49. $\mathbf{F} = \langle 4, 2 \rangle$ **50.** $\mathbf{F} = \langle y^2, x^2 \rangle$

51. $\mathbf{F} = \langle -e^{-x} \sin y, e^{-x} \cos y \rangle$ **52.** $\mathbf{F} = \langle x^2, -2xy \rangle$

Applications

53–56. Ideal flow *A two-dimensional vector field describes **ideal flow** if it has both zero curl and zero divergence on a simply connected region (excluding the origin if necessary).*

  a. Verify that the curl and divergence of the given field is zero.

  b. Find a potential function φ and a stream function ψ for the field.

  c. Verify that φ and ψ satisfy Laplace's equation $\varphi_{xx} + \varphi_{yy} = \psi_{xx} + \psi_{yy} = 0$.

53. $\mathbf{F} = \langle e^x \cos y, -e^x \sin y \rangle$

54. $\mathbf{F} = \langle x^3 - 3xy^2, y^3 - 3x^2y \rangle$

55. $\mathbf{F} = \left\langle \tan^{-1}(y/x), \dfrac{1}{2} \ln(x^2 + y^2) \right\rangle$

56. $\mathbf{F} = \dfrac{\langle x, y \rangle}{x^2 + y^2}$

57. Flow in an ocean basin An idealized two-dimensional ocean is modeled by the square region $R = [-\pi/2, \pi/2] \times [-\pi/2, \pi/2]$

with boundary C. Consider the stream function
$\psi(x, y) = 4 \cos x \cos y$ defined on R (see figure).

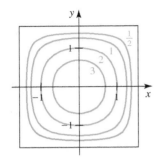

a. The horizontal (east-west) component of the velocity is
$u = \psi_y$ and the vertical (north-south) component of the velocity is $v = -\psi_x$. Sketch a few representative velocity vectors
and show that the flow is counterclockwise around the region.
b. Is the velocity field source free? Explain.
c. Is the velocity field irrotational? Explain.
d. Let C be the boundary of R. Find the total outward flux
across C.
e. Find the circulation on C assuming counterclockwise
orientation.

Additional Exercises

58. Green's Theorem as a Fundamental Theorem of Calculus
Show that if the circulation form of Green's Theorem is applied
to the vector field $\left\langle 0, \dfrac{f(x)}{c} \right\rangle$ and $R = \{(x, y): a \le x \le b,$
$0 \le y \le c\}$, then the result is the Fundamental Theorem of
Calculus,
$$\int_a^b \frac{df}{dx}\, dx = f(b) - f(a).$$

59. Green's Theorem as a Fundamental Theorem of Calculus
Show that if the flux form of Green's Theorem is applied to
the vector field $\left\langle \dfrac{f(x)}{c}, 0 \right\rangle$ and $R = \{(x, y): a \le x \le b,$
$0 \le y \le c\}$, then the result is the Fundamental Theorem of
Calculus,
$$\int_a^b \frac{df}{dx}\, dx = f(b) - f(a).$$

60. What's wrong? Consider the rotation field $\mathbf{F} = \dfrac{\langle -y, x \rangle}{x^2 + y^2}$.

a. Verify that the two-dimensional curl of $\mathbf{F}$ is zero, which suggests that the double integral in the circulation form of Green's
Theorem is zero.
b. Use a line integral to verify that the circulation on the unit
circle of the vector field is 2π.
c. Explain why the results of parts (a) and (b) do not agree.

61. What's wrong? Consider the radial field $\mathbf{F} = \dfrac{\langle x, y \rangle}{x^2 + y^2}$.

a. Verify that the divergence of $\mathbf{F}$ is zero, which suggests that the
double integral in the flux form of Green's Theorem is zero.

b. Use a line integral to verify that the outward flux across the
unit circle of the vector field is 2π.
c. Explain why the results of parts (a) and (b) do not agree.

62. Conditions for Green's Theorem Consider the radial field
$$\mathbf{F} = \langle f, g \rangle = \frac{\langle x, y \rangle}{\sqrt{x^2 + y^2}} = \frac{\mathbf{r}}{|\mathbf{r}|}.$$

a. Explain why the conditions of Green's Theorem do not apply
to $\mathbf{F}$ on a region that includes the origin.
b. Let R be the unit disk centered at the origin and compute
$$\iint_R \left(\frac{\partial f}{\partial x} + \frac{\partial g}{\partial y} \right) dA.$$
c. Evaluate the line integral in the flux form of Green's Theorem
on the boundary of R.
d. Do the results of parts (b) and (c) agree? Explain.

63. Flux integrals Assume the vector field $\mathbf{F} = \langle f, g \rangle$ is source
free (zero divergence) with stream function ψ. Let C be any
smooth simple curve from A to the distinct point B. Show that
the flux integral $\int_C \mathbf{F} \cdot \mathbf{n}\, ds$ is independent of path; that is,
$\int_C \mathbf{F} \cdot \mathbf{n}\, ds = \psi(B) - \psi(A)$.

64. Streamlines are tangent to the vector field Assume that the vec-
tor field $\mathbf{F} = \langle f, g \rangle$ is related to the stream function ψ by $\psi_y = f$
and $\psi_x = -g$ on a region R. Prove that at all points of R, the
vector field is tangent to the streamlines (the level curves of the
stream function).

65. Streamlines and equipotential lines Assume that on $\mathbb{R}^2$ the vec-
tor field $\mathbf{F} = \langle f, g \rangle$ has a potential function φ such that $f = \varphi_x$
and $g = \varphi_y$, and it has a stream function ψ such that $f = \psi_y$ and
$g = -\psi_x$. Show that the equipotential curves (level curves of φ)
and the streamlines (level curves of ψ) are everywhere orthogonal.

66. Channel flow The flow in a long shallow channel is modeled by
the velocity field $\mathbf{F} = \langle 0, 1 - x^2 \rangle$, where $R = \{(x, y): |x| \le 1$
and $|y| < \infty\}$.

a. Sketch R and several streamlines of $\mathbf{F}$.
b. Evaluate the curl of $\mathbf{F}$ on the lines $x = 0$, $x = \frac{1}{4}$, $x = \frac{1}{2}$, and
$x = 1$.
c. Compute the circulation on the boundary of the region
$R = \{(x, y): |x| \le 1, 0 \le y \le 1\}$.
d. How do you explain the fact that the curl of $\mathbf{F}$ is nonzero at
points of R, but the circulation is zero?

QUICK CHECK ANSWERS

1. $g_x - f_y = 0$, which implies zero circulation on a closed
curve.   **2.** $f_x + g_y = 0$, which implies zero flux across a
closed curve.   **3.** $\psi_y = y$ is the x-component of $\mathbf{F} = \langle y, x \rangle$
and $-\psi_x = x$ is the y-component of $\mathbf{F}$. Also the divergence
of $\mathbf{F}$ is $y_x + x_y = 0$.   **4.** If the curl is zero on a region, then
all closed-path integrals are zero, which is a condition
(Section 15.3) for a conservative field. ◀

15.5 Divergence and Curl

Green's Theorem sets the stage for the final act in our exploration of calculus. The last four sections of the book have the following goal: to lift both forms of Green's Theorem out of the plane ($\mathbb{R}^2$) and into space ($\mathbb{R}^3$). It is done as follows.

• The circulation form of Green's Theorem relates a line integral over a simple closed oriented curve in the plane to a double integral over the enclosed region. In an analogous manner, we will see that *Stokes' Theorem* (Section 15.7) relates a line integral over a simple closed oriented curve in $\mathbb{R}^3$ to a double integral over a surface bounded by that curve.

• The flux form of Green's Theorem relates a line integral over a simple closed oriented curve in the plane to a double integral over the enclosed region. Similarly, the *Divergence Theorem* (Section 15.8) relates an integral over a closed oriented surface in $\mathbb{R}^3$ to a triple integral over the region enclosed by that surface.

In order to make these extensions, we need a few more tools.

• The two-dimensional divergence and two-dimensional curl must be extended to three dimensions (this section).

• The idea of a *surface integral* must be introduced (Section 15.6).

The Divergence

> Review: The divergence measures the expansion or contraction of the field at each point. The flux form of Green's Theorem implies that if the two-dimensional divergence of a vector field is zero throughout a simply connected plane region, then the outward flux across the boundary of the region is zero. If the divergence is nonzero, Green's Theorem gives the outward flux across the boundary.

Recall that in two dimensions the divergence of the vector field $\mathbf{F} = \langle f, g \rangle$ is $\dfrac{\partial f}{\partial x} + \dfrac{\partial g}{\partial y}$. The extension to three dimensions is straightforward. If $\mathbf{F} = \langle f, g, h \rangle$ is a differentiable vector field defined on a region of $\mathbb{R}^3$, the divergence is $\dfrac{\partial f}{\partial x} + \dfrac{\partial g}{\partial y} + \dfrac{\partial h}{\partial z}$. The interpretation of the three-dimensional divergence is much the same as it is in two dimensions. It measures the expansion or contraction of the vector field at each point. If the divergence is zero at all points of a region, the vector field is *source free* on that region.

Recall the *del operator* ∇ that was introduced in Section 13.6 to define the gradient:

$$\nabla = \mathbf{i}\frac{\partial}{\partial x} + \mathbf{j}\frac{\partial}{\partial y} + \mathbf{k}\frac{\partial}{\partial z} = \left\langle \frac{\partial}{\partial x}, \frac{\partial}{\partial y}, \frac{\partial}{\partial z} \right\rangle.$$

This object is not really a vector; it is an operation that is applied to a function or a vector field. Applying it directly to a scalar function f results in the gradient of f:

$$\nabla f = \frac{\partial f}{\partial x}\mathbf{i} + \frac{\partial f}{\partial y}\mathbf{j} + \frac{\partial f}{\partial z}\mathbf{k} = \langle f_x, f_y, f_z \rangle.$$

> In evaluating $\nabla \cdot \mathbf{F}$ as a dot product, each component of ∇ is applied to the corresponding component of $\mathbf{F}$, producing $f_x + g_y + h_z$.

However, if we form the *dot product* of ∇ and a vector field $\mathbf{F} = \langle f, g, h \rangle$, the result is

$$\nabla \cdot \mathbf{F} = \left\langle \frac{\partial}{\partial x}, \frac{\partial}{\partial y}, \frac{\partial}{\partial z} \right\rangle \cdot \langle f, g, h \rangle = \frac{\partial f}{\partial x} + \frac{\partial g}{\partial y} + \frac{\partial h}{\partial z},$$

which is the divergence of $\mathbf{F}$, also denoted div $\mathbf{F}$. Like all dot products, the divergence is a scalar; in this case, it is a scalar-valued function.

DEFINITION **Divergence of a Vector Field**

The **divergence** of a vector field $\mathbf{F} = \langle f, g, h \rangle$ that is differentiable on a region of $\mathbb{R}^3$ is

$$\text{div } \mathbf{F} = \nabla \cdot \mathbf{F} = \frac{\partial f}{\partial x} + \frac{\partial g}{\partial y} + \frac{\partial h}{\partial z}.$$

If $\nabla \cdot \mathbf{F} = 0$, the vector field is **source free**.

EXAMPLE 1 **Computing the divergence** Compute the divergence of the following vector fields.

a. $\mathbf{F} = \langle x, y, z \rangle$ (a radial field)

b. $\mathbf{F} = \langle -y, x - z, y \rangle$ (a rotation field)

c. $\mathbf{F} = \langle -y, x, z \rangle$ (a spiral flow)

SOLUTION

a. The divergence is $\nabla \cdot \mathbf{F} = \nabla \cdot \langle x, y, z \rangle = \dfrac{\partial x}{\partial x} + \dfrac{\partial y}{\partial y} + \dfrac{\partial z}{\partial z} = 1 + 1 + 1 = 3.$

Because the divergence is positive, the flow expands outward at all points (Figure 15.37a).

b. The divergence is

$$\nabla \cdot \mathbf{F} = \nabla \cdot \langle -y, x - z, y \rangle = \frac{\partial(-y)}{\partial x} + \frac{\partial(x - z)}{\partial y} + \frac{\partial y}{\partial z} = 0 + 0 + 0 = 0,$$

so the field is source free.

c. This field is a combination of the two-dimensional rotation field $\mathbf{F} = \langle -y, x \rangle$ and a vertical flow in the z-direction; the net effect is a field that spirals upward for $z > 0$ and spirals downward for $z < 0$. The divergence is

$$\nabla \cdot \mathbf{F} = \nabla \cdot \langle -y, x, z \rangle = \frac{\partial(-y)}{\partial x} + \frac{\partial x}{\partial y} + \frac{\partial z}{\partial z} = 0 + 0 + 1 = 1.$$

The rotational part of the field in x and y does not contribute to the divergence. However, the z-component of the field produces a nonzero divergence (Figure 15.37b).

Related Exercises 9–16 ◄

Divergence of a Radial Vector Field The vector field considered in Example 1a is just one of many radial fields that have important applications (for example, the inverse square laws of gravitation and electrostatics). The following example leads to a general result for the divergence of radial vector fields.

QUICK CHECK 1 Show that if a vector field has the form $\mathbf{F} = \langle f(y, z), g(x, z), h(x, y) \rangle$, then div $\mathbf{F} = 0$. ◄

EXAMPLE 2 **Divergence of a radial field** Compute the divergence of the radial vector field

$$\mathbf{F} = \frac{\mathbf{r}}{|\mathbf{r}|} = \frac{\langle x, y, z \rangle}{\sqrt{x^2 + y^2 + z^2}}.$$

SOLUTION This radial field has the property that is it directed outward from the origin and all vectors have unit length ($|\mathbf{F}| = 1$). Let's compute one piece of the divergence;

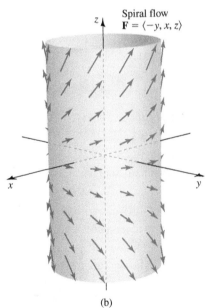

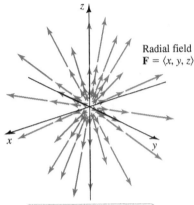

Radial field
$\mathbf{F} = \langle x, y, z \rangle$

$\nabla \cdot \mathbf{F} = 3$ at all points $\Longrightarrow$
vector field expands outward
at all points.

(a)

Spiral flow
$\mathbf{F} = \langle -y, x, z \rangle$

(b)

FIGURE 15.37

the others follow the same pattern. Using the Quotient Rule, the derivative with respect to x of the first component of $\mathbf{F}$ is

$$\frac{\partial}{\partial x}\left(\frac{x}{(x^2 + y^2 + z^2)^{1/2}}\right) = \frac{\sqrt{x^2 + y^2 + z^2} - x^2(x^2 + y^2 + z^2)^{-1/2}}{x^2 + y^2 + z^2} \qquad \text{Quotient Rule}$$

$$= \frac{|\mathbf{r}| - x^2|\mathbf{r}|^{-1}}{|\mathbf{r}|^2} \qquad \sqrt{x^2 + y^2 + z^2} = |\mathbf{r}|$$

$$= \frac{|\mathbf{r}|^2 - x^2}{|\mathbf{r}|^3}. \qquad \text{Simplify.}$$

A similar calculation of the y- and z-derivatives yields $\dfrac{|\mathbf{r}|^2 - y^2}{|\mathbf{r}|^3}$ and $\dfrac{|\mathbf{r}|^2 - z^2}{|\mathbf{r}|^3}$, respectively.

Adding the three terms, we find that

$$\nabla \cdot \mathbf{F} = \frac{|\mathbf{r}|^2 - x^2}{|\mathbf{r}|^3} + \frac{|\mathbf{r}|^2 - y^2}{|\mathbf{r}|^3} + \frac{|\mathbf{r}|^2 - z^2}{|\mathbf{r}|^3}$$

$$= 3\frac{|\mathbf{r}|^2}{|\mathbf{r}|^3} - \frac{x^2 + y^2 + z^2}{|\mathbf{r}|^3} \qquad \text{Collect terms.}$$

$$= \frac{2}{|\mathbf{r}|}. \qquad x^2 + y^2 + z^2 = |\mathbf{r}|^2$$

Related Exercises 17–20◀

Examples 1a and 2 give two special cases of the following theorem about the divergence of radial vector fields (Exercise 71).

> **THEOREM 15.8   Divergence of Radial Vector Fields**
> For a real number p, the divergence of the radial vector field
> $$\mathbf{F} = \frac{\mathbf{r}}{|\mathbf{r}|^p} = \frac{\langle x, y, z\rangle}{(x^2 + y^2 + z^2)^{p/2}} \quad \text{is} \quad \nabla \cdot \mathbf{F} = \frac{3 - p}{|\mathbf{r}|^p}.$$

EXAMPLE 3   Divergence from a graph   To gain some intuition about the divergence, consider the two-dimensional vector field $\mathbf{F} = \langle f, g\rangle = \langle x^2, y\rangle$ and a circle C of radius 2 centered at the origin (Figure 15.38).

a. Without computing it, determine whether the two-dimensional divergence is positive or negative at the point $Q(1, 1)$. Why?

b. Confirm your conjecture in part (a) by computing the two-dimensional divergence at Q.

c. Based on part (b), over what regions within the circle is the divergence positive and over what regions within the circle is the divergence negative?

d. By inspection of the figure, on what part of the circle is the flux across the boundary outward? Is the net flux out of the circle positive or negative?

SOLUTION

a. At $Q(1, 1)$ the x-component and the y-component of the field are increasing ($f_x > 0$ and $g_y > 0$), so the field is expanding at that point and the two-dimensional divergence is positive.

b. Calculating the two-dimensional divergence, we find that

$$\nabla \cdot \mathbf{F} = \frac{\partial}{\partial x}(x^2) + \frac{\partial}{\partial y}(y) = 2x + 1.$$

At $Q(1, 1)$ the divergence is 3, confirming part (a).

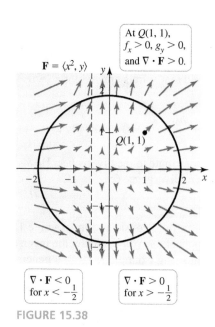

At $Q(1, 1)$, $f_x > 0$, $g_y > 0$, and $\nabla \cdot \mathbf{F} > 0$.

$\mathbf{F} = \langle x^2, y\rangle$

$Q(1, 1)$

$\nabla \cdot \mathbf{F} < 0$ for $x < -\frac{1}{2}$

$\nabla \cdot \mathbf{F} > 0$ for $x > -\frac{1}{2}$

FIGURE 15.38

> To be more specific, as you move through the point Q from left to right, the horizontal components of the vectors increase in length ($f_x > 0$). As you move through the point Q in the upward direction, the vertical components of the vectors also increase in length ($g_y > 0$).

QUICK CHECK 2 Verify the claim made in part (d) of Example 3 by showing that the net outward flux of **F** across C is positive. (*Hint:* If you use Green's Theorem to evaluate the integral $\int_C f\, dy - g\, dx$, convert to polar coordinates.)

c. From part (b) we see that $\nabla \cdot \mathbf{F} = 2x + 1 > 0$, for $x > -\frac{1}{2}$, and $\nabla \cdot \mathbf{F} < 0$, for $x < -\frac{1}{2}$. To the left of the line $x = -\frac{1}{2}$ the field is contracting and to the right of the line the field is expanding.

d. Using Figure 15.38, it appears that the field is tangent to the circle at two points with $x \approx -1$. For points on the circle with $x < -1$, the flow is into the circle; for points on the circle with $x > -1$, the flow is out of the circle. It appears that the net outward flux across C is positive. The points where the field changes from inward to outward may be determined exactly (Exercise 44). *Related Exercises 21–22* ◄

The Curl

> Review: The *two-dimensional curl* $g_x - f_y$ measures the rotation of a vector field at a point. The circulation form of Green's theorem implies that if the two-dimensional curl of a vector field is zero throughout a simply connected region, then the circulation on the boundary of the region is also zero. If the curl is nonzero, Green's Theorem gives the circulation along the curve.

Just as the divergence $\nabla \cdot \mathbf{F}$ is the dot product of the *del operator* and **F**, the three-dimensional curl is the cross product $\nabla \times \mathbf{F}$. If we formally use the notation for the cross product in terms of a 3×3 determinant, we obtain the definition of the curl:

$$\nabla \times \mathbf{F} = \begin{vmatrix} \mathbf{i} & \mathbf{j} & \mathbf{k} \\ \dfrac{\partial}{\partial x} & \dfrac{\partial}{\partial y} & \dfrac{\partial}{\partial z} \\ f & g & h \end{vmatrix} \begin{matrix} \leftarrow \text{Unit vectors} \\ \\ \leftarrow \text{Components of } \nabla \\ \\ \leftarrow \text{Components of } \mathbf{F} \end{matrix}$$

$$= \left(\frac{\partial h}{\partial y} - \frac{\partial g}{\partial z} \right) \mathbf{i} + \left(\frac{\partial f}{\partial z} - \frac{\partial h}{\partial x} \right) \mathbf{j} + \left(\frac{\partial g}{\partial x} - \frac{\partial f}{\partial y} \right) \mathbf{k}.$$

The curl of a vector field, also denoted curl **F**, is a vector with three components. Notice that the **k**-component of the curl $(g_x - f_y)$ is the two-dimensional curl, which gives the rotation in the xy-plane at a point. The **i**- and **j**-components of the curl correspond to the rotation of the vector field in planes parallel to the yz-plane (orthogonal to **i**) and in planes parallel to the xz-plane (orthogonal to **j**) (Figure 15.39).

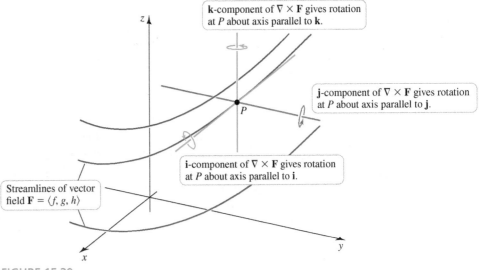

k-component of $\nabla \times \mathbf{F}$ gives rotation at P about axis parallel to **k**.

j-component of $\nabla \times \mathbf{F}$ gives rotation at P about axis parallel to **j**.

i-component of $\nabla \times \mathbf{F}$ gives rotation at P about axis parallel to **i**.

Streamlines of vector field $\mathbf{F} = \langle f, g, h \rangle$

FIGURE 15.39

DEFINITION Curl of a Vector Field

The **curl** of a vector field $\mathbf{F} = \langle f, g, h \rangle$ that is differentiable on a region of $\mathbb{R}^3$ is

$$\nabla \times \mathbf{F} = \text{curl } \mathbf{F}$$

$$= \left(\frac{\partial h}{\partial y} - \frac{\partial g}{\partial z} \right) \mathbf{i} + \left(\frac{\partial f}{\partial z} - \frac{\partial h}{\partial x} \right) \mathbf{j} + \left(\frac{\partial g}{\partial x} - \frac{\partial f}{\partial y} \right) \mathbf{k}.$$

If $\nabla \times \mathbf{F} = \mathbf{0}$, the vector field is **irrotational**.

Curl of a General Rotation Vector Field   We can clarify the physical meaning of the curl by considering the vector field $\mathbf{F} = \mathbf{a} \times \mathbf{r}$, where $\mathbf{a} = \langle a_1, a_2, a_3 \rangle$ is a nonzero constant vector and $\mathbf{r} = \langle x, y, z \rangle$. Writing out its components, we see that

$$\mathbf{F} = \mathbf{a} \times \mathbf{r} = \begin{vmatrix} \mathbf{i} & \mathbf{j} & \mathbf{k} \\ a_1 & a_2 & a_3 \\ x & y & z \end{vmatrix} = (a_2 z - a_3 y)\mathbf{i} + (a_3 x - a_1 z)\mathbf{j} + (a_1 y - a_2 x)\mathbf{k}.$$

This vector field is a *general rotation field* in three dimensions. With $a_1 = a_2 = 0$, and $a_3 = 1$, we have the familiar two-dimensional rotation field $\langle -y, x \rangle$ with its axis in the **k**-direction. More generally, **F** is the superposition of three rotation fields with axes in the **i**-, **j**-, and **k**-directions. The result is a single rotation field with an axis in the direction of **a** (Figure 15.40).

Two calculations tell us a lot about the general rotation field. The first calculation confirms that $\nabla \cdot \mathbf{F} = 0$ (Exercise 42). Just as with rotation fields in two dimensions, the divergence of a general rotation field is zero.

The second calculation (Exercise 43) says that $\nabla \times \mathbf{F} = 2\mathbf{a}$. Therefore, the curl of the general rotation field is in the direction of the axis of rotation **a** (Figure 15.40). The magnitude of the curl is $|\nabla \times \mathbf{F}| = 2|\mathbf{a}|$. It can be shown (Exercise 50) that $|\mathbf{a}|$ is the constant angular speed of rotation of the vector field, denoted ω. The angular speed is the rate (radians per unit time) at which a small particle in the vector field rotates about the axis of the field. Therefore, the angular speed is half the magnitude of the curl, or

$$\omega = |\mathbf{a}| = \frac{1}{2}|\nabla \times \mathbf{F}|.$$

The rotation field $\mathbf{F} = \mathbf{a} \times \mathbf{r}$ suggests a related question. Suppose a paddle wheel is placed in the vector field **F** at a point P with the axis of the wheel in the direction of a unit vector **n** (Figure 15.41). How should **n** be chosen so the paddle wheel spins fastest? The scalar component of **curl F** in the direction of **n** is

$$(\nabla \times \mathbf{F}) \cdot \mathbf{n} = |\nabla \times \mathbf{F}| \cos\theta, \quad (|\mathbf{n}| = 1)$$

where θ is the angle between $\nabla \times \mathbf{F}$ and **n**. The scalar component is greatest in magnitude and the paddle wheel spins fastest when $\theta = 0$ or $\theta = \pi$; that is, when **n** and $\nabla \times \mathbf{F}$ are parallel. If the axis of the paddle wheel is orthogonal to $\nabla \times \mathbf{F}$ ($\theta = \pm\pi/2$), the wheel doesn't spin.

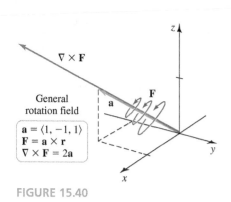

General rotation field

$\mathbf{a} = \langle 1, -1, 1 \rangle$
$\mathbf{F} = \mathbf{a} \times \mathbf{r}$
$\nabla \times \mathbf{F} = 2\mathbf{a}$

FIGURE 15.40

Just as $\nabla f \cdot \mathbf{n}$ is the directional derivative in the direction **n**, $(\nabla \times \mathbf{F}) \cdot \mathbf{n}$ is the directional spin in the direction **n**.

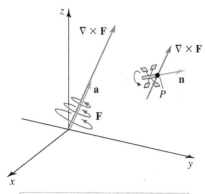

Paddle wheel at P with axis **n** measures rotation about **n**. Rotation is a maximum when $\nabla \times \mathbf{F}$ is parallel to **n**.

FIGURE 15.41

General Rotation Vector Field

The **general rotation vector field** is $\mathbf{F} = \mathbf{a} \times \mathbf{r}$, where the nonzero constant vector $\mathbf{a} = \langle a_1, a_2, a_3 \rangle$ is the axis of rotation and $\mathbf{r} = \langle x, y, z \rangle$. For all nonzero choices of **a**, $|\nabla \times \mathbf{F}| = 2|\mathbf{a}|$ and $\nabla \cdot \mathbf{F} = 0$. The constant angular speed of the vector field is

$$\omega = |\mathbf{a}| = \frac{1}{2}|\nabla \times \mathbf{F}|.$$

QUICK CHECK 3 Show that if a vector field has the form $\mathbf{F} = \langle f(x), g(y), h(z) \rangle$, then $\nabla \times \mathbf{F} = \mathbf{0}$.

EXAMPLE 4   **Curl of a rotation field** Compute the curl of the rotational field $\mathbf{F} = \mathbf{a} \times \mathbf{r}$, where $\mathbf{a} = \langle 1, -1, 1 \rangle$ and $\mathbf{r} = \langle x, y, z \rangle$ (Figure 15.40). What is the direction and the magnitude of the curl?

SOLUTION A quick calculation shows that

$$\mathbf{F} = \mathbf{a} \times \mathbf{r} = (-y - z)\mathbf{i} + (x - z)\mathbf{j} + (x + y)\mathbf{k}.$$

The curl of the field is

$$\nabla \times \mathbf{F} = \begin{vmatrix} \mathbf{i} & \mathbf{j} & \mathbf{k} \\ \dfrac{\partial}{\partial x} & \dfrac{\partial}{\partial y} & \dfrac{\partial}{\partial z} \\ -y - z & x - z & x + y \end{vmatrix} = 2\mathbf{i} - 2\mathbf{j} + 2\mathbf{k} = 2\mathbf{a}.$$

We have confirmed that curl $\mathbf{F} = 2\mathbf{a}$ and that the direction of the curl is the direction of $\mathbf{a}$, which is the axis of rotation. The magnitude of curl $\mathbf{F}$ is $|2\mathbf{a}| = 2\sqrt{3}$, which is twice the angular speed of rotation.   *Related Exercises 23–34*◄

Working with Divergence and Curl

The divergence and curl satisfy many of the same properties that ordinary derivatives satisfy. For example, given a real number c and differentiable vector fields $\mathbf{F}$ and $\mathbf{G}$, we have the following properties.

Divergence Properties	**Curl Properties**
$\nabla \cdot (\mathbf{F} + \mathbf{G}) = \nabla \cdot \mathbf{F} + \nabla \cdot \mathbf{G}$	$\nabla \times (\mathbf{F} + \mathbf{G}) = (\nabla \times \mathbf{F}) + (\nabla \times \mathbf{G})$
$\nabla \cdot (c\mathbf{F}) = c(\nabla \cdot \mathbf{F})$	$\nabla \times (c\mathbf{F}) = c(\nabla \times \mathbf{F})$

These and other properties are explored in Exercises 63–70.

Additional properties that have importance in theory and applications are presented in the following theorems and examples.

THEOREM 15.9   Curl of a Conservative Vector Field
Suppose that $\mathbf{F}$ is a conservative vector field on an open region D of $\mathbb{R}^3$. Let $\mathbf{F} = \nabla\varphi$, where φ is a potential function with continuous second partial derivatives on D. Then $\nabla \times \mathbf{F} = \nabla \times \nabla\varphi = \mathbf{0}$; that is, the curl of the gradient is the zero vector and $\mathbf{F}$ is irrotational.

Proof: We must calculate $\nabla \times \nabla\varphi$:

$$\nabla \times \nabla\varphi = \begin{vmatrix} \mathbf{i} & \mathbf{j} & \mathbf{k} \\ \dfrac{\partial}{\partial x} & \dfrac{\partial}{\partial y} & \dfrac{\partial}{\partial z} \\ \varphi_x & \varphi_y & \varphi_z \end{vmatrix} = \underbrace{(\varphi_{zy} - \varphi_{yz})}_{0}\mathbf{i} + \underbrace{(\varphi_{xz} - \varphi_{zx})}_{0}\mathbf{j} + \underbrace{(\varphi_{yx} - \varphi_{xy})}_{0}\mathbf{k} = \mathbf{0}.$$

The mixed partial derivatives are equal by Clairaut's Theorem (Theorem 13.4).

The converse of this theorem (if $\nabla \times \mathbf{F} = \mathbf{0}$, then $\mathbf{F}$ is a conservative field) is handled in Section 15.7 by means of Stokes' Theorem.   ◄

> First note that $\nabla \times \mathbf{F}$ is a vector, so it makes sense to take the divergence of the curl.

THEOREM 15.10   Divergence of the Curl
Suppose that $\mathbf{F} = \langle f, g, h \rangle$, where f, g, and h have continuous second partial derivatives. Then $\nabla \cdot (\nabla \times \mathbf{F}) = 0$: The divergence of the curl is zero.

Proof: Again, a calculation is needed:

$$\nabla \cdot (\nabla \times \mathbf{F})$$
$$= \frac{\partial}{\partial x}\left(\frac{\partial h}{\partial y} - \frac{\partial g}{\partial z}\right) + \frac{\partial}{\partial y}\left(\frac{\partial f}{\partial z} - \frac{\partial h}{\partial x}\right) + \frac{\partial}{\partial z}\left(\frac{\partial g}{\partial x} - \frac{\partial f}{\partial y}\right)$$
$$= \underbrace{(h_{yx} - h_{xy})}_{0} + \underbrace{(g_{xz} - g_{zx})}_{0} + \underbrace{(f_{zy} - f_{yz})}_{0} = 0.$$

Clairaut's Theorem assures that the mixed partial derivatives are equal.   ◄

The gradient, the divergence, and the curl may be combined in many ways—some of which are undefined. For example, the gradient of the curl ($\nabla(\nabla \times \mathbf{F})$) and the curl of the divergence ($\nabla \times (\nabla \cdot \mathbf{F})$) are undefined. However, a combination that *is* defined and is important is the divergence of the gradient $\nabla \cdot \nabla u$, where u is a scalar-valued function. This combination is denoted $\nabla^2 u$ and is called the **Laplacian** of u; it arises in many physical situations (Exercises 54–56, 60). Carrying out the calculation, we find that

$$\nabla \cdot \nabla u = \frac{\partial}{\partial x}\frac{\partial u}{\partial x} + \frac{\partial}{\partial y}\frac{\partial u}{\partial y} + \frac{\partial}{\partial z}\frac{\partial u}{\partial z} = \frac{\partial^2 u}{\partial x^2} + \frac{\partial^2 u}{\partial y^2} + \frac{\partial^2 u}{\partial z^2}.$$

We close with a result that is useful in its own right but also intriguing because it parallels the Product Rule from single-variable calculus.

THEOREM 15.11   Product Rule for the Divergence
Let u be a scalar-valued function that is differentiable on a region D and let $\mathbf{F}$ be a vector field that is differentiable on D. Then

$$\nabla \cdot (u\mathbf{F}) = \nabla u \cdot \mathbf{F} + u(\nabla \cdot \mathbf{F}).$$

QUICK CHECK 4 Is $\nabla \cdot (u\mathbf{F})$ a vector function or a scalar function? ◄

The rule says that the "derivative" of the product is the "derivative" of the first function multiplied by the second function plus the first function multiplied by the "derivative" of the second function. However, in each instance "derivative" must be interpreted correctly for the operations to make sense. The proof of the theorem requires a direct calculation (Exercise 65). Other similar vector calculus identities are presented in Exercises 66–70.

EXAMPLE 5   More properties of radial fields Let $\mathbf{r} = \langle x, y, z \rangle$ and let
$\varphi = \dfrac{1}{|\mathbf{r}|} = (x^2 + y^2 + z^2)^{-1/2}$ be a potential function.

a. Find the associated gradient field $\mathbf{F} = \nabla\left(\dfrac{1}{|\mathbf{r}|}\right)$.

b. Compute $\nabla \cdot \mathbf{F}$.

SOLUTION

a. The gradient has three components. Computing the first component reveals a pattern:

$$\frac{\partial \varphi}{\partial x} = \frac{\partial}{\partial x}(x^2 + y^2 + z^2)^{-1/2} = -\frac{1}{2}(x^2 + y^2 + z^2)^{-3/2}\, 2x = -\frac{x}{|\mathbf{r}|^3}.$$

Making a similar calculation for the y- and z-derivatives, the gradient is

$$\mathbf{F} = \nabla\left(\frac{1}{|\mathbf{r}|}\right) = -\frac{\langle x, y, z \rangle}{|\mathbf{r}|^3} = -\frac{\mathbf{r}}{|\mathbf{r}|^3}.$$

This result reveals that $\mathbf{F}$ is an inverse square vector field (for example, a gravitational or electric field), and its potential function is $\varphi = \dfrac{1}{|\mathbf{r}|}$.

b. The divergence $\nabla \cdot \mathbf{F} = \nabla \cdot \left(-\dfrac{\mathbf{r}}{|\mathbf{r}|^3}\right)$ involves a product of the vector function
$\mathbf{r} = \langle x, y, z \rangle$ and the scalar function $|\mathbf{r}|^{-3}$. Applying Theorem 15.11, we find that

$$\nabla \cdot \mathbf{F} = \nabla \cdot \left(-\frac{\mathbf{r}}{|\mathbf{r}|^3}\right) = -\nabla \frac{1}{|\mathbf{r}|^3} \cdot \mathbf{r} - \frac{1}{|\mathbf{r}|^3}\, \nabla \cdot \mathbf{r}.$$

A calculation similar to part (a) shows that $\nabla \dfrac{1}{|\mathbf{r}|^3} = -\dfrac{3\,\mathbf{r}}{|\mathbf{r}|^5}$ (Exercise 35). Therefore,

$$\nabla \cdot \mathbf{F} = \nabla \cdot \left(-\dfrac{\mathbf{r}}{|\mathbf{r}|^3}\right) = -\underbrace{\nabla \dfrac{1}{|\mathbf{r}|^3}}_{-3\mathbf{r}/|\mathbf{r}|^5} \cdot \mathbf{r} - \dfrac{1}{|\mathbf{r}|^3}\underbrace{\nabla \cdot \mathbf{r}}_{3}$$

$$= \dfrac{3\,\mathbf{r}}{|\mathbf{r}|^5} \cdot \mathbf{r} - \dfrac{3}{|\mathbf{r}|^3} \qquad \text{Substitute for } \nabla \dfrac{1}{|\mathbf{r}|^3}.$$

$$= \dfrac{3|\mathbf{r}|^2}{|\mathbf{r}|^5} - \dfrac{3}{|\mathbf{r}|^3} \qquad \mathbf{r} \cdot \mathbf{r} = |\mathbf{r}|^2$$

$$= 0.$$

The result is consistent with Theorem 15.8 (with $p = 3$): The divergence of an inverse square vector field in $\mathbb{R}^3$ is zero. It does not happen for any other radial fields of this form.

Related Exercises 35–38 ◄

Summary of Properties of Conservative Vector Fields

We can now extend the list of equivalent properties of conservative vector fields $\mathbf{F}$ defined on an open connected region. Theorem 15.9 is added to the list given at the end of Section 15.3.

Properties of a Conservative Vector Field

Let $\mathbf{F}$ be a conservative vector field whose components have continuous second partial derivatives on an open connected region D in $\mathbb{R}^3$. Then $\mathbf{F}$ has the following equivalent properties.

1. There exists a potential function φ such that $\mathbf{F} = \nabla\varphi$ (definition).

2. $\int_C \mathbf{F} \cdot d\mathbf{r} = \varphi(B) - \varphi(A)$ for all points A and B in D and all smooth oriented curves C from A to B.

3. $\oint_C \mathbf{F} \cdot d\mathbf{r} = 0$ on all simple smooth closed oriented curves C in D.

4. $\nabla \times \mathbf{F} = \mathbf{0}$ at all points of D.

SECTION 15.5 EXERCISES

Review Questions

1. Explain how to compute the divergence of the vector field $\mathbf{F} = \langle f, g, h \rangle$.

2. Interpret the divergence of a vector field.

3. What does it mean if the divergence of a vector field is zero throughout a region?

4. Explain how to compute the curl of the vector field $\mathbf{F} = \langle f, g, h \rangle$.

5. Interpret the curl of a general rotation vector field.

6. What does it mean if the curl of a vector field is zero throughout a region?

7. What is the value of $\nabla \cdot (\nabla \times \mathbf{F})$?

8. What is the value of $\nabla \times \nabla u$?

Basic Skills

9–16. Divergence of vector fields *Find the divergence of the following vector fields.*

9. $\mathbf{F} = \langle 2x, 4y, -3z \rangle$

10. $\mathbf{F} = \langle -2y, 3x, z \rangle$

11. $\mathbf{F} = \langle 12x, -6y, -6z \rangle$

12. $\mathbf{F} = \langle x^2 yz, -xy^2 z, -xyz^2 \rangle$

13. $\mathbf{F} = \langle x^2 - y^2, y^2 - z^2, z^2 - x^2 \rangle$

14. $\mathbf{F} = \langle e^{-x+y}, e^{-y+z}, e^{-z+x} \rangle$

15. $\mathbf{F} = \dfrac{\langle x, y, z \rangle}{1 + x^2 + y^2}$

16. $\mathbf{F} = \langle yz \sin x, xz \cos y, xy \cos z \rangle$

17–20. Divergence of radial fields *Calculate the divergence of the following radial fields. Express the result in terms of the position vector* **r** *and its length* |**r**|. *Check for agreement with Theorem 15.8.*

17. $\mathbf{F} = \dfrac{\langle x, y, z \rangle}{x^2 + y^2 + z^2} = \dfrac{\mathbf{r}}{|\mathbf{r}|^2}$

18. $\mathbf{F} = \dfrac{\langle x, y, z \rangle}{(x^2 + y^2 + z^2)^{3/2}} = \dfrac{\mathbf{r}}{|\mathbf{r}|^3}$

19. $\mathbf{F} = \dfrac{\langle x, y, z \rangle}{(x^2 + y^2 + z^2)^2} = \dfrac{\mathbf{r}}{|\mathbf{r}|^4}$

20. $\mathbf{F} = \langle x, y, z \rangle (x^2 + y^2 + z^2) = \mathbf{r}|\mathbf{r}|^2$

21–22. Divergence and flux from graphs *Consider the following vector fields, the circle C, and two points P and Q.*

a. *Without computing the divergence, does the graph suggest that the divergence is positive or negative at P and Q? Justify your answer.*

b. *Compute the divergence and confirm your conjecture in part (a).*

c. *On what part of C is the flux outward? Inward?*

d. *Is the net outward flux across C positive or negative?*

21. $\mathbf{F} = \langle x, x + y \rangle$

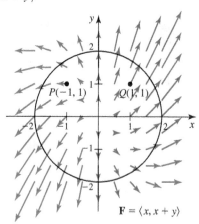

$\mathbf{F} = \langle x, x + y \rangle$

22. $\mathbf{F} = \langle x, y^2 \rangle$

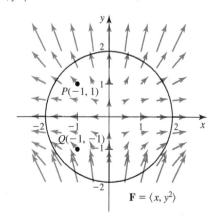

$\mathbf{F} = \langle x, y^2 \rangle$

23–26. Curl of a rotational field *Consider the following vector fields, where* $\mathbf{r} = \langle x, y, z \rangle$.

a. *Compute the curl of the field and verify that it has the same direction as the axis of rotation.*

b. *Compute the magnitude of the curl of the field.*

23. $\mathbf{F} = \langle 1, 0, 0 \rangle \times \mathbf{r}$ **24.** $\mathbf{F} = \langle 1, -1, 0 \rangle \times \mathbf{r}$

25. $\mathbf{F} = \langle 1, -1, 1 \rangle \times \mathbf{r}$ **26.** $\mathbf{F} = \langle 1, -2, -3 \rangle \times \mathbf{r}$

27–34. Curl of a vector field *Compute the curl of the following vector fields.*

27. $\mathbf{F} = \langle x^2 - y^2, xy, z \rangle$ **28.** $\mathbf{F} = \langle 0, z^2 - y^2, -yz \rangle$

29. $\mathbf{F} = \langle x^2 - z^2, 1, 2xz \rangle$ **30.** $\mathbf{F} = \mathbf{r} = \langle x, y, z \rangle$

31. $\mathbf{F} = \dfrac{\langle x, y, z \rangle}{(x^2 + y^2 + z^2)^{3/2}} = \dfrac{\mathbf{r}}{|\mathbf{r}|^3}$

32. $\mathbf{F} = \dfrac{\langle x, y, z \rangle}{(x^2 + y^2 + z^2)^{1/2}} = \dfrac{\mathbf{r}}{|\mathbf{r}|}$

33. $\mathbf{F} = \langle z^2 \sin y, xz^2 \cos y, 2xz \sin y \rangle$

34. $\mathbf{F} = \langle 3xz^3 e^{y^2}, 2xz^3 e^{y^2}, 3xz^2 e^{y^2} \rangle$

35–38. Derivative rules *Prove the following identities. Use Theorem 15.11 (Product Rule) whenever possible.*

35. $\nabla \left(\dfrac{1}{|\mathbf{r}|^3} \right) = \dfrac{-3\mathbf{r}}{|\mathbf{r}|^5}$ (used in Example 5)

36. $\nabla \left(\dfrac{1}{|\mathbf{r}|^2} \right) = \dfrac{-2\mathbf{r}}{|\mathbf{r}|^4}$

37. $\nabla \cdot \nabla \left(\dfrac{1}{|\mathbf{r}|^2} \right) = \dfrac{2}{|\mathbf{r}|^4}$ (use Exercise 36)

38. $\nabla (\ln |\mathbf{r}|) = \dfrac{\mathbf{r}}{|\mathbf{r}|^2}$

Further Explorations

39. Explain why or why not Determine whether the following statements are true and give an explanation or counterexample.

a. For a function f of a single variable, if $f'(x) = 0$ for all x in the domain, then f is a constant function. If $\nabla \cdot \mathbf{F} = 0$ for all points in the domain, then $\mathbf{F}$ is constant.

b. If $\nabla \times \mathbf{F} = \mathbf{0}$, then $\mathbf{F}$ is constant.

c. A vector field consisting of parallel vectors has zero curl.

d. A vector field consisting of parallel vectors has zero divergence.

e. curl $\mathbf{F}$ is orthogonal to $\mathbf{F}$.

40. Another derivative combination Let $\mathbf{F} = \langle f, g, h \rangle$ and let u be a differentiable scalar-valued function.

a. Take the dot product of $\mathbf{F}$ and the del operator; then apply the result to u to show that

$$(\mathbf{F} \cdot \nabla) u = \left(f \frac{\partial}{\partial x} + g \frac{\partial}{\partial y} + h \frac{\partial}{\partial z} \right) u$$

$$= f \frac{\partial u}{\partial x} + g \frac{\partial u}{\partial y} + h \frac{\partial u}{\partial z}.$$

b. Evaluate $(\mathbf{F} \cdot \nabla)(xy^2 z^3)$ at $(1, 1, 1)$, where $\mathbf{F} = \langle 1, 1, 1 \rangle$.

41. Does it make sense? Are the following expressions defined? If so, state whether the result is a scalar or a vector. Assume **F** is a sufficiently differentiable vector field and φ is a sufficiently differentiable scalar-valued function.

a. $\nabla \cdot \varphi$ b. $\nabla \mathbf{F}$ c. $\nabla \cdot \nabla \varphi$
d. $\nabla(\nabla \cdot \varphi)$ e. $\nabla(\nabla \times \varphi)$ f. $\nabla \cdot (\nabla \cdot \mathbf{F})$
g. $\nabla \times \nabla \varphi$ h. $\nabla \times (\nabla \cdot \mathbf{F})$ i. $\nabla \times (\nabla \times \mathbf{F})$

42. Zero divergence of the rotation field Show that the general rotation field $\mathbf{F} = \mathbf{a} \times \mathbf{r}$, where **a** is a nonzero constant vector and $\mathbf{r} = \langle x, y, z \rangle$, has zero divergence.

43. Curl of the rotation field For the general rotation field $\mathbf{F} = \mathbf{a} \times \mathbf{r}$, where **a** is a nonzero constant vector and $\mathbf{r} = \langle x, y, z \rangle$, show that curl $\mathbf{F} = 2\mathbf{a}$.

44. Inward to outward Find the exact points on the circle $x^2 + y^2 = 2$ at which the field $\mathbf{F} = \langle f, g \rangle = \langle x^2, y \rangle$ switches from pointing inward to outward on the circle, or vice versa.

45. Maximum divergence Within the cube $\{(x, y, z): |x| \le 1, |y| \le 1, |z| \le 1\}$, where does div **F** have the greatest magnitude when $\mathbf{F} = \langle x^2 - y^2, xy^2z, 2xz \rangle$?

46. Maximum curl Let $\mathbf{F} = \langle z, 0, -y \rangle$.

a. What is the component of curl **F** in the direction $\mathbf{n} = \langle 1, 0, 0 \rangle$?
b. What is the component of curl **F** in the direction $\mathbf{n} = \langle 1, -1, 1 \rangle$?
c. In what direction **n** is (curl **F**) $\cdot$ **n** a maximum?

47. Zero component of the curl For what vectors **n** is (curl **F**) $\cdot$ **n** $= 0$ when $\mathbf{F} = \langle y, -2z, -x \rangle$?

48–49. Find a vector field Find a vector field **F** with the given curl. In each case, is the vector field you found unique?

48. curl $\mathbf{F} = \langle 0, 1, 0 \rangle$.   **49.** curl $\mathbf{F} = \langle 0, z, -y \rangle$

50. Curl and angular speed Consider the rotational velocity field $\mathbf{v} = \mathbf{a} \times \mathbf{r}$, where **a** is a nonzero constant vector and $\mathbf{r} = \langle x, y, z \rangle$. Use the fact that an object moving in a circular path of radius R with speed $|\mathbf{v}|$ has an angular speed of $\omega = |\mathbf{v}|/R$.

a. Sketch a position vector **a**, which is the axis of rotation for the vector field, and a position vector **r** of a point P in $\mathbb{R}^3$. Let θ be the angle between the two vectors. Show that the perpendicular distance from P to the axis of rotation is $R = |\mathbf{r}| \sin \theta$.
b. Show that the speed of a particle in the velocity field is $|\mathbf{a} \times \mathbf{r}|$ and that the angular speed of the object is $|\mathbf{a}|$.
c. Conclude that $\omega = \frac{1}{2}|\nabla \times \mathbf{v}|$.

51. Paddle wheel in a vector field Let $\mathbf{F} = \langle z, 0, 0 \rangle$ and let **n** be a unit vector aligned with the axis of a paddle wheel located on the x-axis (see figure).

a. If the paddle wheel is oriented with $\mathbf{n} = \langle 1, 0, 0 \rangle$, in what direction (if any) does the wheel spin?
b. If the paddle wheel is oriented with $\mathbf{n} = \langle 0, 1, 0 \rangle$, in what direction (if any) does the wheel spin?

c. If the paddle wheel is oriented with $\mathbf{n} = \langle 0, 0, 1 \rangle$, in what direction (if any) does the wheel spin?

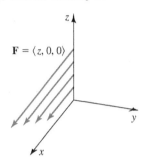

52. Angular speed Consider the rotational velocity field $\mathbf{v} = \langle -2y, 2z, 0 \rangle$.

a. If a paddle wheel is placed in the xy-plane with its axis normal to this plane, what is its angular speed?
b. If a paddle wheel is placed in the xz-plane with its axis normal to this plane, what is its angular speed?
c. If a paddle wheel is placed in the yz-plane with its axis normal to this plane, what is its angular speed?

53. Angular speed Consider the rotational velocity field $\mathbf{v} = \langle 0, 10z, -10y \rangle$. If a paddle wheel is placed in the plane $x + y + z = 1$ with its axis normal to this plane, how fast does the paddle wheel spin (revolutions per unit time)?

Applications

54–56. Heat flux *Suppose a solid object in $\mathbb{R}^3$ has a temperature distribution given by $T(x, y, z)$. The heat-flow vector field in the object is $\mathbf{F} = -k\nabla T$, where the conductivity $k > 0$ is a property of the material. Note that the heat-flow vector points in the direction opposite to that of the gradient, which is the direction of greatest temperature decrease. The divergence of the heat-flow vector is $\nabla \cdot \mathbf{F} = -k\nabla \cdot \nabla T = -k\nabla^2 T$ (the Laplacian of T). Compute the heat-flow vector field and its divergence for the following temperature distributions.*

54. $T(x, y, z) = 100e^{-\sqrt{x^2+y^2+z^2}}$

55. $T(x, y, z) = 100e^{-x^2+y^2+z^2}$

56. $T(x, y, z) = 100(1 + \sqrt{x^2 + y^2 + z^2})$

57. Gravitational potential The potential function for the gravitational force field due to a mass M at the origin acting on a mass m is $\varphi = GMm/|\mathbf{r}|$, where $\mathbf{r} = \langle x, y, z \rangle$ is the position vector of the mass m and G is the gravitational constant.

a. Compute the gravitational force field $\mathbf{F} = -\nabla\varphi$.
b. Show that the field is irrotational; that is $\nabla \times \mathbf{F} = \mathbf{0}$.

58. Electric potential The potential function for the force field due to a charge q at the origin is $\varphi = \frac{1}{4\pi\varepsilon_0} \frac{q}{|\mathbf{r}|}$, where $\mathbf{r} = \langle x, y, z \rangle$ is the position vector of a point in the field and ε_0 is the permittivity of free space.

a. Compute the force field $\mathbf{F} = -\nabla\varphi$.
b. Show that the field is irrotational; that is $\nabla \times \mathbf{F} = \mathbf{0}$.

59. Navier-Stokes equation The Navier-Stokes equation is the fundamental equation of fluid dynamics that models the flow in everything from bathtubs to oceans. In one of its many forms (incompressible, viscous flow), the equation is

$$\rho\left(\frac{\partial \mathbf{V}}{\partial t} + (\mathbf{V} \cdot \nabla)\,\mathbf{V}\right) = -\nabla p + \mu(\nabla \cdot \nabla)\,\mathbf{V}.$$

In this notation $\mathbf{V} = \langle u, v, w \rangle$ is the three-dimensional velocity field, p is the (scalar) pressure, ρ is the constant density of the fluid, and μ is the constant viscosity. Write out the three component equations of this vector equation. (See Exercise 40 for an interpretation of the operations.)

60. Stream function and vorticity The rotation of a three-dimensional velocity field $\mathbf{V} = \langle u, v, w \rangle$ is measured by the **vorticity** $\boldsymbol{\omega} = \nabla \times \mathbf{V}$. If $\boldsymbol{\omega} = \mathbf{0}$ at all points in the domain, the flow is irrotational.

  a. Which of the following velocity fields is irrotational:
$\mathbf{V} = \langle 2, -3y, 5z \rangle$ or $\mathbf{V} = \langle y, x - z, -y \rangle$?

  b. Recall that for a two-dimensional source free flow $\mathbf{V} = (u, v, 0)$, a stream function $\psi(x, y)$ may be defined such that $u = \psi_y$ and $v = -\psi_x$. For such a two-dimensional flow, let $\zeta = \mathbf{k} \cdot \nabla \times \mathbf{V}$ be the $\mathbf{k}$-component of the vorticity. Show that $\nabla^2 \psi = \nabla \cdot \nabla \psi = -\zeta$.

  c. Consider the stream function $\psi(x, y) = \sin x \sin y$ on the square region $R = \{(x, y): 0 \le x \le \pi, 0 \le y \le \pi\}$. Find the velocity components u and v; then sketch the velocity field.

  d. For the stream function in part (c) find the vorticity function ζ as defined in part (b). Plot several level curves of the vorticity function. Where on R is it a maximum? A minimum?

61. Maxwell's equation One of Maxwell's equations for electromagnetic waves (also called Ampere's Law) is $\nabla \times \mathbf{B} = C\dfrac{\partial \mathbf{E}}{\partial t}$, where $\mathbf{E}$ is the electric field, $\mathbf{B}$ is the magnetic field, and C is a constant.

  a. Show that the fields

$$\mathbf{E}(z, t) = A \sin(kz - \omega t)\,\mathbf{i} \qquad \mathbf{B}(z, t) = A \sin(kz - \omega t)\,\mathbf{j}$$

satisfy the equation for constants A, k, and ω, provided $\omega = k/C$.

  b. Make a rough sketch showing the directions of $\mathbf{E}$ and $\mathbf{B}$.

Additional Exercises

62. Splitting a vector field Express the vector field $\mathbf{F} = \langle xy, 0, 0 \rangle$ in the form $\mathbf{V} + \mathbf{W}$, where $\nabla \cdot \mathbf{V} = 0$ and $\nabla \times \mathbf{W} = \mathbf{0}$.

63. Properties of div and curl Prove the following properties of the divergence and curl. Assume $\mathbf{F}$ and $\mathbf{G}$ are differentiable vector fields and c is a real number.

  a. $\nabla \cdot (\mathbf{F} + \mathbf{G}) = \nabla \cdot \mathbf{F} + \nabla \cdot \mathbf{G}$
  b. $\nabla \times (\mathbf{F} + \mathbf{G}) = (\nabla \times \mathbf{F}) + (\nabla \times \mathbf{G})$
  c. $\nabla \cdot (c\mathbf{F}) = c(\nabla \cdot \mathbf{F})$
  d. $\nabla \times (c\mathbf{F}) = c(\nabla \times \mathbf{F})$

64. Equal curls If two functions of one variable, f and g, have the property that $f' = g'$, then f and g differ by a constant. Prove or disprove: If $\mathbf{F}$ and $\mathbf{G}$ are nonconstant vector fields in $\mathbb{R}^2$ with curl $\mathbf{F} = $ curl $\mathbf{G}$ and div $\mathbf{F} = $ div $\mathbf{G}$ at all points of $\mathbb{R}^2$, then $\mathbf{F}$ and $\mathbf{G}$ differ by a constant vector.

65–70. Identities *Prove the following identities. Assume that φ is a differentiable scalar-valued function and $\mathbf{F}$ and $\mathbf{G}$ are differentiable vector fields, all defined on a region of $\mathbb{R}^3$.*

65. $\nabla \cdot (\varphi \mathbf{F}) = \nabla \varphi \cdot \mathbf{F} + \varphi \nabla \cdot \mathbf{F}$ (Product Rule)

66. $\nabla \times (\varphi \mathbf{F}) = (\nabla \varphi \times \mathbf{F}) + (\varphi \nabla \times \mathbf{F})$ (Product Rule)

67. $\nabla \cdot (\mathbf{F} \times \mathbf{G}) = \mathbf{G} \cdot (\nabla \times \mathbf{F}) - \mathbf{F} \cdot (\nabla \times \mathbf{G})$

68. $\nabla \times (\mathbf{F} \times \mathbf{G}) = (\mathbf{G} \cdot \nabla)\mathbf{F} - \mathbf{G}(\nabla \cdot \mathbf{F}) - (\mathbf{F} \cdot \nabla)\mathbf{G} + \mathbf{F}(\nabla \cdot \mathbf{G})$

69. $\nabla(\mathbf{F} \cdot \mathbf{G}) = (\mathbf{G} \cdot \nabla)\mathbf{F} + (\mathbf{F} \cdot \nabla)\mathbf{G} + \mathbf{G} \times (\nabla \times \mathbf{F}) + \mathbf{F} \times (\nabla \times \mathbf{G})$

70. $\nabla \times (\nabla \times \mathbf{F}) = \nabla(\nabla \cdot \mathbf{F}) - (\nabla \cdot \nabla)\mathbf{F}$

71. Divergence of radial fields Prove that for a real number p, with $\mathbf{r} = \langle x, y, z \rangle$, $\nabla \cdot \dfrac{\langle x, y, z \rangle}{|\mathbf{r}|^p} = \dfrac{3 - p}{|\mathbf{r}|^p}$.

72. Gradients and radial fields Prove that for a real number p, with $\mathbf{r} = \langle x, y, z \rangle$, $\nabla\left(\dfrac{1}{|\mathbf{r}|^p}\right) = \dfrac{-p\mathbf{r}}{|\mathbf{r}|^{p+2}}$.

73. Divergence of gradient fields Prove that for a real number p, with $\mathbf{r} = \langle x, y, z \rangle$, $\nabla \cdot \nabla\left(\dfrac{1}{|\mathbf{r}|^p}\right) = \dfrac{p(p - 1)}{|\mathbf{r}|^{p+2}}$.

QUICK CHECK ANSWERS

1. The x-derivative of the divergence is applied to $f(y, z)$, which gives zero. Similarly, the y- and z-derivatives are zero. **2.** Net outward flux is 4π **3.** In the curl, the first component of $\mathbf{F}$ is differentiated only with respect to y and z, so the contribution from the first component is zero. Similarly, the second and third components of $\mathbf{F}$ make no contribution to the curl.   **4.** The divergence is a scalar-valued function.

15.6 Surface Integrals

We have studied integrals on intervals, on regions in the plane, on solid regions in space, and along curves in space. One situation is still unexplored. Suppose a sphere has a known temperature distribution; perhaps it is cold near the poles and warm near the equator. How do you find the average temperature over the entire sphere? In analogy with other average value calculations, we should expect to "add up" the temperature values over the sphere and divide by the surface area of the sphere. Because the temperature varies continuously over the sphere, adding up means integrating. How do you integrate a function over a surface? This question leads to *surface integrals*.

It helps to keep curves, arc length, and line integrals in mind as we discuss surfaces, surface area, and surface integrals. What we discover about surfaces parallels what we already know about curves—all "lifted" up one dimension.

Parallel Concepts	
Curves	**Surfaces**
Arc length	Surface area
Line integrals	Surface integrals
One-parameter description	Two-parameter description

Parameterized Surfaces

A curve in $\mathbb{R}^2$ is defined parametrically by $\mathbf{r}(t) = \langle x(t), y(t) \rangle$, for $a \leq t \leq b$; it requires one parameter and two dependent variables. Stepping up one dimension, to define a surface in $\mathbb{R}^3$ we need *two* parameters and *three* dependent variables. Letting u and v be parameters, the general parametric description of a surface has the form

$$\mathbf{r}(u, v) = \langle x(u, v), y(u, v), z(u, v) \rangle.$$

We make the assumption that the parameters vary over a rectangle $R = \{(u, v): a \leq u \leq b, c \leq v \leq d\}$ (Figure 15.42). As the parameters (u, v) vary over R, the vector $\mathbf{r}(u, v) = \langle x(u, v), y(u, v), z(u, v) \rangle$ sweeps out a surface S in $\mathbb{R}^3$.

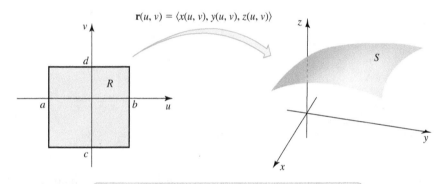

$\mathbf{r}(u, v) = \langle x(u, v), y(u, v), z(u, v) \rangle$

FIGURE 15.42   A rectangle in the *uv*-plane is mapped to a surface in *xyz*-space.

We work extensively with three surfaces that are easily described in parametric form. As with parameterized curves, a parametric description of a surface is not unique.

Cylinders   In Cartesian coordinates, the set

$$\{(x, y, z): x = a \cos \theta, y = a \sin \theta, 0 \leq \theta \leq 2\pi, 0 \leq z \leq h\}$$

is a cylindrical surface of radius a and height h with its axis along the z-axis. Using the parameters $u = \theta$ and $v = z$, a parametric description of the cylinder is

$$\mathbf{r}(u, v) = \langle x(u, v), y(u, v), z(u, v) \rangle = \langle a \cos u, a \sin u, v \rangle,$$

where $0 \leq u \leq 2\pi$ and $0 \leq v \leq h$ (Figure 15.43).

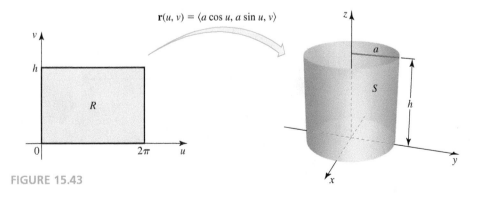

$\mathbf{r}(u, v) = \langle a \cos u, a \sin u, v \rangle$

FIGURE 15.43

QUICK CHECK 1 Describe the surface $\mathbf{r}(u, v) = \langle 2 \cos u, 2 \sin u, v \rangle$, for $0 \leq u \leq \pi$ and $0 \leq v \leq 1$. ◄

Cones   The surface of a cone of height h and radius a with its vertex at the origin is described in cylindrical coordinates by

$$\{(r, \theta, z): 0 \le r \le a, 0 \le \theta \le 2\pi, z = rh/a\}.$$

For a fixed value of z, we have $r = az/h$; therefore, on the surface of the cone

$$x = r \cos \theta = \frac{az}{h} \cos \theta \quad \text{and} \quad y = r \sin \theta = \frac{az}{h} \sin \theta.$$

> Note that when $r = 0, z = 0$ and when $r = a, z = h$.

Using the parameters $u = \theta$ and $v = z$, the parametric description of the conical surface is

$$\mathbf{r}(u, v) = \langle x(u, v), y(u, v), z(u, v) \rangle = \left\langle \frac{av}{h} \cos u, \frac{av}{h} \sin u, v \right\rangle,$$

> Recall the relationships among polar and rectangular coordinates:
>
> $x = r \cos \theta, y = r \sin \theta,$ and $x^2 + y^2 = r^2.$

where $0 \le u \le 2\pi$ and $0 \le v \le h$ (Figure 15.44).

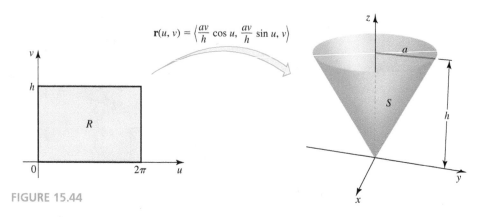

QUICK CHECK 2   Describe the surface $\mathbf{r}(u, v) = \langle v \cos u, v \sin u, v \rangle$, for $0 \le u \le \pi$ and $0 \le v \le 10.$ ◄

FIGURE 15.44

> The complete cylinder, cone, and sphere are generated as the angle variable θ varies over the half-open interval $[0, 2\pi)$. As in previous chapters, we will use the closed interval $[0, 2\pi]$.

Spheres   The parametric description of a sphere of radius a centered at the origin comes directly from spherical coordinates:

$$\{(\rho, \varphi, \theta): \rho = a, 0 \le \varphi \le \pi, 0 \le \theta \le 2\pi\}.$$

Recall the following relationships among spherical and rectangular coordinates (Section 14.5):

$$x = a \sin \varphi \cos \theta, \qquad y = a \sin \varphi \sin \theta, \qquad z = a \cos \varphi.$$

When we define the parameters $u = \varphi$ and $v = \theta$, a parametric description of the sphere is

$$\mathbf{r}(u, v) = \langle a \sin u \cos v, a \sin u \sin v, a \cos u \rangle,$$

where $0 \le u \le \pi$ and $0 \le v \le 2\pi$ (Figure 15.45).

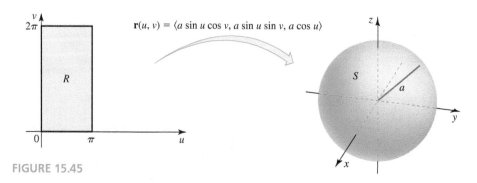

FIGURE 15.45

QUICK CHECK 3 Describe the surface $\mathbf{r}(u, v) = \langle 4 \sin u \cos v, 4 \sin u \sin v, 4 \cos u \rangle$, for $0 \leq u \leq \pi/2$ and $0 \leq v \leq \pi$.

EXAMPLE 1   **Parametric surfaces** Find parametric descriptions for the following surfaces.

a. The plane $3x - 2y + z = 2$
b. The paraboloid $z = x^2 + y^2$, for $0 \leq z \leq 9$

SOLUTION

a. Defining the parameters $u = x$ and $v = y$, we find that

$$z = 2 - 3x + 2y = 2 - 3u + 2v.$$

Therefore, a parametric description of the plane is

$$\mathbf{r}(u, v) = \langle u, v, 2 - 3u + 2v \rangle,$$

for $-\infty < u < \infty$ and $-\infty < v < \infty$.

b. Thinking in terms of polar coordinates, we let $u = \theta$ and $v = \sqrt{z}$, which means that $z = v^2$. The equation of the paraboloid is $x^2 + y^2 = z = v^2$, so v plays the role of the polar coordinate r. Therefore, $x = v \cos \theta$ and $y = v \sin \theta$. A parametric description for the paraboloid is

$$\mathbf{r}(u, v) = \langle v \cos u, v \sin u, v^2 \rangle,$$

where $0 \leq u \leq 2\pi$ and $0 \leq v \leq 3$.
Alternatively, we could choose $u = \theta$ and $v = z$. The resulting description is

$$\mathbf{r}(u, v) = \langle \sqrt{v} \cos u, \sqrt{v} \sin u, v \rangle,$$

where $0 \leq u \leq 2\pi$ and $0 \leq v \leq 9$.

Related Exercises 11–20◄

Surface Integrals of Scalar-Valued Functions

We now develop the surface integral of a scalar-valued function f defined on a smooth parameterized surface S described by the equation

$$\mathbf{r}(u, v) = \langle x(u, v), y(u, v), z(u, v) \rangle,$$

where the parameters vary over a rectangle $R = \{(u, v): a \leq u \leq b, c \leq v \leq d\}$. The functions x, y, and z are assumed to have continuous partial derivatives with respect to u and v. The rectangular region R in the uv-plane is partitioned into rectangles, with sides of length Δu and Δv, that are ordered in some convenient way, for $k = 1, \ldots, n$. The kth rectangle R_k, which has area $\Delta A = \Delta u \Delta v$, corresponds to a curved patch S_k on the surface S (Figure 15.46),

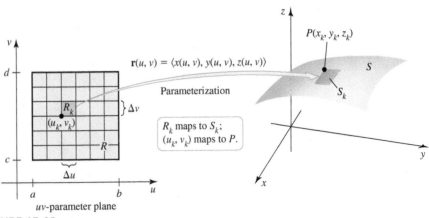

FIGURE 15.46

▶ A more general approach allows (u_k, v_k) to be an arbitrary point in the kth rectangle. The outcome of the two approaches is the same.

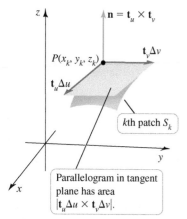

Parallelogram in tangent plane has area $|\mathbf{t}_u \Delta u \times \mathbf{t}_v \Delta v|$.

FIGURE 15.47

▶ In general, the vectors $\mathbf{t}_u$ and $\mathbf{t}_v$ are different for each patch, so they should carry a subscript k. To keep the notation as simple as possible, we have suppressed the subscripts on these vectors with the understanding that they change with k. These tangent vectors are given by partial derivatives because in each case, either u or v is held constant, while the other variable changes.

which has area ΔS_k. We let (u_k, v_k) be the lower-left corner point of R_k. The parameterization then assigns (u_k, v_k) to a point $P(x(u_k, v_k), y(u_k, v_k), z(u_k, v_k))$, or more simply, $P(x_k, y_k, z_k)$, on S_k. To construct the surface integral we define a Riemann sum, which adds up function values multiplied by areas of the respective patches:

$$\sum_{k=1}^{n} f(x(u_k, v_k), y(u_k, v_k), z(u_k, v_k)) \Delta S_k.$$

The crucial step is computing ΔS_k, the area of the kth patch S_k.

Figure 15.47 shows the patch S_k and the point $P(x_k, y_k, z_k)$. Two special vectors are tangent to the surface at P.

• $\mathbf{t}_u$ is a vector tangent to the surface corresponding to a change in u with v constant in the uv-plane.

• $\mathbf{t}_v$ is a vector tangent to the surface corresponding to a change in v with u constant in the uv-plane.

Because the surface S may be written $\mathbf{r}(u, v) = \langle x(u, v), y(u, v), z(u, v) \rangle$, a tangent vector corresponding to a change in u with v fixed is

$$\mathbf{t}_u = \frac{\partial \mathbf{r}}{\partial u} = \left\langle \frac{\partial x}{\partial u}, \frac{\partial y}{\partial u}, \frac{\partial z}{\partial u} \right\rangle.$$

Similarly, a tangent vector corresponding to a change in v with u fixed is

$$\mathbf{t}_v = \frac{\partial \mathbf{r}}{\partial v} = \left\langle \frac{\partial x}{\partial v}, \frac{\partial y}{\partial v}, \frac{\partial z}{\partial v} \right\rangle.$$

Now consider an increment Δu in u with v fixed. The tangent vector $\mathbf{t}_u \Delta u$ forms one side of a parallelogram (Figure 15.47). Similarly, with an increment Δv in v with u fixed, the tangent vector $\mathbf{t}_v \Delta v$ forms the other side of that parallelogram. The area of this parallelogram is an approximation to the area of the patch S_k, which is ΔS_k.

Appealing to the cross product (Section 12.4), the area of the parallelogram is

$$|\mathbf{t}_u \Delta u \times \mathbf{t}_v \Delta v| = |\mathbf{t}_u \times \mathbf{t}_v| \Delta u \, \Delta v \approx \Delta S_k.$$

Note that $\mathbf{t}_u \times \mathbf{t}_v$ is evaluated at (u_k, v_k) and is a vector normal to the surface at P, which we assume to be nonzero at all points of S.

We write the Riemann sum with the observation that the areas of the parallelograms approximate the areas of the patches S_k:

$$\sum_{k=1}^{n} f(x(u_k, v_k), y(u_k, v_k), z(u_k, v_k)) \Delta S_k$$

$$\approx \sum_{k=1}^{n} f(x(u_k, v_k), y(u_k, v_k), z(u_k, v_k)) \underbrace{|\mathbf{t}_u \times \mathbf{t}_v| \Delta u \, \Delta v}_{\approx \, \Delta S_k}.$$

▶ The factor $|\mathbf{t}_u \times \mathbf{t}_v| \, dA$ plays an analogous role in surface integrals as the factor $|\mathbf{r}'(t)| \, dt$ in line integrals.

We now assume that f is continuous on S. As Δu and Δv approach zero, the areas of the parallelograms approach the areas of the corresponding patches on S. In this limit, the Riemann sum approaches the surface integral of f over the surface S, which we write $\iint_S f(x, y, z) \, dS$:

$$\lim_{\Delta u, \, \Delta v \to 0} \sum_{k=1}^{n} f(x(u_k, v_k), y(u_k, v_k), z(u_k, v_k)) |\mathbf{t}_u \times \mathbf{t}_v| \Delta u \, \Delta v$$

$$= \iint_R f(x(u, v), y(u, v), z(u, v)) |\mathbf{t}_u \times \mathbf{t}_v| \, dA$$

$$= \iint_S f(x, y, z) \, dS.$$

The integral over S is evaluated as an ordinary double integral over the region R in the uv-plane. If R is a rectangular region, as we have assumed, the double integral becomes an iterated integral with respect to u and v with constant limits. In the special case that $f(x, y, z) = 1$, the integral gives the surface area of S.

> The condition that $\mathbf{t}_u \times \mathbf{t}_v$ be nonzero means $\mathbf{t}_u$ and $\mathbf{t}_v$ are nonzero and not parallel. If $\mathbf{t}_u \times \mathbf{t}_v \neq \mathbf{0}$ at all points, then the surface is *smooth*. The value of the integral is independent of the parameterization of S.

DEFINITION Surface Integral of Scalar-Valued Functions on Parameterized Surfaces

Let f be a continuous function on a smooth surface S given parametrically by $\mathbf{r}(u, v) = \langle x(u, v), y(u, v), z(u, v) \rangle$, where $R = \{(u, v): a \leq u \leq b, c \leq v \leq d\}$. Assume also that the tangent vectors $\mathbf{t}_u = \dfrac{\partial \mathbf{r}}{\partial u} = \left\langle \dfrac{\partial x}{\partial u}, \dfrac{\partial y}{\partial u}, \dfrac{\partial z}{\partial u} \right\rangle$ and $\mathbf{t}_v = \dfrac{\partial \mathbf{r}}{\partial v} = \left\langle \dfrac{\partial x}{\partial v}, \dfrac{\partial y}{\partial v}, \dfrac{\partial z}{\partial v} \right\rangle$ are continuous on R and the normal vector $\mathbf{n} = \mathbf{t}_u \times \mathbf{t}_v$ is nonzero on R. Then the **surface integral** of the scalar-valued function f over S is

$$\iint\limits_{S} f(x, y, z)\, dS = \iint\limits_{R} f(x(u, v), y(u, v), z(u, v)) |\mathbf{t}_u \times \mathbf{t}_v|\, dA.$$

If $f(x, y, z) = 1$, the integral equals the surface area of S.

EXAMPLE 2 Surface area of a cylinder and sphere Find the surface area of the following surfaces.

a. A cylinder with radius $a > 0$ and height h (excluding the circular ends)

b. A sphere of radius a

SOLUTION The critical step is evaluating the normal vector $\mathbf{t}_u \times \mathbf{t}_v$. It needs to be done only once for any given surface.

a. As shown before, a parametric description of the cylinder is

$$\mathbf{r}(u, v) = \langle x(u, v), y(u, v), z(u, v) \rangle = \langle a \cos u, a \sin u, v \rangle,$$

where $0 \leq u \leq 2\pi$ and $0 \leq v \leq h$. A normal vector is

$$\mathbf{n} = \mathbf{t}_u \times \mathbf{t}_v = \begin{vmatrix} \mathbf{i} & \mathbf{j} & \mathbf{k} \\ \frac{\partial x}{\partial u} & \frac{\partial y}{\partial u} & \frac{\partial z}{\partial u} \\ \frac{\partial x}{\partial v} & \frac{\partial y}{\partial v} & \frac{\partial z}{\partial v} \end{vmatrix} \qquad \text{Definition of cross product}$$

$$= \begin{vmatrix} \mathbf{i} & \mathbf{j} & \mathbf{k} \\ -a \sin u & a \cos u & 0 \\ 0 & 0 & 1 \end{vmatrix} \qquad \text{Evaluate the derivatives.}$$

$$= \langle a \cos u, a \sin u, 0 \rangle. \qquad \text{Compute the cross product.}$$

Notice that the normal vector points outward from the cylinder, away from the z-axis (Figure 15.48). It now follows that

$$|\mathbf{t}_u \times \mathbf{t}_v| = \sqrt{a^2 \cos^2 u + a^2 \sin^2 u} = a.$$

Setting $f(x, y, z) = 1$, the surface area of the cylinder is

$$\iint\limits_{S} 1\, dS = \iint\limits_{R} \underbrace{|\mathbf{t}_u \times \mathbf{t}_v|}_{a}\, dA = \int_{0}^{2\pi} \int_{0}^{h} a\, dv\, du = 2\pi a h,$$

confirming the formula for the surface area of a cylinder (excluding the ends).

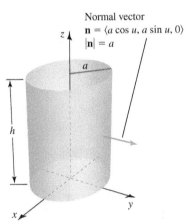

Normal vector
$\mathbf{n} = \langle a \cos u, a \sin u, 0 \rangle$
$|\mathbf{n}| = a$

Cylinder: $\mathbf{r}(u, v) = \langle a \cos u, a \sin u, v \rangle$,
$0 \leq u \leq 2\pi$ and $0 \leq v \leq h$

FIGURE 15.48

Recall that for the sphere, $u = \varphi$ and $v = \theta$, where φ and θ are spherical coordinates. The element of surface area in spherical coordinates is $dS = a^2 \sin \varphi \, d\varphi \, d\theta$.

Sphere:
$\mathbf{r}(u, v) = \langle a \sin u \cos v, a \sin u \sin v, a \cos u \rangle$,
$0 \le u \le \pi$ and $0 \le v \le 2\pi$

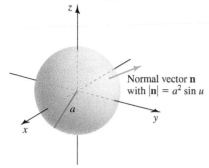

Normal vector $\mathbf{n}$ with $|\mathbf{n}| = a^2 \sin u$

FIGURE 15.49

b. A parametric description of the sphere is

$$\mathbf{r}(u, v) = \langle a \sin u \cos v, a \sin u \sin v, a \cos u \rangle,$$

where $0 \le u \le \pi$ and $0 \le v \le 2\pi$. A normal vector is

$$\mathbf{n} = \mathbf{t}_u \times \mathbf{t}_v = \begin{vmatrix} \mathbf{i} & \mathbf{j} & \mathbf{k} \\ a \cos u \cos v & a \cos u \sin v & -a \sin u \\ -a \sin u \sin v & a \sin u \cos v & 0 \end{vmatrix}$$
$$= \langle a^2 \sin^2 u \cos v, a^2 \sin^2 u \sin v, a^2 \sin u \cos u \rangle.$$

Computing $|\mathbf{t}_u \times \mathbf{t}_v|$ requires several steps (Exercise 70). However, the needed result is quite simple: $|\mathbf{t}_u \times \mathbf{t}_v| = a^2 \sin u$ and the normal vector $\mathbf{n} = \mathbf{t}_u \times \mathbf{t}_v$ points outward from the surface of the sphere (Figure 15.49). With $f(x, y, z) = 1$, the surface area of the sphere is

$$\iint_S 1 \, dS = \iint_R \underbrace{|\mathbf{t}_u \times \mathbf{t}_v|}_{a^2 \sin u} \, dA = \int_0^{2\pi} \int_0^{\pi} a^2 \sin u \, du \, dv = 4\pi a^2,$$

confirming the formula for the surface area of a sphere.

Related Exercises 21–26 ◄

EXAMPLE 3 Surface area of a partial cylinder Find the surface area of the cylinder $\{(r, \theta): r = 4, 0 \le \theta \le 2\pi\}$ between the planes $z = 0$ and $z = 16 - 2x$.

SOLUTION Figure 15.50 shows the cylinder bounded by the two planes. With $u = \theta$ and $v = z$, a parametric description of the cylinder is

$$\mathbf{r}(u, v) = \langle x(u, v), y(u, v), z(u, v) \rangle = \langle 4 \cos u, 4 \sin u, v \rangle.$$

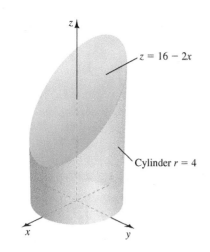

$z = 16 - 2x$

Cylinder $r = 4$

Sliced cylinder is generated by $\mathbf{r}(u, v) = \langle 4 \cos u, 4 \sin u, v \rangle$, where $0 \le u \le 2\pi, 0 \le v \le 16 - 8 \cos u$.

FIGURE 15.50

The challenge is finding the limits on v, which is the z-coordinate. The plane $z = 16 - 2x$ intersects the cylinder in an ellipse; along this ellipse, as u varies between 0 and 2π, the parameter v also changes. To find the relationship between u and v along this intersection curve, notice that at any point on the cylinder, we have $x = 4 \cos u$ (remember that $u = \theta$). Making this substitution in the equation of the plane, we have

$$z = 16 - 2x = 16 - 2(4 \cos u) = 16 - 8 \cos u.$$

Substituting $v = z$, the relationship between u and v is $v = 16 - 8 \cos u$ (Figure 15.51). Therefore, the region of integration in the uv-plane is

$$R = \{(u, v): 0 \le u \le 2\pi, 0 \le v \le 16 - 8 \cos u\}.$$

Recall from Example 2a that for the cylinder, $|\mathbf{t}_u \times \mathbf{t}_v| = a = 4$. Setting $f(x, y, z) = 1$, the surface integral for the area is

$$\iint_S 1 \, dS = \iint_R \underbrace{|\mathbf{t}_u \times \mathbf{t}_v|}_{4} \, dA$$

$$= \int_0^{2\pi} \int_0^{16-8\cos u} 4 \, dv \, du$$

$$= 4 \int_0^{2\pi} (16 - 8 \cos u) \, du \qquad \text{Evaluate the inner integral.}$$

$$= 4(16u - 8 \sin u) \Big|_0^{2\pi} \qquad \text{Evaluate the outer integral.}$$

$$= 128\pi. \qquad \text{Simplify.}$$

Related Exercises 21–26 ◄

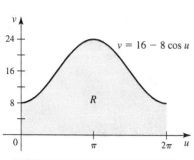

$v = 16 - 8 \cos u$

R

Region of integration in the uv-plane is $R = \{(u, v): 0 \le u \le 2\pi, 0 \le v \le 16 - 8 \cos u\}$.

FIGURE 15.51

EXAMPLE 4   **Average temperature on a sphere**   The temperature on the surface of a sphere of radius a varies with latitude according to the function $T(\varphi, \theta) = 10 + 50 \sin \varphi$, for $0 \le \varphi \le \pi$ and $0 \le \theta \le 2\pi$ (φ and θ are spherical coordinates, so the temperature is 10° at the poles, increasing to 60° at the equator). Find the average temperature over the sphere.

SOLUTION   We use the parametric description of a sphere. With $u = \varphi$ and $v = \theta$, the temperature function becomes $f(u, v) = 10 + 50 \sin u$. Integrating the temperature over the sphere using the fact that $|\mathbf{t}_u \times \mathbf{t}_v| = a^2 \sin u$ (Example 2b), we have

$$\iint_S (10 + 50 \sin u) \, dS = \iint_R (10 + 50 \sin u) \underbrace{|\mathbf{t}_u \times \mathbf{t}_v|}_{a^2 \sin u} \, dA$$

$$= \int_0^\pi \int_0^{2\pi} (10 + 50 \sin u) a^2 \sin u \, dv \, du$$

$$= 2\pi a^2 \int_0^\pi (10 + 50 \sin u) \sin u \, du \qquad \text{Evaluate the inner integral.}$$

$$= 10\pi a^2 (4 + 5\pi). \qquad \text{Evaluate the outer integral.}$$

The average temperature is the integrated temperature $10\pi a^2 (4 + 5\pi)$ divided by the surface area of the sphere $4\pi a^2$; so the average temperature is $(20 + 25\pi)/2 \approx 49.3°$. Notice that the equatorial region has both higher temperatures and greater surface area, so the average temperature is weighted toward the maximum temperature.

Related Exercises 27–30 ◄

Surface Integrals on Explicitly Defined Surfaces

Suppose a smooth surface S is defined not parametrically, but explicitly, in the form $z = g(x, y)$ over a region R in the xy-plane. Such a surface may be treated as a parameterized surface. We simply define the parameters to be $u = x$ and $v = y$. Making these substitutions into the expression for $\mathbf{t}_u$ and $\mathbf{t}_v$, a short calculation (Exercise 71) reveals that $\mathbf{t}_u = \langle 1, 0, z_x \rangle$, $\mathbf{t}_v = \langle 0, 1, z_y \rangle$, and a normal vector is a scalar multiple of

$$\mathbf{n} = \mathbf{t}_u \times \mathbf{t}_v = \langle -z_x, -z_y, 1 \rangle.$$

> This is a familiar result: A normal to the surface $z = g(x, y)$ at a point is a constant multiple of the gradient of $z - g(x, y)$, which is $\langle -g_x, -g_y, 1 \rangle = \langle -z_x, -z_y, 1 \rangle$. The factor $\sqrt{z_x^2 + z_y^2 + 1}$ is analogous to the factor $\sqrt{(f'(x))^2 + 1}$ that appears in arc length integrals.

It follows that

$$|\mathbf{t}_x \times \mathbf{t}_y| = |\langle -z_x, -z_y, 1 \rangle| = \sqrt{z_x^2 + z_y^2 + 1}.$$

With these observations, the surface integral over S can be expressed as a double integral over a region R in the xy-plane.

> If the surface S in Theorem 15.12 is generated by revolving a curve in the xy-plane about the x-axis, the theorem gives the surface area formula derived in Section 6.6 (Exercise 75).

THEOREM 15.12   Evaluation of Surface Integrals of Scalar-Valued Functions on Explicitly Defined Surfaces

Let f be a continuous function on a smooth surface S given by $z = g(x, y)$, for (x, y) in a region R. The surface integral of f over S is

$$\iint_S f(x, y, z) \, dS = \iint_R f(x, y, g(x, y)) \sqrt{z_x^2 + z_y^2 + 1} \, dA.$$

If $f(x, y, z) = 1$, the surface integral equals the area of the surface.

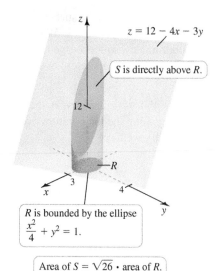

R is bounded by the ellipse $\frac{x^2}{4} + y^2 = 1$.

Area of $S = \sqrt{26} \cdot$ area of R.

FIGURE 15.52

EXAMPLE 5   **Area of a roof over an ellipse**   Find the area of the surface S that lies in the plane $z = 12 - 4x - 3y$ directly above the region R bounded by the ellipse $x^2/4 + y^2 = 1$ (Figure 15.52).

SOLUTION   Because we are computing the area of the surface, we take $f(x, y, z) = 1$. Note that $z_x = -4$ and $z_y = -3$, so the factor $\sqrt{z_x^2 + z_y^2 + 1}$ has the value $\sqrt{(-4)^2 + (-3)^2 + 1} = \sqrt{26}$ (a constant because the surface is a plane). The relevant surface integral is

$$\iint_S 1 \, dS = \iint_R \underbrace{\sqrt{z_x^2 + z_y^2 + 1}}_{\sqrt{26}} \, dA = \sqrt{26} \iint_R dA.$$

The double integral that remains is simply the area of the region R bounded by the ellipse. Because the ellipse has semiaxes of length $a = 2$ and $b = 1$, its area is $\pi ab = 2\pi$. Therefore, the area of S is $2\pi\sqrt{26}$.

This result has a useful interpretation. The plane surface S is not horizontal, so it has a greater area than the horizontal region R beneath it. The factor that converts the area of R to the area of S is $\sqrt{26}$. Notice that if the roof *were* horizontal, then the surface would be $z = c$, the area conversion factor would be 1, and the area of the roof would equal the area of the floor beneath it.

Related Exercises 31–34 ◄

QUICK CHECK 4   The plane $z = y$ forms a 45° angle with the xy-plane. Suppose the plane is the roof of a room and the xy-plane is the floor of the room. Then 1 ft^2 on the floor becomes how many square feet when projected on the roof? ◄

EXAMPLE 6   **Mass of a conical sheet**   A thin conical sheet is described by the surface $z = (x^2 + y^2)^{1/2}$, for $0 \le z \le 4$. The density of the sheet in g/cm^2 is $\rho = f(x, y, z) = (8 - z)$ (decreasing from 8 g/cm^2 at the tip to 4 g/cm^2 at the top; Figure 15.53). What is the mass of the cone?

SOLUTION   We find the mass by integrating the density function over the surface of the cone. The projection of the cone on the xy-plane is found by setting $z = 4$ (the top of the cone) in the equation of the cone. We find that $(x^2 + y^2)^{1/2} = 4$; therefore, the region of integration is the disk $R = \{(x, y): x^2 + y^2 \le 16\}$. We first find z_x and z_y in order to compute $\sqrt{z_x^2 + z_y^2 + 1}$. Differentiating $z^2 = x^2 + y^2$ implicitly gives $2zz_x = 2x$, or $z_x = x/z$. Similarly, $z_y = y/z$. Using the fact that $z^2 = x^2 + y^2$, we have

$$\sqrt{z_x^2 + z_y^2 + 1} = \sqrt{(x/z)^2 + (y/z)^2 + 1} = \sqrt{\underbrace{\frac{x^2 + y^2}{z^2} + 1}_{1}} = \sqrt{2}.$$

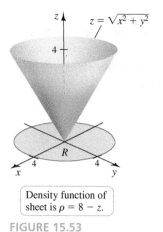

Density function of sheet is $\rho = 8 - z$.

FIGURE 15.53

To integrate the density over the conical surface, we set $f(x, y, z) = 8 - z$. Replacing z in the integrand by $r = (x^2 + y^2)^{1/2}$ and using polar coordinates, the mass in grams is given by

$$\iint_S f(x, y, z) \, dS = \iint_R f(x, y, z) \underbrace{\sqrt{z_x^2 + z_y^2 + 1}}_{\sqrt{2}} \, dA$$

$$= \sqrt{2} \iint_R (8 - z) \, dA \qquad \text{Substitute.}$$

$$= \sqrt{2} \iint_R (8 - \sqrt{x^2 + y^2}) \, dA \qquad z = \sqrt{x^2 + y^2}$$

$$= \sqrt{2} \int_0^{2\pi} \int_0^4 (8 - r)\, r\, dr\, d\theta \qquad \text{Polar coordinates}$$

$$= \sqrt{2} \int_0^{2\pi} \left(4r^2 - \frac{r^3}{3}\right)\bigg|_0^4 d\theta \qquad \text{Evaluate the inner integral.}$$

$$= \frac{128\sqrt{2}}{3} \int_0^{2\pi} d\theta \qquad \text{Simplify.}$$

$$= \frac{256\pi\sqrt{2}}{3} \approx 379. \qquad \text{Evaluate the outer integral.}$$

As a check, note that the surface area of the cone is $\pi r \sqrt{r^2 + h^2} \approx 71 \text{ cm}^2$. If the entire cone had the maximum density $\rho = 8 \text{ g/cm}^2$, its mass would be approximately 568 g. If the entire cone had the minimum density $\rho = 4 \text{ g/cm}^2$, its mass would be approximately 284 g. The actual mass is between these extremes and closer to the low value because the cone is lighter at the top, where the surface area is greater.

Related Exercises 35–42◄

Table 15.2 summarizes the essential relationships for the explicit and parametric descriptions of cylinders, cones, spheres, and paraboloids. The listed normal vectors are chosen to point away from the z-axis.

Table 15.2

Surface	Explicit Description $z = g(x,y)$		Parametric Description	
	Equation	Normal $\mathbf{n} = \pm\langle -z_x, -z_y, 1\rangle$	Equation	Normal $\mathbf{n} = \mathbf{t}_u \times \mathbf{t}_v$
Cylinder	$x^2 + y^2 = a^2,$ $0 \le z \le h$	$\mathbf{n} = \langle x, y, 0\rangle, \ |\mathbf{n}| = a$	$\mathbf{r} = \langle a\cos u, a\sin u, v\rangle,$ $0 \le u \le 2\pi, 0 \le v \le h$	$\mathbf{n} = \langle a\cos u, a\sin u, 0\rangle, \ |\mathbf{n}| = a$
Cone	$z^2 = x^2 + y^2,$ $0 \le z \le h$	$\mathbf{n} = \langle x/z, y/z, -1\rangle,$ $|\mathbf{n}| = \sqrt{2}$	$\mathbf{r} = \langle v\cos u, v\sin u, v\rangle,$ $0 \le u \le 2\pi, 0 \le v \le h$	$\mathbf{n} = \langle v\cos u, v\sin u, -v\rangle,$ $|\mathbf{n}| = \sqrt{2}v$
Sphere	$x^2 + y^2 + z^2 = a^2$	$\mathbf{n} = \langle x/z, y/z, 1\rangle,$ $|\mathbf{n}| = a/z$	$\mathbf{r} = \langle a\sin u\cos v,$ $a\sin u\sin v, a\cos u\rangle,$ $0 \le u \le \pi, 0 \le v \le 2\pi$	$\mathbf{n} = \langle a^2\sin^2 u\cos v, a^2\sin^2 u\sin v,$ $a^2\sin u\cos u\rangle, \ |\mathbf{n}| = a^2\sin u$
Paraboloid	$z = x^2 + y^2,$ $0 \le z \le h$	$\mathbf{n} = \langle 2x, 2y, -1\rangle,$ $|\mathbf{n}| = \sqrt{1 + 4(x^2 + y^2)}$	$\mathbf{r} = \langle v\cos u, v\sin u, v^2\rangle,$ $0 \le u \le 2\pi, 0 \le v \le \sqrt{h}$	$\mathbf{n} = \langle 2v^2\cos u, 2v^2\sin u, -v\rangle,$ $|\mathbf{n}| = v\sqrt{1 + 4v^2}$

QUICK CHECK 5 Explain why the explicit description for a cylinder $x^2 + y^2 = a^2$ cannot be used for a surface integral over a cylinder and a parametric description must be used. ◄

Surface Integrals of Vector Fields

Before beginning a discussion of surface integrals of vector fields, two technical issues about surfaces and normal vectors must be addressed.

The surfaces we consider in this book are called **two-sided**, or **orientable**, surfaces. To be orientable, a surface must have the property that the normal vectors vary continuously over the surface. In other words, when you walk on any closed path on an orientable surface and return to your starting point, your head must point in the same direction it did when you started. The most famous example of a *nonorientable* surface is the Möbius strip (Figure 15.54). Suppose you start walking the length of the Möbius strip at a point P with your head pointing upward. When you return to P, your head points in the opposite direction, or downward. Therefore, the Möbius strip is not orientable.

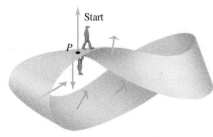

FIGURE 15.54

Closed surfaces are oriented so normal vectors point in the outward direction.

For other surfaces, the orientation of the surface must be specified.

FIGURE 15.55

At any point of a parameterized orientable surface, there are two unit normal vectors. Therefore, the second point concerns the orientation of the surface or, equivalently, the choice of the direction of the normal vectors. Once the orientation is determined, the surface becomes **oriented**.

We make the common assumption that—unless specified otherwise—a closed orientable surface that fully encloses a region (such as a sphere) is oriented so that the normal vectors point in the *outward direction*. For a surface that is not closed, the orientation must be specified in some way. For example, we might specify that the normal vectors for a particular surface point in the positive z-direction (Figure 15.55).

Now recall that the parameterization of a surface defines a normal vector $\mathbf{t}_u \times \mathbf{t}_v$ at each point. In many cases, the normal vectors are consistent with the specified orientation, in which case no adjustments need to be made. If the direction of $\mathbf{t}_u \times \mathbf{t}_v$ is not consistent with the specified orientation, then the sign of $\mathbf{t}_u \times \mathbf{t}_v$ must be reversed before doing calculations. This process is demonstrated in the following examples.

Flux Integrals   It turns out that the most common surface integral of a vector field is a *flux integral*. Consider a vector field $\mathbf{F} = \langle f, g, h \rangle$, continuous on a region in $\mathbb{R}^3$, that represents the flow of a fluid or the transport of a substance. Given a smooth oriented surface S, we aim to compute the net flux of the vector field across the surface. In a small region containing a point P, the flux across the surface is proportional to the component of $\mathbf{F}$ in the direction of the unit normal vector $\mathbf{n}$ at P. If θ is the angle between $\mathbf{F}$ and $\mathbf{n}$, then this component is $\mathbf{F} \cdot \mathbf{n} = |\mathbf{F}| |\mathbf{n}| \cos \theta = |\mathbf{F}| \cos \theta$ (because $|\mathbf{n}| = 1$; Figure 15.56a). We have the following special cases.

- If $\mathbf{F}$ and the unit normal vector are aligned at P ($\theta = 0$), then the component of $\mathbf{F}$ in the direction $\mathbf{n}$ is $\mathbf{F} \cdot \mathbf{n} = |\mathbf{F}|$; that is, all of $\mathbf{F}$ flows across the surface in the direction of $\mathbf{n}$ (Figure 15.56b).

- If $\mathbf{F}$ and the unit normal vector point in opposite directions at P ($\theta = \pi$), then the component of $\mathbf{F}$ in the direction $\mathbf{n}$ is $\mathbf{F} \cdot \mathbf{n} = -|\mathbf{F}|$; that is, all of $\mathbf{F}$ flows across the surface in the direction opposite to that of $\mathbf{n}$ (Figure 15.56c).

- If $\mathbf{F}$ and the unit normal vector are orthogonal at P ($\theta = \pi/2$), then the component of $\mathbf{F}$ in the direction $\mathbf{n}$ is $\mathbf{F} \cdot \mathbf{n} = 0$; that is, none of $\mathbf{F}$ flows across the surface at that point (Figure 15.56d).

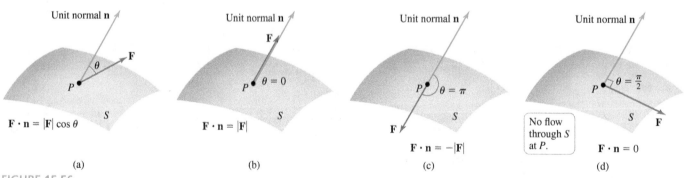

FIGURE 15.56

The flux integral, denoted $\iint_S \mathbf{F} \cdot \mathbf{n} \, dS$ or $\iint_S \mathbf{F} \cdot d\mathbf{S}$, simply adds up the components of $\mathbf{F}$ normal to the surface at all points of the surface. Notice that $\mathbf{F} \cdot \mathbf{n}$ is a scalar-valued function. Here is how the flux integral is computed.

Suppose the smooth oriented surface S is parameterized in the form

$$\mathbf{r}(u, v) = \langle x(u, v), y(u, v), z(u, v) \rangle,$$

> If $\mathbf{t}_u \times \mathbf{t}_v$ is not consistent with the specified orientation, its sign must be reversed.

where u and v vary over a region R in the uv-plane. A normal to the surface at a point is $\mathbf{t}_u \times \mathbf{t}_v$, which we assume to be consistent with the orientation of S. Therefore, the *unit* normal vector consistent with the orientation is $\mathbf{n} = \dfrac{\mathbf{t}_u \times \mathbf{t}_v}{|\mathbf{t}_u \times \mathbf{t}_v|}$. Appealing to the definition of the surface integral for parameterized surfaces, the flux integral is

$$\iint_S \mathbf{F} \cdot \mathbf{n}\, dS = \iint_R \mathbf{F} \cdot \mathbf{n}|\mathbf{t}_u \times \mathbf{t}_v|\, dA \qquad \text{Definition of surface integral}$$

$$= \iint_R \mathbf{F} \cdot \underbrace{\frac{\mathbf{t}_u \times \mathbf{t}_v}{|\mathbf{t}_u \times \mathbf{t}_v|}}_{\mathbf{n}}|\mathbf{t}_u \times \mathbf{t}_v|\, dA \qquad \text{Substitute for } \mathbf{n}.$$

$$= \iint_R \mathbf{F} \cdot (\mathbf{t}_u \times \mathbf{t}_v)\, dA. \qquad \text{Convenient cancellation}$$

The remarkable occurrence in the flux integral is the cancellation of the factor $|\mathbf{t}_u \times \mathbf{t}_v|$. The flux integral turns out to be a double integral with respect to u and v.

The special case in which the surface S is specified in the form $z = g(x, y)$ follows directly by recalling that a vector normal to the surface is $\mathbf{t}_u \times \mathbf{t}_v = \langle -z_x, -z_y, 1 \rangle$. In this case, with $\mathbf{F} = \langle f, g, h \rangle$, the integrand of the surface integral is $\mathbf{F} \cdot (\mathbf{t}_u \times \mathbf{t}_v) = -fz_x - gz_y + h$.

> The value of the surface integral is independent of the parameterization. However, in contrast to a surface integral of a scalar-valued function, the value of a surface integral of a vector field depends on the orientation of the surface. Changing the orientation changes the sign of the result.

DEFINITION Surface Integral of a Vector Field

Suppose $\mathbf{F} = \langle f, g, h \rangle$ is a continuous vector field on a region of $\mathbb{R}^3$ containing a smooth oriented surface S. If S is defined parametrically as $\mathbf{r}(u, v) = \langle x(u, v), y(u, v), z(u, v) \rangle$, for (u, v) in a region R, then

$$\iint_S \mathbf{F} \cdot \mathbf{n}\, dS = \iint_R \mathbf{F} \cdot (\mathbf{t}_u \times \mathbf{t}_v)\, dA,$$

where $\mathbf{t}_u = \dfrac{\partial \mathbf{r}}{\partial u} = \left\langle \dfrac{\partial x}{\partial u}, \dfrac{\partial y}{\partial u}, \dfrac{\partial z}{\partial u} \right\rangle$ and $\mathbf{t}_v = \dfrac{\partial \mathbf{r}}{\partial v} = \left\langle \dfrac{\partial x}{\partial v}, \dfrac{\partial y}{\partial v}, \dfrac{\partial z}{\partial v} \right\rangle$ are continuous on R, the normal vector $\mathbf{n} = \mathbf{t}_u \times \mathbf{t}_v$ is nonzero on R, and the direction of $\mathbf{n}$ is consistent with the orientation of S. If S is defined in the form $z = g(x, y)$, for (x, y) in a region R, then

$$\iint_S \mathbf{F} \cdot \mathbf{n}\, dS = \iint_R (-fz_x - gz_y + h)\, dA.$$

EXAMPLE 7 Rain on a roof Consider the vertical vector field $\mathbf{F} = \langle 0, 0, -1 \rangle$, corresponding to a constant downward flow. Find the flux in the downward (negative z) direction across the surface S, which is the plane $z = 4 - 2x - y$ in the first octant.

SOLUTION In this case, the surface is given explicitly. With $z = 4 - 2x - y$, we have $z_x = -2$ and $z_y = -1$. Therefore, a vector normal to the plane is $\langle -z_x, -z_y, 1 \rangle = \langle 2, 1, 1 \rangle$, which points *upward* (Figure 15.57). Because we are interested in the *downward* flux of $\mathbf{F}$ across S, the surface must be oriented so the normal vectors point in the negative z-direction. So, we take the normal vector to be $\mathbf{n} = \langle -2, -1, -1 \rangle$. Noting that $\mathbf{F} = \langle f, g, h \rangle = \langle 0, 0, -1 \rangle$, the flux integral is

$$\iint_S \mathbf{F} \cdot \mathbf{n}\, dS = \iint_R \langle 0, 0, -1 \rangle \cdot \langle -2, -1, -1 \rangle\, dA = \iint_R dA = \text{area}(R).$$

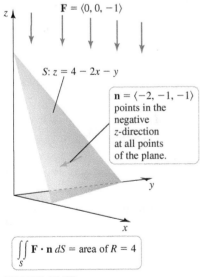

$\mathbf{F} = \langle 0, 0, -1 \rangle$

$S: z = 4 - 2x - y$

$\mathbf{n} = \langle -2, -1, -1 \rangle$ points in the negative z-direction at all points of the plane.

$\iint_S \mathbf{F} \cdot \mathbf{n}\, dS = \text{area of } R = 4$

FIGURE 15.57

The base R is a triangle in the xy-plane with vertices $(0, 0)$, $(2, 0)$, and $(0, 4)$, so its area is 4. Therefore, the *downward* flux across S is 4.

This flux integral has an interesting interpretation. If the vector field $\mathbf{F}$ represents the rate of rainfall with units of, say, g/m^2 per unit time, then the flux integral gives the mass of rain (in grams) that falls on the surface in a unit of time. This result says that (because the vector field is vertical) the mass of rain that falls on the roof equals the mass that would fall on the floor beneath the roof if the roof were not there. This property is explored further in Exercise 73.

Related Exercises 43–48 ◄

EXAMPLE 8   Flux of the radial field   Consider the radial vector field
$\mathbf{F} = \langle f, g, h \rangle = \langle x, y, z \rangle$. Is the *upward* flux of the field greater across the hemisphere $x^2 + y^2 + z^2 = 1$, for $z \geq 0$, or across the paraboloid $z = 1 - x^2 - y^2$, for $z \geq 0$? Note that the two surfaces have the same base in the xy-plane and the same high point $(0, 0, 1)$. Use the explicit description for the hemisphere and a parametric description for the paraboloid.

SOLUTION   The base of both surfaces in the xy-plane is the unit disk
$R = \{ (x, y) : x^2 + y^2 \leq 1 \} = \{ (r, \theta) : 0 \leq r \leq 1, 0 \leq \theta \leq 2\pi \}$. To use the explicit description for the hemisphere, we must compute z_x and z_y. Differentiating $x^2 + y^2 + z^2 = 1$ implicitly, we find that $z_x = -x/z$ and $z_y = -y/z$. Therefore, a normal vector is $\langle x/z, y/z, 1 \rangle$, which points *upward* on the surface. The flux integral is evaluated by substituting for f, g, h, z_x, and z_y; eliminating z from the integrand; and converting the integral in x and y to an integral in polar coordinates:

> Recall that a normal vector for an explicitly defined surface $z = g(x, y)$ is $\langle -z_x, -z_y, 1 \rangle$.

$$
\iint\limits_{S} \mathbf{F} \cdot \mathbf{n} \, dS = \iint\limits_{R} (-f z_x - g z_y + h) \, dA
$$

$$
= \iint\limits_{R} \left(x \frac{x}{z} + y \frac{y}{z} + z \right) dA \qquad \text{Substitute.}
$$

$$
= \iint\limits_{R} \left(\frac{x^2 + y^2 + z^2}{z} \right) dA \qquad \text{Simplify.}
$$

$$
= \iint\limits_{R} \left(\frac{1}{z} \right) dA \qquad x^2 + y^2 + z^2 = 1
$$

$$
= \iint\limits_{R} \left(\frac{1}{\sqrt{1 - x^2 - y^2}} \right) dA \qquad z = \sqrt{1 - x^2 - y^2}
$$

$$
= \int_{0}^{2\pi} \int_{0}^{1} \left(\frac{1}{\sqrt{1 - r^2}} \right) r \, dr \, d\theta \qquad \text{Polar coordinates}
$$

$$
= \int_{0}^{2\pi} \left. (-\sqrt{1 - r^2}) \right|_{0}^{1} d\theta \qquad \begin{array}{l} \text{Evaluate the inner integral} \\ \text{as an improper integral.} \end{array}
$$

$$
= \int_{0}^{2\pi} d\theta = 2\pi. \qquad \text{Evaluate the outer integral.}
$$

For the paraboloid $z = 1 - x^2 - y^2$, we use the parametric description (Example 1b or Table 15.2)

$$
\mathbf{r}(u, v) = \langle x, y, z \rangle = \langle v \cos u, v \sin u, 1 - v^2 \rangle,
$$

for $0 \leq u \leq 2\pi$ and $0 \leq v \leq 1$. A vector normal to the surface is

$$\mathbf{t}_u \times \mathbf{t}_v = \begin{vmatrix} \mathbf{i} & \mathbf{j} & \mathbf{k} \\ -v \sin u & v \cos u & 0 \\ \cos u & \sin u & -2v \end{vmatrix}$$

$$= \langle -2v^2 \cos u, -2v^2 \sin u, -v \rangle.$$

Notice that the normal vectors point *downward* on the surface (because the z-component is negative for $0 \le v \le 1$). In order to find the *upward* flux, we negate the normal vector and use the *upward* normal vector

$$\mathbf{n} = -(\mathbf{t}_u \times \mathbf{t}_v) = \langle 2v^2 \cos u, 2v^2 \sin u, v \rangle.$$

The flux integral is evaluated by substituting for $\mathbf{F} = \langle x, y, z \rangle$ and $\mathbf{n}$, and then evaluating an iterated integral in u and v:

$$\iint\limits_S \mathbf{F} \cdot \mathbf{n} \, dS = \int_0^1 \int_0^{2\pi} \langle v \cos u, v \sin u, 1 - v^2 \rangle \cdot \langle 2v^2 \cos u, 2v^2 \sin u, v \rangle \, du \, dv$$

Substitute for **F** and **n**.

$$= \int_0^1 \int_0^{2\pi} (v^3 + v) \, du \, dv \quad \text{Simplify.}$$

$$= 2\pi \left(\frac{v^4}{4} + \frac{v^2}{2} \right) \Big|_0^1 = \frac{3\pi}{2}. \quad \text{Evaluate integrals.}$$

QUICK CHECK 6 Explain why the upward flux for the radial field in Example 8 is greater for the hemisphere than for the paraboloid. ◄

We see that the upward flux is greater for the hemisphere than for the paraboloid.

Related Exercises 43–48 ◄

SECTION 15.6 EXERCISES

Review Questions

1. Give a parametric description for a cylinder with radius a and height h, including the intervals for the parameters.

2. Give a parametric description for a cone with radius a and height h, including the intervals for the parameters.

3. Give a parametric description for a sphere with radius a, including the intervals for the parameters.

4. Explain how to compute the surface integral of a scalar-valued function f over a cone using an explicit description of the cone.

5. Explain how to compute the surface integral of a scalar-valued function f over a sphere using a parametric description of the sphere.

6. Explain how to compute a surface integral $\iint_S \mathbf{F} \cdot \mathbf{n} \, dS$ over a cone using an explicit description and a given orientation of the cone.

7. Explain how to compute a surface integral $\iint_S \mathbf{F} \cdot \mathbf{n} \, dS$ over a sphere using a parametric description of the sphere and a given orientation.

8. Explain what it means for a surface to be orientable.

9. Describe the usual orientation of a closed surface such as a sphere.

10. Why is the upward flux of a vertical vector field $\mathbf{F} = \langle 0, 0, 1 \rangle$ across a surface equal to the area of the projection of the surface in the xy-plane?

Basic Skills

11–16. Parametric descriptions *Give a parametric description of the form* $\mathbf{r}(u, v) = \langle x(u, v), y(u, v), z(u, v) \rangle$ *for the following surfaces. The descriptions are not unique.*

11. The plane $2x - 4y + 3z = 16$

12. The cap of the sphere $x^2 + y^2 + z^2 = 16$, for $4/\sqrt{2} \le z \le 4$

13. The frustum of the cone $z^2 = x^2 + y^2$, for $2 \le z \le 8$

14. The cone $z^2 = 4(x^2 + y^2)$, for $0 \le z \le 4$

15. The portion of the cylinder $x^2 + y^2 = 9$ in the first octant, for $0 \le z \le 3$

16. The cylinder $y^2 + z^2 = 36$, for $0 \le x \le 9$

17–20. Identify the surface *Describe the surface with the given parametric representation.*

17. $\mathbf{r}(u, v) = \langle u, v, 2u + 3v - 1 \rangle$, for $1 \le u \le 3, 2 \le v \le 4$

18. $\mathbf{r}(u, v) = \langle u, u + v, 2 - u - v \rangle$, for $0 \le u \le 2, 0 \le v \le 2$

19. $\mathbf{r}(u, v) = \langle v \cos u, v \sin u, 4v \rangle$, for $0 \le u \le \pi, 0 \le v \le 3$

20. $\mathbf{r}(u, v) = \langle v, 6 \cos u, 6 \sin u \rangle$, for $0 \le u \le 2\pi, 0 \le v \le 2$

21–26. Surface area using a parametric description *Find the area of the following surfaces using a parametric description of the surface.*

21. The half-cylinder $\{(r, \theta, z): r = 4, 0 \le \theta \le \pi, 0 \le z \le 7\}$

22. The plane $z = 3 - x - 3y$ in the first octant

23. The plane $z = 10 - x - y$ above the square $|x| \le 2, |y| \le 2$

24. The hemisphere $x^2 + y^2 + z^2 = 100$, for $z \ge 0$

25. A cone with base radius r and height h, where r and h are positive constants

26. The cap of the sphere $x^2 + y^2 + z^2 = 4$, for $1 \le z \le 2$

27–30. Surface integrals using a parametric description *Evaluate the surface integral $\iint_S f(x, y, z)\, dS$ using a parametric description of the surface.*

27. $f(x, y, z) = x^2 + y^2$, where S is the hemisphere $x^2 + y^2 + z^2 = 36$, for $z \ge 0$

28. $f(x, y, z) = y$, where S is the cylinder $x^2 + y^2 = 9, 0 \le z \le 3$

29. $f(x, y, z) = x$, where S is the cylinder $x^2 + z^2 = 1, 0 \le y \le 3$

30. $f(\rho, \varphi, \theta) = \cos \varphi$, where S is the part of the unit sphere in the first octant

31–34. Surface area using an explicit description *Find the area of the following surfaces using an explicit description of the surface.*

31. The cone $z^2 = 4(x^2 + y^2)$, for $0 \le z \le 4$

32. The paraboloid $z = 2(x^2 + y^2)$, for $0 \le z \le 8$

33. The trough $z = x^2$, for $-2 \le x \le 2, 0 \le y \le 4$

34. The part of the hyperbolic paraboloid $z = x^2 - y^2$ above the sector $R = \{(r, \theta): 0 \le r \le 4, -\pi/4 \le \theta \le \pi/4\}$

35–38. Surface integrals using an explicit description *Evaluate the surface integral $\iint_S f(x, y, z)\, dS$ using an explicit representation of the surface.*

35. $f(x, y, z) = xy$; S is the plane $z = 2 - x - y$ in the first octant.

36. $f(x, y, z) = x^2 + y^2$; S is the paraboloid $z = x^2 + y^2$, for $0 \le z \le 4$.

37. $f(x, y, z) = 25 - x^2 - y^2$; S is the hemisphere centered at the origin with radius 5, for $z \ge 0$.

38. $f(x, y, z) = e^z$; S is the plane $z = 8 - x - 2y$ in the first octant.

39–42. Average values

39. Find the average temperature on that part of the plane $3x + 4y + z = 6$ over the square $|x| \le 1, |y| \le 1$, where the temperature is given by $T(x, y, z) = e^{-z}$.

40. Find the average squared distance between the origin and the points on the paraboloid $z = 4 - x^2 - y^2$, for $z \ge 0$.

41. Find the average value of the function $f(x, y, z) = xyz$ on the unit sphere in the first octant.

42. Find the average value of the temperature function $T(x, y, z) = 100 - 25z$ on the cone $z^2 = x^2 + y^2$, for $0 \le z \le 2$.

43–48. Surface integrals of vector fields *Find the flux of the following vector fields across the given surface with the specified orientation. You may use either an explicit or parametric description of the surface.*

43. $\mathbf{F} = \langle 0, 0, -1 \rangle$ across the slanted face of the tetrahedron $z = 4 - x - y$ in the first octant; normal vectors point in the positive z-direction.

44. $\mathbf{F} = \langle x, y, z \rangle$ across the slanted face of the tetrahedron $z = 10 - 2x - 5y$ in the first octant; normal vectors point in the positive z-direction.

45. $\mathbf{F} = \langle x, y, z \rangle$ across the slanted surface of the cone $z^2 = x^2 + y^2$, for $0 \le z \le 1$; normal vectors point in the positive z-direction.

46. $\mathbf{F} = \langle e^{-y}, 2z, xy \rangle$ across the curved sides of the surface $S = \{(x, y, z): z = \cos y, |y| \le \pi, 0 \le x \le 4\}$, where normal vectors point upward.

47. $\mathbf{F} = \mathbf{r}/|\mathbf{r}|^3$ across the sphere of radius a centered at the origin, where $\mathbf{r} = \langle x, y, z \rangle$; the normal vectors point outward.

48. $\mathbf{F} = \langle -y, x, 1 \rangle$ across the cylinder $y = x^2$, for $0 \le x \le 1$, $0 \le z \le 4$; normal vectors point in the positive y-direction.

Further Explorations

49. Explain why or why not Determine whether the following statements are true and give an explanation or counterexample.

    a. If the surface S is given by $\{(x, y, z): 0 \le x \le 1, 0 \le y \le 1, z = 10\}$, then $\iint_S f(x, y, z)\, dS = \int_0^1 \int_0^1 f(x, y, 10)\, dx\, dy$.

    b. If the surface S is given by $\{(x, y, z): 0 \le x \le 1, 0 \le y \le 1, z = x\}$, then $\iint_S f(x, y, z)\, dS = \int_0^1 \int_0^1 f(x, y, x)\, dx\, dy$.

    c. The surface $\mathbf{r} = \langle v \cos u, v \sin u, v^2 \rangle$, for $0 \le u \le \pi$, $0 \le v \le 2$, is the same as the surface $\mathbf{r} = \langle \sqrt{v} \cos 2u, \sqrt{v} \sin 2u, v \rangle$, for $0 \le u \le \pi/2, 0 \le v \le 4$.

    d. Given the standard parameterization of a sphere, the normal vectors $\mathbf{t}_u \times \mathbf{t}_v$ are outward normal vectors.

50–53. Miscellaneous surface integrals *Evaluate the following integrals using the method of your choice. Assume normal vectors point either outward or in the positive z-direction.*

50. $\iint_S \nabla \ln |\mathbf{r}| \cdot \mathbf{n}\, dS$, where S is the hemisphere $x^2 + y^2 + z^2 = a^2$, for $z \ge 0$, and where $\mathbf{r} = \langle x, y, z \rangle$

51. $\iint_S |\mathbf{r}|\, dS$, where S is the cylinder $x^2 + y^2 = 4$, for $0 \le z \le 8$, and where $\mathbf{r} = \langle x, y, z \rangle$

52. $\iint_S xyz\, dS$, where S is that part of the plane $z = 6 - y$ that lies in the cylinder $x^2 + y^2 = 4$

53. $\displaystyle \iint_S \frac{\langle x, 0, z \rangle}{\sqrt{x^2 + z^2}} \cdot \mathbf{n}\, dS$, where S is the cylinder $x^2 + z^2 = a^2$, $|y| \le 2$

54. Cone and sphere The cone $z^2 = x^2 + y^2$, for $z \ge 0$, cuts the sphere $x^2 + y^2 + z^2 = 16$ along a curve C.

    a. Find the surface area of the sphere below C, for $z \ge 0$.
    b. Find the surface area of the sphere above C.
    c. Find the surface area of the cone below C, for $z \ge 0$.

55. Cylinder and sphere Consider the sphere $x^2 + y^2 + z^2 = 4$ and the cylinder $(x - 1)^2 + y^2 = 1$, for $z \ge 0$.

    a. Find the surface area of the cylinder inside the sphere.
    b. Find the surface area of the sphere inside the cylinder.

56. Flux on a tetrahedron Find the upward flux of the field $\mathbf{F} = \langle x, y, z \rangle$ across the plane $x/a + y/b + z/c = 1$ in the first octant. Show that the flux equals c times the area of the base of the region. Interpret the result physically.

57. Flux across a cone Consider the field $\mathbf{F} = \langle x, y, z \rangle$ and the cone $z^2 = (x^2 + y^2)/a^2$, for $0 \le z \le 1$.

   a. Show that when $a = 1$, the outward flux across the cone is zero. Interpret the result.

   b. Find the outward flux (away from the z-axis), for any $a > 0$. Interpret the result.

58. Surface area formula for cones Find the general formula for the surface area of a cone with height h and base radius a (excluding the base).

59. Surface area formula for spherical cap A sphere of radius a is sliced parallel to the equatorial plane at a distance $a - h$ from the equatorial plane (see figure). Find the general formula for the surface area of the resulting spherical cap (excluding the base) with thickness h.

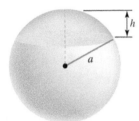

60. Radial fields and spheres Consider the radial field $\mathbf{F} = \mathbf{r}/|\mathbf{r}|^p$, where $\mathbf{r} = \langle x, y, z \rangle$ and p is a real number. Let S be the sphere of radius a centered at the origin. Show that the outward flux of $\mathbf{F}$ across the sphere is $4\pi/a^{p-3}$. It is instructive to do the calculation using both an explicit and parametric description of the sphere.

Applications

61–63. Heat flux *The heat flow vector field for conducting objects is $\mathbf{F} = -k\nabla T$, where $T(x, y, z)$ is the temperature in the object and $k > 0$ is a constant that depends on the material. Compute the outward flux of $\mathbf{F}$ across the following surfaces S for the given temperature distributions. Assume $k = 1$.*

61. $T(x, y, z) = 100e^{-x-y}$; S consists of the faces of the cube $|x| \le 1, |y| \le 1, |z| \le 1$.

62. $T(x, y, z) = 100e^{-x^2-y^2-z^2}$; S is the sphere $x^2 + y^2 + z^2 = a^2$.

63. $T(x, y, z) = -\ln(x^2 + y^2 + z^2)$; S is the sphere $x^2 + y^2 + z^2 = a^2$.

64. Flux across a cylinder Let S be the cylinder $x^2 + y^2 = a^2$, for $-L \le z \le L$.

   a. Find the outward flux of the field $\mathbf{F} = \langle x, y, 0 \rangle$ across S.

   b. Find the outward flux of the field $\mathbf{F} = \dfrac{\langle x, y, 0 \rangle}{(x^2 + y^2)^{p/2}} = \dfrac{\mathbf{r}}{|\mathbf{r}|^p}$ across S, where $|\mathbf{r}|$ is the distance from the z-axis and p is a real number.

   c. In part (b), for what values of p is the outward flux finite as $a \to \infty$ (with L fixed)?

d. In part (b), for what values of p is the outward flux finite as $L \to \infty$ (with a fixed)?

65. Flux across concentric spheres Consider the radial fields
$$\mathbf{F} = \frac{\langle x, y, z \rangle}{(x^2 + y^2 + z^2)^{p/2}} = \frac{\mathbf{r}}{|\mathbf{r}|^p},$$
where p is a real number. Let S consist of the spheres A and B centered at the origin with radii $0 < a < b$, respectively. The total outward flux across S consists of the flux out of S across the outer sphere B minus the flux into S across the inner sphere A.

   a. Find the total flux across S with $p = 0$. Interpret the result.

   b. Show that for $p = 3$ (an inverse square law), the flux across S is independent of a and b.

66–69. Mass and center of mass *Let S be a surface that represents a thin shell with density ρ. The moments about the coordinate planes (see Section 14.6) are $M_{yz} = \iint_S x\rho(x, y, z)\, dS$, $M_{xz} = \iint_S y\rho(x, y, z)\, dS$, and $M_{xy} = \iint_S z\rho(x, y, z)\, dS$. The coordinates of the center of mass of the shell are $\bar{x} = \dfrac{M_{yz}}{m}, \bar{y} = \dfrac{M_{xz}}{m}, \bar{z} = \dfrac{M_{xy}}{m}$, where m is the mass of the shell. Find the mass and center of mass of the following shells. Use symmetry whenever possible.*

66. The constant-density hemispherical shell $x^2 + y^2 + z^2 = a^2, z \ge 0$

67. The constant-density cone with radius a, height h, and base in the xy-plane

68. The constant-density half cylinder $x^2 + z^2 = a^2, -h/2 \le y \le h/2, z \ge 0$

69. The cylinder $x^2 + y^2 = a^2, 0 \le z \le 2$, with density $\rho(x, y, z) = 1 + z$

Additional Exercises

70. Outward normal to a sphere Show that $|\mathbf{t}_u \times \mathbf{t}_v| = a^2 \sin u$ for a sphere of radius a defined parametrically by $\mathbf{r}(u, v) = \langle a \sin u \cos v, a \sin u \sin v, a \cos u \rangle$, where $0 \le u \le \pi$ and $0 \le v \le 2\pi$.

71. Special case of surface integrals of scalar-valued functions Suppose that a surface S is defined as $z = g(x, y)$ on a region R. Show that $\mathbf{t}_x \times \mathbf{t}_y = \langle -z_x, -z_y, 1 \rangle$ and that $\iint_S f(x, y, z)\, dS = \iint_R f(x, y, z) \sqrt{z_x^2 + z_y^2 + 1}\, dA$.

72. Surfaces of revolution Let $y = f(x)$ be a curve in the xy-plane with f continuous and $f(x) > 0$, for $a \le x \le b$. Let S be the surface generated when the graph of f on $[a, b]$ is revolved about the x-axis.

   a. Show that S is described parametrically by $\mathbf{r}(u, v) = \langle u, f(u) \cos v, f(u) \sin v \rangle$, for $a \le u \le b, 0 \le v \le 2\pi$.

   b. Find an integral that gives the surface area of S.

   c. Apply the result of part (b) to find the area of the surface generated with $f(x) = x^3$, for $1 \le x \le 2$.

   d. Apply the result of part (b) to find the area of the surface generated with $f(x) = (25 - x^2)^{1/2}$, for $3 \le x \le 4$.

73. Rain on roofs Let $z = s(x, y)$ define a surface over a region R in the xy-plane, where $z \ge 0$ on R. Show that the downward flux of the vertical vector field $\mathbf{F} = \langle 0, 0, -1 \rangle$ across S equals the area of R. Interpret the result physically.

74. Surface area of a torus

a. Show that a torus with radii $R > r$ (see figure) may be described parametrically by
$r(u, v) = \langle (R + r \cos u) \cos v, (R + r \cos u) \sin v, r \sin u \rangle$,
for $0 \le u \le 2\pi, 0 \le v \le 2\pi$.

b. Show that the surface area of the torus is $4\pi^2 Rr$.

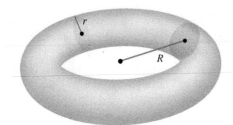

75. Surfaces of revolution—single variable Let f be differentiable and positive on the interval $[a, b]$. Let S be the surface generated when the graph of f on $[a, b]$ is revolved about the x-axis. Use Theorem 15.12 to show that the area of S (as given in Section 6.6) is

$$2\pi \int_a^b f(x) \sqrt{1 + f'(x)^2} \, dx.$$

QUICK CHECK ANSWERS

1. A half cylinder with height 1 and radius 2 with its axis along the z-axis   **2.** A half-cone with height 10 and radius 10   **3.** A quarter-sphere with radius 4   **4.** $\sqrt{2}$ **5.** The cylinder $x^2 + y^2 = a^2$ does not represent a function, so z_x and z_y cannot be computed.   **6.** The vector field is everywhere orthogonal to the hemisphere, so the hemisphere has maximum flux at every point. ◄

15.7 Stokes' Theorem

Born in Ireland, George Gabriel Stokes (1819–1903) led a long and distinguished life as one of the prominent mathematicians and physicists of his day. He entered Cambridge University as a student and remained there as a professor for most of his life, taking the Lucasian chair of mathematics, once held by Sir Isaac Newton. The first statement of Stokes' Theorem was given by William Thomson (Lord Kelvin).

With the divergence, the curl, and surface integrals in hand, we are ready to present two of the crowning results of calculus. Fortunately, all of the heavy lifting has been done. In this section, you will see Stokes' Theorem, and in the next section we present the Divergence Theorem.

Stokes' Theorem

Stokes' Theorem is the three-dimensional version of the circulation form of Green's Theorem. Recall that if C is a closed simple smooth oriented curve in the xy-plane enclosing a simply connected region R and $\mathbf{F} = \langle f, g \rangle$ is a differentiable vector field on R, Green's Theorem says that

$$\underbrace{\oint_C \mathbf{F} \cdot d\mathbf{r}}_{\text{circulation}} = \iint_R \underbrace{(g_x - f_y)}_{\text{curl or rotation}} \, dA.$$

The line integral on the left gives the circulation along the boundary of R. The double integral on the right sums the curl of the vector field over all points of R. If $\mathbf{F}$ represents a fluid flow, the theorem says that the cumulative rotation of the flow within R equals the circulation along the boundary.

In Stokes' Theorem, the plane region R in Green's Theorem becomes an oriented surface S in $\mathbb{R}^3$. The circulation integral in Green's Theorem remains a circulation integral, but now over the closed simple smooth oriented curve C that forms the boundary of S. The double integral of the curl in Green's Theorem becomes a surface integral of the three-dimensional curl (Figure 15.58).

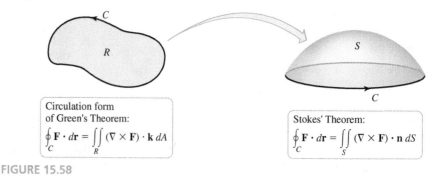

Circulation form of Green's Theorem:
$$\oint_C \mathbf{F} \cdot d\mathbf{r} = \iint_R (\nabla \times \mathbf{F}) \cdot \mathbf{k} \, dA$$

Stokes' Theorem:
$$\oint_C \mathbf{F} \cdot d\mathbf{r} = \iint_S (\nabla \times \mathbf{F}) \cdot \mathbf{n} \, dS$$

FIGURE 15.58

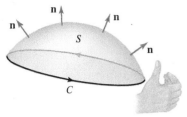

FIGURE 15.59

> The right-hand rule tells you which of two normal vectors at a point of S to use. Remember that the direction of normal vectors changes continuously on an oriented surface.

Stokes' Theorem involves an oriented curve C and an oriented surface S on which there are two unit normal vectors at every point. These orientations must be consistent and the normal vectors must be chosen correctly. Here is the right-hand rule that relates the orientations of S and C, and determines the choice of the normal vectors:

> If the fingers of your right hand curl in the positive direction around C, then your right thumb points in the (general) direction of the vectors normal to S (Figure 15.59).

A common situation occurs when C has a counterclockwise orientation when viewed from above; then, the vectors normal to S point upward.

THEOREM 15.13   Stokes' Theorem

Let S be a smooth oriented surface in $\mathbb{R}^3$ with a smooth closed boundary C whose orientation is consistent with that of S. Assume that $\mathbf{F} = \langle f, g, h \rangle$ is a vector field whose components have continuous first partial derivatives on S. Then

$$\oint_C \mathbf{F} \cdot d\mathbf{r} = \iint_S (\nabla \times \mathbf{F}) \cdot \mathbf{n} \, dS,$$

where $\mathbf{n}$ is the unit vector normal to S determined by the orientation of S.

QUICK CHECK 1 Suppose that S is a region in the xy-plane with a boundary oriented counterclockwise. What is the normal to S? Explain why Stokes' Theorem becomes the circulation form of Green's Theorem. ◄

The meaning of Stokes' Theorem is much the same as for the circulation form of Green's Theorem: Under the proper conditions, the accumulated rotation of the vector field over the surface S (as given by the normal component of the curl) equals the net circulation on the boundary of S. An outline of the proof of Stokes' Theorem is given at the end of this section. First, we look at some special cases that give further insight into the theorem.

If $\mathbf{F}$ is a conservative vector field on a domain D, then it has a potential function φ such that $\mathbf{F} = \nabla\varphi$. Because $\nabla \times \nabla\varphi = \mathbf{0}$, it follows that $\nabla \times \mathbf{F} = \mathbf{0}$ (Theorem 15.9); therefore, the circulation integral is zero on all closed curves in D. Recall that the circulation integral is also a work integral for the force field $\mathbf{F}$, which emphasizes the fact that no work is done in moving an object on a closed path in a conservative force field. Among the important conservative vector fields are the radial fields $\mathbf{F} = \mathbf{r}/|\mathbf{r}|^p$, which generally have zero curl and zero circulation on closed curves.

> Recall that for a constant nonzero vector **a** and the position vector $\mathbf{r} = \langle x, y, z \rangle$, the field $\mathbf{F} = \mathbf{a} \times \mathbf{r}$ is a rotational field. In Example 1,
>
> $$\mathbf{F} = \langle 0, 1, 1 \rangle \times \langle x, y, z \rangle.$$

EXAMPLE 1   Verifying Stokes' Theorem Confirm that Stokes' Theorem holds for the vector field $\mathbf{F} = \langle z - y, x, -x \rangle$, where S is the hemisphere $x^2 + y^2 + z^2 = 4$, for $z \geq 0$, and C is the circle $x^2 + y^2 = 4$ oriented counterclockwise.

SOLUTION The orientation of C says that the vectors normal to S point in the outward direction. The vector field is a rotation field $\mathbf{a} \times \mathbf{r}$, where $\mathbf{a} = \langle 0, 1, 1 \rangle$ and $\mathbf{r} = \langle x, y, z \rangle$; so the axis of rotation points in the direction of the vector $\langle 0, 1, 1 \rangle$ (Figure 15.60). We first compute the circulation integral in Stokes' Theorem. The curve C with the given orientation is parameterized as $\mathbf{r}(t) = \langle 2 \cos t, 2 \sin t, 0 \rangle$, for $0 \leq t \leq 2\pi$; therefore, $\mathbf{r}'(t) = \langle -2 \sin t, 2 \cos t, 0 \rangle$. The circulation integral is

$$\oint_C \mathbf{F} \cdot d\mathbf{r} = \int_0^{2\pi} \mathbf{F} \cdot \mathbf{r}'(t) \, dt \qquad \text{Definition of line integral}$$

$$= \int_0^{2\pi} \langle \underbrace{z - y}_{-2\sin t}, \underbrace{x}_{2\cos t}, -x \rangle \cdot \langle -2 \sin t, 2 \cos t, 0 \rangle \, dt \qquad \text{Substitute.}$$

$$= \int_0^{2\pi} 4(\sin^2 t + \cos^2 t) \, dt \qquad \text{Simplify.}$$

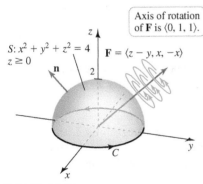

$S: x^2 + y^2 + z^2 = 4$
$z \geq 0$

Axis of rotation of **F** is $\langle 0, 1, 1 \rangle$.

$\mathbf{F} = \langle z - y, x, -x \rangle$

FIGURE 15.60

$$= 4 \int_0^{2\pi} dt$$ $\qquad$ $\sin^2 t + \cos^2 t = 1$

$$= 8\pi.$$ $\qquad$ Evaluate the integral.

The surface integral requires computing the curl of the vector field:

$$\nabla \times \mathbf{F} = \nabla \times \langle z - y, x, -x \rangle = \begin{vmatrix} \mathbf{i} & \mathbf{j} & \mathbf{k} \\ \dfrac{\partial}{\partial x} & \dfrac{\partial}{\partial y} & \dfrac{\partial}{\partial z} \\ z - y & x & -x \end{vmatrix} = \langle 0, 2, 2 \rangle.$$

Recall from Section 15.6 (Table 15.2) that an outward normal to the hemisphere is $\langle x/z, y/z, 1 \rangle$. The region of integration is the base of the hemisphere in the xy-plane, which is

$$R = \{(x, y): x^2 + y^2 \le 4\} = \{(r, \theta): 0 \le r \le 2, 0 \le \theta \le 2\pi\}.$$

Combining these results, the surface integral in Stokes' Theorem is

$$\iint_S \underbrace{(\nabla \times \mathbf{F})}_{\langle 0, 2, 2 \rangle} \cdot \mathbf{n}\, dS = \iint_R \langle 0, 2, 2 \rangle \cdot \left\langle \frac{x}{z}, \frac{y}{z}, 1 \right\rangle dA$$ $\qquad$ Substitute and convert to a double integral over R.

$$= \iint_R \left(\frac{2y}{\sqrt{4 - x^2 - y^2}} + 2 \right) dA$$ $\qquad$ Simplify and use $z = \sqrt{4 - x^2 - y^2}$.

$$= \int_0^{2\pi} \int_0^2 \left(\frac{2r \sin \theta}{\sqrt{4 - r^2}} + 2 \right) r\, dr\, d\theta.$$ $\qquad$ Convert to polar coordinates.

> In eliminating the first term of this double integral, we note that the improper integral $\int_0^2 \dfrac{r^2}{\sqrt{4 - r^2}}\, dr$ has a finite value.

We integrate first with respect to θ because the integral of $\sin \theta$ from 0 to 2π is zero and the first term in the integral is eliminated. Therefore, the surface integral reduces to

$$\iint_S (\nabla \times \mathbf{F}) \cdot \mathbf{n}\, dS = \int_0^2 \int_0^{2\pi} \left(\frac{2r^2 \sin \theta}{\sqrt{4 - r^2}} + 2r \right) d\theta\, dr$$

$$= \int_0^2 \int_0^{2\pi} 2r\, d\theta\, dr$$ $\qquad$ $\int_0^{2\pi} \sin \theta\, d\theta = 0$

$$= 4\pi \int_0^2 r\, dr$$ $\qquad$ Evaluate the inner integral.

$$= 8\pi.$$ $\qquad$ Evaluate the outer integral.

Computed either as a line integral or a surface integral, the vector field has a positive circulation along the boundary of S, which is produced by the net rotation of the field over the surface S.

Related Exercises 5–10◄

In Example 1, it was possible to evaluate both the line integral and the surface integral that appear in Stokes' Theorem. Often the theorem provides an easier way to evaluate difficult line integrals.

EXAMPLE 2 **Using Stokes' Theorem to evaluate a line integral** Evaluate the line integral $\oint_C \mathbf{F} \cdot d\mathbf{r}$, where $\mathbf{F} = z\mathbf{i} - z\mathbf{j} + (x^2 - y^2)\mathbf{k}$ and C consists of the three line segments that bound the plane $z = 8 - 4x - 2y$ in the first octant, oriented as shown in Figure 15.61.

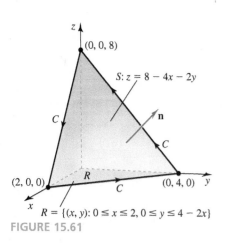

$R = \{(x, y): 0 \le x \le 2, 0 \le y \le 4 - 2x\}$

FIGURE 15.61

SOLUTION Evaluating the line integral directly involves parameterizing the three line segments. Instead, we use Stokes' Theorem to convert the line integral to a surface integral, where S is that portion of the plane $z = 8 - 4x - 2y$ that lies in the first octant. The curl of the vector field is

$$\nabla \times \mathbf{F} = \nabla \times \langle z, -z, x^2 - y^2 \rangle = \begin{vmatrix} \mathbf{i} & \mathbf{j} & \mathbf{k} \\ \dfrac{\partial}{\partial x} & \dfrac{\partial}{\partial y} & \dfrac{\partial}{\partial z} \\ z & -z & x^2 - y^2 \end{vmatrix} = \langle 1 - 2y, 1 - 2x, 0 \rangle.$$

> Recall that for an explicitly defined surface S given by $z = g(x, y)$ over a region R with $\mathbf{F} = \langle f, g, h \rangle$
>
> $$\iint_S \mathbf{F} \cdot \mathbf{n} \, dS = \iint_R (-f z_x - g z_y + h) \, dA.$$
>
> In Example 2, $\mathbf{F}$ is replaced by $\nabla \times \mathbf{F}$.

The appropriate vector normal to the plane $z = 8 - 4x - 2y$ is $\langle -z_x, -z_y, 1 \rangle = \langle 4, 2, 1 \rangle$, which points upward, consistent with the orientation of C. The triangular region R in the xy-plane beneath the plane is found by setting $z = 0$ in the equation of the plane; we find that $R = \{(x, y): 0 \leq x \leq 2, 0 \leq y \leq 4 - 2x\}$. The surface integral in Stokes' Theorem may now be evaluated:

$$\iint_S \underbrace{(\nabla \times \mathbf{F})}_{\langle 1 - 2y, 1 - 2x, 0 \rangle} \cdot \mathbf{n} \, dS = \iint_R \langle 1 - 2y, 1 - 2x, 0 \rangle \cdot \langle 4, 2, 1 \rangle \, dA \qquad \text{Substitute and convert to a double integral over } R.$$

$$= \int_0^2 \int_0^{4-2x} (6 - 4x - 8y) \, dy \, dx \qquad \text{Simplify.}$$

$$= -\frac{88}{3}. \qquad \text{Evaluate the integrals.}$$

The circulation around the boundary of R is negative, indicating a net circulation in the clockwise direction on C (looking from above).   *Related Exercises 11–16* ◄

In other situations, Stokes' Theorem may be used to convert a difficult surface integral into a relatively easy line integral, as illustrated in the next example.

EXAMPLE 3   Using Stokes' Theorem to evaluate a surface integral Evaluate the integral $\iint_S (\nabla \times \mathbf{F}) \cdot \mathbf{n} \, dS$, where $\mathbf{F} = -xz \, \mathbf{i} + yz \, \mathbf{j} + xye^z \, \mathbf{k}$ and S is the cap of the paraboloid $z = 5 - x^2 - y^2$ above the plane $z = 3$ (Figure 15.62). Assume $\mathbf{n}$ points in the positive z-direction on S.

SOLUTION We use Stokes' Theorem to convert the surface integral to a line integral along the curve C that bounds S. That curve is the intersection between the paraboloid $z = 5 - x^2 - y^2$ and the plane $z = 3$. Eliminating z from these equations, we find that C is the circle $x^2 + y^2 = 2$, with $z = 3$. By the orientation of S, we see that C is oriented counterclockwise, so a parametric description of C is $\mathbf{r}(t) = \langle \sqrt{2} \cos t, \sqrt{2} \sin t, 3 \rangle$, which implies that $\mathbf{r}'(t) = \langle -\sqrt{2} \sin t, \sqrt{2} \cos t, 0 \rangle$. The value of the surface integral is

$$\iint_S (\nabla \times \mathbf{F}) \cdot \mathbf{n} \, dS = \oint_C \mathbf{F} \cdot d\mathbf{r} \qquad \text{Stokes' Theorem}$$

$$= \int_0^{2\pi} \mathbf{F} \cdot \mathbf{r}'(t) \, dt \qquad \text{Definition of line integral}$$

$$= \int_0^{2\pi} \langle -xz, yz, xye^z \rangle \cdot \langle -\sqrt{2} \sin t, \sqrt{2} \cos t, 0 \rangle \, dt \qquad \text{Substitute.}$$

$$= \int_0^{2\pi} 12 \sin t \cos t \, dt \qquad \text{Substitute for } x, y, \text{ and } z, \text{ and simplify.}$$

$$= 6 \int_0^{2\pi} \sin 2t \, dt = 0. \qquad \sin 2t = 2 \sin t \cos t$$

Related Exercises 17–20 ◄

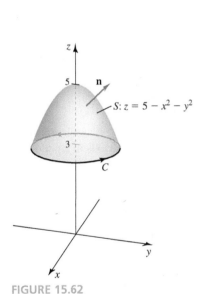

FIGURE 15.62

QUICK CHECK 2 In Example 3, the z-component of the vector field did not enter the calculation; it could have been anything. Explain why. ◄

Interpreting the Curl

Stokes' Theorem leads to another interpretation of the curl at a point in a vector field. We need the idea of the **average circulation**. If C is the boundary of an oriented surface S, we define the average circulation of $\mathbf{F}$ over S as

$$\frac{1}{\text{area}(S)} \oint_C \mathbf{F} \cdot d\mathbf{r} = \frac{1}{\text{area}(S)} \iint_S (\nabla \times \mathbf{F}) \cdot \mathbf{n} \, dS,$$

where Stokes' Theorem is used to convert the circulation integral to a surface integral.

First consider a general rotation field $\mathbf{F} = \mathbf{a} \times \mathbf{r}$, where $\mathbf{a} = \langle a_1, a_2, a_3 \rangle$ is a constant nonzero vector and $\mathbf{r} = \langle x, y, z \rangle$. Recall that $\mathbf{F}$ describes the rotation about an axis in the direction of $\mathbf{a}$ with angular speed $\omega = |\mathbf{a}|$. We also showed that $\mathbf{F}$ has a constant curl, $\nabla \times \mathbf{F} = \nabla \times (\mathbf{a} \times \mathbf{r}) = 2\mathbf{a}$. We now take S to be a small circular disk centered at a point P, whose normal vector $\mathbf{n}$ makes an angle θ with the axis $\mathbf{a}$ (Figure 15.63). Let C be the boundary of S with a counterclockwise orientation.

The average circulation of this vector field on S is

$$\frac{1}{\text{area}(S)} \iint_S \underbrace{(\nabla \times \mathbf{F})}_{\text{constant}} \cdot \mathbf{n} \, dS \qquad \text{Definition}$$

$$= \frac{1}{\text{area}(S)} (\nabla \times \mathbf{F}) \cdot \mathbf{n} \cdot \text{area}(S) \qquad \iint_S dS = \text{area}(S)$$

$$= \underbrace{(\nabla \times \mathbf{F})}_{2\mathbf{a}} \cdot \mathbf{n} \qquad \text{Simplify.}$$

$$= 2|\mathbf{a}| \cos \theta. \qquad |\mathbf{n}| = 1, |\nabla \times \mathbf{F}| = 2|\mathbf{a}|$$

If the normal vector $\mathbf{n}$ is aligned with $\nabla \times \mathbf{F}$ (which is parallel to $\mathbf{a}$), then $\theta = 0$ and the average circulation on S has its maximum value of $2|\mathbf{a}|$. However, if the vector normal to the surface S is orthogonal to the axis of rotation ($\theta = \pi/2$), the average circulation is zero.

We see that for a general rotation field $\mathbf{F} = \mathbf{a} \times \mathbf{r}$, the curl of $\mathbf{F}$ has the following interpretations, where S is a small disk centered at a point P with a normal vector $\mathbf{n}$.

- The scalar component of $\nabla \times \mathbf{F}$ at P in the direction of $\mathbf{n}$, which is $(\nabla \times \mathbf{F}) \cdot n = 2|\mathbf{a}| \cos \theta$, is the average circulation of $\mathbf{F}$ on S.

- The direction of $\nabla \times \mathbf{F}$ at P is the direction that maximizes the average circulation of $\mathbf{F}$ on S. Equivalently, it is the direction in which you should orient the axis of a paddle wheel to obtain the maximum angular speed.

A similar argument may be applied to a general vector field (with a variable curl) to give an analogous interpretation of the curl at a point (Exercise 44).

EXAMPLE 4   Horizontal channel flow Consider the velocity field $\mathbf{v} = \langle 0, 1 - x^2, 0 \rangle$, for $|x| \leq 1$ and $|z| \leq 1$, which represents a horizontal flow in the y-direction (Figure 15.64a).

a. Suppose you place a paddle wheel at the point $P\left(\frac{1}{2}, 0, 0\right)$. Using physical arguments, in which of the coordinate directions should the axis of the wheel point in order for the wheel to spin? In which direction does it spin?

b. Compute and graph the curl of $\mathbf{v}$ and provide an interpretation.

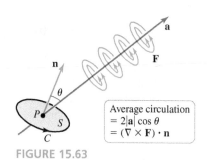

FIGURE 15.63

> Recall that $\mathbf{n}$ is a unit normal vector with $|\mathbf{n}| = 1$. By definition, the dot product gives $\mathbf{a} \cdot \mathbf{n} = |\mathbf{a}| \cos \theta$.

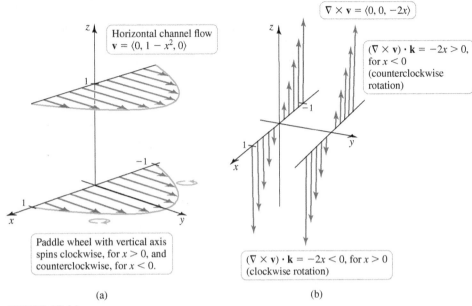

FIGURE 15.64

SOLUTION

a. If the axis of the wheel is aligned with the x-axis at P, the flow strikes the upper and lower halves of the wheel symmetrically and the wheel does not spin. If the axis of the wheel is aligned with the y-axis, the flow strikes the face of the wheel and it does not spin. If the axis of the wheel is aligned with the z-axis at P, the flow in the y-direction is greater for $x < \frac{1}{2}$ than it is for $x > \frac{1}{2}$. Therefore, a wheel located at $(\frac{1}{2}, 0, 0)$ spins in the clockwise direction, looking from above.

b. A short calculation shows that

$$\nabla \times \mathbf{v} = \begin{vmatrix} \mathbf{i} & \mathbf{j} & \mathbf{k} \\ \dfrac{\partial}{\partial x} & \dfrac{\partial}{\partial y} & \dfrac{\partial}{\partial z} \\ 0 & 1 - x^2 & 0 \end{vmatrix} = -2x\,\mathbf{k}.$$

As shown in Figure 15.64b, the curl points in the z-direction, which is the direction of the paddle wheel axis that gives the maximum angular speed of the wheel. Consider the z-component of the curl, which is $(\nabla \times \mathbf{v}) \cdot \mathbf{k} = -2x$. At $x = 0$, this component is zero, meaning the wheel does not spin at any point along the y-axis when its axis is aligned with the z-axis. For $x > 0$, we see that $(\nabla \times \mathbf{v}) \cdot \mathbf{k} < 0$, which corresponds to clockwise rotation of the vector field. For $x < 0$, we have $(\nabla \times \mathbf{v}) \cdot \mathbf{k} > 0$, corresponding to counterclockwise rotation.

Related Exercises 21–24 ◀

QUICK CHECK 3 In Example 4, explain why a paddle wheel with its axis aligned with the z-axis does not spin when placed on the y-axis. ◀

Proof of Stokes' Theorem

The proof of the most general case of Stokes' Theorem is intricate. However, a proof of a special case is instructive and it relies on several previous results.

Consider the case in which the surface S is the graph of the function $z = s(x, y)$, defined on a region in the xy-plane. Let C be the curve that bounds S with a counterclockwise orientation, let R be the projection of S in the xy-plane, and let C' be the projection of C in the xy-plane (Figure 15.65).

Letting $\mathbf{F} = \langle f, g, h \rangle$, the line integral in Stokes' Theorem is

$$\oint_C \mathbf{F} \cdot d\mathbf{r} = \oint_C f\,dx + g\,dy + h\,dz.$$

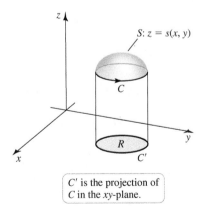

C' is the projection of C in the xy-plane.

FIGURE 15.65

The key observation for this integral is that along C, $dz = z_x\, dx + z_y\, dy$. Making this substitution, we convert the line integral on C to a line integral on C' in the xy-plane:

$$\oint_C \mathbf{F} \cdot d\mathbf{r} = \oint_{C'} f\, dx + g\, dy + h\underbrace{(z_x\, dx + z_y\, dy)}_{dz}$$

$$= \oint_{C'} \underbrace{(f + hz_x)}_{M(x,y)}\, dx + \underbrace{(g + hz_y)}_{N(x,y)}\, dy.$$

We now apply the circulation form of Green's Theorem to this line integral with $M(x, y) = f + hz_x$ and $N(x, y) = g + hz_y$; the result is

$$\oint_{C'} M\, dx + N\, dy = \iint_R (N_x - M_y)\, dA.$$

A careful application of the Chain Rule (remembering that z is a function of x and y, Exercise 45) reveals that

$$M_y = f_y + f_z z_y + hz_{xy} + z_x(h_y + h_z z_y) \quad \text{and}$$
$$N_x = g_x + g_z z_x + hz_{yx} + z_y(h_x + h_z z_x).$$

Making these substitutions in the line integral and simplifying (note that $z_{xy} = z_{yx}$ is needed), we have

$$\oint_C \mathbf{F} \cdot d\mathbf{r} = \iint_R \left(z_x(g_z - h_y) + z_y(h_x - f_z) + (g_x - f_y) \right) dA. \tag{1}$$

Now let's look at the surface integral in Stokes' Theorem. The upward vector normal to the surface is $\langle -z_x, -z_y, 1 \rangle$. Substituting the components of $\nabla \times \mathbf{F}$, the surface integral takes the form

$$\iint_S (\nabla \times \mathbf{F}) \cdot \mathbf{n}\, dS = \iint_R \left((h_y - g_z)(-z_x) + (f_z - h_x)(-z_y) + (g_x - f_y) \right) dA,$$

which upon rearrangement becomes the integral in (1).   ◄

Two Final Notes on Stokes' Theorem

1. Stokes' Theorem allows a surface integral $\iint_S (\nabla \times \mathbf{F}) \cdot \mathbf{n}\, dS$ to be evaluated using only the values of the vector field on the boundary C. This means that if a closed curve C is the boundary of two different smooth oriented surfaces S_1 and S_2, which both have an orientation consistent with that of C, then the integrals of $(\nabla \times \mathbf{F}) \cdot \mathbf{n}$ on the two surfaces are equal; that is,

$$\iint_{S_1} (\nabla \times \mathbf{F}) \cdot \mathbf{n}_1\, dS = \iint_{S_2} (\nabla \times \mathbf{F}) \cdot \mathbf{n}_2\, dS,$$

where $\mathbf{n}_1$ and $\mathbf{n}_2$ are the respective unit normal vectors consistent with the orientation of the surfaces (Figure 15.66a).

Now let's take a different perspective. Suppose S is a *closed* surface consisting of S_1 and S_2 with a common boundary curve C (Figure 15.66b). Let $\mathbf{n}$ be the outward normal vectors for the entire surface S. Either the vectors normal to S_1 point out of the enclosed region (in the direction of $\mathbf{n}$) and the vectors normal to S_2 point

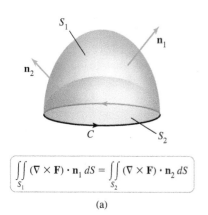

$$\iint_{S_1} (\nabla \times \mathbf{F}) \cdot \mathbf{n}_1\, dS = \iint_{S_2} (\nabla \times \mathbf{F}) \cdot \mathbf{n}_2\, dS$$

(a)

$$S = S_1 \cup S_2$$

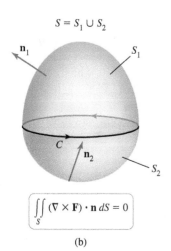

$$\iint_S (\nabla \times \mathbf{F}) \cdot \mathbf{n}\, dS = 0$$

(b)

FIGURE 15.66

into that region (opposite $\mathbf{n}$), or vice versa. In either case, $\iint_{S_1} (\nabla \times \mathbf{F}) \cdot \mathbf{n}_1 \, dS$ and $\iint_{S_2} (\nabla \times \mathbf{F}) \cdot \mathbf{n}_2 \, dS$ are equal in magnitude and of opposite sign; therefore,

$$\iint_S (\nabla \times \mathbf{F}) \cdot \mathbf{n} \, dS = \iint_{S_1} (\nabla \times \mathbf{F}) \cdot \mathbf{n}_1 \, dS + \iint_{S_2} (\nabla \times \mathbf{F}) \cdot \mathbf{n}_2 \, dS = 0.$$

This argument can be adapted to show that $\iint_S (\nabla \times \mathbf{F}) \cdot \mathbf{n} \, dS = 0$ over any closed oriented surface S (Exercise 46).

2. We can now resolve an assertion made in Section 15.5. There we proved (Theorem 15.9) that if $\mathbf{F}$ is a conservative vector field, then $\nabla \times \mathbf{F} = \mathbf{0}$; we claimed, but did not prove, that the converse is true. The converse follows directly from Stokes' Theorem.

THEOREM 15.14   Curl F $=$ 0 Implies F Is Conservative

Suppose that $\nabla \times \mathbf{F} = \mathbf{0}$ throughout an open simply connected region D of $\mathbb{R}^3$. Then $\oint_C \mathbf{F} \cdot d\mathbf{r} = 0$ on all closed simple smooth curves C in D and $\mathbf{F}$ is a conservative vector field on D.

Proof: Given a closed simple smooth curve C, an advanced result states that C is the boundary of at least one smooth oriented surface S in D. By Stokes' Theorem

$$\oint_C \mathbf{F} \cdot d\mathbf{r} = \iint_S \underbrace{(\nabla \times \mathbf{F})}_{0} \cdot \mathbf{n} \, dS = 0.$$

Because the line integral equals zero over all such curves in D, the vector field is conservative on D by Theorem 15.5. ◀

SECTION 15.7 EXERCISES

Review Questions

1. Explain the meaning of the integral $\oint_C \mathbf{F} \cdot d\mathbf{r}$ in Stokes' Theorem.

2. Explain the meaning of the integral $\iint_S (\nabla \times \mathbf{F}) \cdot \mathbf{n} \, dS$ in Stokes' Theorem.

3. Explain the meaning of Stokes' Theorem.

4. Why does a conservative vector field produce zero circulation around a closed curve?

Basic Skills

5–10. Verifying Stokes' Theorem *Verify that the line integral and the surface integral of Stokes' Theorem are equal for the following vector fields, surfaces S, and closed curves C. Assume that C has counterclockwise orientation and S has a consistent orientation.*

5. $\mathbf{F} = \langle y, -x, 10 \rangle$; S is the upper half of the sphere $x^2 + y^2 + z^2 = 1$ and C is the circle $x^2 + y^2 = 1$ in the xy-plane.

6. $\mathbf{F} = \langle 0, -x, y \rangle$; S is the upper half of the sphere $x^2 + y^2 + z^2 = 4$ and C is the circle $x^2 + y^2 = 4$ in the xy-plane.

7. $\mathbf{F} = \langle x, y, z \rangle$; S is the paraboloid $z = 8 - x^2 - y^2$, for $0 \le z \le 8$, and C is the circle $x^2 + y^2 = 8$ in the xy-plane.

8. $\mathbf{F} = \langle 2z, -4x, 3y \rangle$; S is the cap of the sphere $x^2 + y^2 + z^2 = 169$ above the plane $z = 12$ and C is the boundary of S.

9. $\mathbf{F} = \langle y - z, z - x, x - y \rangle$; S is the cap of the sphere $x^2 + y^2 + z^2 = 16$ above the plane $z = \sqrt{7}$ and C is the boundary of S.

10. $\mathbf{F} = \langle -y, -x - z, y - x \rangle$; S is the part of the plane $z = 6 - y$ that lies in the cylinder $x^2 + y^2 = 16$ and C is the boundary of S.

11–16. Stokes' Theorem for evaluating line integrals *Evaluate the line integral $\oint_C \mathbf{F} \cdot d\mathbf{r}$ by evaluating the surface integral in Stokes' Theorem with an appropriate choice of S. Assume that C has a counterclockwise orientation.*

11. $\mathbf{F} = \langle 2y, -z, x \rangle$; C is the circle $x^2 + y^2 = 12$ in the plane $z = 0$.

12. $\mathbf{F} = \langle y, xz, -y \rangle$; C is the ellipse $x^2 + y^2/4 = 1$ in the plane $z = 1$.

13. $\mathbf{F} = \langle x^2 - z^2, y, 2xz \rangle$; C is the boundary of the plane $z = 4 - x - y$ in the first octant.

14. $\mathbf{F} = \langle x^2 - y^2, z^2 - x^2, y^2 - z^2 \rangle$; C is the boundary of the square $|x| \le 1$, $|y| \le 1$ in the plane $z = 0$.

15. $\mathbf{F} = \langle y^2, -z^2, x \rangle$; C is the circle $\mathbf{r}(t) = \langle 3 \cos t, 4 \cos t, 5 \sin t \rangle$, for $0 \le t \le 2\pi$.

16. $\mathbf{F} = \langle 2xy \sin z, x^2 \sin z, x^2 y \cos z \rangle$; C is the boundary of the plane $z = 8 - 2x - 4y$ in the first octant.

17–20. Stokes' Theorem for evaluating surface integrals *Evaluate the line integral in Stokes' Theorem to evaluate the surface integral* $\iint_S (\nabla \times \mathbf{F}) \cdot \mathbf{n} \, dS$. *Assume that* $\mathbf{n}$ *points in the positive z-direction.*

17. $\mathbf{F} = \langle x, y, z \rangle$; S is the upper half of the ellipsoid $x^2/4 + y^2/9 + z^2 = 1$.

18. $\mathbf{F} = \mathbf{r}/|\mathbf{r}|$; S is the paraboloid $x = 9 - y^2 - z^2$, for $0 \le x \le 9$ (excluding its base), where $\mathbf{r} = \langle x, y, z \rangle$.

19. $\mathbf{F} = \langle 2y, -z, x - y - z \rangle$; S is the cap of the sphere (excluding its base) $x^2 + y^2 + z^2 = 25$, for $3 \le x \le 5$.

20. $\mathbf{F} = \langle x + y, y + z, z + x \rangle$; S is the tilted disk enclosed by $\mathbf{r}(t) = \langle \cos t, 2 \sin t, \sqrt{3} \cos t \rangle$.

21–24. Interpreting and graphing the curl *For the following velocity fields, compute the curl, make a sketch of the curl, and interpret the curl.*

21. $\mathbf{v} = \langle 0, 0, y \rangle$

22. $\mathbf{v} = \langle 1 - z^2, 0, 0 \rangle$

23. $\mathbf{v} = \langle -2z, 0, 1 \rangle$

24. $\mathbf{v} = \langle 0, -z, y \rangle$

Further Explorations

25. **Explain why or why not** Determine whether the following statements are true and give an explanation or counterexample.

   a. A paddle wheel with its axis in the direction $\langle 0, 1, -1 \rangle$ would not spin when put in the vector field $\mathbf{F} = \langle 1, 1, 2 \rangle \times \langle x, y, z \rangle$.
   b. Stokes' Theorem relates the flux of a vector field $\mathbf{F}$ across a surface to the values of $\mathbf{F}$ on the boundary of the surface.
   c. A vector field of the form $\mathbf{F} = \langle a + f(x), b + g(y), c + h(z) \rangle$, where a, b, and c are constants, has zero circulation on a closed curve.
   d. If a vector field has zero circulation on all simple closed smooth curves C in a region D, then $\mathbf{F}$ is conservative on D.

26–29. Conservative fields *Use Stokes' Theorem to find the circulation of the following vector fields around any simple closed smooth curve C.*

26. $\mathbf{F} = \langle 2x, -2y, 2z \rangle$

27. $\mathbf{F} = \nabla (x \sin y \, e^z)$

28. $\mathbf{F} = \langle 3x^2y, x^3 + 2yz^2, 2y^2z \rangle$

29. $\mathbf{F} = \langle y^2z^3, 2xyz^3, 3xy^2z^2 \rangle$

30–34. Tilted disks *Let S be the disk enclosed by the curve* $C: \mathbf{r}(t) = \langle \cos \varphi \cos t, \sin t, \sin \varphi \cos t \rangle$, *for* $0 \le t \le 2\pi$, *where* $0 \le \varphi \le \pi/2$ *is a fixed angle.*

30. What is the area of S? Find a vector normal to S.

31. What is the length of C?

32. Use Stokes' Theorem and a surface integral to find the circulation on C of the vector field $\mathbf{F} = \langle -y, x, 0 \rangle$ as a function of φ. For what value of φ is the circulation a maximum?

33. What is the circulation on C of the vector field $\mathbf{F} = \langle -y, -z, x \rangle$ as a function of φ? For what value of φ is the circulation a maximum?

34. Consider the vector field $\mathbf{F} = \mathbf{a} \times \mathbf{r}$, where $\mathbf{a} = \langle a_1, a_2, a_3 \rangle$ is a constant nonzero vector and $\mathbf{r} = \langle x, y, z \rangle$. Show that the circulation is a maximum when $\mathbf{a}$ points in the direction of the normal to S.

35. **Circulation in a plane** A circle C in the plane $x + y + z = 8$ has a radius of 4 and center $(2, 3, 3)$. Evaluate $\oint_C \mathbf{F} \cdot d\mathbf{r}$ for

$\mathbf{F} = \langle 0, -z, 2y \rangle$ where C has a counterclockwise orientation when viewed from above. Does the circulation depend on the radius of the circle? Does it depend on the location of the center of the circle?

36. **No integrals** Let $\mathbf{F} = \langle 2z, z, 2y + x \rangle$ and let S be the hemisphere of radius a with its base in the xy-plane and center at the origin.

   a. Evaluate $\iint_S (\nabla \times \mathbf{F}) \cdot \mathbf{n} \, dS$ by computing $\nabla \times \mathbf{F}$ and appealing to symmetry.
   b. Evaluate the line integral using Stokes' Theorem to check part (a).

37. **Compound surface and boundary** Begin with the paraboloid $z = x^2 + y^2$, for $0 \le z \le 4$, and slice it with the plane $y = 0$. Let S be the surface that remains for $y \ge 0$ (including the planar surface in the xz-plane) (see figure). Let C be the semicircle and line segment that bound the cap of S in the plane $z = 4$ with counterclockwise orientation. Let $\mathbf{F} = \langle 2z + y, 2x + z, 2y + x \rangle$.

   a. Describe the direction of the vectors normal to the surface.
   b. Evaluate $\iint_S (\nabla \times \mathbf{F}) \cdot \mathbf{n} \, dS$.
   c. Evaluate $\oint_C \mathbf{F} \cdot d\mathbf{r}$ and check for agreement with part (b).

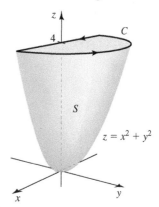

Applications

38. **Ampère's Law** The French physicist André-Marie Ampère (1775–1836) discovered that an electrical current I in a wire produces a magnetic field $\mathbf{B}$. A special case of Ampère's Law relates the current to the magnetic field through the equation $\oint_C \mathbf{B} \cdot d\mathbf{r} = \mu I$, where C is any closed curve through which the wire passes and μ is a physical constant. Assume that the current I is given in terms of the current density $\mathbf{J}$ as $I = \iint_S \mathbf{J} \cdot \mathbf{n} \, dS$, where S is an oriented surface with C as a boundary. Use Stokes' Theorem to show that an equivalent form of Ampère's Law is $\nabla \times \mathbf{B} = \mu \mathbf{J}$.

39. **Maximum surface integral** Let S be the paraboloid $z = a(1 - x^2 - y^2)$, for $z \ge 0$, where $a > 0$ is a real number. Let $\mathbf{F} = \langle x - y, y + z, z - x \rangle$. For what value(s) of a (if any) does $\iint_S (\nabla \times \mathbf{F}) \cdot \mathbf{n} \, dS$ have its maximum value?

40. **Area of a region in a plane** Let R be a region in a plane that has a unit normal vector $\mathbf{n} = \langle a, b, c \rangle$ and boundary C. Let $\mathbf{F} = \langle bz, cx, ay \rangle$.

   a. Show that $\nabla \times \mathbf{F} = \mathbf{n}$.
   b. Use Stokes' Theorem to show that

$$\text{area of } R = \oint_C \mathbf{F} \cdot d\mathbf{r}.$$

c. Consider the curve C given by $\mathbf{r} = \langle 5 \sin t, 13 \cos t, 12 \sin t \rangle$, for $0 \le t \le 2\pi$. Prove that C lies in a plane by showing that $\mathbf{r} \times \mathbf{r}'$ is constant for all t.

d. Use part (b) to find the area of the region enclosed by C in part (c) (*Hint:* Find the unit normal vector that is consistent with the orientation of C.)

41. **Choosing a more convenient surface** The goal is to evaluate $A = \iint_S (\nabla \times \mathbf{F}) \cdot \mathbf{n}\, dS$, where $\mathbf{F} = \langle yz, -xz, xy \rangle$ and S is the surface of the upper half of the ellipsoid $x^2 + y^2 + 8z^2 = 1$ ($z \ge 0$).

a. Evaluate a surface integral over a more convenient surface to find the value of A.

b. Evaluate A using a line integral.

Additional Exercises

42. **Radial fields and zero circulation** Consider the radial vector fields $\mathbf{F} = \mathbf{r}/|\mathbf{r}|^p$, where p is a real number and $\mathbf{r} = \langle x, y, z \rangle$. Let C be any circle in the xy-plane centered at the origin.

a. Evaluate a line integral to show that the field has zero circulation on C.

b. For what values of p does Stokes' Theorem apply? For those values of p, use the surface integral in Stokes' Theorem to show that the field has zero circulation on C.

43. **Zero curl** Consider the vector field

$$\mathbf{F} = \frac{-y}{x^2 + y^2}\, \mathbf{i} + \frac{x}{x^2 + y^2}\, \mathbf{j} + z\, \mathbf{k}.$$

a. Show that $\nabla \times \mathbf{F} = \mathbf{0}$.

b. Show that $\oint_C \mathbf{F} \cdot d\mathbf{r}$ is not zero on a circle C in the xy-plane enclosing the origin.

c. Explain why Theorem 15.13 does not apply in this case.

44. **Average circulation** Let S be a small circular disk of radius R centered at the point P with a unit normal vector $\mathbf{n}$. Let C be the boundary of S.

a. Express the average circulation of the vector field $\mathbf{F}$ on S as a surface integral of $\nabla \times \mathbf{F}$.

b. Argue that for small R, the average circulation approaches $(\nabla \times \mathbf{F})|_P \cdot \mathbf{n}$ (the component of $\nabla \times \mathbf{F}$ in the direction of $\mathbf{n}$ evaluated at P) with the approximation improving as $R \to 0$.

45. **Proof of Stokes' Theorem** Confirm the following step in the proof of Stokes' Theorem. If $z = s(x, y)$ and f, g, and h are functions of x, y, and z, with $M = f + hz_x$ and $N = g + hz_y$, then

$$M_y = f_y + f_z z_y + h z_{xy} + z_x(h_y + h_z z_y) \quad \text{and}$$
$$N_x = g_x + g_z z_x + h z_{yx} + z_y(h_x + h_z z_x).$$

46. **Stokes' Theorem on closed surfaces** Prove that if $\mathbf{F}$ satisfies the conditions of Stokes' Theorem, then $\iint_S (\nabla \times \mathbf{F}) \cdot \mathbf{n}\, dS = 0$, where S is a smooth surface that encloses a region.

47. **Rotated Green's Theorem** Use Stokes' Theorem to write the circulation form of Green's Theorem in the yz-plane.

QUICK CHECK ANSWERS

1. If S is a region in the xy-plane, $\mathbf{n} = \mathbf{k}$, and $(\nabla \times \mathbf{F}) \cdot \mathbf{n}$ becomes $g_x - f_y$. 2. The tangent vector $\mathbf{r}'$ lies in the xy-plane and is orthogonal to the z-component of $\mathbf{F}$. This component does not contribute to the circulation along C. 3. The vector field is symmetric about the y-axis. ◄

15.8 Divergence Theorem

Vector fields can represent electric or magnetic fields, air velocities in hurricanes, or blood flow in an artery. These and other vector phenomena suggest movement of a "substance." A frequent question concerns the amount of a substance that flows across a surface—for example, the amount of water that passes across the membrane of a cell per unit time. Such flux calculations may be done using flux integrals as in Section 15.6. The Divergence Theorem offers an alternative method. In effect, it says that instead of integrating the flow in and out of a region across its boundary, you may also add up all the sources (or sinks) of the flow throughout the region.

> Circulation form of
> Green's Theorem → Stokes' Theorem
>
> Flux form of Green's
> Theorem → Divergence Theorem

Divergence Theorem

The Divergence Theorem is the three-dimensional version of the flux form of Green's Theorem. Recall that if R is a region in the xy-plane, C is the simple closed oriented boundary of R, and $\mathbf{F} = \langle f, g \rangle$ is a vector field, Green's Theorem says that

$$\underbrace{\oint_C \mathbf{F} \cdot \mathbf{n}\, ds}_{\text{flux across } C} = \iint_R \underbrace{(f_x + g_y)\, dA}_{\text{divergence}}.$$

The line integral on the left gives the flux across the boundary of R. The double integral on the right measures the net expansion or contraction of the vector field within R. If $\mathbf{F}$ represents a fluid flow or the transport of a material, the theorem says that the cumulative effect of the sources (or sinks) of the flow within R equals the net flow across its boundary.

The Divergence Theorem is a direct extension of Green's Theorem. The plane region in Green's Theorem becomes a solid region D in $\mathbb{R}^3$, and the closed curve in Green's Theorem becomes the oriented surface S that encloses D. The flux integral in Green's Theorem becomes a surface integral over S, and the double integral in Green's Theorem becomes a triple integral over D of the three-dimensional divergence (Figure 15.67).

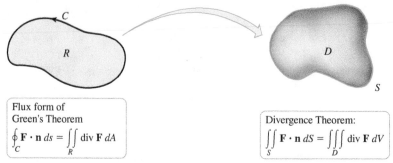

Flux form of Green's Theorem

$$\oint_C \mathbf{F} \cdot \mathbf{n} \, ds = \iint_R \text{div } \mathbf{F} \, dA$$

Divergence Theorem:

$$\iint_S \mathbf{F} \cdot \mathbf{n} \, dS = \iiint_D \text{div } \mathbf{F} \, dV$$

FIGURE 15.67

THEOREM 15.15   Divergence Theorem

Let $\mathbf{F}$ be a vector field whose components have continuous first partial derivatives in a connected and simply connected region D in $\mathbb{R}^3$ enclosed by a smooth oriented surface S. Then

$$\iint_S \mathbf{F} \cdot \mathbf{n} \, dS = \iiint_D \nabla \cdot \mathbf{F} \, dV,$$

where $\mathbf{n}$ is the unit outward normal vector on S.

The surface integral on the left gives the flux of the vector field across the boundary; a positive flux integral means there is a net flow of the field out of the region. The triple integral on the right is the cumulative expansion or contraction of the field over the region D. The proof of a special case of the theorem is given later in this section.

QUICK CHECK 1 Interpret the Divergence Theorem in the case that $\mathbf{F} = \langle a, b, c \rangle$ is a constant vector field and D is a ball. ◄

EXAMPLE 1   Verifying the Divergence Theorem Consider the radial field $\mathbf{F} = \langle x, y, z \rangle$ and let S be the sphere $x^2 + y^2 + z^2 = a^2$ that encloses the region D. Assume $\mathbf{n}$ is the outward normal vector on the sphere. Evaluate both integrals of the Divergence Theorem.

SOLUTION The divergence of $\mathbf{F}$ is

$$\nabla \cdot \mathbf{F} = \frac{\partial}{\partial x}(x) + \frac{\partial}{\partial y}(y) + \frac{\partial}{\partial z}(z) = 3.$$

Integrating over D, we have

$$\iiint_D \nabla \cdot \mathbf{F} \, dV = \iiint_D 3 \, dV = 3 \times \text{volume}(D) = 4\pi a^3.$$

To evaluate the surface integral, we parameterize the sphere (Section 15.6, Table 15.2) in the form

$$\mathbf{r} = \langle x, y, z \rangle = \langle a \sin u \cos v, a \sin u \sin v, a \cos u \rangle,$$

where $R = \{(u, v): 0 \le u \le \pi, 0 \le v \le 2\pi\}$ (u and v are the spherical coordinates φ and θ, respectively). The surface integral is

$$\iint\limits_{S} \mathbf{F} \cdot \mathbf{n}\, dS = \iint\limits_{R} \mathbf{F} \cdot (\mathbf{t}_u \times \mathbf{t}_v)\, dA,$$

where a vector normal to the surface is

$$\mathbf{t}_u \times \mathbf{t}_v = \langle a^2 \sin^2 u \cos v, a^2 \sin^2 u \sin v, a^2 \sin u \cos u \rangle.$$

Substituting for $\mathbf{F} = \langle x, y, z \rangle$ and $\mathbf{t}_u \times \mathbf{t}_v$, we find after simplifying that $\mathbf{F} \cdot (\mathbf{t}_u \times \mathbf{t}_v) = a^3 \sin u$. Therefore, the surface integral becomes

> See Exercise 32 for an alternative evaluation of the surface integral.

$$\iint\limits_{S} \mathbf{F} \cdot \mathbf{n}\, dS = \iint\limits_{R} \underbrace{\mathbf{F} \cdot (\mathbf{t}_u \times \mathbf{t}_v)}_{a^3 \sin u}\, dA$$

$$= \int_0^{2\pi} \int_0^{\pi} a^3 \sin u\, du\, dv \quad \text{Substitute for } \mathbf{F} \text{ and } \mathbf{t}_u \times \mathbf{t}_v.$$

$$= 4\pi a^3. \qquad\qquad\qquad\text{Evaluate integrals.}$$

The two integrals of the Divergence Theorem are equal.

Related Exercises 9–12 ◄

EXAMPLE 2 **Divergence Theorem with a rotation field** Consider the rotation field

$$\mathbf{F} = \mathbf{a} \times \mathbf{r} = \langle 1, 0, 1 \rangle \times \langle x, y, z \rangle = \langle -y, x - z, y \rangle.$$

Let S be the hemisphere $x^2 + y^2 + z^2 = a^2$, for $z \ge 0$, together with its base in the xy-plane. Find the net outward flux across S.

SOLUTION To find the flux using surface integrals, two surfaces must be considered (the hemisphere and its base). The Divergence Theorem gives a simpler solution. Note that

$$\nabla \cdot \mathbf{F} = \frac{\partial}{\partial x}(-y) + \frac{\partial}{\partial y}(x - z) + \frac{\partial}{\partial z}(y) = 0.$$

We see that the flux across the hemisphere is zero.

Related Exercises 13–16 ◄

With Stokes' Theorem, rotation fields are noteworthy because they have a nonzero curl. With the Divergence Theorem, the situation is reversed. As suggested by Example 2, pure rotation fields of the form $\mathbf{F} = \mathbf{a} \times \mathbf{r}$ have zero divergence (Exercise 16). However, with the Divergence Theorem, radial fields are interesting and have many physical applications.

EXAMPLE 3 **Computing flux with the Divergence Theorem** Find the net outward flux of the field $\mathbf{F} = xyz\langle 1, 1, 1 \rangle$ across the boundaries of the cube $D = \{(x, y, z): 0 \le x \le 1, 0 \le y \le 1, 0 \le z \le 1\}$.

SOLUTION Computing a surface integral involves the six faces of the cube. The Divergence Theorem gives the outward flux with a single integral over D. The divergence of the field is

$$\nabla \cdot \mathbf{F} = \frac{\partial}{\partial x}(xyz) + \frac{\partial}{\partial y}(xyz) + \frac{\partial}{\partial z}(xyz) = yz + xz + xy.$$

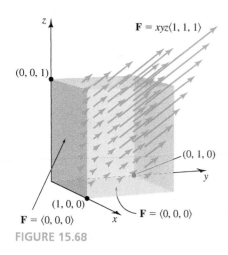

$\mathbf{F} = xyz\langle 1, 1, 1\rangle$

$(0, 0, 1)$

$(0, 1, 0)$

$(1, 0, 0)$

$\mathbf{F} = \langle 0, 0, 0\rangle$

$\mathbf{F} = \langle 0, 0, 0\rangle$

FIGURE 15.68

The integral over D is a standard triple integral:

$$\iiint_D \nabla \cdot \mathbf{F}\, dV = \iiint_D (yz + xz + xy)\, dV$$

$$= \int_0^1 \int_0^1 \int_0^1 (yz + xz + xy)\, dx\, dy\, dz \quad \text{Convert to a triple integral.}$$

$$= \frac{3}{4}. \quad\quad\quad\quad \text{Evaluate integrals.}$$

On three faces of the cube (those that lie in the coordinate planes), we see that $\mathbf{F}(0, y, z) = \mathbf{F}(x, 0, z) = \mathbf{F}(x, y, 0) = \mathbf{0}$, so there is no contribution to the flux on these faces (Figure 15.68). On the other three faces, the vector field has components out of the cube. Therefore, the net outward flux is positive, as calculated.

Related Exercises 17–24◄

> **QUICK CHECK 2** In Example 3, does the vector field have negative components anywhere in the cube D? Is the divergence negative anywhere in D? ◄

> ▷ The mass transport is also called the *flux density*; when multiplied by an area, it gives the flux. We use the convention that flux has units of mass per unit time.

> ▷ Check the units: if $\mathbf{F}$ has units of mass/(area · time), then the flux has units of mass/time ($\mathbf{n}$ has no units).

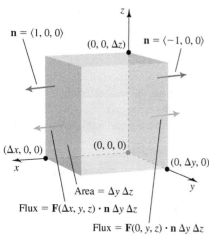

$\mathbf{n} = \langle 1, 0, 0\rangle$

$(0, 0, \Delta z)$

$\mathbf{n} = \langle -1, 0, 0\rangle$

$(\Delta x, 0, 0)$

$(0, 0, 0)$

$(0, \Delta y, 0)$

Area $= \Delta y\, \Delta z$

Flux $= \mathbf{F}(\Delta x, y, z) \cdot \mathbf{n}\, \Delta y\, \Delta z$

Flux $= \mathbf{F}(0, y, z) \cdot \mathbf{n}\, \Delta y\, \Delta z$

FIGURE 15.69

Interpretation of the Divergence Using Mass Transport   Suppose that $\mathbf{v}$ is the velocity field of a material, such as water or molasses, and ρ is its constant density. The vector field $\mathbf{F} = \rho\mathbf{v} = \langle f, g, h\rangle$ describes the **mass transport** of the material, with units of (mass/vol.) × (length/time) = mass/(area · time); typical units of mass transport are $g/m^2/s$. This means that $\mathbf{F}$ gives the mass of material flowing past a point (in each of the three coordinate directions) per unit of surface area per unit of time. When $\mathbf{F}$ is multiplied by an area, the result is the *flux*, with units of mass/unit time.

Now consider a small cube located in the vector field with its faces parallel to the coordinate planes. One vertex is located at $(0, 0, 0)$, the opposite vertex is at $(\Delta x, \Delta y, \Delta z)$, and (x, y, z) is an arbitrary point in the cube (Figure 15.69). The goal is to compute the approximate flux of material across the faces of the cube. We begin with the flux across the two parallel faces $x = 0$ and $x = \Delta x$.

The outward unit vectors normal to the faces $x = 0$ and $x = \Delta x$ are $\langle -1, 0, 0\rangle$ and $\langle 1, 0, 0\rangle$, respectively. Each face has area $\Delta y\, \Delta z$, so the approximate net flux across these faces is

$$\underbrace{\mathbf{F}(\Delta x, y, z)}_{x\,=\,\Delta x\text{ face}} \cdot \underbrace{\mathbf{n}}_{\langle 1, 0, 0\rangle}\, \Delta y\, \Delta z + \underbrace{\mathbf{F}(0, y, z)}_{x\,=\,0\text{ face}} \cdot \underbrace{\mathbf{n}}_{\langle -1, 0, 0\rangle}\, \Delta y\, \Delta z$$

$$= (f(\Delta x, y, z) - f(0, y, z))\, \Delta y\, \Delta z.$$

Note that if $f(\Delta x, y, z) > f(0, y, z)$, the net flux across these two faces of the cube is positive, which means the net flow is *out* of the cube. Letting $\Delta V = \Delta x\, \Delta y\, \Delta z$ be the volume of the cube, we rewrite the net flux as

$$(f(\Delta x, y, z) - f(0, y, z))\, \Delta y\, \Delta z$$

$$= \frac{f(\Delta x, y, z) - f(0, y, z)}{\Delta x}\, \Delta x\, \Delta y\, \Delta z \quad \text{Multiply by } \frac{\Delta x}{\Delta x}$$

$$= \frac{f(\Delta x, y, z) - f(0, y, z)}{\Delta x}\, \Delta V. \quad \Delta V = \Delta x\, \Delta y\, \Delta z$$

A similar argument can be applied to the other two pairs of faces. The approximate net flux across the faces $y = 0$ and $y = \Delta y$ is

$$\frac{g(x, \Delta y, z) - g(x, 0, z)}{\Delta y}\, \Delta V,$$

and the approximate net flux across the faces $z = 0$ and $z = \Delta z$ is

$$\frac{h(x, y, \Delta z) - h(x, y, 0)}{\Delta z}\, \Delta V.$$

Adding these three individual fluxes gives the approximate net flux out of the cube:

$$\text{net flux out of cube} \approx \left(\underbrace{\frac{f(\Delta x, y, z) - f(0, y, z)}{\Delta x}}_{\approx \frac{\partial f}{\partial x}(0,0,0)} + \underbrace{\frac{g(x, \Delta y, z) - g(x, 0, z)}{\Delta y}}_{\approx \frac{\partial g}{\partial y}(0,0,0)} \right.$$

$$\left. + \underbrace{\frac{h(x, y, \Delta z) - h(x, y, 0)}{\Delta z}}_{\approx \frac{\partial h}{\partial z}(0,0,0)} \right) \Delta V$$

$$\approx \left(\frac{\partial f}{\partial x} + \frac{\partial g}{\partial y} + \frac{\partial h}{\partial z} \right) \Bigg|_{(0,0,0)} \Delta V$$

$$= (\nabla \cdot \mathbf{F})(0,0,0) \, \Delta V.$$

Notice how the three quotients approximate partial derivatives when Δx, Δy, and Δz are small. A similar argument may be made at any point in the region.

Taking one more step, we show informally how the Divergence Theorem arises. Suppose the small cube we just analyzed is one of many small cubes of volume ΔV that fill a region D. We label the cubes $k = 1, \ldots, n$ and apply the preceding argument to each cube, letting $(\nabla \cdot \mathbf{F})_k$ be the divergence evaluated at a point in the kth cube. Adding the individual contributions to the net flux from each cube, we obtain the approximate net flux across the boundary of D:

> In making this argument, notice that for two adjacent cubes the flux into one cube equals the flux out of the other cube across the common face. Thus, there is a cancellation of fluxes throughout the interior of D.

$$\text{net flux out of } D \approx \sum_{k=1}^{n} (\nabla \cdot \mathbf{F})_k \, \Delta V.$$

Letting the volume of the cubes ΔV approach 0 and letting the number of cubes n increase, we obtain an integral over D:

$$\text{net flux out of } D = \lim_{n \to \infty} \sum_{k=1}^{n} (\nabla \cdot \mathbf{F})_k \, \Delta V = \iiint_D \nabla \cdot \mathbf{F} \, dV.$$

The net flux across the boundary of D is also given by $\iint_S \mathbf{F} \cdot \mathbf{n} \, dS$. Equating the surface integral and the volume integral gives the Divergence Theorem. Now we look at a formal proof.

QUICK CHECK 3 Draw the unit cube $D = \{(x, y, z): 0 \le x \le 1, 0 \le y \le 1, 0 \le z \le 1\}$ and sketch the vector field $\mathbf{F} = \langle x, -y, 2z \rangle$ on the six faces of the cube. Compute and interpret div $\mathbf{F}$. ◄

Proof of the Divergence Theorem

We prove the Divergence Theorem under special conditions on the region D. Let R be the projection of D in the xy-plane (Figure 15.70); that is,

$$R = \{(x, y): (x, y, z) \text{ is in } D\}.$$

Assume that the boundary of D is S and let $\mathbf{n}$ be the unit vector normal to S that points outward.

Letting $\mathbf{F} = \langle f, g, h \rangle = f\mathbf{i} + g\mathbf{j} + h\mathbf{k}$, the surface integral in the Divergence Theorem is

$$\iint_S \mathbf{F} \cdot \mathbf{n} \, dS = \iint_S (f\mathbf{i} + g\mathbf{j} + h\mathbf{k}) \cdot \mathbf{n} \, dS$$

$$= \iint_S f\mathbf{i} \cdot \mathbf{n} \, dS + \iint_S g\mathbf{j} \cdot \mathbf{n} \, dS + \iint_S h\mathbf{k} \cdot \mathbf{n} \, dS.$$

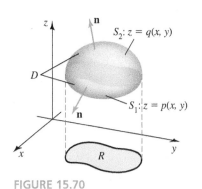

FIGURE 15.70

The volume integral in the Divergence Theorem is

$$\iiint\limits_D \nabla \cdot \mathbf{F}\, dV = \iiint\limits_D \left(\frac{\partial f}{\partial x} + \frac{\partial g}{\partial y} + \frac{\partial h}{\partial z} \right) dV.$$

Matching terms of the surface and volume integrals, the theorem is proved by showing that

$$\iint\limits_S f\mathbf{i} \cdot \mathbf{n}\, dS = \iiint\limits_D \frac{\partial f}{\partial x} dV, \tag{1}$$

$$\iint\limits_S g\mathbf{j} \cdot \mathbf{n}\, dS = \iiint\limits_D \frac{\partial g}{\partial y} dV, \text{ and} \tag{2}$$

$$\iint\limits_S h\mathbf{k} \cdot \mathbf{n}\, dS = \iiint\limits_D \frac{\partial h}{\partial z} dV. \tag{3}$$

We work on equation (3) assuming special properties for D. Suppose D is bounded by two surfaces $S_1: z = p(x, y)$ and $S_2: z = q(x, y)$, where $p(x, y) \le q(x, y)$ on R (Figure 15.70). The Fundamental Theorem of Calculus is used in the triple integral to show that

$$\iiint\limits_D \frac{\partial h}{\partial z} dV = \iint\limits_R \int_{p(x, y)}^{q(x, y)} \frac{\partial h}{\partial z} dz\, dx\, dy$$

$$= \iint\limits_R (h(x, y, q(x, y)) - h(x, y, p(x, y)))\, dx\, dy. \quad \text{Evaluate the inner integral.}$$

Now let's turn to the surface integral in equation (3), $\iint_S h\,\mathbf{k} \cdot \mathbf{n}\, dS$, and note that S consists of three pieces: the lower surface S_1, the upper surface S_2, and the vertical sides S_3 of the surface (if they exist). The normal to S_3 is everywhere orthogonal to $\mathbf{k}$, so $\mathbf{k} \cdot \mathbf{n} = 0$ and the S_3 integral makes no contribution. What remains is to compute the surface integrals over S_1 and S_2.

An outward normal to S_2 (which is the graph of $z = q(x, y)$) is $\langle -q_x, -q_y, 1 \rangle$. An outward normal to S_1 (which is the graph of $z = p(x, y)$) points *downward*, so it is given by $\langle p_x, p_y, -1 \rangle$. The surface integral of (3) becomes

$$\iint\limits_S h\,\mathbf{k} \cdot \mathbf{n}\, dS = \iint\limits_{S_2} h(x, y, z)\,\mathbf{k} \cdot \mathbf{n}\, dS + \iint\limits_{S_1} h(x, y, z)\,\mathbf{k} \cdot \mathbf{n}\, dS$$

$$= \iint\limits_R h(x, y, q(x, y))\,\underbrace{\mathbf{k} \cdot \langle -q_x, -q_y, 1 \rangle}_{1}\, dx\, dy$$

$$+ \iint\limits_R h(x, y, p(x, y))\,\underbrace{\mathbf{k} \cdot \langle p_x, p_y, -1 \rangle}_{-1}\, dx\, dy \qquad \text{Convert to an area integral.}$$

$$= \iint\limits_R h(x, y, q(x, y))\, dx\, dy - \iint\limits_R h(x, y, p(x, y))\, dx\, dy. \quad \text{Simplify.}$$

Observe that both the volume integral and the surface integral of (3) reduce to the same integral over R. Therefore, $\iint_S h \, \mathbf{k} \cdot \mathbf{n} \, dS = \iiint_D \dfrac{\partial h}{\partial z} \, dV$.

Equations (1) and (2) are handled in a similar way.

- To prove (1), we make the special assumption that D is also bounded by two surfaces, $S_1: x = s(y, z)$ and $S_2: x = t(y, z)$, where $s(x, y) \le t(x, y)$.
- To prove (2), we assume that D is bounded by two surfaces, $S_1: y = u(x, z)$ and $S_2: y = v(x, z)$, where $u(x, y) \le v(x, y)$.

When combined, the three equations—(1), (2), and (3)—yield the Divergence Theorem. ◄

Divergence Theorem for Hollow Regions

The Divergence Theorem may be extended to more general solid regions. Here we consider the important case of hollow regions. Suppose that D is a region consisting of all points inside a closed oriented surface S_2 and outside a closed oriented surface S_1, where S_1 lies within S_2 (Figure 15.71). Therefore, the boundary of D consists of S_1 and S_2. (Note that D *is* simply connected.)

We let $\mathbf{n}_1$ and $\mathbf{n}_2$ be the outward unit normal vectors for S_1 and S_2, respectively. Note that $\mathbf{n}_1$ points into D, so the outward normal to S on S_1 is $-\mathbf{n}_1$. With that observation, the Divergence Theorem takes the following form.

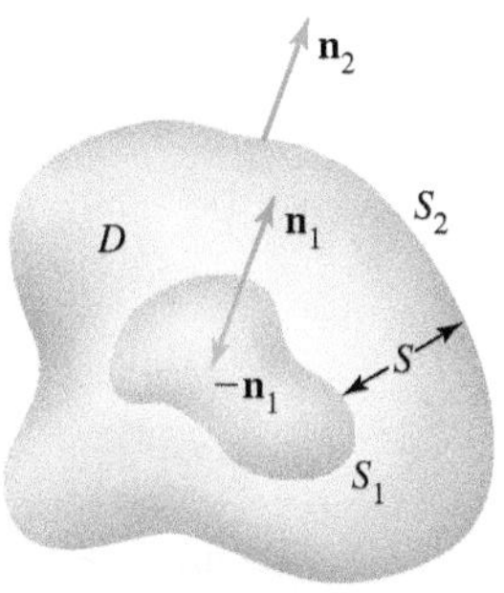

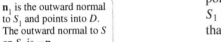

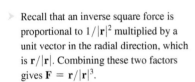

$\mathbf{n}_1$ is the outward normal to S_1 and points into D. The outward normal to S on S_1 is $-\mathbf{n}_1$.

FIGURE 15.71

> It's important to point out again that $\mathbf{n}_1$ is the normal that we would use for S_1 alone, independent of S. It is the outward normal to S_1, but it points into D.

> **THEOREM 15.16   Divergence Theorem for Hollow Regions**
> Suppose the vector field $\mathbf{F}$ satisfies the conditions of the Divergence Theorem on a region D bounded by two smooth oriented surfaces S_1 and S_2, where S_1 lies within S_2. Let S be the entire boundary of D ($S = S_1 \cup S_2$) and let $\mathbf{n}_1$ and $\mathbf{n}_2$ be the outward unit normal vectors for S_1 and S_2, respectively. Then
>
> $$\iiint_D \nabla \cdot \mathbf{F} \, dV = \iint_S \mathbf{F} \cdot \mathbf{n} \, dS = \iint_{S_2} \mathbf{F} \cdot \mathbf{n}_2 \, dS - \iint_{S_1} \mathbf{F} \cdot \mathbf{n}_1 \, dS.$$

This form of the Divergence Theorem is applicable to vector fields that are not differentiable at the origin, as is the case with some important radial vector fields.

EXAMPLE 4   Flux for an inverse square field Consider the inverse square vector field

$$\mathbf{F} = \frac{\mathbf{r}}{|\mathbf{r}|^3} = \frac{\langle x, y, z \rangle}{(x^2 + y^2 + z^2)^{3/2}}.$$

a. Find the net outward flux of $\mathbf{F}$ across the surface of the region $D = \{(x, y, z): a^2 \le x^2 + y^2 + z^2 \le b^2\}$ that lies between concentric spheres with radii a and b.

b. Find the outward flux of $\mathbf{F}$ across any sphere that encloses the origin.

SOLUTION

> Recall that an inverse square force is proportional to $1/|\mathbf{r}|^2$ multiplied by a unit vector in the radial direction, which is $\mathbf{r}/|\mathbf{r}|$. Combining these two factors gives $\mathbf{F} = \mathbf{r}/|\mathbf{r}|^3$.

a. Although the vector field is undefined at the origin, it is defined and differentiable in D, which excludes the origin. In Section 15.5 (Exercise 71) it was shown that the divergence of the radial field $\mathbf{F} = \dfrac{\mathbf{r}}{|\mathbf{r}|^p}$ with $p = 3$ is 0. We let S be the union of S_2, the larger sphere of radius b, and S_1, the smaller sphere of radius a. Because $\iiint_D \nabla \cdot \mathbf{F}\, dV = 0$, the Divergence Theorem implies that

$$\iint_S \mathbf{F} \cdot \mathbf{n}\, dS = \iint_{S_2} \mathbf{F} \cdot \mathbf{n}_2\, dS - \iint_{S_1} \mathbf{F} \cdot \mathbf{n}_1\, dS = 0.$$

Therefore, the next flux across S is zero.

b. Part (a) implies that

$$\underbrace{\iint_{S_2} \mathbf{F} \cdot \mathbf{n}_2\, dS}_{\text{out of } D} = \underbrace{\iint_{S_1} \mathbf{F} \cdot \mathbf{n}_1\, dS}_{\text{into } D}.$$

We see that the flux out of D across S_2 equals the flux into D across S_1. To find that flux, we evaluate the surface integral over S_1 on which $|\mathbf{r}| = a$. (Because the fluxes are equal, S_2 could also be used.)

The easiest way to evaluate the surface integral is to note that on the sphere S_1, the unit outward normal vector is $\mathbf{n}_1 = \mathbf{r}/|\mathbf{r}|$. Therefore, the surface integral is

$$
\begin{aligned}
\iint_{S_1} \mathbf{F} \cdot \mathbf{n}_1\, dS &= \iint_{S_1} \frac{\mathbf{r}}{|\mathbf{r}|^3} \cdot \frac{\mathbf{r}}{|\mathbf{r}|}\, dS && \text{Substitute for } \mathbf{F} \text{ and } \mathbf{n}_1. \\
&= \iint_{S_1} \frac{|\mathbf{r}|^2}{|\mathbf{r}|^4}\, dS && \mathbf{r} \cdot \mathbf{r} = |\mathbf{r}|^2 \\
&= \iint_{S_1} \frac{1}{a^2}\, dS && |\mathbf{r}| = a \\
&= \frac{4\pi a^2}{a^2} && \text{Surface area} = 4\pi a^2 \\
&= 4\pi.
\end{aligned}
$$

The same result is obtained using S_2 or any smooth surface enclosing the origin. The flux of the inverse square field across *any* surface enclosing the origin is 4π. As shown in Exercise 46, among radial fields, this property holds only for the inverse square field ($p = 3$).

Related Exercises 25–30◄

Gauss' Law

Applying the Divergence Theorem to electric fields leads to one of the fundamental laws of physics. The electric field due to a point charge Q located at the origin is given by the inverse square law,

$$\mathbf{E}(x, y, z) = \frac{Q}{4\pi\varepsilon_0} \frac{\mathbf{r}}{|\mathbf{r}|^3},$$

where $\mathbf{r} = \langle x, y, z \rangle$ and ϵ_0 is a physical constant called the *permittivity of free space*.

According to the calculation of Example 4, the flux of the field $\dfrac{\mathbf{r}}{|\mathbf{r}|^3}$ across any surface that encloses the origin is 4π. Therefore, the flux of the electric field across any surface enclosing the origin is $\dfrac{Q}{4\pi\varepsilon_0} \cdot 4\pi = \dfrac{Q}{\varepsilon_0}$ (Figure 15.72). This is one statement of

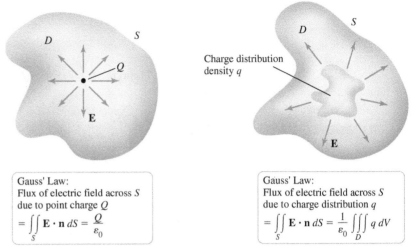

FIGURE 15.72

Gauss' Law: If S is a surface that encloses a point charge Q, then the flux of the electric field across S is

$$\iint_S \mathbf{E} \cdot \mathbf{n} \, dS = \frac{Q}{\varepsilon_0}.$$

In fact, Gauss' Law applies to more general charge distributions (Exercise 39). If $q(x, y, z)$ is a charge density (charge per unit volume) defined on a region D enclosed by S, then the total charge within D is $Q = \iiint_D q(x, y, z) \, dV$. Replacing Q by this triple integral, Gauss' Law takes the form

$$\iint_S \mathbf{E} \cdot \mathbf{n} \, dS = \frac{1}{\varepsilon_0} \underbrace{\iiint_D q(x, y, z) \, dV}_{Q}.$$

Gauss' Law applies to other inverse square fields. In a slightly different form, it also governs heat transfer. If T is the temperature distribution in a solid body D, then the heat flow vector field is $\mathbf{F} = -k\nabla T$. (Heat flows down the temperature gradient.) If $q(x, y, z)$ represents the sources of heat within D, Gauss' Law says

$$\iint_S \mathbf{F} \cdot \mathbf{n} \, dS = -k \iint_S \nabla T \cdot \mathbf{n} \, dS = \iiint_D q(x, y, z) \, dV.$$

We see that, in general, the flux of material (fluid, heat, electric field lines) across the boundary of a region is the cumulative effect of the sources within the region.

A Final Perspective

We now stand back and look at the progression of fundamental theorems of calculus that have appeared throughout this book. Each theorem builds on its predecessors, extending the same basic idea to a different situation or to higher dimensions.

In all cases, the statement is effectively the same: The cumulative (integrated) effect of the *derivatives* of a function throughout a region is determined by the values of the function on the boundary of that region. This principle underlies much of our understanding of the world around us.

Fundamental Theorem of Calculus	$\displaystyle\int_a^b f'(x)\,dx = f(b) - f(a)$	
Fundamental Theorem of Line Integrals	$\displaystyle\int_C \nabla f \cdot d\mathbf{r} = f(B) - f(A)$	
Green's Theorem (Circulation form)	$\displaystyle\iint_R (g_x - f_y)\,dA = \oint_C f\,dx + g\,dy$	
Stokes' Theorem	$\displaystyle\iint_S (\nabla \times \mathbf{F}) \cdot \mathbf{n}\,dS = \oint_C \mathbf{F}\cdot d\mathbf{r}$	
Divergence Theorem	$\displaystyle\iiint_D \nabla \cdot \mathbf{F}\,dV = \iint_S \mathbf{F}\cdot \mathbf{n}\,dS$	

SECTION 15.8 EXERCISES

Review Questions

1. Explain the meaning of the surface integral in the Divergence Theorem.

2. Interpret the volume integral in the Divergence Theorem.

3. Explain the meaning of the Divergence Theorem.

4. What is the net outward flux of the rotation field $\mathbf{F} = \langle 2z + y, -x, -2x \rangle$ across the surface that encloses any region?

5. What is the net outward flux of the radial field $\mathbf{F} = \langle x, y, z \rangle$ across the sphere of radius 2 centered at the origin?

6. What is the divergence of an inverse square vector field?

7. Suppose div $\mathbf{F} = 0$ in a region enclosed by two concentric spheres. What is the relationship between the outward fluxes across the two spheres?

8. If div $\mathbf{F} > 0$ in a region enclosed by a small cube, is the net flux of the field into or out of the cube?

Basic Skills

9–12. Verifying the Divergence Theorem *Evaluate both integrals of the Divergence Theorem for the following vector fields and regions. Check for agreement.*

9. $\mathbf{F} = \langle 2x, 3y, 4z \rangle$; $D = \{(x, y, z): x^2 + y^2 + z^2 \le 4\}$

10. $\mathbf{F} = \langle -x, -y, -z \rangle$; $D = \{(x, y, z): |x| \le 1, |y| \le 1, |z| \le 1\}$

11. $\mathbf{F} = \langle z - y, x, -x \rangle$; $D = \{(x, y, z): x^2/4 + y^2/8 + z^2/12 \le 1\}$

12. $\mathbf{F} = \langle x^2, y^2, z^2 \rangle$; $D = \{(x, y, z): |x| \le 1, |y| \le 2, |z| \le 3\}$

13–16. Rotation fields

13. Find the net outward flux of the field $\mathbf{F} = \langle 2z - y, x, -2x \rangle$ across the sphere of radius 1 centered at the origin.

14. Find the net outward flux of the field $\mathbf{F} = \langle z - y, x - z, y - x \rangle$ across the boundary of the cube $\{(x, y, z): |x| \le 1, |y| \le 1, |z| \le 1\}$.

15. Find the net outward flux of the field $\mathbf{F} = \langle bz - cy, cx - az, ay - bx \rangle$ across any smooth closed surface in $\mathbb{R}^3$, where a, b, and c are constants.

16. Find the net outward flux of $\mathbf{F} = \mathbf{a} \times \mathbf{r}$ across any smooth closed surface in $\mathbb{R}^3$, where $\mathbf{a}$ is a constant nonzero vector and $\mathbf{r} = \langle x, y, z \rangle$.

17–24. Computing flux *Use the Divergence Theorem to compute the net outward flux of the following fields across the given surfaces S.*

17. $\mathbf{F} = \langle x, -2y, 3z \rangle$; S is the sphere $\{(x, y, z): x^2 + y^2 + z^2 = 6\}$.

18. $\mathbf{F} = \langle x^2, 2xz, y^2 \rangle$; S is the surface of the cube cut from the first octant by the planes $x = 1$, $y = 1$, and $z = 1$.

19. $\mathbf{F} = \langle x, 2y, z \rangle$; S is the boundary of the tetrahedron in the first octant formed by the plane $x + y + z = 1$.

20. $\mathbf{F} = \langle x^2, y^2, z^2 \rangle$; S is the sphere $\{(x, y, z): x^2 + y^2 + z^2 = 25\}$.

21. $\mathbf{F} = \langle y - 2x, x^3 - y, y^2 - z \rangle$; S is the sphere $\{(x, y, z): x^2 + y^2 + z^2 = 4\}$.

22. $\mathbf{F} = \langle y + z, x + z, x + y \rangle$; S consists of the faces of the cube $\{(x, y, z): |x| \le 1, |y| \le 1, |z| \le 1\}$.

23. $\mathbf{F} = \langle x, y, z \rangle$; S is the surface of the paraboloid $z = 4 - x^2 - y^2$, for $z \ge 0$, plus its base in the xy-plane.

24. $\mathbf{F} = \langle x, y, z \rangle$; S is the surface of the cone $z^2 = x^2 + y^2$, for $0 \le z \le 4$, plus its top surface in the plane $z = 4$.

25–30. Divergence Theorem for more general regions *Use the Divergence Theorem to compute the net outward flux of the following vector fields across the boundary of the given regions D.*

25. $\mathbf{F} = \langle z - x, x - y, 2y - z \rangle$; D is the region between the spheres of radius 2 and 4 centered at the origin.

26. $\mathbf{F} = \mathbf{r}|\mathbf{r}| = \langle x, y, z \rangle \sqrt{x^2 + y^2 + z^2}$; D is the region between the spheres of radius 1 and 2 centered at the origin.

27. $\mathbf{F} = \dfrac{\mathbf{r}}{|\mathbf{r}|} = \dfrac{\langle x, y, z \rangle}{\sqrt{x^2 + y^2 + z^2}}$; D is the region between the spheres of radius 1 and 2 centered at the origin.

28. $\mathbf{F} = \langle z - y, x - z, 2y - x \rangle$; D is the region between two cubes: $\{(x, y, z): 1 \le |x| \le 3, 1 \le |y| \le 3, 1 \le |z| \le 3\}$.

29. $\mathbf{F} = \langle x^2, -y^2, z^2 \rangle$; D is the region in the first octant between the planes $z = 4 - x - y$ and $z = 2 - x - y$.

30. $\mathbf{F} = \langle x, 2y, 3z \rangle$; D is the region between the cylinders $x^2 + y^2 = 1$ and $x^2 + y^2 = 4$, for $0 \le z \le 8$.

Further Explorations

31. **Explain why or why not** Determine whether the following statements are true and give an explanation or counterexample.

   a. If $\nabla \cdot \mathbf{F} = 0$ at all points of a region D, then $\mathbf{F} \cdot \mathbf{n} = 0$ at all points of the boundary of D.

   b. If $\iint_S \mathbf{F} \cdot \mathbf{n} \, dS = 0$ on all closed surfaces in $\mathbb{R}^3$, then $\mathbf{F}$ is constant.

   c. If $|\mathbf{F}| < 1$, then $\left| \iiint_D \nabla \cdot \mathbf{F} \, dV \right|$ is less than the area of the surface of D.

32. **Flux across a sphere** Consider the radial field $\mathbf{F} = \langle x, y, z \rangle$ and let S be the sphere of radius a centered at the origin. Compute the outward flux of $\mathbf{F}$ across S using the representation $z = \pm \sqrt{a^2 - x^2 - y^2}$ for the sphere (either symmetry or two surfaces must be used).

33–35. Flux integrals *Compute the outward flux of the following vector fields across the given surfaces S. You should decide which integral of the Divergence Theorem to use.*

33. $\mathbf{F} = \langle x^2 e^y \cos z, -4x e^y \cos z, 2x e^y \sin z \rangle$; S is the boundary of the ellipsoid $x^2/4 + y^2 + z^2 = 1$.

34. $\mathbf{F} = \langle -yz, xz, 1 \rangle$; S is the boundary of the ellipsoid $x^2/4 + y^2/4 + z^2 = 1$.

35. $\mathbf{F} = \langle x \sin y, -\cos y, z \sin y \rangle$; S is the boundary of the region bounded by the planes $x = 1$, $y = 0$, $y = \pi/2$, $z = 0$, and $z = x$.

36. **Radial fields** Consider the radial vector field
$$\mathbf{F} = \frac{\mathbf{r}}{|\mathbf{r}|^p} = \frac{\langle x, y, z \rangle}{(x^2 + y^2 + z^2)^{p/2}}.$$ Let S be the sphere of radius a centered at the origin.

   a. Use a surface integral to show that the outward flux of $\mathbf{F}$ across S is $4\pi a^{3-p}$. Recall that the unit normal to the sphere is $\mathbf{r}/|\mathbf{r}|$.

   b. For what values of p does $\mathbf{F}$ satisfy the conditions of the Divergence Theorem? For these values of p, use the fact (Theorem 15.8) that $\nabla \cdot \mathbf{F} = \dfrac{3 - p}{|\mathbf{r}|^p}$ to compute the flux across S using the Divergence Theorem.

37. **Singular radial field** Consider the radial field
$$\mathbf{F} = \frac{\mathbf{r}}{|\mathbf{r}|} = \frac{\langle x, y, z \rangle}{(x^2 + y^2 + z^2)^{1/2}}.$$

   a. Evaluate a surface integral to show that $\iint_S \mathbf{F} \cdot \mathbf{n} \, dS = 4\pi a^2$, where S is the surface of a sphere of radius a centered at the origin.

   b. Note that the first partial derivatives of the components of $\mathbf{F}$ are undefined at the origin, so the Divergence Theorem does not apply directly. Nevertheless the flux across the sphere as computed in part (a) is finite. Evaluate the triple integral of the Divergence Theorem as an improper integral as follows. Integrate div $\mathbf{F}$ over the region between two spheres of radius a and $0 < \varepsilon < a$. Then let $\varepsilon \to 0^+$ to obtain the flux computed in part (a).

38. **Logarithmic potential** Consider the potential function $\varphi(x, y, z) = \frac{1}{2} \ln (x^2 + y^2 + z^2) = \ln |\mathbf{r}|$, where $\mathbf{r} = \langle x, y, z \rangle$.

   a. Show that the gradient field associated with φ is
$$\mathbf{F} = \frac{\mathbf{r}}{|\mathbf{r}|^2} = \frac{\langle x, y, z \rangle}{x^2 + y^2 + z^2}.$$

   b. Show that $\iint_S \mathbf{F} \cdot \mathbf{n} \, dS = 4\pi a$, where S is the surface of a sphere of radius a centered at the origin.

   c. Compute div $\mathbf{F}$.

   d. Note that $\mathbf{F}$ is undefined at the origin, so the Divergence Theorem does not apply directly. Evaluate the volume integral as described in Exercise 37.

Applications

39. **Gauss' Law for electric fields** The electric field due to a point charge Q is $\mathbf{E} = \dfrac{Q}{4\pi \varepsilon_0} \dfrac{\mathbf{r}}{|\mathbf{r}|^3}$, where $\mathbf{r} = \langle x, y, z \rangle$, and ε_0 is a constant.

   a. Show that the flux of the field across a sphere of radius a centered at the origin is $\iint_S \mathbf{E} \cdot \mathbf{n} \, dS = \dfrac{Q}{\varepsilon_0}$.

   b. Let S be the boundary of the region between two spheres centered at the origin of radius a and b with $a < b$. Use the Divergence Theorem to show that the net outward flux across S is zero.

   c. Suppose there is a distribution of charge within a region D. Let $q(x, y, z)$ be the charge density (charge per unit volume). Interpret the statement that
$$\iint_S \mathbf{E} \cdot \mathbf{n} \, dS = \frac{1}{\varepsilon_0} \iiint_D q(x, y, z) \, dV.$$

d. Assuming $\mathbf{E}$ satisfies the conditions of the Divergence Theorem, conclude from part (c) that $\nabla \cdot \mathbf{E} = \dfrac{q}{\varepsilon_0}$.

e. Because the electric force is conservative, it has a potential function φ. From part (d) conclude that $\nabla^2 \varphi = \nabla \cdot \nabla \varphi = \dfrac{q}{\varepsilon_0}$.

40. Gauss' Law for gravitation The gravitational force due to a point mass M at the origin is proportional to $\mathbf{F} = GM\mathbf{r}/|\mathbf{r}|^3$, where $\mathbf{r} = \langle x, y, z \rangle$ and G is the gravitational constant.

a. Show that the flux of the force field across a sphere of radius a centered at the origin is $\iint_S \mathbf{F} \cdot \mathbf{n} \, dS = 4\pi GM$.

b. Let S be the boundary of the region between two spheres centered at the origin of radius a and b with $a < b$. Use the Divergence Theorem to show that the net outward flux across S is zero.

c. Suppose there is a distribution of mass within a region D. Let $\rho(x, y, z)$ be the mass density (mass per unit volume). Interpret the statement that

$$\iint_S \mathbf{F} \cdot \mathbf{n} \, dS = 4\pi G \iiint_D \rho(x, y, z) \, dV$$

d. Assuming $\mathbf{F}$ satisfies the conditions of the Divergence Theorem, conclude from part (c) that $\nabla \cdot \mathbf{F} = 4\pi G\rho$.

e. Because the gravitational force is conservative, it has a potential function φ. From part (d) conclude that $\nabla^2 \varphi = 4\pi G\rho$.

41–45. Heat transfer *Fourier's Law of heat transfer (or heat conduction) states that the heat flow vector $\mathbf{F}$ at a point is proportional to the negative gradient of the temperature; that is, $\mathbf{F} = -k\nabla T$, which means that heat energy flows from hot regions to cold regions. The constant $k > 0$ is called the conductivity, which has metric units of $J/m \cdot s \cdot K$ or $W/m \cdot K$. A temperature function for a region D is given. Find the net outward heat flux $\iint_S \mathbf{F} \cdot \mathbf{n} \, dS = -k \iint_S \nabla T \cdot \mathbf{n} \, dS$ across the boundary S of D. In some cases it may be easier to use the Divergence Theorem and evaluate a triple integral. Assume that $k = 1$.*

41. $T(x, y, z) = 100 + x + 2y + z$;
$D = \{(x, y, z) : 0 \le x \le 1, 0 \le y \le 1, 0 \le z \le 1\}$

42. $T(x, y, z) = 100 + x^2 + y^2 + z^2$;
$D = \{(x, y, z) : 0 \le x \le 1, 0 \le y \le 1, 0 \le z \le 1\}$

43. $T(x, y, z) = 100 + e^{-z}$;
$D = \{(x, y, z) : 0 \le x \le 1, 0 \le y \le 1, 0 \le z \le 1\}$

44. $T(x, y, z) = 100 + x^2 + y^2 + z^2$; D is the unit sphere centered at the origin.

45. $T(x, y, z) = 100e^{-x^2-y^2-z^2}$; D is the sphere of radius a centered at the origin.

Additional Exercises

46. Inverse square fields are special Let $\mathbf{F}$ be a radial field $\mathbf{F} = \mathbf{r}/|\mathbf{r}|^p$, where p is a real number and $\mathbf{r} = \langle x, y, z \rangle$. With $p = 3$, $\mathbf{F}$ is an inverse square field.

a. Show that the net flux across a sphere centered at the origin is independent of the radius of the sphere only for $p = 3$.

b. Explain the observation in part (a) by finding the flux of $\mathbf{F} = \mathbf{r}/|\mathbf{r}|^p$ across the boundaries of a spherical box $\{(\rho, \varphi, \theta) : a \le \rho \le b, \varphi_1 \le \varphi \le \varphi_2, \theta_1 \le \theta \le \theta_2\}$ for various values of p.

47. A beautiful flux integral Consider the potential function $\varphi(x, y, z) = G(\rho)$, where G is any twice differentiable function and $\rho = \sqrt{x^2 + y^2 + z^2}$; therefore, G depends only on the distance from the origin.

a. Show that the gradient vector field associated with φ is

$$\mathbf{F} = \nabla\varphi = G'(\rho) \frac{\mathbf{r}}{\rho}, \text{ where } \mathbf{r} = \langle x, y, z \rangle \text{ and } \rho = |\mathbf{r}|.$$

b. Let S be the sphere of radius a centered at the origin and let D be the region enclosed by S. Show that the flux of $\mathbf{F}$ across S is $\iint_S \mathbf{F} \cdot \mathbf{n} \, dS = 4\pi a^2 G'(a)$.

c. Show that $\nabla \cdot \mathbf{F} = \nabla \cdot \nabla\varphi = \dfrac{2G'(\rho)}{\rho} + G''(\rho)$.

d. Use part (c) to show that the flux across S (as given in part (b)) is also obtained by the volume integral $\iiint_D \nabla \cdot \mathbf{F} \, dV$. (*Hint:* use spherical coordinates and integrate by parts.)

48. Integration by parts (Gauss' Formula) Recall the Product Rule of Theorem 15.11: $\nabla \cdot (u\mathbf{F}) = \nabla u \cdot \mathbf{F} + u(\nabla \cdot \mathbf{F})$.

a. Integrate both sides of this identity over a solid region D with a closed boundary S and use the Divergence Theorem to prove an integration by parts rule:

$$\iiint_D u(\nabla \cdot \mathbf{F}) \, dV = \iint_S u\mathbf{F} \cdot \mathbf{n} \, dS - \iiint_D \nabla u \cdot \mathbf{F} \, dV.$$

b. Explain the correspondence between this rule and the integration by parts rule for single-variable functions.

c. Use integration by parts to evaluate $\iiint_D (x^2y + y^2z + z^2x) \, dV$, where D is the cube in the first octant cut by the planes $x = 1$, $y = 1$, and $z = 1$.

49. Green's Formula Write Gauss' Formula of Exercise 48 in two dimensions—that is, where $\mathbf{F} = \langle f, g \rangle$, D is a plane region R and C is the boundary of R. Show that the result is Green's Formula:

$$\iint_R u(f_x + g_y) \, dA = \oint_C u(\mathbf{F} \cdot \mathbf{n}) \, ds - \iint_R (fu_x + gu_y) \, dA.$$

Show that with $u = 1$, one form of Green's Theorem appears. Which form of Green's Theorem is it?

50. Green's First Identity Prove Green's First Identity for twice differentiable scalar-valued functions u and v defined on a region D:

$$\iiint_D (u\nabla^2 v + \nabla u \cdot \nabla v) \, dV = \iint_S u\nabla v \cdot \mathbf{n} \, dS,$$

where $\nabla^2 v = \nabla \cdot \nabla v$. You may apply Gauss' Formula in Exercise 48 to $\mathbf{F} = \nabla v$ or apply the Divergence Theorem to $\mathbf{F} = u\nabla v$.

51. Green's Second Identity Prove Green's Second Identity for scalar-valued functions u and v defined on a region D:

$$\iiint_D (u\nabla^2 v - v\nabla^2 u) \, dV = \iint_S (u\nabla v - v\nabla u) \cdot \mathbf{n} \, dS.$$

(*Hint:* Reverse the roles of u and v in Green's First Identity.)

52–54. Harmonic functions *A scalar-valued function φ is* **harmonic** *on a region D if $\nabla^2\varphi = \nabla \cdot \nabla\varphi = 0$ at all points of D.*

52. Show that the potential function $\varphi(x, y, z) = |\mathbf{r}|^{-p}$ is harmonic provided $p = 0$ or $p = 1$, where $\mathbf{r} = \langle x, y, z \rangle$. To what vector fields do these potentials correspond?

53. Show that if φ is harmonic on a region D enclosed by a surface S, then $\iint_S \nabla\varphi \cdot \mathbf{n} \, dS = 0$.

54. Show that if u is harmonic on a region D enclosed by a surface S, then $\iint_S u \, \nabla u \cdot \mathbf{n} \, dS = \iiint_D |\nabla u|^2 \, dV$.

55. Miscellaneous integral identities Prove the following identities.

a. $\iiint_D \nabla \times \mathbf{F} \, dV = \iint_S (\mathbf{n} \times \mathbf{F}) \, dS$ (*Hint:* Apply the Divergence Theorem to each component of the identity.)

b. $\iint_S (\mathbf{n} \times \nabla\varphi) \, dS = \oint_C \varphi \, d\mathbf{r}$ (*Hint:* Apply Stokes' Theorem to each component of the identity.)

QUICK CHECK ANSWERS

1. If $\mathbf{F}$ is constant, then $\text{div}(\mathbf{F}) = 0$, so $\iiint_D \nabla \cdot \mathbf{F} \, dV = \iint_S \mathbf{F} \cdot \mathbf{n} \, dS = 0$. This means that all the "material" that flows into one side of D flows out of the other side of D. **2.** The vector field and the divergence are positive throughout D. **3.** The vector field has no flow into or out of the cube on the faces $x = 0$, $y = 0$, and $z = 0$ because the vectors of $\mathbf{F}$ on these faces are parallel to the faces. The vector field points out of the cube on the $x = 1$ and $z = 1$ faces and into the cube on the $y = 1$ face. $\text{div}(\mathbf{F}) = 2$, so there is a net flow out of the cube. ◂

CHAPTER 15   REVIEW EXERCISES

1. Explain why or why not Determine whether the following statements are true and give an explanation or counterexample.

a. The rotational field $\mathbf{F} = \langle -y, x \rangle$ has zero curl and zero divergence.

b. $\nabla \times \nabla\varphi = \mathbf{0}$

c. Two vector fields with the same curl differ by a constant vector field.

d. Two vector fields with the same divergence differ by a constant vector field.

e. If $\mathbf{F} = \langle x, y, z \rangle$ and S encloses a region D, then $\iint_S \mathbf{F} \cdot \mathbf{n} \, dS$ is three times the volume of D.

2. Matching vector fields Match vector fields a–f with the graphs A–F. Let $\mathbf{r} = \langle x, y \rangle$.

a. $\mathbf{F} = \langle x, y \rangle$
b. $\mathbf{F} = \langle -2y, 2x \rangle$
c. $\mathbf{F} = \mathbf{r}/|\mathbf{r}|$
d. $\mathbf{F} = \langle y - x, x \rangle$
e. $\mathbf{F} = \langle e^{-y}, e^{-x} \rangle$
f. $\mathbf{F} = \langle \sin \pi x, \sin \pi y \rangle$

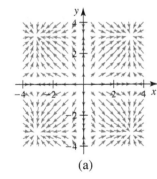

(a)

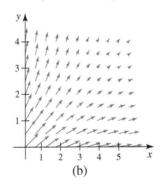

(b)

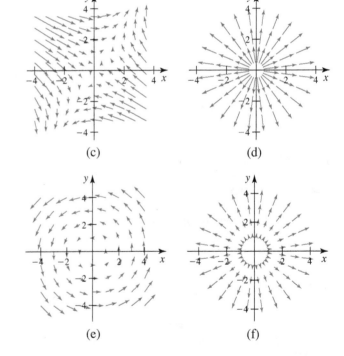

(c)

(d)

(e)

(f)

3–4. Gradient fields in $\mathbb{R}^2$ *Find the vector field $\mathbf{F} = \nabla\varphi$ for the following potential functions. Sketch a few level curves of φ and sketch the general appearance of $\mathbf{F}$ in relation to the level curves.*

3. $\varphi(x, y) = x^2 + 4y^2$, for $|x| \le 5$, $|y| \le 5$

4. $\varphi(x, y) = (x^2 - y^2)/2$, for $|x| \le 2$, $|y| \le 2$

5–6. Gradient fields in $\mathbb{R}^3$ *Find the vector field* $\mathbf{F} = \nabla\varphi$ *for the following potential functions.*

5. $\varphi(x, y, z) = 1/|\mathbf{r}|$, where $\mathbf{r} = \langle x, y, z \rangle$

6. $\varphi(x, y, z) = \dfrac{1}{2}e^{-x^2-y^2-z^2}$

7. Normal component Let C be the circle of radius 2 centered at the origin with counterclockwise orientation.

   a. Give the unit outward normal vector at any point (x, y) on C.
   b. Find the normal component of the vector field $\mathbf{F} = 2\langle y, -x \rangle$ at any point on C.
   c. Find the normal component of the vector field $\mathbf{F} = \dfrac{\langle x, y \rangle}{x^2 + y^2}$ at any point on C.

8–10. Line integrals *Evaluate the following line integrals.*

8. $\displaystyle\int_C (x^2 - 2xy + y^2)\, ds$; C is the upper half of the circle $\mathbf{r}(t) = \langle 5\cos t, 5\sin t \rangle$, for $0 \le t \le \pi$, with counterclockwise orientation.

9. $\displaystyle\int_C ye^{-xz}\, ds$; C is the path $\mathbf{r}(t) = \langle t, 3t, -6t \rangle$, for $0 \le t \le \ln 8$.

10. $\displaystyle\int_C (xz - y^2)\, ds$; C is the line segment from $(0, 1, 2)$ to $(-3, 7, -1)$.

11. Two parameterizations Verify that $\displaystyle\oint_C (x - 2y + 3z)\, ds$ has the same value when C is given by $\mathbf{r}(t) = \langle 2\cos t, 2\sin t, 0 \rangle$, for $0 \le t \le 2\pi$, and by $\mathbf{r}(t) = \langle 2\cos t^2, 2\sin t^2, 0 \rangle$, for $0 \le t \le \sqrt{2\pi}$.

12. Work integral Find the work done in moving an object from $P(1, 0, 0)$ to $Q(0, 1, 0)$ in the presence of the force $\mathbf{F} = \langle 1, 2y, -4z \rangle$ along the following paths.

   a. The line segment from P to Q
   b. The line segment from P to $O(0, 0, 0)$ followed by the line segment from O to Q
   c. The arc of the quarter circle from P to Q
   d. Is the work independent of the path?

13–14. Work integrals in $\mathbb{R}^3$ *Given the following force fields, find the work required to move an object on the given curve.*

13. $\mathbf{F} = \langle -y, z, x \rangle$ on the path consisting of the line segment from $(0, 0, 0)$ to $(0, 1, 0)$ followed by the line segment from $(0, 1, 0)$ to $(0, 1, 4)$

14. $\mathbf{F} = \dfrac{\langle x, y, z \rangle}{(x^2 + y^2 + z^2)^{3/2}}$ on the path $\mathbf{r}(t) = \langle t^2, 3t^2, -t^2 \rangle$, for $1 \le t \le 2$

15–18. Circulation and flux *Find the circulation and the outward flux of the following vector fields for the curve* $\mathbf{r}(t) = \langle 2\cos t, 2\sin t \rangle$, *for* $0 \le t \le 2\pi$.

15. $\mathbf{F} = \langle y - x, y \rangle$ **16.** $\mathbf{F} = \langle x, y \rangle$

17. $\mathbf{F} = \mathbf{r}/|\mathbf{r}|^2$, where $\mathbf{r} = \langle x, y \rangle$ **18.** $\mathbf{F} = \langle x - y, x \rangle$

19. Flux in channel flow Consider the flow of water in a channel whose boundaries are the planes $y = \pm L$ and $z = \pm\frac{1}{2}$. The velocity field in the channel is $\mathbf{v} = \langle v_0(L^2 - y^2), 0, 0 \rangle$. Find the flux across the cross section of the channel at $x = 0$ in terms of v_0 and L.

20–23. Conservative vector fields and potentials *Determine whether the following vector fields are conservative on their domains. If so, find a potential function.*

20. $\mathbf{F} = \langle y^2, 2xy \rangle$ **21.** $\mathbf{F} = \langle y, x + z^2, 2yz \rangle$

22. $\mathbf{F} = \langle e^x \cos y, -e^x \sin y \rangle$ **23.** $\mathbf{F} = e^z \langle y, x, xy \rangle$

24–27. Evaluating line integrals *Evaluate the line integral* $\int_C \mathbf{F} \cdot d\mathbf{r}$ *for the following vector fields* $\mathbf{F}$ *and curves* C *in two ways.*

   a. *By parameterizing* C
   b. *By using the Fundamental Theorem for line integrals, if possible*

24. $\mathbf{F} = \nabla(x^2y)$; $C: \mathbf{r}(t) = \langle 9 - t^2, t \rangle$, for $0 \le t \le 3$

25. $\mathbf{F} = \nabla(xyz)$; $C: \mathbf{r}(t) = \langle \cos t, \sin t, t/\pi \rangle$, for $0 \le t \le \pi$

26. $\mathbf{F} = \langle x, -y \rangle$; C is the square with vertices $(\pm 1, \pm 1)$ with counterclockwise orientation.

27. $\mathbf{F} = \langle y, z, -x \rangle$; $C: \mathbf{r}(t) = \langle \cos t, \sin t, 4 \rangle$, for $0 \le t \le 2\pi$

28. Radial fields in $\mathbb{R}^2$ are conservative Prove that the radial field $\mathbf{F} = \dfrac{\mathbf{r}}{|\mathbf{r}|^p}$, where $\mathbf{r} = \langle x, y \rangle$ and p is a real number, is conservative on $\mathbb{R}^2$ with the origin removed. For what value of p is $\mathbf{F}$ conservative on $\mathbb{R}^2$ (including the origin)?

29–32. Green's Theorem for line integrals *Use either form of Green's Theorem to evaluate the following line integrals.*

29. $\displaystyle\oint_C xy^2\, dx + x^2y\, dy$; C is the triangle with vertices $(0, 0)$, $(2, 0)$, and $(0, 2)$ with counterclockwise orientation.

30. $\displaystyle\oint_C (-3y + x^{3/2})\, dx + (x - y^{2/3})\, dy$; C is the boundary of the half disk $\{(x, y): x^2 + y^2 \le 2, y \ge 0\}$ with counterclockwise orientation.

31. $\displaystyle\oint_C (x^3 + xy)\, dy + (2y^2 - 2x^2y)\, dx$; C is the square with vertices $(\pm 1, \pm 1)$ with counterclockwise orientation.

32. $\displaystyle\oint_C 3x^3\, dy - 3y^3\, dx$; C is the circle of radius 4 centered at the origin with *clockwise* orientation.

33–34. Areas of plane regions *Find the area of the following regions using a line integral.*

33. The region enclosed by the ellipse $x^2 + 4y^2 = 16$

34. The region bounded by the hypocycloid $\mathbf{r}(t) = \langle \cos^3 t, \sin^3 t \rangle$, for $0 \le t \le 2\pi$

35–36. Circulation and flux *Consider the following vector fields.*

a. *Compute the circulation on the boundary of the region R (with counterclockwise orientation).*

b. *Compute the outward flux across the boundary of R.*

35. $\mathbf{F} = \mathbf{r}/|\mathbf{r}|$, where $\mathbf{r} = \langle x, y \rangle$ and R is the half-annulus $\{(r, \theta): 1 \le r \le 3, 0 \le \theta \le \pi\}$

36. $\mathbf{F} = \langle -\sin y, x \cos y \rangle$, where R is the square $\{(x, y): 0 \le x \le \pi/2, 0 \le y \le \pi/2\}$

37. Parameters Let $\mathbf{F} = \langle ax + by, cx + dy \rangle$, where $a, b, c,$ and d are constants.

a. For what values of $a, b, c,$ and d is $\mathbf{F}$ conservative?

b. For what values of $a, b, c,$ and d is $\mathbf{F}$ source free?

c. For what values of $a, b, c,$ and d is $\mathbf{F}$ conservative and source free?

38–41. Divergence and curl *Compute the divergence and curl of the following vector fields. State whether the field is source free or irrotational.*

38. $\mathbf{F} = \langle yz, xz, xy \rangle$

39. $\mathbf{F} = \mathbf{r}|\mathbf{r}| = \langle x, y, z \rangle \sqrt{x^2 + y^2 + z^2}$

40. $\mathbf{F} = \langle \sin xy, \cos yz, \sin xz \rangle$

41. $\mathbf{F} = \langle 2xy + z^4, x^2, 4xz^3 \rangle$

42. Identities Prove that $\nabla\left(\dfrac{1}{|\mathbf{r}|^4}\right) = -\dfrac{4\mathbf{r}}{|\mathbf{r}|^6}$, and use the result to prove that $\nabla \cdot \nabla\left(\dfrac{1}{|\mathbf{r}|^4}\right) = \dfrac{12}{|\mathbf{r}|^6}$.

43. Maximum curl Let $\mathbf{F} = \langle z, x, -y \rangle$.

a. What are the components of curl $\mathbf{F}$ in the directions $\mathbf{n} = \langle 1, 0, 0 \rangle$ and $\mathbf{n} = \langle 0, -1/\sqrt{2}, 1/\sqrt{2} \rangle$?

b. In what direction is the scalar component of curl $\mathbf{F}$ a maximum?

44. Paddle wheel in a vector field Let $\mathbf{F} = \langle 0, 2x, 0 \rangle$ and let $\mathbf{n}$ be a unit vector aligned with the axis of a paddle wheel located on the y-axis.

a. If the axis of the paddle wheel is aligned with $\mathbf{n} = \langle 1, 0, 0 \rangle$, how fast does it spin?

b. If the axis of the paddle wheel is aligned with $\mathbf{n} = \langle 0, 0, 1 \rangle$, how fast does it spin?

c. For what direction $\mathbf{n}$ does the paddle wheel spin fastest?

45–48. Surface areas *Use a surface integral to find the area of the following surfaces.*

45. The hemisphere $x^2 + y^2 + z^2 = 9$, for $z \ge 0$ (excluding the base)

46. The frustum of the cone $z^2 = x^2 + y^2$, for $2 \le z \le 4$ (excluding the bases)

47. The plane $z = 6 - x - y$ above the square $|x| \le 1, |y| \le 1$

48. The surface $f(x, y) = \sqrt{2}\,xy$ above the region $\{(r, \theta): 0 \le r \le 2, 0 \le \theta \le 2\pi\}$

49–51. Surface integrals *Evaluate the following surface integrals.*

49. $\displaystyle\iint_S (1 + yz)\, dS$; S is the plane $x + y + z = 2$ in the first octant.

50. $\displaystyle\iint_S \langle 0, y, z \rangle \cdot \mathbf{n}\, dS$; S is the curved surface of the cylinder $y^2 + z^2 = a^2, |x| \le 8$ with outward normal vectors.

51. $\displaystyle\iint_S (x - y + z)\, dS$; S is the entire surface including the base of the hemisphere $x^2 + y^2 + z^2 = 4$, for $z \ge 0$.

52–53. Flux integrals *Find the flux of the following vector fields across the given surface. Assume the vectors normal to the surface point outward.*

52. $\mathbf{F} = \langle x, y, z \rangle$ across the curved surface of the cylinder $x^2 + y^2 = 1$, for $|z| \le 8$

53. $\mathbf{F} = \mathbf{r}/|\mathbf{r}|$ across the sphere of radius a centered at the origin, where $\mathbf{r} = \langle x, y, z \rangle$

54. Three methods Find the surface area of the paraboloid $z = x^2 + y^2$, for $0 \le z \le 4$, in three ways.

a. Use an explicit description of the surface.

b. Use the parametric description $\mathbf{r} = \langle v \cos u, v \sin u, v^2 \rangle$.

c. Use the parametric description $\mathbf{r} = \langle \sqrt{v} \cos u, \sqrt{v} \sin u, v \rangle$.

55. Flux across hemispheres and paraboloids Let S be the hemisphere $x^2 + y^2 + z^2 = a^2$, for $z \ge 0$, and let T be the paraboloid $z = a - (x^2 + y^2)/a$, for $z \ge 0$, where $a > 0$. Assume the surfaces have outward normal vectors.

a. Verify that S and T have the same base ($x^2 + y^2 \le a^2$) and the same high point $(0, 0, a)$.

b. Which surface has the greater area?

c. Show that the flux of the radial field $\mathbf{F} = \langle x, y, z \rangle$ across S is $2\pi a^3$.

d. Show that the flux of the radial field $\mathbf{F} = \langle x, y, z \rangle$ across T is $3\pi a^3/2$.

56. Surface area of an ellipsoid Consider the ellipsoid $x^2/a^2 + y^2/b^2 + z^2/c^2 = 1$, where $a, b,$ and c are positive real numbers.

a. Show that the surface is described by the parametric equations

$$\mathbf{r}(u, v) = \langle a \cos u \sin v, b \sin u \sin v, c \cos v \rangle$$

for $0 \le u \le 2\pi, 0 \le v \le \pi$.

b. Write an integral for the surface area of the ellipsoid.

57–58. Stokes' Theorem for line integrals *Evaluate the line integral $\oint_C \mathbf{F} \cdot d\mathbf{r}$ using Stokes' Theorem. Assume C has counterclockwise orientation.*

57. $\mathbf{F} = \langle xz, yz, xy \rangle$; C is the circle $x^2 + y^2 = 4$ in the xy-plane.

58. $\mathbf{F} = \langle x^2 - y^2, x, 2yz \rangle$; C is the boundary of the plane $z = 6 - 2x - y$ in the first octant.

59–60. Stokes' Theorem for surface integrals *Use Stokes' Theorem to evaluate the surface integral* $\iint_S (\nabla \times \mathbf{F}) \cdot \mathbf{n}\, dS$. *Assume that* $\mathbf{n}$ *is the outward normal.*

59. $\mathbf{F} = \langle -z, x, y \rangle$, where S is the hyperboloid $z = 10 - \sqrt{1 + x^2 + y^2}$, for $z \geq 0$

60. $\mathbf{F} = \langle x^2 - z^2, y^2, xz \rangle$, where S is the hemisphere $x^2 + y^2 + z^2 = 4$, for $y \geq 0$

61.   Conservative fields Use Stokes' Theorem to find the circulation of the vector field $\mathbf{F} = \nabla(10 - x^2 + y^2 + z^2)$ around any smooth closed curve C with counterclockwise orientation.

62–64. Computing fluxes *Use the Divergence Theorem to compute the outward flux of the following vector fields across the given surfaces S.*

62. $\mathbf{F} = \langle -x, x - y, x - z \rangle$; S is the surface of the cube cut from the first octant by the planes $x = 1$, $y = 1$, and $z = 1$.

63. $\mathbf{F} = \langle x^3, y^3, z^3 \rangle / 3$; S is the sphere $\{(x, y, z): x^2 + y^2 + z^2 = 9\}$.

64. $\mathbf{F} = \langle x^2, y^2, z^2 \rangle$; S is the cylinder $\{(x, y, z): x^2 + y^2 = 4, 0 \leq z \leq 8\}$.

65–66. General regions *Use the Divergence Theorem to compute the outward flux of the following vector fields across the boundary of the given regions D.*

65. $\mathbf{F} = \langle x^3, y^3, 10 \rangle$; D is the region between the hemispheres of radius 1 and 2 centered at the origin with bases in the xy-plane.

66. $\mathbf{F} = \dfrac{\mathbf{r}}{|\mathbf{r}|^3} = \dfrac{\langle x, y, z \rangle}{(x^2 + y^2 + z^2)^{3/2}}$; D is the region between two spheres with radii 1 and 2 centered at $(5, 5, 5)$.

67.   Flux integrals Compute the outward flux of the field $\mathbf{F} = \langle x^2 + x \sin y, y^2 + 2 \cos y, z^2 + z \sin y \rangle$ across the surface S that is the boundary of the prism bounded by the planes $y = 1 - x$, $x = 0$, $y = 0$, $z = 0$, and $z = 4$.

68.   Stokes' Theorem on a compound surface Consider the surface S consisting of the quarter-sphere $x^2 + y^2 + z^2 = a^2$, for $z \geq 0$ and $x \geq 0$, and the half-disk in the yz-plane $y^2 + z^2 \leq a^2$, for $z \geq 0$. The boundary of S in the xy-plane is C, which consists of the semicircle $x^2 + y^2 = a^2$, for $x \geq 0$, and the line segment $[-a, a]$ on the y-axis, with a counterclockwise orientation. Let $\mathbf{F} = \langle 2z - y, x - z, y - 2x \rangle$.

  a. Describe the direction in which the normal vectors point on S.

  b. Evaluate $\oint_C \mathbf{F} \cdot d\mathbf{r}$.

  c. Evaluate $\iint_S (\nabla \times \mathbf{F}) \cdot \mathbf{n}\, dS$ and check for agreement with part (b).

Chapter 15 Guided Projects

Applications of the material in this chapter and related topics can be found in the following Guided Projects. For additional information, see the Preface.

- Ideal fluid flow
- Maxwell's equations

- Planimeters and vector fields
- Vector calculus in other coordinate systems

Answers

CHAPTER 1

Section 1.1 Exercises, pp. 9–12

1. A function is a rule that assigns to each value of the independent variable in the domain a unique value of the dependent variable in the range. **3.** A graph is that of a function provided no vertical line intersects the graph at more than one point. **5.** The first statement is true of a function, by definition. **7.** $2; -2$
9. $f(-x) = f(x)$

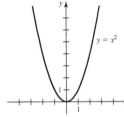

11. B **13.** $D = \mathbb{R}, R = [-10, \infty)$ **15.** $D = [-2, 2], R = [0, 2]$
17. $D = \mathbb{R}, R = \mathbb{R}$ **19.** $D = [-3, 3]; R = [0, 27]$ **21.** The independent variable is t; the dependent variable is d. $D = [0, 8]$
23. The independent variable is h; the dependent variable is V.
$D = [0, 50]$. **25.** 96 **27.** $1/z^3$ **29.** $1/(y^3 - 3)$ **31.** $(u^2 - 4)^3$
33. $\dfrac{x - 3}{10 - 3x}$ **35.** x **37.** $g(x) = x^3 - 5; f(x) = x^{10}; D = \mathbb{R}$
39. $g(x) = x^4 + 2, f(x) = \sqrt{x}; D = \mathbb{R}$
41. $(f \circ g)(x) = |x^2 - 4|; D = \mathbb{R}$
43. $(f \circ G)(x) = \dfrac{1}{|x - 2|}; \quad D = \{x: x \ne 2\}$
45. $(G \circ g \circ f)(x) = \dfrac{1}{x^2 - 6}; \quad D = \{x: x \ne \sqrt{6}, -\sqrt{6}\}$
47. $x^4 - 8x^2 + 12$ **49.** $f(x) = x - 3$ **51.** $f(x) = x^2$
53. $f(x) = x^2$ **55. a.** 4 **b.** 1 **c.** 3 **d.** 3 **e.** 7 **f.** 8
57. $2x + h; x + a$ **59.** $-\dfrac{2}{x(x + h)}; -\dfrac{2}{ax}$
61. $\dfrac{1}{(x + h + 1)(x + 1)}; \dfrac{1}{(a + 1)(x + 1)}$
63. $3x^2 + 3xh + h^2 - 2; x^2 + ax + a^2 - 2$
65. $\dfrac{4(2x + h)}{x^2(x + h)^2}; \dfrac{4(x + a)}{a^2 x^2}$
67. a.

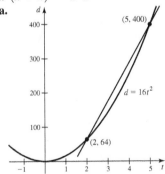

b. $m_{\text{sec}} = 112$ ft/s; the object falls at an average rate of 112 ft/s.

69. a.

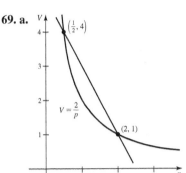

b. $m_{\text{sec}} = -2$ cm^3/atmosphere; the volume decreases at an average rate of 2 cm^3/atmosphere over the interval $0.5 \le p \le 2$.

71. y-axis **73.** No symmetry **75.** x-axis, y-axis, origin **77.** Origin
79. A is even, B is odd, C is even **81. a.** True **b.** False **c.** True **d.** False **e.** False **f.** True **g.** True **h.** False **i.** True.
83.

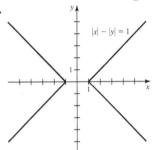

85. $f(x) = 3x - 2$ **87.** $f(x) = x^2 - 6$
89. $\dfrac{1}{\sqrt{x + h} + \sqrt{x}}; \dfrac{1}{\sqrt{x} + \sqrt{a}}$
91. $\dfrac{3}{\sqrt{x}(x + h) + x\sqrt{x + h}}; \dfrac{3}{x\sqrt{a} + a\sqrt{x}}$
93. a. $[0, 3 + \sqrt{14}]$
b.

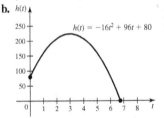

At time $t = 3$, the maximum height is 224 ft.

95. None **97.** Symmetry about the origin **99.** y-axis **101.** y-axis
103. a. 4 **b.** 1 **c.** 3 **d.** -2 **e.** -1 **f.** 7

Section 1.2 Exercises, pp. 21–26

1. A formula, a graph, a table, words **3.** Set of all real numbers except points at which the denominator is zero
5.

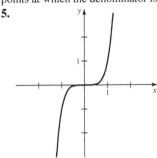

7. Shift the graph to the left 2 units.   **9.** Compress the graph horizontally by a factor of 3.   **11.** $y = -\frac{2}{3}x - 1$
13. $y = 2x + 1$

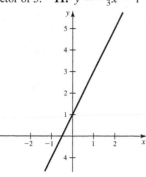

15. $d = -3p/50 + 27; D = [0, 450]$

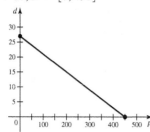

17. $p(t) = 24t + 500; 860$
19. $y = \begin{cases} x + 3 & \text{if } x < 0 \\ -\frac{1}{2}x + 3 & \text{if } x \geq 0 \end{cases}$
21. $c(t) = \begin{cases} 0.05t & \text{if } 0 \leq t \leq 60 \\ 1.2 + 0.03t & \text{if } 60 < t \leq 120 \end{cases}$

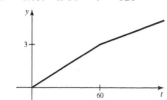

23.
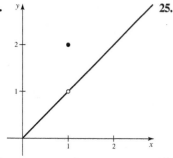
25.

27.
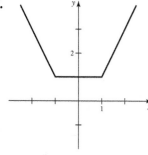

29. a.
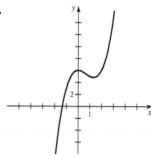

b. Polynomial function; $D = \mathbb{R}$
c. One peak near $x = 0$; one valley near $x = 4/3$; x-intercept approx $(-1.34, 0)$, y-intercept $(0, 6)$
31. a.
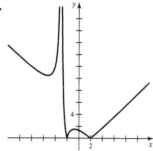

b. Absolute value of a rational function; $D = \{x : x \neq -3\}$
c. Undefined at $x = -3$; a valley near $x = -5.2$; x-intercepts (and valleys) at $x = -2$ and $x = 2$; a peak near $x = -0.8$; y-intercept $\left(0, \frac{4}{3}\right)$
33. a.
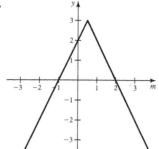

b. $D = (-\infty, \infty)$.   **c.** One peak at $x = \frac{1}{2}$.
35. $s(x) = 2$
37. $s(x) = \begin{cases} 1 & \text{if } x \leq 0 \\ -\frac{1}{2} & \text{if } x > 0 \end{cases}$
39. a. 12   **b.** 36   **c.** $A(x) = 6x$ **41. a.** 12   **b.** 21
c. $A(x) = \begin{cases} 8x - x^2 & \text{if } 0 \leq x \leq 3 \\ 2x + 9 & \text{if } x > 3 \end{cases}$
43. $f(x) = |x - 2| + 3; g(x) = -|x + 2| - 1$
45. a. Shift 3 units to the right.

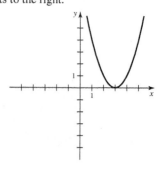

b. Compress horizontally by a factor of 2, then shift 2 units to the right.

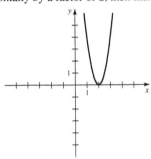

c. Shift to the right 2 units, vertical scaling and flip by a factor of 3, shift up 4 units.

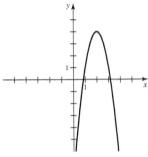

d. Horizontal scaling by a factor of $\frac{1}{3}$, horizontal shift right 2 units, vertical scaling by a factor of 6, vertical shift up 1 unit

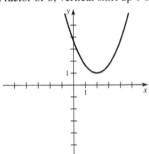

47. Shift the graph of $y = x^2$ right 2 units and up 1 unit.

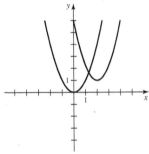

49. Stretch the graph of $y = x^2$ vertically by a factor of 3 and reflect across the x-axis.   **51.** Shift the graph of $y = x^2$ left 3 units and stretch vertically by a factor of 2.   **53.** Shift the graph of $y = x^2$ to the left $\frac{1}{2}$ unit, stretch vertically by a factor of 4, reflect through the x-axis, and then shift up 13 units to obtain the graph of h.
55. a. True   **b.** False   **c.** True   **d.** False   **57.** $(0, 0)$ and $(4, 16)$

59. $y = \sqrt{x} - 1$
61. $y = 5x; D = [0, 4]$

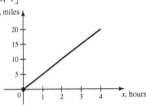

63. $y = 3200/x; D = (0, 5]$

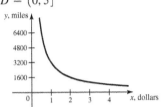

65. $y = \lceil x \rceil$

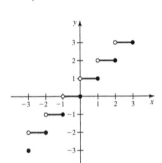

67.

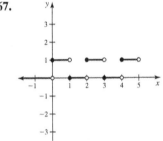

69.

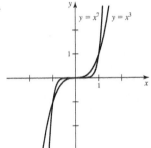

71. a.

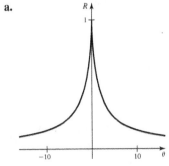

b. $\theta = 0$; vision is sharpest when we look straight ahead.
c. $|\theta| \le 0.19°$ (less than $\frac{1}{5}$ of a degree).
73. a. $p(t) = 328.3t + 1875$ **b.** 4830
75. a. $f(m) = 350m + 1200$ **b.** Buy
77. $0 \le h \le 2$

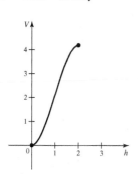

79. a. $S(x) = x^2 + \dfrac{500}{x}$ **b.** ≈ 6.30 ft

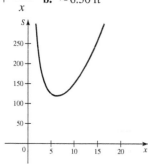

83. a.

n	1	2	3	4	5
$f(n)$	1	2	6	24	120

b.   **c.** 10

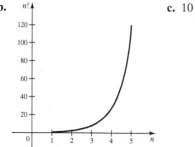

85. a.

n	1	2	3	4	5	6	7	8	9	10
$T(n)$	1	5	14	30	55	91	140	204	285	385

b. $D = \{n: n \text{ is a positive integer}\}$ **c.** 14

Section 1.3 Exercises, pp. 35–38

1. $D = \mathbb{R}$; $R = \{y: y > 0\}$ **3.** If a function f is not one-to-one, there are domain values, x_1 and x_2, such that $x_1 \ne x_2$ but $f(x_1) = f(x_2)$. If f^{-1} exists, by definition $f^{-1}(f(x_1)) = x_1$ and $f^{-1}(f(x_2)) = x_2$ so that f^{-1} assigns two different range values to the single domain value of $f(x_1)$.

5.

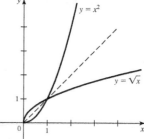

7. The expression $\log_b x$ represents the power to which b must be raised to obtain x.   **9.** $D = (0, \infty)$; $R = \mathbb{R}$
11. $(-\infty, -1], [-1, 1], [1, \infty)$
13.

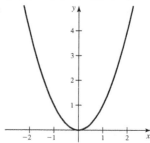

15. $(-\infty, \infty)$ **17.** $(-\infty, 5) \cup (5, \infty)$ **19.** $(-\infty, 0), (0, \infty)$
21. a. $f^{-1}(x) = \frac{1}{2}x$ **23. a.** $f^{-1}(x) = (6 - x)/4$
25. a. $f^{-1}(x) = (x - 5)/3$ **27. a.** $f^{-1}(x) = x^2 - 2, x \ge 0$
29. a. $f_1(x) = \sqrt{1 - x^2};\ \ 0 \le x \le 1$
     $f_2(x) = \sqrt{1 - x^2};\ \ -1 \le x \le 0$
     $f_3(x) = -\sqrt{1 - x^2};\ \ -1 \le x \le 0$
     $f_4(x) = -\sqrt{1 - x^2};\ \ 0 \le x \le 1$
b. $f_1^{-1}(x) = \sqrt{1 - x^2};\ \ 0 \le x \le 1$
     $f_2^{-1}(x) = -\sqrt{1 - x^2};\ \ 0 \le x \le 1$
     $f_3^{-1}(x) = -\sqrt{1 - x^2};\ \ -1 \le x \le 0$
     $f_4^{-1}(x) = \sqrt{1 - x^2};\ \ -1 \le x \le 0$
31. $f^{-1}(x) = \dfrac{8 - x}{4}$ **33.** $f^{-1}(x) = x^2, x \ge 0$

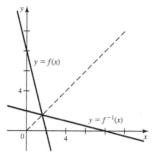

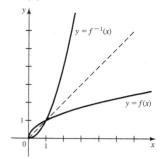

35. $f^{-1}(x) = \sqrt[4]{x - 4}, x \ge 4$ **37.** $f^{-1}(x) = \sqrt{x - 5} + 1, x \ge 5$

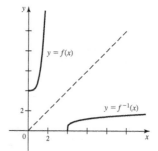

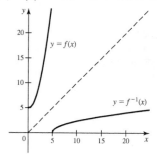

39.

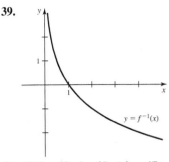

$y = f^{-1}(x)$

41. 1000   **43.** 2   **45.** $1/e$ **47.** -0.2 **49.** 1.19   **51.** $-0.09\overline{6}$
53. $\ln 21 / \ln 7$ **55.** $\ln 5/(3 \ln 3) + 5/3$ **57.** 451 years
59. $\ln 15 / \ln 2 \approx 3.9069$ **61.** $\ln 40 / \ln 4 \approx 2.6610$ **63.** $e^{x \ln 2}$
65. $\log_5 |x| / \log_5 e$ **67.** e **69. a.** False   **b.** False   **c.** False
d. True   **e.** False   **f.** False   **g.** True
71. A is $y = \log_2 x$. B is $y = \log_4 x$. C is $y = \log_{10} x$.
73.

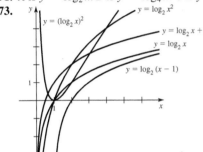

$y = \log_2 x^2$
$y = (\log_2 x)^2$
$y = \log_2 x + 1$
$y = \log_2 x$
$y = \log_2 (x - 1)$

75. $f^{-1}(x) = \sqrt[3]{x} - 1, D = \mathbb{R}$
77. $f_1^{-1}(x) = \sqrt{2/x - 2}, D_1 = (0, 1]; f_2^{-1}(x) = -\sqrt{2/x - 2},$

$D_2 = (0, 1]$ **79. b.** $\dfrac{p(t + 12)}{p(t)} = 2$ **c.** 38,400   **d.** 19.0 hr

e. 72.7 hr   **81. a.** No   **b.** $f^{-1}(h) = 2 - \sqrt{\dfrac{64 - h}{16}}$

c. $f^{-1}(h) = 2 + \sqrt{\dfrac{64 - h}{16}}$ **d.** 0.5423 s   **e.** 3.8371 s

83. Let $y = \log_b x$. Then $b^y = x$ and $(1/b)^y = 1/x$. Hence,
$y = -\log_{1/b} x$. Thus, $\log_{1/b} x = -y = -\log_b x$.
87. a.

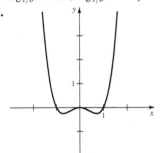

f is one-to-one
on the intervals
$(-\infty, -1/\sqrt{2}], [-1/\sqrt{2}, 0],$
$[0, 1/\sqrt{2}], [1/\sqrt{2}, \infty)$

b. $x = \sqrt{\dfrac{1 \pm \sqrt{4y + 1}}{2}}, -\sqrt{\dfrac{1 \pm \sqrt{4y + 1}}{2}}$

Section 1.4 Exercises, pp. 47–51

1. $\sin \theta = $ opp/hyp; $\cos \theta = $ adj/hyp; $\tan \theta = $ opp/adj;
$\cot \theta = $ adj/opp; $\sec \theta = $ hyp/adj; $\csc \theta = $ hyp/opp
3. The radian measure of an angle θ is the length of an arc s on the unit
circle associated with θ.   **5.** $\sin^2 \theta + \cos^2 \theta = 1, 1 + \cot^2 \theta = \csc^2 \theta,$
$\tan^2 \theta + 1 = \sec^2 \theta$ **7.** $\{x: x$ is an odd multiple of $\pi/2\}$ **9.** Sine is
not one-to-one on its domain.   **11.** Yes; no   **13.** Vertical asymptotes

at $x = \pi/2$ and $x = -\pi/2$ **15.** $-\frac{1}{2}$ **17.** 1   **19.** $-1/\sqrt{3}$
21. $1/\sqrt{3}$ **23.** 1   **25.** -1 **27.** Undefined
29. $\sec \theta = \dfrac{r}{x} = \dfrac{1}{x/r} = \dfrac{1}{\cos \theta}$ **31.** Dividing both sides of
$\cos^2 \theta + \sin^2 \theta = 1$ by $\cos^2 \theta$ gives $1 + \tan^2 \theta = \sec^2 \theta$.
33. If α and β are complementary angles, then $\cos \alpha = \sin \beta$. Thus
$1/(\cos \alpha) = 1/(\sin \beta)$. Letting $\alpha = \pi/2 - \theta$

and $\beta = \theta, \sec (\pi/2 - \theta) = \csc \theta$.   **35.** $\dfrac{\sqrt{2 + \sqrt{3}}}{2}$ or $\dfrac{\sqrt{6} + \sqrt{2}}{4}$
37. $\pi/4 + n\pi, n = 0, \pm 1, \pm 2, \ldots$
39. $\pi/6, 5\pi/6, 7\pi/6, 11\pi/6$
41. $\pi/4 + 2n\pi, 3\pi/4 + 2n\pi, n = 0, \pm 1, \pm 2, \ldots$
43. $\pi/12, 5\pi/12, 3\pi/4, 13\pi/12, 17\pi/12, 7\pi/4$
45. $0, \pi/2, \pi, 3\pi/2$ **47.** $\pi/2$ **49.** $\pi/4$ **51.** $\pi/3$ **53.** $2\pi/3$

55. -1 **57.** $\sqrt{1 - x^2}$ **59.** $\dfrac{\sqrt{4 - x^2}}{2}$ **61.** $2x\sqrt{1 - x^2}$

63. $\cos^{-1} x + \cos^{-1} (-x) = \theta + (\pi - \theta) = \pi$

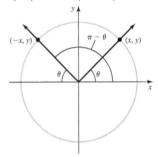

$(-x, y)$ $\pi - \theta$ (x, y)
θ θ

65. The functions are equal.   **67.** $\pi/3$ **69.** $\pi/3$ **71.** $\pi/4$

73. $\pi/2 - 2$ **75.** $\dfrac{1}{\sqrt{x^2 + 1}}$ **77.** $1/x$ **79.** $x/\sqrt{x^2 + 16}$

81. $\sin^{-1} \dfrac{x}{6} = \tan^{-1}\left(\dfrac{x}{\sqrt{36 - x^2}}\right) = \sec^{-1}\left(\dfrac{6}{\sqrt{36 - x^2}}\right)$

83. a. False   **b.** False   **c.** False   **d.** False   **e.** True   **f.** False
g. True   **h.** False   **85.** $\sin \theta = \frac{12}{13}; \tan \theta = \frac{12}{5}; \sec \theta = \frac{13}{5};$
$\csc \theta = \frac{13}{12}; \cot \theta = \frac{5}{12}$ **87.** $\sin \theta = \frac{12}{13}; \cos \theta = \frac{5}{13}; \tan \theta = \frac{12}{5};$
$\sec \theta = \frac{13}{5}; \cot \theta = \frac{5}{12}$ **89.** Amp $= 3$; period $= 6\pi$
91. Amp $= 3.6$; period $= 48$ **93.** Stretch the graph of $y = \cos x$
horizontally by a factor of 3; stretch vertically by a factor of 2; and
reflect through the x-axis.

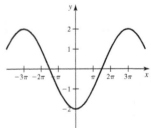

95. Stretch the graph of $y = \cos x$ horizontally by a factor of $24/\pi$;
then stretch it vertically by a factor of 3.6 and shift it up 2 units.

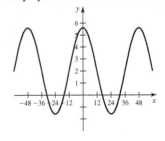

97. $y = 3 \sin (\pi x/12 - 3\pi/4) + 13$ **99.** About 6 ft
101. $d(t) = 10 \cos (4\pi t/3)$ **103.** $\sqrt{a^2 - h^2} + k$
105. $s(t) = 117.5 - 87.5 \sin \left(\dfrac{\pi}{182.5} (t - 95) \right)$

$S(t) = 844.5 + 87.5 \sin \left(\dfrac{\pi}{182.5} (t - 67) \right)$

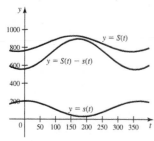

107. Area of circle is πr^2; $\theta/(2\pi)$ represents the proportion of area swept out by a central angle θ. Thus, the area of such a sector is $(\theta/2\pi)\pi r^2 = r^2\theta/2$.

Chapter 1 Review Exercises, pp. 51–53

1. a. True **b.** False **c.** False **d.** True **e.** False
f. False **g.** True
3. a.

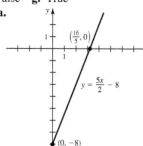

b.

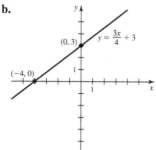

c.

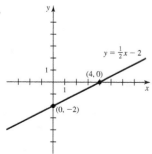

5. $f(x) = \begin{cases} 0 & \text{if } x \geq 0 \\ 4x & \text{if } x < 0 \end{cases}$

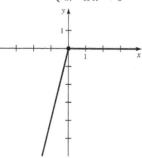

7. a.

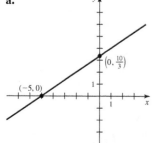

b.

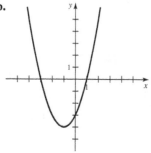

c.

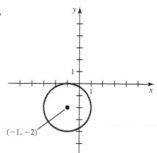

d.

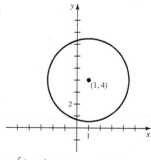

9. $D_f = \mathbb{R}, R_f = \mathbb{R}; D_g = [0, \infty), R_g = [0, \infty)$
11. $B = -\dfrac{1}{500} a + 212$
13. a.

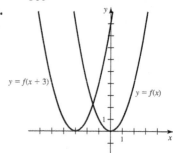

b.

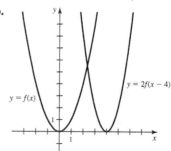

c.

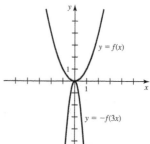

d.

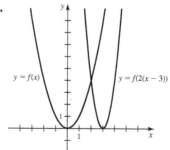

15. a. 1 **b.** $\sqrt{x^3}$ **c.** $\sin^3\sqrt{x}$ **d.** $\mathbb{R}$ **e.** $[-1, 1]$
17. $2x + h - 2; x + a - 2$ **19.** $3x^2 + 3xh + h^2; x^2 + ax + a^2$
21. a. y-axis **b.** y-axis **c.** x-axis, y-axis, origin **23.** $x = 2$; base does not matter **25.** $(-\infty, 0], [0, 2],$ and $[2, \infty)$
27. $f^{-1}(x) = 2 + \sqrt{x - 1}$

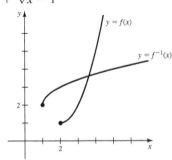

29. a. $3\pi/4$ **b.** $144°$ **c.** $40\pi/3$ **31. a.** $f(t) = -2\cos\left(\dfrac{\pi t}{3}\right)$
b. $f(t) = 5\sin\left(\dfrac{\pi t}{12}\right) + 15$ **33. a.** F **b.** E **c.** D **d.** B
e. C **f.** A **35.** $(7\pi/6, -1/2); (11\pi/6, -1/2)$ **37.** $\pi/6$
39. $-\pi/2$ **41.** x **43.** $\cos\theta = \frac{5}{13}; \tan\theta = \frac{12}{5}; \cot\theta = \frac{5}{12};$
$\sec\theta = \frac{13}{5}; \csc\theta = \frac{13}{12}$ **45.** $\dfrac{\sqrt{4 - x^2}}{2}$ **47.** $\pi/2 - \theta$ **49.** 0
51. $1 - 2x^2$

CHAPTER 2

Section 2.1 Exercises, pp. 59–60

1. $\dfrac{s(b) - s(a)}{b - a}$ **3.** $\dfrac{f(b) - f(a)}{b - a}$ **5.** The instantaneous velocity at $t = a$ is the slope of the line tangent to the position curve at $t = a$.
7. 20 **9. a.** 48 **b.** 64 **c.** 80 **d.** $16(6 - h)$ **11. a.** 36 **b.** 44
c. 52 **d.** 60 **13.** $m_{\text{sec}} = 60$; the slope is the average velocity of the object over the interval $[0.5, 2]$.

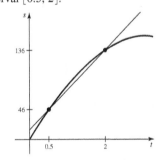

15.

Time interval	Average velocity
$[1, 2]$	80
$[1, 1.5]$	88
$[1, 1.1]$	94.4
$[1, 1.01]$	95.84
$[1, 1.001]$	95.984
$v_{\text{inst}} = 96$	

17. 47.84, 47.984, 47.9984; instantaneous velocity appears to be 48.

19.

Time interval	Average velocity
$[2, 3]$	20
$[2.9, 3]$	5.60
$[2.99, 3]$	4.16
$[2.999, 3]$	4.016
$[2.9999, 3]$	4.002
$v_{\text{inst}} = 4$	

21.

Time interval	Average velocity
$[3, 3.5]$	-24
$[3, 3.1]$	-17.6
$[3, 3.01]$	-16.16
$[3, 3.001]$	-16.016
$[3, 3.0001]$	-16.002
$v_{\text{inst}} = -16$	

23.

Time interval	Average velocity
$[0, 1]$	36.372
$[0, 0.5]$	67.318
$[0, 0.1]$	79.468
$[0, 0.01]$	79.995
$[0, 0.001]$	80.000
$v_{\text{inst}} = 80$	

25.

Interval	Slope of secant line
$[1, 2]$	6
$[1.5, 2]$	7
$[1.9, 2]$	7.8
$[1.99, 2]$	7.98
$[1.999, 2]$	7.998
$m_{\text{tan}} = 8$	

27.

Interval	Slope of secant line
$[0, 1]$	1.718
$[0, 0.5]$	1.297
$[0, 0.1]$	1.052
$[0, 0.01]$	1.005
$[0, 0.001]$	1.001
$m_{\text{tan}} = 1$	

29. a.

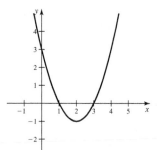

b. $(2, -1)$

c.

Interval	Slope of secant line
$[2, 2.5]$	0.5
$[2, 2.1]$	0.1
$[2, 2.01]$	0.01
$[2, 2.001]$	0.001
$[2, 2.0001]$	0.0001
$m_{\tan} = 0$	

31. a.

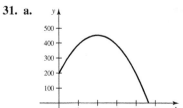

b. $t = 4$

c.

Interval	Slope of secant line
$[4, 4.5]$	-8
$[4, 4.1]$	-1.6
$[4, 4.01]$	-0.16
$[4, 4.001]$	-0.016
$[4, 4.0001]$	-0.0016
$v_{\text{inst}} = 0$	

d. $0 \le t < 4$ **e.** $4 < t \le 9$ **33.** 0.6366, 0.9589, 0.9996, 1

Section 2.2 Exercises, pp. 65–69

1. As x approaches a from either side, the values of $f(x)$ approach L.
3. As x approaches a from the right, the values of $f(x)$ approach L.
5. $L = M$.   **7. a.** 5   **b.** 3   **c.** Does not exist   **d.** 1   **e.** 2
9. a. -1 **b.** 1   **c.** 2   **d.** 2
11. a.

x	$f(x)$	x	$f(x)$
1.9	3.9	2.1	4.1
1.99	3.99	2.01	4.01
1.999	3.999	2.001	4.001
1.9999	3.9999	2.0001	4.0001

b. 4

13. a.

t	$g(t)$	t	$g(t)$
8.9	5.983287	9.1	6.016621
8.99	5.998333	9.01	6.001666
8.999	5.999833	9.001	6.000167

b. 6

15. From the graph and table, the limit appears to be 0.

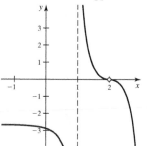

x	1.99	1.999	1.9999	2.0001	2.001	2.01
$f(x)$	0.0021715	0.00014476	0.000010857	-0.000010857	-0.00014476	-0.0021715

17. From the graph and table, the limit appears to be 2.

x	0.9	0.99	0.999	1.001	1.01	1.1
$f(x)$	1.993342	1.999933	1.999999	1.999999	1.999933	1.993342

19. $\lim\limits_{x \to 5^+} f(x) = 10$; $\lim\limits_{x \to 5^-} f(x) = 10$; $\lim\limits_{x \to 5} f(x) = 10$
21. a. 0   **b.** 1   **c.** 0   **d.** Does not exist; $\lim\limits_{x \to 1^-} f(x) \ne \lim\limits_{x \to 1^+} f(x)$
23. a. 3   **b.** 2   **c.** 2   **d.** 2   **e.** 2   **f.** 4   **g.** 1   **h.** Does not exist.
i. 3   **j.** 3   **k.** 3   **l.** 3
25. a.

x	$\sin\left(1/x\right)$
$2/\pi$	1
$2/(3\pi)$	-1
$2/(5\pi)$	1
$2/(7\pi)$	-1
$2/(9\pi)$	1
$2/(11\pi)$	-1

The value alternates between 1 and -1.

b. The function alternates between 1 and -1 infinitely many times on the interval $(0, h)$ no matter how small $h > 0$ becomes.
c. $\lim\limits_{x \to 0} \sin\left(1/x\right)$ does not exist.   **27. a.** False   **b.** False   **c.** False
29.

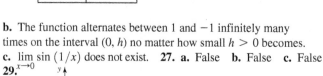

31. Approximately 403.4   **33.** 1   **35. a.** $-2, -1, 1, 2$ **b.** $2, 2, 2$
c. $\lim\limits_{x \to a^-} \lfloor x \rfloor = a - 1$ and $\lim\limits_{x \to a^+} \lfloor x \rfloor = a$, if a is an integer
d. $\lim\limits_{x \to a^-} \lfloor x \rfloor = \lfloor a \rfloor$ and $\lim\limits_{x \to a^+} \lfloor x \rfloor = \lfloor a \rfloor$, if a is not an integer
e. $\lim\limits_{x \to a} \lfloor x \rfloor = \lfloor a \rfloor$ provided a is not an integer.   **37.** 0   **39.** 16

41. a. 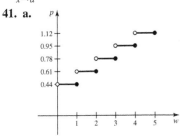   **b.** \$0.95

c. $\lim\limits_{x \to 1^+} f(w)$ is the cost of a letter that weighs just over 1 oz; $\lim\limits_{x \to 1^-} f(w)$ is the cost of a letter that weighs just under 1 oz.   **d.** No; $\lim\limits_{x \to 4^+} f(w) \neq \lim\limits_{x \to 4^-} f(w)$ **43. a.** 8   **b.** 5   **45. a.** 2; 3; 4   **b.** p

47. $\dfrac{p}{q}$

Section 2.3 Exercises, pp. 77–80

1. $\lim\limits_{x \to a} f(x) = f(a)$ **3.** Those values of a for which the denominator is not zero.   **5.** $\dfrac{x^2 - 7x + 12}{x - 3} = x - 4$ for $x \neq 3$.   **7.** 20   **9.** 4

11. 5   **13.** -45 **15.** 4   **17.** 32; Constant Multiple Law   **19.** 5; Difference Law   **21.** 12; Quotient and Product Laws   **23.** 32; Power Law   **25.** 8   **27.** 3   **29.** 3   **31.** -5 **33. a.** 2   **b.** 0   **c.** Does not exist   **35. a.** 0   **b.** $\sqrt{x - 2}$ is not defined for $x < 2$.
37. $\lim\limits_{x \to 0^-} |x| = \lim\limits_{x \to 0^-} (-x) = 0$ and $\lim\limits_{x \to 0^+} |x| = \lim\limits_{x \to 0^+} x = 0$ **39.** 2
41. -8 **43.** -1 **45.** -12 **47.** $\frac{1}{6}$ **49.** $2\sqrt{a}$ **51.** $\frac{1}{8}$

53. a. 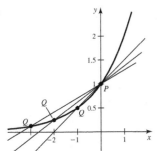   **b.** $\dfrac{2^x - 1}{x}$

c.

x	$\dfrac{2^x - 1}{x}$
-1	0.5
-0.1	0.6697
-0.01	0.6908
-0.001	0.6929
-0.0001	0.6931
-0.00001	0.6931
Limit $\approx$ 0.693	

55. a. Because $\left| \sin \dfrac{1}{x} \right| \leq 1$ for all $x \neq 0$, we have that

$$|x| \left| \sin \frac{1}{x} \right| \leq |x|.$$

That is, $\left| x \sin \dfrac{1}{x} \right| \leq |x|$, so that $-|x| \leq x \sin \dfrac{1}{x} \leq |x|$ for all $x \neq 0$.

b.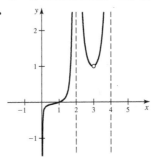

c. $\lim\limits_{x \to 0} -|x| = 0$ and $\lim\limits_{x \to 0} |x| = 0$; by part (a) and the Squeeze Theorem, $\lim\limits_{x \to 0} x \sin \dfrac{1}{x} = 0$

57. a.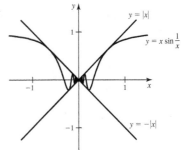

b. $\lim\limits_{x \to 0} \dfrac{\sin x}{x} = 1$ **59. a.** False   **b.** False   **c.** False   **d.** False
e. False   **61.** 8   **63.** 5   **65.** 10   **67.** -3 **69.** $a = -13$;
$\lim\limits_{x \to -1} g(x) = 6$ **71.** 6   **73.** $5a^4$ **75.** $\frac{1}{3}$ **77.** 2   **79.** -54
81. $f(x) = x - 1, g(x) = \dfrac{5}{x - 1}$ **83.** $b = 2$ and $c = -8$; yes
85. $\lim\limits_{S \to 0^+} r(S) = 0$; the radius of the cylinder approaches 0 as the surface area of the cylinder approaches 0.   **87.** 0.0435 N/C   **89.** 6; 4

Section 2.4 Exercises, pp. 86–89

1. $\lim\limits_{x \to a^+} f(x) = -\infty$ means that as x approaches a from the right, the values of $f(x)$ are negative and become arbitrarily large in magnitude.
3. A vertical line $x = a$ that the graph of a function approaches as x approaches a **5.** $-\infty$ **7.** ∞ **9. a.** ∞ **b.** ∞ **c.** ∞ **d.** ∞
e. $-\infty$ **f.** Does not exist   **11. a.** $-\infty$ **b.** $-\infty$ **c.** $-\infty$ **d.** ∞
e. $-\infty$ **f.** Does not exist   **13. a.** ∞ **b.** $-\infty$ **c.** $-\infty$ **d.** ∞
15.

17. a. ∞ **b.** $-\infty$ **c.** Does not exist   **19. a.** $-\infty$ **b.** $-\infty$
c. $-\infty$ **21. a.** ∞ **b.** $-\infty$ **c.** Does not exist   **23.** -5 **25.** ∞
27. a. $-\infty$ **b.** $-\infty$ **c.** $-\infty$ **29. a.** $1/10$ **b.** $-\infty$ **c.** ∞; vertical
asymptote: $x = -5$ **31.** $x = 3$; $\lim\limits_{x\to3^+} f(x) = -\infty$; $\lim\limits_{x\to3^-} f(x) = \infty$;
$\lim\limits_{x\to3} f(x)$ does not exist.   **33.** $x = 0$ and $x = 2$; $\lim\limits_{x\to0^+} f(x) = \infty$;
$\lim\limits_{x\to0^-} f(x) = -\infty$; $\lim\limits_{x\to0} f(x)$ does not exist; $\lim\limits_{x\to2^+} f(x) = \infty$;
$\lim\limits_{x\to2^-} f(x) = \infty$; $\lim\limits_{x\to2} f(x) = \infty$ **35.** ∞ **37.** $-\infty$ **39. a.** $-\infty$
b. ∞ **c.** $-\infty$ **d.** ∞ **41. a.** False   **b.** True   **c.** False
43. $f(x) = \dfrac{1}{x - 6}$ **45.** $x = 0$ **47.** $x = -1$ **49.** $\theta = 10k + 5$,
for any integer k **51.** $x = 0$ **53. a.** $a = 4$ or $a = 3$ **b.** Either
$a > 4$ or $a < 3$ **c.** $3 < a < 4$ **55. a.** $\dfrac{1}{\sqrt[3]{h}}$, regardless of the sign
of h **b.** $\lim\limits_{h\to0^+} \dfrac{1}{\sqrt[3]{h}} = \infty$; $\lim\limits_{h\to0^-} \dfrac{1}{\sqrt[3]{h}} = -\infty$; the tangent line
at $(0, 0)$ is vertical.

Section 2.5 Exercises, pp. 98–100

1. The values of $f(x)$ approaches 10 as x increases without bound
negatively.   **3.** 0   **5.** $\lim\limits_{x\to\infty} f(x) = -\infty$; $\lim\limits_{x\to-\infty} f(x) = \infty$ **7.** ∞; 0; 0
9. 3   **11.** 0   **13.** 0   **15.** ∞ **17.** 0   **19.** ∞ **21.** $-\infty$ **23.** 0
25. $\lim\limits_{x\to\infty} f(x) = \lim\limits_{x\to-\infty} f(x) = \frac{1}{5}$; $y = \frac{1}{5}$
27. $\lim\limits_{x\to\infty} f(x) = 2$; $\lim\limits_{x\to-\infty} f(x) = 2$; $y = 2$
29. $\lim\limits_{x\to\infty} f(x) = \lim\limits_{x\to-\infty} f(x) = 0$; $y = 0$
31. $\lim\limits_{x\to\infty} f(x) = \lim\limits_{x\to-\infty} f(x) = 0$; $y = 0$ **33.** $\lim\limits_{x\to\infty} f(x) = \infty$;
$\lim\limits_{x\to-\infty} f(x) = -\infty$; none   **35. a.** $y = x - 6$ **b.** $x = -6$
c.

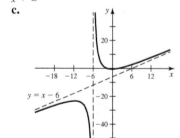

37. a. $y = \frac{1}{3}x - \frac{4}{9}$ **b.** $x = \frac{2}{3}$
c.

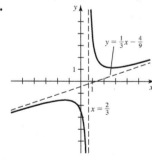

39. a. $y = 4x + 4$ **b.** No vertical asymptotes

c.

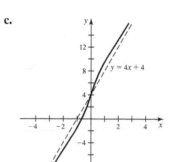

41. $\lim\limits_{x\to\infty} f(x) = \frac{2}{3}$; $\lim\limits_{x\to-\infty} f(x) = -2$; $y = \frac{2}{3}$; $y = -2$
43. $\lim\limits_{x\to\infty} f(x) = \lim\limits_{x\to-\infty} f(x) = \dfrac{1}{4 + \sqrt{3}}$; $y = \dfrac{1}{4 + \sqrt{3}}$
45. $\lim\limits_{x\to\infty} (-3e^{-x}) = 0$; $\lim\limits_{x\to-\infty} (-3e^{-x}) = -\infty$

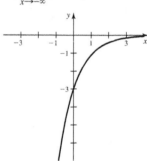

47. $\lim\limits_{x\to\infty} (1 - \ln x) = -\infty$; $\lim\limits_{x\to0^+} (1 - \ln x) = \infty$

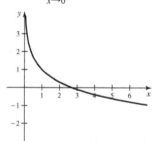

49. $\lim\limits_{x\to\infty} \sin x$ does not exist; $\lim\limits_{x\to-\infty} \sin x$ does not exist

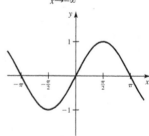

51. a. False   **b.** False   **c.** True
53. a. $\lim\limits_{x\to\infty} f(x) = 2$; $\lim\limits_{x\to-\infty} f(x) = 2$; $y = 2$
b. $x = 0$; $\lim\limits_{x\to0^+} f(x) = \infty$; $\lim\limits_{x\to0^-} f(x) = -\infty$
55. a. $\lim\limits_{x\to\infty} f(x) = 3$; $\lim\limits_{x\to-\infty} f(x) = 3$; $y = 3$
b. $x = -3$ and $x = 4$; $\lim\limits_{x\to-3^-} f(x) = \infty$; $\lim\limits_{x\to-3^+} f(x) = -\infty$;
$\lim\limits_{x\to4^-} f(x) = -\infty$; $\lim\limits_{x\to4^+} f(x) = \infty$

57. a. $\lim\limits_{x\to\infty} f(x) = 1$; $\lim\limits_{x\to-\infty} f(x) = 1$; $y = 1$
b. $x = 0$; $\lim\limits_{x\to0^+} f(x) = \infty$; $\lim\limits_{x\to0^-} f(x) = -\infty$
59. a. $\lim\limits_{x\to\infty} f(x) = 1$; $\lim\limits_{x\to-\infty} f(x) = -1$; $y = 1$ and $y = -1$
b. No vertical asymptotes **61. a.** $\lim\limits_{x\to\infty} f(x) = 0$; $\lim\limits_{x\to-\infty} f(x) = 0$;
$y = 0$ **b.** No vertical asymptotes **63. a.** $\dfrac{\pi}{2}$ **b.** $\dfrac{\pi}{2}$

65. a. $\lim\limits_{x\to\infty} \sinh x = \infty$; $\lim\limits_{x\to-\infty} \sinh x = -\infty$
b. $\sinh 0 = 0$

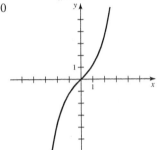

67.

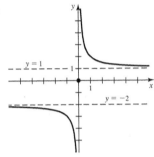

69. $x = 0$ is a vertical asymptote; $y = 2$ is a horizontal asymptote
71. 3500 **73.** No steady state **75.** 2 **77.** 1 **79.** 0
81. a. No. f has a horizontal asymptote if $m = n$ and it has a slant
asymptote if $m = n + 1$. **b.** Yes; $f(x) = x^4/\sqrt{x^6 + 1}$.
83. $\lim\limits_{x\to\infty} f(x) = 0$; $\lim\limits_{x\to-\infty} f(x) = \infty$; $y = 0$

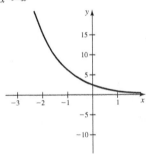

Section 2.6 Exercises, pp. 109–112

1. a, c **3.** A function is continuous on an interval if it is
continuous at each point of the interval. If the interval contains endpoints, then the function must be continuous
there. **5. a.** $\lim\limits_{x\to a^-} f(x) = f(a)$
b. $\lim\limits_{x\to a^+} f(x) = f(a)$ **7.** $\{x: x \neq 0\}$, $\{x: x \neq 0\}$ **9.** $a = 2$,
item 3; $a = 3$, item 2; $a = 1$, item 1 **11.** $a = 1$, item 1;
$a = 2$, item 2; $a = 3$, item 1 **13.** Yes; $\lim\limits_{x\to5} f(x) = f(5)$
15. No; $f(1)$ is undefined. **17.** No; $\lim\limits_{x\to1} f(x) = 2$ but $f(1) = 3$.
19. No; $f(4)$ is undefined. **21.** $(-\infty, \infty)$

23. $(-\infty, -3), (-3, 3), (3, \infty)$ **25.** $(-\infty, -2), (-2, 2), (2, \infty)$ **27.** 1
29. 16 **31.** $[0, 1), (1, 2), (2, 3], (3, 4]$ **33.** $[0, 1), (1, 2), [2, 3), (3, 5]$
35. a. $\lim\limits_{x\to1} f(x)$ does not exist. **b.** From the right
c. $(-\infty, 1), [1, \infty)$ **37.** $(-\infty, -2\sqrt{2}]; [2\sqrt{2}, \infty)$ **39.** $(-\infty, \infty)$
41. $(-\infty, \infty)$ **43.** 3 **45.** 4
47. $(n\pi, (n + 1)\pi)$, where n is an integer; $\sqrt{2}, -\infty$
49. $\left(\dfrac{n\pi}{2}, \left(\dfrac{n}{2} + 1\right)\dfrac{\pi}{2}\right)$, where n is an odd integer; $\infty, \sqrt{3} - 2$
51. $(-\infty, 0), (0, \infty)$; ∞; $-\infty$

53. a. A is continuous on $[0, 0.08]$ and 7000 is between $A(0) = 5000$
and $A(0.08) = 11{,}098.20$. So, by the Intermediate Value Theorem,
there is at least one c in $(0, 0.08)$ such that $A(c) = 7000$.
b. $\qquad\qquad\qquad\qquad\qquad c \approx 0.034$ or 3.4%

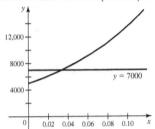

55. b. $x \approx 0.835$ **57. b.** $x \approx -0.285$; $x \approx 0.778$; $x \approx 4.507$
59. b. -0.567
61. a. True **b.** True **c.** False **d.** True **63.** $(-\infty, \infty)$
65. $[0, 16), (16, \infty)$ **67.** 1 **69.** 2 **71.** $-\frac{1}{2}$ **73.** 0 **75.** $-\infty$
77. The vertical line segments should not appear.

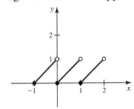

79. a, b.

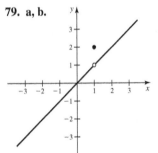

81. a. 2 **b.** 8 **c.** No; $\lim\limits_{x\to1^-} g(x) = 2$ and $\lim\limits_{x\to1^+} g(x) = 8$
83. $\lim\limits_{x\to0} f(x) = 6$, $\lim\limits_{x\to-\infty} f(x) = 10$, and $\lim\limits_{x\to\infty} f(x) = 2$; no vertical
asymptotes; and $y = 2$ and $y = 10$ are the horizontal asymptotes.

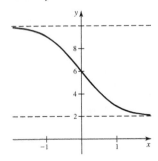

85. $c_1 = \frac{1}{7}$; $c_2 = \frac{1}{2}$; $c_3 = \frac{3}{5}$ **87. a.** $A(r)$ is continuous on $[0.01, 0.10]$ and $A(0.01) = 2615.55$, while $A(0.10) = 3984.36$. Thus, $A(0.01) < 3500 < A(0.10)$. So, by the Intermediate Value Theorem, there exists c in $(0.01, 0.10)$ such that $A(c) = 3500$. Therefore, c is the desired interest rate. **b.** $r \approx 7.28\%$ **89.** Yes. Imagine there is a clone of the monk who walks down the path at the same time the monk walks up the path. The monk and his clone must cross paths with his clone at some time between dawn and dusk. **91.** No; f cannot be made continuous at $x = a$ by redefining $f(a)$. **93.** $\lim_{x \to 2} f(x) = -3$; define $f(2)$ to be -3. **95. a.** Yes **b.** No **97.** $a = 0$ removable discontinuity; $a = 1$ infinite discontinuity.

Section 2.7 Exercises, pp. 121–124

1. 1 **3.** c **5.** Given any $\varepsilon > 0$, there exists a $\delta > 0$ such that $|f(x) - L| < \varepsilon$ whenever $0 < |x - a| < \delta$. **7.** $0 < \delta < 2$
9. a. $\delta = 1$ **b.** $\delta = \frac{1}{2}$ **11. a.** $\delta = 2$ **b.** $\delta = \frac{1}{2}$ **13. a.** $\delta = 1$
b. $\delta = 0.79$ **15. a.** $\delta = 1$ **b.** $\delta = \frac{1}{2}$ **c.** $\delta = \varepsilon$ **17. a.** $\delta = 1$
b. $\delta = 1/2$ **c.** $\delta = \varepsilon/2$ **19.** $\delta = \varepsilon/8$ **21.** $\delta = \varepsilon$ **23.** $\delta = \sqrt{\varepsilon}$
27. a. Use any $\delta > 0$ **b.** $\delta = \varepsilon$ **29.** $\delta = 1/\sqrt{N}$
31. $\delta = 1/\sqrt{N-1}$ **33. a.** False **b.** False **c.** True **d.** True
35. $\delta = \min\{1, 6\varepsilon\}$ **37.** $\delta = \min\{1/20, \varepsilon/200\}$ **39.** For
$x > a$, $|x - a| = x - a$. **41. a.** $\delta = \varepsilon/2$ **b.** $\delta = \varepsilon/3$
c. Since $\lim_{x \to 0^+} f(x) = \lim_{x \to 0^-} f(x) = -4$, $\lim_{x \to 0} f(x) = -4$.
43. $\delta = \varepsilon^2$ **45. a.** For each $N > 0$, there is a corresponding $\delta > 0$ such that $f(x) > N$ whenever $a < x < a + \delta$. **b.** For each $N < 0$, there is a corresponding $\delta > 0$ such that $f(x) < N$ whenever $a - \delta < x < a$. **c.** For each $N > 0$, there is a corresponding $\delta > 0$ such that $f(x) > N$ whenever $a - \delta < x < a$. **47.** $\delta = 1/N$
49. $\delta = (-1/M)^{1/4}$ **51.** $N = 1/\varepsilon$ **53.** $N = M - 1$

Chapter 2 Review Exercises, pp. 124–126

1. a. False **b.** False **c.** False **d.** True **e.** False **f.** False
g. False **h.** True **3.** $x = -1$; $\lim_{x \to -1} f(x)$ does not exist; $x = 1$;
$\lim_{x \to 1} f(x) \neq f(1)$; $x = 3$; $f(3)$ is undefined. **5. a.** 1.414 **b.** $\sqrt{2}$
7.

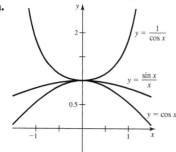

9. $\sqrt{11}$ **11.** 2 **13.** $\frac{1}{3}$ **15.** $-\frac{1}{16}$ **17.** 108 **19.** $\frac{1}{108}$ **21.** 0
23. a.

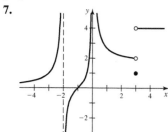

b. $\lim_{x \to 0} \cos x \le \lim_{x \to 0} \frac{\sin x}{x} \le \lim_{x \to 0} \frac{1}{\cos x}$;

$$1 \le \lim_{x \to 0} \frac{\sin x}{x} \le 1;$$

$$\lim_{x \to 0} \frac{\sin x}{x} = 1$$

25. $-\infty$ **27.** ∞ **29.** $-\infty$ **31.** $\frac{1}{2}$ **33.** ∞

35. $3\pi/2 + 2$ **37.** $\lim_{x \to \infty} f(x) = -4$; $\lim_{x \to -\infty} f(x) = -4$

39. $\lim_{x \to \infty} f(x) = 1$; $\lim_{x \to -\infty} f(x) = -\infty$ **41.** Horizontal asymptotes at $y = 2/\pi$ and $y = -2/\pi$; vertical asymptote at $x = 0$ **43. a.** ∞; $-\infty$

b. $y = \dfrac{3x}{4} + \dfrac{5}{16}$ is the slant asymptote. **45. a.** $-\infty$; ∞

b. $y = -x - 2$ is the slant asymptote. **47.** No; $f(5)$ does not exist.
49. Yes; $\lim_{x \to 3.01} h(x) = h(3.01)$ **51.** $(-\infty, -\sqrt{5}]$ and
$[\sqrt{5}, \infty)$; left-continuous at $-\sqrt{5}$ and right-continuous at $\sqrt{5}$
53. $(-\infty, -5)$, $(-5, 0)$, $(0, 5)$, and $(5, \infty)$ **55.** $a = 3, b = 0$
57.

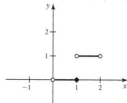

59. a. $m(0) < 30 < m(5)$ and $m(5) > 30 > m(15)$. **b.** $m = 30$ when $t \approx 2.4$ and $t \approx 10.8$. **c.** No; the maximum amount is approximately $m(5.5) \approx 38.5$. **61.** $\delta = \varepsilon$ **63.** $\delta = 1/\sqrt[4]{N}$.

CHAPTER 3

Section 3.1 Exercises, pp. 137–141

1. Given the point $(a, f(a))$ and any point $(x, f(x))$ near $(a, f(a))$, the slope of the secant line joining these points is $\dfrac{f(x) - f(a)}{x - a}$. The limit of this quotient as x approaches a is the slope of the tangent line at the point. **3.** The average rate of change over the interval $[a, x]$ is $\dfrac{f(x) - f(a)}{x - a}$. The limit $\lim_{x \to a} \dfrac{f(x) - f(a)}{x - a}$ is the slope of the tangent line; it is also the limit of average rates of change, which is the instantaneous rate of change at $x = a$. **5.** $f'(a)$ is the slope of the tangent line at $(a, f(a))$ or the instantaneous rate of change of f at a. **7.** $\dfrac{dy}{dx}$ is the limit of $\dfrac{\Delta y}{\Delta x}$ and is the rate of change of y with respect to x. **9.** No.
11. a. 6 **b.** $y = 6x - 14$ **c.**

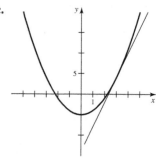

13. a. -5 **b.** $y = -5x + 1$
c.

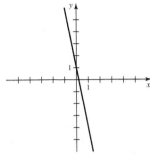

15. a. -1 **b.** $y = -x - 2$
c.

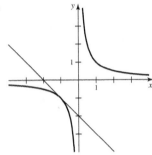

17. a. 2 **b.** $y = 2x + 1$ **19. a.** 4 **b.** $y = 4x - 8$
21. a. 3 **b.** $y = 3x - 2$ **23. a.** $\frac{2}{25}$ **b.** $y = \frac{2}{25}x + \frac{7}{25}$
25. a. $\frac{1}{4}$ **b.** $y = \frac{1}{4}x + \frac{7}{4}$ **27. a.** $f'(-3) = 8$ **b.** $y = 8x$
29. a. $f'(-2) = -14$ **b.** $y = -14x - 16$ **31. a.** $f'\left(\frac{1}{4}\right) = -4$

b. $y = -4x + 3$ **33. a.** $\frac{1}{3}$ **b.** $y = \frac{1}{3}x + \frac{5}{3}$ **35. a.** $-\frac{1}{100}$

b. $y = -\frac{x}{100} + \frac{3}{20}$ **37. a.** $f'(x) = 6x + 2$ **b.** $y = 8x - 13$

c.

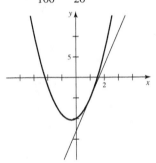

39. a. $f'(x) = 10x - 6$ **b.** $y = 14x - 19$
c.

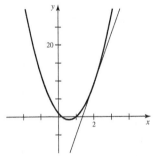

41. a. $2ax + b$ **b.** $8x - 3$ **43.** $-\frac{1}{4}$ **45.** $\frac{1}{5}$

47.

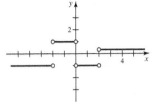

49. a–D; b–C; c–B; d–A   **51.**

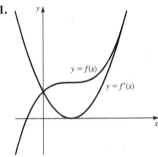

53. a. $x = 1$ **b.** $x = 1, x = 2$ **c.**

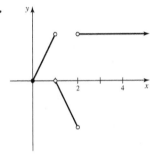

55. a. True **b.** False **c.** True **d.** True

57. a. $f'(x) = \dfrac{3}{2\sqrt{3x + 1}}$ **b.** $y = 3x/10 + 13/5$

59. a. $f'(x) = \dfrac{-6}{(3x + 1)^2}$ **b.** $y = -3x/2 - 5/2$

61. a. C, D **b.** A, B, E **c.** A, B, E, D, C
63. Yes.

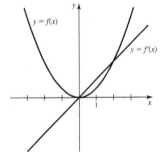

65. a. Approximately 10 kW; approximately -5 kW **b.** $t = 6$ and $t = 18$ **c.** $t = 12$ **67. b.** $f'_+(2) = 1, f'_-(2) = -1$ **c.** f is continuous but not differentiable at $x = 2$.
69. a.   Vertical tangent line $x = 2$

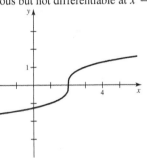

b.

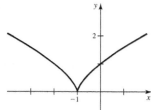

Vertical tangent line $x = -1$

c.

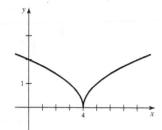

Vertical tangent line $x = 4$

d.

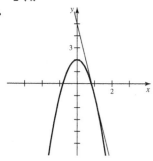

Vertical tangent line $x = 0$

71. $f'(x) = \dfrac{1}{3}x^{-2/3}$ and $\displaystyle\lim_{x \to 0^-} |f'(x)| = \lim_{x \to 0^+} |f'(x)| = \infty$

73. $f(x) = \dfrac{1}{x+1}$; $a = 2$; $-\dfrac{1}{9}$ **75.** $f(x) = x^4$; $a = 2$; 32

77. No; f is not continuous at $x = 2$.   **79.** $a = 4$

Section 3.2 Exercises, pp. 148–151

1. Using the definition can be tedious.   **3.** $f(x) = e^x$ **5.** Take the product of the constant and the derivative of the function.   **7.** $5x^4$
9. 0   **11.** 1   **13.** $15x^2$ **15.** 8   **17.** $200t$ **19.** $12x^3 + 7$
21. $40x^3 - 32$ **23.** $6w^2 + 6w + 10$ **25.** $18x^2 + 6x + 4$
27. $4x^3 + 4x$ **29.** $2w$ for $w \neq 0$ **31.** 1   for $x \neq 1$

33. $\dfrac{1}{2\sqrt{x}}$ for $x \neq a$ **35. a.** $y = -6x + 5$

b.

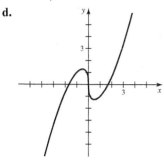

37. a. $y = 3x + 3 - 3\ln 3$ **b.**

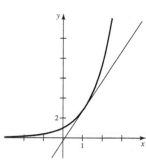

39. a. $x = 3$ **b.** $x = 4$ **41. a.** $(-1, 11), (2, -16)$ **b.** $(-3, -41)$, $(4, 36)$ **43. a.** $(4, 4)$ **b.** $(16, 0)$ **45.** $f'(x) = 20x^3 + 30x^2 + 3$; $f''(x) = 60x^2 + 60x$; $f^{(3)}(x) = 120x + 60$
47. $f'(x) = 1$; $f''(x) = f^{(3)}(x) = 0$ for $x \neq -1$
49. a. False   **b.** True   **c.** False   **d.** False   **e.** False
51. a. $y = 7x - 1$ **b.** $y = -2x + 5$ **c.** $y = 16x + 4$ **53.** -10

55. 4   **57.** 7.5   **59. a.** $f(x) = \sqrt{x}$; $a = 9$ **b.** $f'(9) = \dfrac{1}{6}$

61. a. $f(x) = x^{100}$; $a = 1$ **b.** $f'(1) = 100$ **63.** 3   **65.** 1
67. $f(x) = e^x$; $a = 0$; $f'(0) = 1$ **69. a.** $d'(t) = 32\,t$; ft/s; the velocity of the stone.   **b.** 576 ft; approx. 131 mi/hr

71. a. $\dfrac{dD}{dg} = 0.10g + 35$; mi/gal; the rate of change of mi driven per gal of gas consumed   **b.** 35 mi/gal, 35.5 mi/gal, 36 mi/gal; the gas mileage improves when driving longer distances.   **c.** Approx. 427 mi

Section 3.3 Exercises, pp. 158–160

1. $\dfrac{d}{dx}[f(x) \cdot g(x)] = f'(x)\,g(x) + f(x)\,g'(x)$ **3.** $\dfrac{d}{dx}(x^n) = nx^{n-1}$
for any integer n **5.** $y' = ke^{kx}$ for any real number k **7.** $36x^5 - 12x^3$
9. $e^t t^4(t + 5)$ **11.** $4x^3$ **13.** $e^w(w^3 + 3w^2 - 1)$ **15. a.** $6x + 1$
17. a. $18y^5 - 52y^3 + 8y$ **19.** $\dfrac{1}{(x+1)^2}$ **21.** $\dfrac{e^x}{(e^x + 1)^2}$
23. $e^{-x}(1 - x)$ **25.** $\dfrac{-1}{(t-1)^2}$ **27.** $\dfrac{e^x(x^2 - 2x - 1)}{(x^2 - 1)^2}$
29. a. $2w$ for $w \neq 0$ **31.** 1   **33. a.** $y = -3x/2 + 17/2$
b.

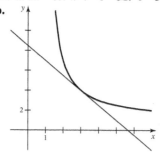

35. a. $y = 3x + 1$ **b.**

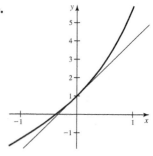

37. $-27x^{-10}$ **39.** $6t - 42/t^8$ **41.** $-3/t^2 - 2/t^3$ **43.** $e^{7x}(7x + 1)$
45. $45e^{3x}$ **47.** $e^{-3x}(1 - 3x)$ **49.** $\frac{2}{3}e^x - e^{-x}$

51. a. $p'(t) = \left(\dfrac{20}{t + 2}\right)^2$ **b.** $p'(5) \approx 8.16$ **c.** $t = 0$
d. $\lim\limits_{t \to \infty} p'(t) = 0$; the population approaches a steady state.
e.

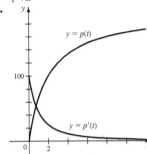

53. a. $Q'(t) = -1.386e^{-0.0693t}$ **b.** -1.386 mg/hr; -1.207 mg/hr
c. $\lim\limits_{t \to \infty} Q(t) = 0$—eventually none of the drug remains in the
bloodstream; $\lim\limits_{t \to \infty} Q'(t) = 0$—the rate at which the body excretes the
drug goes to zero over time.   **55. a.** $x = -\frac{1}{2}$ **b.** The line tangent to
the graph of $f(x)$ at $x = -\frac{1}{2}$ is horizontal.   **57.** $\dfrac{e^x(x^2 - x - 5)}{(x - 2)^2}$

59. $\dfrac{e^x(x^2 + x + 1)}{(x + 1)^2}$ **61. a.** False   **b.** False   **c.** False   **d.** True

63. $f'(x) = x\,e^{3x}(3x + 2)$
       $f''(x) = e^{3x}(9x^2 + 12x + 2)$
       $f^{(3)}(x) = 9e^{3x}(3x^2 + 6x + 2)$

65. $f'(x) = \dfrac{x^2 + 2x - 7}{(x + 1)^2}$
       $f''(x) = \dfrac{16}{(x + 1)^3}$
       $f^{(3)}(x) = \dfrac{-48}{(x + 1)^4}$

67. $8x - \dfrac{2}{(5x + 1)^2}$ **69.** $\dfrac{r - 6\sqrt{r} - 1}{2\sqrt{r}\,(r + 1)^2}$
71. $300x^9 + 135x^8 + 105x^6 + 120x^3 + 45x^2 + 15$

73. a. $y = -\dfrac{108}{169}x + \dfrac{567}{169}$ **b.**

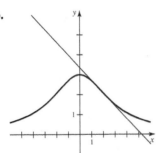

75. $-\frac{3}{2}$ **77.** $\frac{1}{9}$ **79.** $\frac{7}{8}$ **81. a.** $F'(x) = -\dfrac{1.8 \times 10^{10}\,Qq}{x^3}$ N/m
b. -1.8×10^{19} N/m   **c.** $|F'(x)|$ decreases as x increases.
83. One possible pair: $f(x) = e^{ax}$ and $g(x) = e^{bx}$,
where $b = \dfrac{a}{a - 1}$, $a \neq 1$.   **87.** $f''g + 2f'g' + fg''$
91. a. $f'gh + fg'h + fgh'$ **b.** $2e^{2x}(x^2 + 3x - 2)$

Section 3.4 Exercises, pp. 167–169

1. $\dfrac{\sin x}{x}$ is undefined at $x = 0$.   **3.** The tangent and cotangent functions
are defined as ratios of the sine and cosine functions.   **5.** -1

7. 3   **9.** $\dfrac{7}{3}$ **11.** 5   **13.** 7   **15.** $\frac{1}{4}$ **17.** $\cos x - \sin x$

19. $e^{-x}(\cos x - \sin x)$ **21.** $\sin x + x \cos x$ **23.** $-\dfrac{1}{1 + \sin x}$

25. $\cos^2 x - \sin^2 x = \cos 2x$ **27.** $-2 \sin x \cos x = -\sin 2x$

33. $\sec x \tan x - \csc x \cot x$ **35.** $e^{5x} \csc x(5 - \cot x)$ **37.** $-\dfrac{\csc x}{1 + \csc x}$

39. $\cos^2 z - \sin^2 z = \cos 2z$ **41.** $2 \cos x - x \sin x$ **43.** $2e^x \cos x$
45. $2 \csc^2 x \cot x$ **47.** $2\,(\sec^2 x \tan x + \csc^2 x \cot x)$ **49. a.** False
b. False   **c.** True   **d.** True   **51.** a/b **53.** $\frac{3}{4}$ **55.** 0

57. $x \cos 2x + \frac{1}{2} \sin 2x$ **59.** $-\dfrac{2}{1 + \sin x}$ **61.** $\dfrac{2 \sin x}{(1 + \cos x)^2}$

63. a. $y = \sqrt{3}x + 2 - \pi\sqrt{3}/6$ **b.**

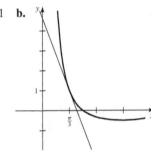

65. a. $y = -2\sqrt{3}x + 2\sqrt{3}\pi/3 + 1$ **b.**

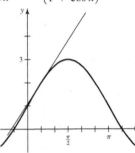

67. $x = 7\pi/6 + 2k\pi$ and $x = 11\pi/6 + 2k\pi$, where k is any integer
69. a.

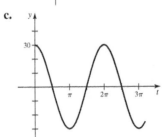

b. $v(t) = 30 \cos t$

c.

d. $v(t) = 0$ for $t = (2k + 1)\dfrac{\pi}{2}$,
where k is any nonnegative integer
and the position is
$\left((2k + 1)\dfrac{\pi}{2}, 0\right)$ if k is even or
$\left((2k + 1)\dfrac{\pi}{2}, -60\right)$ if k is odd.

e. $v(t)$ is at a maximum at $t = 2k\pi$, where k is a nonnegative integer; the position is $(2k\pi, -30)$.

f. $a(t) = -30 \sin t$

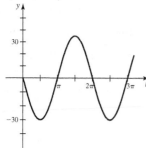

77. $a = 0$ **79. a.** $2 \sin x \cos x$ **b.** $3 \sin^2 x \cos x$ **c.** $4 \sin^3 x \cos x$

d. $n \sin^{n-1} x \cos x$ The conjecture is true for $n = 1$. If it holds for

$n = k$, then when $n = k + 1$, we have $\dfrac{d}{dx}(\sin^{k+1} x) =$

$\dfrac{d}{dx}(\sin^k x \cdot \sin x) = \sin^k x \cos x + \sin x \cdot k \sin^{k-1} x \cos x =$

$(k + 1) \sin^k x \cos x$. **81. a.** $f(x) = \sin x; a = \pi/6$ **b.** $\sqrt{3}/2$

83. a. $f(x) = \cot x; a = \pi/4$ **b.** -2

Section 3.5 Exercises, pp. 177–181

1. The average rate of change is $\dfrac{f(x + \Delta x) - f(x)}{\Delta x}$, whereas the

instantaneous rate of change is the limit as Δx goes to zero in this
quotient. **3.** Small **5.** If the position of the object at time t is $s(t)$,
then the acceleration at time t is $a(t) = d^2 s/dt^2$. **7.** Each of the first
200 stoves costs, on average, \$70 to produce. When 200 stoves have
already been produced, the 201st stove costs \$65 to produce.
9. a. 40 mi/hr **b.** 40 mi/hr; yes **c.** -60 mi/hr; -60 mi/hr; south
d. The police car drives away from the police station going north until
about 10:08, when it turns around and heads south, toward the police
station. It continues south until it passes the police station at about
11:02 and keeps going south until about 11:40, when it turns around
and heads north.
11. a.

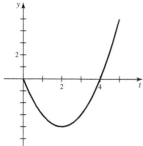

b. $v(t) = 2t - 4$; stationary at
$t = 2$, to the right on $(2, 5]$, to the
left on $[0, 2)$

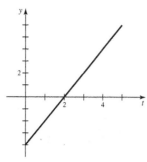

c. $v(1) = -2$ ft/s; $a(1) = 2$ ft/s² **d.** $a(2) = 2$ ft/s²

13. a.

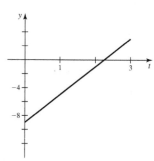

b. $v(t) = 4t - 9$; stationary at
$t = \frac{9}{4}$, to the right on $\left(\frac{9}{4}, 3\right]$, to the
left on $\left[0, \frac{9}{4}\right)$

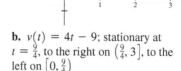

c. $v(1) = -5$ ft/s; $a(1) = 4$ ft/s² **d.** $a\left(\frac{9}{4}\right) = 4$ ft/s²

15. a.

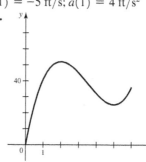

b. $v(t) = 6t^2 - 42t + 60$; stationary at $t = 2$ and $t = 5$, to the right
on $[0, 2)$ and $(5, 6]$, to the left on $(2, 5)$

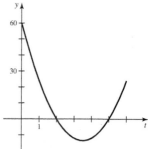

c. $v(1) = 24$ ft/s; $a(1) = -30$ ft/s² **d.** $a(2) = -18$ ft/s;
$a(5) = 18$ ft/s² **17. a.** $v(t) = -32t + 64$ **b.** At $t = 2$
c. 96 ft **d.** At $2 + \sqrt{6}$ **e.** $-32\sqrt{6}$ ft/s
19. a. 98,300 people/year **b.** 99,920 people/year in 1997;
95,600 people/year in 2005 **c.** $p'(t) = -0.54t + 101$; population
increased, growth rate is positive but decreasing.

21. a. $\overline{C}(x) = \dfrac{1000}{x} + 0.1; C'(x) = 0.1$

b. $\overline{C}(2000) = \$0.60/\text{item}; C'(2000) = \$0.10/\text{item}$
c. The average cost per item when 2000 items are produced is
\$0.60/item. The cost of producing the 2001st item is \$0.10.
23. a. $\overline{C}(x) = -0.01x + 40 + 100/x; C'(x) = -0.02x + 40$

b. $\overline{C}(1000) = \$30.10/$item; $C'(1000) = \$20/$item   **c.** The average cost per item is about \$30.10 when 1000 items are produced. The cost of producing the 1001st item is \$20.   **25. a.** False   **b.** True   **c.** False   **d.** True   **27.** 240 ft   **29.** 64 ft/s   **31. a.** $t = 1, 2, 3$ **b.** It is moving in the positive direction for t in $(0, 1)$ and $(2, 3)$; it is moving in the negative direction for t in $(1, 2)$ and $t > 3$.

c.
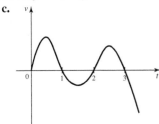

33. a. $P(x) = 0.02x^2 + 50x - 100$

b. $\dfrac{P(x)}{x} = 0.02x + 50 - \dfrac{100}{x}$; $\dfrac{dP}{dx} = 0.04x + 50$

c. $\dfrac{P(500)}{500} = 59.8$; $\dfrac{dp}{dx}(500) = 70$ **d.** The profit, on average, for each of the first 500 items produced is 59.8; the profit for the 501st item produced is 70.   **35. a.** $P(x) = 0.04x^2 + 100x - 800$

b. $\dfrac{P(x)}{x} = 0.04x + 100 - \dfrac{800}{x}$; $\dfrac{dp}{dx} = 0.08x + 100$

c. $\dfrac{P(1000)}{1000} = 139.2$; $p'(1000) = 180$ **d.** The average profit per item for each of the first 1000 items produced is \$139.20. The profit for the 1001st item produced is \$180.   **37. a.** 1930, 1.1 million people/yr   **b.** 1960, 2.9 million people/yr   **c.** The population did not decrease.   **d.** $[1905, 1915], [1930, 1960], [1980, 1990]$

39. a.
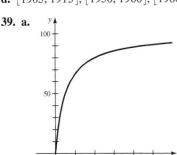
b. $v = \dfrac{100}{(t + 1)^2}$

c.
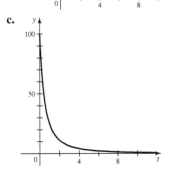

The marble moves fastest at the beginning and slows considerably over the first 5 s. It continues to slow but never actually stops.
d. $t = 4$ s   **e.** $t = -1 + \sqrt{2} \approx 0.414$ s

41. a. $C'(x) = -\dfrac{125,000,000}{x^2} + 1.5$;

$\overline{C}(x) = \dfrac{C(x)}{25,000} = 50 + \dfrac{5000}{x} + 0.00006x$

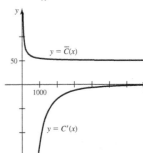

b. $C'(5000) = -3.5$; $\overline{C}(5000) = 51.3$ **c.** Marginal cost: If the batch size is increased from 5000 to 5001, then the cost of producing 25,000 gadgets would *decrease* by about \$3.50.   Average cost: When batch size is 5000, it costs \$51.30 *per item* to produce all 25,000 gadgets.

43. a.
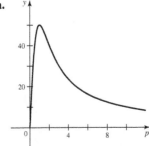

b. $R'(p) = \dfrac{100(1 - p^2)}{(p^2 + 1)^2}$ **c.** $p = 1$

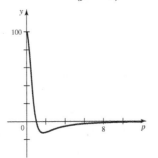

45. a.
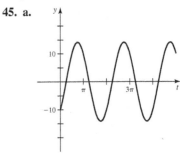

b. $dx/dt = 10 \cos t + 10 \sin t$ **c.** $t = 3\pi/4 + k\pi$, where k is any positive integer.   **d.** The graph implies that the spring never stops oscillating. In reality, the weight would eventually come to rest.

47. a. Juan starts faster than Jean and opens up a big lead. Then, Juan slows down while Jean speeds up. Jean catches up, and the race finishes in a tie.   **b.** Same average velocity   **c.** Tie   **d.** At $t = 2$, $\theta'(2) = \pi/2$ rad/min; $\theta'(4) = \pi =$ Jean's greatest velocity   **e.** At $t = 2, \varphi'(2) = \pi/2$ rad/min; $\varphi'(0) = \pi =$ Juan's greatest velocity

49. a.

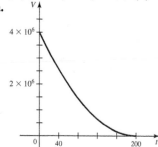

$V(0) = 4{,}000{,}000 \text{ m}^3$

b. 200 hr

c.

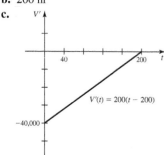

$V'(t) = 200(t - 200)$

d. The magnitude of the flow rate is greatest (most negative) at $t = 0$ and least (zero) at $t = 200$.

51. a. $v(t) = -15e^{-t}(\sin t + \cos t); v(1) \approx -7.6 \text{ m/s}$, $v(3) \approx 0.63 \text{ m/s}$ **b.** Down $(0, 2.4)$ and $(5.5, 8.6)$; up $(2.4, 5.5)$ and $(8.6, 10)$ **c.** ≈ 0.65 m/s   **53. a.** $-T'(1) = -80, -T'(3) = 80$ **b.** $-T'(x) < 0$ for $0 \le x < 2; -T'(x) > 0$ for $2 < x \le 4$ **c.** Near $x = 0$, with $x > 0, -T'(x) < 0$, so heat flows toward the end of the rod. Similarly, near $x = 4$, with $x < 4, -T'(x) > 0$.

Section 3.6 Exercises, pp. 187–190

1. $\dfrac{dy}{dx} = \dfrac{dy}{du} \cdot \dfrac{du}{dx}; \dfrac{d}{dx}(f(g(x))) = f'(g(x)) \cdot g'(x)$ **3.** $g(x), x$

5. Outer: $f(x) = x^{-5}$; inner: $u = x^2 + 10$ **7.** $30(3x + 7)^9$

9. $5 \sin^4 x \cos x$ **11.** $5e^{5x-7}$ **13.** $\dfrac{x}{\sqrt{x^2 + 1}}$ **15.** $10x \sec^2 5x^2$

17. $e^x \sec e^x \tan e^x$ **19.** $10(6x + 7)(3x^2 + 7x)^9$ **21.** $\dfrac{5}{\sqrt{10x + 1}}$

23. $-\dfrac{315x^2}{(7x^3 + 1)^4}$ **25.** $3 \sec(3x + 1) \tan(3x + 1)$ **27.** $e^x \sec^2 e^x$

29. $(12x^2 + 3) \cos(4x^3 + 3x + 1)$ **31.** $\dfrac{\cos(2\sqrt{x})}{\sqrt{x}}$

33. $5 \sec x (\sec x + \tan x)^5$ **35. a.** $u = \cos x, y = u^3$; $\dfrac{dy}{dx} = -3 \cos^2 x \sin x$ **b.** $u = x^3, y = \cos u; \dfrac{dy}{dx} = -3x^2 \sin x^3$

37. a. 100   **b.** -100 **c.** -16 **d.** 40   **e.** 40

39. $y' = 25(12x^5 - 9x^2)(2x^6 - 3x^3 + 3)^{24}$

41. $y' = 30(1 + 2\tan x)^{14} \sec^2 x$ **43.** $y' = -\dfrac{\cot x \csc^2 x}{\sqrt{1 + \cot^2 x}}$

45. $e^x \cos(\sin(e^x)) \cos(e^x)$

47. $y' = -15 \sin^4(\cos 3x)(\sin 3x)[\cos(\cos 3x)]$

49. $y' = \dfrac{3e^{\sqrt{3x}}}{2\sqrt{3x}} \sec^2(e^{\sqrt{3x}})$ **51.** $y' = \dfrac{1}{2\sqrt{x + \sqrt{x}}}\left(1 + \dfrac{1}{2\sqrt{x}}\right)$

53. $y' = f'(g(x^2))g'(x^2) 2x$ **55.** $\dfrac{5x^4}{(x + 1)^6}$

57. $x e^{x^2+1}(2 \sin x^3 + 3x \cos x^3)$

59. $5\theta^2 \sec 5\theta \tan 5\theta + 2\theta \sec 5\theta$

61. $4(x + 2)^3(x^2 + 1)^3(3x^2 + 4x + 1)$ **63.** $\dfrac{2x^3 - \sin 2x}{\sqrt{x^4 + \cos 2x}}$

65. $2(p + \pi)(\sin p^2 + p(p + \pi) \cos p^2)$ **67. a.** True   **b.** True

c. True   **d.** False   **69.** $\dfrac{d^2 y}{dx^2} = 2 \cos x^2 - 4x^2 \sin x^2$

71. $\dfrac{d^2 y}{dx^2} = 4 e^{-2x^2}(4x^2 - 1)$ **73.** $y' = \dfrac{f'(x)}{2\sqrt{f(x)}}$

75. $y = -9x + 35$

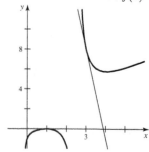

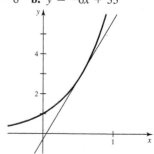

77. a. $h(4) = 9, h'(4) = -6$ **b.** $y = -6x + 33$

79. $y = 6x + 3 - 3 \ln 3$

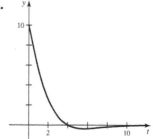

81. a. -3π **b.** -5π **83. a.** $\dfrac{d^2 y}{dt^2} = \dfrac{-y_0 k}{m} \cos\left(t\sqrt{\dfrac{k}{m}}\right)$

85. a.

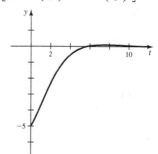

b. $v(t) = -5e^{-t/2}\left[\dfrac{\pi}{4} \sin\left(\dfrac{\pi t}{8}\right) + \cos\left(\dfrac{\pi t}{8}\right)\right]$

87. a. 10.88 hr **b.** $D'(t) = \dfrac{6\pi}{365} \sin\left(\dfrac{2\pi(t + 10)}{365}\right)$

c. 2.87 min/day; on March 1, the length of day is increasing at a rate of about 2.87 min/day.

d.

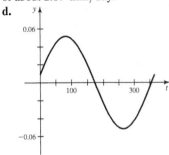

e. Most rapidly: Approximately March 22 and September 22; least rapidly: approximately December 21 and June 21

89. a. $E'(t) = 400 + 200 \cos\left(\dfrac{\pi t}{12}\right)$ MW **b.** At noon;

$E'(0) = 600$ MW **c.** At midnight; $E'(12) = 200$ MW

d.

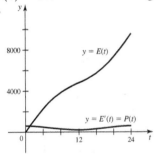

91. a. $f'(x) = -2 \cos x \sin x + 2 \sin x \cos x = 0$
b. $f(0) = \cos^2 0 + \sin^2 0 = 1$; $f(x) = 1$ for all x, by part (b); that is, $\cos^2 x + \sin^2 x = 1$ **95. a.** $h(x) = (x^2 - 3)^5$; $a = 2$ **b.** 20
97. a. $h(x) = \sin(x^2)$; $a = \pi/2$ **b.** $\pi \cos(\pi^2/4)$
99. $\displaystyle\lim_{x \to 5} \dfrac{f(x)^2 - f(25)}{x - 5} = 10 f'(25)$

Section 3.7 Exercises, pp. 196–198

1. There may be more than one expression for y or y'. **3.** When derived implicitly, dy/dx is usually given in terms of both x and y.

5. a. $\dfrac{dy}{dx} = -\dfrac{x^3}{y^3}$ **b.** 1 **7. a.** $\dfrac{dy}{dx} = \dfrac{2}{y}$ **b.** 1 **9. a.** $\dfrac{dy}{dx} = \dfrac{20x^3}{\cos y}$

b. -20 **11. a.** $\dfrac{dy}{dx} = -\dfrac{1}{\sin y}$ **b.** -1 **13.** $\dfrac{dy}{dx} = \dfrac{1 - y \cos(xy)}{x \cos(xy) - 1}$

15. $-\dfrac{1}{1 + \sin y}$ **17.** $\dfrac{dy}{dx} = \dfrac{1}{2y \sin(y^2) + e^y}$

19. $\dfrac{dy}{dx} = \dfrac{3x^2(x - y)^2 + 2y}{2x}$ **21.** $\dfrac{dy}{dx} = \dfrac{13y - 18x^2}{21y^2 - 13x}$

23. $\dfrac{dy}{dx} = \dfrac{5\sqrt{x^4 + y^2} - 2x^3}{y - 6y^2\sqrt{x^4 + y^2}}$ **25. a.** $2^2 + 2 \cdot 1 + 1^2 = 7$

b. $y = -5x/4 + 7/2$ **27. a.** $\sin \pi + 5\left(\dfrac{\pi^2}{5}\right) = \pi^2$

b. $y = \dfrac{\pi(1 + \pi)}{1 + 2\pi} + \dfrac{5}{1 + 2\pi} x$

29. a. $\cos\left(\dfrac{\pi}{2} - \dfrac{\pi}{4}\right) + \sin\dfrac{\pi}{4} = \sqrt{2}$ **b.** $y = \dfrac{x}{2}$

31. $\dfrac{d^2 y}{dx^2} = -\dfrac{1}{4y^3}$ **33.** $\dfrac{\sin y}{(\cos y - 1)^3}$ **35.** $\dfrac{d^2 y}{dx^2} = \dfrac{4e^{2y}}{(1 - 2e^{2y})^3}$

37. $\dfrac{dy}{dx} = \dfrac{5}{4}x^{1/4}$ **39.** $\dfrac{dy}{dx} = \dfrac{10}{3(5x + 1)^{1/3}}$

41. $\dfrac{dy}{dx} = -\dfrac{3}{2^{7/4} x^{3/4}(4x - 3)^{5/4}}$ **43.** $\dfrac{2}{9x^{2/3}\sqrt[3]{1 + \sqrt[3]{x}}}$

45. $-\frac{1}{4}$ **47.** $-\frac{24}{13}$ **49.** -5 **51. a.** False **b.** True **c.** False
d. False **53. a.** $y = x - 1$ and $y = -x + 2$
b.

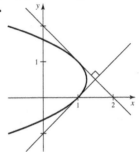

55. a. $y' = -\dfrac{2xy}{x^2 + 4}$ **b.** $y = \frac{1}{2}x + 2, y = -\frac{1}{2}x + 2$

c. $-\dfrac{16x}{(x^2 + 4)^2}$ **57. a.** $\left(\frac{5}{4}, \frac{1}{2}\right)$ **b.** No

59. a. $\dfrac{dy}{dx} = 0$ on the $y = 1$ branch; $\dfrac{dy}{dx} = \dfrac{1}{2y + 1}$ on the other two branches.

b. $f_1(x) = 1, f_2(x) = \dfrac{-1 + \sqrt{4x - 3}}{2}, f_3(x) = \dfrac{-1 - \sqrt{4x - 3}}{2}$

c.

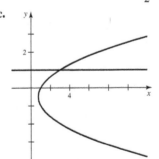

61. a. $\dfrac{dy}{dx} = \dfrac{x - x^3}{y}$ **b.** $f_1(x) = \sqrt{x^2 - \dfrac{x^4}{2}}; f_2(x) = -\sqrt{x^2 - \dfrac{x^4}{2}}$

c.

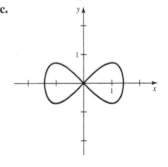

63. $y = \dfrac{4x}{5} - \dfrac{3}{5}$

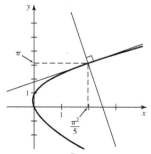

65. $y = -\dfrac{1 + 2\pi}{5} x + \pi\left(\dfrac{25 + \pi + 2\pi^2}{25}\right)$

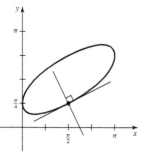

67. $y = -2x + \dfrac{5\pi}{4}$

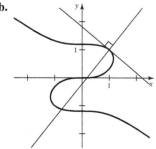

69. a. $y = -\dfrac{9x}{11} + \dfrac{20}{11}$ and $y = \dfrac{11x}{9} - \dfrac{2}{9}$

b.

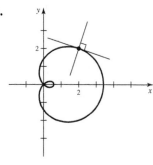

71. a. $y = -\dfrac{x}{3} + \dfrac{8}{3}$ and $y = 3x - 4$

b.

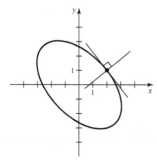

73. a. $\dfrac{dK}{dL} = \dfrac{-K}{2L}$ **b.** -4 **75.** $\dfrac{dr}{dh} = \dfrac{h - 2r}{h}; -3$

77. Note that for $y = mx$, $dy/dx = m = y/x$; for $x^2 + y^2 = a^2$, $dy/dx = -x/y$.   **79.** For $xy = a$, $dy/dx = -y/x$. For $x^2 - y^2 = b$, $dy/dx = x/y$. Since $(-y/x) \cdot (x/y) = -1$, the families of curves are orthogonal trajectories.   **81.** $y' = \dfrac{7y^2 - 3x^2 - 4xy^2 - 4x^3}{2y(2x^2 + 2y^2 - 7x)}$

83. $\dfrac{d^2 y}{dx^2} = \dfrac{2y^2(5 + 8x\sqrt{y})}{(1 + 2x\sqrt{y})^3}$

Section 3.8 Exercises, pp. 206–209

1. $x = e^y \Rightarrow 1 = e^y y'(x) \Rightarrow y'(x) = 1/e^y = 1/x.$

3. $\dfrac{d}{dx}(\ln kx) = \dfrac{d}{dx}(\ln k + \ln x) = \dfrac{d}{dx}(\ln x)$

5. $f'(x) = \dfrac{1}{x \ln b}$. If $b = e$, then $f'(x) = \dfrac{1}{x}$.   **7.** $f(x) = e^{h(x) \ln g(x)}$

9. $\dfrac{1}{x}$ **11.** $2/x$ **13.** $\cot x$ **15.** $-2/(x^2 - 1)$

17. $(x^2 + 1)/x + 2x \ln x$ **19.** $1/(x \ln x)$

21. $\dfrac{1}{x(\ln x + 1)^2}$ **23.** $8^x \ln 8$ **25.** $y' = 5 \cdot 4^x \ln 4$

27. $y' = 3^x \cdot x^2 (x \ln 3 + 3)$ **29.** $A' = 1000(1.045)^{4t} \ln(1.045)$

31. a. About 28.7 s   **b.** -46.512 s/1000 ft   **c.** $dT/da = -2.74 \cdot 2^{-0.274a} \ln 2$

At $t = 8, \dfrac{dT}{da} = -0.4156$ min/1000 ft

$$= -24.938 \text{ s}/1000 \text{ ft.}$$

If a plane is traveling at 30,000 feet and it increases its altitude by 1,000 feet, the time of useful consciousness would decrease by about 25 seconds.

33. a. About 67.19 hr

b. $Q'(12) = -9.815$ μCi/hr

$Q'(24) = -5.201$ μCi/hr

$Q'(48) = -1.461$ μCi/hr

The rate at which iodine-123 leaves the body decreases with time.

35. $2^x \ln 2$ **37.** $g'(y) = e^y y^{e-1} (y + e)$ **39.** $r' = 2e^{2\theta}$

41. $f'(x) = \dfrac{\sqrt{x}}{2}(10x - 9)$ **43.** $\dfrac{2^x \ln 2}{(2^x + 1)^2}$

45. $x^{\cos x - 1}(\cos x - x \ln x \sin x); -\ln(\pi/2)$

47. $x^{\sqrt{x}}\left(\dfrac{2 + \ln x}{2\sqrt{x}}\right); 4(2 + \ln 4)$

49. $\dfrac{(\sin x)^{\ln x}(\ln (\sin x) + x(\ln x) \cot x)}{x}; 0$

51. $y = x \sin 1 + 1 - \sin 1$ **53.** $y = e^{2/e}$ and $y = e^{-2/e}$

55. $y' = \dfrac{8x}{(x^2 - 1) \ln 3}$ **57.** $y' = -\sin x (\ln (\cos^2 x) + 2)$

59. $y' = -\dfrac{\ln 4}{x \ln^2 x}$ **61.** $f'(x) = \dfrac{(x + 1)^{10}}{(2x - 4)^8}\left[\dfrac{10}{x + 1} - \dfrac{8}{x - 2}\right]$

63. $f'(x) = 2x^{(\ln x) - 1} \ln x$

65. $f'(x) = \dfrac{(x + 1)^{3/2} (x - 4)^{5/2}}{(5x + 3)^{2/3}} \cdot$

$$\left[\dfrac{3}{2(x + 1)} + \dfrac{5}{2(x - 4)} - \dfrac{10}{3(5x + 3)}\right]$$

67. $f'(x) = (\sin x)^{\tan x}\left[1 + \sec^2 x \ln (\sin x)\right]$

69. a. False   **b.** False   **c.** False   **d.** False   **e.** True

71. $-\dfrac{1}{x^2 \ln 10}$ **73.** $2/x$ **75.** $y' = 3^x \ln 3$ **77.** $f'(x) = 12/(3x + 1)$

79. $f'(x) = 1/(2x)$ **81.** $f'(x) = \dfrac{2}{2x - 1} + \dfrac{3}{x + 2} + \dfrac{8}{1 - 4x}$

83. $y = 2$

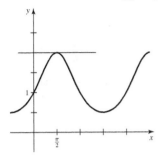

85. $10x^{10x}(1 + \ln x)$

87. $x^{\cos x}\left(\dfrac{\cos x}{x} - \ln x \sin x\right)$

89. $\left(1 + \dfrac{1}{x}\right)^x \left[\ln\left(1 + \dfrac{1}{x}\right) - \dfrac{1}{x + 1}\right]$

91. $x^{9 + x^{10}}(1 + 10 \ln x)$

93. a.

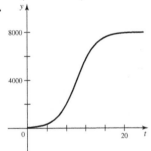

b. $t = 2 \ln (265) \approx 11.2$ years; about 14.5 years
c. $P'(0) \approx 25$ fish/year; $P'(5) \approx 264$ fish/year
d.

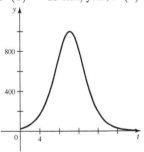

The population is growing fastest after about 10 years.

95. b. $r(11) \approx 0.0133$; $r(21) \approx 0.0118$; the relative growth rate is decreasing.   **c.** $\lim\limits_{t \to \infty} r(t) = 0$; as the population gets close to carrying capacity, the growth rate approaches zero.

97. a. $A(5) = \$17{,}443$
$A(15) = \$72{,}705$
$A(25) = \$173{,}248$
$A(35) = \$356{,}178$
$\$5526.20/\text{year}$, $\$10{,}054.30/\text{year}$, $\$18{,}293/\text{year}$
b. $A(40) = \$497{,}873$
c. $\dfrac{dA}{dt} = 600{,}000 \ln (1.005)\left[(1.005)^{12t}\right]$
$\approx (2992.5)(1.005)^{12t}$
A increases at an increasing rate.

99. $p = e^{1/e}$; (e, e) **101.** $1/e$ **103.** $27(1 + \ln 3)$

Section 3.9 Exercises, pp. 216–219

1. $\dfrac{d}{dx}(\sin^{-1} x) = \dfrac{1}{\sqrt{1 - x^2}}$; $\dfrac{d}{dx}(\tan^{-1} x) = \dfrac{1}{1 + x^2}$;

$\dfrac{d}{dx}(\sec^{-1} x) = \dfrac{1}{|x|\sqrt{x^2 - 1}}$ **3.** $\frac{1}{5}$ **5.** $\frac{1}{4}$ **7.** $\dfrac{2}{\sqrt{1 - 4x^2}}$

9. $-\dfrac{4w}{\sqrt{1 - 4w^2}}$ **11.** $-\dfrac{2e^{-2x}}{\sqrt{1 - e^{-4x}}}$ **13.** $\dfrac{10}{100x^2 + 1}$

15. $\dfrac{4y}{1 + (2y^2 - 4)^2}$ **17.** $-\dfrac{1}{2\sqrt{z}(1 + z)}$ **19.** $\dfrac{1}{|x|\sqrt{x^2 - 1}}$

21. $-\dfrac{1}{|2u + 1|\sqrt{u^2 + u}}$ **23.** $\dfrac{2y}{(y^2 + 1)^2 + 1}$

25. $\dfrac{1}{x|\ln x|\sqrt{(\ln x)^2 - 1}}$ **27.** $-\dfrac{e^x \sec^2 (e^x)}{|\tan e^x|\sqrt{\tan^2 e^x - 1}}$

29. $-\dfrac{e^s}{1 + e^{2s}}$ **31.** $y = x + \dfrac{\pi}{4} - \dfrac{1}{2}$ **33.** $y = -\dfrac{4}{\sqrt{6}}x + \dfrac{\pi}{3} + \dfrac{2}{\sqrt{3}}$

35. a. ≈ -0.00055 rad/m
b.

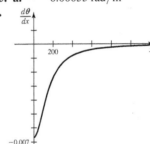

The magnitude of the change in angular size, $|d\theta/dx|$, is greatest when the boat is at the skyscraper (i.e., at $x = 0$).

37. $\frac{1}{3}$ **39.** $-\frac{1}{5}$ **41.** $\frac{1}{2}$ **43.** 4 **45.** $\frac{1}{12}$ **47.** $\frac{1}{4}$ **49.** $\frac{5}{4}$
51. a. True   **b.** False   **c.** True   **d.** True   **e.** True
53. a.

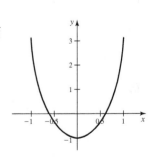

b. $f'(x) = 2x \sin^{-1} x + \dfrac{x^2 - 1}{\sqrt{1 - x^2}}$

55. a.

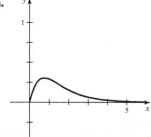

b. $f'(x) = \dfrac{e^{-x}}{1+x^2} - e^{-x}\tan^{-1}(x)$

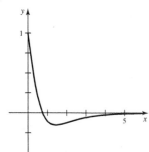

57. $(f^{-1})'(x) = \frac{1}{3}$ **59.** $(f^{-1})'(x) = 1/(2\sqrt{x+4})$

61. $(f^{-1})'(x) = 2x$ **63.** $(f^{-1})'(x) = -2/x^3$

65. a. $\sin\theta = \dfrac{10}{\ell}$ implies $\theta = \sin^{-1}\dfrac{10}{\ell}$.

Thus, $\dfrac{d\theta}{d\ell} = \dfrac{1}{\sqrt{1-\left(\dfrac{10}{\ell}\right)^2}} \cdot (-10\ell^{-2}) = -\dfrac{10}{\ell\sqrt{\ell^2-100}}$.

b. $d\theta/d\ell = -0.0041, -0.0289,$ and -0.1984

c. $\lim\limits_{\ell \to 10^+} d\theta/d\ell = -\infty$ **d.** The length ℓ is decreasing.

67. a. $d\theta/dc = 1/\sqrt{R^2-c^2}$ **b.** $1/R$

71. Use the identity $\cot^{-1}(x) + \tan^{-1}(x) = \pi/2$.

Section 3.10 Exercises, pp. 222–227

1. As the side length s of a cube changes, the surface area $6s^2$ changes as well.   **3.** The other two opposite sides decrease in length.

5. a. $40\ \text{m}^2/\text{s}$ **b.** $80\ \text{m}^2/\text{s}$

c.

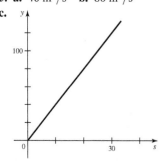

7. a. $4\ \text{m}^2/\text{s}$ **b.** $\sqrt{2}\ \text{m}^2/\text{s}$ **c.** $2\sqrt{2}\ \text{m/s}$ **9. a.** $\dfrac{1}{4\pi}\ \text{cm/s}$

b. $\dfrac{1}{2}\ \text{cm/s}$ **11.** $-40\pi\ \text{ft}^2/\text{min}$ **13.** $\dfrac{3}{80\pi}\ \text{in./min}$

17. At the point $\left(\dfrac{1}{2}, \dfrac{1}{4}\right)$ **19.** $\dfrac{1}{500}\ \text{m/min};\ 2000\ \text{min}$

21. $10\tan 20°\ \text{km/hr} \approx 3.6\ \text{km/hr}$ **23.** $\dfrac{5}{24}\ \text{ft/s}$

25. $-\dfrac{8}{3}\ \text{ft/s}, -\dfrac{32}{3}\ \text{ft/s}$ **27.** $2592\pi\ \text{cm}^3/\text{s}$ **29.** $-\dfrac{8}{9\pi}\ \text{ft/s}$

31. $9\pi\ \text{ft}^3/\text{min}$ **33.** $\dfrac{2}{5}\ \text{m}^2/\text{min}$ **35.** $57.89\ \text{ft/s}$ **37.** $4.66\ \text{in./s}$

39. $\dfrac{3\sqrt{5}}{2}\ \text{ft/s}$ **41.** $\approx 720.3\ \text{mi/hr}$ **43.** $11.06\ \text{m/hr}$

45. a. $187.5\ \text{ft/s}$ **b.** $0.938\ \text{rad/s}$ **47.** $\dfrac{d\theta}{dt} = 0.543\ \text{rad/hr}$

49. $\dfrac{d\theta}{dt} = \dfrac{1}{5}\ \text{rad/s}, \dfrac{d\theta}{dt} = \dfrac{1}{8}\ \text{rad/s}$ **51.** $\dfrac{d\theta}{dt} = 0\ \text{rad/s}$ for all $t \geq 0$

53. $-0.0201\ \text{rad/s}$ **55. a.** $-\dfrac{\sqrt{3}}{10}\ \text{m/hr}$ **b.** $-1\ \text{m}^2/\text{hr}$

Review Exercises, pp. 227–230

1. a. False   **b.** False   **c.** False   **d.** False   **e.** True

3. a. 16 **b.** $y = 16x - 10$

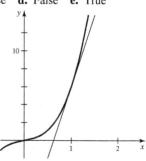

5. a. $-\frac{3}{4}$ **b.** $y = -\dfrac{3x}{4} + \dfrac{1}{2}$

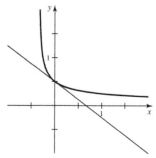

7. a. 2.70 million people/year   **b.** The slope of the secant line through the two points is approximately equal to the slope of that tangent line at $t = 55$.   **c.** 2.217 million people/year   **9. a.** $\approx 40\ \text{m/s}$

b. $\approx 7\ \text{m/s}$ **c.** $\approx 18\ \text{m/s}$

d.

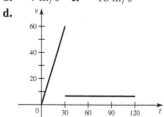

e. The skydiver deployed the parachute.

13.

15. $2x^2 + 2\pi x + 7$ **17.** $5t^2 \cos t + 10t \sin t$

19. $(8\theta + 12) \sec^2(\theta^2 + 3\theta + 2)$ **21.** $\dfrac{32u^2 + 8u + 1}{(8u + 1)^2}$

23. $\sec^2(\sin\theta) \cdot \cos\theta$ **25.** $\dfrac{9x \sin x - 2 \sin x + 6x^2 \cos x - 2x \cos x}{\sqrt{3x - 1}}$

27. $(2 + \ln x) \ln x$ **29.** $(2x - 1)\, 2^{x^2 - x} \ln 2$ **31.** $-\dfrac{1}{|x|\sqrt{x^2 - 1}}$

33. 1   **35.** $\sqrt{3} + \pi/6$ **37.** $\dfrac{dy}{dx} = \dfrac{y \cos x}{e^y - 1 - \sin x}$

39. $\dfrac{dy}{dx} = -\dfrac{xy}{x^2 + 2y^2}$ **41.** $y = x$ **43.** $y = -\dfrac{4x}{5} + \dfrac{24}{5}$

45. $x = 4; x = 6$ **47.** $y' = \dfrac{\cos\sqrt{x}}{2\sqrt{x}}, y'' = -\dfrac{\sqrt{x}\sin\sqrt{x} + \cos\sqrt{x}}{4x^{3/2}},$

$y''' = \dfrac{3\sqrt{x}\sin\sqrt{x} + (3 - x)\cos\sqrt{x}}{8x^{5/2}}$ **49.** $x^2 f'(x) + 2x f(x)$

51. $\dfrac{g(x)(x f'(x) + f(x)) - x f(x) g'(x)}{g^2(x)}$ **53. a.** 27 **b.** $\frac{25}{27}$ **c.** 294

55. $f(x) = \tan(\pi\sqrt{3x - 11}),\ a = 5;\ f'(5) = 3\pi/4$ **57.** -1

59. $(f^{-1})'(x) = -3/x^4$ **61. a.** $(f^{-1})'(1/\sqrt{2}) = \sqrt{2}$

63. a. $\overline{C}(3000) = \$341.67;\ C'(3000) = \$280$ **b.** The average cost of producing the first 3000 lawnmowers is $341.67 per mower. The cost of producing the 3001st lawnmower is $280.   **65. a.** 6550 people/year   **b.** $p'(40) = 4800$ people/year   **67.** 50 mi/hr

69. $-5 \sin(65°)$ ft/s or ≈ -4.5 ft/s   **71.** -0.166 rad/s

CHAPTER 4

Section 4.1 Exercises, pp. 237–240

1. f has an absolute maximum at c in $[a, b]$ if $f(x) \le f(c)$ for all x in $[a, b]$. f has an absolute minimum at c in $[a, b]$ if $f(x) \ge f(c)$ for all x in $[a, b]$.   **3.** The function must be continuous on a closed interval.

5.
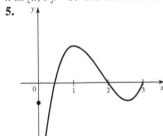

7.
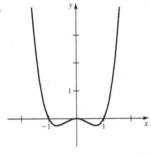

9. Evaluate the function at the critical points and at the endpoints of the interval.   **11.** Abs. min at $x = c_2$; abs. max at $x = b$ **13.** Abs. min at $x = a$; no abs. max   **15.** Local min at $x = q, s$; local max at $x = p, r$; abs. min at $x = a$; abs. max at $x = b$ **17.** Local max at $x = p$ and $x = r$; local min at $x = q$; abs. max at $x = p$; abs. min at $x = b$

19.
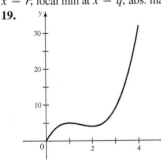

21.
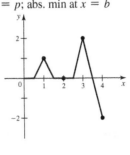

23. a. $x = \frac{2}{3}$ **b.** Local min   **25. a.** $x = \pm 3$ **b.** $x = -3$ local max, $x = 3$ local min.   **27. a.** $x = -\frac{2}{3}, \frac{1}{3}$ **b.** $x = -\frac{2}{3}$ local max, $x = \frac{1}{3}$ local min.   **29. a.** $x = \pm 1$ **b.** $x = -1$ local min; $x = 1$ local max   **31. a.** $x = 0$ **b.** Local min   **33. a.** No critical points   **35. a.** $x = -\frac{4}{5}, 0$ **b.** $x = -\frac{4}{5}$ local max, $x = 0$ local min.

37. a. $x = 0$ **b.** Abs. max: -1 at $x = 3$; abs. min: -10 at $x = 0$

c.
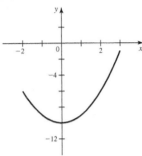

39. a. $x = \pi/2$ **b.** Abs. max: 1 at $x = 0, \pi$; abs. min: 0 at $x = \pi/2$

c.
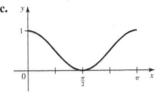

41. a. $x = \pm\pi/6$ **b.** Abs. max: 1 at $x = \pi/6$; abs. min: -1 at $x = -\pi/6$ **c.**
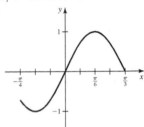

43. a. $x = 1/(2e)$ **b.** Abs. min: $(\sqrt{1/e})^{1/e}$ at $x = 1/(2e)$; abs. max: 2 at $x = 1$ **c.**
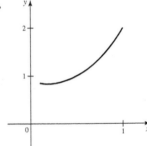

45. a. $x = 1/\sqrt{2}$ **b.** Abs. max: $1 + \pi$ at $x = -1$; abs. min: 1 at $x = 1$ **c.**
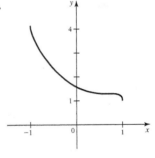

47. a. 1, 4 **b.** Abs max: 11 at $x = 1$; abs. min: -16 at $x = 4$
c.

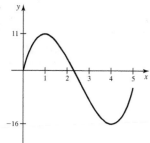

c.

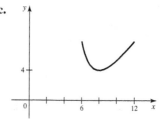

49. a. $x = -3, \frac{1}{2}$ **b.** Abs. max: 27 at $x = -3$; abs. min: $-\frac{19}{12}$ at $x = \frac{1}{2}$ **c.**

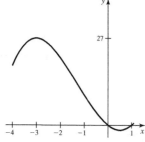

51. $t = 2$ s **53. a.** 50 **b.** 45 **55. a.** False **b.** False **c.** False **d.** True **e.** False **57. a.** $x = -0.96, 2.18, 5.32$ **b.** Abs. max: 3.72 at $x = 2.18$; abs. min: -32.80 at $x = 5.32$
c.

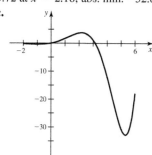

59. a. $x = 0$ **b.** Abs. max: $\sqrt{2}$ at $x = \pm \pi/4$; abs. min: 1 at $x = 0$
c.

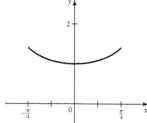

61. a. $x = 0$ and $x = 3$ **b.** Abs. max: $27/e^3$ at $x = 3$; abs. min: $-e$ at $x = -1$ **c.**

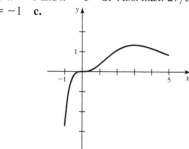

63. a. $x = 8$ **b.** Abs. max: $3\sqrt{2}$ at $x = 6$ and $x = 12$; abs. min: 4 at $x = 8$

65. If $a \geq 0$, there is no critical point. If $a < 0$, $x = 2a/3$ is the only critical point. **67.** $x = \pm a$ **69. a.** $x = \tan^{-1} 2 + k\pi$, for $k = -2, -1, 0, 1$ **b.** $x = \tan^{-1} 2 + k\pi$, for $k = -2, 0$ correspond to local max; $x = \tan^{-1} 2 + k\pi$, for $k = -1, 1$ correspond to local min. **c.** Abs. max: 2.24; abs. min: -2.24 **71. a.** $x = -\frac{1}{8}$ and $x = 3$ **b.** $x = -\frac{1}{8}$ corresponds to a local min; $x = 3$ is neither **c.** Abs. max: 51.23; abs. min: -12.52 **73. a.** $x = 5 - 4\sqrt{2}$ **b.** $x = 5 - 4\sqrt{2}$ corresponds to a local max. **c.** No abs. max or min **75.** Abs. max: 4 at $x = -1$; abs. min: -8 at $x = 3$

77. a. $T(x) = \dfrac{\sqrt{2500 + x^2}}{2} + \dfrac{50 - x}{4}$ **b.** $x = 50/\sqrt{3}$

c. $T(50/\sqrt{3}) = 34.15$, $T(0) = 37.50, T(50) = 35.36$ **d.**

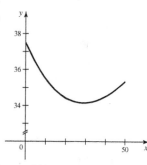

79. a. 1, 3, 0, 1 **b.** Since $g'(2) = 0$, g could have a local extreme value at $x = 2$. Since $h'(2) \neq 0$, h does not have a local extreme value at $x = 2$. **81. a.** A local min at $x = -c$ **b.** A local max at $x = -c$ **83. a.** $f(x) - f(c) \leq 0$ for all x near c

b. $\displaystyle\lim_{x \to c^+} \frac{f(x) - f(c)}{x - c} \leq 0$ **c.** $\displaystyle\lim_{x \to c^-} \frac{f(x) - f(c)}{x - c} \geq 0$

d. Since $f'(c)$ exists, $\displaystyle\lim_{x \to c^+} \frac{f(x) - f(c)}{x - c} = \lim_{x \to c^-} \frac{f(x) - f(c)}{x - c}$. By parts (b) and (c), we must have that $f'(c) = 0$.

Section 4.2 Exercises pp. 251–255

1. f is increasing on I if $f'(x) > 0$ for all x in I; f is decreasing on I if $f'(x) < 0$ for all x in I. **3.**

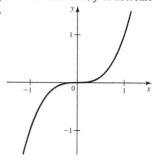

5. Because f has a local maximum at c, $f'(x) > 0$, for x near c and $x < c$, and $f'(x) < 0$, for x near c and $x > c$. Therefore, f' is decreasing near c and $f''(c) < 0$. **7.** A point in the domain at which f changes concavity. **9.** Yes. Consider the graph of $y = \sqrt{x}$ on $(0, \infty)$.

11.

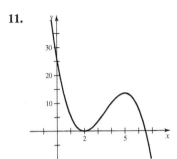

13. 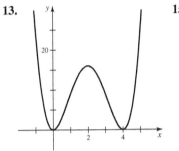 **15.**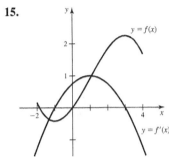

$x = 2$ **61.** Concave down on $(-\infty, 1)$; concave up on $(1, \infty)$; inflection point at $x = 1$. **63.** Concave up on $(-1/\sqrt{3}, 1/\sqrt{3})$; concave down on $(-\infty, -1/\sqrt{3})$; $(1/\sqrt{3}, \infty)$; inflection points at $x = \pm 1/\sqrt{3}$ **65.** Concave up on $(-\infty, -1)$ and $(1, \infty)$; concave down on $(-1, 1)$; inflection points at $x = \pm 1$ **67.** Concave up on $(0, 1)$; concave down on $(1, \infty)$; inflection point at $x = 1$ **69.** Concave up on $(0, 2)$ and $(4, \infty)$; concave down on $(-\infty, 0)$ and $(2, 4)$; inflection points at $x = 0, 2, 4$ **71.** Critical pt. $x = 0, 2$; local max at $x = 0$; local min at $x = 2$ **73.** Critical pt. at $x = 0$; local max at $x = 0$ **75.** Critical pt. at $x = 6$; local min at $x = 6$ **77.** Critical pt. at $x = 0$ and $x = 1$; local max at $x = 0$; local min at $x = 1$ **79.** Critical pts. at $x = 0$ and $x = 2$; local min at $x = 0$; local max at $x = 2$ **81.** Critical pt. at $x = e^5$; local min at $x = e^5$ **83. a.** True **b.** False **c.** True **d.** False **e.** False **85.**

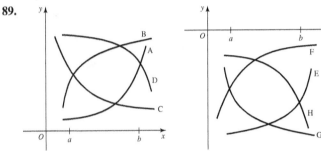

87. a–f–g, b–e–i, c–d–h

17. Increasing on $(-\infty, 0)$; decreasing on $(0, \infty)$ **19.** Decreasing on $(-\infty, 1)$; increasing on $(1, \infty)$ **21.** Increasing on $(-\infty, 1/2)$; decreasing on $(1/2, \infty)$ **23.** Increasing on $(-\infty, 0)$, $(1, 2)$; decreasing on $(0, 1)$, $(2, \infty)$ **25.** Increasing on $\left(-\dfrac{1}{\sqrt{e}}, 0\right)$, $\left(\dfrac{1}{\sqrt{e}}, \infty\right)$; decreasing on $\left(-\infty, -\dfrac{1}{\sqrt{e}}\right)$, $\left(0, \dfrac{1}{\sqrt{e}}\right)$ **27.** Increasing on the intervals $(-\pi, -2\pi/3)$, $(-\pi/3, 0)$, $(\pi/3, 2\pi/3)$; decreasing on the intervals $(-2\pi/3, -\pi/3)$, $(0, \pi/3)$, $(2\pi/3, \pi)$ **29.** Increasing on $(0, \infty)$; decreasing on $(-\infty, 0)$ **31.** Increasing on $(-\infty, \infty)$ **33.** Decreasing on $(-\infty, 1)$, $(4, \infty)$; increasing on $(1, 4)$ **35.** Increasing on $\left(-\infty, -\dfrac{1}{2}\right)$, $\left(0, \dfrac{1}{2}\right)$; decreasing on $\left(-\dfrac{1}{2}, 0\right)$, $\left(\dfrac{1}{2}, \infty\right)$. **37.** Increasing on $(0, \infty)$; decreasing on $(-\infty, 0)$. **39. a.** $x = 0$ **b.** Local min at $x = 0$ **c.** Abs. min: 3 at $x = 0$; abs. max: 12 at $x = -3$ **41. a.** $x = \pm 3/\sqrt{2}$ **b.** Local min at $x = -3/\sqrt{2}$; local max at $x = 3/\sqrt{2}$ **c.** Abs. max: $9/2$ at $x = 3/\sqrt{2}$; abs. min: $-9/2$ at $x = -3/\sqrt{2}$ **43. a.** $x = \pm\sqrt{3}$ **b.** local min at $x = -\sqrt{3}$; local max at $x = \sqrt{3}$ **c.** Abs. max: 28 at $x = -4$; abs. min: $-6\sqrt{3}$ at $x = -\sqrt{3}$ **45. a.** $x = 8/5$ and $x = 0$ **b.** Local max at $x = 0$; local min at $x = 8/5$ **c.** Abs. min: -26.32 at $x = -5$; abs. max: 2.92 at $x = 5$ **47. a.** $x = e^{-2}$ **b.** Local min at $x = e^{-2}$ **c.** Abs. min: $-2/e$ at $x = e^{-2}$; no abs. max **49.** Abs. max: $1/e$ at $x = 1$ **51.** Abs. min: $36\sqrt[3]{\pi/6}$ at $x = \sqrt[3]{6/\pi}$.

53. 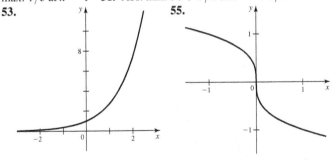 **55.**

89.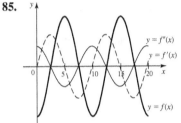

91. 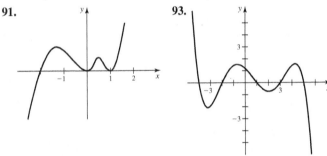 **93.**

95. a. Increasing on $(-2, 2)$; decreasing on $(-3, -2)$ **b.** Critical pts. at $x = -2$ and $x = 0$; local min at $x = -2$; neither a local max or min at $x = 0$ **c.** Inflection pts. at $x = -1$ and $x = 0$ **d.** Concave up on $(-3, -1)$ and $(0, 2)$; concave down on $(-1, 0)$

e. **f.**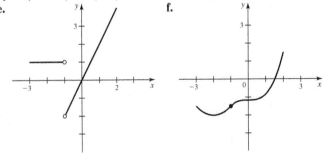

57. Concave up on $(-\infty, 0)$ and $(1, \infty)$; concave down on $(0, 1)$; inflection points at $x = 0$ and $x = 1$ **59.** Concave up on $(-\infty, 0)$ and $(2, \infty)$; concave down on $(0, 2)$; inflection points at $x = 0$ and

97. Critical pt. at $x = -3$ and $x = 4$; local min at $x = -3$; inconclusive at $x = 4$ **99.** No critical pts. **101. a.** $E = \dfrac{p}{p - 50}$ **b.** -1.4%

c. $E'(p) = -\dfrac{ab}{(a - bp)^2} < 0$, for $p \geq 0, p \neq a/b$ **d.** $E(p) = -b$,

for $p \geq 0$ **103. a.** 300 **b.** $t = \sqrt{10}$ **c.** $t = \sqrt{b/3}$

105. a. $f''(x) = 6x + 2a = 0$ when $x = -a/3$

b. $f(-a/3) - f(-a/3 + x) = (a^2/3)x - bx - x^3$; also,

$f(-a/3 - x) - f(-a/3) = (a^2/3)x - bx - x^3$

Section 4.3 Exercises, pp. 262–265

1. We need to know over which interval(s) to graph f. **3.** No; the domain of any polynomial is $(-\infty, \infty)$; there are no vertical asymptotes. Also, $\lim\limits_{x \to \pm\infty} p(x) = \pm\infty$ where p is any polynomial; there are no horizontal asymptotes. **5.** Evaluate the function at the critical points and at the endpoints. Then find the largest and smallest values among those candidates.

7.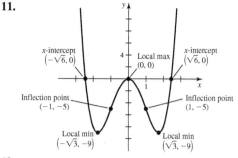

9.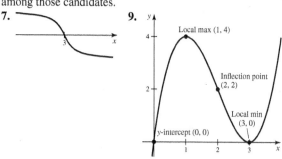

11.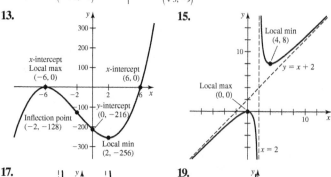

13.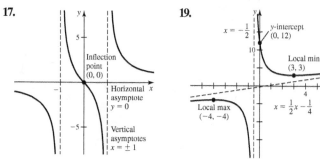

15.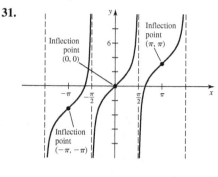

17.

19.

21.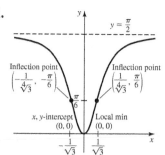

23.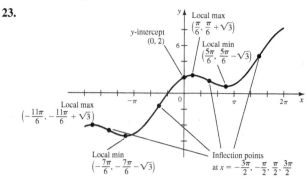

25.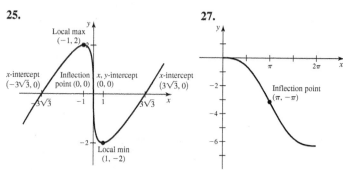

27.

29.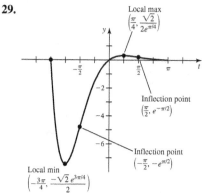

31.

33.

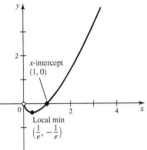

49. Critical pts. at $x = 1, 3$; local max at $x = 1$; local min at $x = 3$; inflection pt. at $x = 2$; increasing on $(0, 1)$, $(3, 4)$; decreasing on $(1, 3)$; concave up on $(2, 4)$; concave down on $(0, 2)$

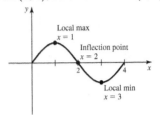

35.

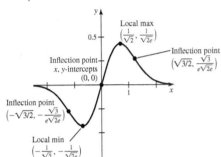

51.

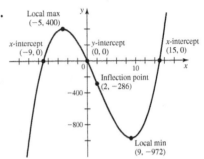

37.

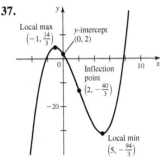

39.

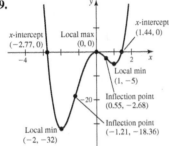

53.

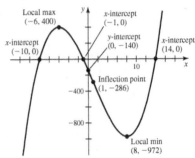

41.

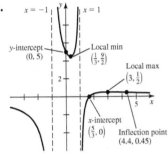

43. a. False **b.** False
c. False **d.** True

55. Local max at $\left(e, e^{1/e}\right)$

57.

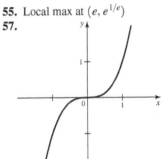

59.

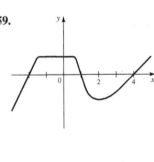

45.

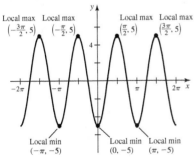

61.

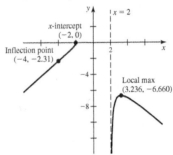

47.

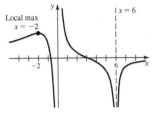

63. a.

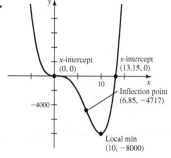

b.

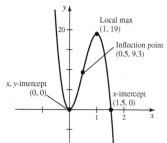

65.

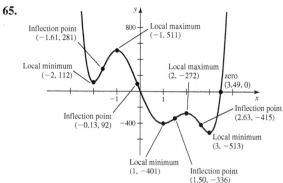

67.

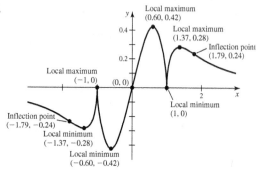

69. a.

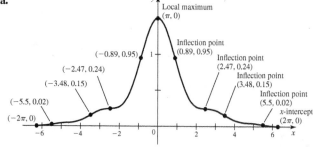

b.

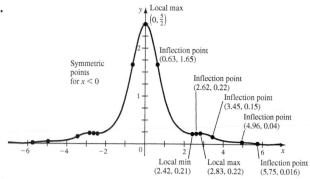

71. (A) a. h

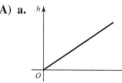

b. Water is being added at all times **c.** No concavity   **d.** h' has an abs. max at all points of $[0, 10]$.

(B) a. h

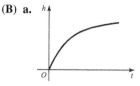

c. Concave down **d.** h' has abs. max at $t = 0$.

(C) a. h

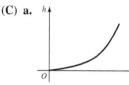

c. Concave up **d.** h' has abs. max at $t = 10$.

(D) a. h

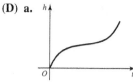

c. Concave up on $(0, 5)$, then concave down on $(5, 10)$; inflection pt. at $t = 5$ **d.** h' has abs. max at $t = 0$ and $t = 10$.

(E) a. h

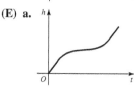

c. First, no concavity; then, concave down, no concavity, concave up, and, finally, no concavity   **d.** h' has abs. max at all points of an interval $[0, a]$ and $[b, 10]$.

(F) a. h

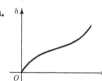

c. Concave down on $(0, 5)$; concave up on $(5, 10)$; inflection pt. at $t = 5$ **d.** h' has abs. max at $t = 0$ and $t = 10$.

73. $f'(0)$ does not exist.

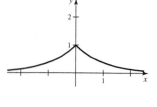

75.

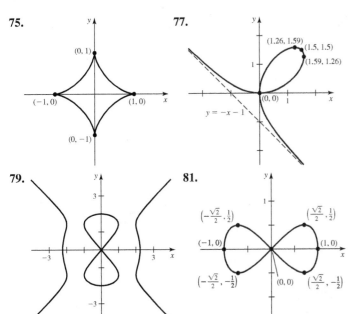

77.

79.

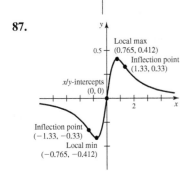

81.

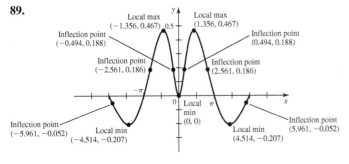

83.

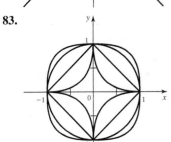

85. a. $\{x: x < a\}$
b. $f(a) = 0$, $\lim_{x \to -\infty} f(x) = 0$
c. $f'(x) = (a - x)^{x-1} \times [(a - x) \ln (a - x) - x]$
d. See part (c).
e. z and $f(z)$ increase as a increases.

87.

89.

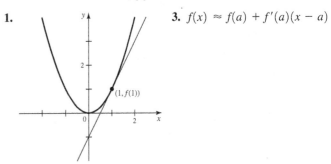

Section 4.4 Exercises, pp. 269–275

1. Objective function, constraints **3.** $Q = x^2(10 - x)$;
$Q = (10 - y)^2 y$ **5.** Width = length = $\frac{5}{2}$ m
7. Width = length = 10 **9.** $\frac{23}{2}$ and $\frac{23}{2}$ **11.** $5\sqrt{2}$ and $5\sqrt{2}$
13. $x = \sqrt{6}, y = 2\sqrt{6}$ **15.** Length = width = height = $\sqrt[3]{100}$

17. $\dfrac{4}{\sqrt[3]{5}}$ ft by $\dfrac{4}{\sqrt[3]{5}}$ ft by $5^{2/3}$ ft **19.** $(5, 15)$, distance ≈ 47.4
21. a. A point $8/\sqrt{5}$ mi from the point on the shore nearest the woman in the direction of the restaurant **b.** $9/\sqrt{13}$ mi/hr
23. 18.2 ft **25.** $\dfrac{10}{\sqrt{2}}$ cm by $\dfrac{5}{\sqrt{2}}$ cm **27.** $h = 2\sqrt{\dfrac{5}{3}}; r = 2\sqrt{\dfrac{10}{3}}$
29. $\sqrt{15}$ m by $2\sqrt{15}$ m **31.** $r/h = \sqrt{2}$ **33.** $r = h = \sqrt[3]{450/\pi}$ m
35. The point $12/(\sqrt[3]{2} + 1) \approx 5.3$ m from the weaker source
37. A point $7\sqrt{3}/6$ mi from the point on shore nearest the island, in the direction of the power station **39. a.** $P = 2/\sqrt{3}$ units from the midpoint of the base **41.** $r = \sqrt{6}, h = \sqrt{3}$
43. For $L \le 4r$, max at $\theta = 0$ and $\theta = 2\pi$; min at $\theta = \cos^{-1}(-L/(4r))$ and $\theta = 2\pi - \cos^{-1}(-L/(4r))$.
For $L > 4r$, max at $\theta = 0$ and $\theta = 2\pi$; min at $\theta = \pi$.
45. a. $r = \sqrt[3]{177/\pi} \approx 3.83$ cm; $h = 2\sqrt[3]{177/\pi} \approx 7.67$ cm
b. $r = \sqrt[3]{177/2\pi} \approx 3.04$ cm; $h = 2\sqrt[3]{708/\pi} \approx 12.17$ cm.
Part (b) is closer to the real can. **47.** $\sqrt{30} \approx 5.5$ ft **49.** When the seat is at its lowest point **51.** $r = \sqrt{2}R/\sqrt{3}; h = 2R/\sqrt{3}$
53. a. $r = 2R/3; h = \frac{1}{3}H$ **b.** $r = R/2; h = H/2$ **55.** 3:1
57. $(1 + \sqrt{3})$ mi ≈ 2.732 mi **59.** You can run 12 mi/hr if you run toward the point $3/16$ mi ahead of the locomotive (when it passes the point nearest you). **61. a.** $(-6/5, 2/5)$ **b.** Approx $(0.59, 0.65)$
c. (i) $\left(p - \frac{1}{2}, \sqrt{p - \frac{1}{2}}\right)$ **(ii)** $(0, 0)$ **63. a.** 0, 30, 25
b. 42.5 mi/hr **c.** The units of $p/g(v)$ are \$/mi and so are the units of w/v. Thus, $L\left(\dfrac{p}{g(v)} + \dfrac{w}{v}\right)$ gives the total cost of a trip of L miles.
d. ≈ 62.9 mi/hr **e.** Neither; the zeros of $C'(v)$ are independent of L.
f. Decreased slightly, to 62.5 mi/hr **g.** Decreased to 60.8 mi/hr
65. b. Because the speed of light is constant, travel time is minimized when distance is minimized. **67.** Let the angle of the cuts be ϕ_1 and ϕ_2, where $\phi_1 + \phi_2 = \theta$. The volume of the notch is proportional to $\tan \phi_1 + \tan \phi_2 = \tan \phi_1 + \tan (\theta - \phi_1)$, which is minimized when $\phi_1 = \phi_2 = \dfrac{\theta}{2}$. **69.** $x \approx 38.81, y \approx 55.03$

Section 4.5 Exercises, pp. 282–283

1.

3. $f(x) \approx f(a) + f'(a)(x - a)$

5. $dy = f'(x)\, dx$ **7.** 61 mi/hr; 61.02 mi/hr
9. $L(x) = T(0) + T'(0)(x - 0) = D - (D/60)x = D(1 - x/60)$
11. 84 min; 84.21 min
13. a. $L(x) = -4x + 16$ **b.**

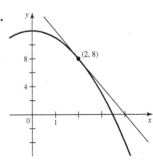

c. 7.6   **d.** 0.13% error   **15. a.** $L(x) = x$ **b.**

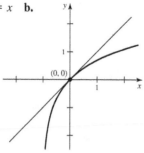

a.

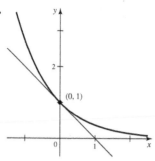

b. $e^{-0.03} \approx 0.97$ **c.** 0.05% error

c. 0.9   **d.** 40% error   **17. a.** $L(x) = 1$ **b.**

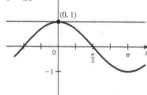

57. $L(x) = 2 + (x - 8)/12$

x	Linear Approximation	Exact Value	Percent Error
8.1	$2.008\overline{3}$	2.00829885	1.717×10^{-3}
8.01	$2.0008\overline{3}$	2.000832986	1.734×10^{-5}
8.001	$2.00008\overline{3}$	2.00008333	1.736×10^{-7}
8.0001	$2.000008\overline{3}$	2.000008333	1.736×10^{-9}
7.9	$1.991\overline{6}$	1.991631701	1.756×10^{-3}
7.99	$1.99991\overline{6}$	1.999166319	1.738×10^{-5}
7.999	$1.999991\overline{6}$	1.999916663	1.736×10^{-7}
7.9999	$1.9999991\overline{6}$	1.999991667	1.736×10^{-9}

c. 1   **d.** 0.005% error   **19. a.** $y = \dfrac{1}{2} - \dfrac{x}{48}$

b.

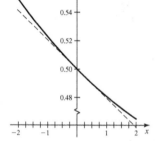

c. 0.50   **d.** 0.003% error

59. a. f; the rate at which f' is changing at 1 is smaller than the rate at which g' is changing at 1. The graph of f bends away from the linear function more slowly than the graph of g.   **b.** The larger the value of $|f''(a)|$, the greater the deviation of the curve $y = f(x)$ from the tangent line at points near $x = a$.

Section 4.6 Exercises, pp. 288–289

1. If f is a continuous function on the closed interval $[a, b]$ and is differentiable on (a, b) and the slope of the secant line that joins $(a, f(a))$ to $(b, f(b))$ is zero, then there is at least one value c in (a, b) at which the slope of the line tangent to f at $(c, f(c))$ is also zero.

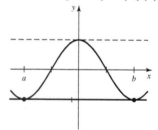

21. $y = 1/x$ near $a = 200$; $\frac{1}{203} \approx 0.004925$ **23.** $y = \sqrt{x}$ near $a = 144$; $\sqrt{146} \approx 12\frac{1}{12}$ **25.** $y = \ln x$ near $a = 1$; $\ln(1.05) \approx 0.05$ **27.** $y = e^x$ near $a = 0$; $e^{0.06} \approx 1.06$

29. $y = \dfrac{1}{\sqrt[3]{x}}$ near $a = 512$; $\dfrac{1}{\sqrt[3]{510}} \approx \dfrac{769}{6144} \approx 0.125$

31. $\Delta V \approx 10\pi \text{ ft}^3$ **33.** $\Delta V \approx -40\pi \text{ cm}^3$

35. $\Delta S \approx -\dfrac{59\pi}{5\sqrt{34}} \text{ m}^2$ **37.** $dy = 2\,dx$ **39.** $dy = -\dfrac{3}{x^4}\,dx$

41. $dy = a \sin x\,dx$ **43.** $dy = (9x^2 - 4)\,dx$

45. $dy = \sec^2 x\,dx$ **47. a.** True **b.** False **c.** True   **49.** 2.7

51. $L(x) = 1 - x$; **a.**

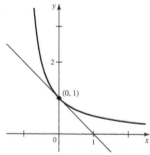

3. $f(x) = |x|$ is not differentiable at 0.

5.

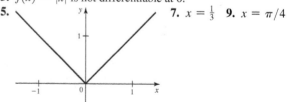

7. $x = \frac{1}{3}$ **9.** $x = \pi/4$

b. $1/1.1 \approx 0.9$ **c.** 1% error   **53.** $L(x) = 1 - x$

11. Does not apply   **13.** $x = \frac{5}{3}$ **15.** Average lapse rate $= -6.3°/\text{km}$. You cannot conclude that the lapse rate at a point exceeds the critical value.

17. a. Yes **b.** $c = \frac{1}{2}$ **c.**

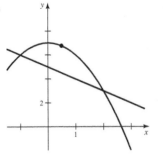

19. a. Yes **b.** $c = \ln\left(\dfrac{3}{\ln 4}\right)$ **c.**

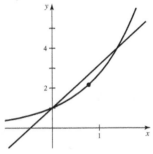

21. a. Yes **b.** $c = \sqrt{1 - 9/\pi^2}$ **c.**

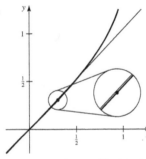

23. a. Does not apply **25. a.** False **b.** True **c.** False **27.** h and p
29.

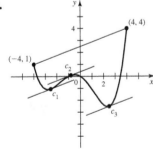

31. The car's average velocity is $(30 - 0)/(28/60) = 64.3$ mi/hr. By the MVT, the car's instantaneous velocity was 64.3 mi/hr at some time.
33. Average speed $= 11.6$ mi/hr. By MVT, the speed was exactly 11.6 mi/hr at least once. By the Intermediate Value Theorem, all speeds between 0 and 11.6 mi/hr were reached. Because the initial and final speed was 0 mi/hr, the speed of 11 mi/hr was reached at least twice.
35. $\dfrac{f(b) - f(a)}{b - a} = A(a + b) + B$ and $f'(x) = 2Ax + B$;

$2Ax + B = A(a + b) + B$ implies that $x = \dfrac{a + b}{2}$, the midpoint of $[a, b]$. **37.** $\tan^2 x$ and $\sec^2 x$ differ by a constant; in fact, $\tan^2 x - \sec^2 x = -1$. **39.** Bolt's average speed was 37.58 km/hr, so he exceeded 37 km/hr during the race. **41. b.** $c = \frac{1}{2}$

Section 4.7 Exercises, pp. 300–302

1. If $\lim_{x \to a} f(x) = 0$ and $\lim_{x \to a} g(x) = 0$, then we say $\lim_{x \to a} f(x)/g(x)$ is of indeterminate form $0/0$. **3.** Take the limit of the quotient of the derivatives of the functions. **5.** If $\lim_{x \to a} f(x)g(x)$ has the indeterminate form $0 \cdot \infty$, then $\lim_{x \to a} \left(\dfrac{f(x)}{1/g(x)}\right)$ has the indeterminate form $0/0$ or ∞/∞. **7.** If $\lim_{x \to a} f(x) = 1$ and $\lim_{x \to a} g(x) = \infty$, then $f(x)^{g(x)} \to 1^\infty$ as $x \to a$, which is meaningless; so direct substitution does not work. **9.** $\lim_{x \to \infty} \dfrac{g(x)}{f(x)} = 0$ **11.** $\ln x, x^3, 2^x, x^x$ **13.** -1
15. $1/2$ **17.** $1/e$ **19.** $\frac{12}{5}$ **21.** 4 **23.** $\frac{9}{16}$ **25.** $\frac{1}{2}$ **27.** $1/24$
29. 1 **31.** 4 **33.** $-\frac{1}{2}$ **35.** $1/\pi^2$ **37.** $\frac{1}{2}$ **39.** $-\frac{2}{3}$ **41.** 1
43. $\frac{1}{3}$ **45.** 1 **47.** $\frac{7}{6}$ **49.** 1 **51.** 0 **53.** 0 **55.** 1 **57.** 1
59. e **61.** e^a **63.** e^{a+1} **65.** 1 **67.** e **69.** $e^{0.01x}$
71. Comparable growth rates **73.** x^x **75.** 1.00001^x **77.** x^x
79. e^{x^2} **81. a.** False **b.** False **c.** False **d.** False **e.** True
f. True **83.** $\frac{2}{5}$ **85.** $-\frac{9}{4}$ **87.** 0 **89.** $\frac{1}{6}$ **91.** ∞ **93.** $(\ln 3)/(\ln 2)$
95. $\frac{1}{2}$ **97. a.** Approx. 3.44×10^{15} **b.** Approx. 3536 **c.** e^{100}
d. Approx. 163 **99.** 1 **101.** $\ln a - \ln b$

103. b. $\lim_{m \to \infty} (1 + r/m)^m = \lim_{m \to \infty} \left(1 + \dfrac{1}{(m/r)}\right)^{(m/r)r} = e^r$

105. $\sqrt{a/c}$ **107.** $\lim_{x \to \infty} \dfrac{x^p}{b^x} = \lim_{t \to \infty} \dfrac{\ln^p t}{t \ln^p b} = 0$ (let $t = b^x$, see

Example 8) **109.** Show $\lim_{x \to \infty} \dfrac{\log_a x}{\log_b x} = \dfrac{\ln b}{\ln a} \neq 0$. **111.** $1/3$

115. a. $b > e$ **b.** e^{ax} grows faster than e^x as $x \to \infty$, for $a > 1$; e^{ax} grows slower than e^x as $x \to \infty$, for $0 < a < 1$.

Section 4.8 Exercises, pp. 309–311

1. Newton's method generates a sequence of x-intercepts of lines tangent to the graph of f to approximate the roots of f. **3.** Generally, if two successive Newton approximations agree in their first p digits, then those approximations have p digits of accuracy. The method is terminated when the desired accuracy is reached.

5. $x_{n+1} = x_n - \dfrac{x_n^2 - 6}{2x_n} = \dfrac{x_n^2 + 6}{2x_n}$; $x_1 = 2.4, x_2 = 2.45$

7. $x_{n+1} = x_n - \dfrac{e^{-x_n} - x_n}{e^{-x_n} - 1}$; $x_1 = 0.564382, x_2 = 0.567142$

9.

k	x_k
0	4.000000
1	3.250000
2	3.163462
3	3.162278
4	3.162278
5	3.162278
6	3.162278
7	3.162278
8	3.162278
9	3.162278
10	3.162278

11.

k	x_k
0	1.500000
1	0.101436
2	0.501114
3	0.510961
4	0.510973
5	0.510973
6	0.510973
7	0.510973
8	0.510973
9	0.510973
10	0.510973

13.

k	x_k
0	1.500000
1	1.443890
2	1.361976
3	1.268175
4	1.196179
5	1.168571
6	1.165592
7	1.165561
8	1.165561
9	1.165561
10	1.165561

15. $x \approx 0, 1.895494, -1.895494$ **17.** $x \approx -2.114908, 0.254102,$
1.860806 **19.** $x \approx 0.062997, 2.230120$ **21.** $x \approx 2.798386$
23. $x \approx -0.666667, 1.5, 1.666667$ **25.** The method converges more
slowly for f, because of the double root at $x = 1$.

k	x_k for f	x_k for g
0	2	2
1	1.5	1.25
2	1.25	1.025
3	1.125	1.0003
4	1.0625	1
5	1.03125	1
6	1.01563	1
7	1.00781	1
8	1.00391	1
9	1.00195	1
10	1.00098	1

27. a. True. **b.** False. **c.** False   **29.** $x \approx 1.153467, 2.423622,$
-3.57709 **31.** $x = 0$ and $x \approx 1.047198$ **33.** $x \approx -0.335408,$
1.333057 **35.** $x \approx 0.179295$ **37.** $x \approx 0.620723, 3.03645$
39.

k	x_k	Error	Residual
0	0.5	0.5	0.000976563
1	0.45	0.45	0.000340506
2	0.405	0.405	0.000118727
3	0.3645	0.3645	0.0000413976
4	0.32805	0.32805	0.0000144345
5	0.295245	0.295245	5.03298×10^{-6}
6	0.265721	0.265721	1.75489×10^{-6}
7	0.239148	0.239148	6.11893×10^{-7}
8	0.215234	0.215234	2.13354×10^{-7}
9	0.193710	0.193710	7.43919×10^{-8}
10	0.174339	0.174339	2.59389×10^{-8}

41. $a = e$ **43.** $x \approx 0.142857$ is approximately $\frac{1}{7}$.
45. a. $t = \pi/4 \approx 0.785398$ **b.** $t \approx 1.33897$ **c.** $t \approx 2.35619$
d. $t \approx 2.90977$ **47.** $\lambda = 1.29011, 2.37305, 3.40918$

Section 4.9 Exercises, pp. 320–322

1. the derivative, an antiderivative   **3.** $x + C$, where C is any real number
5. $\dfrac{x^{p+1}}{p + 1} + C$, where C is any real number and $p \neq -1$
7. $\ln|x| + C$ **9.** 0   **11.** $x^5 + C$ **13.** $-\frac{1}{2}\cos 2x + C$
15. $3\tan x + C$ **17.** $y^{-2} + C$ **19.** $e^x + C$ **21.** $\tan^{-1}s + C$
23. $\frac{1}{2}x^6 - \frac{1}{2}x^{10} + C$ **25.** $\frac{8}{3}x^{3/2} - 8x^{1/2} + C$
27. $\frac{25}{3}s^3 + 15s^2 + 9s + C$ **29.** $\frac{9}{4}x^{4/3} + 6x^{2/3} + 6x + C$
31. $-x^3 + \frac{11}{2}x^2 + 4x + C$ **33.** $-x^{-3} + 2x + 3x^{-1} + C$
35. $x^4 - 3x^2 + C$ **37.** $-\frac{1}{2}\cos 2y + \frac{1}{3}\sin 3y + C$
39. $\tan x - x + C$ **41.** $\tan\theta + \sec\theta + C$ **43.** $t^3 + \frac{1}{2}\tan 2t + C$
45. $\frac{1}{4}\sec 4\theta + C$ **47.** $\frac{1}{2}\ln|y| + C$ **49.** $6\sin^{-1}(x/5) + C$
51. $\frac{1}{10}\sec^{-1}|x/10| + C$ **53.** $\frac{1}{5}\sec^{-1}|\frac{x}{5}| + C$

55. $t + \ln|t| + C$ **57.** $e^{x+2} + C$
59. $F(x) = x^6/6 + 2/x + x - 19/6$ **61.** $F(v) = \sec v + 1$
63. $2x^4 + 2x^{-1} + 1$ **65.** $y^3 + 5\ln|y| + 2$
67. $f(x) = x^2 - 3x + 4$ **69.** $g(x) = \dfrac{7}{8}x^8 - \dfrac{x^2}{2} + \dfrac{13}{8}$
71. $f(u) = 4\sin u + 2\cos 2u - 3$ **73.** $3\ln|t| + 6t + 2$
75. $\sqrt{2}\sin\theta + \tan\theta + 1$
77. $f(x) = x^2 - 5x + 4$

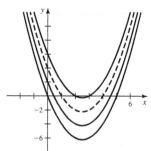

79. $f(x) = \dfrac{3x^2}{2} - \dfrac{\cos(\pi x)}{\pi} + \dfrac{1 - 3\pi}{\pi}$

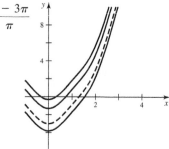

81. $f(t) = \ln t + 4$

83. $s(t) = t^2 + 4t$

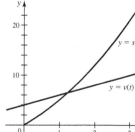

85. $s(t) = \frac{4}{3}t^{3/2} + 1$

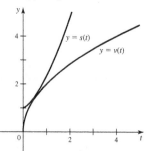

87. $s(t) = 2t^3 + 2t^2 - 10t$

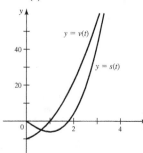

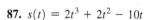

89. $-16t^2 + 20t$ **91.** $\frac{1}{30}t^3 + 1$ **93.** $-\frac{3}{4}\sin 2t + \frac{5}{2}t + 10$
95. Runner A overtakes runner B at $t = \pi/2$.
97. a. $v(t) = -9.8t + 30$ **b.** $s(t) = -4.9t^2 + 30t$ **c.** 45.92 m at
time $t = 3.06$ **d.** $t = 6.12$ **99. a.** $v(t) = -9.8t + 10$
b. $s(t) = -4.9t^2 + 10t + 400$ **c.** 405.10 m at time $t = 1.02$

d. $t = 10.11$ **101. a.** True **b.** False **c.** True **d.** False
e. False **103.** $(e^{2x} + e^{-2x})/4 + C$
105. $-\cot\theta + 2\theta^3/3 - 3\theta^2/2 + C$ **107.** $\ln|x| + 2\sqrt{x} + C$
109. $\frac{4}{15}x^{15/2} - \frac{24}{11}x^{11/6} + C$ **111.** $F(x) = -\cos x + 3x + 3 - 3\pi$
113. $F(x) = 2x^8 + x^4 + 2x + 1$ **115. a.** $Q(t) = 10t - t^3/30$ gal

b.

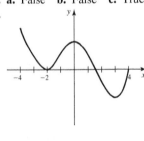

c. $\dfrac{200}{3}$ gal

117. $\displaystyle\int \sin^2 x\, dx = x/2 - (\sin 2x)/4 + C;$

$\displaystyle\int \cos^2 x\, dx = x/2 + (\sin 2x)/4 + C$

Review Exercises, pp. 322–325

1. a. False **b.** False **c.** True **d.** True **e.** True **f.** False
3.

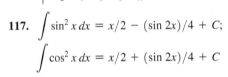

5.

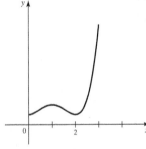

7. $x = 3$ and $x = -2$; no abs. max or min
9. $x = 1/e$; abs. min at $(1/e, 10 - 2/e)$
11.

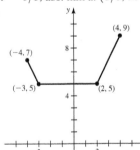

Critical pts.: x in the interval $[-3, 2]$; abs. max: $(4, 9)$; abs. and local min at $(x, 5)$ for all x in $[-3, 2]$; local max. at $(x, 5)$ for all x in $(-3, 2)$

13.

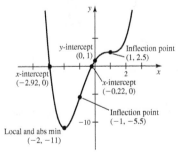

15.

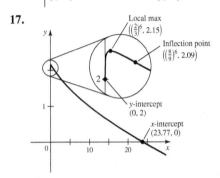

17.

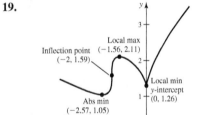

19.

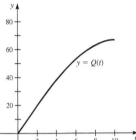

21. $r = 4\sqrt{6}/3; h = 4\sqrt{3}/3$ **23.** $x = 14, y = 7$
25. $p = q = 5\sqrt{2}$ **27. a.** $L(x) = \frac{2}{9}x + 3$ **b.** $\frac{85}{9} \approx 9.44$
29. $f(x) = 1/x^2; a = 4; 1/4.2^2 \approx 9/160 = 0.05625$
31. $\Delta h \approx -112$ ft **33. a.** $\frac{100}{9}$ cells/week **b.** $t = 2$ weeks
35. $-0.434259, 0.767592, 1$ **37.** $0, \pm 0.948683$ **39.** 0 **41.** $2\sqrt{3} - \frac{4}{3}$
43. $\frac{2}{3}$ **45.** ∞ **47.** 0 **49.** 1 **51.** 0 **53.** 1 **55.** 1 **57.** $1/e^3$
59. 1 **61.** $x^{1/2}$ **63.** $\sqrt{x}$ **65.** 3^x **67.** Comparable growth rates
69. $\frac{4}{3}x^3 + 2x^2 + x + C$ **71.** $-\dfrac{1}{x} + \dfrac{4}{3}x^{-3/2} + C$
73. $\theta + \frac{1}{3}\sin 3\theta + C$ **75.** $\frac{1}{2}\sec 2x + C$ **77.** $12\ln|x| + C$
79. $\tan^{-1} x + C$ **81.** $\frac{4}{7}x^{7/4} + \frac{2}{7}x^{7/2} + C$
83. $f(t) = -\cos t + t^2 + 6$
85. $h(x) = \dfrac{x}{2} - \dfrac{1}{4}\sin 2x + \left(\dfrac{1}{2} + \dfrac{\sin 2}{4}\right)$
87. $v(t) = -9.8t + 120; s(t) = -4.9t^2 + 120t + 125$
The rocket reaches a height of 859.69 m at time $t = 12.24$ s and then falls to the ground, hitting at time $t = 25.49$ s. **89.** $1; 1$ **91.** 0
93. $\lim_{x\to 0^+} f(x) = 1; \lim_{x\to 0^+} g(x) = 0$

CHAPTER 5

Section 5.1 Exercises, pp. xxx–xxx

1.

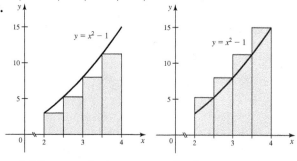

Displacement = 105 m

3. Subdivide the interval $[0, \pi/2]$ into several subintervals, which will be the bases of rectangles that fit under the curve. The heights of the rectangles can be computed by taking the value of $\cos x$ at the right-hand endpoint of each base. We can calculate the area of each rectangle and add them to get a lower bound on the area.
5. $\frac{1}{2}$; 1, 1.5, 2, 2.5, 3; 1, 1.5, 2, 2.5; 1.5, 2, 2.5, 3; 1.25, 1.75, 2.25, 2.75
7. Underestimate; the rectangles all fit under the curve.   **9. a.** 67 ft
b. 67.75 ft   **11.** 40 m   **13.** 2.78 m   **15.** 148.96 mi   **17.** 20; 25
19. a. c.

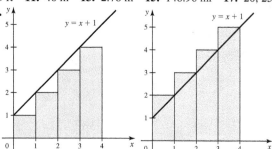

Left Riemann sum underestimates.   Right Riemann sum overestimates.
b. $\Delta x = 1; x_0 = 0, x_1 = 1, x_2 = 2, x_3 = 3, x_4 = 4$ **d.** 10, 14
21. a. c.

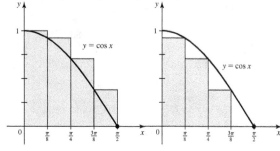

Left Riemann sum overestimates.   Right Riemann sum underestimates.
b. $\Delta x = \pi/8; 0, \pi/8, \pi/4, 3\pi/8, \pi/2$ **d.** 1.18; 0.79
23. a. c.

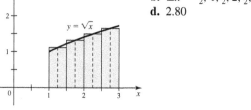

Left Riemann sum underestimates.   Right Riemann sum overestimates.

b. $\Delta x = \frac{1}{2}$; 2, 2.5, 3, 3.5, 4   **d.** 13.75; 19.75
25. a. c.

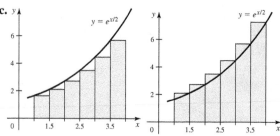

Left Riemann sum underestimates.   Right Riemann sum overestimates.
b. $\Delta x = 0.5; x_0 = 1, x_1 = 1.5, x_2 = 2, x_3 = 2.5, x_4 = 3, x_5 = 3.5,$
$x_6 = 4$ **d.** 10.11, 12.98   **27.** 670
29. a. c.

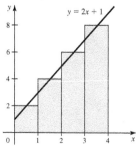

b. $\Delta x = 1; x_0 = 0, x_1 = 1, x_2 = 2, x_3 = 3, x_4 = 4$ **d.** 20
31. a. c.   **b.** $\Delta x = \frac{1}{2}$; 1, $\frac{3}{2}$, 2, $\frac{5}{2}$, 3
        d. 2.80

33. a. c.   **b.** $\Delta x = 1$; 1, 2, 3, 4, 5, 6
        d. 1.76

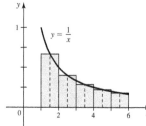

35. 5.5, 3.5   **37. b.** 110, 117.5   **39. a.** $\sum_{k=1}^{5} k$ **b.** $\sum_{k=1}^{6} (k + 3)$

c. $\sum_{k=1}^{4} k^2$ **d.** $\sum_{k=1}^{4} \frac{1}{k}$ **41. a.** 55 **b.** 48 **c.** 30 **d.** 60 **e.** 6 **f.** 6

g. 85 **h.** 0 **43. a.** $\frac{1}{10} \sum_{k=1}^{40} \sqrt{\frac{k-1}{10}} \approx 5.227$; $\frac{1}{10} \sum_{k=1}^{40} \sqrt{\frac{k}{10}} \approx 5.427$;

$\frac{1}{10} \sum_{k=1}^{40} \sqrt{\frac{2k-1}{20}} \approx 5.3$ **b.** $\frac{16}{3}$ **45. a.** $\frac{1}{15} \sum_{k=1}^{75} \left[\left(\frac{k+29}{15} \right)^2 - 1 \right] =$

$\frac{14{,}198}{135} \approx 105.17$; $\frac{1}{15} \sum_{k=1}^{75} \left[\left(\frac{k+30}{15} \right)^2 - 1 \right] = \frac{14{,}603}{135} \approx 108.17$;

$\frac{1}{15} \sum_{k=1}^{75} \left[\left(\frac{2k+59}{30} \right)^2 - 1 \right] = \frac{57{,}599}{540} \approx 106.66$ **b.** 106.7

47.

n	Right Riemann sum
10	10.56
30	10.65
60	10.664
80	10.665

The sums approach $10\frac{2}{3}$.

49.

n	Right Riemann sum
10	5.655
30	6.074
60	6.178
80	6.205

The sums approach 2π.
53. a. True **b.** False
c. True

71. $s(t) = \begin{cases} 30t & \text{if } 0 \le t \le 2 \\ 50t - 40 & \text{if } 2 < t \le 2.5 \\ 44t - 25 & \text{if } 2.5 < t \le 3 \end{cases}$

73.

n	Midpoint Riemann sum
16	0.503906
32	0.500977
64	0.500244

The sums approach 0.5.

75.

n	Midpoint Riemann sum
16	4.7257
32	4.7437
64	4.7485

The sums approach 4.75.

51.

n	Right Riemann sum
10	1.0844
30	1.0285
60	1.0143
80	1.0107

The sums approach 1.

55. $\sum_{k=1}^{50}\left(\frac{4k}{50}+1\right)\cdot\frac{4}{50}=\frac{304}{25}=12.16$

57. $\sum_{k=1}^{32}\left(3+\frac{2k-1}{8}\right)^3\cdot\frac{1}{4}\approx 3639.1$

59. Left; $[2,6]$; 4 or Right; $[1,5]$; 4 **61.** Midpoint; $[2,6]$; 4
63. a.

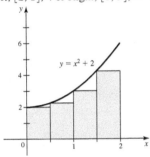

Left Riemann sum is
$\frac{23}{4}=5.75$.

b.

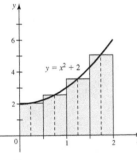

Midpoint Riemann sum
is $\frac{53}{8}=6.625$.

c.

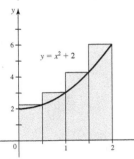

Right Riemann sum is
$\frac{31}{4}=7.75$.

65. Left sum: 34; right sum: 24 **67. a.** The object is speeding up on
the interval $[0,1]$, moving at a constant rate on $[1,3]$, slowing down
on $[3,5]$, and maintaining a constant velocity on $[5,6]$. **b.** 30 m
c. 50 m **d.** $s(t)=30+10t$ **69. a.** 14.5 g **b.** 29.5 g **c.** 44 g
d. $x=6\frac{1}{3}$ cm

Section 5.2 Exercises, pp. 351–354

1. The area of the regions above the x-axis minus the area of the
regions below the x-axis. **3.** When the function is nonnegative on the
entire interval; when the function has negative values on the interval
5. Both integrals $= 0$. **7.** The length of the interval $[a, a]$ is
$a - a = 0$, so the net area is 0. **9.** $\frac{a^2}{2}$

11. a.

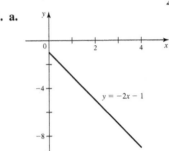

b. $-16, -24, -20$

13. a.

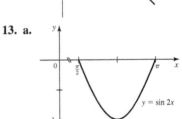

b. $\approx -0.948, \approx -0.948,$
≈ -1.026

15. a.

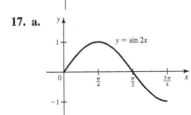

b. $4, -4, 0$ **c.** Positive contributions on $[0, 2)$; negative
contributions on $(2, 4]$.

17. a.

b. $\approx 0.735, \approx 0.146, \approx 0.530$
c. Positive contribution on
$(0, \pi/2)$; negative contribution
on $(\pi/2, 3\pi/4)$.

19. a.
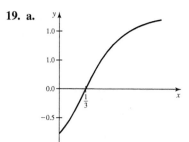

b. 0.0823315; 0.555468; 0.325932

c. Positive contributions on $\left(\frac{1}{3}, 1\right)$; negative contributions on $\left(0, \frac{1}{3}\right)$.   **21.** $\int_0^2 (x^2 + 1)\, dx$ **23.** $\int_1^2 x \ln x\, dx$

25. 16
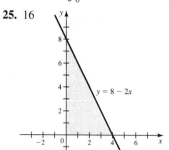

27. $-\frac{5}{2}$
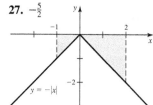

29. 4π
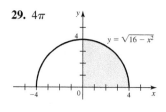

31. 26
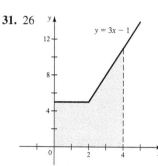

33. 16   **35.** 6   **37.** π **39.** -2π **41. a.** -32 **b.** $\frac{32}{3}$ **c.** -64
d. Not possible   **43. a.** 10   **b.** -3 **c.** -16 **d.** 3   **45. a.** $\frac{3}{2}$
b. $-\frac{3}{4}$ **47.** 6   **49.** 104   **51.** 18   **53. a.** True   **b.** True   **c.** True
d. False   **e.** False

55. a.
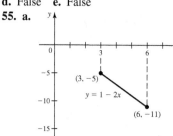

b. $\Delta x = \frac{1}{2}$; 3, 3.5, 4, 4.5, 5, 5.5, 6   **c.** -22.5; -25.5
d. the left Riemann sum overestimates; the right Riemann sum underestimates.

57. a.
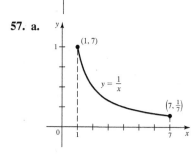

b. $\Delta x = 1$; 1, 2, 3, 4, 5, 6, 7   **c.** $\frac{49}{20}$; $\frac{223}{140}$ **d.** The left Riemann sum overestimates; the right Riemann sum underestimates.

59. a.

Left: $\displaystyle\sum_{k=1}^{20}\left[\left(\frac{k-1}{20}\right)^2 + 1\right]\cdot\frac{1}{20} = 1.30875$;

right: $\displaystyle\sum_{k=1}^{20}\left[\left(\frac{k}{20}\right)^2 + 1\right]\cdot\frac{1}{20} = 1.35875$

Left: $\displaystyle\sum_{k=1}^{50}\left[\left(\frac{k-1}{50}\right)^2 + 1\right]\cdot\frac{1}{50} = 1.3234$;

right: $\displaystyle\sum_{k=1}^{50}\left[\left(\frac{k}{50}\right)^2 + 1\right]\cdot\frac{1}{50} = 1.3434$

Left: $\displaystyle\sum_{k=1}^{100}\left[\left(\frac{k-1}{100}\right)^2 + 1\right]\cdot\frac{1}{100} = 1.32835$;

right: $\displaystyle\sum_{k=1}^{100}\left[\left(\frac{k}{100}\right)^2 + 1\right]\cdot\frac{1}{100} = 1.33835$ **b.** 1.33

61. a. Left: $\displaystyle\sum_{k=1}^{20}\cos^{-1}\left(\frac{k-1}{20}\right)\frac{1}{20} = 1.03619$;

right: $\displaystyle\sum_{k=1}^{20}\cos^{-1}\left(\frac{k}{20}\right)\frac{1}{20} = 0.95765$;

Left: $\displaystyle\sum_{k=1}^{50}\cos^{-1}\left(\frac{k-1}{50}\right)\frac{1}{50} = 1.01491$;

right: $\displaystyle\sum_{k=1}^{50}\cos^{-1}\left(\frac{k}{50}\right)\frac{1}{50} = 0.983494$;

Left: $\displaystyle\sum_{k=1}^{100}\cos^{-1}\left(\frac{k-1}{100}\right)\frac{1}{100} = 1.00757$;

right: $\displaystyle\sum_{k=1}^{100}\cos^{-1}\left(\frac{k}{100}\right)\frac{1}{100} = 0.99186$ **b.** 1.

63. a. $\displaystyle\sum_{k=1}^{n}\frac{6}{n}\sqrt{\frac{2n + 6k - 3}{2n}}$

b.

n	Midpoint Riemann sum
20	9.33380
50	9.33341
100	9.33335

Estimate: 9.33

65. a. $\displaystyle\sum_{k=1}^{n}(2k - 1)(2n + 1 - 2k)\cdot\frac{16}{n^3}$

b.

n	Midpoint Riemann sum
20	10.6800
50	10.6688
100	10.6672

Estimate: 10.67

67. a. 15   **b.** 5   **c.** 3   **d.** -2 **e.** 24   **f.** -10

69.

The area is 12; the net area is 0.

71.

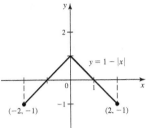

The area is 2; the net area is 0.

73. 17   **75.** $25\pi/2$ **77.** 25   **81.** For any such partition on the interval $[0, 1]$, the grid points are $x_k = k/n$, for $k = 0, 1, \ldots, n$. That is, x_k is rational for each k so that $f(x_k) = 1$, for $k = 0, 1, \ldots, n$. Thus, the left, right, and midpoint Riemann sums are $\sum_{k=1}^{n} 1 \cdot (1/n) = 1$.

Section 5.3 Exercises, pp. 365–369

1. A is an antiderivative of f; $A'(x) = f(x)$

3. Let f be continuous on $[a, b]$. Then $\int_a^b f(x)\, dx = F(b) - F(a)$, where F is any antiderivative of f.   **5.** Increasing   **7.** The derivative of the integral of f is f, or $\dfrac{d}{dx}\left(\int_a^x f(t)\, dt\right) = f(x)$.   **9.** $f(x), 0$

11. a. 0   **b.** -9 **c.** 25   **d.** 0   **e.** 16
13. a.

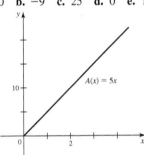

b. $A'(x) = 5$

15. a.

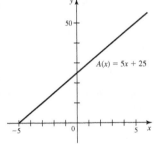

b. $A'(x) = 5$

17. a. $A(2) = 2, A(4) = 8; A(x) = \frac{1}{2}x^2$ **b.** $F(4) = 6, F(6) = 16$; $F(x) = \frac{1}{2}x^2 - 2$ **c.** $A(x) - F(x) = \frac{1}{2}x^2 - \left(\frac{1}{2}x^2 - 2\right) = 2$
19. a.

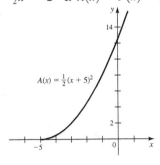

b. $A'(x) = \left[\frac{1}{2}(x + 5)^2\right]' = x + 5 = f(x)$
21. a.

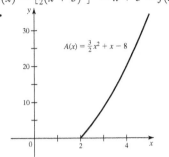

b. $A'(x) = \left(\frac{3}{2}x^2 + x - 8\right)' = 3x + 1 = f(x)$ **23.** $\frac{7}{3}$
25. $-\frac{125}{6}$ **27.** $-\frac{10}{3}$

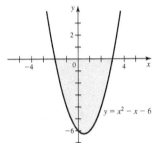

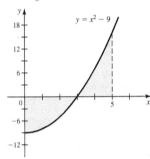

29. 16   **31.** $\frac{7}{6}$ **33.** 8   **35.** $-\frac{32}{3}$ **37.** $-\frac{5}{2}$ **39.** 1   **41.** $-\frac{3}{8}$
43. $\frac{9}{2}$ **45.** $3\ln 2$ **47.** $\sqrt{2}/4$ **49.** $\pi/12$
51. (i) $\frac{14}{3}$ **(ii)** $\frac{14}{3}$ **53. (i)** -51.2 **(ii)** 51.2

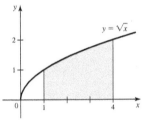

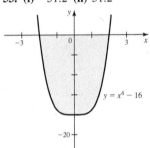

55. Area $= \frac{94}{3}$ **57.** Area $= \ln 2$ **59.** Area $= 2$ **61.** $x^2 + x + 1$
63. $3/x^4$ **65.** $-\sqrt{x^4 + 1}$ **67.** $2\sqrt{1 + x^2}$ **69.** a–C, b–B, c–D, d–A
71. a. $x = 0, x \approx 3.5$ **b.** Local min at $x \approx 1.5$; local max at $x \approx 8.5$
c.

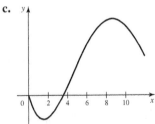

73. a. $x = 0, 10$ **b.** Local max at $x = 5$

c.
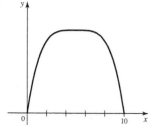

75. $-\pi, -\pi + \frac{9}{2}, -\pi + 9, 5 - \pi$ **77. a.** $A(x) = e^x - 1$
b.
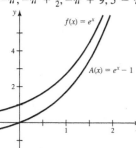
c. $A(b) = 1; A(c) = 3$

79. a. $A(x) = \dfrac{1}{\pi} \sin \pi x$ **c.** $A(b) = 1/\pi; A(c) = 0$

b.
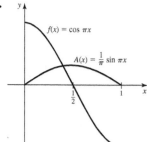

81. a.
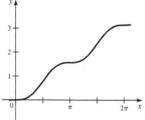
b. $g'(x) = \sin^2(x)$

c.
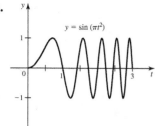

83. a.
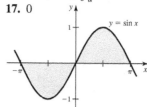
b. $g'(x) = \sin(\pi x^2)$

c.
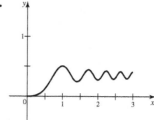

85. a. True   **b.** True   **c.** False   **d.** True   **e.** True   **87.** $\frac{2}{3}$ **89.** 1
91. $\frac{45}{4}$ **93.** $\frac{3}{2} + 4 \ln 2$
95.
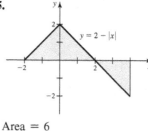

Area = 6

97.
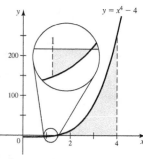

Area ≈ 194.05

99. $f(8) - f(3)$ **101.** $-(\cos^4 x + 6) \sin x$
103. a.
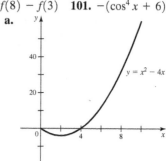
b. $b = 6$

c. $b = \dfrac{3a}{2}$

105. 3   **107.** $f(x) = -2 \sin x + 3$ **109.** $\pi/2 \approx 1.57$

111. $\left[S'(x) \right]^2 + \left[\dfrac{S''(x)}{2x} \right]^2 = [\sin x^2]^2 + \left[\dfrac{2x \cos x^2}{2x} \right]^2$
$$= \sin^2 x^2 + \cos^2 x^2 = 1$$

Section 5.4 Exercises, pp. 374–376

1. If f is odd, the region between f and the positive x-axis and between f and the negative x-axis are reflections of each other through the origin. Thus, on $[-a, a]$, the areas cancel each other out.   **3.** Even; even
5. If f is continuous on $[a, b]$, then there is a c in (a, b) such that
$$f(c) = \frac{1}{b - a} \int_a^b f(x)\, dx$$ **7.** 0   **9.** $\frac{1000}{3}$ **11.** $-\frac{88}{3}$ **13.** 0   **15.** 0
17. 0
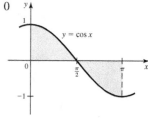
19. 0

21. 0

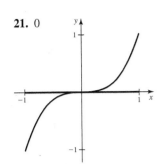

23. $\dfrac{\pi}{4}$

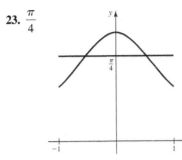

25. $1/(e-1)$

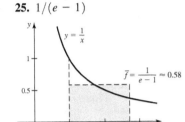

27. $2/\pi$

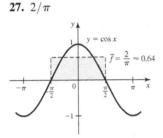

29. $1/(n+1)$ **31.** $2000/3$ **33.** $20/\pi$ **35.** $c=2$
37. $c=a/\sqrt{3}$ **39.** $c=\pm\frac{1}{2}$ **41. a.** True **b.** True **c.** True
d. False **43.** 2 **45.** 0 **47.** 420 ft **51. a.** 9 **b.** 0
53. $f(g(-x))=f(g(x))\Rightarrow$ the integrand is even;

$$\int_{-a}^{a}f(g(x))\,dx=2\int_{0}^{a}f(g(x))\,dx$$

55. $p(g(-x))=p(g(x))\Rightarrow$ the integrand is even;

$$\int_{-a}^{a}p(g(x))\,dx=2\int_{0}^{2}p(g(x))\,dx$$ **57. a.** $a/6$

b. $(3\pm\sqrt{3})/6$, independent of a **61.** $c=\sqrt[4]{12}$
65.

Even	Even
Even	Odd

Section 5.5 Exercises, pp. 383–386

1. The Chain Rule **3.** $u=g(x)$ **5.** We let a become $g(a)$ and
b become $g(b)$. **7.** $\dfrac{x}{2}+\dfrac{\sin 2x}{4}+C$ **9.** $\dfrac{(x+1)^{13}}{13}+C$

11. $\dfrac{(2x+1)^{3/2}}{3}+C$ **13.** $\dfrac{(x^2+1)^5}{5}+C$ **15.** $\frac{1}{4}\sin^4 x+C$

17. $\dfrac{(x^2-1)^{100}}{100}+C$ **19.** $-\dfrac{(1-4x^3)^{1/2}}{3}+C$

21. $\dfrac{(x^2+x)^{11}}{11}+C$ **23.** $\dfrac{(x^4+16)^7}{28}+C$ **25.** $\dfrac{\sin^{-1}(3x)}{3}+C$

27. $\dfrac{(x^6-3x^2)^5}{30}+C$ **29.** $\frac{1}{3}\sin^{-1}3x+C$ **31.** $2\sec^{-1}2x+C$

33. $\frac{2}{3}(x-4)^{1/2}(x+8)+C$ **35.** $\frac{3}{5}(x+4)^{2/3}(x-6)+C$
37. $\frac{3}{112}(2x+1)^{4/3}(8x-3)+C$ **39.** $\frac{7}{2}$ **41.** $\frac{1}{3}$ **43.** $(e^9-1)/3$

45. $\sqrt{2}-1$ **47.** $\pi/6$ **49.** $\frac{1}{2}\ln 17$ **51.** $\dfrac{\pi}{9}$ **53.** π

55. $\dfrac{\theta}{2}-\dfrac{1}{4}\sin\left(\dfrac{6\theta+\pi}{3}\right)+C$ **57.** $\dfrac{\pi}{4}$ **59.** $\ln\dfrac{9}{8}$ **61. a.** True
b. True **c.** False **d.** False **e.** False **63.** $\frac{1}{10}\tan(10x)+C$

65. $\dfrac{1}{2}\tan^2 x+C$ **67.** $\frac{1}{7}\sec^7 x+C$ **69.** $\frac{1}{3}$ **71.** $\frac{3}{4}(4-3^{2/3})$

73. $\frac{32}{3}$ **75.** $-\ln 3$ **77.** $\dfrac{1}{7}$ **79.** 1 **81.** $\dfrac{64}{5}$ **83.** $\frac{2}{3}$; constant

85. a. π/p **b.** 0 **87. a.** 160 **b.** $\dfrac{4800}{49}\approx 98$

c. $\Delta p=\displaystyle\int_{0}^{T}\dfrac{200}{(t+1)^r}\,dt$; decreases as r increases **d.** $r\approx 1.28$

e. As $t\to\infty$, the population approaches 100. **89.** $2/\pi$

93. One area is $\displaystyle\int_{4}^{9}\dfrac{(\sqrt{x}-1)^2}{2\sqrt{x}}\,dx$. Changing variables by letting
$u=\sqrt{x}-1$ yields $\int_{1}^{2}u^2\,du$, which is the other area. **95.** $7297/12$

97. $\dfrac{[f^{(p)}(x)]^{n+1}}{n+1}+C$ **99.** $\frac{2}{15}(3-2a)(1+a)^{3/2}+\frac{4}{15}a^{5/2}$

101. $\frac{1}{3}\sec^3\theta+C$ **103. a.** $I=\int\left(\frac{1}{2}\sin 2x\right)^2 dx=\frac{1}{8}x-\frac{1}{32}\sin 4x+C$

b. $I=\int(\sin^2 x-\sin^4 x)\,dx=\frac{1}{8}x-\frac{1}{32}\sin 4x+C$

107. $\dfrac{4}{3}(-2+\sqrt{1+x})\sqrt{1+\sqrt{1+x}}$ **109.** $-4+\sqrt{17}$

Chapter 5 Review Exercises, pp. 386–389

1. a. True **b.** False **c.** True **d.** True **e.** False **f.** True
g. True **3. a.** 8.5 **b.** -4.5 **c.** 0 **d.** 11.5 **5.** 4π
7. a. $1[(3\cdot 2-2)+(3\cdot 3-2)+(3\cdot 4-2)]=21$

b. $\displaystyle\sum_{k=1}^{n}\dfrac{3}{n}\left[3\left(1+\dfrac{3k}{n}\right)-2\right]$ **c.** $\dfrac{33}{2}$ **9.** $-\frac{16}{3}$ **11.** 56

13. $\displaystyle\int_{0}^{4}(1+x^8)\,dx=\dfrac{36+4^9}{9}$ **15.** $\frac{212}{5}$ **17.** 20

19. x^9-x^7+C **21.** $\frac{7}{6}$ **23.** $\dfrac{\pi}{6}$ **25.** 1 **27.** $\frac{1}{2}\theta-\frac{1}{20}\sin 10\theta+C$

29. $\frac{1}{3}\ln|x^3+3x^2-6x|+C$ **31.** $\frac{256}{3}$ **33.** 8 **35.** $\frac{-4}{15};\frac{4}{15}$
37. a. 20 **b.** 0 **c.** 80 **d.** 10 **e.** 0 **39.** 18 **41.** 10 **43.** Not
enough information **45.** Displacement $=0$; distance $=20/\pi$
47. a. $5/2, c=3.5$ **b.** $3, c=3$ and $c=5$ **49.** 24
51. $f(1)=0; f'(x)>0$ on $[1,\infty); f''(x)<0$ on $[1,\infty)$

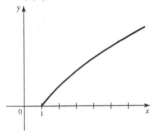

57. $\cos\dfrac{1}{x}+C$ **59.** $\ln|\tan^{-1}x|+C$ **61.** $\ln(e^x+e^{-x})+C$

63. Differentiating the first equation gives the second equation; no.
65. a. Increasing on $(-\infty,1)$ and $(2,\infty)$; decreasing on $(1,2)$
b. Concave up on $(\frac{13}{8},\infty)$; concave down on $(-\infty,\frac{13}{8})$
c. Local max at $x=1$; local min at $x=2$
d. Inflection point at $x=\frac{13}{8}$

CHAPTER 6

Section 6.1 Exercises, pp. 398–403

1. The position, $s(t)$, is the location of the object relative to the origin. The displacement between time $t = a$ and $t = b$ is $s(b) - s(a)$.

The distance traveled between $t = a$ and $t = b$ is $\int_a^b |v(t)|\,dt$,

where $v(t)$ is the velocity at time t. **3.** The displacement between

$t = a$ and $t = b$ is $\int_a^b v(t)\,dt$. **5.** $Q(t) = Q(0) + \int_0^t Q'(x)\,dx$

7. a. 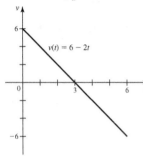   Positive direction for $0 \le t < 3$; negative direction for $3 < t \le 6$
b. 0   **c.** 18 m

9. a. 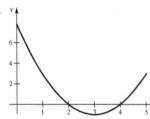   Positive direction for $0 \le t < 2$ and $4 < t \le 5$; negative direction for $2 < t < 4$ **b.** 20/3 m   **c.** 28/3 m

11. a. 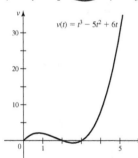   Positive direction for $0 < t < 2$ and $3 < t \le 5$; negative direction for $2 < t < 3$

b. $\dfrac{275}{12}$ m   **c.** 23.75 m

13. Positive direction for $0 < t < \pi$; negative direction for $\pi < t < 2\pi$.
a. 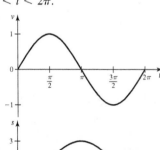   **b.** $s(t) = -\cos t + 2$

c.

15. a. 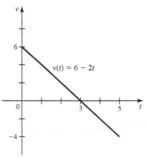   Positive direction for $0 \le t < 3$; negative direction for $3 < t \le 5$

b. $s(t) = 6t - t^2$

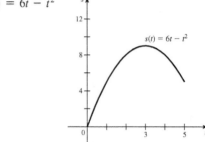

17. a. 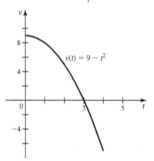   Positive direction for $0 \le t < 3$; negative direction for $3 < t \le 4$

b. $s(t) = 9t - \dfrac{t^3}{3} - 2$ **c.**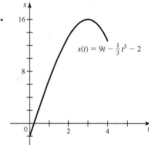

19. a. $s(t) = 2 \sin \pi t$ **b.** 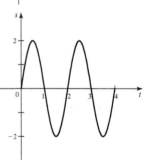   **c.** $\frac{3}{2}, \frac{7}{2}, \frac{11}{2}$ **d.** $\frac{1}{2}, \frac{5}{2}, \frac{9}{2}$

21. a. $s(t) = 10t(48 - t^2)$ **b.** 880 mi

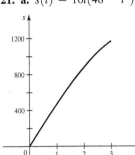

c. $\dfrac{2720\sqrt{6}}{9} \approx 740.29$ mi

b. Theo   **c.** Sasha   **d.** Theo hits the 10-mi mark before Sasha; Sasha and Theo hit the 15-mi mark at the same time; Sasha hits the 20-mi mark before Theo.   **e.** Sasha   **f.** Theo

57. a. Abe initially runs into a headwind; Bess initially runs with a tailwind.

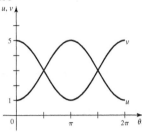

23.

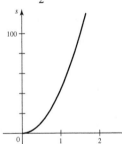

a. Velocity is a maximum for $20 \leq t \leq 45$; $v = 0$ at $t = 0$ and $t = 60$ **b.** 1200 m
c. 2550 m   **d.** 2100 m in the positive direction from $s(0)$

b. Both runners have an average speed of 3 mi/hr.   **c.** $\pi\sqrt{5}/25$ hr.

59. a. $\dfrac{10^7(1 - e^{-kt})}{k}$ **b.** $\dfrac{10^7}{k}$ = total amount of barrels of oil

extracted if the nation extracts the oil indefinitely where it is assumed

that the nation has at least $\dfrac{10^7}{k}$ barrels of oil in reserve

c. $k = \dfrac{1}{200} = 0.005$ **d.** Approximately 138.6 yr

25. $v(t) = -32t + 70$; $s(t) = -16t^2 + 70t + 10$
27. $v(t) = -9.8t + 20$; $s(t) = -4.9t^2 + 20t$
29. $v(t) = -\frac{1}{200}t^2 + 10$; $s(t) = -\frac{1}{600}t^3 + 10t$
31. $v(t) = \dfrac{1}{2}\sin 2t + 5$; $s(t) = -\dfrac{1}{4}\cos 2t + 5t + \dfrac{29}{4}$

61. a. $\dfrac{120}{\pi} + 40 \approx 78.20$ m^3 **b.** $Q(t) = 20\left[t + \dfrac{12}{\pi}\sin\left(\dfrac{\pi}{12}t\right)\right]$

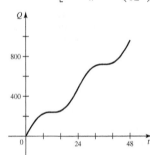

33.

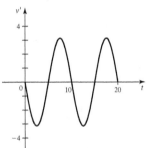

a. $s(t) = 44t^2$ ft
b. 704 ft
c. $\sqrt{30} \approx 5.477$ s
d. $\dfrac{5\sqrt{33}}{11} \approx 2.611$ s
e. $\dfrac{89^2}{44} \approx 180.023$ ft

c. After ≈ 122.6 hr   **63. a.**

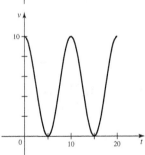

35. 6.154 mi; 1.465 mi   **37. a.** 27,250 barrels   **b.** 31,000 barrels
c. 4000 barrels   **39. a.** $\approx$ 2639 people
b. $P(t) = 250 + 20t^{3/2} + 30t$ people   **41. a.** 1897 cells; 1900 cells
b. $N(t) = -400e^{-0.25t} + 1900$ cells   **43. a.** \$96,875   **b.** \$86,875
45. a. \$69,583.33   **b.** \$139,583.33   **47. a.** False   **b.** True
c. True   **d.** True   **49. a.** 3   **b.** $\frac{13}{3}$ **c.** 3

d. $s(t) = \begin{cases} -\dfrac{t^2}{2} + 2t, & 0 \leq t \leq 3 \\ \dfrac{3t^2}{2} - 10t + 18, & 3 < t \leq 4 \\ -t^2 + 10t - 22, & 4 < t \leq 5 \end{cases}$

b. $V(t) = 5\cos\left(\dfrac{\pi t}{5}\right) + 5$

51. $\frac{2}{3}$ **53.** $\dfrac{25}{3}$ **55. a.**

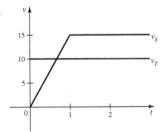

c. 6 breaths/min   **65. a.** 7200 MWh or 2.592×10^{13} J
b. 16,000 kg; 5,840,000 kg   **c.** 450 g; 164,250 g
d. About 1500 turbines

Section 6.2 Exercises, pp. 408–412

1.

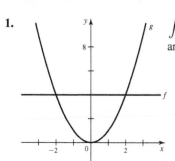

$\int_{-2}^{2} (f(x) - g(x))\, dx$ represents the area between these curves.

3. See solution to Exercise 1.   **5.** $\dfrac{9}{2}$ **7.** $\dfrac{5}{2} - \dfrac{1}{\ln 2}$ **9.** $\dfrac{25}{2}$ **11.** $\dfrac{81}{32}$

13. $\pi - 2$ **15.** $2 - \sqrt{2}$ **17.** $\frac{1}{2} + \ln 2$ **19.** 3   **21.** 3

23. 48   **25.** $\dfrac{1}{6}$

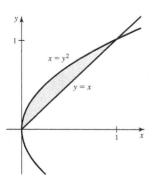

27. a. $\displaystyle\int_{-\sqrt{2}}^{-1} (2 - x^2)\, dx + \int_{-1}^{0} (-x)\, dx$

b. $\displaystyle\int_{-1}^{0} (y + \sqrt{y + 2})\, dy$

29. a. $\displaystyle 2\int_{-3}^{-2} \sqrt{x + 3}\, dx + \int_{-2}^{6}\left(\sqrt{x + 3} - \dfrac{x}{2}\right) dx$

b. $\displaystyle\int_{-1}^{3} (2y - (y^2 - 3))\, dy$ **31.**

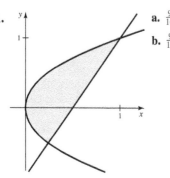

a. $\frac{9}{16}$
b. $\frac{9}{16}$

33. $\frac{64}{5}$ **35.** $\ln 2$ **37.** $\frac{5}{24}$ **39. a.** False   **b.** False   **c.** True

41. $\frac{1}{6}$ **43.** $\frac{9}{2}$ **45.** $\frac{32}{3}$ **47.** $\frac{63}{4}$ **49.** $\frac{15}{8} - 2\ln 2$

51. a. Area $(R_1) = \dfrac{p - 1}{2(p + 1)}$ for all positive integers p; area

$(R_2) = \dfrac{q - 1}{2(q + 1)}$ for all positive integers q; they are the same.

b. R_1 has greater area.   **c.** R_2 has greater area.

53. $\dfrac{135 + 17\sqrt{17} - 128\sqrt{2}}{96}$ **55.** $\dfrac{81}{2}$ **57.** $\dfrac{n - 1}{2(n + 1)}$

59. $A_n = \dfrac{n - 1}{n + 1}$; $\lim_{n \to \infty} A_n = 1$; the region approximates a square with side length of 1.   **61. a.** The lowest $p\%$ of households owns exactly $p\%$ of the wealth for $0 \le p \le 100$.   **b.** The function must be increasing and concave up because the poorest $p\%$ cannot own more than $p\%$ of the wealth.   **c.** $p = 1.1$ is most equitable; $p = 4$ is least equitable.

e. $G(p) = 1 - \dfrac{2}{p + 1}$ **f.** $0 \le G \le 1$ for $p \ge 1$.   **g.** $\dfrac{5}{18}$ **63.** -1

65. $\frac{4}{9}$ **67. a.** $F(a) = ab^3/6 - b^4/12$; $F(a) = 0$ if $a = b/2$

b. Since $A'(b/2) = 0$ and $A''(b/2) > 0$, A has a minimum at $a = b/2$. The maximum value of $b^4/12$ occurs if $a = 0$ or $a = b$.

69. a.

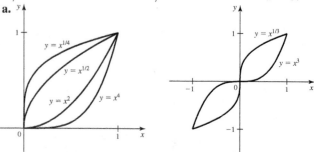

b. $A_n(x)$ is the net area of the region between the graphs of f and g from 0 to x.   **c.** $x = n^{n/(n^2 - 1)}$; the roots decrease with n.

Section 6.3 Exercises, pp. 419–423

1. $A(x)$ is the area of the cross section through the solid at the point x.

3. $V = \displaystyle\int_{0}^{2} \pi\,(4x^2 - x^4)\, dx$ **5.** The cross sections are disks and $A(x)$ is the area of a disk.   **7.** $\frac{64}{15}$ **9.** 1   **11.** $\frac{1000}{3}$ **13.** $\frac{\pi}{3}$

15. $\dfrac{16\sqrt{2}}{3}$ **17.** 36π **19.** $15\pi/32$ **21.** $\pi^2/2$ **23.** $\pi^2/6$

25. $\pi^2/2$ **27.** $32\pi/3$ **29.** $5\pi/6$ **31.** $117\pi/5$ **33.** $(4\pi - \pi^2)/4$

35. 54π **37.** $64\pi/5$ **39.** $32\pi/3$ **41.** Volumes are equal.

43. x-axis   **45. a.** False   **b.** True   **c.** True   **47.** $\pi \ln 3$

49. $\dfrac{\pi}{2}(e^4 - 1)$ **51.** $49\pi/2$ **53.** Volume $S = 8\pi a^{5/2}/15$;

volume $T = \pi a^{5/2}/3$

55. a.

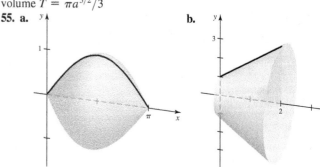

57. a. $\frac{1}{3}V_C$ **b.** $\frac{2}{3}V_C$ **59.** $24\pi^2$ **61. b.** $2/\sqrt{\pi}$ m

Section 6.4 Exercises, pp. 432–435

1. $\displaystyle\int_{a}^{b} 2\pi x(f(x) - g(x))\, dx$ **3.** $x; y$ **5.** $\dfrac{\pi}{6}$ **7.** $\pi \ln 5$ **9.** π

11. $\dfrac{\pi}{5}$ **13.** π **15.** 8π **17.** $\dfrac{32\pi}{3}$ **19.** $\dfrac{2\pi}{3}$ **21.** $\dfrac{81\pi}{2}$

23. 90π **25.** π **27.** 24π **29.** 54π **31.** $16\sqrt{2}\,\pi/3$

33. $\dfrac{11\pi}{6}$ **35.** $\dfrac{23\pi}{15}$ **37.** $\dfrac{704\pi}{15}$ **39.** $\dfrac{192\pi}{5}$ **41.** $4\pi/15$; shell
method **43.** $8\pi/27$; shell method **45.** $\pi\,(\sqrt{e}-1)^2$; shell method
47. $\dfrac{\pi}{9}$; washer method **49. a.** True **b.** False **c.** True **51.** $4\pi\ln 2$
53. $2\pi e(e-1)$ **55.** $16\pi/3$ **57.** $608\pi/3$ **59.** $\pi/4$ **61.** $\pi/3$
63. a. $V_1 = \dfrac{\pi}{15}(3a^2 + 10a + 15)$

$\qquad V_2 = \dfrac{\pi}{2}(a+2)$

b. $V(S_1) = V(S_2)$ for $a=0$ and $a=-\frac{5}{6}$ **67.** $\dfrac{\pi h^2}{3}(24-h)$
69. $24\pi^2$ **73.** 10π **75. a.** $27\sqrt{3}\pi r^3/8$ **b.** $54\sqrt{2}/(3+\sqrt{2})^3$
c. $500\pi/3$

Section 6.5 Exercises, pp. 440–442

1. Determine if f has a continuous derivative on $[a,b]$. If so, calculate
$f'(x)$ and $f'(x)^2$. Then evaluate the integral $\displaystyle\int_a^b \sqrt{1+f'(x)^2}\,dx$.

3. $4\sqrt{5}$ **5.** 168 **7.** $\frac{4}{3}$ **9.** $\frac{123}{32}$ **11. a.** $\displaystyle\int_{-1}^{1}\sqrt{1+4x^2}\,dx$ **b.** 2.96

13. a. $\displaystyle\int_1^4 \sqrt{1+\dfrac{1}{x^2}}\,dx$ **b.** 3.34 **15. a.** $\displaystyle\int_3^4 \sqrt{\dfrac{4x-7}{4x-8}}\,dx$ **b.** 1.08

17. a. $\displaystyle\int_0^\pi \sqrt{1+4\sin^2(2x)}\,dx$ **b.** 5.27 **19. a.** $\displaystyle\int_1^{10}\sqrt{1+1/x^4}\,dx$
b. 9.15 **21.** $7\sqrt{5}$ **23.** $\frac{123}{32}$ **25. a.** False **b.** True **c.** False
27. a. $f(x) = \pm 4x^3/3 + C$ **b.** $f(x) = \pm 3\sin 2x + C$
29. $y = 1 - x^2$ **31.** Approximately 1326 m **33. a.** $L/2$ **b.** L/c

Section 6.6 Exercises, pp. 448–450

1. 15π **3.** Evaluate $\displaystyle\int_a^b 2\pi f(x)\sqrt{1+f'(x)^2}\,dx$. **5.** $156\sqrt{10}\pi$

7. $\dfrac{2912\pi}{3}$ **9.** $\dfrac{53\pi}{9}$ **11.** $\dfrac{\pi}{8}(16+e^8-e^{-8})$ **13.** $\dfrac{275\pi}{32}$ **15.** $\frac{9\pi}{125}\,\text{m}^2$

17. $\dfrac{\pi}{9}(17^{3/2}-1)$ **19.** $15\sqrt{17}\,\pi$ **21. a.** False **b.** False

c. True **d.** False **23.** $\dfrac{48{,}143\pi}{48}$ **25.** $\dfrac{1{,}256{,}001\pi}{1024}\approx 3853.36$

27. b. Approximately 7.21 **29. b.** Approximately 3.84 **31.** $\dfrac{12\pi a^2}{5}$

35. a. $6/a$ **b.** $3/a$ **c.** $\dfrac{3}{2a}+\dfrac{3a}{2\sqrt{a^2-1}}\sin^{-1}\left(\dfrac{\sqrt{a^2-1}}{a}\right)$

37. a. $c^2 A$ **b.** A

Section 6.7 Exercises, pp. 458–462

1. 150 g **3.** 25 J **5.** Different volumes of water are moved different
distances. **7.** 39,200 N/m² **9.** $\pi+2$ **11.** 3 **13.** $(2\sqrt{2}-1)/3$
15. 10 **17.** 9 J **19. a.** $k=150$ **b.** 12 J **c.** 6.75 J **d.** 9 J
21. a. 112.5 J **b.** 12.5 J **23. a.** 31.25 J **b.** 312.5 J **25.** 525 J
27. 11,484,375 J **29.** 3,940,814 J **31. a.** $66{,}150\pi$ J **b.** No
33. a. $200{,}704{,}000\pi/3$ J **b.** $120{,}422{,}400\pi$ J **35. a.** 32,667 J
b. Yes **37.** 7696.9 J **39.** 14,700,000 N **41.** 29,400,000 N

43. 800,000 N **45.** 6737.5 N **47. a.** True **b.** True **c.** True
d. False **49. a.** Compared to a linear spring $F(x)=16x$, the
restoring force is less for large displacements. **b.** 17.87 J
c. 31.6 J **51.** 0.28 J **53. a.** 8.87×10^9 J
b. $500\,GMx/(R(x+R)) = (2\times 10^{17})x/(R(x+R))$ J
c. GMm/R **d.** $v=\sqrt{2GM/R}$ **55. a.** $2250g$ J **b.** $3750g$ J
59. The left-hand plate **61. a.** Yes **b.** 4.296 m

Section 6.8 Exercises, pp. 470–472

1. $D=(0,\infty), R=(-\infty,\infty)$ **3.** $\dfrac{4^x}{\ln 4}+C$

5. $e^{x\ln 3}, e^{\pi\ln x}, e^{(\sin x)(\ln x)}$ **7.** 3 **9.** $\cos(\ln x)/x, x\in(0,\infty)$

11. $-\dfrac{5}{x(\ln 2x)^6}$ **13.** $6(1-\ln 2)$ **15.** $\dfrac{3}{8}$ **17.** $\dfrac{1}{2}\ln(4+e^{2x})+C$

19. $\dfrac{1}{\ln 2}-\dfrac{1}{\ln 3}$ **21.** $4-\dfrac{4}{e^2}$ **23.** $2e^{\sqrt{x}}+C$ **25.** $\ln|e^x-e^{-x}|+C$

27. $\dfrac{99}{10\ln 10}$ **29.** 3 **31.** $\dfrac{6^{x^3+8}}{3\ln 6}+C$

33. $4^{2x+1}x^{4x}(1+\ln 2x)$ **35.** $(\ln 2)\,2^{x^2+1}\,x$

37. $2(x+1)^{2x}\left[\dfrac{x}{x+1}+\ln(x+1)\right]$

39. $y^{\sin y}\left(\cos y\ln y+\dfrac{\sin y}{y}\right)$ **41. a.** True **b.** False **c.** False

d. False **e.** False

43.

h	$(1+2h)^{1/h}$	h	$(1+2h)^{1/h}$
10^{-1}	6.1917	-10^{-1}	9.3132
10^{-2}	7.2446	-10^{-2}	7.5404
10^{-3}	7.3743	-10^{-3}	7.4039
10^{-4}	7.3876	-10^{-4}	7.3905
10^{-5}	7.3889	-10^{-5}	7.3892
10^{-6}	7.3890	-10^{-6}	7.3891

$\displaystyle\lim_{h\to 0}(1+2h)^{1/h}=e^2$

45.

x	$\dfrac{2^x-1}{x}$	x	$\dfrac{2^x-1}{x}$
10^{-1}	0.71773	-10^{-1}	0.66967
10^{-2}	0.69556	-10^{-2}	0.69075
10^{-3}	0.69339	-10^{-3}	0.69291
10^{-4}	0.69317	-10^{-4}	0.69312
10^{-5}	0.69315	-10^{-5}	0.69314
10^{-6}	0.69315	-10^{-6}	0.69315

$\displaystyle\lim_{x\to 0}\dfrac{2^x-1}{x}=\ln 2$

47. a. No **b.** No **49.** $\dfrac{\ln p}{p-1}, 0$ **51.** $-20xe^{-10x^2}$

53. $-(1/x)^x(1+\ln x)$ **55.** $\left[-\dfrac{4}{x+4}+\ln\left(\dfrac{x+4}{x}\right)\right]\left(1+\dfrac{4}{x}\right)^x$

57. $-\sin(x^{2\sin x})\,x^{2\sin x}\left(\dfrac{2\sin x}{x}+2\cos x\ln x\right)$ **59.** $-\dfrac{1}{9^x\ln 9}+C$

61. $\dfrac{10^{x^3}}{3\ln 10}+C$ **63.** $\dfrac{3\cdot 3^{\ln 2}-1}{\ln 3}$ **65.** $\frac{32}{3}$ **67.** $\dfrac{1}{3}\ln\dfrac{65}{16}$

69. $\frac{1}{2}(\ln 2 + 1) \approx 0.85$

73. $\ln 2 = \int_1^2 \frac{dt}{t} < L_2 = \frac{5}{6} < 1$

$\ln 3 = \int_1^3 \frac{dt}{t} > R_7$

$= 2\left(\frac{1}{9} + \frac{1}{11} + \frac{1}{13} + \frac{1}{15} + \frac{1}{17} + \frac{1}{19} + \frac{1}{21}\right) > 1$

Section 6.9 Exercises, pp. 479–481

1. The relative growth is constant.   **3.** The time it takes for a function to double in value   **5.** $T_2 = \ln 2/k$ **7.** Compound interest, world population   **9.** $\frac{df}{dt} = 10.5; \frac{dg}{dt} \cdot \frac{1}{g} = \frac{10e^{t/10}}{100e^{t/10}} = \frac{1}{10}$
11. $P(t) = 90{,}000e^{0.024\,t}$ people with $t = 0$ in 2010; in 2039
13. 60,500   **15.** \$134.39   **17. a.** $T_2 \approx 87$ yr;
2050 pop ≈ 425 million   **b.** $T_2 \approx 116$ yr; 2050 pop ≈ 393 million
$T_2 \approx 70$ yr; 2050 pop ≈ 460 million   **19.** About 33 million
21. $H(t) = 800e^{-0.030t}$ homicides/yr with $t = 0$ in 2010; in 2019
23. 18,928 ft; 125,754 ft **25.** About 9.82 million; the population decline may stop if the economy improves.   **27. a.** 15.87 mg
b. after 119.59 hr ≈ 5 days   **29.** ≈ 1.055 billion yr   **31. a.** False
b. False   **c.** True   **d.** True   **e.** True   **33.** If $A(t) = A_0e^{kt}$ and
$A(T) = 2A_0$, then $e^{kt} = 2$ and $T = (\ln 2)/k$. Thus the doubling time
is a constant.   **35. a.** Bob; Abe
b. $y = 4 \ln (t + 1)$ and $y = 8 - 8e^{-t/2}$; Bob

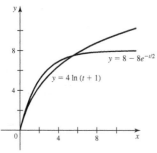

37. $\approx 10.034\%$; no   **39.** ≈ 1.2643 s   **41.** ≈ 1044 days   **43.** \$50
45. $k = \ln(1 + r); r = 2^{(1/T_2)} - 1; T_2 = (\ln 2)/k$

Section 6.10 Exercises, pp. 494–498

1. $\cosh x = \dfrac{e^x + e^{-x}}{2}$; $\sinh x = \dfrac{e^x - e^{-x}}{2}$ **3.** $\cosh^2 x - \sinh^2 x = 1$
5. $\sinh^{-1} x = \ln(x + \sqrt{x^2 + 1})$ **7.** Evaluate $\sinh^{-1}\frac{1}{5}$.
9. $\displaystyle\int \frac{dx}{16 - x^2} = \frac{1}{4}\coth^{-1}\frac{x}{4} + C$ when $|x| > 4$; in this case, the
values in the interval of integration $6 \le x \le 8$ satisfy $|x| > 4$.
23. $2 \cosh x \sinh x$ **25.** $2 \tanh x \operatorname{sech}^2 x$ **27.** $-2 \tanh 2x$
29. $2x \cosh 3x(3x \sinh 3x + \cosh 3x)$ **31.** $(\sinh 2x)/2 + C$
33. $\ln(1 + \cosh x) + C$ **35.** $x - \tanh x + C$
37. $(\cosh^4 3 - 1)/12 \approx 856$ **39.** $\ln(5/4)$
41. $(x^2 + 1)/(2x) + C$ **43. a.** The values of $y = \coth x$ are very
close to 1 on $[5,10]$.   **b.** $\ln(\sinh 10) - \ln(\sinh 5) \approx 5.0000454$;
$|\text{error}| \approx 0.0000454$

45.

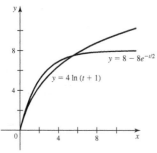

a. $x = \sinh^{-1} 1 = \ln(1 + \sqrt{2})$ **b.** $\pi/4 - \ln\sqrt{2} \approx 0.44$
47. $4/\sqrt{16x^2 - 1}$ **49.** $2v/\sqrt{v^4 + 1}$ **51.** $\sinh^{-1} x$
53. $\dfrac{1}{2\sqrt{2}}\coth^{-1}\left(\dfrac{x}{2\sqrt{2}}\right) + C$ **55.** $\tanh^{-1}(e^x/6)/6 + C$
57. $-\operatorname{sech}^{-1}(x^4/2)/8 + C$ **59.** $\sinh^{-1} 2 = \ln(2 + \sqrt{5})$
61. $-(\ln 5)/3 \approx -0.54$ **63.** $3\ln\left(\frac{\sqrt{5}+2}{\sqrt{2}+1}\right) = 3(\sinh^{-1} 2 - \sinh^{-1} 1)$
65. $\dfrac{1}{15}\left(17 - \dfrac{8}{\ln(5/3)}\right) \approx 0.09$
67. a. sag $= f(50) - f(0) = a(\cosh(50/a) - 1) = 10$;
now divide by a.   **b.** $t \approx 0.08$ **c.** $a = 10/t \approx 125$;
$L = 250 \sinh(2/5) \approx 102.7$ ft   **69.** $\lambda \approx 32.81$ m
71. b. When $d/\lambda < 0.05$, $2\pi d/\lambda$ is small. Because $\tanh x \approx x$
for small values of x, $\tanh(2\pi d/\lambda) \approx 2\pi d/\lambda$; therefore,
$v = \sqrt{\dfrac{g\lambda}{2\pi}}\tanh\left(\dfrac{2\pi d}{\lambda}\right) \approx \sqrt{\dfrac{g\lambda}{2\pi} \cdot \dfrac{2\pi d}{\lambda}} = \sqrt{gd}.$
c. $v = \sqrt{gd}$ is a function of depth alone; when depth d decreases, v
also decreases.   **73. a.** False   **b.** False   **c.** False   **d.** True
e. False   **75. a.** 1   **b.** 0   **c.** Undefined   **d.** 1   **e.** $13/12$ **f.** $40/9$
g. $\left(\dfrac{e^2 + 1}{2e}\right)^2$ **h.** Undefined   **i.** $\ln 4$ **j.** 1   **77.** $x = 0$
79. $x = \pm\tanh^{-1}(1/\sqrt{3}) = \pm\ln(2 + \sqrt{3})/2 \approx \pm 0.658$
81. $\tan^{-1}(\sinh 1) - \pi/4 \approx 0.08$ **83.** Applying l'Hôpital's Rule
twice brings you back to the initial limit; $\lim_{x\to\infty} \tanh x = 1$.   **85.** $2/\pi$
87. 1   **89.** $-\operatorname{csch} z + C$ **91.** $\ln\sqrt{3} \cdot \ln(4/3) \approx 0.158$
93. $12(3\ln(3 + \sqrt{8}) - \sqrt{8}) \approx 29.5$ **95. a.** ≈ 360.8 m
b. first 100 m: $t \approx 4.72$ s, $v_{\text{av}} \approx 21.2$ m/s; second 100 m: $t \approx 2.25$ s,
$v_{\text{av}} \approx 44.5$ m/s   **97. a.** $\sqrt{mg/k}$ **b.** $35\sqrt{3} \approx 60.6$ m/s
c. $t = \sqrt{\dfrac{m}{kg}}\tanh^{-1}(0.95) = \dfrac{1}{2}\sqrt{\dfrac{m}{kg}}\ln 39$ **d.** ≈ 736.5 m
109. $\ln(21/4) \approx 1.66$

Chapter 6 Review Exercises, pp. 498–502

1. a. True   **b.** True   **c.** True   **d.** False   **e.** False
f. False   **g.** True
3. $s(t) = 20t - 5t^2$; displacement $(t) = 20t - 5t^2$;
$D(t) = \begin{cases} 20t - 5t^2 & 0 \le t < 2 \\ 5t^2 - 20t + 40 & 2 \le t \le 4 \end{cases}$
5. a. $v(t) = -\dfrac{8}{\pi}\cos\dfrac{\pi t}{4}$
$s(t) = -\dfrac{32}{\pi^2}\sin\dfrac{\pi t}{4}$
b. min value $= -\dfrac{32}{\pi^2}$; max value $= \dfrac{32}{\pi^2}$ **c.** 0; 0   **7. a.** $R(t) = 3t^{4/3}$
b. $R(t) = \begin{cases} 3t^{4/3} & \text{if } 0 \le t \le 8 \\ 2t + 32 & \text{if } t > 8 \end{cases}$ **c.** $t = 59$ min

9. a.

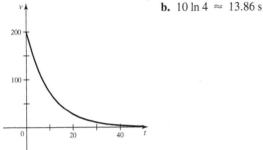

b. $10 \ln 4 \approx 13.86$ s

c. $s(t) = 2000(1 - e^{-t/10})$
d. No

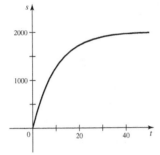

11. a. $s_{\text{Tom}}(t) = -10e^{-2t} + 10$
$s_{\text{Sue}}(t) = -15e^{-t} + 15$

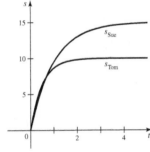

b. $t = 0$ and $t = \ln 2$ **c.** Sue   **13.** $\dfrac{21\pi}{4}$

15. R_1: 17/6; R_2: 47/6; R_3: 11/2   **17.** 8   **19.** 1   **21.** $\dfrac{1}{3}$ **23.** 16

25. $\dfrac{8\pi}{5}$ **27.** $\dfrac{\pi r^2 h}{3}$ **29.** π **31. a.** V_y **b.** V_y

c. $V_x = \begin{cases} \pi\left(\dfrac{a^{1-2p} - 1}{1 - 2p}\right) & \text{if } p \neq 1/2 \\ \pi \ln a & \text{if } p = 1/2 \end{cases}$

d. $V_y = \begin{cases} 2\pi\left(\dfrac{a^{2-p} - 1}{2 - p}\right) & \text{if } p \neq 2 \\ 2\pi \ln a & \text{if } p = 2 \end{cases}$

33. 1   **35.** $2\sqrt{3} - \dfrac{4}{3}$

37. $\sqrt{b^2 + 1} - \sqrt{2} + \ln\left(\dfrac{(\sqrt{b^2 + 1} - 1)(1 + \sqrt{2})}{b}\right)$;

$b \approx 2.715$ **39. a.** 9π **b.** $\dfrac{9\pi}{2}$ **41. a.** $\dfrac{263,439\pi}{4096}$ **b.** $\dfrac{483}{64}$

c. $\dfrac{\pi}{8}(84 + \ln 2)$ **d.** $\dfrac{264,341\pi}{18,432}$ **43.** $\left(450 - \dfrac{450}{e}\right)$ g   **45.** 562.5 J

47. 5.2×10^7 J   **49.** $\ln 4$ **51.** $\frac{1}{2}\ln(x^2 + 8x + 25) + C$
53. $\cosh^{-1}(x/3) + C = \ln(x + \sqrt{x^2 - 9}) + C$

55. $\tanh^{-1}(1/3)/9 = (\ln 2)/18 \approx 0.0385$ **57.** 48.37 yr
59. Local max at $x = -\frac{1}{2}(\sqrt{5} + 1)$;
local min at $x = \frac{1}{2}(\sqrt{5} - 1)$;
inflection points at $x = -3$ and $x = 0$;
$\lim\limits_{x \to -\infty} f(x) = 0$; $\lim\limits_{x \to \infty} f(x) = \infty$.

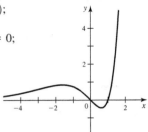

61. a.

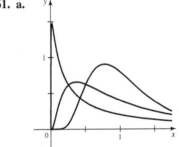

b. $\lim\limits_{x \to 0} f(x) = 0$ **c.** $f'(x^*) = 0$ **d.** $f(x^*) = \dfrac{1}{\sqrt{2\pi}}\dfrac{e^{\sigma^2/2}}{\sigma}$
e. $\sigma = 1$ **63. a.** $\cosh x$ **b.** $\operatorname{sech} x(1 - x \tanh x)$
65. $L(x) = \frac{5}{3} + \frac{4}{3}(x - \ln 3)$; $\cosh 1 \approx 1.535$

CHAPTER 7

Section 7.1 Exercises, pp. 506–508

1. $u = 4 - 7x$ **3.** $\sin^2 x = \dfrac{1 - \cos 2x}{2}$

5. Complete the square in $x^2 - 4x - 9$

7. $\dfrac{1}{15(3 - 5x)^3} + C$ **9.** $\dfrac{\sqrt{2}}{4}$ **11.** $\frac{1}{2}\ln^2 2x + C$

13. $\ln(e^x + 1) + C$ **15.** $\frac{1}{2}\ln|e^{2x} - 2| + C$ **17.** $\frac{32}{3}$
19. $-\frac{1}{5}\cot^5 x + C$ **21.** $x - \ln|x + 1| + C$

23. $\dfrac{1}{2}\ln(x^2 + 4) + \tan^{-1}\dfrac{x}{2} + C$

25. $\dfrac{\sec^2 t}{2} + \sec t + C$ or $\dfrac{\tan^2 t}{2} + \sec t + C$

27. $3\sqrt{1 - x^2} + 2\sin^{-1} x + C$ **29.** $x - 2\ln|x + 4| + C$

31. $\dfrac{t^3}{3} - \dfrac{t^2}{2} + t - 3\ln|t + 1| + C$ **33.** $\dfrac{1}{3}\tan^{-1}\left(\dfrac{x - 1}{3}\right) + C$

35. $\sin^{-1}\left(\dfrac{\theta + 3}{6}\right) + C$ **37.** $\tan\theta - \sec\theta + C$

39. $-x - \cot x - \csc x + C$
41. a. False   **b.** False   **c.** False   **d.** False

43. $\dfrac{\ln 4 - \pi}{4}$ **45.** $\dfrac{2\sin^3 x}{3} + C$ **47.** $2\tan^{-1}\sqrt{x} + C$

49. $\dfrac{1}{2}\ln(x^2 + 6x + 13) - \dfrac{5}{2}\tan^{-1}\left(\dfrac{x + 3}{2}\right) + C$

51. $-\dfrac{1}{e^x + 1} + C$ **53.** $\frac{1}{2}$ **55.   a.** $\dfrac{\tan^2 x}{2} + C$ **b.** $\dfrac{\sec^2 x}{2} + C$

c. The derivative of part (a) equals the derivative of part (b).

57.   a. $\frac{1}{2}(x + 1)^2 - 2(x + 1) + \ln|x + 1| + C$

b. $\dfrac{x^2}{2} - x + \ln|x + 1| + C$

c. The derivative of part (a) equals the derivative of part (b).

59. $\dfrac{\ln 26}{3}$ **61.   a.** $\dfrac{14\pi}{3}$ **b.** $\frac{2}{3}(5\sqrt{5} - 1)\pi$ **63.** $\dfrac{2048 + 1763\sqrt{41}}{9375}$

65. $\pi\left(\dfrac{9}{2} - \dfrac{5\sqrt{5}}{6}\right)$

Section 7.2 Exercises, pp. 512–515

1. The Product Rule   **3.** $u = x^n$ **5.** Products for which the choice for dv is easily integrated and when the resulting new integral is no more difficult than the original

7. $x \sin x + \cos x + C$ **9.** $te^t - e^t + C$

11. $\frac{2}{3}(x - 2)\sqrt{x + 1} + C$ **13.** $\dfrac{x^3}{3}(\ln x^3 - 1) + C$

15. $\dfrac{x^3}{9}(3 \ln x - 1) + C$ **17.** $-\dfrac{1}{9x^9}\left(\ln x + \dfrac{1}{9}\right) + C$

19. $x \tan^{-1} x - \frac{1}{2}\ln(x^2 + 1) + C$ **21.** $\dfrac{1}{8}\sin 2x - \dfrac{x}{4}\cos 2x + C$

23. $-e^{-t}(t^2 + 2t + 2) + C$

25. $-\dfrac{e^{-x}}{17}(\sin 4x + 4 \cos 4x) + C$

27. $\dfrac{e^x}{2}(\sin x + \cos x) + C$

29. $\frac{1}{4}(1 - 2x^2)\cos 2x + \frac{1}{2}x \sin 2x + C$ **31.** π **33.** $-\frac{1}{2}$

35. $\frac{1}{9}(5e^6 + 1)$ **37.** $\left(\dfrac{2\sqrt{3} - 1}{12}\right)\pi + \dfrac{1 - \sqrt{3}}{2}$ **39.** $\pi(1 - \ln 2)$

41. $\dfrac{2\pi}{27}(13e^6 - 1)$ **43.   a.** False   **b.** True   **c.** True

45. Let $u = x^n$ and $dv = \cos ax\, dx$.   **47.** Let $u = \ln^n x$ and $dv = dx$.

49. $\dfrac{x^2 \sin 5x}{5} + \dfrac{2x \cos 5x}{25} - \dfrac{2 \sin 5x}{125} + C$

51. $x \ln^4 x - 4x \ln^3 x + 12x \ln^2 x - 24x \ln x + 24x + C$

53. $(\tan x + 2)\ln(\tan x + 2) - \tan x + C$

55. $\displaystyle\int \log_b x\, dx = \int \dfrac{\ln x}{\ln b}\, dx = \dfrac{1}{\ln b}(x \ln x - x) + C$

57. $2\sqrt{x} \sin \sqrt{x} + 2 \cos \sqrt{x} + C$ **59.** $2e^3$ **61.** $\pi(\pi - 2)$

63. x-axis: $\dfrac{\pi^2}{2}$; y-axis: $2\pi^2$ **65.   a.** Let $u = x$ and $dv = f'(x)\, dx$.

b. $\dfrac{e^{3x}}{9}(3x - 1) + C$ **67.** Use $u = \sec x$ and $dv = \sec^2 x\, dx$.

69.   a.

$t = k\pi$ for $k = 0, 1, 2, \ldots$

b. $\dfrac{e^{-\pi} + 1}{2\pi}$

c. $(-1)^n\left(\dfrac{e^{\pi} + 1}{2\pi e^{(n+1)\pi}}\right)$

d. $a_n = a_{n-1} \cdot \dfrac{1}{e^{\pi}}$

71. $\displaystyle\int_a^b u\, dv + \int_a^b v\, du = A + B = f(b)\, g(b) - f(a)\, g(a) = uv\Big|_a^b$

75.   a. $I_1 = -\frac{1}{2}e^{-x^2} + C$ **b.** $I_3 = -\frac{1}{2}e^{-x^2}(x^2 + 1) + C$

c. $I_5 = -\frac{1}{2}e^{-x^2}(x^4 + 2x^2 + 2) + C$

d. $I_{2n+1} = -\frac{1}{2}e^{-x^2}x^{2n} + n\, I_{2n-1}$

Section 7.3 Exercises, pp. 521–523

1. $\sin^2 x = \frac{1}{2}(1 - \cos 2x)$; $\cos^2 x = \frac{1}{2}(1 + \cos 2x)$

3. Rewrite $\sin^3 x$ as $(1 - \cos^2 x)\sin x$.   **5.** A reduction formula expresses an integral with a power in the integrand in terms of another integral with a smaller power in the integrand.

7. Let $u = \tan x$.   **9.** $\dfrac{x}{2} - \dfrac{1}{4}\sin 2x + C$ **11.** $\sin x - \dfrac{\sin^3 x}{3} + C$

13. $-\cos x + \dfrac{2}{3}\cos^3 x - \dfrac{\cos^5 x}{5} + C$ **15.** $\dfrac{1}{8}x - \dfrac{1}{32}\sin 4x + C$

17. $\dfrac{\cos^5 x}{5} - \dfrac{\cos^3 x}{3} + C$ **19.** $\frac{2}{3}\sin^{3/2}x - \frac{2}{7}\sin^{7/2} x + C$

21. $\sec x + 2 \cos x - \dfrac{\cos^3 x}{3} + C$

23. $\dfrac{\sin^3 x \cos^3 x}{6} + \dfrac{1}{16}x - \dfrac{1}{64}\sin 4x + C$ **25.** $\tan x - x + C$

27. $-\dfrac{\cot^3 x}{3} + \cot x + x + C$

29. $4 \tan^5 x - \dfrac{20}{3}\tan^3 x + 20 \tan x - 20x + C$

31. $\tan^{10} x + C$ **33.** $\dfrac{\sec^3 x}{3} + C$

35. $\frac{1}{8}\tan^2 4x + \frac{1}{4}\ln|\cos 4x| + C$ **37.** $\frac{2}{3}\tan^{3/2} x + C$

39. $\tan x - \cot x + C$ **41.** $\frac{4}{3}$ **43.** $\frac{4}{3} - \ln \sqrt{3}$

45.   a. True   **b.** False   **49.** $\frac{1}{2}\ln\left(\sqrt{2} + \frac{3}{2}\right)$

51. $\frac{1}{3}\tan(\ln \theta)\sec^2(\ln \theta) + \frac{2}{3}\tan(\ln \theta) + C$ **53.** $\ln 4$

55. $8\sqrt{2}/3$ **57.** $\ln|\sec(e^x + 1) + \tan(e^x + 1)| + C$

59. $\sqrt{2}$ **61.** $2\sqrt{2}/3$ **63.** $\ln(\sqrt{2} + 1)$ **65.** $\frac{1}{2} - \ln \sqrt{2}$

67. $\dfrac{\cos 4x}{8} - \dfrac{\cos 10x}{20} + C$ **69.** $\dfrac{\sin x}{2} - \dfrac{\sin 5x}{10} + C$

73. $\displaystyle\int_0^\pi \sin^2 nx\, dx = \int_0^\pi \cos^2 nx\, dx = \pi/2, \quad n = 1, 2, 3, \ldots$

$\displaystyle\int_0^\pi \sin^4 nx\, dx = \dfrac{3\pi}{8}, \quad n = 1, 2, 3, \ldots$

Section 7.4 Exercises, pp. 529–532

1. $x = 3 \sec \theta$ **3.** $x = 10 \sin \theta$ **5.** $\sqrt{4 - x^2}/x$ **7.** $\pi/6$

9. $25\left(\dfrac{2\pi}{3} - \dfrac{\sqrt{3}}{2}\right)$ **11.** $\dfrac{\pi}{12} - \dfrac{\sqrt{3}}{8}$ **13.** $\sin^{-1}\dfrac{x}{4} + C$

15. $3 \ln\left|\dfrac{\sqrt{9 - x^2} - 3}{x}\right| + \sqrt{9 - x^2} + C$

17. $\dfrac{x}{2}\sqrt{64 - x^2} + 32 \sin^{-1}\dfrac{x}{8} + C$ **19.** $\dfrac{x}{\sqrt{1 - x^2}} + C$

21. $\dfrac{-\sqrt{x^2 + 9}}{9x} + C$ **23.** $\sin^{-1}\dfrac{x}{6} + C$

25. $\ln(\sqrt{x^2 - 81} + x) + C$ **27.** $x/\sqrt{1 + 4x^2} + C$

29. $8 \sin^{-1}(x/4) - x\sqrt{16 - x^2}/2 + C$

31. $\sqrt{x^2 - 9} - 3\sec^{-1}(x/3) + C$

33. $\dfrac{x}{2}\sqrt{4 + x^2} - 2\ln(x + \sqrt{4 + x^2}) + C$

35. $\sin^{-1}\left(\dfrac{x + 1}{2}\right) + C$ **37.** $\dfrac{9}{10}\cos^{-1}\dfrac{5}{3x} - \dfrac{\sqrt{9x^2 - 25}}{2x^2} + C$

39. $\dfrac{1}{10}\left[\tan^{-1}\dfrac{x}{5} - \dfrac{5x}{25 + x^2}\right] + C$

41. $x/\sqrt{100 - x^2} - \sin^{-1}(x/10) + C$

43. $81/(2(81 - x^2)) + \ln(\sqrt{81 - x^2}) + C$

45. $-1/\sqrt{x^2 - 1} - \sec^{-1}x + C$ **47.** $\ln\left(\dfrac{1 + \sqrt{17}}{4}\right)$

49. $2 - \sqrt{2}$ **51.** $\dfrac{1}{3} + \dfrac{\ln 3}{4}$ **53.** $\sqrt{2}/6$

55. $\frac{1}{16}\left[1 - \sqrt{3} - \ln(21 - 12\sqrt{3})\right]$

57. a. False   **b.** True   **c.** False   **d.** False

59. $\dfrac{1}{3}\tan^{-1}\left(\dfrac{x + 3}{3}\right) + C$

61. $\left(\dfrac{x - 1}{2}\right)\sqrt{x^2 - 2x + 10}$
$\quad -\dfrac{9}{2}\ln(x - 1 + \sqrt{x^2 - 2x + 10}) + C$

63. $\dfrac{x - 4}{\sqrt{9 + 8x - x^2}} - \sin^{-1}\left(\dfrac{x - 4}{5}\right) + C$ **65.** $\dfrac{\pi\sqrt{2}}{48}$

67. a. $A_{\text{seg}} = A_{\text{sector}} - A_{\text{triangle}} = \dfrac{\theta r^2}{2} - \dfrac{r^2\sin\theta}{2} = \dfrac{r^2}{2}(\theta - \sin\theta)$

69. a. $\ln 3$ **b.** $\dfrac{\pi}{3}\tan^{-1}\dfrac{4}{3}$ **c.** 4π.

71. $\dfrac{1}{4a}\left[20a\sqrt{1 + 400a^2} + \ln(20a + \sqrt{1 + 400a^2})\right]$

73. $\frac{1}{81} + \frac{\ln 3}{108}$

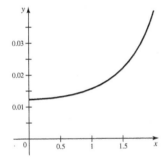

75. $25(\sqrt{3} - \ln\sqrt{2 + \sqrt{3}})$

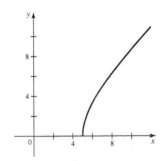

77. $\ln((2 + \sqrt{3})(\sqrt{2} - 1))$ **79.** $192\pi^2$

81. b. $\displaystyle\lim_{L\to\infty}\dfrac{kQ}{a\sqrt{a^2 + L^2}} = \lim_{L\to\infty}2\rho k\dfrac{1}{a\sqrt{\left(\dfrac{a}{L}\right)^2 + 1}} = \dfrac{2\rho k}{a}$

83. a. $\dfrac{1}{\sqrt{g}}\left[\dfrac{\pi}{2} - \sin^{-1}\left(\dfrac{2\cos b - \cos a + 1}{\cos a + 1}\right)\right]$

b. For $b = \pi$, the descent time is $\dfrac{\pi}{\sqrt{g}}$, a constant.

87. $\pi - 3\sqrt{3}$

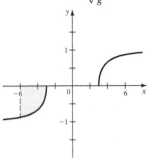

Section 7.5 Exercises, pp. 540–542

1. Rational functions   **3. a.** $\dfrac{A}{x - 3}$ **b.** $\dfrac{A_1}{x - 4}, \dfrac{A_2}{(x - 4)^2}, \dfrac{A_3}{(x - 4)^3}$

c. $\dfrac{Ax + B}{x^2 + 2x + 6}$ **5.** $\dfrac{\frac{1}{3}}{x - 4} + \dfrac{-\frac{1}{3}}{x + 2}$ **7.** $\dfrac{2}{x - 1} + \dfrac{3}{x - 2}$

9. $\dfrac{\frac{1}{2}}{x - 4} + \dfrac{\frac{1}{2}}{x + 4}$ **11.** $-\dfrac{3}{x - 1} + \dfrac{1}{x} + \dfrac{2}{x - 2}$

13. $\ln\left|\dfrac{x - 1}{x + 2}\right| + C$ **15.** $3\ln\left|\dfrac{x - 1}{x + 1}\right| + C$

17. $\ln|(x - 3)^3(x + 2)^2| + C$ **19.** $\ln|(x - 6)^6(x + 4)^4| + C$

21. $\ln\left|\dfrac{(x - 2)^2(x + 1)}{(x + 2)^2(x - 1)}\right| + C$ **23.** $\ln\left|\dfrac{x(x - 2)^3}{(x + 2)^3}\right| + C$

25. $\ln\left|\dfrac{(x - 3)^{1/3}(x + 1)}{(x + 3)^{1/3}(x - 1)}\right|^{1/16} + C$ **27.** $\dfrac{9}{x} + \ln\left|\dfrac{x - 9}{x}\right| + C$

29. $\ln|x + 3| + \dfrac{3}{x + 3} + C$ **31.** $-\dfrac{2}{x} + \ln\left|\dfrac{x + 1}{x}\right|^2 + C$

33. $\dfrac{5}{x} + \ln\left|\dfrac{x}{x + 1}\right|^6 + C$ **35.** $-\dfrac{6}{x - 3} + \ln\left|\dfrac{(x - 2)^2}{x - 3}\right| + C$

37. $\dfrac{3}{x - 1} + \ln\left|\dfrac{(x - 1)^5}{x^4}\right| + C$

39. $\dfrac{A}{x - 1} + \dfrac{B}{(x - 1)^2} + \dfrac{Cx + D}{x^2 + 1}$

41. $\dfrac{A}{x - 4} + \dfrac{B}{(x - 4)^2} + \dfrac{Cx + D}{x^2 + 3x + 4}$

43. $\ln|x + 1| + \tan^{-1}x + C$ **45.** $\ln(x + 1)^2 + \tan^{-1}(x + 1) + C$

47. $\ln\left|\dfrac{(x - 1)^2}{x^2 + 4x + 5}\right| + 14\tan^{-1}(x + 2) + C$

49. $\ln|(x - 1)^{1/5}(x^2 + 4)^{2/5}| + \dfrac{2}{5}\tan^{-1}\dfrac{x}{2} + C$

51. a. False   **b.** False   **c.** False   **d.** True   **53.** $\ln 6$

55. $4\sqrt{2} + \frac{1}{3}\ln\left(\frac{3 - 2\sqrt{2}}{3 + 2\sqrt{2}}\right)$ **57.** $\left(\dfrac{24}{5} - 2\ln 5\right)\pi$

59. $\frac{2}{3}\pi\ln 2$ **61.** $2\pi\left(3 + \ln\frac{2}{5}\right)$ **63.** $x - \ln(1 + e^x) + C$

65. $3x + \ln\dfrac{(x - 2)^{14}}{|x - 1|} + C$ **67.** $\ln\sqrt{2e^t + 1} + C$

69. $\frac{1}{2}(\sec\theta\tan\theta - \sec^2\theta + \ln|\sec\theta + \tan\theta|) + C$

71. $\ln \left| \dfrac{e^x - 1}{e^x + 2} \right|^{1/3} + C$ **73.** $-\dfrac{1}{2(e^{2x} + 1)} + C$

77. $\dfrac{4}{3}(x + 2)^{3/4} - 2(x + 2)^{1/2} + 4(x + 2)^{1/4}$
$\quad - \ln\left((x + 2)^{1/4} + 1\right)^4 + C$

79. $2\sqrt{x} - 3\sqrt[3]{x} + 6\sqrt[6]{x} - \ln\left(\sqrt[6]{x} + 1\right)^6 + C$

81. $\dfrac{4}{3}\sqrt{1 + \sqrt{x}}\left(\sqrt{x} - 2\right) + C$ **83.** $\ln\left(\dfrac{x^2}{x^2 + 1}\right) + \dfrac{1}{x^2 + 1} + C$

85. $\dfrac{1}{50}\left[\dfrac{5(3x + 4)}{x^2 + 2x + 2} + 11\tan^{-1}(1 + x) + \ln\left|\dfrac{(x - 1)^2}{x^2 + 2x + 2}\right|\right] + C$

87. $\ln\sqrt{\left|\dfrac{x - 1}{x + 1}\right|} + C$ **89.** $\tan x - \sec x + C$

91. $-\cot x - \csc x + C$

93. $\dfrac{\sqrt{2}}{2}\ln\left(\dfrac{\sqrt{2} + 1 + \tan(\theta/2)}{\sqrt{2} - 1 - \tan(\theta/2)}\right) + C$

95. a. Car A   **b.** Car C
c. $S_A(t) = 88t - 88\ln|t + 1|$;

$\quad S_B(t) = 88\left[t - \ln(t + 1)^2 - \dfrac{1}{t + 1} + 1\right]$;

$\quad S_C(t) = 88(t - \tan^{-1}t)$
d. Car C

97. Because $\dfrac{x^4(1 - x)^4}{1 + x^2} > 0$ on $(0, 1)$, $\displaystyle\int_0^1 \dfrac{x^4(1 - x^4)}{1 + x^2}\,dx > 0$;

$\quad$ thus, $\dfrac{22}{7} > \pi$.

Section 7.6 Exercises, pp. 546–548

1. Substitutions, integration by parts, partial fractions
3. The CAS may not include the constant of integration and it may use a trigonometric identity or other algebraic simplification.
5. $x\cos^{-1}x - \sqrt{1 - x^2} + C$ **7.** $\ln\left(x + \sqrt{16 + x^2}\right) + C$

9. $\dfrac{3}{4}(2u - 7\ln|7 + 2u|) + C$ **11.** $-\dfrac{1}{4}\cot 2x + C$

13. $\dfrac{1}{12}(2x - 1)\sqrt{4x + 1} + C$ **15.** $\dfrac{1}{3}\ln\left|x + \sqrt{x^2 - \left(\frac{10}{3}\right)^2}\right| + C$

17. $\dfrac{x}{16\sqrt{16 + 9x^2}} + C$ **19.** $-\dfrac{1}{12}\ln\left|\dfrac{12 + \sqrt{144 - x^2}}{x}\right| + C$

21. $2x + x\ln^2 x - 2x\ln x + C$

23. $\dfrac{x + 5}{2}\sqrt{x^2 + 10x} - \dfrac{25}{2}\ln\left|x + 5 + \sqrt{x^2 + 10x}\right| + C$

25. $\dfrac{1}{3}\tan^{-1}\left(\dfrac{x + 1}{3}\right) + C$ **27.** $\ln x - \dfrac{1}{10}\ln(x^{10} + 1) + C$

29. $2\ln\left(\sqrt{x - 6} + \sqrt{x}\right) + C$ **31.** $\ln\left(e^x + \sqrt{4 + e^{2x}}\right) + C$

33. $-\dfrac{1}{2}\ln\left|\dfrac{2 + \sin x}{\sin x}\right| + C$ **35.** $-\dfrac{\tan^{-1}x^3}{3x^3} + \ln\left|\dfrac{x}{(x^6 + 1)^{1/6}}\right| + C$

37. $\dfrac{2\ln^2 x - 1}{4}\sin^{-1}(\ln x) + \dfrac{\ln x\sqrt{1 - \ln^2 x}}{4} + C$

39. $4\sqrt{17} + \ln(4 + \sqrt{17})$ **41.** $\sqrt{5} - \sqrt{2} + \ln\left(\dfrac{2 + 2\sqrt{2}}{1 + \sqrt{5}}\right)$

43. $\dfrac{128\pi}{3}$ **45.** $\dfrac{\pi^2}{4}$ **47.** $\dfrac{(x - 3)\sqrt{3 + 2x}}{3} + C$

49. $\dfrac{1}{3}\tan 3x - x + C$

51. $\dfrac{(x^2 - a^2)^{3/2}}{3} - a^2\sqrt{x^2 - a^2} + a^3\cos^{-1}\dfrac{a}{x} + C$

53. $-\dfrac{x}{8}(2x^2 - 5a^2)\sqrt{a^2 - x^2} + \dfrac{3a^4}{8}\sin^{-1}\dfrac{x}{a} + C$

55. $\dfrac{\left(\frac{4}{5}\right)^9 - \left(\frac{2}{3}\right)^9}{9}$ **57.** $\dfrac{1540 + 243\ln 3}{8}$ **59.** $\dfrac{\pi}{4}$

61. $2 - \dfrac{\pi^2}{12} - \ln 4$ **63. a.** True   **b.** True

67. $\dfrac{1}{8}e^{2x}(4x^3 - 6x^2 + 6x - 3) + C$

69. $\dfrac{\tan^3 3y}{9} - \dfrac{\tan 3y}{3} + y + C$

71. $\dfrac{1}{16}\left((8x^2 - 1)\sin^{-1}2x + 2x\sqrt{1 - 4x^2}\right) + C$

73. $-\dfrac{\tan^{-1}x}{x} + \ln\left(\dfrac{|x|}{\sqrt{x^2 + 1}}\right) + C$ **75. b.** $\dfrac{\pi}{8}\ln 2$

77. a.

θ_0	T
0.10	6.27927
0.20	6.26762
0.30	6.24854
0.40	6.22253
0.50	6.19021
0.60	6.15236
0.70	6.10979
0.80	6.06338
0.90	6.01399
1.00	5.96247

b. All are within 10%.

79. $\dfrac{1}{a^2}(ax - b\ln|b + ax|) + C$

81. $\dfrac{1}{a^2}\left[\dfrac{(ax + b)^{n+2}}{n + 2} - \dfrac{b(ax + b)^{n+1}}{n + 1}\right] + C$

83. b. $\dfrac{63\pi}{512}$ **c.** Decrease

Section 7.7 Exercises, pp. 556–558

1. $\dfrac{1}{2}$ **3.** The Trapezoid Rule approximates areas under curves using trapezoids.   **5.** $-1, 1, 3, 5, 7, 9$ **7.** 1.59×10^{-3}; 5.04×10^{-4}
9. 1.72×10^{-3}; 6.32×10^{-4} **11.** 576; 640; 656
13. 0.643950551   **15.** 704; 672; 664   **17.** 0.622
19. $M(25) = 0.63703884$, $T(25) = 0.63578179$; 6.58×10^{-4}, 1.32×10^{-3}
21.

n	$M(n)$	$T(n)$	Abs. Error $M(n)$	Abs. Error $T(n)$
4	99	102	1.00	2.00
8	99.75	100.5	0.250	0.500
16	99.9375	100.125	0.0625	0.125
32	99.984375	100.03125	0.0156	0.0313

23.

n	$M(n)$	$T(n)$	Abs. Error $M(n)$	Abs. Error $T(n)$
4	1.50968181	1.48067370	9.68×10^{-3}	1.93×10^{-2}
8	1.50241228	1.49517776	2.41×10^{-3}	4.82×10^{-3}
16	1.50060256	1.49879502	6.03×10^{-4}	1.20×10^{-3}
32	1.50015061	1.49969879	1.51×10^{-4}	3.01×10^{-4}

25.

n	$M(n)$	$T(n)$	Abs. Error $M(n)$	Abs. Error $T(n)$
4	-1.96×10^{-16}	0	1.96×10^{-16}	0
8	7.63×10^{-17}	-1.41×10^{-16}	7.63×10^{-17}	1.42×10^{-16}
16	1.61×10^{-16}	1.09×10^{-17}	1.61×10^{-16}	1.09×10^{-17}
32	6.27×10^{-17}	-4.77×10^{-17}	6.27×10^{-17}	4.77×10^{-17}

27. Simpson's Rule: $\dfrac{164}{3} \approx 54.7$ **29.** $\dfrac{421}{12} \approx 35.1$

31. a. $T(25) = 3.19623162$
$T(50) = 3.19495398$
b. $S(50) = 3.19452809$
c. $e_T(50) = 4.26 \times 10^{-4}$
$e_S(50) = 4.05 \times 10^{-8}$

33. a. $T(50) = 1.00008509$
$T(100) = 1.00002127$
b. $S(100) = 1.00000000$
c. $e_T(100) = 2.13 \times 10^{-5}$
$e_S(100) = 4.57 \times 10^{-9}$

35.

n	$T(n)$	$S(n)$	Error $T(n)$	Error $S(n)$
4	1820.0000	—	284	—
8	1607.7500	1537.0000	71.8	1
16	1553.9844	1536.0625	18.0	6.25×10^{-2}
32	1540.4990	1536.0039	4.50	3.90×10^{-3}

37.

n	$T(n)$	$S(n)$	Error $T(n)$	Error $S(n)$
4	0.46911538	—	5.25×10^{-2}	—
8	0.50826998	0.52132152	1.33×10^{-2}	2.85×10^{-4}
16	0.51825968	0.52158957	3.35×10^{-3}	1.74×10^{-5}
32	0.52076933	0.52160588	8.38×10^{-4}	1.08×10^{-6}

39. a. True **b.** False **c.** True

41.

n	$M(n)$	$T(n)$	Abs. Error $M(n)$	Abs. Error $T(n)$
4	0.40635058	0.40634782	1.38×10^{-6}	1.38×10^{-6}
8	0.40634920	0.40634920	7.6×10^{-10}	7.62×10^{-10}
16	0.40634920	0.40634920	6.55×10^{-13}	6.56×10^{-13}
32	0.40634920	0.40634920	8.88×10^{-16}	7.77×10^{-16}

43.

n	$M(n)$	$T(n)$	Abs. Error $M(n)$	Abs. Error $T(n)$
4	4.72531819	4.72507878	0.00012	0.00012
8	4.72519850	4.72519849	9.12×10^{-9}	9.12×10^{-9}
16	4.72519850	4.72519850	0.	8.88×10^{-16}
32	4.72519850	4.72519850	0.	8.88×10^{-16}

49. Approximations will vary; exact value is 38.753792 . . . .
51. Approximations will vary; exact value is 68.26894921 . . . .
53. a. Approximately 1.6×10^{11} barrels
b. Approximately 6.8×10^{10} barrels
55. a. $T(40) = 0.874799972 \ldots$
b. $f''(x) = e^x \cos e^x - e^{2x} \sin e^x$ **d.** $E_T \le \dfrac{1}{3200}$
59. Overestimate

Section 7.8 Exercises, pp. 567–570

1. The interval of integration is infinite or the integrand is unbounded on the interval of integration.

3. $\displaystyle\int_0^1 \frac{1}{\sqrt{x}}\,dx = \lim_{b \to 0^+} \int_b^1 \frac{1}{\sqrt{x}}\,dx$ **5.** 1 **7.** $\dfrac{1}{e}$ **9.** Diverges **11.** $\dfrac{1}{2}$

13. $\dfrac{1}{a}$ **15.** $\dfrac{1}{(p-1)\,2^{p-1}}$ **17.** $\dfrac{1}{2}$ **19.** $\dfrac{1}{\pi}$ **21.** $\dfrac{\pi}{4}$ **23.** $\ln 2$

25. Diverges **27.** Diverges **29.** $\dfrac{\pi}{3}$ **31.** $3\pi/2$ **33.** $\pi/(\ln 2)$

35. 6 **37.** 2 **39.** Diverges **41.** $2(e-1)$ **43.** Diverges
45. $4 \cdot 10^{3/4}/3$ **47.** -2 **49.** π **51.** 2π **53.** $\dfrac{72 \cdot 2^{1/3}\,\pi}{5}$

55. 48 **57.** 0.76 **59.** 10 mi
61. a. True **b.** False **c.** False **d.** True **e.** True

63. a. 2 **b.** 0 **65.** $\displaystyle\int_0^{\infty} e^{-x^2}\,dx \approx 0.886227$ **67.** $-\dfrac{1}{4}$

69. $\displaystyle\int_0^{\infty} xe^{-x^2}\,dx = \tfrac{1}{2}$; $\displaystyle\int_0^{\infty} x^2 e^{-x^2}\,dx = \sqrt{\pi}/4 \approx 0.443$

71. $1/b - 1/a$ **73. a.** $A(a,b) = \dfrac{e^{-ab}}{a}$, for $a > 0$

b. $b = g(a) = -\dfrac{1}{a}\ln 2a$ **c.** $b^* = -2/e$

75. a. $p < \tfrac{1}{2}$ **b.** $p < 2$ **81.** \$41,666.67 **85.** 20,000 hr
87. a. $6.28 \times 10^7 m$ J **b.** 11.2 km/s **c.** ≤ 9 mm
89. a.

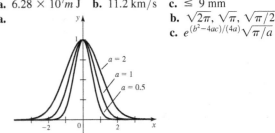

b. $\sqrt{2\pi},\ \sqrt{\pi},\ \sqrt{\pi/2}$
c. $e^{(b^2-4ac)/(4a)}\sqrt{\pi/a}$

95. a. π **b.** $\pi/(4e^2)$
97. $p > 1$

Chapter 7 Review Exercises, pp. 571–573

1. a. True **b.** False **c.** False **d.** True **e.** False
3. $2(x-8)\sqrt{x+4} + C$ **5.** $\pi/4$
7. $\sqrt{t-1} - \tan^{-1}\sqrt{t-1} + C$ **9.** $\dfrac{1}{3}\sqrt{x+2}\,(x-4) + C$

11. $x\cosh x - \sinh x + C$ **13.** $4/105$ **15.** $\dfrac{1}{5}\tan^5 t + C$
17. $\tfrac{1}{5}\sec^5\theta - \tfrac{1}{3}\sec^3\theta + C$ **19.** $\sqrt{3} - 1 - \pi/12$
21. $\tfrac{1}{3}(x^2-8)\sqrt{x^2+4} + C$ **23.** $2\ln|x| + 3\tan^{-1}(x+1) + C$

25. $\dfrac{1}{x + 1} + \ln |(x + 1)(x^2 + 4)| + C$

27. $\dfrac{\sqrt{6}}{3} \tan^{-1}\left(\sqrt{\dfrac{2x - 3}{3}}\right) + C$

29. $\frac{1}{4} \sec^3 x \tan x + \frac{3}{8} \sec x \tan x + \frac{3}{8} \ln |\sec x + \tan x| + C$

31. 1.196288 **33. a.** $T(6) = 9.125, M(6) = 8.9375$
b. $T(12) = 9.03125, M(12) = 8.984375$
35. 1 **37.** $\pi/2$ **39.** $-\cot \theta - \csc \theta + C$

41. $\dfrac{e^x}{2} (\sin x - \cos x) + C$ **43.** $\theta/2 + (1/16) \sin (8\theta) + C$

45. $(\sec^5 z)/5 + C$ **47.** $(256 - 147\sqrt{3})/480$

49. $\sin^{-1} (x/2) + C$ **51.** $-\dfrac{1}{9y} \sqrt{9 - y^2} + C$

53. $\pi/9$ **55.** $-\operatorname{sech} x + C$ **57.** $\pi/3$

59. $\dfrac{1}{8} \ln \left|\dfrac{x - 5}{x + 3}\right| + C$ **61.** $\dfrac{\ln 2}{4} + \dfrac{\pi}{8}$

63. $\dfrac{1}{3} \ln \left|\dfrac{x - 2}{x + 1}\right| + C$ **65.** $2(x - 2 \ln |x + 2|) + C$

67. $e^{2t}/2\sqrt{1 + e^{4t}} + C$ **69.** $\pi(e - 2)$ **71.** $\dfrac{\pi}{2}(e^2 - 3)$

73. y-axis   **75. a.** 1.603 **b.** 1.870 **c.** $b \ln b - b = a \ln a - a$
d. Decreasing   **77.** $20/(3\pi)$ **79.** 1901 cars

81. a. $I(p) = \dfrac{1}{(p - 1)^2} (1 - pe^{1-p}) \text{ if } p \neq 1, I(1) = \dfrac{1}{2}$

b. $0, \infty$ **c.** $I(0) = 1$ **83.** 0.4054651 **85.** $n = 2$
87. a. $V_1(a) = \pi(a \ln^2 a - 2a \ln a + 2(a - 1))$

b. $V_2(a) = \dfrac{\pi}{2} (2a^2 \ln a - a^2 + 1)$

c. $V_2(a) > V_1(a)$ for all $a > 1$

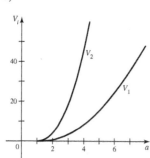

89. $a = \ln 2/(2b)$

CHAPTER 8

Section 8.1 Exercises, pp. 580–582

1. 2 **3.** 2 **5.** Yes   **15.** $y = 3t - \dfrac{e^{-2t}}{2} + C$

17. $y = 2 \ln |\sec 2x| - 3 \sin x + C$
19. $y = 2t^6 + 6t^{-1} - 2t^2 + C_1 t + C_2$
21. $u = \dfrac{x^{11}}{2} + \dfrac{x^9}{2} - \dfrac{x^7}{2} + \dfrac{5}{x} + C_1 x + C_2$

23. $y = e^t + t + 3$ **25.** $y = x^3 + x^{-3} - 2$ **27.** $y = -t^5 + 2t^3 + 1$
29. a. $s = -4.9t^2 + 29.4t + 30, v = -9.8t + 29.4$ **b.** Highest point
of 74.1 m is reached at $t = 3$ s   **31.** The amount of resource is
increasing for $H < 75$, and the amount of the resource is constant
if $H = 75$. Approximately 28 time units.

33. $h = (1.4 - 0.2t\sqrt{2g})^2 \approx (1.4 - 0.44t)^2$; tank is empty
after approximately 3.16 s.

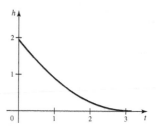

35. a. False   **b.** False   **c.** True

37. $u = \ln (x^2 + 4) - \tan^{-1}\dfrac{x}{2} + C$ **39.** $y = \sin^{-1} x + C_1 x + C_2$

41. $u = \dfrac{1}{4} \tan^{-1}\dfrac{x}{4} - 4x + 2$ **43.** $y = e^t(t - 2) + 2(t + 1)$

51. c. $y = C_1 \sin kt + C_2 \cos kt$ **53. b.** $C = \dfrac{K - 50}{50}$

c.

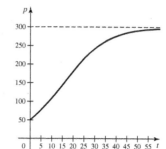

d. 300

55. c. The decay rate is greater for the $n = 1$ model.

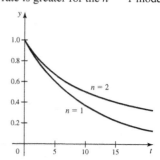

Section 8.2 Exercises, pp. 588–591

1. At selected points (t_0, y_0) in the region of interest draw a short line
segment with slope $f(t_0, y_0)$.   **3.** $y(3.1) \approx 1.6$
5.

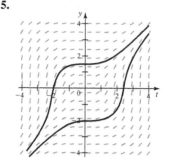

7. a. D **b.** B **c.** A **d.** C **9.** An initial condition of $y(0) = -1$ leads to a constant solution. For any other initial condition, the solutions are increasing over time.

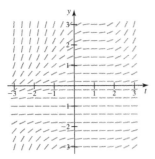

11. An initial condition of $y(0) = 1$ leads to a constant solution. Initial conditions $y(0) = A$ lead to solutions that are increasing over time if $A > 1$.

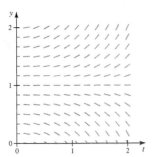

13.

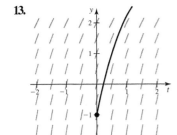

15.

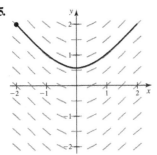

17. a. $y = 1, y = -1$ **b.** Solutions are increasing for $|y| > 1$; decreasing for $|y| < 1$. **c.** Initial conditions $y(0) = A$ lead to increasing solutions if $|A| > 1$ and decreasing solutions if $|A| < 1$.
d.

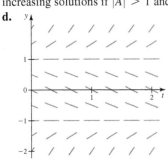

19. a. $y = \pi/2, y = -\pi/2$ **b.** Solutions are increasing for $|y| < \pi/2$, decreasing for $|y| > \pi/2$. **c.** Initial conditions

$y(0) = A$ lead to increasing solutions if $|A| < \pi/2$ and decreasing solutions if $\pi/2 < |A| < \pi$. **d.**

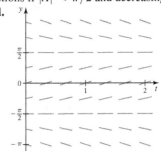

21. The equilibrium solutions are $P = 0$ and $P = 500$.

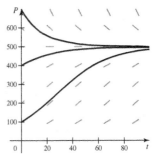

23. The equilibrium solutions are $P = 0$ and $P = 3200$.

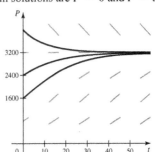

25. $y(0.5) \approx u_1 = 4; y(1) \approx u_2 = 8$
27. $y(0.1) \approx u_1 = 1.1; y(0.2) \approx u_2 = 1.19$
29. a.

Δt	approximation to $y(0.2)$	approximation to $y(0.4)$
0.20000	0.80000	0.64000
0.10000	0.81000	0.65610
0.05000	0.81451	0.66342
0.02500	0.81665	0.66692

b.

Δt	errors for $y(0.2)$	errors for $y(0.4)$
0.20000	0.01873	0.03032
0.10000	0.00873	0.01422
0.05000	0.00422	0.00690
0.02500	0.00208	0.00340

c. Time step $\Delta t = 0.025$; smaller time steps generally produce more accurate results. **d.** Halving the time steps results in approximately halving the error.

31. a.

Δt	approximation to $y(0.2)$	approximation to $y(0.4)$
0.20000	3.20000	3.36000
0.10000	3.19000	3.34390
0.05000	3.18549	3.33658
0.02500	3.18335	3.33308

b.

Δt	errors for $y(0.2)$	errors for $y(0.4)$
0.20000	0.01873	0.03032
0.10000	0.00873	0.01422
0.05000	0.00422	0.00690
0.02500	0.00208	0.00340

c. Time step $\Delta t = 0.025$; smaller time steps generally produce more accurate results.   **d.** Halving the time steps results in approximately halving the error.   **33. a.** $y(2) \approx 0.00604662$ **b.** 0.012269
c. $y(2) \approx 0.0115292$ **d.** Error in part (c) is approximately half of the error in part (b).   **35. a.** $y(4) \approx 3.05765$ **b.** 0.0339321
c. $y(4) \approx 3.0739$ **d.** Error in part (c) is approximately half of the error in part (b).   **37. a.** True   **b.** False   **39. a.** $y = 3$
b, c.

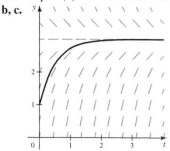

41. a. $y = 0$ and $y = 3$ **b, c.**

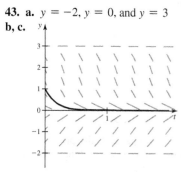

43. a. $y = -2$, $y = 0$, and $y = 3$
b, c.

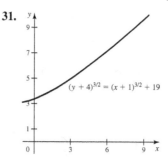

45. a. $\Delta t = \dfrac{b - a}{N}$ **b.** $u_1 = A + f(a, A)\dfrac{b - a}{N}$

c. $u_{k+1} = u_k + f(t_k, u_k)\dfrac{b - a}{N}$, where $u_0 = A$ and

$t_k = a + k(b - a)/N$, for $k = 0, 1, 2, \ldots, N - 1$.

47. a.

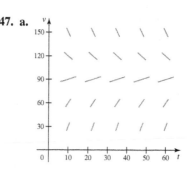

b. Increasing for $A < 98$ and decreasing for $A > 98$ **c.** $v(t) = 98$

Section 8.3 Exercises, pp. 595–598

1. A first-order separable differential equation has the form
$g(y)\, y'(t) = h(t)$, where the factor $g(y)$ is a function of y and
$h(t)$ is a function of t.   **3.** No   **5.** $y = \dfrac{t^4}{4} + C$

7. $y = \pm\sqrt{2t^3 + C}$ **9.** $y = -2\ln\left(\dfrac{1}{2}\cos t + C\right)$

11. $y = \dfrac{x}{1 + Cx}$ **13.** $y = \pm\dfrac{1}{\sqrt{C - \cos t}}$ **15.** $u = \ln\left(\dfrac{e^{2x}}{2} + C\right)$

17. $y = \ln t + 2$ **19.** $y = \sqrt{t^3 + 81}$ **21.** Not separable
23. $y = \sqrt{e^t - 1}$ **25.** $y = \ln(e^x + 2)$
27.

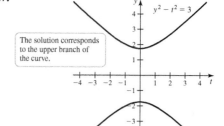

The solution corresponds to the upper branch of the curve.

$y^2 - t^2 = 3$

29.

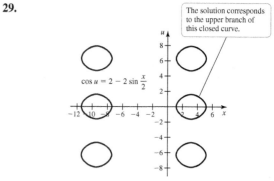

$\cos u = 2 - 2\sin\dfrac{x}{2}$

The solution corresponds to the upper branch of this closed curve.

31.

$(y + 4)^{3/2} = (x + 1)^{3/2} + 19$

33. a.

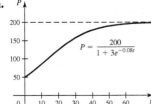

b. 200

$P = \dfrac{200}{1 + 3e^{-0.08t}}$

35. a. True **b.** False **c.** True **37.** $y = \dfrac{t^3}{2 - t^3}$

39. $y = \dfrac{3}{2}(-2 + 2^{1/5}(6 + 5t)^{1/5})$

41. a. $y = -2\ln\left(\dfrac{x^2}{4} + \cos(x^2) + C\right)$ **b.** $C = 0, 1, 1 - \dfrac{\pi}{8}$

c.

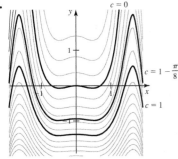

43. $y = kx$ **45. b.** $\sqrt{gm/k}$ **c.** $v = \sqrt{\dfrac{g}{a}} \dfrac{Ce^{2\sqrt{ag}\,t} - 1}{Ce^{2\sqrt{ag}\,t} + 1}$,

where $a = \dfrac{k}{m}$

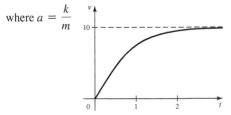

47. a. $h = (\sqrt{H} - kt)^2$ **b.** $h = (\sqrt{0.5} - 0.1t)^2$

c. ≈ 7.07 s

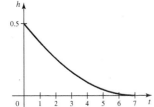

49. a.

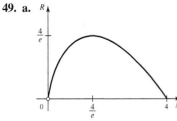

R is positive if $0 < M < 4$; R has a maximum value when $M = \dfrac{4}{e}$; $\displaystyle\lim_{M \to 0} R(M) = 0$.

b. $M(t) = 4^{1 - e^{-t}}$; the tumor grows quickly at first and then the rate of growth slows down; the limiting size of the tumor is 4.

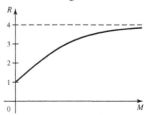

c. K is the limiting size of the tumor. **51. a.** $y = \dfrac{1}{1 - t}$

b. $y = \dfrac{1}{\sqrt{2}\sqrt{1 - t}}$ **c.** $y = \dfrac{1}{(n(1 - t))^{1/n}}$; as $t \to 1^-$, $y \to \infty$

53. a. $y = \pm\sqrt{t^2 + e^t + C}$

b. $y = \sqrt{t^2 + e^t - 1/e}$; $y = \sqrt{t^2 + e^t + 3 - 1/e}$

c. As t increases, y increases without bound.

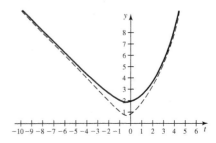

d. $y = -\sqrt{t^2 + e^t - 1/e}$; $y = -\sqrt{t^2 + e^t + 3 - 1/e}$

e. As t increases, y decreases without bound.

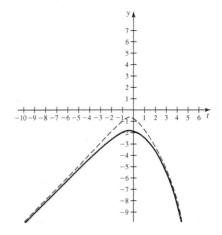

Section 8.4 Exercises, pp. 603–605

1. $y = 17e^{-10t} - 13$ **3.** $y = Ce^{-4t} + \dfrac{3}{2}$ **5.** $y = Ce^{3t} + \dfrac{4}{3}$

7. $y = Ce^{-2x} - 2$ **9.** $u = Ce^{-12t} + \dfrac{5}{4}$ **11.** $y = 7e^{3t} + 2$

13. $y = 4(e^{2t} - 1)$ **15.** $y = 4(2e^{3t-3} - 1)$

17. $y = \frac{3}{2}$; unstable

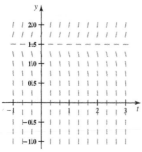

19. $y = -3$; stable

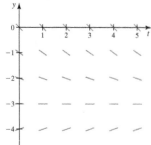

21. $u = -3$; stable

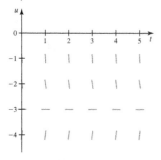

23. $B = 100{,}000 - 50{,}000\,e^{0.005t}$; reaches a balance of zero after approximately 139 months

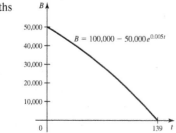

25. $B = 200{,}000 - 100{,}000\,e^{0.0075t}$; reaches a balance of zero after approximately 93 months

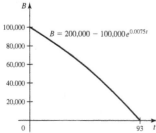

27. ≈ 32 min   **29.** ≈ 14 min   **31. a.** False   **b.** True   **c.** False

d. False   **33.** $y = 1 + \dfrac{t}{2} + \dfrac{5}{2t}$ **35.** $y = \dfrac{1}{2}e^{3t} + \dfrac{7}{2}e^{t}$

37. a. $B = 20{,}000 + 20{,}000\,e^{0.03t}$; the unpaid balance is growing because the monthly payment of \$600 is less than the interest on the unpaid balance.   **b.** \$20,000   **c.** $\dfrac{m}{r}$

39. a.

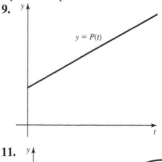

b. 150   **c.** ≈ 115.1 hr

41. a. $h = 16\ \text{yr}^{-1}$ **b.** 25,000   **45.** $y(t) = \dfrac{6}{t}$

47. $y = \dfrac{9t^5 + 20t^3 + 15t + 76}{15(t^2 + 1)}$

Section 8.5 Exercises, pp. 612–615

1. The growth rate function specifies the rate of growth of the population. The population is increasing when the growth rate function is positive, and the population is decreasing when the growth rate function is negative.   **3.** If the growth rate function is positive (it does not matter if it is increasing or decreasing), then the population is increasing.   **5.** It is a linear, first-order differential equation.   **7.** The solution curves in the FH-plane are closed curves that circulate around the equilibrium point.

9.

11.

13.

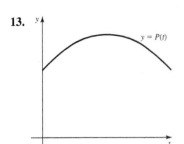

15. $P' = 0.2 P\left(1 - \dfrac{P}{300}\right); P = \dfrac{300}{5e^{-0.2t} + 1}$

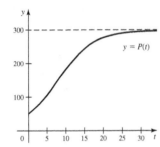

17. $P = \dfrac{2000}{9e^{-\ln(27/7)t} + 1}$

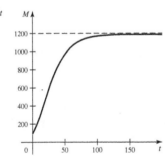

19. $M = K\left(\dfrac{M_0}{K}\right)^{e^{-rt}}$

21. $M = 1200 \cdot 0.075e^{0.05t}$

23. a. $m'(t) = -0.008t + 80, m(0) = 0$
b. $m = e^{-0.008t}(10,000\, e^{0.008t} - 10,000)$

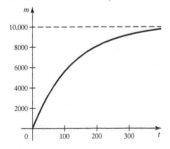

25. a. $m'(t) = -0.005\, t + 100, m(0) = 80,000$
b. $m = 60,000\, e^{-0.005t} + 20,000$

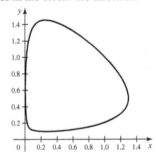

27. a. x is the predator population; y is the prey population.
b. $x' = 0$ on the lines $x = 0$ and $y = \frac{1}{2}$; $y' = 0$ on the lines $y = 0$ and $x = \frac{1}{4}$.   **c.** $(0,0), (\frac{1}{4}, \frac{1}{2})$
d. $x' > 0$ and $y' > 0$ for $0 < x < \frac{1}{4}, y > \frac{1}{2}$
  $x' > 0$ and $y' < 0$ for $x > \frac{1}{4}, y > \frac{1}{2}$
  $x' < 0$ and $y' < 0$ for $x > \frac{1}{4}, 0 < y < \frac{1}{2}$
  $x' < 0$ and $y' > 0$ for $0 < x < \frac{1}{4}, 0 < y < \frac{1}{2}$
e. Solution evolves in the clockwise direction.

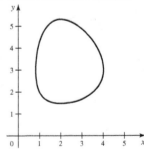

29. a. x is the predator population; y is the prey population.
b. $x' = 0$ on the lines $x = 0$ and $y = 3$; $y' = 0$ on the lines $y = 0$ and $x = 2$.   **c.** $(0,0), (2, 3)$
d. $x' > 0$ and $y' > 0$ for $0 < x < 2, y > 3$
  $x' > 0$ and $y' < 0$ for $x > 2, y > 3$
  $x' < 0$ and $y' < 0$ for $x > 2, 0 < y < 3$
  $x' < 0$ and $y' > 0$ for $0 < x < 2, 0 < y < 3$
e. Solution evolves in the clockwise direction.

31. a. True   **b.** True   **c.** True   **35. c.** $\lim\limits_{t \to \infty} m(t) = C_i V$, which is the amount of substance in the tank when the tank is filled with the inflow solution.   **d.** Increasing R increases the rate at which the solution in the tank reaches the steady state concentration.

37. a. $I = \dfrac{V}{R}e^{-t/(RC)}$ **b.** $Q = VC(1 - e^{-t/(RC)})$

39. a. $y'(x) = \dfrac{y(c - dx)}{x(-a + by)}$ **c.**

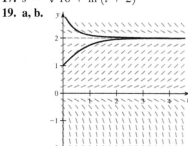

Chapter 8 Review Exercises, pp. 615–616

1. a. False   **b.** False   **c.** True   **d.** True   **e.** False
3. $y = Ce^{-2t} + 3$ **5.** $y = Ce^{t^2}$ **7.** $y = Ce^{\tan^{-1}t}$
9. $y = \tan(t^2 + t + C)$ **11.** $y = \sin t + t^2 + 1$
13. $Q = 8(1 - e^{t-1})$ **15.** $u = (3 + t^{2/3})^{3/2}$
17. $s = \sqrt{16 + \ln(t + 2)}$
19. a, b.

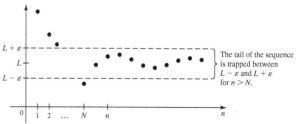

c. $0 < A < 2$
d. $A > 2$ or $A < 0$
e. $y = 0$ and $y = 2$

21. a. 1.05, 1.09762   **b.** 1.04939, 1.09651
c. 0.00217, 0.00106; the error in part (b) is smaller.
23. $y = -3$ (unstable), $y = 0$ (stable), $y = 5$ (unstable)
25. $y = -1$ (unstable), $y = 0$ (stable), $y = 2$ (unstable)
27. a. 0.0713   **b.** $P = \dfrac{1600}{79\,e^{-0.0713t} + 1}$
c. Approximately 61 hours
29. a. $m = 2000(1 - e^{-0.005t})$ **b.** 2000 g
c. Approximately 599 minutes
31. a. x represents the predator.   **b.** $x'(t) = 0$ when $x = 0$ and
$y = 2$. $y'(t) = 0$ when $y = 0$ and $x = 5$.   **c.** $(0, 0)$ and $(5, 2)$
d. $x' > 0, y' > 0$ when $0 < x < 5$ and $y > 2$; $x' > 0, y' < 0$
when $x > 5$ and $y > 2$; $x' < 0, y' < 0$ when $x > 5$ and
$0 < y < 2$; $x' < 0, y' > 0$ when $0 < x < 5$ and $0 < y < 2$
e. Clockwise direction

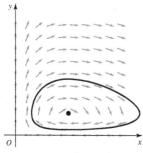

33. a. $p_1 = 3, p_2 = -4$ **b.** $y(t) = t^3 - t^{-4}$

Section 9.1 Exercises, pp. 625–627

1. A sequence is an ordered list of numbers. Example: $1, \frac{1}{3}, \frac{1}{9}, \frac{1}{27}, \dots$
3. 1, 1, 2, 6, 24   **5.** Given a sequence $\{a_1, a_2, \dots\}$, an infinite series
is the sum $a_1 + a_2 + a_3 + \dots$. Example: $\sum\limits_{k=1}^{\infty} \dfrac{1}{k^2}$ **7.** 1, 5, 14, 30
9. $\frac{1}{10}, \frac{1}{100}, \frac{1}{1000}, \frac{1}{10,000}$ **11.** $-\frac{1}{2}, \frac{1}{4}, -\frac{1}{8}, \frac{1}{16}$ **13.** $\frac{4}{3}, \frac{8}{5}, \frac{16}{9}, \frac{32}{17}$
15. 2, 1, 0, 1   **17.** 2, 4, 8, 16   **19.** 10, 18, 42, 114   **21.** 0, 2, 15, 679
23. a. $1/32, 1/64$ **b.** $a_1 = 1, a_{n+1} = \dfrac{1}{2}a_n$, for $n \geq 1$
c. $a_n = \dfrac{1}{2^{n-1}}$, for $n \geq 1$ **25. a.** $-5, 5$ **b.** $a_1 = -5, a_{n+1} = -a_n$,
for $n \geq 1$ **c.** $a_n = (-1)^n \cdot 5$, for $n \geq 1$ **27. a.** 32, 64
b. $a_1 = 1, a_{n+1} = 2a_n$, for $n \geq 1$ **c.** $a_n = 2^{n-1}$, for $n \geq 1$
29. a. 243, 729   **b.** $a_1 = 1, a_{n+1} = 3a_n$, for $n \geq 1$ **c.** $a_n = 3^{n-1}$,
for $n \geq 1$ **31.** 9, 99, 999, 9999; diverges   **33.** $\frac{1}{10}, \frac{1}{100}, \frac{1}{1000}, \frac{1}{10,000}$;
converges to 0   **35.** $-1, \frac{1}{2}, -\frac{1}{3}, \frac{1}{4}$; converges to 0   **37.** 2, 2, 2, 2;
converges to 2   **39.** 100, 100, 100, 100; converges to 100   **41.** 0
43. Diverges   **45.** 1   **47. a.** $\frac{5}{2}, \frac{9}{4}, \frac{17}{8}, \frac{33}{16}$ **b.** 2   **49.** 4   **51.** Diverges
53. 4   **55. a.** $20, 10, 5, \frac{5}{2}$ **b.** $h_n = 20\left(\frac{1}{2}\right)^n$, for $n \geq 0$
57. a. $30, \frac{15}{2}, \frac{15}{8}, \frac{15}{32}$ **b.** $h_n = 30\left(\frac{1}{4}\right)^n$, for $n \geq 0$ **59.** $S_1 = 0.3$,
$S_2 = 0.33, S_3 = 0.333, S_4 = 0.3333; \frac{1}{3}$ **61.** $S_1 = 4, S_2 = 4.9$,
$S_3 = 4.99, S_4 = 4.999$; 5   **63. a.** $\frac{2}{3}, \frac{4}{5}, \frac{6}{7}, \frac{8}{9}$ **b.** $S_n = \dfrac{2n}{2n + 1}$
c. $\lim\limits_{n\to\infty} S_n = 1$ **65. a.** $\frac{1}{3}, \frac{2}{5}, \frac{3}{7}, \frac{4}{9}$ **b.** $S_n = \dfrac{n}{2n + 1}$ **c.** $\lim\limits_{n\to\infty} S_n = \frac{1}{2}$
67. a. True **b.** False **c.** True   **69. a.** 40, 70, 92.5, 109.375 **b.** 160
71. a. 0.9, 0.99, 0.999, 0.9999   **b.** 1   **73. a.** $\frac{1}{3}, \frac{4}{9}, \frac{13}{27}, \frac{40}{81}$
b. $\frac{1}{2}$ **75. a.** $-1, 0, -1, 0$ **b.** Diverges   **77. a.** 0.3, 0.33, 0.333,
0.3333   **b.** $\frac{1}{3}$ **79. a.** $20, 10, 5, \frac{5}{2}, \frac{5}{4}$ **b.** $M_n = 20\left(\frac{1}{2}\right)^n$, for $n \geq 0$
c. $M_0 = 20, M_{n+1} = \frac{1}{2}M_n$, for $n \geq 0$ **d.** $\lim\limits_{n\to\infty} a_n = 0$ **81. a.** 200,
190, 180.5, 171.475, 162.90125 **b.** $d_n = 200(0.95)^n$, for $n \geq 0$
c. $d_0 = 200, d_{n+1} = (0.95)d_n$, for $n \geq 0$ **d.** $\lim\limits_{n\to\infty} d_n = 0$.

Section 9.2 Exercises, pp. 637–640

1. $a_n = \dfrac{1}{n}$, $n \geq 1$ **3.** $a_n = \dfrac{n}{n + 1}$, $n \geq 1$ **5.** Converges for
$-1 < r \leq 1$, diverges otherwise   **7.** A sequence $\{a_n\}_{n=1}^{\infty}$ converges
to L if, given any $\varepsilon > 0$, there exists a positive integer N such that
whenever $n > N$, $|a_n - L| < \varepsilon$.

9. 0   **11.** 3/2   **13.** 3   **15.** $\pi/2$ **17.** 0   **19.** e^2 **21.** $e^{1/4}$ **23.** 0
25. 1   **27.** 0   **29.** 0   **31.** 6   **33.** Limit does not exist.
35. Limit doesn't exist.   **37.** 0   **39.** 2   **41.** 0   **43.** The limit
doesn't exist.   **45.** Converges monotonically; 0   **47.** Converges
by oscillation; 0   **49.** Diverges monotonically   **51.** Diverges by
oscillation   **53.** 0   **55.** 0   **57.** 0   **59. a.** $d_{n+1} = \frac{1}{2}d_n + 80$, $n \geq 1$
b. 160 mg   **61. a.** $0, \$100, \$200.75, \$302.26, \$404.53$

b. $B_{n+1} = 1.0075 B_n + 100$, $n \geq 0$ **c.** During the 43rd month
63. 0 **65.** Diverges **67.** 0 **69.** Given a tolerance $\varepsilon > 0$, look beyond a_N where $N > 1/\varepsilon$. **71.** Given a tolerance $\varepsilon > 0$, look beyond a_N where $N > \frac{1}{4}\sqrt{3/\varepsilon}$, provided $\varepsilon < \frac{3}{4}$ **73.** Given a tolerance $\varepsilon > 0$, look beyond a_N where $N > c/(\varepsilon b^2)$. **75. a.** True **b.** False **c.** True **d.** True **e.** False **f.** True **77.** $\{n^2 + 2n - 17\}$
79. 0 **81.** 1 **83.** 1 **85.** Diverges **87.** $1/2$ **89.** 0 **91.** $n = 4$, $n = 6, n = 25$ **93. a.** $\{h_n\} = \{(200 + 5n)(0.65 - 0.01n) - 0.45n\}$
b. The profit is maximized after 8 days. **95.** 0.607
97. b. 1, 1.4142, 1.5538, 1.5981, 1.6119 **c.** Limit ≈ 1.618

e. $\dfrac{1 + \sqrt{1 + 4p}}{2}$ **99. b.** 1, 2, 1.5, 1.6667, 1.6 **c.** Limit ≈ 1.618

e. $\dfrac{a + \sqrt{a^2 + 4b}}{2}$ **101. a.** 1, 1, 2, 3, 5, 8, 13, 21, 34, 55 **b.** No

Section 9.3 Exercises, pp. 644–647

1. Consecutive terms differ by a constant ratio. Example:
$2 + 1 + \frac{1}{2} + \frac{1}{4} + \cdots$ **3.** The constant r in the series $\sum\limits_{k=0}^{\infty} ar^k$.

5. No **7.** 9841 **9.** ≈ 1.1905 **11.** ≈ 0.5392 **13.** $\dfrac{1 - \pi^7}{1 - \pi}$ **15.** 1

17. $\frac{1093}{2916}$ **19.** $\frac{4}{3}$ **21.** 10 **23.** Diverges **25.** $\dfrac{1}{e^2 - 1}$ **27.** $\dfrac{1}{7}$

29. $\dfrac{1}{500}$ **31.** $\dfrac{\pi}{\pi - e}$ **33.** $\frac{312,500}{19}$ **35.** $\dfrac{10}{19}$ **37.** $\dfrac{3\pi}{\pi + 1}$ **39.** $\dfrac{9}{460}$

41. a. $0.\overline{3} = \sum\limits_{k=1}^{\infty} 3(0.1)^k$ **b.** $\frac{1}{3}$ **43. a.** $0.\overline{1} = \sum\limits_{k=1}^{\infty}(0.1)^k$ **b.** $\frac{1}{9}$

45. a. $0.\overline{09} = \sum\limits_{k=1}^{\infty} 9(0.01)^k$ **b.** $\frac{1}{11}$ **47. a.** $0.\overline{037} = \sum\limits_{k=1}^{\infty} 37(0.001)^k = \frac{1}{27}$

49. $0.\overline{12} = \sum\limits_{k=0}^{\infty} 0.12(0.01)^k = \dfrac{4}{33}$

51. $0.\overline{456} = \sum\limits_{k=0}^{\infty} 0.456(0.001)^k = \dfrac{152}{333}$

53. $0.00\overline{952} = \sum\limits_{k=0}^{\infty} 0.00952(0.001)^k = \dfrac{952}{99,900}$

55. $S_n = \dfrac{1}{2} - \dfrac{1}{n+2}; \dfrac{1}{2}$ **57.** $S_n = \dfrac{1}{7} - \dfrac{1}{n+7}; \dfrac{1}{7}$

59. $S_n = \dfrac{1}{9} - \dfrac{1}{4n+9}; \dfrac{1}{9}$ **61.** $S_n = \ln(n + 1)$; diverges

63. $S_n = \dfrac{1}{p+1} - \dfrac{1}{n+p+1}; \dfrac{1}{p+1}$

65. $S_n = \left(\dfrac{1}{\sqrt{2}} + \dfrac{1}{\sqrt{3}}\right) - \left(\dfrac{1}{\sqrt{n+2}} + \dfrac{1}{\sqrt{n+3}}\right); \dfrac{1}{\sqrt{2}} + \dfrac{1}{\sqrt{3}}$

67. $S_n = -\dfrac{n+1}{4n+3}; -\frac{1}{4}$ **69. a.** True **b.** True **c.** False **71.** $-\frac{2}{15}$

73. $\dfrac{1}{\ln 2}$ **75.** $\frac{4}{3}$ **77.** $\sum\limits_{k=0}^{\infty}\left(\dfrac{1}{4}\right)^k A_1 = \dfrac{A_1}{1 - 1/4} = \dfrac{4}{3}A_1$

79. 462 months **81.** 0 **83.** There will be twice as many children.

85. $\sqrt{\dfrac{20}{g}}\dfrac{1 + \sqrt{p}}{1 - \sqrt{p}}$ s **87. a.** $L_n = 3\left(\dfrac{4}{3}\right)^n$, so $\lim\limits_{n\to\infty} L_n = \infty$

b. $\lim\limits_{n\to\infty} A_n = \dfrac{2\sqrt{3}}{5}$

89. $R_n = |S - S_n| = \left| \dfrac{1}{1-r} - \left(\dfrac{1 - r^n}{1 - r}\right)\right| = \left|\dfrac{r^n}{1 - r}\right|$

91. a. 60 **b.** 9 **93. a.** 13 **b.** 15 **95. a.** $1, \frac{5}{6}, \frac{2}{3}$, undefined, undefined **b.** $(-1, 1)$ **97.** Converges for x in $(-\infty, -2)$ or $(0, \infty); f(x) = 3$ for $x = \frac{1}{2}$

Section 9.4 Exercises, pp. 659–661

1. Computation may not show whether the sequence of partial sums diverges or converges. **3.** Yes, if the terms are positive and decreasing. **5.** Converges for $p > 1$ and diverges for $p \leq 1$.
9. Diverges **11.** Diverges **13.** Inconclusive **15.** Diverges
17. Diverges **19.** Diverges **21.** Converges **23.** Diverges
25. Converges **27.** Test does not apply. **29.** Converges

31. Converges **33.** Diverges **35. a.** $\dfrac{1}{5n^5}$ **b.** 3

c. $L_n = \sum\limits_{k=1}^{n} \dfrac{1}{k^6} + \dfrac{1}{5(n+1)^5}$ $\quad U_n = \sum\limits_{k=1}^{n} \dfrac{1}{k^6} + \dfrac{1}{5n^2}$

d. $(1.017342754, 1.017343512)$ **37. a.** $\dfrac{3^{-n}}{\ln 3}$ **b.** 7

c. $L_n = \sum\limits_{k=1}^{n} 3^{-k} + \dfrac{3^{-n-1}}{\ln 3}$ $\quad U_n = \sum\limits_{k=1}^{n} 3^{-k} + \dfrac{3^{-n}}{\ln 3}$

d. $(0.499996671, 0.500006947)$ **39. a.** $\dfrac{2}{\sqrt{n}}$ **b.** $4 \cdot 10^6 + 1$

c. $L_n = \sum\limits_{k=1}^{n} \dfrac{1}{k^{3/2}} + \dfrac{2}{\sqrt{n+1}}$ $\quad U_n = \sum\limits_{k=1}^{n} \dfrac{1}{k^{3/2}} + \dfrac{2}{\sqrt{n}}$

d. $(2.598359183, 2.627792025)$ **41. a.** $\dfrac{1}{2n^2}$ **b.** 23

c. $L_n = \sum\limits_{k=1}^{n} \dfrac{1}{k^3} + \dfrac{1}{2(n+1)^2}$ $\quad U_n = \sum\limits_{k=1}^{n} \dfrac{1}{k^3} + \dfrac{1}{2n^2}$

d. $(1.201664217, 1.202531986)$ **43.** $\frac{4}{11}$ **45.** -2 **47.** $\frac{113}{30}$ **49.** $\frac{17}{10}$
51. a. True **b.** True **c.** False **d.** False **e.** False **f.** False
53. Converges **55.** Diverges **57.** Converges **59. a.** $p > 1$

b. $\sum\limits_{k=2}^{\infty} \dfrac{1}{k(\ln k)^2}$ converges more quickly.

65. $\zeta(3) \approx 1.202, \zeta(5) \approx 1.037$
67. $\frac{\pi^2}{8}$ **69. a.** $\frac{1}{2}, \frac{7}{12}, \frac{37}{60}$ **71. a.** $\sum\limits_{k=2}^{n} \dfrac{1}{k}$ **b.** Infinitely many

Section 9.5 Exercises, pp. 668–670

5. Ratio Test **7.** $S_{n+1} - S_n = a_{n+1} > 0$ thus $S_{n+1} > S_n$
9. Converges **11.** Converges **13.** Converges **15.** Diverges
17. Converges **19.** Converges **21.** Converges **23.** Converges
25. Converges **27.** Converges **29.** Diverges **31.** Converges
33. Converges **35.** Diverges **37.** Diverges **39. a.** False **b.** True
c. True **41.** Diverges **43.** Converges **45.** Converges
47. Diverges **49.** Diverges **51.** Converges **53.** Diverges
55. Converges **57.** Converges **59.** Converges **61.** Diverges
63. Converges **65.** Diverges **67.** Converges **69.** Converges
71. $p > 1$ **73.** $p > 1$ **75.** $p > 2$ **77.** Diverges for all p
79. Diverges if $|r| \geq 1$ **83.** $x < 1$ **85.** $x \leq 1$ **87.** $x < 2$
89. a. e^2 **b.** 0

Section 9.6 Exercises, pp. 677–679

1. Because $S_{n+1} - S_n = (-1)^n a_{n+1}$ alternates sign.   **3.** Because $\lim\limits_{k \to \infty} a_k = 0$ and the terms $\{a_k\}$ alternate in sign.
5. $R_n = |S - S_n| \le |S_{n+1} - S_n| = a_{n+1}$ **7.** No; if a series of positive terms converges, it does so absolutely and not conditionally.   **9.** Yes, $\sum\limits_{k=1}^{\infty} \dfrac{(-1)^k}{k^2}$ has this property.

11. Converges   **13.** Diverges   **15.** Converges   **17.** Converges
19. Diverges   **21.** Diverges   **23.** Converges   **25.** Diverges
27. Converges   **29.** 10,000   **31.** 5000   **33.** 10   **35.** 3334   **37.** 6
39. −0.973   **41.** −0.269 (the sum of the first 999 terms)   **43.** −0.783
45. Converges conditionally   **47.** Converges absolutely   **49.** Converges absolutely   **51.** Diverges   **53.** Diverges   **55.** Converges absolutely
57. a. False **b.** True **c.** True **d.** True **e.** False **f.** True **g.** True
61. The conditions of the Alternating Series Test are met; thus
$\sum\limits_{k=1}^{\infty} r^k$ converges for $-1 < r < 0$.   **65.** x and y are divergent series.

Chapter 9 Review Exercises, pp. 679–681

1. a. False **b.** False **c.** True **d.** False **e.** True **f.** False **g.** False
h. True   **3.** 0   **5.** 1   **7.** $1/e$ **9.** Diverges   **11. a.** $\frac{1}{3}, \frac{11}{24}, \frac{21}{40}, \frac{17}{30}$
b. $S_1 = \dfrac{1}{3}, S_n = \dfrac{1}{2}\left(\dfrac{3}{2} - \dfrac{1}{n+1} - \dfrac{1}{n+2}\right), n \ge 2$ **c.** $3/4$
13. Diverges   **15.** 1   **17.** 3   **19.** $2/9$ **21. a.** Yes; 1.5
b. Convergence uncertain   **c.** Appears to diverge   **23.** Diverges
25. Converges   **27.** Converges   **29.** Converges   **31.** Converges
33. Converges   **35.** Converges   **37.** Converges   **39.** Diverges
41. Diverges   **43.** Converges absolutely   **45.** Converges absolutely
47. Converges absolutely   **49.** Diverges   **51. a.** 0 **b.** $\frac{5}{9}$
53. $\lim\limits_{k \to \infty} a_k = 0, \lim\limits_{n \to \infty} S_n = 8$ **55.** $0 < p \le 1$ **57.** 0.25 (to 14 digits);
6.5×10^{-15} **59.** 100   **61. a.** 803 m, 1283 m, $2000(1 - 0.95^N)$ m
b. 2000 m   **63. a.** $\dfrac{\pi}{2^{n-1}}$ **b.** 2π
65. a. $B_{n+1} = 1.0025B_n + 100, B_0 = 100$
b. $B_n = 40,000(1.0025^{n+1} - 1)$ **67. a.** $T_1 = \dfrac{\sqrt{3}}{16}, T_2 = \dfrac{7\sqrt{3}}{64}$
b. $T_n = \dfrac{\sqrt{3}}{4}\left[1 - \left(\dfrac{3}{4}\right)^n\right]$ **c.** $\lim\limits_{n \to \infty} T_n = \dfrac{\sqrt{3}}{4}$ **d.** 0

CHAPTER 10

Section 10.1 Exercises, pp. 692–694

1. $f(0) = p(0), f'(0) = p'(0),$ and $f''(0) = p''(0)$
3. 1, 1.05, 1.04875   **5.** $R_n(x) = f(x) - p_n(x)$
7. a. $p_1(x) = 8 + 12(x - 1)$ **b.** $p_2(x) = 8 + 12(x - 1) + 3(x - 1)^2$
c. 9.2; 9.23   **9. a.** $p_1(x) = 1 - x$ **b.** $p_2(x) = 1 - x + \dfrac{x^2}{2}$
c. 0.8, 0.82   **11. a.** $p_1(x) = 1 - x$ **b.** $p_2(x) = 1 - x + x^2$
c. 0.95, 0.9525   **13. a.** $p_1(x) = 2 + \frac{1}{12}(x - 8)$
b. $p_2(x) = 2 + \frac{1}{12}(x - 8) - \frac{1}{288}(x - 8)^2$ **c.** $1.958\overline{3}$, 1.95747
15. a. $p_0(x) = 1, p_1(x) = 1, p_2(x) = 1 - \dfrac{x^2}{2}$

b.

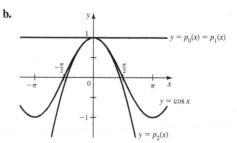

17. a. $p_0(x) = 0, p_1(x) = -x, p_2(x) = -x - \dfrac{x^2}{2}$
b.

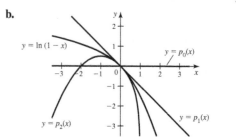

19. a. $p_0(x) = 0, p_1(x) = x, p_2(x) = x$
b.

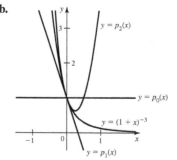

21. a. $p_0(x) = 1, p_1(x) = 1 - 3x, p_2(x) = 1 - 3x + 6x^2$
b.

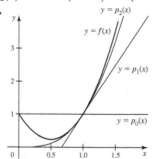

23. a. 1.0247 **b.** 7.58×10^{-6} **25. a.** 0.9624 **b.** 1.50×10^{-4}
27. a. 0.8613 **b.** 5.42×10^{-4}
29. a. $p_0(x) = 1, p_1(x) = 1 + 3(x - 1),$
$p_2(x) = 1 + 3(x - 1) + 3(x - 1)^2$
b.

31. a. $p_0(x) = \dfrac{\sqrt{2}}{2}$, $p_1(x) = \dfrac{\sqrt{2}}{2} + \dfrac{\sqrt{2}}{2}\left(x - \dfrac{\pi}{4}\right)$,

$p_2(x) = \dfrac{\sqrt{2}}{2} + \dfrac{\sqrt{2}}{2}\left(x - \dfrac{\pi}{4}\right) - \dfrac{\sqrt{2}}{4}\left(x - \dfrac{\pi}{4}\right)^2$

b.

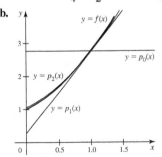

33. a. $p_0(x) = 3$, $p_1(x) = 3 + \dfrac{(x - 9)}{6}$,

$p_2(x) = 3 + \dfrac{(x - 9)}{6} - \dfrac{(x - 9)^2}{216}$

b.

35. a. $p_0(x) = 1$, $p_1(x) = 1 + \dfrac{x - e}{e}$,

$p_2(x) = 1 + \dfrac{x - e}{e} - \dfrac{(x - e)^2}{2e^2}$

b.

37. a. $p_0(x) = 2 + \dfrac{\pi}{4}$, $p_1(x) = 2 + \dfrac{\pi}{4} + \dfrac{5}{2}(x - 1)$,

$p_2(x) = 2 + \dfrac{\pi}{4} + \dfrac{5}{2}(x - 1) + \dfrac{3}{4}(x - 1)^2$

b.

39. a. 1.12749 **b.** 8.85×10^{-6} **41. a.** -0.100333
b. 1.34×10^{-6} **43. a.** 1.029564 **b.** 4.86×10^{-7}
45. a. 10.04987563 **b.** 3.88×10^{-9} **47. a.** 0.520833

b. 0.000261972 **49.** $R_n(x) = \dfrac{\sin^{(n+1)}(c)}{(n + 1)!} x^{n+1}$ for some c between

x and 0. **51.** $R_n(x) = \dfrac{(-1)^{n+1} e^{-c}}{(n + 1)!} x^{n+1}$ for some c between x and 0.

53. $R_n(x) = \dfrac{\sin^{(n+1)}(c)}{(n + 1)!}\left(x - \dfrac{\pi}{2}\right)^{n+1}$ for some c between x and $\dfrac{\pi}{2}$.

55. 2.03×10^{-5} **57.** 1.63×10^{-5} $(e^{0.25} < 2)$ **59.** 2.60×10^{-4}
61. With $n = 4$, max error $= 2.49 \times 10^{-3}$
63. With $n = 2$, max error $= 4.17 \times 10^{-2}$ $(e^{0.5} < 2)$
65. With $n = 2$, max error $= 5.4 \times 10^{-3}$ **67.** 4 **69.** 3 **71.** 1
73. a. False **b.** True **c.** True **75. a.** C **b.** E **c.** A **d.** D **e.** B
f. F **77. a.** $0.1; 1.67 \times 10^{-4}$
b. $0.2; 1.33 \times 10^{-3}$ **79. a.** $0.995; 4.17 \times 10^{-6}$
b. $0.98; 6.67 \times 10^{-5}$ **81. a.** $1.05; \frac{1}{800}$ **b.** $1.1; \frac{1}{200}$
83. a. $1.1; \frac{1}{100}$ **b.** $1.2; \frac{1}{25}$
85. a.

x	$|\sin x - p_3(x)|$	$|\sin x - p_5(x)|$
-0.2	2.7×10^{-6}	2.5×10^{-9}
-0.1	8.3×10^{-8}	2.0×10^{-11}
0.0	0	0
0.1	8.3×10^{-8}	2.0×10^{-11}
0.2	2.7×10^{-6}	2.5×10^{-9}

b. The error increases as $|x|$ increases.

87. a.

x	$|e^{-x} - p_1(x)|$	$|e^{-x} - p_2(x)|$
-0.2	2.1×10^{-2}	1.4×10^{-3}
-0.1	5.2×10^{-3}	1.7×10^{-4}
0.0	0	0
0.1	4.8×10^{-3}	1.6×10^{-4}
0.2	1.9×10^{-2}	1.3×10^{-3}

b. The error increases as $|x|$ increases.

89. a.

x	$|\tan x - p_1(x)|$	$|\tan x - p_3(x)|$
-0.2	2.7×10^{-3}	4.3×10^{-5}
-0.1	3.3×10^{-4}	1.3×10^{-6}
0.0	0	0
0.1	3.3×10^{-4}	1.3×10^{-6}
0.2	2.7×10^{-3}	4.3×10^{-5}

b. The error increases as $|x|$ increases. **91.** Centered at $x = 0$ for
all n **93. a.** $y = f(a) + f'(a)(x - a)$

Section 10.2 Exercises, pp. 702–704

1. $c_0 + c_1 x + c_2 x^2 + c_3 x^3$ **3.** Ratio and Root Test **5.** The radius of
convergence does not change. The interval of convergence may change.
7. $|x| < \frac{1}{4}$ **9.** $R = \frac{1}{2}; \left(-\frac{1}{2}, \frac{1}{2}\right)$ **11.** $R = 1; [0, 2)$
13. $R = 0; \{x: x = 0\}$ **15.** $R = \infty; (-\infty, \infty)$ **17.** $R = 3; (-3, 3)$
19. $R = \infty; (-\infty, \infty)$ **21.** $R = \infty; (-\infty, \infty)$
23. $R = \sqrt{3}; (-\sqrt{3}, \sqrt{3})$ **25.** $R = 1; (0, 2)$

27. $R = \infty$; $(-\infty, \infty)$ **29.** $\displaystyle\sum_{k=0}^{\infty}(3x)^k$; $\left(-\frac{1}{3}, \frac{1}{3}\right)$ **31.** $2\displaystyle\sum_{k=0}^{\infty}x^{k+3}$; $(-1, 1)$

33. $4\displaystyle\sum_{k=0}^{\infty}x^{k+12}$; $(-1, 1)$ **35.** $-\displaystyle\sum_{k=1}^{\infty}\frac{(3x)^k}{k}$; $\left[-\frac{1}{3}, \frac{1}{3}\right)$ **37.** $-\displaystyle\sum_{k=1}^{\infty}\frac{x^{k+1}}{k}$;

$[-1, 1)$ **39.** $-2\displaystyle\sum_{k=1}^{\infty}\frac{x^{k+6}}{k}$; $[-1, 1)$ **41.** $g(x) = \displaystyle\sum_{k=1}^{\infty}kx^{k-1}$; $(-1, 1)$

43. $g(x) = \displaystyle\sum_{k=3}^{\infty}\frac{k(k-1)(k-2)}{6}x^{k-3}$; $(-1, 1)$

45. $g(x) = -\displaystyle\sum_{k=1}^{\infty}\frac{3^k x^k}{k}$; $\left[-\frac{1}{3}, \frac{1}{3}\right)$ **47.** $\displaystyle\sum_{k=0}^{\infty}(-x^2)^k$; $(-1, 1)$

49. $\displaystyle\sum_{k=0}^{\infty}\left(-\frac{x}{3}\right)^k$; $(-3, 3)$ **51.** $\ln 2 - \frac{1}{2}\displaystyle\sum_{k=1}^{\infty}\frac{x^{2k}}{k4^k}$; $(-2, 2)$

53. a. True **b.** True **c.** True **d.** True   **55.** e **57.** $\displaystyle\sum_{k=0}^{\infty}\frac{(-1)^k x^k}{k+1}$

59. $\displaystyle\sum_{k=1}^{\infty}\frac{(-x^2)^k}{k!}$ **61.** $|x - a| < R$ **63.** $f(x) = \dfrac{1}{3 - \sqrt{x}}$;

$1 < x < 9$ **65.** $f(x) = \dfrac{e^x}{e^x - 1}$; $0 < x < \infty$

67. $f(x) = \dfrac{3}{4 - x^2}$; $-2 < x < 2$ **69.** $\displaystyle\sum_{k=0}^{\infty}\frac{(-x)^k}{k!}$; $-\infty < x < \infty$

71. $\displaystyle\sum_{k=0}^{\infty}\frac{(-3x)^k}{k!}$; $-\infty < x < \infty$

73. $\displaystyle\lim_{k\to\infty}\left|\frac{c_{k+1}x^{k+1}}{c_k x^k}\right| = \lim_{k\to\infty}\left|\frac{c_{k+1}x^{k+m+1}}{c_k x^{k+m}}\right|$, so by the Ratio Test the two series converge on the same interval.
75. a. $f(x) \cdot g(x) = c_0 d_0 + (c_0 d_1 + c_1 d_0)x$
$\qquad\qquad\qquad + (c_0 d_2 + c_1 d_1 + c_2 d_0)x^2 + \cdots$.

b. $\displaystyle\sum_{k=0}^{n}c_k d_{n-k}$ **77. b.** $n = 112$

Section 10.3 Exercises, pp. 714–716

1. The nth Taylor polynomial is the nth partial sum of the corresponding Taylor series.   **3.** Calculate $c_k = \dfrac{f^{(k)}(a)}{k!}$ for $k = 0, 1, 2, \ldots$.
5. Replace x by x^2 in the Taylor series for $f(x)$; $|x| < 1$.   **7.** The Taylor series for a function f converges to f on an interval if, for all x in the interval, $\displaystyle\lim_{n\to\infty}R_n(x) = 0$, where $R_n(x)$ is the remainder at x.

9. a. $1 - x + \dfrac{x^2}{2!} - \dfrac{x^3}{3!}$ **b.** $\displaystyle\sum_{k=0}^{\infty}\frac{(-1)^k x^k}{k!}$ **c.** $(-\infty, \infty)$

11. a. $1 - x^2 + x^4 - x^6$ **b.** $\displaystyle\sum_{k=0}^{n}(-1)^k x^{2k}$ **c.** $(-1, 1)$

13. a. $1 + 2x + \dfrac{(2x)^2}{2!} + \dfrac{(2x)^3}{3!}$ **b.** $\displaystyle\sum_{k=0}^{\infty}\frac{(2x)^k}{k!}$ **c.** $(-\infty, \infty)$

15. a. $x - \dfrac{x^3}{3} + \dfrac{x^5}{5} - \dfrac{x^7}{7}$ **b.** $\displaystyle\sum_{k=0}^{\infty}\frac{(-1)^k x^{2k+1}}{2k+1}$ **c.** $[-1, 1]$

17. a. $1 + (\ln 3)x + \dfrac{\ln^2 3}{2}x^2 + \dfrac{\ln^3 3}{6}x^3$ **b.** $\displaystyle\sum_{k=0}^{\infty}\frac{\ln^k 3}{k!}x^k$ **c.** $(-\infty, \infty)$

19. a. $1 + \dfrac{x^2}{2} + \dfrac{x^4}{24} + \dfrac{x^6}{720}$ **b.** $\displaystyle\sum_{k=0}^{\infty}\frac{x^{2k}}{(2k)!}$ **c.** $(-\infty, \infty)$

21. a. $1 - \dfrac{(x - \pi/2)^2}{2!} + \dfrac{(x - \pi/2)^4}{4!} - \dfrac{(x - \pi/2)^6}{6!}$

b. $\displaystyle\sum_{k=0}^{\infty}\frac{(-1)^k}{(2k)!}(x - \pi/2)^{2k}$ **23. a.** $1 - (x - 1) + (x - 1)^2 - (x - 1)^3$

b. $\displaystyle\sum_{k=0}^{\infty}(-1)^k(x - 1)^k$ **25. a.** $\ln 3 + \dfrac{(x - 3)}{3} - \dfrac{(x - 3)^2}{3^2 \cdot 2} + \dfrac{(x - 3)^3}{3^3 \cdot 3}$

b. $\ln 3 + \displaystyle\sum_{k=1}^{\infty}\frac{(-1)^{k+1}(x - 3)^k}{k3^k}$ **27. a.** $2 + 2\ln 2(x - 1) +$

$\ln^2 2(x - 1)^2 + \dfrac{\ln^3 2}{3}(x - 1)^3$ **b.** $\displaystyle\sum_{k=0}^{\infty}\frac{2(x - 1)^k \ln^k 2}{k!}$

29. $x^2 - \dfrac{x^4}{2} + \dfrac{x^6}{3} - \dfrac{x^8}{4} + \cdots$ **31.** $1 + 2x + 4x^2 + 8x^3$

33. $1 + \dfrac{x}{2} + \dfrac{x^2}{6} + \dfrac{x^3}{24} + \cdots$ **35.** $1 - x^4 + x^8 - x^{12} + \cdots$

37. $x^2 + \dfrac{x^6}{6} + \dfrac{x^{10}}{120} + \dfrac{x^{14}}{5040}$ **39. a.** $1 - 2x + 3x^2 - 4x^3$ **b.** 0.826

41. a. $1 + \frac{1}{4}x - \frac{3}{32}x^2 + \frac{7}{128}x^3$ **b.** 1.029
43. a. $1 - \frac{2}{3}x + \frac{5}{9}x^2 - \frac{40}{81}x^3$ **b.** 0.895

45. $1 + \dfrac{x^2}{2} - \dfrac{x^4}{8} + \dfrac{x^6}{16} - \cdots$; $[-1, 1]$

47. $3 - \dfrac{3x}{2} - \dfrac{3x^2}{8} - \dfrac{3x^3}{16} - \cdots$; $[-1, 1)$

49. $a + \dfrac{x^2}{2a} - \dfrac{x^4}{8a^3} + \dfrac{x^6}{16a^5} - \cdots$; $|x| \le a$

51. $1 - 8x + 48x^2 - 256x^3 + \cdots$

53. $\dfrac{1}{16} - \dfrac{x^2}{32} + \dfrac{3x^4}{256} - \dfrac{x^6}{256} + \cdots$

55. $\dfrac{1}{9} - \dfrac{2}{9}\left(\dfrac{4x}{3}\right) + \dfrac{3}{9}\left(\dfrac{4x}{3}\right)^2 - \dfrac{4}{9}\left(\dfrac{4x}{3}\right)^3 + \cdots$

57. $R_n(x) = \dfrac{f^{(n+1)}(c)}{(n+1)!}x^{n+1}$, where c is between 0 and x and

$f^{(n+1)}(c) = \pm\sin c$ or $\pm\cos c$. Thus, $|R_n(x)| \le \dfrac{|x|^{n+1}}{(n+1)!} \to 0$ as

$n \to \infty$, for $-\infty < x < \infty$.

59. $R_n(x) = \dfrac{f^{(n+1)}(c)}{(n+1)!}x^{n+1}$, where c is between 0 and x and

$f^{(n+1)}(c) = (-1)^n e^{-c}$

Thus, $\displaystyle\lim_{n\to\infty}|R_n(x)| = \lim_{n\to\infty}\left|\frac{x^{n+1}}{e^c(n+1)!}\right| = 0$ and so $\displaystyle\lim_{n\to\infty}R_n(x) = 0$,

for $-\infty < x < \infty$.   **61. a.** False **b.** True **c.** False **d.** False

e. True   **63. a.** $1 + \dfrac{x^2}{2!} + \dfrac{x^4}{4!} + \dfrac{x^6}{6!} + \cdots$ **b.** $R = \infty$

65. a. $1 - \frac{2}{3}x^2 + \frac{5}{9}x^4 - \frac{40}{81}x^6 + \cdots$ **b.** $R = 1$
67. a. $1 - \frac{1}{2}x^2 - \frac{1}{8}x^4 - \frac{1}{16}x^6 - \cdots$ **b.** $R = 1$
69. a. $1 - 2x^2 + 3x^4 - 4x^6 + \cdots$ **b.** $R = 1$ **71.** $\sqrt[3]{60} \approx 3.9149$
using the first four terms   **73.** $\sqrt[4]{13} \approx 1.8989$ using the first four terms

79. $\displaystyle\sum_{k=0}^{\infty}\left(\frac{x - 4}{2}\right)^k$ **81.** $\dfrac{1 \cdot 3 \cdot 5 \cdot 7}{2 \cdot 4 \cdot 6 \cdot 8}x^4, \dfrac{-1 \cdot 3 \cdot 5 \cdot 7 \cdot 9}{2 \cdot 4 \cdot 6 \cdot 8 \cdot 10}x^5$

83. Use three terms of the Taylor series for $\cos x$ centered at $a = n/4$; $\cos 40° = \cos(40\pi/180) \approx 0.766$ **85.** Use six terms of the Taylor series for $\sqrt[3]{x}$ centered at $a = 64$; $\sqrt[3]{83} \approx 4.362$ **87. a.** Use three terms of the Taylor series for $\sqrt[3]{125 + x}$ centered at $a = 0$; $\sqrt[3]{128} \approx 5.03968$ **b.** Use three terms of the Taylor series for $\sqrt[3]{x}$ centered at $a = 125$; $\sqrt[3]{128} \approx 5.03968$ **c.** Yes

Section 10.4 Exercises, pp. 723–725

1. Replace f and g by their Taylor series centered at a and evaluate the limit.   **3.** Substitute $x = -0.6$ into the Taylor series for e^x centered at 0. Because the resulting series is an alternating series, the error can be estimated.   **5.** $f'(x) = \sum_{k=1}^{\infty} kc_k x^{k-1}$ **7.** 1   **9.** $\frac{1}{2}$ **11.** 2   **13.** $\frac{2}{3}$

15. $\frac{2}{5}$ **17.** $\frac{3}{5}$ **19.** $-\frac{1}{6}$ **21.** 1   **23.** $\frac{5}{4}$

25. a. $1 + x + \frac{x^2}{2!} + \cdots + \frac{x^n}{n!} + \cdots$ **b.** e^x

c. $-\infty < x < \infty$ **27. a.** $1 - x + x^2 - \cdots (-1)^{n-1} x^{n-1} + \cdots$

b. $\frac{1}{1+x}$ **c.** $|x| < 1$

29. a. $-2 + 4x - 8 \cdot \frac{x^2}{2!} + \cdots + (-2)^n \frac{x^{n-1}}{(n-1)!} + \cdots$

b. $-2e^{-2x}$ **c.** $-\infty < x < \infty$ **31. a.** $1 - x^2 + x^4 - \cdots$

b. $\frac{1}{1+x^2}$ **c.** $-1 < x < 1$ **33. a.** $2 + 2t + \frac{2t^2}{2!} + \cdots + \frac{2t^n}{n!} + \cdots$

b. $y(t) = 2e^t$

35. a. $2 + 16t + 24t^2 + 24t^3 + \cdots + \frac{3^{n-1} \cdot 16}{n!} t^n + \cdots$

b. $y(t) = \frac{16}{3} e^{3t} - \frac{10}{3}$ **37.** 0.2448   **39.** 0.6958

41. $\left(\frac{0.35^2}{2} - \frac{0.35^4}{12} \right) \approx 0.0600$ **43.** 0.4994

45. $e^2 = \sum_{k=0}^{\infty} \frac{2^k}{k!} = 1 + 2 + \frac{2^2}{2!} + \frac{2^3}{3!} + \cdots$

47. $\cos 2 = \sum_{k=0}^{\infty} \frac{(-1)^k 2^{2k}}{(2k)!} = 1 - 2 + \frac{2}{3} - \frac{4}{45} + \cdots$

49. $\ln (3/2) = \sum_{k=1}^{\infty} \frac{(-1)^{k+1}}{k2^k} = \frac{1}{2} - \frac{1}{8} + \frac{1}{24} - \frac{1}{64} + \cdots$

51. $\frac{e^x - 1}{x} = \sum_{k=0}^{\infty} \frac{x^k}{(k+1)!}$; Therefore, $\sum_{k=0}^{\infty} \frac{1}{(k+1)!} = e - 1$.

53. $\sum_{k=1}^{\infty} \frac{(-1)^{k+1} x^k}{k}$ for $-1 < x \le 1$. At $x = 1$, $\sum_{k=1}^{\infty} \frac{(-1)^{k+1}}{k} = \ln 2$.

55. $f(x) = \frac{2}{2-x}$ **57.** $f(x) = \frac{4}{4+x^2}$ **59.** $f(x) = -\ln (1 - x)$

61. $f(x) = \frac{-3x^2}{(3+x)^2}$ **63.** $f(x) = \frac{6x^2}{(3-x)^3}$ **65. a.** False

b. False **c.** True   **67.** $\frac{a}{b}$ **69.** $e^{-1/6}$ **71.** $f^{(3)}(0) = 0$;

$f^{(4)}(0) = 4e$ **73.** $f^{(3)}(0) = 2$; $f^{(4)}(0) = 0$ **75.** 2

77. a. 1.5741 using four terms **b.** At least three **c.** More terms would be needed.   **79. a.** $S'(x) = \sin (x^2)$; $C'(x) = \cos (x^2)$

b. $\frac{x^3}{3} - \frac{x^7}{7 \cdot 3!} + \frac{x^{11}}{11 \cdot 5!} - \frac{x^{15}}{15 \cdot 7!}$; $x - \frac{x^5}{5 \cdot 2!} + \frac{x^9}{9 \cdot 4!} - \frac{x^{13}}{13 \cdot 6!}$

c. $S(0.05) \approx 0.00004166664807$; $C(-0.25) \approx -0.2499023614$

d. 1 **e.** 2   **81. a.** $1 - \frac{x^2}{4} + \frac{x^4}{64} - \frac{x^6}{2304}$ **b.** $-\infty < x < \infty, R = \infty$

c. $\left(-\frac{x^2}{2} + \frac{3x^4}{16} - \frac{5x^6}{384} \right) + \left(-\frac{x^2}{2} + \frac{x^4}{16} - \frac{x^6}{384} \right) +$

$\left(x^2 - \frac{x^4}{4} + \frac{x^6}{64} \right) = 0$ **83. a.** The Maclaurin series for $\cos x$ consists of even powers of x, which are even functions. **b.** The Maclaurin series for $\sin x$ consists of odd powers of x, which are odd functions.

Chapter 10 Review Exercises, pp. 726–727

1. a. True **b.** False **c.** True **d.** True   **3.** $p_2(x) = 1$

5. $p_3(x) = x - \frac{x^2}{2} + \frac{x^3}{3}$ **7.** $p_2(x) = (x - 1) - \frac{(x-1)^2}{2}$

9. $p_3(x) = \frac{5}{4} + \frac{3}{4}(x - \ln 2) + \frac{5}{8}(x - \ln 2)^2 + \frac{1}{8}(x - \ln 2)^3$

11. a. $p_2(x) = 1 + x + \frac{x^2}{2}$ **b.**

n	$p_n(x)$	Error
0	1	7.7×10^{-2}
1	0.92	3.1×10^{-3}
2	0.9232	8.4×10^{-5}

13. a. $p_2(x) = \frac{\sqrt{2}}{2} + \frac{\sqrt{2}}{2}\left(x - \frac{\pi}{4} \right) - \frac{\sqrt{2}}{4}\left(x - \frac{\pi}{4} \right)^2$

b.

n	$p_n(x)$	Error
0	0.7071	1.2×10^{-1}
1	0.5960	8.2×10^{-3}
2	0.5873	4.7×10^{-4}

15. $R_3(x) = \frac{\sin c}{4!} x^4, |c| < \pi; |R_3| < \frac{\pi^4}{4!}$ **17.** $(-\infty, \infty), R = \infty$

19. $(-\infty, \infty), R = \infty$ **21.** $(-9, 9), R = 9$ **23.** $[-4, 0), R = 2$

25. $\sum_{k=0}^{\infty} x^{2k}; (-1, 1)$ **27.** $\sum_{k=0}^{\infty} 3^k x^k; \left(-\frac{1}{3}, \frac{1}{3} \right)$ **29.** $\sum_{k=1}^{\infty} kx^{k-1}; (-1, 1)$

31. $1 + 3x + \frac{9x^2}{2!}; \sum_{k=0}^{\infty} \frac{(3x)^k}{k!}$

33. $-(x - \pi/2) + \frac{(x - \pi/2)^3}{3!} - \frac{(x - \pi/2)^5}{5!};$

$\sum_{k=0}^{\infty} (-1)^{k+1} \frac{(x - \pi/2)^{2k+1}}{(2k+1)!}$ **35.** $x - \frac{x^3}{3} + \frac{x^5}{5}; \sum_{k=0}^{\infty} \frac{(-1)^k x^{2k+1}}{2k+1}$

37. $1 + \frac{9x^2}{2!} + \frac{81x^4}{4!}; \sum_{k=0}^{\infty} \frac{(3x)^{2k}}{(2k)!}$ **39.** $1 + \frac{x}{3} - \frac{x^2}{9} + \cdots$

41. $1 - \frac{3}{2}x + \frac{3}{2}x^2 - \cdots$ **43.** $R_n(x) = \frac{(-1)^{n+1} e^{-c}}{(n+1)!} x^{n+1}$, where

c is between 0 and x. $\lim_{n \to \infty} |R_n(x)| = \lim_{n \to \infty} \frac{|x^{n+1}|}{e^{|x|}} \cdot \frac{1}{(n+1)!} = 0$ for

$-\infty < x < \infty$.   **45.** $R_n(x) = \frac{(-1)^n (1 + c)^{-(n+1)}}{n + 1} x^{n+1}$

where c is between 0 and x.

$\lim_{n \to \infty} |R_n(x)| = \lim_{n \to \infty} \left(\frac{|x|}{1+c} \right)^{n+1} \cdot \frac{1}{n+1} < \lim_{n \to \infty} 1^{n+1} \cdot \frac{1}{n+1} = 0$

for $|x| \le \frac{1}{2}$.   **47.** $\frac{1}{24}$ **49.** $\frac{1}{8}$ **51.** $\frac{1}{6}$ **53.** 0.4615   **55.** 0.3819

57. $11 - \frac{1}{11} - \frac{1}{2 \cdot 11^3} - \frac{1}{2 \cdot 11^5}$ **59.** $-\frac{1}{3} + \frac{1}{3 \cdot 3^3} - \frac{1}{5 \cdot 3^5} + \frac{1}{7 \cdot 3^7}$

61. $y(x) = 4 + 4x + \frac{4^2}{2!}x^2 + \frac{4^3}{3!}x^3 + \cdots + \frac{4^n}{n!}x^n + \cdots$

$= 3 + e^{4x}$.   **63. a.** $\sum_{k=1}^{\infty} \frac{(-1)^{k+1}}{k}$ **b.** $\sum_{k=1}^{\infty} \frac{1}{k2^k}$ **c.** $2\sum_{k=0}^{\infty} \frac{x^{2k+1}}{2k+1}$

d. $x = \frac{1}{3}; 2\sum_{k=0}^{\infty} \frac{1}{3^{2k+1}(2k+1)}$ **e.** Series in part (d)

CHAPTER 11

Section 11.1 Exercises, pp. 735–739

1. If $x = g(t)$ and $y = h(t)$, for $a \le t \le b$, then plotting the set $\{(g(t), h(t)): a \le t \le b\}$ results in a graph in the xy-plane.
3. $x = R \cos(\pi t/5), y = R \sin(\pi t/5)$
5. $x = t, y = t^2, -\infty < t < \infty$
7. a.

t	-10	-8	-6	-4	-2	0	2	4	6	8	10
x	-20	-16	-12	-8	-4	0	4	8	12	16	20
y	-34	-28	-22	-16	-10	-4	2	8	14	20	26

b. 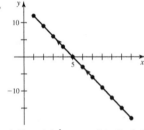　　**c.** $y = \frac{3}{2}x - 4$

d. A line rising up and to the right as t increases
9. a.

t	-5	-4	-3	-2	-1	0	1	2	3	4	5
x	11	10	9	8	7	6	5	4	3	2	1
y	-18	-15	-12	-9	-6	-3	0	3	6	9	12

b. 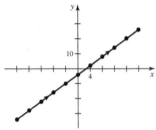　　**c.** $y = -3x + 15$

d. A line rising up and to the left as t increases
11. a. $y = 3x - 12$　**b.** A line rising up and to the right as t increases　**13. a.** $y = 1 - x^2, -1 \le x \le 1$　**b.** A parabola opening downward with a vertex at $(0, 1)$ starting at $(1, 0)$ and ending at $(-1, 0)$　**15. a.** $y = (x + 1)^3$　**b.** A cubic function rising up and to the right as t increases　**17.** Center $(0, 0)$; radius 3; lower half of circle generated counterclockwise　**19.** $x^2 + (y - 1)^2 = 1$; a complete circle of radius 1 centered at $(0, 1)$ traversed counterclockwise starting at $(1, 1)$　**21.** Center $(0, 0)$; radius 7; circle generated counterclockwise　**23.** $x = 4 \cos t, y = 4 \sin t, 0 \le t \le 2\pi$: The circle has equation $x^2 + y^2 = 16$.

25. $x = \cos t + 2, y = \sin t + 3, 0 \le t \le 2\pi$; $(x - 2)^2 + (y - 3)^2 = 1$

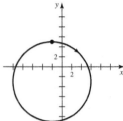

27. $x = 8 \sin t - 2, y = 8 \cos t - 3, 0 \le t \le 2\pi$: The circle has equation $(x + 2)^2 + (y + 3)^2 = 64$.

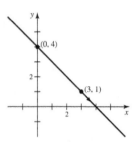

29. $x = 400 \cos\left(\dfrac{4\pi t}{3}\right), y = 400 \sin\left(\dfrac{4\pi t}{3}\right),$
$0 \le t \le 1.5$　**31.** $x = 50 \cos\left(\dfrac{\pi t}{12}\right), y(t) = 50 \sin\left(\dfrac{\pi t}{12}\right),$
$0 \le t \le 24$
33. Slope: -1; point: $(3, 1)$

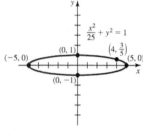

35. Slope: 0; point: $(8, 1)$

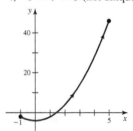

37. $x = 2t, y = 8t, 0 \le t \le 1$
39. $x = -1 + 7t, y = -3 - 13t, 0 \le t \le 1$
41. $x = t, y = 2t^2 - 4, -1 \le t \le 5$ (not unique)

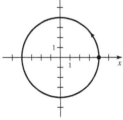

43. $x = 4t - 2, y = -6t + 3, 0 \le t \le 1$;
$x = t + 1, y = 8t - 11, 1 \le t \le 2$ (not unique)

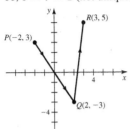

45. 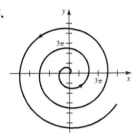   **47.**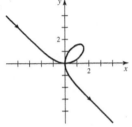

49. 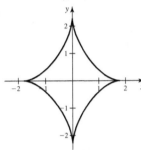   **51.**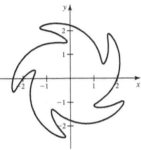

53.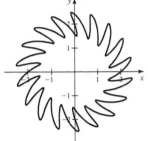

55. a. $\dfrac{dy}{dx} = -2; -2$ **b.**

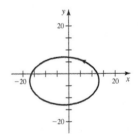

57. a. $\dfrac{dy}{dx} = -8 \cot t; 0$ **b.**

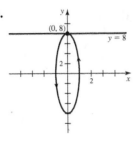

59. a. $\dfrac{dy}{dx} = \dfrac{t^2 + 1}{t^2 - 1}, t \ne 0$; undefined   **b.**

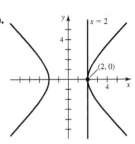

61. a. False   **b.** True   **c.** False   **d.** True   **63.** $y = \dfrac{13}{4}x + \dfrac{1}{4}$

65. $y = x - \dfrac{\pi\sqrt{2}}{4}$ **67.** $x = 1 + 2t, y = 1 + 4t, -\infty < t < \infty$

69. $x = t^2, y = t, t \ge 0$

71. $0 \le t \le 2\pi$

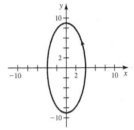

73. $x = 3\cos t, y = \tfrac{3}{2}\sin t, 0 \le t \le 2\pi; \left(\dfrac{x}{3}\right)^2 + \left(\dfrac{2y}{3}\right)^2 = 1$;
in the counterclockwise direction

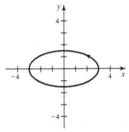

75. $x = 15\cos t - 2, y = 10\sin t - 3, 0 \le t \le 2\pi$;
$\left(\dfrac{x + 2}{15}\right)^2 + \left(\dfrac{y + 3}{10}\right)^2 = 1$; in the counterclockwise direction

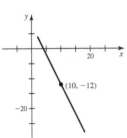

77. a and b   **79.** $x^2 + y^2 = 4$ **81.** $y = \sqrt{4 - x^2}$ **83.** $y = x^2$

85. $\left(-\dfrac{4}{\sqrt{5}}, \dfrac{8}{\sqrt{5}}\right)$ and $\left(\dfrac{4}{\sqrt{5}}, -\dfrac{8}{\sqrt{5}}\right)$ **87.** There is no such point.

89. $a = p, b = p + \dfrac{2\pi}{3}$, for all real p **91. a.** $(0, 2)$ and $(0, -2)$

b. $(1, \sqrt{2}), (1, -\sqrt{2}), (-1, \sqrt{2}), (-1, -\sqrt{2})$

93. a. $x = \pm a\cos^{2/n}(t), y = \pm b\sin^{2/n}(t)$ **c.** The curves become more square as n increases.

99. a.

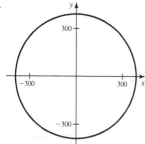

b.

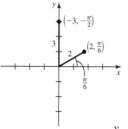

c.

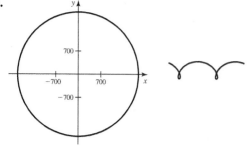

101. ≈ 2857 m

Section 11.2 Exercises, pp. 748–752

1.

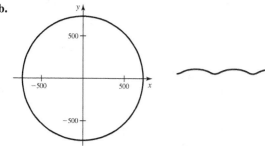

$(-2, -5\pi/6), (2, 13\pi/6);$
$(3, \pi/2), (3, 5\pi/2)$

3. $r^2 = x^2 + y^2, \tan\theta = \dfrac{y}{x}$ **5.** $r\cos\theta = 5$ or $r = 5\sec\theta$

7. x-axis symmetry occurs if (r, θ) on the graph implies $(r, -\theta)$ is on the graph. y-axis symmetry occurs if (r, θ) on the graph implies $(r, \pi - \theta) = (-r, -\theta)$ is on the graph. Symmetry about the origin occurs if (r, θ) on the graph implies $(-r, \theta) = (r, \theta + \pi)$ is on the graph.

9.

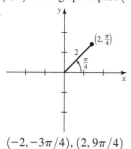

11.

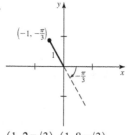

$(-2, -3\pi/4), (2, 9\pi/4)$ $(1, 2\pi/3), (1, 8\pi/3)$

13.

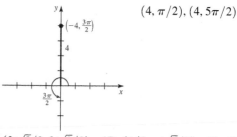

$(4, \pi/2), (4, 5\pi/2)$

15. $(3\sqrt{2}/2, 3\sqrt{2}/2)$ **17.** $(1/2, -\sqrt{3}/2)$ **19.** $(2\sqrt{2}, -2\sqrt{2})$
21. $(2\sqrt{2}, \pi/4), (-2\sqrt{2}, 5\pi/4)$ **23.** $(2, \pi/3), (-2, 4\pi/3)$
25. $(8, 2\pi/3), (-8, -\pi/3)$ **27.** $x = -4$; vertical line passing through $(-4, 0)$ **29.** $x^2 + y^2 = 4$ (circle centered at $(0, 0)$ of radius 2)   **31.** $(x - 1)^2 + (y - 1)^2 = 2$ (circle of radius $\sqrt{2}$ centered at $(1, 1)$)   **33.** $x^2 + (y - 1)^2 = 1$; circle of radius 1 centered at $(0, 1)$ and $x = 0$; y-axis   **35.** $x^2 + (y - 4)^2 = 16$; circle of radius 4 centered at $(0, 4)$

37.

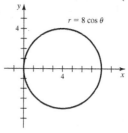

39.

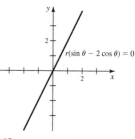

41.

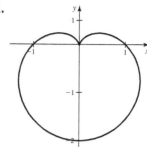

43.

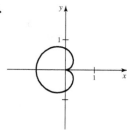

45.

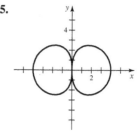

47.

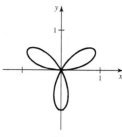

49.

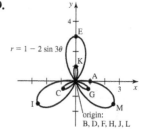

51.

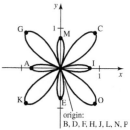

53.

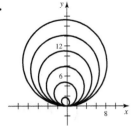

No interval $[0, P]$ generates the entire curve; $-\infty < \theta < \infty$
55. $[0, 2\pi]$ **57.** $[0, 5\pi]$

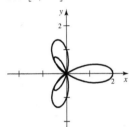   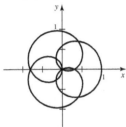

59. $[0, 2\pi]$

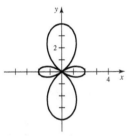

61. a. True   **b.** True   **c.** False   **d.** True   **e.** True
63. $r = \tan\theta\sec\theta$ **65.** $r^2 = \sec\theta\csc\theta$ or $r^2 = 2\csc(2\theta)$
67.   **69.**

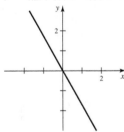

71.   **73.**

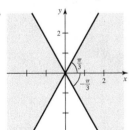

77. A circle of radius 4 and center $(2, \pi/3)$ (polar coordinates)

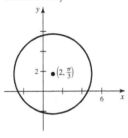

79. A circle of radius 4 centered at $(2, 3)$ (Cartesian coordinates)

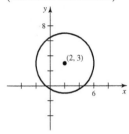

81. A circle of radius 3 centered at $(-1, 2)$ (Cartesian coordinates)

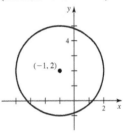

83. Same graph on all three intervals.

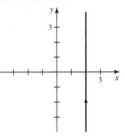

85.

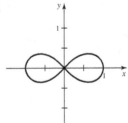

$y = -\dfrac{x}{\sqrt{3}} + 2\sqrt{3}$

87.

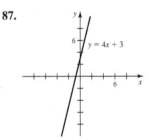

$y = 4x + 3$

89. a. A   **b.** C   **c.** B   **d.** D   **e.** E   **f.** F
91.   **93.**

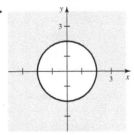   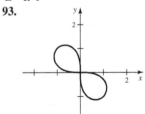

95.   **97.**

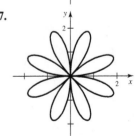

101.

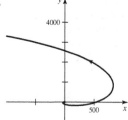

For $a = -1$, the spiral winds inward toward the origin.

103. $(2, 0)$ and $(0, 0)$

105. $(0, 0), \left(\dfrac{2 - \sqrt{2}}{2}, 3\pi/4\right), \left(\dfrac{2 + \sqrt{2}}{2}, 7\pi/4\right)$

107. a.

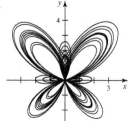

109. a.

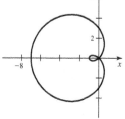

111. $r = a \cos\theta + b \sin\theta = \dfrac{a}{r}(r\cos\theta) + \dfrac{b}{r}(r\sin\theta) = \dfrac{a}{r}x + \dfrac{b}{r}y$

Thus, $\left(x - \dfrac{a}{2}\right)^2 + \left(y - \dfrac{b}{2}\right)^2 = \dfrac{a^2 + b^2}{4}$. Center: $\left(\dfrac{a}{2}, \dfrac{b}{2}\right)$; radius:

$\dfrac{\sqrt{a^2 + b^2}}{2}$ **113.** Symmetry about the x-axis

Section 11.3 Exercises, pp. 758–760

1. $x = f(\theta)\cos\theta, y = f(\theta)\sin\theta$ **3.** The slope of the tangent line is the rate of change of the vertical coordinate with respect to the horizontal coordinate.   **5.** $0; \theta = \pi/2$ **7.** $-\sqrt{3}; \theta = 0$ **9.** Undefined, undefined; the curve does not intersect the origin.   **11.** 0 at $(-4, \pi/2)$ and $(-4, 3\pi/2)$, undefined at $(4, 0)$ and $(4, \pi)$; $\theta = \pi/4, \theta = 3\pi/4$ **13.** $\pm 1; \theta = \pm\pi/4$ **15.** Horizontal at $(2\sqrt{2}, \pi/4), (-2\sqrt{2}, 3\pi/4)$; vertical at $(0, \pi/2), (4, 0)$ **17.** Horizontal: $(0, 0)$ $(0.943, 0.955)$, $(-0.943, 2.186), (0.943, 4.097), (-0.943, 5.328)$; vertical: $(0, 0)$, $(0.943, 0.615), (-0.943, 2.526), (0.943, 3.757), (-0.943, 5.668)$

19. Horizontal at $\left(\dfrac{1}{2}, \dfrac{\pi}{6}\right), \left(\dfrac{1}{2}, \dfrac{5\pi}{6}\right), \left(2, \dfrac{3\pi}{2}\right)$; vertical at

$\left(\dfrac{3}{2}, \dfrac{7\pi}{6}\right), \left(\dfrac{3}{2}, \dfrac{11\pi}{6}\right), \left(0, \dfrac{\pi}{2}\right)$

21.

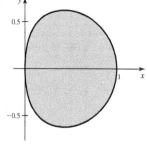

23. 16π **25.** $9\pi/2$

27. $\dfrac{\pi}{12}$

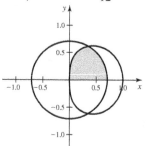

29. $\dfrac{1}{24}(3\sqrt{3} + 2\pi)$

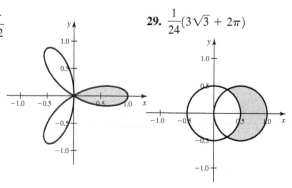

31. $\dfrac{1}{4}(2 - \sqrt{3}) + \dfrac{\pi}{12}$

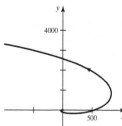

33. $\pi/20$ **35.** $4(4\pi/3 - \sqrt{3})$ **37.** $(0, 0), (3/\sqrt{2}, \pi/4)$

39. $\left(1 + \dfrac{1}{\sqrt{2}}, \dfrac{\pi}{4}\right), \left(1 - \dfrac{1}{\sqrt{2}}, \dfrac{5\pi}{4}\right), (0, 0)$ **41.** $\dfrac{9}{8}(\pi - 2)$ **43.** $\dfrac{3\pi}{2} - 2\sqrt{2}$

45. a. False   **b.** False   **47.** $2\pi/3 - \sqrt{3}/2$ **49.** $9\pi + 27\sqrt{3}$

51. Horizontal: $(0, 0), (4.05, 2.03), (9.83, 4.91)$; vertical: $(1.72, 0.86), (6.85, 3.43), (12.87, 6.44)$

53. a. $A_n = \dfrac{1}{4e^{(4n+2)\pi}} - \dfrac{1}{4e^{4n\pi}} - \dfrac{1}{4e^{(4n-2)\pi}} + \dfrac{1}{4e^{(4n-4)\pi}}$ **b.** 0

c. $e^{-4\pi}$ **55.** 6 **57.** 18π **59.** $(a^2 - 2)\theta^* + \pi - \sin 2\theta^*$, where $\theta^* = \cos^{-1}(a/2)$.   **61.** $a^2(\pi/2 + a/3)$

Section 11.4 Exercises, pp. 770–773

1. A parabola is the set of all points in a plane equidistant from a fixed point and a fixed line.   **3.** A hyperbola is the set of all points in a plane, the difference of whose distances from two fixed points is constant.

5. Parabola:

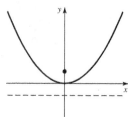

Hyperbola:

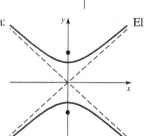

Ellipse:

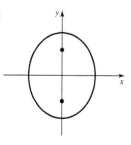

7. $\left(\dfrac{x}{a}\right)^2 + \dfrac{y^2}{a^2 - c^2} = 1$ **9.** $(\pm ae, 0)$ **11.** $y = \pm\dfrac{b}{a}x$

13.

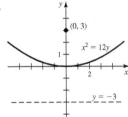

15.

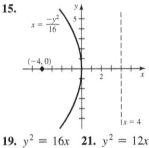

17.

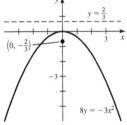

19. $y^2 = 16x$ **21.** $y^2 = 12x$

23. $x^2 = -\dfrac{2}{3}y$ **25.** $y^2 = 4(x + 1)$

27.

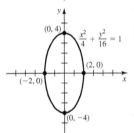

Vertices: $(\pm 2, 0)$; foci: $(\pm\sqrt{3}, 0)$; major axis has length 4; minor axis has length 2.

29.

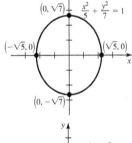

Vertices: $(0, \pm 4)$; foci: $(0, \pm 2\sqrt{3})$; major axis has length 8; minor axis has length 4.

31.

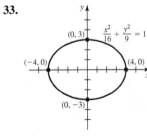

Vertices: $(0, \pm\sqrt{7})$; foci: $(0, \pm\sqrt{2})$; major axis has length $2\sqrt{7}$; minor axis has length $2\sqrt{5}$.

33.

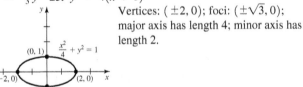

35.

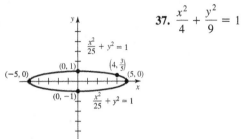

37. $\dfrac{x^2}{4} + \dfrac{y^2}{9} = 1$

39.

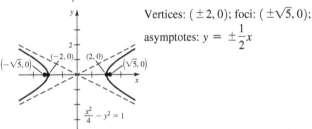

Vertices: $(\pm 2, 0)$; foci: $(\pm\sqrt{5}, 0)$; asymptotes: $y = \pm\dfrac{1}{2}x$

41.

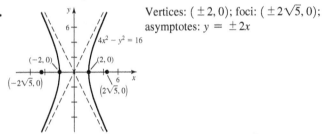

Vertices: $(\pm 2, 0)$; foci: $(\pm 2\sqrt{5}, 0)$; asymptotes: $y = \pm 2x$

43.

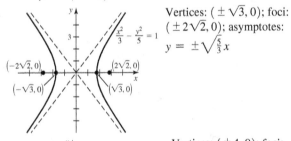

Vertices: $(\pm\sqrt{3}, 0)$; foci: $(\pm 2\sqrt{2}, 0)$; asymptotes: $y = \pm\sqrt{\dfrac{5}{3}}x$

45.

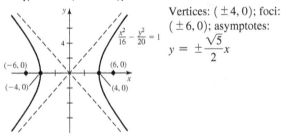

Vertices: $(\pm 4, 0)$; foci: $(\pm 6, 0)$; asymptotes: $y = \pm\dfrac{\sqrt{5}}{2}x$

47.

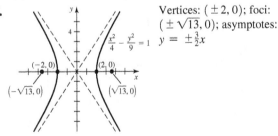

Vertices: $(\pm 2, 0)$; foci: $(\pm\sqrt{13}, 0)$; asymptotes: $y = \pm\dfrac{3}{2}x$

49. $\dfrac{x^2}{16} - \dfrac{y^2}{9} = 1$ **51.** $\dfrac{x^2}{81} + \dfrac{y^2}{72} = 1$

Directrices:
$x = \pm 27$

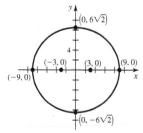

53. $x^2 - \dfrac{y^2}{8} = 1$

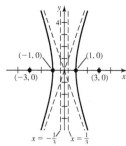

55.

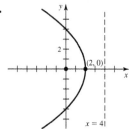

Vertex: $(2, 0)$; focus: $(0, 0)$;
directrix: $x = 4$

57.

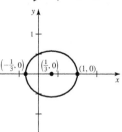

Vertices: $(1, 0)$, $(-\frac{1}{3}, 0)$; center:
$(\frac{1}{3}, 0)$; foci: $(0, 0)$, $(\frac{2}{3}, 0)$; directrices:
$x = -1, x = \frac{5}{3}$

59.

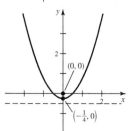

Vertex: $(0, -\frac{1}{4})$; focus: $(0, 0)$;
directrix: $y = -\frac{1}{2}$

61.

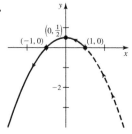

The parabola starts at $(1, 0)$ and goes
through quadrants I, II, and III for θ in
$[0, 3\pi/2]$; then it approaches $(1, 0)$
by traveling through quadrant IV on
$(3\pi/2, 2\pi)$.

63.

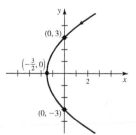

The parabola begins in the first quadrant and passes through the points
$(0, 3)$ and then $(-\frac{3}{2}, 0)$ and $(0, -3)$ as
θ ranges from 0 to 2π.

65. The parabolas open to the right if $p > 0$, open to the left if $p < 0$,
and are more vertically compressed as $|p|$ decreases.   **67. a.** True
b. True   **c.** True   **d.** True   **69.** $y = 2x + 6$ **71.** $y = -\frac{3}{40}x - \frac{4}{5}$

73. $r = \dfrac{4}{1 - 2\sin\theta}$ **77.** $\dfrac{dy}{dx} = \left(-\dfrac{b^2}{a^2}\right)\left(\dfrac{x}{y}\right)$, so

$\dfrac{y - y_0}{x - x_0} = \left(-\dfrac{b^2}{a^2}\right)\left(\dfrac{x_0}{y_0}\right)$, which is equivalent to the given equation.

79. $\dfrac{4\pi b^2 a}{3}$; $\dfrac{4\pi a^2 b}{3}$; yes, if $a \neq b$ **81. a.** $\dfrac{\pi b^2}{3a^2} \cdot (a - c)^2(2a + c)$

b. $\dfrac{4\pi b^4}{3a}$ **91.** $2p$ **97. a.** $u(m) = \dfrac{2m^2 - \sqrt{3m^2 + 1}}{m^2 - 1}$;

$v(m) = \dfrac{2m^2 + \sqrt{3m^2 + 1}}{m^2 - 1}$; 2 intersection points for $|m| > 1$

b. $\frac{5}{4}, \infty$ **c.** $2, 2$ **d.** $2\sqrt{3} - \ln(\sqrt{3} + 2)$

Chapter 11 Review Exercises, pp. 774–776

1. a. False   **b.** False   **c.** True   **d.** False   **e.** True   **f.** True
3. a.   **b.** $y = 3/x^2$

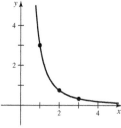

c. The right branch of the function $y = 3/x^2$.   **d.** $\dfrac{dy}{dx} = -6$
5. a.   **b.** $y = 16x$

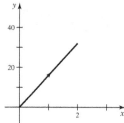

c. A line segment from $(0, 0)$ to $(2, 32)$ **d.** $\dfrac{dy}{dx} = 16$
7. $\dfrac{x^2}{16} + \dfrac{y^2}{9} = 1$; ellipse generated counterclockwise

9. $(x + 3)^2 + (y - 6)^2 = 1$; right half of a circle centered at $(-3, 6)$
of radius 1 generated clockwise   **11.** $x = 3\sin t, y = 3\cos t$, for
$0 \leq t \leq 2\pi$ **13.** $x = 3\cos t, y = 2\sin t$, for $-\pi/2 \leq t \leq \pi/2$
15. $x = -1 + 2t, y = t$, for $0 \leq t \leq 1$; $x = 1 - 2t, y = 1 - t$, for
$0 \leq t \leq 1$

17. At $t = \pi/6$: $y = (2 + \sqrt{3})x + \left(2 - \dfrac{\pi}{3} - \dfrac{\pi\sqrt{3}}{6}\right)$; at $t = \dfrac{2\pi}{3}$: $y = \dfrac{x}{\sqrt{3}} + 2 - \dfrac{2\pi}{3\sqrt{3}}$

19.

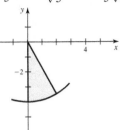

21. Liz should choose $r = 1 - \sin\theta$.

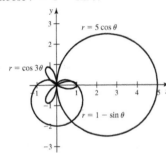

23. $(x - 3)^2 + (y + 1)^2 = 10$; a circle of radius $\sqrt{10}$ centered at $(3, -1)$ **25.** $r = 8\cos\theta, 0 \le \theta \le \pi$

27. a.

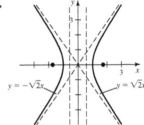

4 intersection points

b. $(1, 1.32), (1, 4.97), (-1, 0.7), (-1, 5.56)$

29. a. $(4.73, 2.77), (4.73, 0.38); (6, \pi/2), (2, 3\pi/2)$ **b.** There is no point at the origin.   **c.**

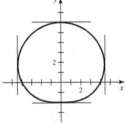

31. a. Horizontal tangent lines at $(1, \pi/6), (1, 5\pi/6), (1, 7\pi/6)$, and $(1, 11\pi/6)$; vertical tangent lines at $(\sqrt{2}, 0)$ and $(\sqrt{2}, \pi)$
b. Tangent lines at the origin have slopes ± 1.
c.

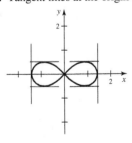

33. $\dfrac{19\pi}{2}$

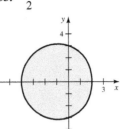

35. $\frac{1}{4}(\sqrt{255} - \cos^{-1}(1/16))$

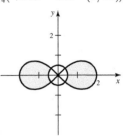

37. 4   **39. a.** Hyperbola   **b.** Foci $(\pm\sqrt{3}, 0)$, vertices $(\pm 1, 0)$, directrices $x = \pm\dfrac{1}{\sqrt{3}}$ **c.** $e = \sqrt{3}$

d.

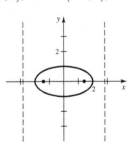

41. a. Hyperbola   **b.** Foci $(0, \pm 2\sqrt{5})$, vertices $(0, \pm 4)$, directrices $y = \pm\dfrac{8}{\sqrt{5}}$ **c.** $e = \dfrac{\sqrt{5}}{2}$ **d.**

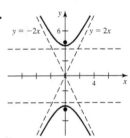

43. a. Ellipse   **b.** Foci $(\pm\sqrt{2}, 0)$, vertices $(\pm 2, 0)$, directrices $x = \pm 2\sqrt{2}$ **c.** $e = \dfrac{\sqrt{2}}{2}$ **d.**

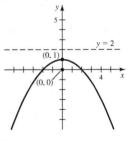

45. $y = \frac{3}{2}x - 2$ **47.** $y = -\frac{3}{5}x - 10$ **49.**

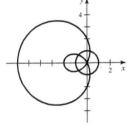

51. 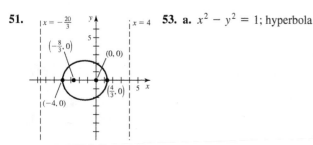   **53. a.** $x^2 - y^2 = 1$; hyperbola

b. $(\pm 1, 0), (\pm \sqrt{2}, 0); x = \pm \dfrac{1}{\sqrt{2}}; e = \sqrt{2}$

c.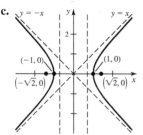

55. $\dfrac{y^2}{16} + \dfrac{25x^2}{336} = 1$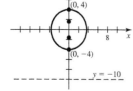

57. $\dfrac{y^2}{4} - \dfrac{x^2}{12} = 1$;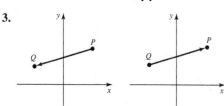

59. $e = 2/3, y = \pm 9, (\pm 2\sqrt{5}, 0)$ **61.** $(0, 0), (0.97, 0.97)$
63. $(0, 0)$ and $(r, \theta) = ((2n - 1)\pi, 0), n = 1, 2, 3, \ldots$
65. $\dfrac{2a}{\sqrt{2}} \cdot \dfrac{2b}{\sqrt{2}}; 2ab$ **67.** $m = \dfrac{b}{a}$ **71.** $r = \dfrac{3}{3 - \sin \theta}$

CHAPTER 12

Section 12.1 Exercises, pp. 787–790

3.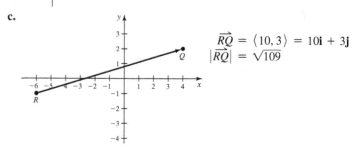

5. There are infinitely many vectors with the same direction and length as **v**.   **7.** If the scalar c is positive, extend the given vector by a multiple of c in the same direction. If $c < 0$, reverse the direction of the vector and extend it by a multiple of $|c|$.   **9.** $\mathbf{u} + \mathbf{v} = \langle u_1 + v_1, u_2 + v_2 \rangle$

11. $|\langle v_1, v_2 \rangle| = \sqrt{v_1^2 + v_2^2}$ **13.** If P has coordinates (p_1, p_2) and Q has coordinates (q_1, q_2) then the magnitude of $\overrightarrow{PQ}$ is given by $\sqrt{(q_1 - p_1)^2 + (q_2 - p_2)^2}$.   **15.** Divide **v** by its length and multiply the result by 10.   **17.** a, c, e   **19. a.** 3v   **b.** 2u   **c.** −3u   **d.** −2u   **e.** v   **21. a.** 3u + 3v   **b.** u + 2v   **c.** 2u + 5v   **d.** −2u + 3v   **e.** 3u + 2v   **f.** −3u − 2v   **g.** −2u − 4v   **h.** u − 4v   **i.** −u − 6v
23. a.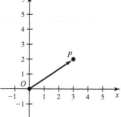
$\overrightarrow{OP} = \langle 3, 2 \rangle = 3\mathbf{i} + 2\mathbf{j}$
$|\overrightarrow{OP}| = \sqrt{13}$

b.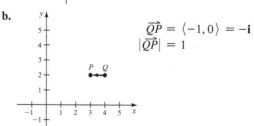
$\overrightarrow{QP} = \langle -1, 0 \rangle = -\mathbf{i}$
$|\overrightarrow{QP}| = 1$

c.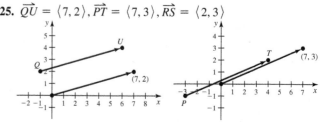
$\overrightarrow{RQ} = \langle 10, 3 \rangle = 10\mathbf{i} + 3\mathbf{j}$
$|\overrightarrow{RQ}| = \sqrt{109}$

25. $\overrightarrow{QU} = \langle 7, 2 \rangle, \overrightarrow{PT} = \langle 7, 3 \rangle, \overrightarrow{RS} = \langle 2, 3 \rangle$
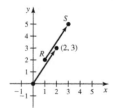

27. $\overrightarrow{QT}$ **29.** $\langle -4, 10 \rangle$ **31.** $\langle 12, -10 \rangle$ **33.** $\langle -28, 82 \rangle$ **35.** $2\sqrt{2}$
37. $\sqrt{194}$ **39.** $\langle 3, 3 \rangle, \langle -3, -3 \rangle$ **41.** $\mathbf{w} - \mathbf{u}$
43. $-\mathbf{i} + 10\mathbf{j}$ **45.** $\pm \dfrac{1}{\sqrt{61}} \langle 6, 5 \rangle$
47. $\left\langle -\dfrac{28}{\sqrt{74}}, \dfrac{20}{\sqrt{74}} \right\rangle, \left\langle \dfrac{28}{\sqrt{74}}, -\dfrac{20}{\sqrt{74}} \right\rangle$
49. $5\sqrt{65}$ km/hr ≈ 40.3 km/hr   **51.** 349.43 mi/hr in the direction 4.64° south of west   **53.** 1 m/s in the direction 30° east of north

55. a. $\langle 20, 20\sqrt{3}\rangle$ **b.** Yes   **c.** No   **57.** $250\sqrt{2}$ lb   **59. a.** True
b. True   **c.** False   **d.** False   **e.** False   **f.** False   **g.** False
h. True   **61. a.** $\langle \frac{3}{5}, -\frac{4}{5}\rangle$ and $\langle -\frac{3}{5}, \frac{4}{5}\rangle$ **b.** $b = \pm\frac{2\sqrt{2}}{3}$

c. $a = \frac{\pm 3}{\sqrt{10}}$ **63.** $\mathbf{x} = \langle \frac{1}{5}, -\frac{3}{10}\rangle$

65. $\mathbf{x} = \langle \frac{4}{3}, -\frac{11}{3}\rangle$ **67.** $4\mathbf{i} - 8\mathbf{j}$

69. $\langle a, b\rangle = \left(\frac{a+b}{2}\right)\mathbf{u} + \left(\frac{b-a}{2}\right)\mathbf{v}$ **71.** $\mathbf{u} = \frac{1}{5}\mathbf{i} + \frac{3}{5}\mathbf{j}$,

$\mathbf{v} = \frac{1}{5}\mathbf{i} - \frac{2}{5}\mathbf{j}$ **73.** $\langle \frac{15}{13}, -\frac{36}{13}\rangle$ **75.** $\langle 9, 3\rangle$ **77. a.** 0

b. The 6:00 vector   **c.** Sum any six consecutive vectors.   **d.** A vector pointing from 12:00 to 6:00 with a length 12 times the radius of the
clock   **79.** 50 lb in the direction 36.87° north of east
81. $\mathbf{u} + \mathbf{v} = \langle u_1, u_2\rangle + \langle v_1, v_2\rangle = \langle u_1 + v_1, u_2 + v_2\rangle$
$\qquad = \langle v_1 + u_1, v_2 + u_2\rangle = \langle v_1, v_2\rangle + \langle u_1, u_2\rangle$
$\qquad = \mathbf{v} + \mathbf{u}$
83. $a(c\mathbf{v}) = a(c\langle v_1, v_2\rangle) = a\langle cv_1, cv_2\rangle$
$\qquad = \langle acv_1, acv_2\rangle = \langle (ac)v_1, (ac)v_2\rangle$
$\qquad = ac\langle v_1, v_2\rangle = (ac)\mathbf{v}$
89. a. $\{\mathbf{u}, \mathbf{v}\}$ are linearly dependent. $\{\mathbf{u}, \mathbf{w}\}$ and $\{\mathbf{v}, \mathbf{w}\}$ are linearly independent.   **b.** Two linearly dependent vectors are parallel.
Two linearly independent vectors are not parallel.   **91. a.** $\frac{5}{3}$ **b.** -15

Section 12.2 Exercises, pp. 797–801

1. Move 3 units from the origin in the direction of the positive x-axis,
then 2 units in the direction of the negative y-axis, and then 1 unit in
the direction of the positive z-axis.   **3.** It is parallel to the yz-plane
and contains the point $(4, 0, 0)$.   **5.** $\mathbf{u} + \mathbf{v} = \langle 9, 0, -6\rangle$;
$3\mathbf{u} - \mathbf{v} = \langle 3, 20, -22\rangle$ **7.** $(0, 0, -4)$ **9.** $A(3, 0, 5), B(3, 4, 0)$,
$C(0, 4, 5)$ **11.** $A(3, -4, 5), B(0, -4, 0), C(0, -4, 5)$
13. a.
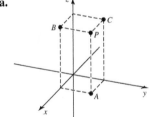
b.
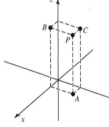
c.
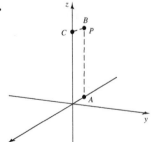
15.

17.
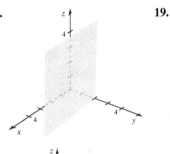
19.

21.
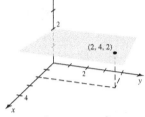

23. $(x - 1)^2 + (y - 2)^2 + (z - 3)^2 = 16$
25. $(x + 2)^2 + y^2 + (z - 4)^2 \le 1$
27. $\left(x - \frac{3}{2}\right)^2 + \left(y - \frac{3}{2}\right)^2 + (z - 7)^2 = \frac{13}{2}$ **29.** Sphere centered at
$(1, 0, 0)$ with radius 3   **31.** A sphere centered at $(0, 1, 2)$ with radius 3
33. All points on or outside the sphere with center $(0, 7, 0)$ and radius 6
35. The ball centered at $(4, 7, 9)$ with radius 15   **37.** The single point
$(1, -3, 0)$ **39.** $\langle 12, -7, 2\rangle; \langle 16, -13, -1\rangle; 5$ **41.** $\langle -4, 5, -4\rangle;$
$\langle -9, 3, -9\rangle; 3\sqrt{2}$ **43.** $\langle -15, 23, 22\rangle; \langle -31, 49, 33\rangle; 3\sqrt{5}$
45. a. $\overrightarrow{PQ} = \langle 2, 6, 2\rangle = 2\mathbf{i} + 6\mathbf{j} + 2\mathbf{k}$ **b.** $|\overrightarrow{PQ}| = 2\sqrt{11}$
c. $\left\langle \frac{1}{\sqrt{11}}, \frac{3}{\sqrt{11}}, \frac{1}{\sqrt{11}}\right\rangle$ and $\left\langle -\frac{1}{\sqrt{11}}, -\frac{3}{\sqrt{11}}, -\frac{1}{\sqrt{11}}\right\rangle$
47. a. $\overrightarrow{PQ} = \langle 0, -5, 1\rangle$ **b.** $|\overrightarrow{PQ}| = \sqrt{26}$ **c.** $\left\langle 0, -\frac{5}{\sqrt{26}}, \frac{1}{\sqrt{26}}\right\rangle$
and $\left\langle 0, \frac{5}{\sqrt{26}}, -\frac{1}{\sqrt{26}}\right\rangle$ **49. a.** $\overrightarrow{PQ} = \langle -2, 4, -2\rangle$
b. $|\overrightarrow{PQ}| = 2\sqrt{6}$ **c.** $\left\langle -\frac{1}{\sqrt{6}}, \frac{2}{\sqrt{6}}, -\frac{1}{\sqrt{6}}\right\rangle$ and $\left\langle \frac{1}{\sqrt{6}}, -\frac{2}{\sqrt{6}}, \frac{1}{\sqrt{6}}\right\rangle$
51. a. $20\mathbf{i} + 20\mathbf{j} - 10\mathbf{k}$;   **b.** 30 mi/hr
53. The speed of the plane is approximately 220 mi/hr; the direction is
slightly south of east and upward.
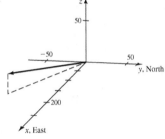

55. $5\sqrt{6}$ knots to the east, $5\sqrt{6}$ knots to the north, 10 knots upward
57. a. False   **b.** False   **c.** False   **d.** True   **59.** All points in $\mathbb{R}^3$
except those on the coordinate axes.

61. A circle of radius 1 centered at $(0, 0, 0)$ in the xy-plane

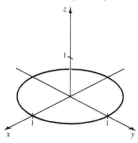

63. A circle of radius 2 centered at $(0, 0, 1)$ in the horizontal plane $z = 1$ **65.** $(x - 2)^2 + (z - 1)^2 = 9, y = 4$ **67.** $\langle 12, -16, 0 \rangle$, $\langle -12, 16, 0 \rangle$ **69.** $\langle -\sqrt{3}, -\sqrt{3}, \sqrt{3} \rangle, \langle \sqrt{3}, \sqrt{3}, -\sqrt{3} \rangle$
71. a. Collinear; Q is between P and R.   **b.** Collinear; P is between Q and R.   **c.** Noncollinear   **d.** Noncollinear   **73.** $\sqrt{29}$ ft for each piece   **75.** $\dfrac{250}{3} \left\langle -\dfrac{1}{\sqrt{3}}, 1, 2 \right\rangle, \dfrac{250}{3} \left\langle -\dfrac{1}{\sqrt{3}}, -1, -2 \right\rangle$, $\dfrac{500}{3} \left\langle \dfrac{1}{\sqrt{3}}, 0, -1 \right\rangle$ **77.** $(3, 8, 9), (-1, 0, 3)$, or $(1, 0, -3)$

Section 12.3 Exercises, pp. 808–812

1. $\mathbf{u} \cdot \mathbf{v} = |\mathbf{u}||\mathbf{v}| \cos \theta$ **3.** -40
5. $\cos \theta = \dfrac{\mathbf{u} \cdot \mathbf{v}}{|\mathbf{u}||\mathbf{v}|}$, so $\theta = \cos^{-1} \left(\dfrac{\mathbf{u} \cdot \mathbf{v}}{|\mathbf{u}||\mathbf{v}|} \right)$
7. Scalar, $\mathbf{u} = |\mathbf{u}| \cos \theta$ is the signed length of the projection of $\mathbf{u}$ in the direction of $\mathbf{v}$.   **9.** $0, 90°$ **11.** $100, 45°$ **13.** $\frac{1}{2}$ **15.** $0; \pi/2$
17. $1; \pi/3$ **19.** $-2, 93.2°$ **21.** $2, 87.2°$ **23.** $-4, 104°$
25. $\langle 3, 0 \rangle, 3$ **27.** $\langle 0, 3 \rangle, 3$ **29.** $\frac{6}{5} \langle -2, 1 \rangle, \dfrac{6}{\sqrt{5}}$
31. $\langle -1, 1, -2 \rangle; -\sqrt{6}$ **33.** $\dfrac{14}{19} \langle -1, -3, 3 \rangle, -\dfrac{14}{\sqrt{19}}$
35. $-\mathbf{i} + \mathbf{j} - 2\mathbf{k}; \sqrt{6}$ **37.** $750\sqrt{3}$ ft · lb   **39.** $25\sqrt{2}$ J   **41.** 400 J
43. $\langle 5, -5 \rangle, \langle -5, -5 \rangle$ **45.** $\langle -5\sqrt{3}, -5 \rangle, \langle 5\sqrt{3}, -5 \rangle$
47. a. False   **b.** True   **c.** True   **d.** False   **e.** False   **f.** True
49. $\{\langle 1, a, 4a - 2 \rangle : a \in \mathbb{R}\}$ **51.** $\left\langle \dfrac{1}{\sqrt{2}}, \dfrac{1}{\sqrt{2}}, 0 \right\rangle$, $\left\langle -\dfrac{1}{\sqrt{2}}, \dfrac{1}{\sqrt{2}}, 0 \right\rangle, \langle 0, 0, 1 \rangle$ (one possibility)
53. a. $\text{proj}_{\mathbf{k}}\mathbf{u} = |\mathbf{u}| \cos 60° \left(\dfrac{\mathbf{k}}{|\mathbf{k}|} \right) = \dfrac{1}{2}\mathbf{k}$ for all such $\mathbf{u}$ **b.** Yes
55. The heads of the vectors lie on the line $y = 3 - x$.   **57.** The heads of the vectors lie on the plane $z = 3$.
59. $\mathbf{u} = \left\langle -\dfrac{4}{5}, -\dfrac{2}{5} \right\rangle + \left\langle -\dfrac{6}{5}, \dfrac{12}{5} \right\rangle$
61. $\mathbf{u} = \left\langle 1, \dfrac{1}{2}, \dfrac{1}{2} \right\rangle + \left\langle -2, \dfrac{3}{2}, \dfrac{5}{2} \right\rangle$ **63. e.** $|\mathbf{w}| = \dfrac{28\sqrt{5}}{5}$
65. e. $|\mathbf{w}| = \sqrt{\dfrac{326}{109}}$
67. $\mathbf{I} = \dfrac{1}{\sqrt{2}}\mathbf{i} + \dfrac{1}{\sqrt{2}}\mathbf{j}, \mathbf{J} = -\dfrac{1}{\sqrt{2}}\mathbf{i} + \dfrac{1}{\sqrt{2}}\mathbf{j}$; $\mathbf{i} = \dfrac{1}{\sqrt{2}}(\mathbf{I} - \mathbf{J}), \mathbf{j} = \dfrac{1}{\sqrt{2}}(\mathbf{I} + \mathbf{J})$
69. a. $|\mathbf{I}| = |\mathbf{J}| = |\mathbf{K}| = 1$ **b.** $\mathbf{I} \cdot \mathbf{J} = 0, \mathbf{I} \cdot \mathbf{K} = 0, \mathbf{J} \cdot \mathbf{K} = 0$ **c.** $\langle 1, 0, 0 \rangle = \frac{1}{2}\mathbf{I} - (1/\sqrt{2})\mathbf{J} + \frac{1}{2}\mathbf{K}$

71. $\angle P = 78.8°, \angle Q = 47.2°, \angle R = 54.0°$ **73. a.** The faces on $y = 0$ and $z = 0$ **b.** The faces on $y = 1$ and $z = 1$ **c.** The faces on $x = 0$ and $x = 1$ **d.** 0 **e.** 1 **f.** 2 **75. a.** $\left(\dfrac{2}{\sqrt{3}}, 0, \dfrac{2\sqrt{2}}{3} \right)$
b. $\mathbf{r}_{OP} = \langle \sqrt{3}, -1, 0 \rangle, \mathbf{r}_{OQ} = \langle \sqrt{3}, 1, 0 \rangle, \mathbf{r}_{PQ} = \langle 0, 2, 0 \rangle$, $\mathbf{r}_{OR} = \left\langle \dfrac{2}{\sqrt{3}}, 0, \dfrac{2\sqrt{2}}{3} \right\rangle, \mathbf{r}_{PR} = \left\langle -\dfrac{\sqrt{3}}{3}, 1, \dfrac{2\sqrt{2}}{3} \right\rangle$
83. a. $\cos^2 \alpha + \cos^2 \beta + \cos^2 \gamma$
$$= \left(\dfrac{\mathbf{v} \cdot \mathbf{i}}{|\mathbf{v}||\mathbf{i}|} \right)^2 + \left(\dfrac{\mathbf{v} \cdot \mathbf{j}}{|\mathbf{v}||\mathbf{j}|} \right)^2 + \left(\dfrac{\mathbf{v} \cdot \mathbf{k}}{|\mathbf{v}||\mathbf{k}|} \right)^2$$
$$= \dfrac{a^2}{a^2 + b^2 + c^2} + \dfrac{b^2}{a^2 + b^2 + c^2} + \dfrac{c^2}{a^2 + b^2 + c^2} = 1$$
b. $\langle 1, 1, 0 \rangle, 90°$ **c.** $\left\langle \dfrac{1}{\sqrt{2}}, \dfrac{1}{\sqrt{2}}, 1 \right\rangle, 45°$
d. No. If so, $\left(\dfrac{\sqrt{3}}{2} \right)^2 + \left(\dfrac{\sqrt{3}}{2} \right)^2 + \cos^2 \gamma = 1$, which has no solution.
e. $54.7°$ **85.** $|\mathbf{u} \cdot \mathbf{v}| = 33 = \sqrt{33} \cdot \sqrt{33} < \sqrt{70} \cdot \sqrt{74} = |\mathbf{u}||\mathbf{v}|$

Section 12.4 Exercises, pp. 817–820

1. $|\mathbf{u} \times \mathbf{v}| = |\mathbf{u}||\mathbf{v}|\sin \theta$, where $0 \le \theta \le \pi$ is the angle between $\mathbf{u}$ and $\mathbf{v}$ **3.** 0 **5.** $\mathbf{u} \times \mathbf{v} = \begin{vmatrix} \mathbf{i} & \mathbf{j} & \mathbf{k} \\ u_1 & u_2 & u_3 \\ v_1 & v_2 & v_3 \end{vmatrix}$ **7.** $15\mathbf{k}$
9. 0 **11.** 18

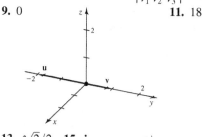

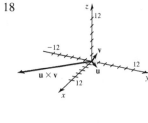

13. $\sqrt{2}/2$ **15.** $\mathbf{i}$

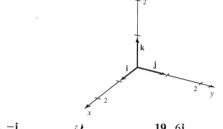

17. $-\mathbf{i}$ **19.** $6\mathbf{j}$

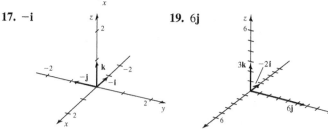

21. 11 **23.** $3\sqrt{10}$ **25.** $\sqrt{11}/2$ **27.** $4\sqrt{2}$
29. $\mathbf{u} \times \mathbf{v} = \langle -30, 18, 9 \rangle, \mathbf{v} \times \mathbf{u} = \langle 30, -18, -9 \rangle$
31. $\mathbf{u} \times \mathbf{v} = \langle 6, 11, 5 \rangle, \mathbf{v} \times \mathbf{u} = \langle -6, -11, -5 \rangle$
33. $\mathbf{u} \times \mathbf{v} = \langle 8, 4, 10 \rangle, \mathbf{v} \times \mathbf{u} = \langle -8, -4, -10 \rangle$
35. $\langle 3, -4, 2 \rangle$ **37.** $\langle -8, -40, 16 \rangle$ **39.** $5/\sqrt{2}$ N · m
41. $\langle 0, 20, -20 \rangle$ **43.** The force $\mathbf{F} = 5\mathbf{i} - 5\mathbf{k}$ produces the greater torque.

45. The magnitude is $20\sqrt{2}$ at a $135°$ angle with the positive x-axis in the xy-plane.

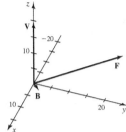

47. $4.53 \times 10^{-14} \text{ kg} \cdot \text{m/s}^2$ **49. a.** False   **b.** False   **c.** False **d.** True   **e.** False   **51.** Not collinear   **53.** $\langle b^2 - a^2, 0, a^2 - b^2 \rangle$. The vectors are parallel when $a = \pm b \neq 0$.   **55.** $9\sqrt{2}$ **57.** $\dfrac{7\sqrt{6}}{2}$

59. $\{\langle u_1, u_1 + 2, u_1 + 1 \rangle : u_1 \in \mathbb{R}\}$ **61.** $\dfrac{\sqrt{(ab)^2 + (ac)^2 + (bc)^2}}{2}$

63. $|\mathbf{u} \cdot (\mathbf{v} \times \mathbf{w})| = |\mathbf{u}||\mathbf{v} \times \mathbf{w}||\cos\theta|$ where $|\mathbf{v} \times \mathbf{w}|$ is the area of the base of the parallelepiped and $|\mathbf{u}||\cos\theta|$ is its height. **65.** $|\tau| = 26.4 \text{ N} \cdot \text{m}$, direction: into the page.   **67.** $1.76 \times 10^7 \text{ m/s}$

Section 12.5 Exercises, pp. 826–829

1. One   **3.** Its output is a vector.
5. $\langle x, y, z \rangle = \langle x_0, y_0, z_0 \rangle + t\langle x_1 - x_0, y_1 - y_0, z_1 - z_0 \rangle$
7. $\lim\limits_{t \to a} \mathbf{r}(t) = \lim\limits_{t \to a} f(t)\mathbf{i} + \lim\limits_{t \to a} g(t)\mathbf{j} + \lim\limits_{t \to a} h(t)\mathbf{k}$
9. $\mathbf{r}(t) = \langle 0, 0, 1 \rangle + t\langle 4, 7, 0 \rangle$
11. $\langle x, y, z \rangle = \langle 0, 0, 1 \rangle + t\langle 0, 1, 0 \rangle$ **13.** $\langle x, y, z \rangle = t\langle 1, 2, 3 \rangle$
15. $\langle x, y, z \rangle = \langle -3, 4, 6 \rangle + t\langle 8, -5, -6 \rangle$
17. $\mathbf{r}(t) = t\langle -2, 8, -4 \rangle$ **19.** $\mathbf{r}(t) = t\langle -2, -1, 1 \rangle$
21. $\mathbf{r}(t) = \langle -2, 5, 3 \rangle + t\langle 0, 2, -1 \rangle$
23. $\mathbf{r}(t) = \langle 1, 2, 3 \rangle + t\langle -4, 6, 14 \rangle$ **25.** $\langle x, y, z \rangle = t\langle 1, 2, 3 \rangle$, $0 \le t \le 1$ **27.** $\langle x, y, z \rangle = \langle 2, 4, 8 \rangle + t\langle 5, 1, -5 \rangle, 0 \le t \le 1$
29.

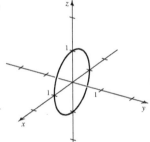

31.

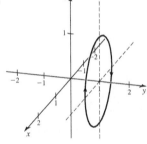

33.

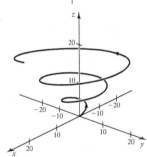

35.

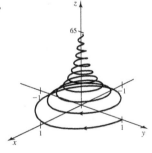

37.

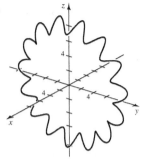

39. When viewed from the top, the curve is a portion of the parabola $y = x^2$.

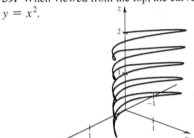

41. $-\mathbf{i} - 4\mathbf{j} + \mathbf{k}$ **43.** $-2\mathbf{j} + \dfrac{\pi}{2}\mathbf{k}$ **45.** $\mathbf{i}$ **47. a.** True   **b.** False
c. True   **d.** True   **49.** $\mathbf{r}(t) = \langle 4, 3, 3 \rangle + t\langle 0, -9, 6 \rangle$
51. The lines intersect at $(1, 3, 2)$.   **53.** Skew
55. These equations describe the same line.   **57.** $\{t : |t| \le 2\}$
59. $\{t : 0 \le t \le 2\}$ **61.** $(21, -6, 4)$ **63.** $(16, 0, -8)$
65. $(4, 8, 16)$ **67. a.** E   **b.** D   **c.** F   **d.** C
e. A   **f.** B   **69. a.** $(50, 0, 0)$ **b.** 5k   **c.**

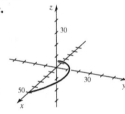

d. $x^2 + y^2 = (50e^{-t})^2$ so $r = 50e^{-t}$. Hence $z = 5 - 5e^{-t} = 5 - \dfrac{r}{10}$.

71. a.

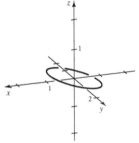

Curve is a tilted circle of radius 1 centered at the origin.
73. $\langle cf - ed, be - af, ad - bc \rangle$ or any scalar multiple
75.

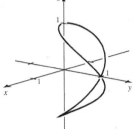

The curve lies on the sphere $x^2 + y^2 + z^2 = 1$.

77. $\dfrac{2\pi}{(m,n)}$, where $(m, n) =$ greatest common factor of m and n.

Section 12.6 Exercises, pp. 835–837

1. $\mathbf{r}(t) = \langle f'(t), g'(t), h'(t) \rangle$ **3.** $\mathbf{T}(t) = \dfrac{\mathbf{r}'(t)}{|\mathbf{r}'(t)|}$

5. $\displaystyle\int \mathbf{r}(t)\, dt = \left(\int f(t)\, dt\right)\mathbf{i} + \left(\int g(t)\, dt\right)\mathbf{j} + \left(\int h(t)\, dt\right)\mathbf{k}$

7. $\langle -\sin t, 2t, \cos t \rangle$ **9.** $\left\langle 6t^2, \dfrac{3}{\sqrt{t}}, -\dfrac{3}{t^2} \right\rangle$ **11.** $\langle e^t, -2e^{-t}, -8e^{2t} \rangle$

13. $\langle e^{-t}(1 - t), 1 + \ln t, \cos t - t \sin t \rangle$ **15.** $\langle 1, 6, 3 \rangle$
17. $\langle 1, 0, 0 \rangle$ **19.** $\langle 8, 9, -10 \rangle$ **21.** $\langle 2/3, 2/3, 1/3 \rangle$
23. $\dfrac{\langle 0, -\sin 2t, 2\cos 2t \rangle}{\sqrt{1 + 3\cos^2 2t}}$ **25.** $\dfrac{t^2}{\sqrt{t^4 + 4}}\left\langle 1, 0, -\dfrac{2}{t^2} \right\rangle$

27. $\langle 0, 0, -1 \rangle$ **29.** $\left\langle \dfrac{2}{\sqrt{5}}, 0, -\dfrac{1}{\sqrt{5}} \right\rangle$

31. $\langle 30t^{14} + 24t^3, 14t^{13} - 12t^{11} + 9t^2 - 3, -96t^{11} - 24 \rangle$
33. $4t(2t^3 - 1)(t^3 - 2)\langle 3t(t^3 - 2), 1, 0 \rangle$
35. $e^t(2t^3 + 6t^2) - 2e^{-t}(t^2 - 2t - 1) - 16e^{-2t}$
37. $5te^t(t + 2) - 6t^2e^{-t}(t - 3)$

39. $-3t^2\sin t + 6t\cos t + 2\sqrt{t}\cos 2t + \dfrac{1}{2\sqrt{t}}\sin 2t$

41. $\langle 2, 0, 0 \rangle$, $\langle 0, 0, 0 \rangle$ **43.** $\langle -9\cos 3t, -16\sin 4t, -36\cos 6t \rangle$, $\langle 27\sin 3t, -64\cos 4t, 216\sin 6t \rangle$

45. $\left\langle -\dfrac{1}{4}(t + 4)^{-3/2}, -2(t + 1)^{-3}, 2e^{-t^2}(1 - 2t^2) \right\rangle$,

$\left\langle \dfrac{3}{8}(t + 4)^{-5/2}, 6(t + 1)^{-4}, -4te^{-t^2}(3 - 2t^2) \right\rangle$

47. $\left\langle \dfrac{t^5}{5} - \dfrac{3t^2}{2}, t^2 - t, 10t \right\rangle + \mathbf{C}$

49. $\left\langle 2\sin t, -\dfrac{2}{3}\cos 3t, \dfrac{1}{2}\sin 8t \right\rangle + \mathbf{C}$

51. $\frac{1}{3}e^{3t}\mathbf{i} + \tan^{-1}t\,\mathbf{j} - \sqrt{2t}\,\mathbf{k} + \mathbf{C}$
53. $\mathbf{r}(t) = \langle e^t + 1, 3 - \cos t, \tan t + 2 \rangle$
55. $\mathbf{r}(t) = \langle t + 3, t^2 + 2, t^3 - 6 \rangle$
57. $\mathbf{r}(t) = \langle \frac{1}{2}e^{2t} + \frac{1}{2}, 2e^{-t} + t - 1, t - 2e^t + 3 \rangle$ **59.** $\langle 2, 0, 2 \rangle$
61. $\mathbf{i}$ **63.** $\langle 0, 0, 0 \rangle$ **65.** $(e^2 + 1)\langle 1, 2, -1 \rangle$ **67. a.** False
b. True   **c.** True   **69.** $\langle 2 - t, 3 - 2t, \pi/2 + t \rangle$

71. $\langle 2 + 3t, 9 + 7t, 1 + 2t \rangle$ **73.** $\langle 2e^{2t}, -2e^t, 0 \rangle$ **75.** $\left\langle 4, -\dfrac{2}{\sqrt{t}}, 0 \right\rangle$

77. $\langle 1 + 6t^2, 4t^3, -2 - 3t^2 \rangle$ **79.** $\langle 1, 0 \rangle$ **81.** $\langle 1, 0, 0 \rangle$
83. $\mathbf{r}(t) = \langle a_1t, a_2t, a_3t \rangle$ or $\mathbf{r}(t) = \langle a_1e^{kt}, a_2e^{kt}, a_3e^{kt} \rangle$, where a_i and k are real numbers

Section 12.7 Exercises, pp. 847–851

1. $\mathbf{v}(t) = \mathbf{r}'(t)$, speed $= |\mathbf{r}'(t)|$, $\mathbf{a}(t) = \mathbf{r}''(t)$ **3.** $m\mathbf{a}(t) = \mathbf{F}$

5. $\mathbf{v}(t) = \displaystyle\int \mathbf{a}(t)\, dt = \langle v_1(t), v_2(t) \rangle + \mathbf{C}$. Use initial conditions to

find $\mathbf{C}$.   **7. a.** $\langle 6t, 8t \rangle$, $10t$ **b.** $\langle 6, 8 \rangle$ **9. a.** $\mathbf{v}(t) = \langle 2, -4 \rangle$,
$|\mathbf{v}(t)| = 2\sqrt{5}$ **b.** $\mathbf{a}(t) = \langle 0, 0 \rangle$ **11. a.** $\mathbf{v}(t) = \langle 8\cos t, -8\sin t \rangle$,
$|\mathbf{v}(t)| = 8$ **b.** $\mathbf{a}(t) = \langle -8\sin t, -8\cos t \rangle$ **13. a.** $\langle 2t, 2t, t \rangle$, $3t$
b. $\langle 2, 2, 1 \rangle$ **15. a.** $\mathbf{v}(t) = \langle 1, -4, 6 \rangle$, $|\mathbf{v}(t)| = \sqrt{53}$
b. $\mathbf{a}(t) = \langle 0, 0, 0 \rangle$ **17. a.** $\mathbf{v}(t) = \langle 0, 2t, -e^{-t} \rangle$,
$|\mathbf{v}(t)| = \sqrt{4t^2 + e^{-2t}}$ **b.** $\mathbf{a}(t) = \langle 0, 2, e^{-t} \rangle$ **19. a.** $[c, d] = [0, 1]$

b. $\langle 1, 2t \rangle$, $\langle 2, 8t \rangle$
c.

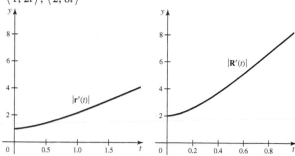

21. a. $\left[0, \dfrac{2\pi}{3} \right]$ **b.** $\mathbf{V_r}(t) = \langle -\sin t, 4\cos t \rangle$, $\mathbf{V_R}(t) = \langle -3\sin 3t, 12\cos 3t \rangle$
c.

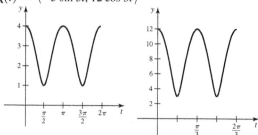

23. a. $[1, e^{36}]$

b. $\mathbf{V_r}(t) = \langle 2t, -8t^3, 18t^5 \rangle$, $\mathbf{V_R}(t) = \left\langle \dfrac{1}{t}, -\dfrac{4}{t}\ln t, \dfrac{9}{t}\ln^2 t \right\rangle$

c.

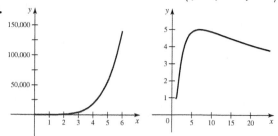

25. $\mathbf{r}(t)$ lies on a circle of radius 8;
$\langle -16\sin 2t, 16\cos 2t \rangle \cdot \langle 8\cos 2t, 8\sin 2t \rangle = 0$.
27. $\mathbf{r}(t)$ lies on a sphere of radius 2;
$\langle \cos t - \sqrt{3}\sin t, \sqrt{3}\cos t + \sin t \rangle$
$\cdot \langle \sin t + \sqrt{3}\cos t, \sqrt{3}\sin t - \cos t \rangle = 0$.
29. $\mathbf{r}(t)$ does not lie on a sphere.

31. $\mathbf{v}(t) = \langle 2, t + 3 \rangle$; $\mathbf{r}(t) = \left\langle 2t, \dfrac{t^2}{2} + 3t \right\rangle$

33. $\mathbf{v}(t) = \langle 0, 10t + 5 \rangle$, $\mathbf{r}(t) = \langle 1, 5t^2 + 5t - 1 \rangle$
35. $\mathbf{v}(t) = \langle \sin t, -2\cos t + 3 \rangle$, $\mathbf{r}(t) = \langle -\cos t + 2, -2\sin t + 3t \rangle$
37. a. $\mathbf{v}(t) = \langle 30, -9.8t + 6 \rangle$, $\mathbf{r}(t) = \langle 30t, -4.9t^2 + 6t \rangle$
b.

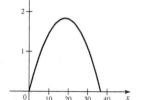

c. $T \approx 1.22$ s, range ≈ 36.7 m
d. 1.84 m

39. a. $\mathbf{v}(t) = \langle 80, 10 - 32t \rangle$, $\mathbf{r}(t) = \langle 80t, -16t^2 + 10t + 6 \rangle$

b.

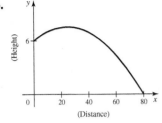

(Height) / (Distance)

c. 1 s, 80 ft

d. max. height ≈ 7.56 ft

41. a. $\mathbf{v}(t) = \langle 125, -32t + 125\sqrt{3} \rangle$,

$\mathbf{r}(t) = \langle 125t, -16t^2 + 125\sqrt{3}t + 20 \rangle$

b.

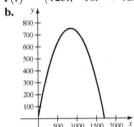

c. 13.6 s; 1702.5 ft   **d.** 752.4 ft

43. $\mathbf{v}(t) = \langle 1, 5, 10t \rangle$, $\mathbf{r}(t) = \langle t, 5t + 5, 5t^2 \rangle$

45. $\mathbf{v}(t) = \langle -\cos t + 1, \sin t + 2, t \rangle$,

$\mathbf{r}(t) = \left\langle -\sin t + t, -\cos t + 2t + 1, \dfrac{t^2}{2} \right\rangle$

47. a. $\mathbf{v}(t) = \langle 200, 200, -9.8t \rangle$, $\mathbf{r}(t) = \langle 200t, 200t, -4.9t^2 + 1 \rangle$

b.

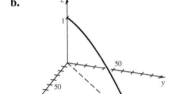

c. 0.452 s, 127.8 m   **d.** 1 m

49. a. $\mathbf{v}(t) = \langle 60 + 10t, 80, 80 - 32t \rangle$,

$\mathbf{r}(t) = \langle 60t + 5t^2, 80t, 80t - 16t^2 + 3 \rangle$

b.

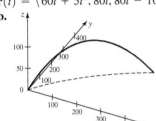

c. 5.04 s, 589 ft

d. max. height = 103 ft

51. a. $\mathbf{v}(t) = \langle 300, 2.5t + 400, -9.8t + 500 \rangle$,

$\mathbf{r}(t) = \langle 300t, 1.25t^2 + 400t, -4.9t^2 + 500t + 10 \rangle$

b.

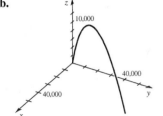

c. 102.1 s, 61,941.5 m

d. 12,765.1 m

53. a. False   **b.** True   **c.** False   **d.** True   **e.** False   **f.** True

g. True   **55.** 15.3 s, 1988.3 m, 287.0 m   **57.** 21.7 s, 4330.1 ft, 1875 ft   **59.** Approximately 27.4° and 62.6°   **61. a.** The direction of $\mathbf{r}$ does not change.   **b.** Constant in direction, not in magnitude

63. a. $\left[0, \dfrac{2\pi}{\omega} \right]$ **b.** $\mathbf{v}(t) = \langle -A\omega \sin \omega t, A\omega \cos \omega t \rangle$ is not constant, $|\mathbf{v}(t)| = |A\omega|$ is constant.   **c.** $\mathbf{a}(t) = \langle -A\omega^2 \cos \omega t, -A\omega^2 \sin \omega t \rangle$

d. $\mathbf{r}$ and $\mathbf{v}$ are orthogonal, $\mathbf{r}$ and $\mathbf{a}$ are in opposite directions.

e.

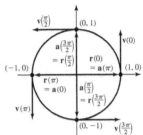

65. a. $\mathbf{r}(t) = \langle 5 \sin (\pi t/6), 5 \cos (\pi t/6) \rangle$

b. $\mathbf{r}(t) = \left\langle 5 \sin \left(\dfrac{1 - e^{-t}}{5} \right), 5 \cos \left(\dfrac{1 - e^{-t}}{5} \right) \right\rangle$

67. a. $\mathbf{v}(t) = \langle -a \sin t, b \cos t \rangle$; $|\mathbf{v}(t)| = \sqrt{a^2 \sin^2 t + b^2 \cos^2 t}$

b.

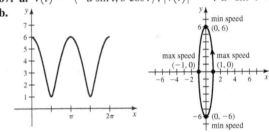

c. Yes   **d.** max $\left\{ \dfrac{a}{b}, \dfrac{b}{a} \right\}$

69. a. $\mathbf{r}(0) = \langle 50, 0, 0 \rangle$, $\lim\limits_{t \to \infty} \mathbf{r}(t) = \langle 0, 0, 5 \rangle$ **b.** At $t = 0$

c.

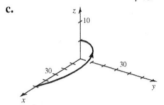

71. Approximately 0.41 rad (23.5°) or 1.04 rad (59.6°)   **73.** 113.4 ft/s

75. a. 1.2 ft, 0.46 s   **b.** 0.88 ft/s   **c.** 0.85 ft   **d.** More curve in the second half.   **e.** $c = 28.17$ ft/s^2

77. $T = \dfrac{|\mathbf{v}_0| \sin \alpha + \sqrt{|\mathbf{v}_0|^2 \sin^2 \alpha + 2gy_0}}{g}$, range $= |\mathbf{v}_0| (\cos \alpha) T$,

max. height $= y_0 + \dfrac{|\mathbf{v}_0|^2 \sin^2 \alpha}{2g}$ **79.** $\{ (\cos t, \sin t, c \sin t) : t \in \mathbb{R} \}$

satisfies the equations $x^2 + y^2 = 1$ and $z - cy = 0$ so that $\langle \cos t, \sin t, c \sin t \rangle$ lies on the intersection of a right circular cylinder and a plane, which is an ellipse.

83. a. $a^2 + c^2 + e^2 = b^2 + d^2 + f^2$ and $ab + cd + ef = 0$

b. $a^2 + c^2 = b^2 + d^2$, $ab + cd = 0$, and $a + c = -e$ and $b + d = -f$

Section 12.8 Exercises, pp. 860–862

1. $\sqrt{5}(b - a)$ **3.** $\displaystyle\int_a^b |\mathbf{v}(t)| \, dt$ **5.** 20π **7.** If the parameter t used

to describe a trajectory also measures the arc length s of the curve that is generated, we say the curve has been parametrized by its arc length.

9. 5   **11.** 3π **13.** $\dfrac{\pi^2}{8}$ **15.** $5\sqrt{34}$ **17.** $4\pi\sqrt{65}$ **19.** 9   **21.** $\frac{3}{2}$

23. $3t^2\sqrt{30}$; $64\sqrt{30}$ **25.** 26; 26π **27.** 19.38   **29.** 32.50   **31.** πa

33. $\frac{8}{3}[(1+\pi^2)^{3/2}-1]$ **35.** 32   **37.** $63\sqrt{5}$ **39.** $\dfrac{2\pi - 3\sqrt{3}}{8}$

41. Yes   **43.** No; $\mathbf{r}(s) = \left\langle \dfrac{s}{\sqrt{5}}, \dfrac{2s}{\sqrt{5}} \right\rangle, 0 \le s \le 3\sqrt{5}$

45. No; $\mathbf{r}(s) = \left\langle 2\cos\dfrac{s}{2}, 2\sin\dfrac{s}{2} \right\rangle, 0 \le s \le 4\pi$

47. No; $\mathbf{r}(s) = \langle \cos s, \sin s \rangle, 0 \le s \le \pi$

49. No; $\mathbf{r}(s) = \left\langle \dfrac{s}{\sqrt{3}}+1, \dfrac{s}{\sqrt{3}}+1, \dfrac{s}{\sqrt{3}}+1 \right\rangle, s \ge 0$ **51. a.** True

b. True   **c.** True   **d.** False   **53. a.** If $a^2 = b^2 + c^2$ then
$|\mathbf{r}(t)|^2 = (a\cos t)^2 + (b\sin t)^2 + (c\sin t)^2 = a^2$ so that $\mathbf{r}(t)$ is a
circle centered at the origin of radius $|a|$.   **b.** $2\pi a$
c. If $a^2 + c^2 + e^2 = b^2 + d^2 + f^2$ and $ab + cd + ef = 0$,
then $\mathbf{r}(t)$ is a circle of radius $\sqrt{a^2 + c^2 + e^2}$ and its arc length
is $2\pi\sqrt{a^2 + c^2 + e^2}$.

55. a. $\displaystyle\int_a^b \sqrt{[Ah'(t)]^2 + [Bh'(t)]^2}\, dt$

$= \displaystyle\int_a^b \sqrt{(A^2 + B^2)\,(h'(t))^2}\, dt = \sqrt{A^2 + B^2}\int_a^b |h'(t)|\, dt$

b. $64\sqrt{29}$ **c.** $\dfrac{7\sqrt{29}}{4}$ **57.** $\dfrac{\sqrt{1+a^2}}{a}$ (where $a > 0$)   **59.** 12.85

61. 26.73   **63. a.** 5.102 s   **b.** $\displaystyle\int_0^{5.102} \sqrt{400 + (25 - 9.8t)^2}\, dt$

c. 124.43 m   **d.** 102.04 m   **65.** $|\mathbf{v}(t)| = \sqrt{a^2 + b^2 + c^2} = 1$,
if $a^2 + b^2 + c^2 = 1$.

67. $\displaystyle\int_a^b |\mathbf{r}'(t)|\, dt = \int_a^b \sqrt{[cf'(t)]^2 + [cg'(t)]^2}\, dt$

$= |c|\displaystyle\int_a^b \sqrt{(f'(t))^2 + (g'(t))^2}\, dt = |c|L.$

69. If $\mathbf{r}(t) = \langle t, f(t)\rangle$, then by definition the arc length

is $\displaystyle\int_a^b \sqrt{(t')^2 + [f'(t)]^2}\, dt = \int_a^b \sqrt{1 + (f'(t))^2}\, dt$

$= \displaystyle\int_a^b \sqrt{1 + (f'(x))^2}\, dx.$

Section 12.9 Exercises, pp. 874–876

1. 0   **3.** $\kappa = \dfrac{1}{|\mathbf{v}|}\left|\dfrac{d\mathbf{T}}{dt}\right|$ or $\kappa = \dfrac{|\mathbf{v}\times\mathbf{a}|}{|\mathbf{v}|^3}$ **5.** $\mathbf{N} = \dfrac{d\mathbf{T}/dt}{|d\mathbf{T}/dt|}$

7. These three unit vectors are mutually orthogonal at all points of the
curve.   **9.** The torsion measures the rate at which the curve rises or
twists out of the **TN**-plane at a point.

11. $\mathbf{T} = \dfrac{\langle 1, 2, 3\rangle}{\sqrt{14}}, \kappa = 0$ **13.** $\mathbf{T} = \dfrac{\langle 1, 2\cos t, -2\sin t\rangle}{\sqrt{5}}, \kappa = \dfrac{1}{5}$

15. $\mathbf{T} = \dfrac{\langle \sqrt{3}\cos t, \cos t, -2\sin t\rangle}{2}, \kappa = \dfrac{1}{2}$ **17.** $\mathbf{T} = \dfrac{\langle 1, 4t\rangle}{\sqrt{1 + 16t^2}},$

$\kappa = \dfrac{4}{(1 + 16t^2)^{3/2}}$ **19.** $\mathbf{T} = \left\langle \cos\left(\dfrac{\pi t^2}{2}\right), \sin\left(\dfrac{\pi t^2}{2}\right)\right\rangle, \kappa = \pi t$

21. $\dfrac{1}{3}$ **23.** $\dfrac{2}{(4t^2 + 1)^{3/2}}$ **25.** $\dfrac{2\sqrt{5}}{(20\sin^2 t + \cos^2 t)^{3/2}}$

27. $\mathbf{T} = \langle \cos t, -\sin t\rangle, \mathbf{N} = \langle -\sin t, -\cos t\rangle$ **29.** $\mathbf{T} = \dfrac{\langle t, -3, 0\rangle}{\sqrt{t^2 + 9}},$
$\mathbf{N} = \dfrac{\langle 3, t, 0\rangle}{\sqrt{t^2 + 9}}$ **31.** $\mathbf{T} = \langle -\sin t^2, \cos t^2\rangle, \mathbf{N} = \langle -\cos t^2, -\sin t^2\rangle$

33. $\mathbf{T} = \dfrac{\langle 2t, 1\rangle}{\sqrt{4t^2 + 1}}, \mathbf{N} = \dfrac{\langle 1, -2t\rangle}{\sqrt{4t^2 + 1}}$ **35.** $a_N = a_T = 0$

37. $a_T = \sqrt{3}\,e^t; a_N = \sqrt{2}e^t$ **39.** $\mathbf{a} = \dfrac{6t}{\sqrt{9t^2 + 4}}\mathbf{N} + \dfrac{18t^2 + 4}{\sqrt{9t^2 + 4}}\mathbf{T}$

41. $\mathbf{B}(t) = \langle 0, 0, -1\rangle, \tau = 0$ **43.** $\mathbf{B}(t) = \langle 0, 0, 1\rangle, \tau = 0$

45. $\mathbf{B}(t) = \dfrac{\langle -\sin t, \cos t, 2\rangle}{\sqrt{5}}, \tau = -\dfrac{1}{5}$

47. $\mathbf{B}(t) = \dfrac{\langle 5, 12\sin t, -12\cos t\rangle}{13}, \tau = \dfrac{12}{169}$ **49. a.** False

b. False   **c.** False   **d.** True   **e.** False   **f.** False   **g.** False

51. $\kappa = \dfrac{2}{(1 + 4x^2)^{3/2}}$ **53.** $\kappa = \dfrac{x}{(x^2 + 1)^{3/2}}$

57. $\kappa = \dfrac{|ab|}{(a^2\cos^2 t + b^2\sin^2 t)^{3/2}}$ **59.** $\kappa = \dfrac{2|a|}{(1 + 4a^2 t^2)^{3/2}}$

61. b. $\mathbf{v}_A(t) = \langle 1, 2, 3\rangle, \mathbf{a}_A(t) = \langle 0, 0, 0\rangle$ and $\mathbf{v}_B(t) = \langle 2t, 4t, 6t\rangle$,
$\mathbf{a}_B(t) = \langle 2, 4, 6\rangle$; A has constant velocity and zero acceleration
while B has increasing speed and constant acceleration.
c. $\mathbf{a}_A(t) = 0\mathbf{N} + 0\mathbf{T}$, $\mathbf{a}_B(t) = 0\mathbf{N} + 2\sqrt{14}\,\mathbf{T}$; both normal
components are zero since the path is a straight line $(\kappa = 0)$.
63. b. $\mathbf{v}_A(t) = \langle -\sin t, \cos t\rangle, \mathbf{a}_A(t) = \langle -\cos t, -\sin t\rangle$
$\mathbf{v}_B(t) = \langle -2t\sin t^2, 2t\cos t^2\rangle$
$\mathbf{a}_B(t) = \langle -4t^2\cos t^2 - 2\sin t^2, -4t^2\sin t^2 + 2\cos t^2\rangle$
c. $\mathbf{a}_A(t) = \mathbf{N} + 0\mathbf{T}$, $\mathbf{a}_B(t) = 4t^2\mathbf{N} + 2\mathbf{T}$; for A, the acceleration is
always normal to the curve, but this is not true for B.

65. b. $\kappa = \dfrac{1}{2\sqrt{2(1 - \cos t)}}$ **c.**

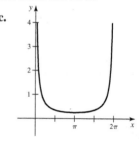

d. Minimum curvature at $\left(\pi, \frac{1}{4}\right)$ **67. b.** $\kappa = \dfrac{1}{t(1 + t^2)^{3/2}}$

c.

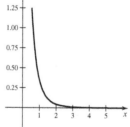

d. No maximum or minimum curvature

69. $\kappa = \dfrac{e^x}{(1 + e^{2x})^{3/2}}, \left(-\dfrac{\ln 2}{2}, \dfrac{1}{\sqrt{2}}\right), \dfrac{2\sqrt{3}}{9}$

71. $\dfrac{1}{\kappa} = \dfrac{1}{2}; x^2 + \left(y - \dfrac{1}{2}\right)^2 = \dfrac{1}{4}$

73. $\dfrac{1}{\kappa} = 4; (x - \pi)^2 + (y + 2)^2 = 16$

75. $\kappa\left(\dfrac{\pi}{2n}\right) = n^2$; κ increases as n increases.

77. a. speed $= \sqrt{V_0^2 - 2V_0\, gt \sin \alpha + g^2 t^2}$.

b. $\kappa(t) = \dfrac{g V_0 \cos \alpha}{(V_0^2 - 2V_0\, gt \sin \alpha + g^2 t^2)^{3/2}}.$ **c.** Speed has a minimum

at $t = \dfrac{V_0 \sin \alpha}{g}$ and $\kappa(t)$ has a maximum at $t = \dfrac{V_0 \sin \alpha}{g}$.

79. $\kappa = \dfrac{1}{|\mathbf{v}|} \cdot \left|\dfrac{d\mathbf{T}}{dt}\right|$, where $\mathbf{T} = \dfrac{\langle b, d, f \rangle}{\sqrt{b^2 + d^2 + f^2}}$ for b, d, f all

constant. Thus, $\dfrac{d\mathbf{T}}{dt} = \mathbf{0}$ so $\kappa = 0$.

81. a. $\kappa_1(x) = \dfrac{2}{(1 + 4x^2)^{3/2}}$

$\kappa_2(x) = \dfrac{12x^2}{(1 + 16x^6)^{3/2}}$

$\kappa_3(x) = \dfrac{30x^4}{(1 + 36x^{10})^{3/2}}$

b.

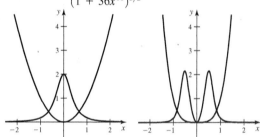

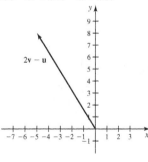

c. κ_1 has its maximum at $x = 0$, κ_2 has its maxima at $x = \pm\sqrt[6]{\frac{1}{56}}$, κ_3 has its maxima at $x = \pm\sqrt[10]{\frac{1}{99}}$.   **d.** $\displaystyle\lim_{n \to \infty} z_n = 1$; the maximum

curvature of $y = f_n(x)$ occurs closer and closer to the point $(1, 1)$ as $n \to \infty$.

Chapter 12 Review Exercises, pp. 876–879

1. a. True   **b.** False   **c.** True   **d.** True   **e.** False   **f.** False
3.
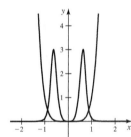
5.

7. $\sqrt{221}$ **9.** $\pm\left\langle -\dfrac{60}{\sqrt{35}}, \dfrac{100}{\sqrt{35}}, \dfrac{20}{\sqrt{35}} \right\rangle$

11. $2\langle 29, 13, 22 \rangle, -2\langle 29, 13, 22 \rangle, 3\sqrt{166}$
13. a. $\mathbf{v} = -275\sqrt{2}\mathbf{i} + 275\sqrt{2}\mathbf{j}$ **b.** $-275\sqrt{2}\mathbf{i} + (275\sqrt{2} + 40)\mathbf{j}$
15. $\{(x, y, z): (x - 1)^2 + y^2 + (z + 1)^2 = 16\}$
17. $\{(x, y, z): x^2 + (y - 1)^2 + z^2 > 4\}$ **19.** A ball centered at
$\left(\frac{1}{2}, -2, 3\right)$ of radius $\frac{3}{2}$ **21.** All points outside of a sphere of radius 10
centered at $(3, 0, 10)$ **23.** 50.15 m/s; $85.4°$ below the horizontal in
the northerly horizontal direction.   **25.** A circle of radius 1 centered
at $(0, 2, 0)$ in the vertical plane $y = 2$.   **27. a.** 0.68 radian

b. $\dfrac{7}{9}\langle 1, 2, 2 \rangle$; $\dfrac{7}{3}$ **c.** $\dfrac{7}{3}\langle -1, 2, 2 \rangle$; 7 **29.** $\pm\left\langle \dfrac{12}{\sqrt{197}}, \dfrac{7}{\sqrt{197}}, \dfrac{2}{\sqrt{197}} \right\rangle$

31. $T(\theta) = 39.2 \sin \theta$ has a maximum value of 39.2 N $\cdot$ m

$\left(\text{when } \theta = \dfrac{\pi}{2}\right)$ and a minimum value of 0 N $\cdot$ m when $\theta = 0$.

Direction does *not* change.
33. $\langle x, y, z \rangle = \langle 0, -3, 9 \rangle + t\langle 2, -5, -8 \rangle, 0 \leq t \leq 1$
35. $\langle t, 1 + 6t, 1 + 2t \rangle$ **37.** 11
39.   **41.**

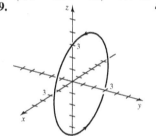

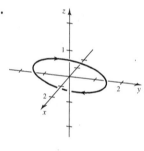

43. a. $(116, 30)$ **b.** 39.1 ft   **c.** 2.315 s

d. $\displaystyle\int_0^{2.315} \sqrt{50^2 + (-32t + 50)^2}\, dt$ **e.** 129 ft   **f.** $41.4°$ to $79.4°$
45. 25.6 ft/s   **47.** 12   **49. a.** $\mathbf{v}(t) = \mathbf{i} + t\sqrt{2}\mathbf{j} + t^2\mathbf{k}$ **b.** 12
51. 40.09
53.

$\mathbf{r}(s) = \left\langle (\sqrt{1 + s} - 1)^2, \dfrac{4\sqrt{2}}{3}(\sqrt{1 + s} - 1)^{3/2}, 2(\sqrt{1 + s} - 1) \right\rangle,$

for $s \geq 0$ **55. a.** $\mathbf{v} = \langle -6 \sin t, 3 \cos t \rangle$, $\mathbf{T} = \dfrac{\langle -2 \sin t, \cos t \rangle}{\sqrt{1 + 3 \sin^2 t}}$

b. $\kappa(t) = \dfrac{2}{3(1 + 3 \sin^2 t)^{3/2}}$

c. $\mathbf{N} = \left\langle -\dfrac{\cos t}{\sqrt{1 + 3 \sin^2 t}}, -\dfrac{2 \sin t}{\sqrt{1 + 3 \sin^2 t}} \right\rangle$

d. $|\mathbf{N}| = \sqrt{\dfrac{\cos^2 t + 4 \sin^2 t}{1 + 3 \sin^2 t}} = \sqrt{\dfrac{(\cos^2 t + \sin^2 t) + 3 \sin^2 t}{1 + 3 \sin^2 t}}$

$= 1$

$\mathbf{T} \cdot \mathbf{N} = \dfrac{2 \sin t \cos t - 2 \sin t \cos t}{1 + 3 \sin^2 t} = 0$

e.

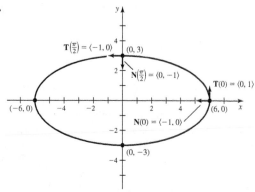

57. a. $\mathbf{v}(t) = \langle -\sin t, -2\sin t, \sqrt{5}\cos t \rangle,$

$\mathbf{T}(t) = \left\langle -\dfrac{1}{\sqrt{5}}\sin t, -\dfrac{2}{\sqrt{5}}\sin t, \cos t \right\rangle$

b. $\kappa(t) = \dfrac{1}{\sqrt{5}}$ **c.** $\mathbf{N}(t) = \left\langle -\dfrac{1}{\sqrt{5}}\cos t, -\dfrac{2}{\sqrt{5}}\cos t, -\sin t \right\rangle$

d. $|\mathbf{N}(t)| = \sqrt{\dfrac{1}{5}\cos^2 t + \dfrac{4}{5}\cos^2 t + \sin^2 t} = 1;$

$\mathbf{T} \cdot \mathbf{N} = \left(\dfrac{1}{5}\cos t \sin t + \dfrac{4}{5}\cos t \sin t \right) - \sin t \cos t = 0$

e.

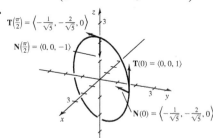

59. a. $\mathbf{a}(t) = 2\mathbf{N} + 0\mathbf{T} = 2\langle -\cos t, -\sin t \rangle$
b.

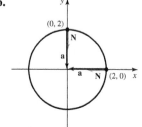

61. a. $a_T = \dfrac{2t}{\sqrt{t^2 + 1}}$ and $a_N = \dfrac{2}{\sqrt{t^2 + 1}}$

b.

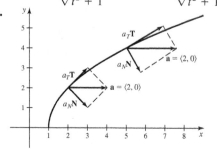

63. a. $a(x - x_0) + b(y - y_0) = 0$
b. $a(y - y_0) - b(x - x_0) = 0$

65. a. $\mathbf{B}(1) = \dfrac{\langle 3, -3, 1 \rangle}{\sqrt{19}}; \tau = \dfrac{3}{19}$

67. a. $\mathbf{T}(t) = \dfrac{1}{5}\langle 3\cos t, -3\sin t, 4 \rangle$ **b.** $\mathbf{N}(t) = \langle -\sin t, -\cos t, 0 \rangle$

e. $\mathbf{B}(t) = \dfrac{1}{5}\langle 4\cos t, -4\sin t, -3 \rangle$ **g.** Check that $\mathbf{T}, \mathbf{N},$ and $\mathbf{B}$ have unit length and are mutually orthogonal.   **h.** $\tau = -\dfrac{4}{25}$

69. a. Let $\mathbf{r}(t) = \langle x(t), y(t), z(t) \rangle$ and show there are constants $a, b,$ and c such that $ax + by + cz = 1$, for all t in the interval.
b. $\mathbf{B}$ is always normal to the plane and has length 1. Therefore, $\dfrac{d\mathbf{B}}{ds} = \mathbf{0}$ and $\tau = 0$.   **c.** $x + y - z = 4$

CHAPTER 13

Section 13.1 Exercises, pp. 892–895

1. One point and a normal vector   **3.** $x = -6, y = -4, z = 3$
5. z-axis; x-axis; y-axis   **7.** Intersection of the surface with a plane parallel to one of the coordinate planes   **9.** Ellipsoid
11. $x + y - z = 4$ **13.** $-x + 2y - 3z = 4$
15. $2x + y - 2z = -2$ **17.** $7x + 2y + z = 10$
19. $4x + 27y + 10z = 21$ **21.** Intercepts $x = 2, y = -3, z = 6$.
Traces $3x - 2y = 6, z = 0; -2y + z = 6, x = 0;$ and
$3x + z = 6, y = 0$

23. Intercepts $x = 30, y = 10, z = -6$. Traces $x + 3y - 30 = 0,$
$z = 0; x - 5z - 30 = 0, y = 0;$ and $3y - 5z - 30 = 0, x = 0$

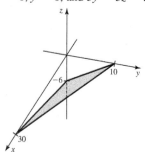

25. Orthogonal   **27.** Neither   **29.** Q and T are identical; $Q, R,$ and T are parallel; S is orthogonal to $Q, R,$ and T.
31. $-x + 2y - 4z = -17$ **33.** $4x + 3y - 2z = -5$
35. $x = t, y = 1 + 2t, z = -1 - 3t$
37. $x = \frac{7}{5} + 2t, y = \frac{9}{5} + t, z = -t$

39. a. Parallel to x-axis   **b.**

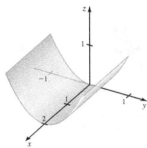

41. a. Parallel to y-axis   **b.**

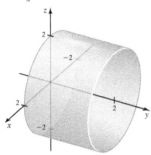

43. a. z-axis   **b.**

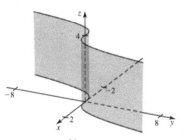

45. a. x-axis   **b.**

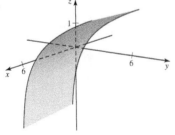

47. a. $x = \pm 1, y = \pm 2, z = \pm 3$ **b.** $x^2 + \dfrac{y^2}{4} = 1, x^2 + \dfrac{z^2}{9} = 1,$
$\dfrac{y^2}{4} + \dfrac{z^2}{9} = 1$ **c.**

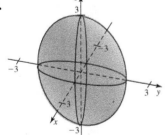

49. a. $x = \pm 3, y = \pm 1, z = \pm 6$ **b.** $\dfrac{x^2}{3} + 3y^2 = 3, \dfrac{x^2}{3} + \dfrac{z^2}{12} = 3,$
$3y^2 + \dfrac{z^2}{12} = 3$ **c.**

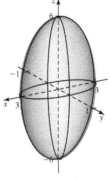

51. a. $x = y = z = 0$ **b.** $x = y^2, x = z^2$, origin
c.

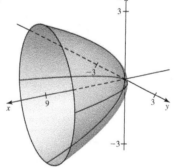

53. a. $x = y = z = 0$ **b.** Origin, $x - 9y^2 = 0, 9x - \dfrac{z^2}{4} = 0$
c.

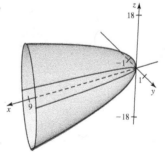

55. a. $x = \pm 5, y = \pm 3$, no z-intercepts
b. $\dfrac{x^2}{25} + \dfrac{y^2}{9} = 1, \dfrac{x^2}{25} - z^2 = 1, \dfrac{y^2}{9} - z^2 = 1$
c.

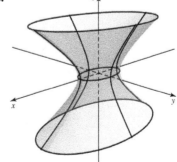

57. a. No x-intercepts, $y = \pm 12$, $z = \pm\dfrac{1}{2}$ **b.** $-\dfrac{x^2}{4} + \dfrac{y^2}{16} = 9$,

$-\dfrac{x^2}{4} + 36z^2 = 9, \dfrac{y^2}{16} + 36z^2 = 9$

c.

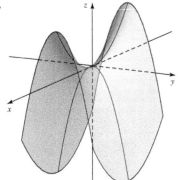

59. a. $x = y = z = 0$ **b.** $\dfrac{x^2}{9} - y^2 = 0$, $z = \dfrac{x^2}{9}$, $z = -y^2$

c.

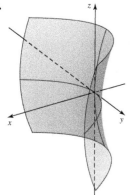

61. a. $x = y = z = 0$

b. $5x - \dfrac{y^2}{5} = 0$, $5x + \dfrac{z^2}{20} = 0$, $-\dfrac{y^2}{5} + \dfrac{z^2}{20} = 0$

c.

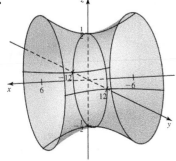

63. a. $x = y = z = 0$ **b.** Origin, $\dfrac{y^2}{4} = z^2$, $x^2 = z^2$

c.

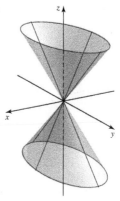

65. a. $x = y = z = 0$ **b.** $\dfrac{y^2}{18} = 2x^2$, $\dfrac{z^2}{32} = 2x^2$, origin

c.

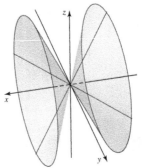

67. a. No x-intercepts, $y = \pm 2$, no z-intercepts   **b.** $-x^2 + \dfrac{y^2}{4} = 1$,

no xz-trace, $\dfrac{y^2}{4} - \dfrac{z^2}{9} = 1$

c.

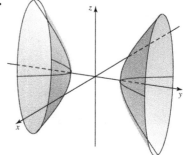

69. a. No x-intercepts, $y = \pm\dfrac{\sqrt{3}}{3}$, no z-intercepts

b. $-\dfrac{x^2}{3} + 3y^2 = 1$, no xz-trace, $3y^2 - \dfrac{z^2}{12} = 1$

c.

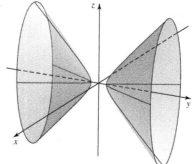

71. a. True **b.** False **c.** False **d.** True **e.** False **f.** False
g. False **73.** $\langle 2 + 2t, 1 - 4t, 3 + t \rangle$ **75.** $6x - 4y + z = d$
77. The planes intersect in the point $(3, 6, 0)$. **79. a.** D **b.** A
c. E **d.** F **e.** B **f.** C **81.** Hyperbolic paraboloid **83.** Elliptic
paraboloid **85.** Hyperboloid of one sheet **87.** Hyperbolic cylinder
89. Hyperboloid of two sheets **91.** $P(3, 9, 27)$ and $Q(-5, 25, 75)$
93. $P\left(\dfrac{6\sqrt{10}}{5}, \dfrac{2\sqrt{10}}{5}, \dfrac{3\sqrt{10}}{10}\right)$ and $Q\left(-\dfrac{6\sqrt{10}}{5}, -\dfrac{2\sqrt{10}}{5}, -\dfrac{3\sqrt{10}}{10}\right)$
95. $\theta = \cos^{-1}\left(-\dfrac{\sqrt{105}}{14}\right) \approx 2.392$ rad; $137°$ **97.** All except the
hyperbolic paraboloid **99. a.**

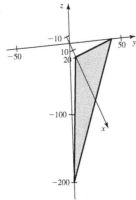

b. Positive **c.** $2x + y = 40$, line in the xy-plane **101. a.** $z = cy$
b. $\theta = \tan^{-1} c$ **103. a.** The length of the orthogonal projection of
$\overrightarrow{PQ}$ onto the normal vector $\mathbf{n}$ is the magnitude of the scalar component
of $\overrightarrow{PQ}$ in the direction of $\mathbf{n}$, which is $\dfrac{|\overrightarrow{PQ} \cdot \mathbf{n}|}{|\mathbf{n}|}$. **b.** $\dfrac{13}{\sqrt{14}}$

Section 13.2 Exercises, pp. 904–907

1. Independent: x and y; dependent: z
3. $D = \{(x, y): x \neq 0 \text{ and } y \neq 0\}$ **5.** Three **7.** Circles **9.** $n = 6$
11. $\mathbb{R}^2$ **13.** $\{(x, y): x^2 + y^2 \leq 25\}$ **15.** $D = \{(x, y): y \neq 0\}$
(xy-plane without the x-axis) **17.** $D = \{(x, y): y < x^2\}$
19. $D = \{(x, y): xy \geq 0, (x, y) \neq (0, 0)\}$; first and third quadrant,
origin excluded **21.** Plane; domain $= \mathbb{R}^2$, range $= \mathbb{R}$

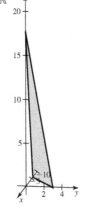

23. Hyperbolic paraboloid; domain $= \mathbb{R}^2$, range $= \mathbb{R}$

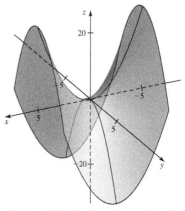

25. Lower part of a hyperboloid of two sheets; domain $= \mathbb{R}^2$,
range $= (-\infty, -1]$

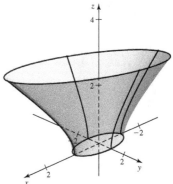

27. Upper half of a hyperboloid of one sheet;
domain $= \{(x, y): x^2 + y^2 \geq 1\}$, range $= [0, \infty)$

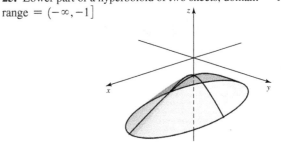

29. a. A **b.** D **c.** B **d.** C **31.**

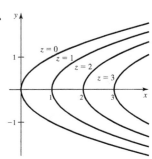

33.

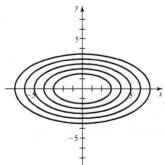

35.

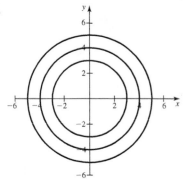

37.

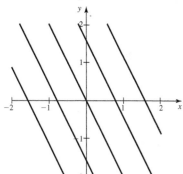

39. a.

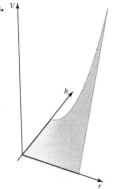

b. $D = \{(r, h): r > 0, h > 0\}$ **c.** $h = 300/(\pi r^2)$

41. a.

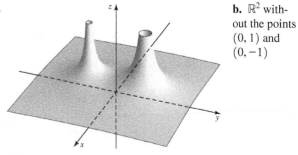

b. $\mathbb{R}^2$ without the points $(0, 1)$ and $(0, -1)$

c. $\varphi(2, 3)$ is greater.   **d.**

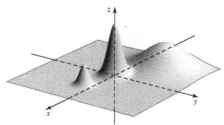

43. a.

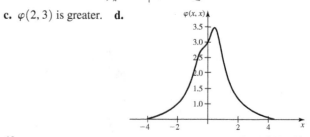

b. $R(10, 10) = 5$
c. $R(x, y) = R(y, x)$

45. a.

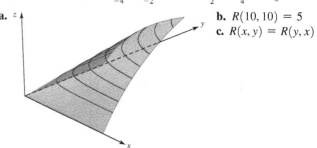

b. $(0, 0), (-5, 3), (4, -1)$
c. $f(0, 0) = 10.17, f(-5, 3) = 5.00, f(4, -1) = 4.00$
47. $D = \{(x, y, z): x \neq z\}$; all points not on the plane $x = z$
49. $D = \{(x, y, z): y \geq z\}$; all points on or below the plane $y = z$
51. $D = \{(x, y, z): x^2 \leq y\}$; all points on the side of the vertical
cylinder $y = x^2$ that contains the positive y-axis   **53. a.** False
b. False   **c.** True   **55. a.** $D = \mathbb{R}^2$, range $= [0, \infty)$
b.

57. a. $D = \{(x, y): x \neq y\}$, range $= \mathbb{R}$
b.

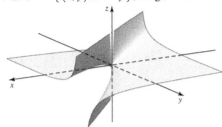

59. a. $D = \{(x, y): y \neq x + \pi/2 + n\pi \text{ for any integer } n\}$, range $= [0, \infty)$ **b.**

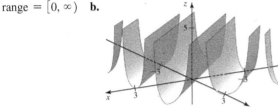

61. Peak at the origin **63.** Depression at $(1, 0)$ **65.** The level curves are $ax + by = d - cz_0$, where c is a constant, which are parallel lines with slope $-a/b$. **67.** $z = x^2 + y^2 - C$; paraboloids with vertices at $(0, 0, -C)$ **69.** $x^2 + 2z^2 = C$; elliptic cylinders parallel to the y-axis **71. a.** $P = \dfrac{20,000r}{(1 + r)^{240} - 1}$ **b.** $P = \dfrac{Br}{(1 + r)^{240} - 1}$, with $B = 5000, 10,000, 15,000, 25,000$

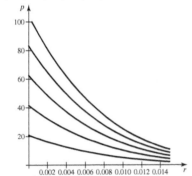

73. a.

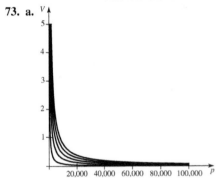

b.

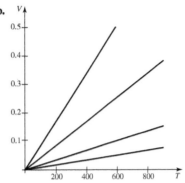

c.

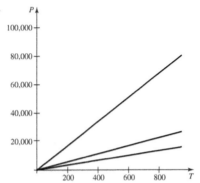

75. $D = \{(x, y): x - 1 \leq y \leq x + 1\}$
77. $D = \{(x, y, z): (x \leq z \text{ and } y \geq -z) \text{ or } (x \geq z \text{ and } y \leq -z)\}$

Section 13.3 Exercises, pp. 914–916

1. The values of $f(x, y)$ are arbitrarily close to L for all (x, y) in a sufficiently small disk centered at (a, b). **3.** Limits are obtained by evaluating the function at a point. **5.** If the function approaches different values along different paths, the limit does not exist. **7.** f must be defined, the limit must exist, and the limit must equal the function value. **9.** At any point where the denominator is nonzero **11.** 101
13. 27 **15.** $1/(2\pi)$ **17.** 2 **19.** 6 **21.** -1 **23.** 2
25. $1/(2\sqrt{2}) = \sqrt{2}/4$ **27.** $L = 1$ along $y = 0$, and $L = -1$ along $x = 0$ **29.** $L = 1$ along $x = 0$, and $L = -2$ along $y = 0$
31. $L = 2$ along $y = x$, and $L = 0$ along $y = -x$ **33.** $\mathbb{R}^2$
35. All points except $(0, 0)$ **37.** $\{(x, y): x \neq 0\}$ **39.** All points except $(0, 0)$ **41.** $\mathbb{R}^2$ **43.** $\mathbb{R}^2$ **45.** $\mathbb{R}^2$ **47.** All points except $(0, 0)$ **49.** $\mathbb{R}^2$ **51.** $\mathbb{R}^2$ **53.** 6 **55.** -1 **57.** 2 **59. a.** False
b. False **c.** True **d.** False **61.** $\frac{1}{2}$ **63.** 0 **65.** Does not exist
67. $\frac{1}{4}$ **69.** Does not exist **71.** Does not exist **73.** $b = 1$ **77.** 1
79. 1 **81.** 0

Section 13.4 Exercises, pp. 925–929

1. $f_x(a, b)$ is the slope of the surface in the direction parallel to the x-axis, $f_y(a, b)$ is the slope of the surface in the direction parallel to the y-axis, both taken at (a, b). **3.** $f_x(x, y) = \cos(xy) - xy \sin(xy)$, $f_y(x, y) = -x^2 \sin(xy)$ **5.** Think of x and y as being fixed, and take the derivative with respect to the variable z.
7. $f_x(x, y) = 6x; f_y(x, y) = 12y^2$ **9.** $f_x(x, y) = 6xy, f_y(x, y) = 3x^2$
11. $f_x(x, y) = e^y; f_y(x, y) = xe^y$ **13.** $g_x(x, y) = -2y \sin(2xy)$, $g_y(x, y) = -2x \sin(2xy)$ **15.** $f_x(x, y) = 2xye^{x^2y}; f_y(x, y) = x^2 e^{x^2y}$
17. $f_w(w, z) = \dfrac{z^2 - w^2}{(w^2 + z^2)^2}$, $f_z(w, z) = -\dfrac{2wz}{(w^2 + z^2)^2}$

19. $s_y(y, z) = z^3 \sec^2(yz)$, $s_z(y, z) = 2z \tan(yz) + yz^2 \sec^2(yz)$

21. $G_s(s, t) = \dfrac{\sqrt{st}(t - s)}{2s(s + t)^2}$, $G_t(s, t) = \dfrac{\sqrt{st}(s - t)}{2t(s + t)^2}$

23. $f_x(x, y) = 2yx^{2y-1}$; $f_y(x, y) = 2x^{2y} \ln x$ **25.** $h_{xx}(x, y) = 6x$,

$h_{xy}(x, y) = 2y$, $h_{yx}(x, y) = 2y$, $h_{yy}(x, y) = 2x$ **27.** $f_{xx}(x, y) = 2y^3$,

$f_{xy}(x, y) = f_{yx} = 6xy^2$, $f_{yy}(x, y) = 6x^2y$ **29.** $f_{xx}(x, y) = -16y^3 \sin 4x$,

$f_{xy}(x, y) = 12y^2 \cos 4x$, $f_{yx}(x, y) = 12y^2 \cos 4x$, $f_{yy}(x, y) = 6y \sin 4x$

31. $p_{uu}(u, v) = \dfrac{-2u^2 + 2v^2 + 8}{(u^2 + v^2 + 4)^2}$, $p_{uv}(u, v) = -\dfrac{4uv}{(u^2 + v^2 + 4)^2}$,

$p_{vu}(u, v) = -\dfrac{4uv}{(u^2 + v^2 + 4)^2}$, $p_{vv}(u, v) = \dfrac{2u^2 - 2v^2 + 8}{(u^2 + v^2 + 4)^2}$

33. $F_{rr}(r, s) = 0$, $F_{rs}(r, s) = e^s$, $F_{sr}(r, s) = e^s$, $F_{ss}(r, s) = re^s$

41. $f_x(x, y, z) = y + z$, $f_y(x, y, z) = x + z$, $f_z(x, y, z) = x + y$

43. $h_x(x, y, z) = h_y(x, y, z) = h_z(x, y, z) = -\sin(x + y + z)$

45. $F_u(u, v, w) = \dfrac{1}{v + w}$, $F_v(u, v, w) = F_w(u, v, w) = -\dfrac{u}{(v + w)^2}$

47. $f_w(w, x, y, z) = 2wxy^2$, $f_x(w, x, y, z) = w^2y^2 + y^3z^2$,

$f_y(w, x, y, z) = 2w^2xy + 3xy^2z^2$, $f_z(w, x, y, z) = 2xy^3z$

49. $h_w(w, x, y, z) = \dfrac{z}{xy}$, $h_x(w, x, y, z) = -\dfrac{wz}{x^2y}$,

$h_y(w, x, y, z) = -\dfrac{wz}{xy^2}$, $h_z(w, x, y, z) = \dfrac{w}{xy}$ **51. a.** $\dfrac{\partial V}{\partial P} = -\dfrac{kT}{P^2}$,

volume decreases with pressure at fixed temperature **b.** $\dfrac{\partial V}{\partial T} = \dfrac{k}{P}$,

volume increases with temperature at fixed pressure

c.

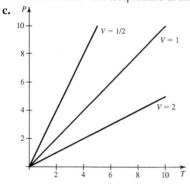

53. a. No **b.** f is not differentiable at $(0, 0)$.

c. $f_x(0, 0) = f_y(0, 0) = 0$ **d.** f_x and f_y are not continuous at $(0, 0)$.

55. a. False **b.** False **c.** True **57.** 1.41 **59.** 1.55 (answer will vary)

61. $f_x(x, y) = -\dfrac{2x}{1 + (x^2 + y^2)^2}$ $f_y(x, y) = -\dfrac{2y}{1 + (x^2 + y^2)^2}$

63. $h_x(x, y, z) = z(1 + x + 2y)^{z-1}$, $h_y(x, y, z) = 2z(1 + x + 2y)^{z-1}$,

$h_z(x, y, z) = (1 + x + 2y)^z \ln(1 + x + 2y)$

65. a. $z_x(x, y) = \dfrac{1}{y^2}$, $z_y(x, y) = -\dfrac{2x}{y^3}$

b.

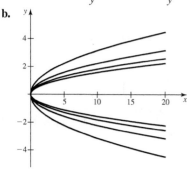

c. z increases as x increases.   **d.** z increases as y increases when $y < 0$,
z is undefined for $y = 0$, and z decreases as y increases for $y > 0$.

67. a. $\dfrac{\partial c}{\partial a} = \dfrac{2a - b}{2\sqrt{a^2 + b^2 - ab}}$, $\dfrac{\partial c}{\partial b} = \dfrac{2b - a}{2\sqrt{a^2 + b^2 - ab}}$

b. $\dfrac{\partial c}{\partial a} = \dfrac{2a - b}{2c}$, $\dfrac{\partial c}{\partial b} = \dfrac{2b - a}{2c}$ **c.** $a > \frac{1}{2}b$

69. a. $\varphi_x(x, y) = -\dfrac{2x}{(x^2 + (y - 1)^2)^{3/2}} - \dfrac{x}{(x^2 + (y + 1)^2)^{3/2}}$,

$\varphi_y(x, y) = -\dfrac{2(y - 1)}{(x^2 + (y - 1)^2)^{3/2}} - \dfrac{y + 1}{(x^2 + (y + 1)^2)^{3/2}}$

b. They both approach zero.   **c.** $\varphi_x(0, y) = 0$

d. $\varphi_y(x, 0) = \dfrac{1}{(x^2 + 1)^{3/2}}$

71. a. $\dfrac{\partial R}{\partial R_1} = \dfrac{R_2^2}{(R_1 + R_2)^2}$, $\dfrac{\partial R}{\partial R_2} = \dfrac{R_1^2}{(R_1 + R_2)^2}$

b. $\dfrac{\partial R}{\partial R_1} = \dfrac{R^2}{R_1^2}$, $\dfrac{\partial R}{\partial R_2} = \dfrac{R^2}{R_2^2}$ **c.** Increase **d.** Decrease

73. $\dfrac{\partial^2 u}{\partial t^2} = -4c^2 \cos[2(x + ct)] = c^2\dfrac{\partial^2 u}{\partial x^2}$

75. $\dfrac{\partial^2 u}{\partial t^2} = c^2Af''(x + ct) + c^2Bg''(x - ct) = c^2\dfrac{\partial^2 u}{\partial x^2}$

77. $u_{xx} = 6x$ $u_{yy} = -6x$

79. $u_{xx} = \dfrac{2(x - 1)y}{[(x - 1)^2 + y^2]^2} - \dfrac{2(x + 1)y}{[(x + 1)^2 + y^2]^2}$,

$u_{yy} = -\dfrac{2(x - 1)y}{[(x - 1)^2 + y^2]^2} + \dfrac{2(x + 1)y}{[(x + 1)^2 + y^2]^2}$

81. $u_t = -16e^{-4t} \cos 2x = u_{xx}$ **83.** $u_t = -a^2Ae^{-a^2t} \cos ax = u_{xx}$

85. $\varepsilon_1 = \Delta y, \varepsilon_2 = 0$ or $\varepsilon_1 = 0, \varepsilon_2 = \Delta x$ **87. a.** f is continuous at

$(0, 0)$. **b.** f is differentiable at $(0, 0)$. **c.** $f_x(0, 0) = f_y(0, 0) = 0$

d. f_x and f_y are not continuous at $(0, 0)$. **89. a.** $f_x(x, y) = -h(x)$,

$f_y(x, y) = h(y)$ **b.** $f_x(x, y) = yh(xy), f_y(x, y) = xh(xy)$

Section 13.5 Exercises, pp. 934–937

1. One dependent, two intermediate, and one independent variable
3. Multiply each of the partial derivatives of w by the t-derivative of
the corresponding function, and add all these expressions.

5.

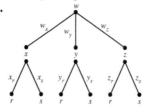

7. $4t^3 + 3t^2$ **9.** $z'(t) = 2t \sin 4t^3 + 12t^4 \cos 4t^3$

11. $w'(t) = -\sin t \sin 3t^4 + 12t^3 \cos t \cos 3t^4$

13. $w'(t) = 20t^4 \sin(t + 1) + 4t^5 \cos(t + 1)$

15. $U'(t) = \dfrac{1 + 2t + 3t^2}{t + t^2 + t^3}$

17. a. $V'(t) = 2\pi r(t)h(t)r'(t) + \pi r(t)^2h'(t)$ **b.** $V'(t) = 0$

c. The volume remains constant. **19.** $z_s = 2(s - t) \sin t^2$;

$z_t = 2(s - t)(t(s - t) \cos t^2 - \sin t^2)$

21. $z_s = 2s - 3s^2 - 2st + t^2$, $z_t = -s^2 - 2t + 2st + 3t^2$

23. $z_s = (t + 1)e^{st+s+t}$, $z_t = (s + 1)e^{st+s+t}$

25. $w_s = -\dfrac{2t(t+1)}{(st+s-t)^2}$, $w_t = \dfrac{2s}{(st+s-t)^2}$

27.

$$\frac{dw}{dt} = \frac{dw}{dz}\left(\frac{\partial z}{\partial x}\frac{dx}{dt} + \frac{\partial z}{\partial y}\frac{dy}{dt}\right)$$

29.

$$\frac{\partial u}{\partial z} = \frac{du}{dv}\left(\frac{\partial v}{\partial w}\frac{dw}{dz} + \frac{\partial v}{\partial x}\frac{\partial x}{\partial z} + \frac{\partial v}{\partial y}\frac{\partial y}{\partial z}\right)$$

31. $\dfrac{dy}{dx} = \dfrac{x}{2y}$ **33.** $\dfrac{dy}{dx} = -\dfrac{y}{x}$

35. $\dfrac{dy}{dx} = -\dfrac{x+y}{2y^3+x}$ **37.** $\dfrac{\partial s}{\partial x} = \dfrac{2x}{\sqrt{x^2+y^2}}$, $\dfrac{\partial s}{\partial y} = \dfrac{2y}{\sqrt{x^2+y^2}}$

39. a. False   **b.** False   **41.** $z'(t) = -\dfrac{2t+2}{(t^2+2t)^2} - \dfrac{3t^2}{(t^3-2)^2}$

43. $w'(t) = 0$ **45.** $\dfrac{\partial z}{\partial x} = -\dfrac{z^2}{x^2}$ **47. a.** $w'(t) = af_x + bf_y + cf_z$

b. $w'(t) = ayz + bxz + cxy = 3abct^2$

c. $w'(t) = \sqrt{a^2+b^2+c^2}\,\dfrac{t}{|t|}$

d. $w''(t) = a^2 f_{xx} + b^2 f_{yy} + c^2 f_{zz} + 2abf_{xy} + 2acf_{xz} + 2bcf_{yz}$

49. $\dfrac{\partial z}{\partial x} = -\dfrac{y+z}{x+y}$, $\dfrac{\partial z}{\partial y} = -\dfrac{x+z}{x+y}$ **51.** $\dfrac{\partial z}{\partial x} = -\dfrac{yz+1}{xy-1}$, $\dfrac{\partial z}{\partial y} = -\dfrac{xz+1}{xy-1}$

53. a. $z'(t) = -2x\sin t + 8y\cos t = 3\sin 2t$ **b.** $0 < t < \pi/2$ and $\pi < t < 3\pi/2$ **55. a.** $z'(t) = \dfrac{(x+y)e^{-t}}{\sqrt{1-x^2-y^2}} = \dfrac{2e^{-2t}}{\sqrt{1-2e^{-2t}}}$

b. All $t \geq \tfrac{1}{2}\ln 2$ **57.** $E'(t) = mx'x'' + my'y'' + mgy' = 0$

59. a. The volume increases.   **b.** The volume decreases.

61. a. $\dfrac{\partial P}{\partial V} = -\dfrac{P}{V}$, $\dfrac{\partial T}{\partial P} = \dfrac{V}{k}$, $\dfrac{\partial V}{\partial T} = \dfrac{k}{P}$ **b.** Follows directly from part (a)

63. a. $w'(t) = \dfrac{2t(t^2+1)\cos 2t - (t^2-1)\sin 2t}{2(t^2+1)^2}$

b. Max. value of $t \approx 0.838$, $(x,y,z) \approx (0.669, 0.743, 0.838)$

65. a. $z_x = \dfrac{x}{r}z_r - \dfrac{y}{r^2}z_\theta$, $z_y = \dfrac{y}{r}z_r + \dfrac{x}{r^2}z_\theta$

b. $z_{xx} = \dfrac{x^2}{r^2}z_{rr} + \dfrac{y^2}{r^4}z_{\theta\theta} - \dfrac{2xy}{r^3}z_{r\theta} + \dfrac{y^2}{r^3}z_r + \dfrac{2xy}{r^4}z_\theta$

c. $z_{yy} = \dfrac{y^2}{r^2}z_{rr} + \dfrac{x^2}{r^4}z_{\theta\theta} + \dfrac{2xy}{r^3}z_{r\theta} + \dfrac{x^2}{r^3}z_r - \dfrac{2xy}{r^4}z_\theta$

d. Add the results from (b) and (c).   **67. a.** $\left(\dfrac{\partial z}{\partial x}\right)_y = -\dfrac{F_x}{F_z}$

b. $\left(\dfrac{\partial y}{\partial z}\right)_x = -\dfrac{F_z}{F_y}$, $\left(\dfrac{\partial x}{\partial y}\right)_z = -\dfrac{F_y}{F_x}$ **c.** Follows from (a) and (b) by multiplication   **d.** $\left(\dfrac{\partial w}{\partial x}\right)_{y,z}\left(\dfrac{\partial z}{\partial w}\right)_{x,y}\left(\dfrac{\partial y}{\partial z}\right)_{x,w}\left(\dfrac{\partial x}{\partial y}\right)_{z,w} = 1$

69. a. $\left(\dfrac{\partial w}{\partial x}\right)_y = f_x + f_z\dfrac{dz}{dx} = 18$ **b.** $\left(\dfrac{\partial w}{\partial x}\right)_z = f_x + f_y\dfrac{dy}{dx} = 8$

d. $\left(\dfrac{\partial w}{\partial y}\right)_x = -5$, $\left(\dfrac{\partial w}{\partial y}\right)_z = 4$, $\left(\dfrac{\partial w}{\partial z}\right)_x = \dfrac{5}{2}$, $\left(\dfrac{\partial w}{\partial z}\right)_y = \dfrac{9}{2}$

Section 13.6 Exercises, pp. 947–950

1. Form the dot product between the unit direction vector **u** and the gradient of the function.   **3.** Direction of steepest ascent   **5.** The gradient is orthogonal to the level curves of f.

7. a.

	$(a,b) = (2,0)$	$(a,b) = (0,2)$	$(a,b) = (1,1)$
$\theta = \pi/4$	$-\sqrt{2}$	$-2\sqrt{2}$	$-3\sqrt{2}/2$
$\theta = 3\pi/4$	$\sqrt{2}$	$-2\sqrt{2}$	$-\sqrt{2}/2$
$\theta = 5\pi/4$	$\sqrt{2}$	$2\sqrt{2}$	$3\sqrt{2}/2$

b.

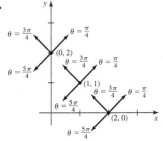

9. $\nabla f(x,y) = \langle 6x, -10y\rangle$, $\nabla f(2,-1) = \langle 12, 10\rangle$
11. $\nabla g(x,y) = \langle 2(x-4xy-4y^2), -4x(x+4y)\rangle$, $\nabla g(-1,2) = \langle -18, 28\rangle$ **13.** $\nabla f(x,y) = e^{2xy}\langle 1+2xy, 2x^2\rangle$; $\nabla f(1,0) = \langle 1, 2\rangle$ **15.** $\nabla F(x,y) = -2e^{-x^2-2y^2}\langle x, 2y\rangle$, $\nabla F(-1,2) = 2e^{-9}\langle 1, -4\rangle$ **17.** -6 **19.** $\dfrac{27}{2} - 6\sqrt{3}$

21. $-\dfrac{2}{\sqrt{5}}$ **23.** -2 **25.** 0 **27. a.** Steepest ascent: $\dfrac{1}{\sqrt{65}}\langle 1, 8\rangle$; steepest descent: $-\dfrac{1}{\sqrt{65}}\langle 1, 8\rangle$

b. $\langle -8, 1\rangle$ **29. a.** Steepest ascent: $\dfrac{1}{\sqrt{5}}\langle -2, 1\rangle$; steepest descent: $\dfrac{1}{\sqrt{5}}\langle 2, -1\rangle$ **b.** $\langle 1, 2\rangle$ **31. a.** Steepest ascent: $\dfrac{1}{\sqrt{2}}\langle 1, -1\rangle$; steepest descent: $\dfrac{1}{\sqrt{2}}\langle -1, 1\rangle$ **b.** $\langle 1, 1\rangle$

33. a. $\nabla f(3,2) = -12\mathbf{i} - 12\mathbf{j}$ **b.** Max. increase, $\theta = \dfrac{5\pi}{4}$; max. decrease, $\theta = \dfrac{\pi}{4}$; no change, $\theta = \dfrac{3\pi}{4}, \dfrac{7\pi}{4}$
c. $g(\theta) = -12\cos\theta - 12\sin\theta$ **d.** $\theta = \tfrac{5}{4}\pi$, $g\left(\tfrac{5}{4}\pi\right) = 12\sqrt{2}$
e. $\nabla f(3,2) = 12\sqrt{2}\left\langle \cos\tfrac{5}{4}\pi, \sin\tfrac{5}{4}\pi\right\rangle$, $|\nabla f(3,2)| = 12\sqrt{2}$
35. a. $\nabla f(\sqrt{3},1) = \dfrac{\sqrt{6}}{6}\langle\sqrt{3}, 1\rangle$ **b.** Max. increase, $\theta = \dfrac{\pi}{6}$; max. decrease, $\theta = \dfrac{7\pi}{6}$; no change, $\theta = \dfrac{2\pi}{3}, \dfrac{5\pi}{3}$
c. $g(\theta) = \dfrac{\sqrt{2}}{2}\cos\theta + \dfrac{\sqrt{6}}{6}\sin\theta$ **d.** $\theta = \dfrac{\pi}{6}$, $g\left(\dfrac{\pi}{6}\right) = \dfrac{\sqrt{6}}{3}$
e. $\nabla f(\sqrt{3},1) = \dfrac{\sqrt{6}}{3}\left\langle\cos\tfrac{\pi}{6}, \sin\tfrac{\pi}{6}\right\rangle$, $|\nabla f(\sqrt{3},1)| = \dfrac{\sqrt{6}}{3}$
37. a. $\nabla F(-1,0) = \dfrac{2}{e}\mathbf{i}$ **b.** Max. increase, $\theta = 0$; max. decrease, $\theta = \pi$; no change, $\theta = \pm\dfrac{\pi}{2}$ **c.** $g(\theta) = \dfrac{2}{e}\cos\theta$ **d.** $\theta = 0$, $g(0) = \dfrac{2}{e}$
e. $\nabla F(-1,0) = \dfrac{2}{e}\langle\cos 0, \sin 0\rangle$, $|\nabla F(-1,0)| = \dfrac{2}{e}$

39.

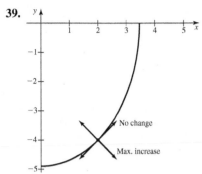

41.

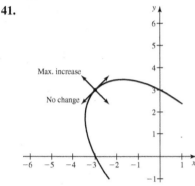

43. $y' = 0$ **45.** Vertical tangent   **47.** $y' = -2/\sqrt{3}$ **49.** Vertical
tangent   **51. a.** $\nabla f = \langle 1, 0 \rangle$ **b.** $x = 4 - t, y = 4, t \ge 0$
53. a. $\nabla f = \langle -2x, -4y \rangle$ **b.** $y = x^2, x \ge 1$
55. a. $\nabla f(x, y, z) = 2x\mathbf{i} + 4y\mathbf{j} + 8z\mathbf{k}, \nabla f(1, 0, 4) = 2\mathbf{i} + 32\mathbf{k}$

b. $\dfrac{1}{\sqrt{257}}(\mathbf{i} + 16\mathbf{k})$ **c.** $2\sqrt{257}$ **d.** $17\sqrt{2}$ **57. a.** $\nabla f(x, y, z) =$
$4yz\mathbf{i} + 4xz\mathbf{j} + 4xy\mathbf{k}, \nabla f(1, -1, -1) = 4\mathbf{i} - 4\mathbf{j} - 4\mathbf{k}$

b. $\dfrac{1}{\sqrt{3}}(\mathbf{i} - \mathbf{j} - \mathbf{k})$ **c.** $4\sqrt{3}$ **d.** $\dfrac{4}{\sqrt{3}}$

59. a. $\nabla f(x, y, z) = \cos(x + 2y - z)(\mathbf{i} + 2\mathbf{j} - \mathbf{k})$
$\nabla f\left(\dfrac{\pi}{6}, \dfrac{\pi}{6}, -\dfrac{\pi}{6}\right) = -\dfrac{1}{2}\mathbf{i} - \mathbf{j} + \dfrac{1}{2}\mathbf{k}$ **b.** $\dfrac{1}{\sqrt{6}}(-\mathbf{i} - 2\mathbf{j} + \mathbf{k})$

c. $\sqrt{6}/2$ **d.** $-\dfrac{1}{2}$

61. a. $\nabla f(x, y, z) = \dfrac{2}{1 + x^2 + y^2 + z^2}(x\mathbf{i} + y\mathbf{j} + z\mathbf{k})$,
$\nabla f(1, 1, -1) = \dfrac{1}{2}\mathbf{i} + \dfrac{1}{2}\mathbf{j} - \dfrac{1}{2}\mathbf{k}$ **b.** $\dfrac{1}{\sqrt{3}}(\mathbf{i} + \mathbf{j} - \mathbf{k})$ **c.** $\dfrac{\sqrt{3}}{2}$ **d.** $\dfrac{5}{6}$

63. a. False   **b.** False   **c.** False   **d.** True   **65.** $\pm\dfrac{1}{\sqrt{5}}(\mathbf{i} - 2\mathbf{j})$

67. $\pm\dfrac{1}{\sqrt{2}}(\mathbf{i} + \mathbf{j})$ **69.** $x = x_0 + at, y = y_0 + bt$

71. a. $\nabla f(x, y, z) = \langle 2x, 2y, 2z \rangle, \nabla f(1, 1, 1) = \langle 2, 2, 2 \rangle$
b. $x + y + z = 3$ **73. a.** $\nabla f(x, y, z) = e^{x+y-z}\langle 1, 1, -1 \rangle$,
$\nabla f(1, 1, 2) = \langle 1, 1, -1 \rangle$ **b.** $x + y - z = 0$
75. a.

b. $\mathbf{v} = \pm\langle 1, 1 \rangle$ **c.** $\mathbf{v} = \pm\langle 1, -1 \rangle$
79. $\langle u, v \rangle = \langle \pi \cos \pi x \sin 2\pi y, 2\pi \sin \pi x \cos 2\pi y \rangle$
83. $\nabla f(x, y) = \dfrac{1}{(x^2 + y^2)^2}\langle y^2 - x^2 - 2xy, x^2 - y^2 - 2xy \rangle$

85. $\nabla f(x, y, z) = -\dfrac{1}{\sqrt{25 - x^2 - y^2 - z^2}}\langle x, y, z \rangle$

87. $\nabla f(x, y, z) = \dfrac{(y + xz)\langle 1, z, y \rangle - (x + yz)\langle z, 1, x \rangle}{(y + xz)^2}$

$= \dfrac{1}{(y + xz)^2}\langle y(1 - z^2), x(z^2 - 1), y^2 - x^2 \rangle$

Section 13.7 Exercises, pp. 957–961

1. The gradient of f is a multiple of $\mathbf{n}$.
3. $F_x(a, b, c)(x - a) + F_y(a, b, c)(y - b) + F_z(a, b, c)(z - c) = 0$
5. Multiply the change in x by $f_x(a, b)$ and the change in y by $f_y(a, b)$,
and add both terms to f.   **7.** $dz = f_x(a, b)\, dx + f_y(a, b)\, dy$
9. $2x + y + z = 4; 4x + y + z = 7$
11. $x + y + z = 6; 3x + 4y + z = 12$
13. $x + \dfrac{1}{2}y + \sqrt{3}z = 2 + \dfrac{\sqrt{3}\pi}{6}$ and $\dfrac{1}{2}x + y + \sqrt{3}z = \dfrac{5\sqrt{3}\pi}{6} - 2$
15. $\frac{1}{2}x + \frac{2}{3}y + 2\sqrt{3}z = -2$ and $x - 2y + 2\sqrt{14}z = 2$
17. $z = -8x - 4y + 16$ and $z = 4x + 2y + 7$
19. $z = y + 1; z = x + 1$ **21.** $z = 8x - 4y - 4$ and
$z = -x - y - 1$ **23.** $z = \frac{7}{25}x - \frac{1}{25}y - \frac{2}{5}$ and $z = -\frac{7}{25}x + \frac{1}{25}y + \frac{6}{5}$
25. a. $L(x, y) = 4x + y - 6$ **b.** $L(2.1, 2.99) = 5.39$
27. a. $L(x, y) = -6x - 4y + 7$ **b.** $L(3.1, -1.04) = -7.44$
29. a. $L(x, y) = x + y$ **b.** $L(0.1, -0.2) = -0.1$
31. $dz = -6dx - 5dy = -0.1$ **33.** $dz = dx + dy = 0.05$
35. a. The surface area decreases.   **b.** Impossible to tell

c. $dS \approx 53.3$ **d.** $dS = 33.95$ **e.** $RdR = rdr$ **37.** $\dfrac{dA}{A} = 3.5\%$
39. $dw = (y^2 + 2xz)\, dx + (2xy + z^2)\, dy + (x^2 + 2yz)\, dz$
41. $dw = \dfrac{dx}{y + z} - \dfrac{u + x}{(y + z)^2}\, dy - \dfrac{u + x}{(y + z)^2}\, dz + \dfrac{du}{y + z}$

43. a. $dc = 0.035$ **b.** When $\theta = \dfrac{\pi}{20}$ **45. a.** True   **b.** True

c. False   **47.** $z = \dfrac{1}{2}x + \dfrac{1}{2}y + \dfrac{\pi}{4} - 1$

49. $\dfrac{1}{6}(x - \pi) + \dfrac{\pi}{6}(y - 1) + \pi\left(z - \dfrac{1}{6}\right) = 0$ **51.** $(1, -1, 1)$ and

$(1, -1, -1)$ **53.** Points with $x = 0, \pm\dfrac{\pi}{2}, \pm\pi$ and $y = \pm\dfrac{\pi}{2}$, or

points with $x = \pm\dfrac{\pi}{4}, \pm\dfrac{3\pi}{4}$ and $y = 0, \pm\pi$ **55. a.** $dS = 0.749$

b. More sensitive to changes of r **57. a.** $dA = \dfrac{2}{1225} = 0.00163$

b. No. The batting average increases more if he gets a hit than it
would decrease if he fails to get a hit.   **c.** Yes. The answer depends on
whether A is less than 0.500 or greater than 0.500.

59. a. $dV = \dfrac{21}{5000} = 0.0042$ **b.** $\dfrac{dV}{V} = -4\%$ **c.** $2p\%$

61. a. $f_r = n(1 - r)^{n-1}, f_n = -(1 - r)^n \ln(1 - r)$
b. $\Delta P \approx 0.027$,   **c.** $\Delta P \approx 2 \times 10^{-20}$ **63.** $dR = 7/540 \approx 0.013$
65. a. Apply the Chain Rule.   **b.** Follows directly from (a)

c. $d(\ln(xy)) = \dfrac{dx}{x} + \dfrac{dy}{y}$ **d.** $d(\ln(x/y)) = \dfrac{dx}{x} - \dfrac{dy}{y}$

e. $\dfrac{df}{f} = \dfrac{dx_1}{x_1} + \dfrac{dx_2}{x_2} + \cdots + \dfrac{dx_n}{x_n}$

Section 13.8 Exercises, pp. 968–971

1. It is locally the highest point on the surface; you cannot get to a higher point in any direction.   **3.** The partial derivatives are both zero, or do not exist.   **5.** The discriminant is a determinant; it is defined as $D(a, b) = f_{xx}(a, b)f_{yy}(a, b) - f_{xy}^2(a, b)$.   **7.** f has an absolute minimum value at (a, b) if $f(x, y) \geq f(a, b)$ for all (x, y) in the domain of f.   **9.** $(0, 0)$ **11.** $\left(\frac{2}{3}, 4\right)$ **13.** $(0, 0), (2, 2)$, and $(-2, -2)$
15. $(0, 2), (\pm 1, 2)$ **17.** $(-3, 0)$ **19.** Local min. at $(0, 0)$
21. Saddle point at $(0, 0)$ **23.** Saddle point at $(0, 0)$, local min. at $(1, 1)$ and at $(-1, -1)$ **25.** Local min. at $(2, 0)$ **27.** Saddle point at $(0, 0)$, local max. at $\left(\dfrac{1}{\sqrt{2}}, \dfrac{1}{\sqrt{2}}\right)$ and $\left(-\dfrac{1}{\sqrt{2}}, -\dfrac{1}{\sqrt{2}}\right)$, local min. at $\left(\dfrac{1}{\sqrt{2}}, -\dfrac{1}{\sqrt{2}}\right)$ and $\left(-\dfrac{1}{\sqrt{2}}, \dfrac{1}{\sqrt{2}}\right)$ **29.** Local min.: $(-1, 0)$; local max.: $(1, 0)$ **31.** Saddle point: $(0, 1)$; local min.: $(\pm 2, 0)$ **33.** Saddle point at $(0, 0)$ **35.** Height $= 32$ in, base is 16 in $\times$ 16 in; volume is 8192 in^3 **37.** 2 m $\times$ 2 m $\times$ 1 m   **39.** Critical point at $(0, 0)$, $D(0, 0) = 0$, absolute min.   **41.** Critical points along the x- and y-axes, all absolute min.   **43.** Absolute min.: $0 = f(0, 1)$; absolute max.: $9 = f(0, -2)$ **45.** Absolute min.: $4 = f(0, 0)$; absolute max.: $7 = f(\pm 1, \pm 1)$ **47.** Absolute min.: $0 = f(1, 0)$; absolute max.: $3 = f(1, 1) = f(1, -1)$ **49.** Absolute max.: $4 = f(1, -1)$; absolute min.: $1 = f(1, -2) = f(1, 0)$ **51.** Absolute min.: $-4 = f(0, 0)$; no absolute max. on R **53.** Absolute max.: $2 = f(0, 0)$; no absolute min. on R **55.** $P\left(-\frac{5}{3}, \frac{4}{3}, \frac{13}{3}\right)$ **57.** $\left(\frac{1}{2}, \frac{1}{4}\right)$; $\left(\frac{7}{8}, -\frac{1}{8}\right)$ **59. a.** True **b.** False
c. True **d.** True   **61.** Local minimum at $(0.3, -0.3)$, saddle point at $(0, 0)$ **63.** $P\left(\frac{4}{3}, \frac{2}{3}, \frac{4}{3}\right)$ **65.** $x = y = z = \dfrac{200}{3}$ in all four parts
67. a. $P\left(1, \frac{1}{3}\right)$ **b.** $P\left(\frac{1}{3}(x_1 + x_2 + x_3), \frac{1}{3}(y_1 + y_2 + y_3)\right)$
c. $P(\bar{x}, \bar{y})$, where $\bar{x} = \dfrac{1}{n}\sum_{k=1}^{n} x_k$ and $\bar{y} = \dfrac{1}{n}\sum_{k=1}^{n} y_k$
d. $d(x, y) = \sqrt{x^2 + y^2} + \sqrt{(x - 2)^2 + y^2} + \sqrt{(x - 1)^2 + (y - 1)^2}$. The absolute min. of this function is $1 + \sqrt{3} = f\left(1, \dfrac{1}{\sqrt{3}}\right)$.   **71.** $y = \dfrac{22}{13}x + \dfrac{46}{13}$ **73.** $a = b = c = 3$

75. a. $\nabla d_1(x, y) = \dfrac{x - x_1}{d_1(x, y)}\mathbf{i} + \dfrac{y - y_1}{d_1(x, y)}\mathbf{j}$
b. $\nabla d_2(x, y) = \dfrac{x - x_2}{d_2(x, y)}\mathbf{i} + \dfrac{y - y_2}{d_2(x, y)}\mathbf{j}$,
$\nabla d_3(x, y) = \dfrac{x - x_3}{d_3(x, y)}\mathbf{i} + \dfrac{y - y_3}{d_3(x, y)}\mathbf{j}$

c. Follows from $\nabla f = \nabla d_1 + \nabla d_2 + \nabla d_3$ **d.** Three unit vectors add to zero.   **e.** P is the vertex at the large angle.   **f.** $P(0.255457, 0.304504)$
77. a. Local max. at $(1, 0), (-1, 0)$ **b.** $(1, 0)$ and $(-1, 0)$

Section 13.9 Exercises, pp. 977–979

1. The level curve of f must be tangential to the curve $g = 0$ at the optimal point; thus, the gradients are parallel.   **3.** $2x = 2\lambda, 2y = 3\lambda,$ $2z = -5\lambda, 2x + 3y - 5z + 4 = 0$

5. Max. value: $2\sqrt{5}$ at $\left(\frac{2}{\sqrt{5}}, \frac{4}{\sqrt{5}}\right)$; min. value: $-2\sqrt{5}$ at $\left(-\frac{2}{\sqrt{5}}, -\frac{4}{\sqrt{5}}\right)$
7. Min. value: -2 at $(-1, -1)$; max. value: 2 at $(1, 1)$
9. Min. value: -3 at $(-\sqrt{3}, \sqrt{3})$ and $(\sqrt{3}, -\sqrt{3})$; max. value: 9 at $(3, 3)$ and $(-3, -3)$ **11.** Min. value: e^{-16} at $(2\sqrt{2}, -2\sqrt{2})$ and $(-2\sqrt{2}, 2\sqrt{2})$; max. value: e^{16} at $(-2\sqrt{2}, -2\sqrt{2})$ and $(2\sqrt{2}, 2\sqrt{2})$
13. Min. value: -16 at $(\pm 2, 0)$; max. value: 2 at $(0, \pm\sqrt{2})$
15. Max. value: $2\sqrt{11}$ at $\left(\frac{2}{\sqrt{11}}, \frac{6}{\sqrt{11}}, -\frac{2}{\sqrt{11}}\right)$; min. value: $-2\sqrt{11}$ at $\left(-\frac{2}{\sqrt{11}}, -\frac{6}{\sqrt{11}}, \frac{2}{\sqrt{11}}\right)$;   **17.** Min. value: $-\dfrac{\sqrt{5}}{2}$ at $\left(-\dfrac{\sqrt{5}}{2}, 0, \dfrac{1}{2}\right)$; max. value: $\dfrac{\sqrt{5}}{2}$ at $\left(\dfrac{\sqrt{5}}{2}, 0, \dfrac{1}{2}\right)$ **19.** Min. value: $\dfrac{1}{3}$ at $\left(-\dfrac{1}{\sqrt{6}}, \dfrac{1}{\sqrt{6}}, 0\right)$ and $\left(\dfrac{1}{\sqrt{6}}, -\dfrac{1}{\sqrt{6}}, 0\right)$; max. value: 1 at $(0, 0, \pm 1)$ **21.** Min. value: -10 at $(-5, 0, 0)$; max. value: $\dfrac{29}{2}$ at $\left(2, 0, \pm\sqrt{\dfrac{21}{2}}\right)$ **23.** Min. value: $6\sqrt[3]{2} = f(\pm\sqrt[3]{4}, \pm\sqrt[3]{4}, \pm\sqrt[3]{4})$; no upper bound   **25.** 18 in $\times$ 18 in $\times$ 36 in   **27.** Min. distance: 0.6731; max. distance: 1.1230   **29.** 2×1 **31.** $\left(-\dfrac{3}{17}, \dfrac{29}{17}, -3\right)$ **33.** Min. distance: $\sqrt{38 - 6\sqrt{29}}$; max. distance: $\sqrt{38 + 6\sqrt{29}}$ **35.** $\ell = 3$ and $g = \frac{3}{2}$; $U = 15\sqrt{2}$ **37.** $\ell = \frac{16}{5}$ and $g = 1$; $U = 20.287$ **39. a.** True **b.** False
41. $\dfrac{\sqrt{6}}{3}$ m $\times \dfrac{\sqrt{6}}{3}$ m $\times \dfrac{\sqrt{6}}{6}$ m   **43.** $2 \times 1 \times \frac{2}{3}$ **45.** $P\left(\frac{4}{3}, \frac{2}{3}, \frac{4}{3}\right)$
47. Min. value: $-\dfrac{7 + \sqrt{661}}{2}$; max. value: $\dfrac{\sqrt{661} - 7}{2}$
49. Min. value: 0; max. value: $6 + 4\sqrt{2}$ **51.** Min. value: 1; max. value: 8   **53.** $K = 7.5$ and $L = 5$ **55.** $K = aB/p$ and $L = (1 - a)B/q$ **57.** Max.: 8   **59.** Max.: $\sqrt{a_1^2 + a_2^2 + a_3^2 + \cdots + a_n^2}$ **61. a.** Gradients are perpendicular to level surfaces.   **b.** If the gradient was not in the plane spanned by ∇g and ∇h, f could be increased (decreased) by moving the point slightly.   **c.** ∇f is a linear combination of ∇g and ∇h, since it belongs to the plane spanned by these two vectors.   **d.** The gradient condition from part (c), as well as the constraints, must be satisfied.   **63.** Min.: $2 - 4\sqrt{2}$; max.: $2 + 4\sqrt{2}$ **65.** Min.: $\frac{5}{4} = f\left(\frac{1}{2}, 0, 1\right)$; max.: $\frac{125}{36} = f\left(-\frac{5}{6}, 0, \frac{5}{3}\right)$

Chapter 13 Review Exercises, pp. 980–983

1. a. False **b.** False **c.** False **d.** False **e.** True
3. a. $18x - 9y + 2z = 6$ **b.** $x = \frac{1}{3}, y = -\frac{2}{3}, z = 3$
c.

5. $x = t, y = 12 - 9t, z = -6 + 6t$ **7.** $3x + y + 7z = 4$
9. a. Hyperbolic paraboloid **b.** $y^2 = 4x^2, z = \dfrac{x^2}{36}, z = -\dfrac{y^2}{144}$

c. $x = y = z = 0$ **d.**

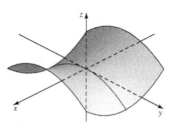

11. a. Elliptic cone   **b.** $y^2 = 4x^2$, the xz-trace reduces to the origin, $y^2 = \dfrac{z^2}{25}$.   **c.** Origin   **d.**

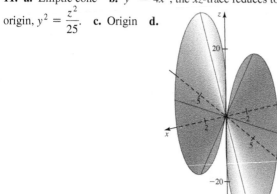

13. a. Elliptic paraboloid   **b.** Origin, $z = \dfrac{x^2}{16}, z = \dfrac{y^2}{36}$ **c.** Origin
d.

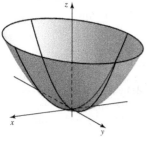

15. a. Hyperboloid of one sheet   **b.** $y^2 - 2x^2 = 1, 4z^2 - 2x^2 = 1$, $y^2 + 4z^2 = 1$ **c.** No x-intercept, $y = \pm1, z = \pm\frac{1}{2}$
d.

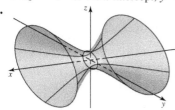

17. a. Hyperboloid of one sheet
b. $\dfrac{x^2}{4} + \dfrac{y^2}{16} = 4, \dfrac{x^2}{4} - z^2 = 4, \dfrac{y^2}{16} - z^2 = 4$
c. $x = \pm4, y = \pm8$, no z-intercept
d.

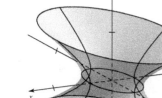

19. a. Ellipsoid   **b.** $\dfrac{x^2}{4} + \dfrac{y^2}{16} = 4, \dfrac{x^2}{4} + z^2 = 4, \dfrac{y^2}{16} + z^2 = 4$
c. $x = \pm4, y = \pm8, z = \pm2$ **d.**

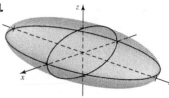

21. a. Elliptic cone   **b.** The xy-trace reduces to the origin, $\dfrac{x^2}{9} = \dfrac{z^2}{64}, \dfrac{y^2}{49} = \dfrac{z^2}{64}$.   **c.** Origin   **d.**

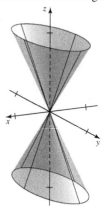

23. $D = \{(x, y): (x, y) \neq (0, 0)\}$

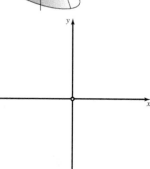

25. $D = \{(x, y): x \geq y^2\}$

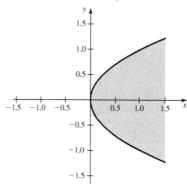

27. a. A   **b.** D   **c.** C   **d.** B   **29.**

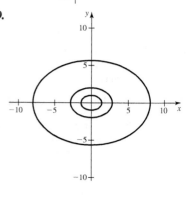

31. 2   **33.** Does not exist   **35.** $\frac{2}{3}$ **37.** 4

39. $f_x = 6xy^5; f_y = 15x^2y^4$ **41.** $f_x = \dfrac{2xy^2}{(x^2 + y^2)^2}; f_y = -\dfrac{2x^2y}{(x^2 + y^2)^2}$

43. $\dfrac{\partial}{\partial x}[xye^{xy}] = y(1 + xy)e^{xy}, \dfrac{\partial}{\partial y}[xye^{xy}] = x(1 + xy)e^{xy}$

45. $f_x(x, y, z) = e^{x+2y+3z}, f_y(x, y, z) = 2e^{x+2y+3z},$

$f_z(x, y, z) = 3e^{x+2y+3z}$ **47.** $\dfrac{\partial^2 u}{\partial x^2} = 6y = -\dfrac{\partial^2 u}{\partial y^2}$ **49. a.** V increases

with R if r is fixed, $V_R > 0$; V decreases if r increases and R is fixed, $V_r < 0$.   **b.** $V_r = -4\pi r^2, V_R = 4\pi R^2$ **c.** The volume increases

more if R is increased.   **51.** $w'(t) = -\dfrac{\cos t \sin t}{\sqrt{1 + \cos^2 t}}$

53. $w_r = \dfrac{3r + s}{r(r + s)}; w_s = \dfrac{r + 3s}{s(r + s)}; w_t = \dfrac{1}{t}$

55. $\dfrac{dy}{dx} = -\dfrac{2xy}{2y^2 + (x^2 + y^2)\ln(x^2 + y^2)}$

57. a. $z'(t) = -24 \sin t \cos t = -12 \sin(2t)$

b. $z'(t) > 0$ for $\dfrac{\pi}{2} < t < \pi$ and $\dfrac{3\pi}{2} < t < 2\pi$

59.

	$(a, b) = (0, 0)$	$(a, b) = (2, 0)$	$(a, b) = (1, 1)$
$\theta = \pi/4$	0	$4\sqrt{2}$	$-2\sqrt{2}$
$\theta = 3\pi/4$	0	$-4\sqrt{2}$	$-6\sqrt{2}$
$\theta = 5\pi/4$	0	$-4\sqrt{2}$	$2\sqrt{2}$

61. $\nabla g = \langle 2xy^3, 3x^2y^2 \rangle; \nabla g(-1, 1) = \langle -2, 3 \rangle; D_{\mathbf{u}} g(-1, 1) = 2$

63. $\nabla h(x, y) = \left\langle \dfrac{x}{\sqrt{2 + x^2 + 2y^2}}, \dfrac{2y}{\sqrt{2 + x^2 + 2y^2}} \right\rangle$

$\nabla h(2, 1) = \left\langle \dfrac{\sqrt{2}}{2}, \dfrac{\sqrt{2}}{2} \right\rangle, D_{\mathbf{u}} h(2, 1) = \dfrac{7\sqrt{2}}{10}$

65. $\nabla f(x, y, z) = \langle \cos(x + 2y - z),$
$2 \cos(x + 2y - z), -\cos(x + 2y - z) \rangle,$

$\nabla f\left(\dfrac{\pi}{6}, \dfrac{\pi}{6}, -\dfrac{\pi}{6}\right) = \left\langle -\dfrac{1}{2}, -1, \dfrac{1}{2} \right\rangle, D_{\mathbf{u}} f\left(\dfrac{\pi}{6}, \dfrac{\pi}{6}, -\dfrac{\pi}{6}\right) = -\dfrac{1}{2}$

67. a. Steepest ascent: $\mathbf{u} = \dfrac{\sqrt{2}}{2}\mathbf{i} - \dfrac{\sqrt{2}}{2}\mathbf{j};$

steepest descent: $\mathbf{u} = -\dfrac{\sqrt{2}}{2}\mathbf{i} + \dfrac{\sqrt{2}}{2}\mathbf{j}$

b. No change: $\mathbf{u} = \pm\left(\dfrac{\sqrt{2}}{2}\mathbf{i} + \dfrac{\sqrt{2}}{2}\mathbf{j}\right)$

69. Tangent line is vertical, $\nabla f(2, 0) = -8\mathbf{i}$

71. $E = \dfrac{kx}{x^2 + y^2}\mathbf{i} + \dfrac{ky}{x^2 + y^2}\mathbf{j}$

73. $y = 2$ and $12x + 3y - 2z = 12$

75. $16x + 2y + z - 8 = 0$ and $8x + y + 8z + 16 = 0$

77. $z = \ln 3 + \dfrac{2}{3}(x - 1) + \dfrac{1}{3}(y - 2);$

$z = \ln 3 - \dfrac{1}{3}(x + 2) - \dfrac{2}{3}(y + 1)$ **79.** $L(x, y) = x + 5y,$

$L(1.95, 0.05) = 2.2$ **81.** -4% **83. a.** $dV = -0.1\pi$ m^3
b. $dS = -0.05\pi$ m^2 **85.** Saddle point: $(0, 0)$; local min.: $(2, -2)$
87. Saddle points: $(0, 0)$ and $(-2, 2)$; local max.: $(0, 2)$; local min.: $(-2, 0)$ **89.** Absolute min.: $-1 = f(1, 1) = f(-1, -1)$; absolute

max.: $49 = f(2, -2) = f(-2, 2)$ **91.** Absolute min.:

$-\dfrac{1}{2} = f\left(-\dfrac{1}{\sqrt{2}}, \dfrac{1}{\sqrt{2}}\right)$; absolute max.: $\dfrac{1}{2} = f\left(\dfrac{1}{\sqrt{2}}, \dfrac{1}{\sqrt{2}}\right)$

93. Max.: $\dfrac{29}{2} = f\left(\dfrac{5}{3}, \dfrac{7}{6}\right)$; min.: $\dfrac{23}{2} = f\left(\dfrac{1}{3}, \dfrac{5}{6}\right)$

95. Max.: $f\left(\dfrac{\sqrt{6}}{6}, \dfrac{\sqrt{6}}{3}, -\dfrac{\sqrt{6}}{6}\right) = \sqrt{6}$

min.: $f\left(-\dfrac{\sqrt{6}}{6}, -\dfrac{\sqrt{6}}{3}, \dfrac{\sqrt{6}}{6}\right) = -\sqrt{6}$ **97.** $\dfrac{2a^2}{\sqrt{a^2 + b^2}}$ by $\dfrac{2b^2}{\sqrt{a^2 + b^2}}$

99. $x = \dfrac{1}{2} + \dfrac{\sqrt{10}}{20}, y = \dfrac{3}{2} + \dfrac{3\sqrt{10}}{20} = 3x, z = \dfrac{1}{2} + \dfrac{\sqrt{10}}{2} = \sqrt{10}x$

CHAPTER 14

Section 14.1 Exercises, pp. 991–994

1. $\displaystyle\int_0^2 \int_1^3 xy \, dy \, dx$ or $\displaystyle\int_1^3 \int_0^2 xy \, dx \, dy$ **3.** $\displaystyle\int_{-2}^4 \int_1^5 f(x, y) \, dy \, dx$ or

$\displaystyle\int_1^5 \int_{-2}^4 f(x, y) \, dx \, dy$ **5.** 4   **7.** $\frac{32}{3}$ **9.** 4   **11.** $\frac{224}{9}$ **13.** 7

15. $10 - 2e$ **17.** $\frac{117}{2} = 58.5$ **19.** 15   **21.** $\frac{4}{3}$ **23.** $\dfrac{9 - e^2}{2}$

25. $\frac{4}{11}$ **27.** $e^2 - 3$ **29.** $e^{16} - 17$ **31.** $\ln \frac{5}{3}$ **33.** $\dfrac{1}{2 \ln 2}$

35. $8/3$ **37. a.** True   **b.** False   **c.** True   **39. a.** 1475
b. The sum of products of population densities and areas is a
Riemann sum.   **41.** 60

43. $\frac{1}{2}$ **45.** $10\sqrt{5} - 4\sqrt{2} - 14$ **47.** 3   **49.** 136   **51.** $a = \pi/6, 5\pi/6$
53. $a = \sqrt{6}$ **55. a.** $\frac{1}{2}\pi^2 + \pi$ **b.** $\frac{1}{2}\pi^2 + \pi$ **c.** $\frac{1}{2}\pi^2 + 2$
57. $\int_c^d \int_a^b f(x) \, dy \, dx = (c - d) \int_a^b f(x) \, dx$. The integral is the area of
the cross section of S.   **59.** $f(a, b) - f(a, 0) - f(0, b) + f(0, 0)$
61. Use substitution ($u = x^r y^s$ and then $v = x^r$).

Section 14.2 Exercises, pp. 1001–1005

1.

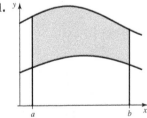

3. $dx \, dy$ **5.** $\displaystyle\int_0^1 \int_{x^2}^{\sqrt{x}} f(x, y) \, dy \, dx$ **7.** $\displaystyle\int_0^2 \int_{x^3}^{4x} f(x, y) \, dy \, dx$

9.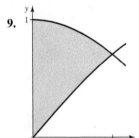

$$\int_0^{\pi/4}\int_{\sin x}^{\cos x} f(x,y)\,dy\,dx$$

11.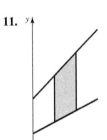

$$\int_1^2\int_{x+1}^{2x+4} f(x,y)\,dy\,dx$$

13.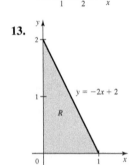

$$\int_0^1\int_0^{-2x+2} f(x,y)\,dy\,dx$$

15.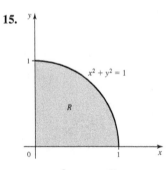

$$\int_0^1\int_0^{\sqrt{1-x^2}} f(x,y)\,dy\,dx$$

17. 2   **19.** $\frac{8}{3}$ **21.** $\sqrt{2}$ **23.** 0   **25.** $e-1$ **27.** 2   **29.** 12

31. $\displaystyle\int_0^{18}\int_{y/2}^{(y+9)/3} f(x,y)\,dx\,dy$ **33.** $\displaystyle\int_0^{23}\int_{(y-3)/2}^{(y+7)/3} f(x,y)\,dx\,dy$

35. $\displaystyle\int_1^4\int_0^{4-y} f(x,y)\,dx\,dy$ **37.** $\displaystyle\int_0^1\int_y^{2-y} f(x,y)\,dx\,dy$

39. 9      **41.** 0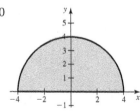

43. $\dfrac{\ln^3 2}{6}$ 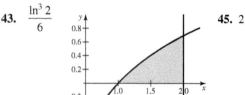   **45.** 2

47. 5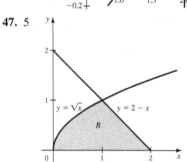

49. 14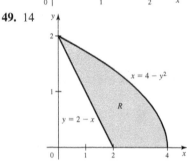

51. 32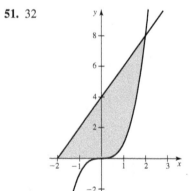

53. $\dfrac{32}{3}$ **55.** 12π **57.** $\displaystyle\int_0^4\int_{y/2}^{\sqrt{y}} f(x,y)\,dx\,dy$

59. $\displaystyle\int_0^{\ln 2}\int_{1/2}^{e^{-x}} f(x,y)\,dy\,dx$ **61.** $\displaystyle\int_0^{\pi/2}\int_0^{\cos x} f(x,y)\,dy\,dx$

63. $\frac{1}{2}(e-1)$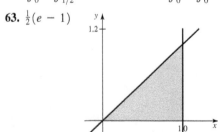

65. 0

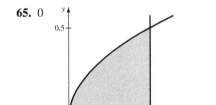

67. $\frac{2}{3}$

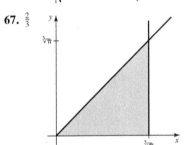

69. $\frac{2}{3}$ **71.** $81\pi/2$ **73.** $\frac{43}{6}$

75. $\frac{32}{3}$

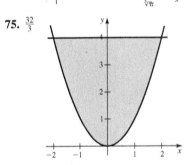

77. 1

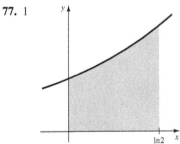

79. $\frac{140}{3}$

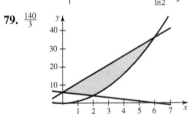

81. a. False **b.** False **c.** False **83.** $\frac{9}{8}$ **85.** $\frac{1}{4}\ln 2$

87. $\displaystyle\int_1^e \int_{-\ln x}^{\ln x} f(x,y)\, dy\, dx$

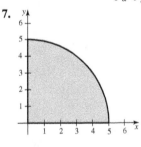

89. $a/3$ **91. a.**

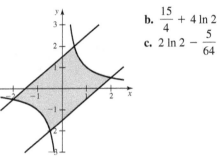

b. $\dfrac{15}{4} + 4\ln 2$

c. $2\ln 2 - \dfrac{5}{64}$

93. $\dfrac{3}{8e^2}$ **95.** 1 **97.** 30 **99.** 16 **101.** $4a\pi$

103. The integral over R_1

Section 14.3 Exercises, pp. 1012–1015

1. It is a polar rectangle because r and θ each vary between two constants.

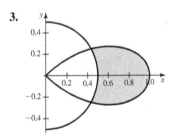

3.

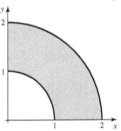

5. Evaluate the integral $\displaystyle\int_\alpha^\beta \int_{g(\theta)}^{h(\theta)} r\, dr\, d\theta$

7.

9.

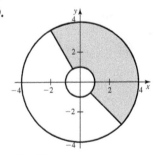

11. $7\pi/2$ **13.** $9\pi/2$ **15.** $\dfrac{62 - 10\sqrt{5}}{3}\,\pi$ **17.** $\dfrac{37\pi}{3}$ **19.** π

21. $\pi/2$ **23.** 128π

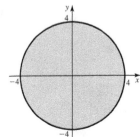

25. 0

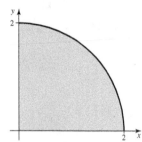

27. $(2 - \sqrt{3})\pi$

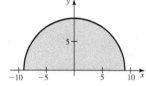

29. $(8 - 24e^{-2})\pi$ **31.** $\dfrac{15625\pi}{3}$

33.

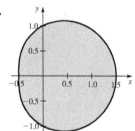

$$\int_0^{2\pi} \int_0^{1+\frac{1}{2}\cos\theta} f(r,\theta)r \, dr \, d\theta$$

35.

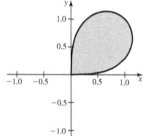

$$\int_0^{\pi/2} \int_0^{\sqrt{2\sin 2\theta}} f(r,\theta)r \, dr \, d\theta$$

37.

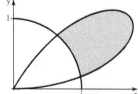

$$\int_{\pi/18}^{5\pi/18} \int_1^{2\sin 3\theta} f(r,\theta)r \, dr \, d\theta$$

39. $3\pi/2$

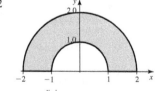

41. π

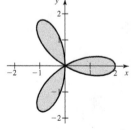

43. $\dfrac{3\pi}{2} - 2\sqrt{2}$

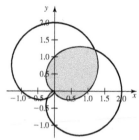

45. $2a/3$ **47.** $\frac{5}{2}$ **49. a.** False   **b.** True   **c.** True
51. $2\pi/5$

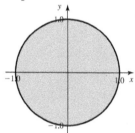

53. $\frac{1}{3}$

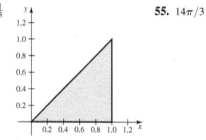

55. $14\pi/3$

57. $2\pi\left(1 - 2\ln\left(\frac{3}{2}\right)\right)$

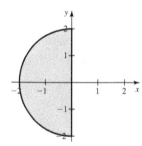

59. The hyperboloid $\left(V = \frac{112}{3}\pi\right)$
61. a. $R = \left\{(r,\theta) : -\pi/4 \le \theta \le \pi/4 \text{ or } 3\pi/4 \le \theta \le 5\pi/4\right\}$
b. $\dfrac{a^4}{4}$ **63.** 1   **65.** $\pi/4$ **67. a.** $9\pi/2$ **b.** $\pi + 3\sqrt{3}$
c. $\pi - 3\sqrt{3}/2$ **69.** $30\pi + 42$ **71. b.** $\sqrt{\pi}/2, \frac{1}{2}$, and $\sqrt{\pi}/4$
73. a. $I = \frac{\sqrt{2}}{2}\tan^{-1}\left(\frac{\sqrt{2}}{2}\right)$
b. $I = \frac{\sqrt{2}}{4}\tan^{-1}\left(\frac{\sqrt{2}}{2}a\right) + \dfrac{a}{2\sqrt{a^2+1}}\tan^{-1}\dfrac{1}{\sqrt{a^2+1}}$ **c.** $\dfrac{\sqrt{2}\pi}{8}$

Section 14.4 Exercises, pp. 1023–1027

1.

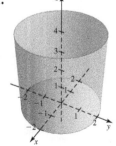

3. $\int_{-9}^{9} \int_{-\sqrt{81-x^2}}^{\sqrt{81-x^2}} \int_{-\sqrt{81-x^2-y^2}}^{\sqrt{81-x^2-y^2}} f(x, y, z)\, dz\, dy\, dx$

5. $\int_{0}^{1} \int_{0}^{\sqrt{1-z^2}} \int_{0}^{\sqrt{1-z^2-x^2}} f(x, y, z)\, dy\, dx\, dz$ **7.** 24   **9.** 8

11. $2/\pi$ **13.** 0   **15.** 8   **17.** $\dfrac{32(\sqrt{2}-1)}{3}\pi$ **19.** $\frac{16}{3}$

21. $\dfrac{2\pi(1 + 19\sqrt{19} - 20\sqrt{10})}{3}$ **23.** 12π **25.** $\frac{2}{3}$ **27.** 128π

29. $(10\sqrt{10} - 1)\dfrac{\pi}{6}$ **31.** $\dfrac{3\ln 2}{2} + \dfrac{e}{16} - 1$ **33.** $\frac{256}{9}$

35. $\int_{0}^{4} \int_{y/4-1}^{0} \int_{0}^{5} dz\, dx\, dy = 10$

37. $\int_{0}^{1} \int_{0}^{\sqrt{1-x^2}} \int_{0}^{\sqrt{1-x^2}} dz\, dy\, dx = \dfrac{2}{3}$ **39.** $\dfrac{7}{\ln^3 2}$ **41.** $\dfrac{10}{3}$ **43.** $\dfrac{3}{2}$

45. a. False   **b.** False   **c.** False   **47.** 1   **49.** $\frac{16}{3}$ **51.** 2

53. $\frac{224}{3}$ and $\frac{160}{3}$ **55.** $V = \pi r^2 h/3$ **57.** $V = \dfrac{\pi h^2}{3}(3R - h)$

59. $V = 4\pi abc/3$ **61.** $\frac{1}{24}$

Section 14.5 Exercises, pp. 1039–1043

1. r measures the distance from the point to the z axis, θ is the angle that the segment from the point to the z-axis makes with the positive xz-plane, and z is the directed distance from the point to the xy-plane.
3. A cone   **5.** It approximates the volume of the cylindrical wedge formed by the changes Δr, $\Delta\theta$, and Δz.

7. $\int_{\alpha}^{\beta} \int_{g(\theta)}^{h(\theta)} \int_{G(r,\theta)}^{H(r,\theta)} f(r, \theta, z)\, r\, dz\, dr\, d\theta$ **9.** Cylindrical coordinates

11.

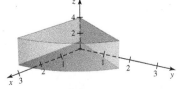

Wedge

13.

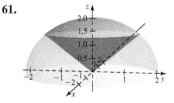

Solid bounded by cone and plane

15. 2π **17.** $4\pi/5$ **19.** $\pi(1 - e^{-1})/2$ **21.** $9\pi/4$
23. 560π **25.** 396π **27.** The paraboloid ($V = 44\pi/3$)

29. $\dfrac{2\pi + 14\pi\sqrt{17}}{3}$ **31.** $\dfrac{(16 + 17\sqrt{29})\pi}{3}$ **33.** $\frac{1}{3}$

35.

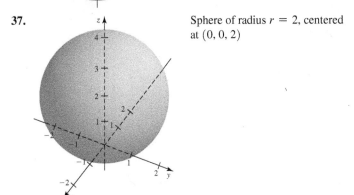

Hollow ball

37.

Sphere of radius $r = 2$, centered at $(0, 0, 2)$

39. $\pi/2$ **41.** $4\pi \ln 2$ **43.** $\pi\left(\dfrac{188}{9} - \dfrac{32\sqrt{3}}{3}\right)$ **45.** $32\pi\sqrt{3}/9$

47. $5\pi/12$ **49.** $\dfrac{8\pi}{3}$ **51.** $\dfrac{8\pi}{3}(9\sqrt{3} - 11)$ **53. a.** True   **b.** True
55. $z = \sqrt{x^2 + y^2} - 1$; upper half of a hyperboloid of one sheet
57. $\dfrac{8\pi}{3}(1 - e^{-512}) \approx \dfrac{8\pi}{3}$ **59.** 32π

61.

$\int_{0}^{2\pi} \int_{0}^{\sqrt{2}} \int_{r}^{\sqrt{4-r^2}} f(r, \theta, z)\, r\, dz\, dr\, d\theta,$

$\int_{0}^{2\pi} \int_{0}^{\sqrt{2}} \int_{0}^{z} f(r, \theta, z)\, r\, dr\, dz\, d\theta$

$+ \int_{0}^{2\pi} \int_{\sqrt{2}}^{2} \int_{0}^{\sqrt{4-z^2}} f(r, \theta, z)\, r\, dr\, dz\, d\theta,$

$\int_{0}^{\sqrt{2}} \int_{r}^{\sqrt{4-r^2}} \int_{0}^{2\pi} f(r, \theta, z)\, r\, d\theta\, dz\, dr$

63.

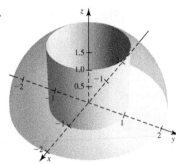

$$\int_{\pi/6}^{\pi/2} \int_0^{2\pi} \int_{\csc\varphi}^2 f(\rho, \varphi, \theta)\, \rho^2 \sin\varphi \, d\rho \, d\theta \, d\varphi,$$

$$\int_{\pi/6}^{\pi/2} \int_{\csc\varphi}^2 \int_0^{2\pi} f(\rho, \varphi, \theta)\, \rho^2 \sin\varphi \, d\theta \, d\rho \, d\varphi$$

65. $32\sqrt{3}\pi/9$ **67.** $2\sqrt{2}/3$ **69.** $7\pi/2$ **71.** $\frac{16}{3}$ **73.** 95.6036

77. $V = \dfrac{\pi r^2 h}{3}$ **79.** $V = \dfrac{\pi}{3}(R^2 + rR + r^2)h$

81. $V = \dfrac{\pi R^3(8r - 3R)}{12r}$

Section 14.6 Exercises, pp. 1051–1053

1. The pivot should be located at the center of mass of the system.
3. Use a double integral. Integrate the density function over the region occupied by the plate.   **5.** Use a triple integral to find the mass of the object and the three moments.

7.

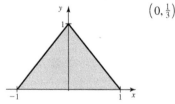

$\frac{27}{13}$ **9.** mass is $2 + \pi$; $\bar{x} = \frac{\pi}{2}$

11. mass is $\frac{20}{3}$; $\bar{x} = \frac{9}{5}$
13. mass is 10; $\bar{x} = \frac{8}{3}$

15.

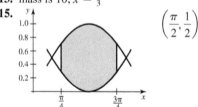

$\left(\dfrac{\pi}{2}, \dfrac{1}{2}\right)$

17.

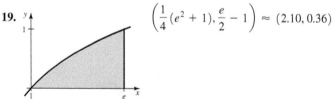

$\left(0, \dfrac{1}{3}\right)$

19.

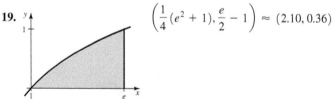

$\left(\dfrac{1}{4}(e^2 + 1), \dfrac{e}{2} - 1\right) \approx (2.10, 0.36)$

21. $\left(\frac{7}{3}, 1\right)$, density increases to the right.   **23.** $\left(\frac{16}{11}, \frac{16}{11}\right)$, density increases toward the hypotenuse of the triangle.

25. $\left(0, \dfrac{16 + 3\pi}{16 + 12\pi}\right) \approx (0, 0.4735)$; density increases away from the x-axis.

27.

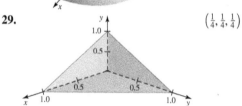

$\left(0, 0, \frac{3}{2}\right)$

29.

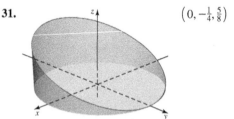

$\left(\frac{1}{4}, \frac{1}{4}, \frac{1}{4}\right)$

31.

$\left(0, -\frac{1}{4}, \frac{5}{8}\right)$

33. $\left(\frac{7}{3}, \frac{1}{2}, \frac{1}{2}\right)$ **35.** $\left(0, 0, \frac{198}{85}\right)$ **37.** $\left(\frac{2}{3}, \frac{7}{3}, \frac{1}{3}\right)$ **39. a.** False   **b.** True
c. False   **d.** False   **41.** $\bar{x} = \dfrac{\ln(1 + L^2)}{2\tan^{-1} L}$, $\displaystyle\lim_{L\to\infty} \bar{x} = \infty$

43. $\left(0, \frac{8}{9}\right)$ **45.** $\left(0, \dfrac{8}{3\pi}\right)$ **47.** $\left(\frac{5}{6}, 0\right)$ **49.** $\left(\dfrac{128}{105\pi}, \dfrac{128}{105\pi}\right)$

51. On the line of symmetry, $2a/\pi$ units above the diameter
53. $\left(\dfrac{2a}{3(4 - \pi)}, \dfrac{2a}{3(4 - \pi)}\right)$ **55.** $h/4$ units   **57.** $h/3$ units, where h
is the height of the triangle   **59.** $3a/8$ units

61. a. $\left(0, \dfrac{4(1 + a + a^2)}{3(1 + a)\pi}\right)$

b. $a = \dfrac{1}{2}\left(-1 + \sqrt{1 + \dfrac{16}{3\pi - 4}}\right) \approx 0.4937$

63. Depth $= \dfrac{40\sqrt{10} - 4}{333}$ cm ≈ 0.3678 cm

65. a. $(\bar{x}, \bar{y}) = \left(\dfrac{-r^2}{R + r}, 0\right)$ (origin at center of large circle);

$(\bar{x}, \bar{y}) = \left(\dfrac{R^2 + Rr + r^2}{R + r}, 0\right)$ (origin at common point of the circles)
b. *Hint:* Solve $\bar{x} = R - 2r$.

Section 14.7 Exercises, pp. 1063–1066

1. The image of S is the 2×2 square with vertices at $(0, 0)$, $(2, 0)$, $(2, 2)$, and $(0, 2)$.   **3.** $\displaystyle\int_0^1 \int_0^1 f(u + v, u - v)\, 2\, du\, dv$
5. The rectangle with vertices at $(0, 0)$, $(2, 0)$, $\left(2, \frac{1}{2}\right)$, and $\left(0, \frac{1}{2}\right)$
7. The diamond with vertices at $(0, 0)$, $\left(\frac{1}{2}, \frac{1}{2}\right)$, $(1, 0)$, and $\left(\frac{1}{2}, -\frac{1}{2}\right)$
9. The region above the x-axis and bounded by the curves $y^2 = 4 \pm 4x$ **11.** The upper half of the unit circle

13.

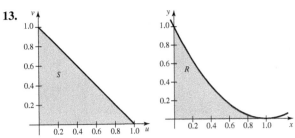

b. $0 \leq u \leq 1, 0 \leq v \leq 1 - u$ **c.** $J(u, v) = 2$ **d.** $256\sqrt{2}/945$

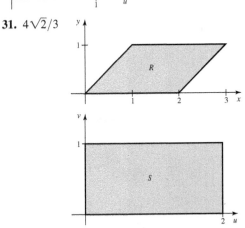

15.

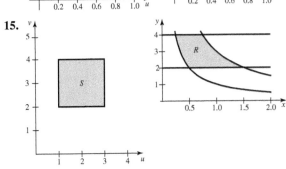

17. -9 **19.** $-4(u^2 + v^2)$ **21.** -1

23. $x = (u + v)/3, y = (2u - v)/3; -\frac{1}{3}$

25. $x = -(u + 3v), y = -(u + 2v); -1$

27. a.

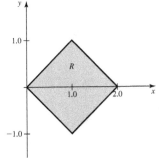

b. $0 \leq u \leq 1, 0 \leq v \leq 1$ **c.** $J(u, v) = -2$ **d.** 0

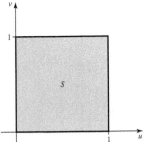

29. a.

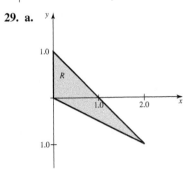

31. $4\sqrt{2}/3$

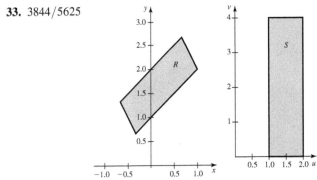

33. $3844/5625$

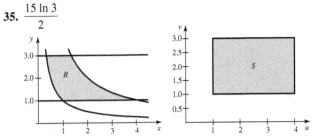

35. $\dfrac{15 \ln 3}{2}$

37. 2 **39.** $2w(u^2 - v^2)$ **41.** 5 **43.** $1024\pi/3$ **45. a.** True
b. True   **c.** True

47. *Hint:* $J(\rho, \varphi, \theta) = \begin{vmatrix} \sin \varphi \cos \theta & \rho \cos \varphi \cos \theta & -\rho \sin \varphi \sin \theta \\ \sin \varphi \sin \theta & \rho \cos \varphi \sin \theta & \rho \sin \varphi \cos \theta \\ \cos \varphi & -\rho \sin \varphi & 0 \end{vmatrix}$

49. $a^2 b^2/2$ **51.** $(a^2 + b^2)/4$ **53.** $\dfrac{4\pi abc}{3}$

55. $(\bar{x}, \bar{y}, \bar{z}) = \left(0, 0, \dfrac{3c}{8} \right)$ **57. a.** $x = a^2 - \dfrac{y^2}{4a^2}$

b. $x = \dfrac{y^2}{4b^2} - b^2$ **c.** $J(u, v) = 4(u^2 + v^2)$ **d.** $\dfrac{80}{3}$ **e.** 160

f. Vertical lines become parabolas opening downward with vertices on the positive y-axis, and horizontal lines become parabolas opening upward with vertices on the negative y-axis.   **59. a.** S is stretched in the positive u- and v-directions but not in the w-direction. The amount of stretching increases with u and v.   **b.** $J(u, v, w) = ad$

c. Volume $= ad$ **d.** $\left(\dfrac{a + b + c}{2}, \dfrac{d + e}{2}, \dfrac{1}{2} \right)$

Chapter 14 Review Exercises, pp. 1066–1069

1. a. False   **b.** True   **c.** False   **3.** $\frac{26}{3}$ **5.** $\displaystyle\int_0^1 \int_{-\sqrt{y}}^{\sqrt{y}} f(x, y) \, dx \, dy$

7. $\displaystyle\int_0^1 \int_0^{\sqrt{1-x^2}} f(x, y) \, dy \, dx$ **9.** $\frac{304}{3}$

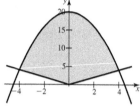

11. $\dfrac{\sqrt{17} - \sqrt{2}}{2}$ **13.** 8π **15.** $\dfrac{2}{7\pi^2}$ **17.** $\dfrac{1}{5}$

19. $\dfrac{9\pi}{2}$

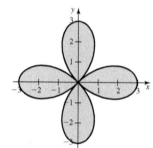

21. $6\pi - 16$

23. 2   **25.** $\displaystyle\int_0^4 \int_0^{\sqrt{16-z^2}} \int_0^{\sqrt{16-y^2-z^2}} f(x, y, z) \, dx \, dy \, dz$ **27.** $\pi - \dfrac{4}{3}$

29. $8 \sin^2 2 = 4(1 - \cos 4)$ **31.** $\dfrac{848}{9}$ **33.** $\dfrac{16}{3}$ **35.** $\dfrac{128}{3}$

37. $\dfrac{\pi}{6} - \dfrac{\sqrt{3}}{2} + \dfrac{1}{2}$ **39. a.** $\frac{512}{15}$ **b.** Five   **c.** $\dfrac{2^{pq+q+1}}{q(p + 1)^2 + p + 1}$

41. $\frac{1}{3}$ **43.** π **45.** 4π **47.** $\dfrac{28\pi}{3}$ **49.** $\dfrac{2048\pi}{105}$

51.

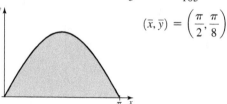

$(\bar{x}, \bar{y}) = \left(\dfrac{\pi}{2}, \dfrac{\pi}{8} \right)$

53.

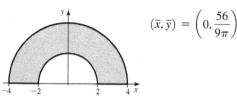

$(\bar{x}, \bar{y}) = \left(0, \dfrac{56}{9\pi} \right)$

55. $(\bar{x}, \bar{y}, \bar{z}) = (0, 0, 24)$ **57.** $(\bar{x}, \bar{y}, \bar{z}) = \left(0, 0, \frac{63}{10} \right)$ **59.** $\dfrac{h}{3}$

61. $\dfrac{1}{6} \sqrt{4s^2 - b^2} = \dfrac{h}{3}$, where h is the height of the triangle.

63. a. $\dfrac{4\pi}{3}$ **b.** $\dfrac{16Q}{3}$ **65.** $R = \{ 0 \leq x \leq 1, 0 \leq y \leq 1 \}$

67. The diamond with vertices at $(0, 0)$, $\left(\frac{1}{2}, -\frac{1}{2} \right)$, $(1, 0)$, and $\left(\frac{1}{2}, \frac{1}{2} \right)$.

69. 14   **71.** 6

73. a.

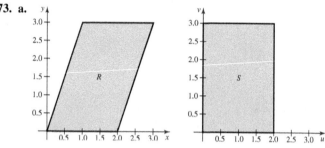

b. $0 \leq u \leq 2, 0 \leq v \leq 3$ **c.** $J(u, v) = 1$ **d.** $\frac{63}{2}$

75. a.

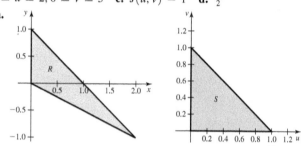

b. $0 \leq u \leq 1, 0 \leq v \leq 1 - u$ **c.** $J(u, v) = 2$ **d.** $\dfrac{256\sqrt{2}}{945}$

77. 42

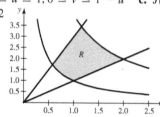

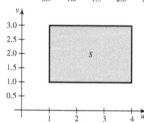

79. $-\dfrac{7}{16}$

CHAPTER 15

Section 15.1 Exercises, pp. 1077–1080

1. $\mathbf{F} = \langle f, g, h \rangle$ evaluated at (x, y, z) is the velocity vector of an air particle at (x, y, z) at a fixed point in time.   **3.** At selected points (a, b), plot the vector $\langle f(a, b), g(a, b) \rangle$.   **5.** It shows the direction in which the temperature increases the fastest and the amount of increase.

7.
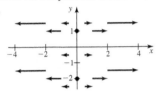

9.
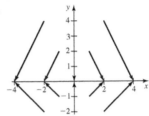

11.
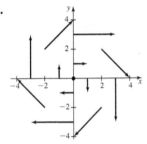

13.
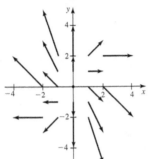

15.
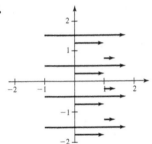

17.
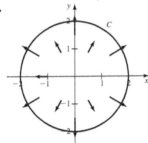

Normal at all points of C

19.
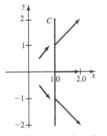

Normal to C at $(1, 0)$

21.
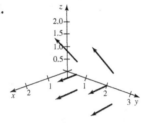

23.
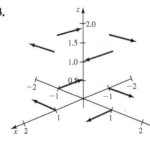

25.
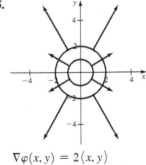

$\nabla \varphi(x, y) = 2 \langle x, y \rangle$

27. $\nabla \varphi = \langle 1, 1 \rangle$
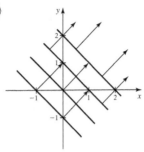

29. $\nabla \varphi(x, y) = \langle 2xy - y^2, x^2 - 2xy \rangle$
31. $\nabla \varphi(x, y) = \langle 1/y, -x/y^2 \rangle$ **33.** $\nabla \varphi(x, y, z) = \langle x, y, z \rangle = \mathbf{r}$

35. $\nabla \varphi(x, y, z) = -(x^2 + y^2 + z^2)^{-3/2} \langle x, y, z \rangle = -\dfrac{\mathbf{r}}{|\mathbf{r}|^3}$

37. a. $\nabla \varphi(x, y) = \langle 2, 3 \rangle$ **b.** $y' = -2/3, \langle 1, -\frac{2}{3} \rangle \cdot \nabla \varphi(1, 1) = 0$
c. $y' = -2/3, \langle 1, -\frac{2}{3} \rangle \cdot \nabla \varphi(x, y) = 0$ **d.**
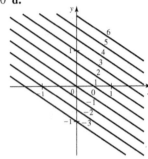

39. a. $\nabla \varphi(x, y) = \langle e^{x-y}, -e^{x-y} \rangle = e^{x-y} \langle 1, -1 \rangle$
b. $y' = 1, \langle 1, 1 \rangle \cdot \nabla \varphi(1, 1) = 0$
c. $y' = 1, \langle 1, 1 \rangle \cdot \nabla \varphi(x, y) = 0$
d.
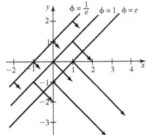

41. a. True **b.** False **c.** True
43.
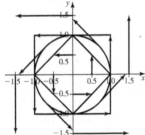

a. For S and D, the vectors with maximum magnitude occur at the vertices; on C all vectors on the boundary have the same maximum magnitude ($|\mathbf{F}| = 1$). **b.** For S and D the field is directed out of the region on line segments between any vertex and the midpoint of the boundary line when proceeding in a counterclockwise direction; on C the vector field is tangent to the boundary curve everywhere.
45. $\mathbf{F} = \langle -y, x \rangle$ or $\mathbf{F} = \langle -1, 1 \rangle$

47. $\mathbf{F}(x, y) = \dfrac{\langle x, y \rangle}{\sqrt{x^2 + y^2}} = \dfrac{\mathbf{r}}{|\mathbf{r}|}$, $\mathbf{F}(0, 0) = \mathbf{0}$

49. a. $\mathbf{E} = \dfrac{c}{x^2 + y^2} \langle x, y \rangle$ **b.** $|\mathbf{E}| = \left| \dfrac{c}{|\mathbf{r}|^2} \mathbf{r} \right| = \dfrac{c}{r}$

c. *Hint:* The equipotential curves are circles centered at the origin.
51. The slope of the streamline at (x, y) is $y'(x)$, which equals the slope of the vector $\mathbf{F}(x, y)$, which is $\frac{g}{f}$. Therefore, $y'(x) = \frac{g}{f}$.

53.

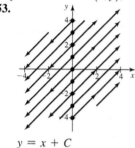

$y = x + C$

55.

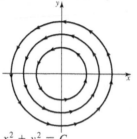

$x^2 + y^2 = C$

57. For $\theta = 0$: $\mathbf{u}_r = \mathbf{i}$ and $\mathbf{u}_\theta = \mathbf{j}$
for $\theta = \frac{\pi}{2}$: $\mathbf{u}_r = \mathbf{j}$ and $\mathbf{u}_\theta = -\mathbf{i}$
for $\theta = \pi$: $\mathbf{u}_r = -\mathbf{i}$ and $\mathbf{u}_\theta = -\mathbf{j}$
for $\theta = \frac{3\pi}{2}$: $\mathbf{u}_r = -\mathbf{j}$ and $\mathbf{u}_\theta = \mathbf{i}$

59.

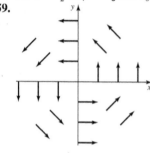

$\mathbf{F} = \dfrac{1}{\sqrt{x^2 + y^2}} \langle -y, x \rangle$

61.

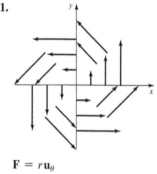

$\mathbf{F} = r\mathbf{u}_\theta$

Section 15.2 Exercises, pp. 1094–1097

1. A line integral is taken along a curve, an ordinary single-variable integral is taken along an interval.   **3.** $\sqrt{1 + 4t^2}$ **5.** The integrand of the alternate form is a dot product of $\mathbf{F}$ and $\mathbf{T}\, ds$.   **7.** Take the line integral of $\mathbf{F} \cdot \mathbf{T}$ along the curve with arc length as the parameter.
9. Take the line integral of $\mathbf{F} \cdot \mathbf{n}$ along the curve with arc length as the parameter, where $\mathbf{n}$ is the outward normal vector of the curve.
11. 0   **13.** $-\frac{32}{3}$ **15. a.** $\mathbf{r}(t) = \langle 4 \cos t, 4 \sin t \rangle$, $0 \le t \le 2\pi$
b. $|\mathbf{r}'(t)| = 4$ **c.** 128π **17. a.** $\mathbf{r}(t) = \langle t, t \rangle$, $1 \le t \le 10$

b. $|\mathbf{r}'(t)| = \sqrt{2}$ **c.** $\dfrac{\sqrt{2}}{2} \ln 10$ **19. a.** $\mathbf{r}(t) = \langle 2 \cos t, 4 \sin t \rangle$,

$0 \le t \le \dfrac{\pi}{2}$ **b.** $|\mathbf{r}'(t)| = 2\sqrt{1 + 3 \cos^2 t}$ **c.** $\dfrac{112}{9}$

21. $\dfrac{15}{2}$ **23.** $\dfrac{1431}{268}$ **25.** 0   **27.** $\dfrac{3\sqrt{14}}{2}$ **29.** $-2\pi^2\sqrt{10}$

31. $\sqrt{101}$ **33.** $\frac{17}{2}$ **35.** 49   **37.** $\dfrac{3}{4\sqrt{10}}$ **39.** 0   **41.** 16

43. 0   **45.** $\dfrac{3\sqrt{3}}{10}$ **47. b.** 0   **49. a.** Negative   **b.** -4π

51. a. True   **b.** True   **c.** True   **d.** True   **53. a.** Both paths require the same work: $W = 28{,}200$.   **b.** Both curves require the

same work: $W = 28{,}200$.   **55. a.** $\dfrac{5\sqrt{5} - 1}{12}$ **b.** $\dfrac{5\sqrt{5} - 1}{12}$

c. The results are identical.

57. *Hint:* $\displaystyle\int_C \mathbf{F} \cdot \mathbf{T}\, ds = \pi r^2 (c - b)$

59. *Hint:* $\displaystyle\int_C \mathbf{F} \cdot \mathbf{n}\, ds = \pi r^2 (a + d)$ **61.** The work equals zero for

all three paths.   **63.** 409.5   **65. a.** $\ln a$ **b.** No   **c.** $\dfrac{1}{6}\left(1 - \dfrac{1}{a^2}\right)$

d. Yes   **e.** $W = \dfrac{3^{1-p/2}}{2 - p}(a^{2-p} - 1)$, for $p \ne 2$; otherwise $W = \ln a$.

f. $p > 2$ **67.** ab

Section 15.3 Exercises, pp. 1104–1106

1. A simple curve has no self-intersections; the initial and terminal points of a closed curve are identical.   **3.** Test for equality of partial derivatives as given in Theorem 15.3.   **5.** Integrate f with respect to x and make the constant of integration a function of y to obtain $\varphi = \int f\, dx + h(y)$; finally set $\frac{\partial \varphi}{\partial y} = g$ in order to determine h.
7. The integral must be zero.   **9.** Conservative   **11.** Conservative
13. Conservative   **15.** $\varphi(x, y) = \frac{1}{2}(x^2 + y^2)$ **17.** Not conservative
19. $\varphi(x, y) = \sqrt{x^2 + y^2}$ **21.** $\varphi(x, y, z) = xz + y$
23. $\varphi(x, y, z) = xy + yz + zx$ **25.** $\varphi(x, y) = \sqrt{x^2 + y^2 + z^2}$
27. a, b. 0   **29. a, b.** 4   **31. a, b.** 2   **33.** 0   **35.** 0   **37.** 0
39. a. False   **b.** True   **c.** True   **d.** True   **41.** $-\frac{1}{2}$ **43.** 0   **45.** 10
47. 25   **49.** C_1 negative, C_2 positive   **53. a.** Compare partial derivatives.

b. $\varphi(x, y, z) = \dfrac{GMm}{\sqrt{x^2 + y^2 + z^2}} = \dfrac{GMm}{|\mathbf{r}|}$

c. $\varphi(B) - \varphi(A) = GMm\left(\dfrac{1}{r_2} - \dfrac{1}{r_1}\right)$.   **d.** No

55. a. $\dfrac{\partial}{\partial y}\left[\dfrac{-y}{(x^2 + y^2)^{p/2}}\right] = \dfrac{-x^2 + (p - 1)y^2}{(x^2 + y^2)^{1+p/2}}$ and

$\dfrac{\partial}{\partial x}\left[\dfrac{x}{(x^2 + y^2)^{p/2}}\right] = \dfrac{-(p - 1)x^2 + y^2}{(x^2 + y^2)^{1+p/2}}$
b. The two partial derivatives in (a) are equal if $p = 2$.
c. $\varphi(x, y) = \tan^{-1}(y/x)$ **59.** $\varphi(x, y) = \frac{1}{2}(x^2 + y^2)$
61. $\varphi(x, y) = \frac{1}{2}(x^4 + x^2y^2 + y^4)$

Section 15.4 Exercises, pp. 1117–1119

1. In both forms the integral of a *derivative* is computed from boundary data.   **3.** y^2 **5.** Area $= \frac{1}{2}\oint_C (x\, dy - y\, dx)$, where C encloses the region   **7.** The integral in the flux form of Green's Theorem vanishes.   **9.** $\mathbf{F} = \langle y, x \rangle$

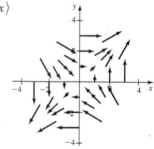

11. a. 0   **b.** Both integrals are zero.   **c.** Yes   **13. a.** -4
b. Both integrals equal -8.   **c.** No   **15. a.** 0   **b.** Both integrals
are zero.   **c.** Yes   **17.** 25π **19.** 16π **21.** 32   **23. a.** 2
b. Both integrals equal 8π **c.** No   **25. a.** 0   **b.** Both integrals
equal zero.   **c.** Yes   **27. a.** 0   **b.** Both integrals equal zero.

c. Yes   **29.** 6; not source free   **31.** $\dfrac{8}{3}$; not source free

33. $8 - \dfrac{\pi}{2}$; not conservative   **35. a.** The circulation is zero.

b. The outward flux equals 3π.   **37. a.** The circulation is zero.

b. The outward flux equals $-\dfrac{15\pi}{2}$.   **39. a.** True   **b.** False

c. True   **41.** The circulation is zero; the outward flux equals 2π.
43. The circulation is 5702.4; the outward flux equals zero.

45. Note: $\dfrac{\partial f}{\partial y} = 0 = \dfrac{\partial g}{\partial x}$ **47.** The integral becomes $\iint_R 2\, dA$.

49. a. $f_x = g_y = 0$ **b.** $\psi(x, y) = -2x + 4y$
51. a. $f_x = e^{-x} \sin y = -g_y$ **b.** $\psi(x, y) = e^{-x} \cos y$
53. a. *Hint:* $f_x = e^x \cos y, f_y = -e^x \sin y$,
$g_x = -e^x \sin y, g_y = -e^x \cos y$
b. $\varphi(x, y) = e^x \cos y, \psi(x, y) = e^x \sin y$

55. a. *Hint:* $f_x = -\dfrac{y}{x^2 + y^2}, f_y = \dfrac{x}{x^2 + y^2}$,

$g_x = \dfrac{x}{x^2 + y^2}, g_y = \dfrac{y}{x^2 + y^2}$.

b. $\varphi(x, y) = x \tan^{-1} \dfrac{y}{x} + \dfrac{y}{2} \ln (x^2 + y^2) - y$,

$\psi(x, y) = y \tan^{-1} \dfrac{y}{x} - \dfrac{x}{2} \ln (x^2 + y^2) + x$

57. a.

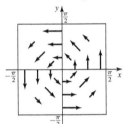

$\mathbf{F} = \langle -4 \cos x \sin y, 4 \sin x \cos y \rangle$ **b.** Yes, the divergence equals
zero.   **c.** No, the two-dimensional curl equals $8 \cos x \cos y$.
d. The total flux across the boundary is zero.   **e.** The total

circulation along C is 32.   **59.** $\mathbf{F} = \left\langle \dfrac{f(x)}{d - c}, 0 \right\rangle$ for the rectangle

$[a, b] \times [c, d]$.   **61. c.** The vector field is undefined at the origin.
63.

Basic ideas: Let C_1 and C_2 be two smooth simple curves from A to B.
$$\int_{C_1} \mathbf{F} \cdot \mathbf{n}\, ds - \int_{C_2} \mathbf{F} \cdot \mathbf{n}\, ds = \oint_C \mathbf{F} \cdot \mathbf{n}\, ds = \iint_R \operatorname{div} \mathbf{F}\, dA = 0$$
and $\displaystyle\int_{C_1} \mathbf{F} \cdot \mathbf{n}\, ds = \int_{C_1} \psi_x\, dx + \psi_y\, dy = \int_{C_1} d\psi = \psi(B) - \psi(A)$
65. Use $\nabla\varphi \cdot \nabla\psi = \langle f, g \rangle \cdot \langle -g, f \rangle = 0$

Section 15.5 Exercises, pp. 1127–1130

1. Compute $f_x + g_y + h_z$.   **3.** There are no sources or sinks.
5. It indicates the axis and the angular speed of the circulation
at a point.   **7.** Zero   **9.** 3   **11.** 0   **13.** $2(x + y + z)$

15. $\dfrac{x^2 + y^2 + 3}{(1 + x^2 + y^2)^2}$ **17.** $\dfrac{1}{|\mathbf{r}|^2}$ **19.** $-\dfrac{1}{|\mathbf{r}|^4}$ **21. a.** Positive for both

points   **b.** div $\mathbf{F} = 2$ **c.** Outward everywhere   **d.** Positive
23. a. curl $\mathbf{F} = 2\mathbf{i}$ **b.** $|$curl $\mathbf{F}| = 2$
25. a. curl $\mathbf{F} = 2\mathbf{i} - 2\mathbf{j} + 2\mathbf{k}$ **b.** $|$curl $\mathbf{F}| = 2\sqrt{3}$
27. $3y\mathbf{k}$ **29.** $-4z\mathbf{j}$ **31.** 0   **33.** 0   **35.** Follows from

partial differentiation of $\dfrac{1}{(x^2 + y^2 + z^2)^{3/2}}$

37. Combine Exercise 36 with Theorem 15.8.   **39. a.** False
b. False   **c.** False   **d.** False   **e.** False   **41. a.** No
b. No   **c.** Yes, scalar function   **d.** No   **e.** No   **f.** No   **g.** Yes,
vector field   **h.** No   **i.** Yes, vector field   **43.** Compute an explicit
expression for $\mathbf{a} \times \mathbf{r}$ and then take the required partial derivatives.
45. div $\mathbf{F} = 6$ at $(1, 1, 1)$, $(1, -1, -1)$, $(-1, 1, 1)$, and $(-1, -1, -1)$.
47. $\mathbf{n} = \langle a, b, 2a + b \rangle$, where a and b are real numbers
49. $\mathbf{F} = \frac{1}{2}(y^2 + z^2)\mathbf{i}$ **51. a.** The wheel does not spin.
b. Clockwise, looking in the positive y-direction

c. The wheel does not spin.   **53.** $\omega = \dfrac{10}{\sqrt{3}}$, or $\dfrac{5}{\sqrt{3}\pi} = 0.9189$

revolutions per unit time.
55. $\mathbf{F} = -200ke^{-x^2+y^2+z^2}(-x\mathbf{i} + y\mathbf{j} + z\mathbf{k})$
$\nabla \cdot \mathbf{F} = -200k(1 + 2(x^2 + y^2 + z^2))e^{-x^2+y^2+z^2}$

57. a. $\mathbf{F} = -\dfrac{GMm\mathbf{r}}{|\mathbf{r}|^3}$ **b.** See Theorem 15.9.

59. $\rho\left(\dfrac{\partial u}{\partial t} + u\dfrac{\partial u}{\partial x} + v\dfrac{\partial u}{\partial y} + w\dfrac{\partial u}{\partial z}\right) = -\dfrac{\partial p}{\partial x} + \mu\left(\dfrac{\partial^2 u}{\partial x^2} + \dfrac{\partial^2 u}{\partial y^2} + \dfrac{\partial^2 u}{\partial z^2}\right)$

$\rho\left(\dfrac{\partial v}{\partial t} + u\dfrac{\partial v}{\partial x} + v\dfrac{\partial v}{\partial y} + w\dfrac{\partial v}{\partial z}\right) = -\dfrac{\partial p}{\partial y} + \mu\left(\dfrac{\partial^2 v}{\partial x^2} + \dfrac{\partial^2 v}{\partial y^2} + \dfrac{\partial^2 v}{\partial z^2}\right)$

$\rho\left(\dfrac{\partial w}{\partial t} + u\dfrac{\partial w}{\partial x} + v\dfrac{\partial w}{\partial y} + w\dfrac{\partial w}{\partial z}\right) = -\dfrac{\partial p}{\partial z} + \mu\left(\dfrac{\partial^2 w}{\partial x^2} + \dfrac{\partial^2 w}{\partial y^2} + \dfrac{\partial^2 w}{\partial z^2}\right)$

61. a. Use $\nabla \times \mathbf{B} = -Ak \cos(kz - \omega t)\mathbf{i}$ and
$\dfrac{\partial \mathbf{E}}{\partial t} = -A\omega \cos(kz - \omega t)\mathbf{i}$.   **b.**

Section 15.6 Exercises, pp. 1143–1146

1. $\mathbf{r}(u, v) = \langle a \cos u, a \sin u, v \rangle, 0 \le u \le 2\pi, 0 \le v \le h$
3. $\mathbf{r}(u, v) = \langle a \sin u \cos v, a \sin u \sin v, a \cos u \rangle, 0 \le u \le \pi$,
$0 \le v \le 2\pi$ **5.** Use the parameterization from Problem 3 and

compute $\displaystyle\int_0^\pi \int_0^{2\pi} f(a \sin u \cos v, a \sin u \sin v, a \cos u)\, a^2 \sin u\, dv\, du$.

7. Use the parametrization from Exercise 3 and compute

$\displaystyle\int_0^\pi \int_0^{2\pi} a^2 \sin u\, (f \sin u \cos v + g \sin u \sin v + h \cos u)\, dv\, du$.

9. The normal vectors point outward.   **11.** $\langle u, v, \frac{1}{3}(16 - 2u + 4v)\rangle$, $|u| < \infty$, $|v| < \infty$ **13.** $\langle v \cos u, v \sin u, v\rangle$, $0 \le u \le 2\pi$, $2 \le v \le 8$ **15.** $\langle 3 \cos u, 3 \sin u, v\rangle$, $0 \le u \le \frac{\pi}{2}$, $0 \le v \le 3$

17. The plane $z = 2x + 3y - 1$ **19.** Part of the upper half of the cone $z^2 = 16x^2 + 16y^2$ of height 12 and radius 3 (with $y \ge 0$)
21. 28π **23.** $16\sqrt{3}$ **25.** $\pi r \sqrt{r^2 + h^2}$ **27.** 1728π
29. 0   **31.** $4\pi\sqrt{5}$ **33.** $8\sqrt{17} + 2 \ln(\sqrt{17} + 4) = 37.1743$
35. $\dfrac{2\sqrt{3}}{3}$ **37.** $\dfrac{1250\pi}{3}$ **39.** $\dfrac{1}{48}(e - e^{-5} - e^{-7} + e^{-13})$ **41.** $\dfrac{1}{4\pi}$
43. -8 **45.** 0   **47.** 4π **49. a.** True   **b.** False   **c.** True
d. True   **51.** $8\pi(4\sqrt{17} + \ln(\sqrt{17} + 4))$ **53.** $8\pi a$ **55. a.** 8
b. $4\pi - 8$ **57. a.** 0   **b.** 0; the flow is tangent to the surface (radial flow).   **59.** $2\pi ah$ **61.** $-400\left(e - \dfrac{1}{e}\right)^2$
63. $8\pi a$ **65. a.** $4\pi(b^3 - a^3)$ **b.** The net flux is zero.
67. $\left(0, 0, \frac{2}{3}h\right)$ **69.** $\left(0, 0, \frac{7}{6}\right)$ **73.** Flux $= \displaystyle\iint_S \mathbf{F} \cdot \mathbf{n}\, dS = \iint_A dx\, dy$

Section 15.7 Exercises, pp. 1153–1155

1. The integral measures the circulation along the closed curve C.
3. The circulation along a closed curve can be calculated by integrating the dot product of the curl and the normal vector on an enclosed surface.   **5.** -2π for both integrals.   **7.** Both integrals are zero.
9. -18π for both integrals.   **11.** -24π **13.** $-\frac{128}{3}$ **15.** 15π
17. 0   **19.** 0   **21.** $\nabla \times \mathbf{v} = \langle 1, 0, 0\rangle$; a paddle wheel with its axis aligned with the x-axis will spin with maximum angular speed counterclockwise (looking in the negative x-direction) at all points.
23. $\nabla \times \mathbf{v} = \langle 0, -2, 0\rangle$; a paddle wheel with its axis aligned with the y-axis will spin with maximum angular speed clockwise (looking in the negative y-direction) at all points.   **25. a.** False   **b.** False
c. True   **d.** True   **27.** The circulation is zero.   **29.** The circulation is zero.   **31.** 2π **33.** $\pi(\cos\varphi - \sin\varphi)$, maximum for $\varphi = 0$
35. The circulation is 48π; it depends on the radius of the circle but not on the center.   **37. a.** The normal vectors point toward the z-axis on the curved surface of S and in the direction of $\langle 0, 1, 0\rangle$ on the flat surface of S.   **b.** 2π **c.** 2π **39.** The integral is π for all a.   **41.** The integral is zero for (a) and (b).   **43. b.** 2π for any circle of radius r centered at the origin.   **c.** $\mathbf{F}$ is not differentiable along the z-axis.

45. Apply the Chain Rule.   **47.** $\displaystyle\int_C \mathbf{F} \cdot d\mathbf{r} = \iint_R \left(\frac{\partial h}{\partial y} - \frac{\partial g}{\partial z}\right) dA$

Section 15.8 Exercises, pp. 1164–1167

1. The surface integral measures the flow across the boundary.
3. The flux across the boundary equals the cumulative expansion or contraction of the vector field inside the region.   **5.** 32π
7. The outward fluxes are equal to each other.   **9.** Both integrals equal 96π.   **11.** Both integrals are zero.   **13.** The net flux is zero.
15. The net flux is zero.   **17.** $16\sqrt{6}\pi$ **19.** $\frac{2}{3}$ **21.** $-\frac{128}{3}\pi$ **23.** 24π
25. -224π **27.** 12π **29.** 20   **31. a.** False   **b.** False   **c.** True
33. 0   **35.** $\frac{3}{2}$ **37. b.** The net flux between the two spheres is $4\pi(a^2 - \varepsilon^2)$.   **39. b.** Use $\nabla \cdot \mathbf{E} = 0$.   **c.** The flux across S is the *sum* of the contributions from the individual charges.   **d.** For an arbitrary volume, we find

$$\frac{1}{\varepsilon_0} \iiint_D q(x, y, z)\, dV = \iint_S \mathbf{E} \cdot \mathbf{n}\, dS = \iiint \nabla \cdot \mathbf{E}\, dV.$$

e. Use $\nabla^2 \varphi = \nabla \cdot \nabla\varphi$.   **41.** 0   **43.** $-(1 - e^{-1})$ **45.** $800\pi a^3 e^{-a^2}$

Chapter 15 Review Exercises, pp. 1167–1170

1. a. False   **b.** True   **c.** False   **d.** False   **e.** True
3. $\nabla\varphi = \langle 2x, 8y\rangle$

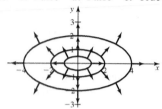

5. $-\dfrac{\mathbf{r}}{|\mathbf{r}|^3}$ **7. a.** $\mathbf{n} = \frac{1}{2}\langle x, y\rangle$ **b.** 0   **c.** $\frac{1}{2}$ **9.** $\dfrac{\sqrt{46}}{4}(e^{6(\ln 8)^2} - 1)$
11. Both integrals are zero.   **13.** 0   **15.** The circulation is -4π; the outward flux is zero.   **17.** The circulation is zero; the outward flux is 2π.   **19.** $\dfrac{4v_0 L^3}{3}$ **21.** $\varphi(x, y, z) = xy + yz^2$ **23.** $\varphi(x, y, z) = xye^z$
25. 0 for both methods   **27. a.** $-\pi$ **b.** $\mathbf{F}$ is not conservative.   **29.** 0
31. $\frac{20}{3}$ **33.** 8π **35.** The circulation is zero; the outward flux equals 2π.   **37. a.** $b = c$ **b.** $a + d = 0$ **c.** $a + d = 0$ and $b = c$
39. $\nabla \cdot \mathbf{F} = 4\sqrt{x^2 + y^2 + z^2} = 4|\mathbf{r}|$, $\nabla \times \mathbf{F} = \mathbf{0}$, $\nabla \cdot \mathbf{F} \ne 0$
41. $\nabla \cdot \mathbf{F} = 2y + 12xz^2$, $\nabla \times \mathbf{F} = \mathbf{0}$, $\nabla \cdot \mathbf{F} \ne 0$ **43. a.** -1 and 0
b. $\mathbf{n} = \dfrac{1}{\sqrt{3}}\langle -1, 1, 1\rangle$ **45.** 18π **47.** $4\sqrt{3}$ **49.** $\dfrac{8\sqrt{3}}{3}$ **51.** 8π
53. $4\pi a^2$ **55. a.** Use $x = y = 0$ to confirm the highest point; use $z = 0$ to confirm the base.   **b.** The hemisphere S has the greater surface area—$2\pi a^2$ for S versus $\dfrac{5\sqrt{5} - 1}{6}\pi a^2$ for T.   **57.** 0
59. 99π **61.** 0   **63.** $\dfrac{972}{5}\pi$ **65.** $\dfrac{124}{5}\pi$ **67.** $\dfrac{32}{3}$

APPENDIX A

Exercises, pp. 1177–1178

1. The set of real numbers greater than -4 and less than or equal to 10; $(-4, 10]$;
3. $|x| = \begin{cases} x & \text{if } x \ge 0 \\ -x & \text{if } x < 0 \end{cases}$ **5.** $2x - 4 \ge 3$ or $2x - 4 \le -3$
7. Take the square root of the sum of the squares of the differences of the x- and y-coordinates.   **9.** $y = \sqrt{36 - x^2}$
11. $m = \dfrac{y + 2}{x - 4}$ or $y = m(x - 4) - 2$ **13.** They are equal.
15. 4   **17.** $4uv$ **19.** $-\dfrac{h}{x(x + h)}$ **21.** $(y - y^{-1})(y + y^{-1})$
23. $u = \pm\sqrt{2}, \pm 3$ **25.** $3x^2 + 3xh + h^2$
27. $(1, 5)$
29. $(-\infty, 4] \cup [5, 6)$
31. $\{x: x < -4/3 \text{ or } x > 4\}$; $\left(-\infty, -\frac{4}{3}\right) \cup (4, \infty)$

33. $\{x: -2 < x < -1 \ \ \text{or} \ \ 2 < x < 3\}; (-2, -1) \bigcup (2, 3)$

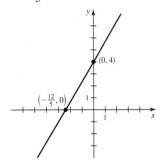

35. $y = 2 - \sqrt{9 - (x + 1)^2}$

37. $y = \dfrac{5}{3}x + 4$

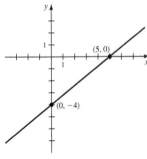

39. $y = \dfrac{4}{5}x - 4$

41. $x + 2y = 24$

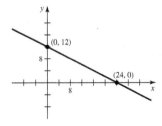

43. $y = \dfrac{1}{3}x - 7$ **45. a.** False **b.** True **c.** False **d.** False
e. False **f.** True **g.** False **47.** $\{x: |x - 1| \geq 3\}$
49.

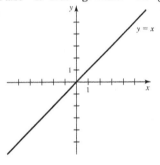

ALGEBRA

Exponents and Radicals

$$x^a x^b = x^{a+b} \qquad \frac{x^a}{x^b} = x^{a-b} \qquad x^{-a} = \frac{1}{x^a} \qquad (x^a)^b = x^{ab} \qquad \left(\frac{x}{y}\right)^a = \frac{x^a}{y^a}$$

$$x^{1/n} = \sqrt[n]{x} \qquad x^{m/n} = \sqrt[n]{x^m} = (\sqrt[n]{x})^m \qquad \sqrt[n]{xy} = \sqrt[n]{x}\sqrt[n]{y} \qquad \sqrt[n]{x/y} = \sqrt[n]{x}/\sqrt[n]{y}$$

Factoring Formulas

$$a^2 - b^2 = (a - b)(a + b) \qquad\qquad a^2 + b^2 \text{ does not factor over real numbers}$$
$$a^3 - b^3 = (a - b)(a^2 + ab + b^2) \qquad a^3 + b^3 = (a + b)(a^2 - ab + b^2)$$
$$a^n - b^n = (a - b)(a^{n-1} + a^{n-2}b + a^{n-3}b^2 + \cdots + ab^{n-2} + b^{n-1})$$

Binomials

$$(a \pm b)^2 = a^2 \pm 2ab + b^2$$
$$(a \pm b)^3 = a^3 \pm 3a^2b + 3ab^2 \pm b^3$$

Binomial Theorem

$$(a + b)^n = a^n + \binom{n}{1}a^{n-1}b + \binom{n}{2}a^{n-2}b^2 + \cdots + \binom{n}{n-1}ab^{n-1} + b^n,$$

$$\text{where } \binom{n}{k} = \frac{n(n-1)(n-2)\cdots(n-k+1)}{k(k-1)(k-2)\cdots 3 \cdot 2 \cdot 1} = \frac{n!}{k!(n-k)!}$$

Quadratic Formula

The solutions of $ax^2 + bx + c = 0$ are

$$x = \frac{-b \pm \sqrt{b^2 - 4ac}}{2a}$$

GEOMETRY

Parallelogram

$A = bh$

Triangle

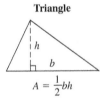

$A = \frac{1}{2}bh$

Trapezoid

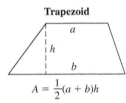

$A = \frac{1}{2}(a + b)h$

Circle

$A = \pi r^2$
$C = 2\pi r$

Sector

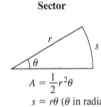

$A = \frac{1}{2}r^2\theta$
$s = r\theta$ (θ in radians)

Cylinder

$V = \pi r^2 h$
$S = 2\pi rh$
(lateral surface area)

Cone

$V = \frac{1}{3}\pi r^2 h$
$S = \pi r\ell$
(lateral surface area)

Sphere

$V = \frac{4}{3}\pi r^3$
$S = 4\pi r^2$

Equations of Lines and Circles

$$m = \frac{y_2 - y_1}{x_2 - x_1} \qquad \text{slope of line through } (x_1, y_1) \text{ and } (x_2, y_2)$$

$$y - y_1 = m(x - x_1) \qquad \text{point-slope form of line through } (x_1, y_1) \text{ with slope } m$$

$$y = mx + b \qquad \text{slope-intercept form of line with slope } m \text{ and } y\text{-intercept } (0, b)$$

$$(x - h)^2 + (y - k)^2 = r^2 \qquad \text{circle of radius } r \text{ with center } (h, k)$$

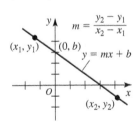

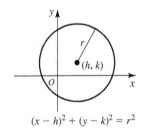

TRIGONOMETRY

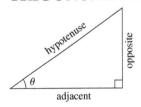

$$\cos\theta = \frac{\text{adj}}{\text{hyp}} \qquad \sin\theta = \frac{\text{opp}}{\text{hyp}} \qquad \tan\theta = \frac{\text{opp}}{\text{adj}}$$

$$\sec\theta = \frac{\text{hyp}}{\text{adj}} \qquad \csc\theta = \frac{\text{hyp}}{\text{opp}} \qquad \cot\theta = \frac{\text{adj}}{\text{opp}}$$

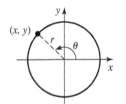

$$\cos\theta = \frac{x}{r} \qquad \sec\theta = \frac{r}{x}$$

$$\sin\theta = \frac{y}{r} \qquad \csc\theta = \frac{r}{y}$$

$$\tan\theta = \frac{y}{x} \qquad \cot\theta = \frac{x}{y}$$

(Continued)

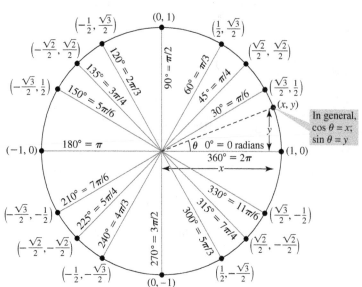

Reciprocal Identities

$$\tan \theta = \frac{\sin \theta}{\cos \theta} \quad \cot \theta = \frac{\cos \theta}{\sin \theta} \quad \sec \theta = \frac{1}{\cos \theta} \quad \csc \theta = \frac{1}{\sin \theta}$$

Pythagorean Identities

$$\sin^2 \theta + \cos^2 \theta = 1 \quad \tan^2 \theta + 1 = \sec^2 \theta \quad 1 + \cot^2 \theta = \csc^2 \theta$$

Sign Identities

$$\sin (-\theta) = -\sin \theta \quad \cos (-\theta) = \cos \theta \quad \tan (-\theta) = -\tan \theta$$
$$\csc (-\theta) = -\csc \theta \quad \sec (-\theta) = \sec \theta \quad \cot (-\theta) = -\cot \theta$$

Double-Angle Identities

$$\sin 2\theta = 2 \sin \theta \cos \theta \qquad \cos 2\theta = \cos^2 \theta - \sin^2 \theta$$
$$= 2 \cos^2 \theta - 1$$
$$\tan 2\theta = \frac{2 \tan \theta}{1 - \tan^2 \theta} \qquad\qquad\quad = 1 - 2 \sin^2 \theta$$

Half-Angle Formulas

$$\cos^2 \theta = \frac{1 + \cos 2\theta}{2} \qquad \sin^2 \theta = \frac{1 - \cos 2\theta}{2}$$

Addition Formulas

$$\sin (\alpha + \beta) = \sin \alpha \cos \beta + \cos \alpha \sin \beta \qquad \sin (\alpha - \beta) = \sin \alpha \cos \beta - \cos \alpha \sin \beta$$
$$\cos (\alpha + \beta) = \cos \alpha \cos \beta - \sin \alpha \sin \beta \qquad \cos (\alpha - \beta) = \cos \alpha \cos \beta + \sin \alpha \sin \beta$$
$$\tan (\alpha + \beta) = \frac{\tan \alpha + \tan \beta}{1 - \tan \alpha \tan \beta} \qquad\qquad \tan (\alpha - \beta) = \frac{\tan \alpha - \tan \beta}{1 + \tan \alpha \tan \beta}$$

Law of Sines

$$\frac{\sin \alpha}{a} = \frac{\sin \beta}{b} = \frac{\sin \gamma}{c}$$

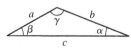

Law of Cosines

$$a^2 = b^2 + c^2 - 2bc \cos \alpha$$

Graphs of Trigonometric Functions and Their Inverses

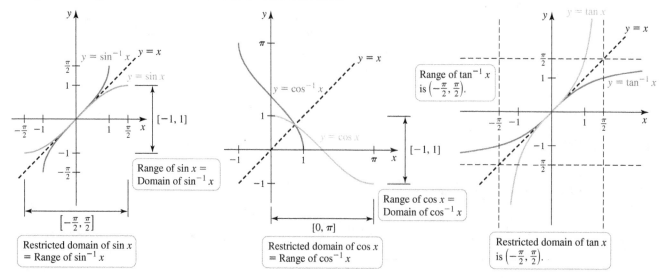

Credits

Page 232, Figure 4.2; Page 233, Figure 4.5; Page 234, Figure 4.7; Page 246, Figure 4.27; Page 250, Figure 4.36; Page 406, Figure 6.17; Page 412, Figure 6.23; Page 416, Figure 6.30; Figure 6.31; Page 417, Figure 6.32; Page 417, Figure 6.33; Page 423, Section 6.3, Figure for Exercise 61; Page 425, Figure 6.38; Page 761, Figure 11.41; Page 769, Figure 11.58; Page 812, Figure 12.55; Page 812, Figure 12.56; Page 814, Figure 12.59; Page 819, Section 12.4, Figure for Exercise 63; Page 884, Figure 13.8; Page 995, Figure 14.12; Page 1000, Figure 14.24; Page 1006, Figure 14.30; Page 1029, Figure 14.50; Page 1035, Figure 14.58; Page 1139, Figure 15.54, *Thomas' Calculus: Early Transcendentals* by George B. Thomas, Maurice D. Weir, Joel Hass, and Frank Giordano. Copyright © 2008, 2007, 2006, 2005 Pearson Education, Inc. Printed and Electronically reproduced by permission of Pearson Education, Inc., Upper Saddle River, New Jersey.; **Page 273, Section 4.4, Exercise 57,** *Problems for Mathematicians, Young and Old* by Paul R. Halmos. Copyright © 1991 Mathematical Association of America. Reprinted by permission. All rights reserved.; **Page 274, Section 4.4, Exercise 64,** "Do Dogs Know Calculus?" by Tim Pennings from *The College Mathematics Journal*, Vol. 34, No.6. Copyright © 2003 Mathematical Association of America. Reprinted by permission. All rights reserved.; **Page 532, Section 7.4, Exercise 89,** *The College Mathematics Journal*, Vol. 34, No.3. Copyright © 2003 Mathematical Association of America. Reprinted by permission. All rights reserved.; **Page 778, Figure 12.2c,** LBNL/Photo Researchers, Inc.; **Page 789, Section 12.1, Exercise 77,** *Calculus* by Gilbert Strang. Copyright © 1991 Wellesley-Cambridge Press. Reprinted by permission of the author. **Page 898, Figure 13.26,** © 2003 National Geographic (www.nationalgeographic.com/ topo); **Page 903, Figure 13.36; Page 1071, Figure 15.2b, Figure 15.2c,** © COMSOL AB. COMSOL and COMSOL Multiphysics are trademarks of COMSOL AB. COMSOL materials are reprinted with the permission of COMSOL AB.; **Page 908, Figure 13.38,** *Calculus* 2nd edition by George B. Thomas and Ross L. Finney. Copyright © 1994, 1990, by Addison Wesley Longman Inc. Printed and Electronically reproduced by permission of Pearson Education, Inc., Upper Saddle River, New Jersey; **Page 970, Section 13.8, Exercise 66,** *Math Horizons*, April 2004. Copyright © 2004 Mathematical Association of America. Reprinted by permission. All rights reserved. **Page 1071, Figure 15.2a,** Courtesy of GFDL/NOAA.

Index